# TOXICOLOGY

## Principles
## and
## Applications

Raymond J.M. Niesink

•

John de Vries

•

Mannfred A. Hollinger

**CRC Press**
**Boca Raton   New York   London   Tokyo**

**Library of Congress Cataloging-in-Publication Data**

Toxicologie. English
   Toxicology : principles and applications / [edited by] Raymond
J.M. Niesink, John de Vries, Mannfred A. Hollinger.
      p.      cm.
   Includes bibliographical references and index.
   ISBN 0-8493-9232-2 (hardcover : alk. paper)
   1. Toxicology.   I. Niesink, Raymundus Johannes Maria, 1953-
II. De Vries, John, 1936-   .   III. Hollinger, Mannfred A.
IV. Title.
   [DNLM: 1. Toxicology.   QV 600 T547 1996a]
RA1211.T62713 1996
615.9—dc20
DNLM/DLC
for Library of Congress                                                                                                95-23711
                                                                                                                                    CIP

© 1996 by CRC Press, Inc. and Open University of The Netherlands **Ou**

No claim to original U.S. Government works
International Standard Book Number 0-8493-9232-2
Library of Congress Card Number 95-23711
Printed in the United States of America   1   2   3   4   5   6   7   8   9   0
Printed on acid-free paper

# Foreword

EUROTOX - the organisation of European toxicologists and national societies of toxicology - has a long tradition in the education and training in toxicology, as had its predecessor, the European Society of Toxicology.

In 1989, the EUROTOX Subcommittee on Education and Training started discussions on needs and possibilities for the harmonisation of education schemes and qualifications in toxicology throughout Europe. It was soon recognised that there was a need for a high quality textbook covering the important areas of toxicology which could be used both for taught courses and for self-education and distance learning.

During the discussions EUROTOX became aware of the courses Toxicology I and II of the Netherlands Open University, and was impressed by the quality of the accompanying course books.

Following discussions with the faculty of Natural Sciences of the Netherlands Open University, sample chapters of these course books were translated into English and presented at the 1991 EUROTOX Congress in Maastricht, The Netherlands.

The enthusiastic response with which these chapters were met convinced EUROTOX that it had found its high quality textbook, and resulted in an agreement with the Open University to have the aforementioned course books translated, edited and published. This textbook is the result of that effort, which should serve the toxicological community, throughout Europe and world-wide, as a basic textbook for everyone interested in the field of toxicology.

EUROTOX's discussions on harmonisation of education and qualification in toxicology are continuing, and this textbook should cover the core syllabus considered necessary for training in toxicology.

*Toxicology: Principles and Applications* has resulted from a close collaboration between EUROTOX and the Netherlands Open University. EUROTOX is proud to have helped in making it available. Special thanks go to Professor John de Vries, Netherlands Open University, for his enthusiastic support and to Dr. Susan Boobis for her English scientific editing on behalf of EUROTOX.

Oslo, November, 1995

Erik Dybing
EUROTOX President

# Preface

The term *toxicology* is derived from the Greek word τοξικοσ (toxicos) the adjective of τοξον (toxon = bow); the historian Herodotus used the word τοξικον (toxikon) for poison-arrow.

Toxicology is the study of the harmful interactions between foreign chemicals (xenobiotics) and biological systems. It is a discipline that requires the integration of many areas of knowledge: basic biochemistry, chemistry (analytical and organic), pathology, and physiology.

The ultimate objective of the discipline of toxicology is protection of life—in particular, that of man—against external harmful factors. Health protection is a concern of scientists, manufacturers, politicians and the public. Therefore, education in toxicology should create a knowledge base in students as well as extending the expertise of professionals. In order to achieve this, education in toxicology should be continuous and predicated upon the major determinants of health: environmental, nutritional and occupational factors. The present textbook is the direct result of many years of teaching toxicology. It was originally designed as a course for distance education in toxicology for students of the Open University of the Netherlands. In practice, it was also used for continuous education. Its success in the Netherlands, as well as other European countries, merited its availability to students studying toxicology in North America and elsewhere.

The main objective of this textbook is to provide toxicological information at an introductory level while incorporating enough comprehensive information to meet the needs of a variety of toxicology students. The text has been written with its primary target group—advanced undergraduates and graduate students—in mind. The text will provide them with an appreciation of the theoretical foundation of toxicology as well as the application of basic principles and concepts. However, the text is also suitable as a reference book for graduate biologists, chemists, physicians, and veterinarians who wish to obtain additional knowledge of toxicology.

The design of the text emphasizes "supervised self study" of toxicology units. Each study unit contains a table of contents, an introduction, a learning core, a summary, a self test and a feedback section. The table of contents lists the main topics to be covered in that unit. It helps the student to see the material that follows in perspective. The introduction refers to the position of the unit in the course and is followed by specific learning objectives and specific study hints for the unit. The learning core contains the main text, applications, figures, tables, illustrations, questions and assignments. Cross references to related material in earlier chapters enable students to refresh their memories quickly. Key words are defined when they appear in the text. In the main text, many analogies and references to everyday experiences are included to help students relate to the toxicological concepts presented. A summary following the core text enables the student to focus on the main concepts before moving on. The self test at the end of the study unit tests whether the learning objectives of the unit have been met, it includes multiple choice questions as well as essay questions. The feedback section consists of feedback referring to questions and findings in the core and feedback referring to questions in the self test.

The structure of the textbook emphasizes four major themes: fundamental principles of toxicology, molecular aspects of toxicity, organ toxicology and applications of toxicology. These themes are further divided into 6 parts.

Part one deals with exposure to chemical substances and the conversion of toxic substances into less or more harmful metabolites, or into substances that are more readily excreted. Students are introduced to the absorption, distribution, biotransformation and excretion of foreign substances, in both a qualitative and quantitative sense. In addition, attention is paid to the relationship between dose and toxic effects and to the influence of time on toxicity.

Part two discusses the mechanisms underlying damage at the cellular level as a result of exposure to toxic substances. The relationships between the structural characteristics of molecules and the eventual toxic effect are described in the unit on Structure-Activity Relationships. The unit on the toxicity of mixtures deals with the influence of combined exposure on the eventual toxic effect. Considerable attention is paid to the mechanisms of mutagenicity and carcinogenicity and to the natural defense mechanisms of organisms against mutation. Mutagenicity and carcinogenicity screening tests are also covered. This part ends with an introduction to cancer risk assessment and cancer risk evaluation.

Part three begins with toxicological safety standards and legislation concerning harmful substances. It includes a discussion of the various steps involved in setting standards and the agencies concerned. It also describes the way in which toxicity tests are carried out and the extrapolation of results obtained in experimental animals to the human situation. The next units of this part describe the cellular and morphological aspects of cellular degeneration. Here the microscopic, ultramicroscopic and biochemical aspects of toxicity studies are discussed.

Parts four and five deal with the organ-specific functions that play a role in the development of the toxic effect. The specific histological, pathological and functional changes are described. Where relevant, the specific techniques for studying functional or structural changes are discussed as well. In addition to pathological and pathophysiological changes resulting from exposure to xenobiotics, the specific problems related to exposure under experimental conditions are discussed. Pulmonary, hepatic and renal toxicity receive particular emphasis.

Part five also deals with the toxicology of a number of organs and organ systems that are involved in the communication within the body (nervous system, endocrine system) or in its defense (blood, immune system). Three study units discuss the nervous system at various levels: the effects of neurotoxic substances at the anatomical and biochemical level, their effects on the electrophysiological level, and the effects of these substances on behavior.

Part six deals with a number of important applications of toxicological knowledge: nutritional toxicology, ecotoxicology, medical toxicology and occupational toxicology.

The textbook concludes with an achievement test, an examination that allows the student to check for him/herself whether he or she has a thorough command of the subject matter. The answers to this achievement test are given in a feedback session.

A full glossary has been included for quick reference to key words that occur throughout the book. In addition to the glossary and index, a chemistry appendix and a list of commonly used abbreviations in toxicology are provided.

Finally, the editors urge the student to contact them if this textbook displays errors or significant omissions.

ACKNOWLEDGMENT

The editors gratefully acknowledge the many people who helped with the original Dutch edition and this new English version. Claire and Phillip Chambers are acknowledged for their assistance in scientific editing of a number of chapters. A special thank-you goes to Hanneke Drijver-De Haas and Susan Boobis, for language editing and Evelin Karsten, for typewriting and lay-out assistance for figures and tables. The Board of Governors of the Open University, the Executive Committee and the Education Subcommittee of Eurotox are gratefully acknowledged for creating organizational and financial opportunities to realize this project.

Heerlen, June 1995

The editors

Raymond J.M. Niesink
John de Vries,
Manfred A. Hollinger

# Contributors

**Prof. Dr. A. Bast**
Section Pharmacochemistry
Chemistry Department
Free University
Amsterdam

**Dr. R.B. Beems**
Department of Toxicology
National Institute of Public Health and Environmental
   Protection
Bilthoven

**Dr. B.J. Blaauboer**
Research Institute for Toxicology
University of Utrecht

**Dr. P.J.A. Borm**
Department of Health Risk Analysis and Toxicology
State University of Limburg
Maastricht

**Dr. H. Van Cauteren**
Department of Toxicology
Janssen Pharmaceutica N.V.
Beerse, Belgium

**W. Coussement, D.V.M., D.V.Sc.**
Department of Toxicology
Janssen Pharmaceutica N.V.
Beerse, Belgium

**J.M. Garbis-Berkvens, B.A.**
Unit Teratology, Endocrinology and Perinatal Screening
National Institute of Public Health and Environmental
   Protection
Bilthoven

**Prof. Dr. V.J. Feron**
TNO Toxicology and Nutrition Institute
Zeist

**Prof. Dr. P.Th. Henderson**
Section Industrial Medicine
Environmental Medicine and Toxicology
State University of Limburg
Maastricht

**Dr. J.L.M. Hermens**
Research Institute for Toxicology
University of Utrecht

**Prof. Dr. J.C.S. Kleinjans**
Department of Health Risk Analysis and Toxicology
State University of Limburg
Maastricht

**Prof. Dr. J.H. Koeman**
Department of Toxicology
Agricultural University of Wageningen
Wageningen

**Dr. Th.M.C.M. de Kok**
Faculty of Natural Sciences
Open University
Heerlen

**Dr. A.Sj. Koster**
Section of Pharmacology
Department of Pharmacy
University of Utrecht

**Dr. M.A.M. Krajnc-Franken**
Unit Teratology, Endocrinology and Perinatal Screening
National Institute of Public Health and Environmental
   Protection
Bilthoven

**Dr. F.X.R. van Leeuwen**
Unit Teratology, Endocrinology and Perinatal Screening
National Institute of Public Health and Environmental
   Protection
Bilthoven

**Dr. J.G. Loeber**
Unit Teratology, Endocrinology and Perinatal Screening
National Institute of Public Health and Environmental
   Protection
Bilthoven

**Dr. H. van Loveren**
Laboratory of Pathology
National Institute of Public Health and Environmental
   Protection
Bilthoven

**Dr. J.J.M. Marx**
Department of Haematology
University Hospital
University of Utrecht

**Dr. A. Musch**
Werkhoven

**Dr. J.F. Nagelkerke**
Centre for Bio-pharmaceutical Sciences
Department of Toxicology
State University of Leiden

**Dr. R.J.M. Niesink**
Faculty of Natural Sciences
Open University
Heerlen

**Dr. P.C. Noordam**
General Directorate of Labour
Voorburg

**Dr. A. Penninks**
TNO Toxicology and Nutrition Institute
Zeist

**Prof. Dr. P.W.J. Peters**
Unit Teratology, Endocrinology and Perinatal Screening
National Institute of Public Health and Environmental
    Protection
Bilthoven

**Drs. P.G.J. Reuzel**
Medical Faculty
State University Leiden

**Prof. Dr. B. Sangster**
General Directorate of Health
Rijswijk

**Dr. F.- J. van Schooten**
Department of Health Risk Analysis and Toxicology
State University of Limburg
Maastricht

**Prof. Dr. N.M. van Straalen**
Section Ecology and Ecotoxicology
Subfaculty of Biology
Free University
Amsterdam

**J. Vandeberghe, D.V.M., Lic. Vet. Sci.**
Department of Toxicology
Janssen Research Foundation
Beerse
Belgium

**Dr. Ph. Vanparys**
Department of Genetic and *in vitro* Toxicology
Janssen Pharmaceutica N.V.
Beerse
Belgium

**Dr. A. Verheyen**
Department of Haematology
Janssen Research Foundation
Beerse
Belgium

**Prof. Dr. T.A. de Vlieger**
Section Neurophysiology and Behavioural Physiology
Department of Neurophysiology, Faculty of Biology
Free University
Amsterdam

**Prof. Dr. J.G. Vos**
Laboratory of Pathology
National Institute of Public Health and Environmental
    Protection
Bilthoven

**Prof. Dr. J. de Vries**
Faculty of Natural Sciences
Open University
Heerlen

**Dr. K.N. Woodward**
Veterinary Medicines Directorate
Surrey
United Kingdom

**Dr. A. Zwart**
TNO Toxicology and Nutrition Institute
Zeist

# Contents

# TOXICOLOGY

## Principles

## and

## Applications

# Contents Study unit 1
# Toxicology: history and scope of the field

0-8493-9232-2/96/$0.00 + $.50
© 1996 by CRC Press, Inc.

# Study unit 1

# Toxicology, history and scope of the field

*J. H. Koeman*

## INTRODUCTION

*Definition of the field of study*

Toxicology can be defined as the branch of science which is concerned with the harmful effects of chemicals on organisms and with the interaction of these substances with organisms.

*Gr. toxikon = poison*

Toxicology literally means "study of poisons". Being poisoned implies that a substance disturbs the physiological balance to such an extent that the condition of the organism concerned can no longer be considered healthy. In other words, the organism becomes ill.

Scientists who study the toxicity of chemicals and poisoning (intoxication) are known as toxicologists.

*Social objectives*

The main *social objectives* of toxicology are:

1 to elucidate the poisonous (toxic) properties of chemicals
2 to carry out scientific research in order to increase knowledge regarding the toxic properties of chemicals
3 to evaluate the hazards of chemicals to organisms in relation to the concentrations in which these substances are present in the environment (risk estimation)
4 to advise society on measures to control or prevent the harmful effects of chemicals (hazard control).

The present study unit has a dual purpose. Firstly, the nature of the field of study and its social functions are elaborated on in some detail. Secondly, the general principles relating to the processes and circumstances which determine the development of toxic effects are discussed. These general principles will be dealt with in more detail in subsequent study units.

LEARNING OBJECTIVES

After studying this unit, you are expected to:
— know the main objectives of toxicology
— have a general insight into the historical development of the discipline
— be able to give an outline of toxicology as a scientific discipline and of the most important areas of toxicology with regard to society
— have a good understanding of the qualitative aspects of toxic effects of chemicals and be able to explain or define the following concepts:
  — exposure phase
  — toxicokinetic phase

3

- — toxicodynamic phase
- — biotransformation
- — toxicity
- — intoxication
- — (bio)activation
- — detoxication
- — primary lesion
- — substance-receptor interaction
- — target organ
- — structure-activity relationship (SAR)
- — have a good understanding of the quantitative aspects of the toxic effects of chemicals and be able to explain or define the following concepts:
  - — dose-response relationship
  - — dose-time relationship
  - — acute intoxication as opposed to chronic intoxication
  - — no-effect level
  - — additive effects
  - — synergism
  - — quantitative structure-activity relationship (QSAR)
  - — selective toxicity
- — be able to clarify the above learning objectives using examples (of substances) mentioned in this study unit.

*Study hints*

The subject matter of this unit is intended to assist you in forming a mental framework (or testing framework) so that you will be able to deal with data in an orderly manner when evaluating toxicological matters or when giving advice on them. This involves logical presentation, checking completeness of the available data, insight into modes of action, etc.

The concise summaries of the various sections of the study core are the basic ingredients for such a mental framework.

The study load for this unit is estimated at between 2 and $2\frac{1}{2}$ student learning hours.

STUDY CORE

## 1    Historical aspects

*Poisonous substances of natural origin (vegetable/animal) are called toxins.*

From earliest times, man has been confronted with the poisonous properties of certain plants and animals. Poisonous substances are indeed common in nature. People who still live in close contact with nature, for example Indians, African tribes and people in Asia, possess an extensive empirical knowledge of poisonous animals and plants. Poisons were, and still are, used by these people for a wide range of applications (catching fish, poisoning arrowheads, in magic rituals and as medicines). Information on poisons was first documented by the ancient civilized races. The German scholar Ebers described Egyptian papyrus scrolls (the so-called Ebers scrolls) dating from 1550 *BC* which show that the ancient Egyptians had an extensive knowledge of the toxic and curative properties of natural products. A good deal is known about the information regarding toxic substances possessed by the Greeks and Romans. They were very interested in poisons and used them to carry out executions. For the execution of

Socrates, for example, an extract of hemlock *(Conium maculatum)* was used. It was also not unusual to use a poison to murder political opponents. Poisons were ideal for that purpose, since it was usually impossible to establish the cause of death by examining the victim. To do so would have required advanced methods of chemical analysis which were not available at the time. Early European literature also includes a considerable number of writings on toxins, including the so-called herbals, such as the Dutch "Herbarium of Kruidtboeck" by Petrus Nylandt, dating from 1673.

Poisoning sometimes assumed the character of a true environmental disaster. One example is poisoning by the fungus *Claviceps purpurea*, which occurs as a parasite in grain, particularly in rye (spurred rye) and causes the condition known as ergotism. In the past, this type of epidemic killed thousands of people who ingested the fungus with their bread. There are detailed accounts of such calamities. For example, in 992, an estimated 40 000 people died of ergotism in France and Spain. The high mortality rate was the result of the lack of knowledge of the toxic properties of the fungus (ergot alkaloids). They simply were unaware that death was caused by eating contaminated bread. It was not until much later that it was understood that large-scale cultivation of grain involved this kind of risk.

*Paracelsus introduces the principle of the dose*

During the emergence of the scientific renaissance of the 16th century, the famous Swiss physician Paracelsus (1493–1541) drew attention to the dose–dependency of the toxic effect of substances. In the words of Paracelsus, "Alle Ding sind Gifft . . . allein die Dosis macht das ein Ding kein Gifft is" (Everything is a poison . . . it is only the dose that makes it not a poison.) This principle is just as valid today.

*Bonaventura Orfila, founder of modern toxicology*

The Spanish chemist and physician Bonaventura Orfila, born on Minorca in 1787, can be considered as the founder of modern toxicology. He was the first scientist to make systematic use of test animals and also to develop methods for chemical analysis to identify poisons in tissue and body fluids. His standard work, "Traité des Poisons", was published in 1814–1815. During the 19th century, many researchers carried out experiments to investigate the effects of toxic substances. A notable example is the elucidation of the actions of carbon monoxide and curare by the French physiologist Claude Bernard (1813–1878). Towards the end of the century, numerous manuals were published, especially in German, describing both current experimental methods and the effects of a large number of substances. The introduction of legislation on foodstuffs around the turn of the century gave the impetus to the development of more or less standardized toxicological tests for coloring agents and preservatives. It was not until after World War II that a large number of new research methods were developed under the pressure of the greatly increasing range of chemicals appearing on the market. Archives für Toxikologie, the first journal explicitly created for experimental toxicology, was first published in 1930. Toxicological research is now in its heyday. From the 1960s onwards, interest in toxicology in universities has increased considerably. This is related mainly to the realization that, for the protection of our health and the quality of the environment, it is essential to have a thorough understanding of the risks that may be attached to the numerous substances produced by our society.

*Summary*

Problems connected with the toxic properties of substances are as old as mankind. The introduction of the dose principle by Paracelsus in the 16th century was a milestone in the history of toxicology. Early in the 19th century, Orfila laid the foundation for modern toxicology. The present era of major progress in toxicology has to do not only with the large number of newly developed substances, but also with the realization that a thorough understanding of the risks involved is essential for adequate protection of man and his environment.

## 2 Toxicology as a scientific discipline and description of subdisciplines

To obtain insight into the mechanisms and processes underlying the effects of poisons, in principle all basic medical–biological and chemical sciences should be integrated in toxicological research.

See section 3

Toxicology is supported by physiology, pathology, biochemistry and analytical chemistry in the study of the toxic effects and behavior of substances at the higher physiological integration levels (organism, organ).
To explain the underlying causes of toxicological processes down to the molecular level, further integration is necessary with basic disciplines such as cell biology, immunology, molecular sciences and organic chemistry (see Figure 1.1).

*"Vertical" integration with basic disciplines*

Depending on the nature of the connection between toxicological research and these basic disciplines, various subdisciplines can be distinguished. Examples are neurotoxicology, immunotoxicology, molecular toxicology, (analytical) chemical toxicology, and genetic toxicology.

*"Horizontal" integration with fields of applied research*

Apart from vertical integration with fundamental research that expands the frontiers of the life sciences, there is also *horizontal* integration with various fields of applied research in the health and environmental sciences. It is only at this level that an evaluation of the risks posed by chemicals to our health is made, and on the basis of which, society is advised by toxicologists. The main subdisciplines in which toxicology has a clear social function are clinical toxicology, nutritional toxicology, environmental (and eco-)toxicology and occupational toxicology.

Clinical toxicology
See Study Unit 38

*Clinical toxicology* is concerned with the diagnosis and treatment of poisoning, with the evaluation of methods of detection and intoxication, and with mechanisms of action in patients, both in man (human toxicology, pharmaceutical toxicology) and in animals (veterinary toxicology). It integrates toxicology, clinical medicine and clinical biochemistry or pharmacy.

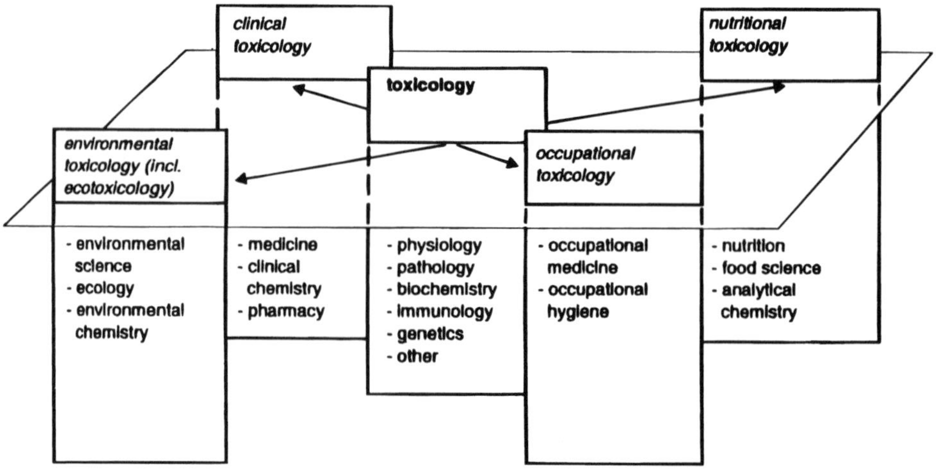

FIGURE 1.1
The position of toxicology in relation to the basic sciences and related fields.

*Nutritional toxicology*
See Study unit 40

*Nutritional toxicology* is the subdiscipline that focuses on the toxicological aspects of foodstuffs and nutritional habits. Here, risk evaluation and advice to society are based on the combination of toxicology with nutrition and food science.

*Occupational toxicology*
See Study unit 4

*Occupational toxicology* combines toxicology with occupational medicine and occupational hygiene.

*Environmental (and eco-)toxicology*
See Study unit 39

*Environmental (and eco-)toxicology* integrates the science of toxicology with subdisciplines such as (environmental) health sciences, ecology and environmental chemistry. Figure 1.1 gives a schematic overview of the various subdisciplines in toxicology.

*Interdisciplinary nature*

Toxicology is typically a *multidisciplinary* field of science, which, to an increasing extent, assumes the character of an *interdiscipline*. This implies that the integration of various disciplines in toxicology not only means that the various sciences are applied simultaneously, but also that integration poses its own specific problems.

*Summary*

Toxicology is based primarily on physiology and pathology, but is also related (vertical integration) to a number of other medical–biological and chemical sciences. Its orientation towards practical applications is expressed in its horizontal integration with clinical medicine, nutrition, work and the environment.

3    **Qualitative aspects of toxic effects**

Intoxication manifests itself in signs or symptoms of illness varying from restricted local effects to complex syndromes that may result in the death of the organism concerned.

*Intoxication as a sequence of events*
*Exposure phase*

Intoxication can be viewed as a *sequence of events* that starts with the exposure of an organism to a substance, the so-called *exposure phase*.

See also Study units 2 and 5

Subsequently, absorption of the substance can occur via various routes, followed by its distribution within the body.

*Equal and unequal distribution*

The distribution may be *equal*, which means that the substance can be found in virtually all compartments of the body (organs, tissues and body fluids). Distribution may also be unequal, in which case the substance is found in only one or a few compartments. Various organic solvents, such as benzene, are distributed equally throughout the body. An example of a substance with unequal distribution is the herbicide paraquat, which is found mainly in lung tissue (this is also the case when it has been ingested orally).

*dose = amount of the substance taken up by the body*

The amount of a substance which is taken up by the body thereby causing a certain internal exposure (body burden) is called the *dose*.

*metabolites = conversion products of substances*
*(bio)activation = production of metabolites that are more toxic than the parent substance*
*detoxication = production of metabolites that are less toxic than the parent substance*
See also Study units 3–6
*Toxicokinetic phase*
*kinêtikos (Gr.) = putting in motion*

The conversion of a substance may produce metabolites that are more toxic than the parent substance (*(bio)activation*) or less toxic (*detoxication*). Recent research has shown that (bio)activation is much more common than was previously thought. Examples of substances for which this is the case are parathion, benzo[*a*]pyrene, hexane, vinyl chloride, aflatoxin B-1 and chloroform.

The whole process of absorption, distribution, transformation and excretion is usually referred to as the *toxicokinetic phase* or *kinetics* of a substance.

*Toxicodynamic phase*
*dynamis (Gr.) = power*
*Receptors*

The *toxicodynamic phase* comprises the sequence of events following the interaction with target molecules that eventually results in a toxic effect. It therefore concerns the mode of action of a substance. All cases of poisoning are based on a molecular reaction between the substance (or a metabolite) on the one hand and endogenous molecules on the other. The endogenous molecules may be DNA, molecular structures in membranes, or enzymes. These endogenous sites of action are known as *receptors*.

Study unit 7 deals in detail with the meaning of the term "receptor" in toxicology.

*primary lesion = damage resulting from reaction between substance and receptor*
*laesio (Lat.) = injury*
*Levels of biological integration*

The primary injury resulting from the reaction at the molecular level is termed a primary or biochemical lesion. It occurs at the subcellular or cellular level.

If a relatively large number of cells are affected, the organ involved will no longer be able to function normally and the toxic effect will become apparent as an illness. The process of intoxication progresses from the molecular level to higher levels of biological integration in the following order: cell, tissue, organ, organism, population, ecosystem. The fact that, at any given level, toxic effects become manifest, also implies that the extent of the molecular lesion is such that compensatory repair and regenerative mechanisms have *failed*. An important consequence of this is that the absence of toxic symptoms at a particular level does not necessarily mean that no damage has been inflicted at lower levels of biological integration. This aspect will be dealt with in more detail in the following section. Figure 1.2 gives a schematic representation of the phased nature of intoxication.

*Target organs*
*hepar = liver*
*nephros = kidney*
*neuron = nerve*

Many cases of intoxication involve effects which are organ-specific, that is, they manifest themselves only in certain organs (target organs) and not in others. This may be because a substance (or metabolite) reacts specifically with receptors that are characteristic of a certain organ or organ system, and has no affinity with

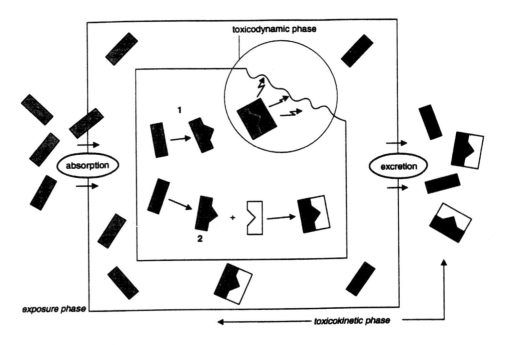

FIGURE 1.2

Sequence of events in the different stages of the toxic effect of a chemical.

After absorption, the substance enters the bloodstream, and subsequently an organ. In this example, biotransformation of the substance activates it. Some of the metabolites react with receptors, resulting in primary lesions and injuries to the organ (1). Others are detoxified by biotransformation enzymes, for example through conjugation with glucuronic acid or glutathione (2). The parent substance as well as detoxication products are excreted.

For glucuronic acid, see Study unit 3

other receptors. On the basis of this phenomenon, many substances can be classified according to the organ-specific nature of their effect. Effects may, for example, be termed hepatotoxic (toxic to the liver, e.g. carbon tetrachloride), nephrotoxic (toxic to the kidney, e.g. mercuric chloride) or neurotoxic (toxic to the nervous system, e.g. cyclohexane). An organ-specific effect may, however, also result from unequal distribution of the substance in the body, causing the exposure of certain organs to be much greater than that of others. The fact that paraquat, which was mentioned in the previous section, is found primarily in the lungs after it has entered the body, probably explains why symptoms of intoxication mainly become manifest in that organ.

There are, however, also substances that display multiple organ toxicity, in that they affect several organs. Depending on the dose and duration of exposure, a substance such as lead affects the intestines, kidneys, nervous system and bone marrow.

*Lead and cadmium have several target organs*

Cadmium is primarily nephrotoxic, in other words, the kidney is the most sensitive organ, although the liver, testis, placenta and bone tissue may also be affected at certain exposure levels. In order to evaluate toxicological risks and set standards, it is essential that the organ functions which are most sensitive to a given substance are identified.

*High toxicity often corresponds with blockage of receptors in physiologically key positions*

Most toxic substances known to date are, without exception, substances that react highly selectively with receptors having a function in physiological key positions. An example is botulin (a toxin from the bacillus *Clostridium botulinum*, the most toxic substance known!), that selectively blocks the release of acetylcholine at nerve endings. One of its effects is that the muscles become completely paralyzed. Another example is tetrodotoxin, produced in the Japanese puffer fish, which blocks the transport of sodium in nerve fibers, also causing complete paralysis. It is, incidentally, interesting that the most toxic substances known are of natural origin. An exception to this is tetrachlorodibenzodioxin, a man-made poison tragically associated with events in the Italian town of Seveso. This dioxin blocks receptors that play a vital role in the genetic control of cellular metabolism in various organs, including the liver.

*Prediction of toxicity using SARs*

The primary toxic lesion is caused by a reaction at the molecular level between a foreign toxicant and endogenous molecules. This reaction is determined by the properties of both the components involved. It is therefore important to find out to what degree the toxic potency of a substance can be derived from its structure. Knowledge of this could, for example, lead to recognition of hazardous substances, and to the development of chemical technology that would avoid the synthesis of dangerous structures.

See also Study unit 8
*Structure–activity relationship*

Molecular toxicological research is particularly involved with the analysis of so-called *structure–activity relationships (SARs)*. A number of dangerous structures are now known. Most organophosphorous esters, for example, inhibit the enzyme acetylcholinesterase, while alkylating substances are usually mutagenic. Aromatic amines are not infrequently carcinogenic. Current progress in the fields of organic chemistry and pharmacology, together with growing interest in the study of toxicological mechanisms, suggests that knowledge of structure-activity relationships is likely to increase significantly in the near future.

*Summary*

A toxic effect is viewed as the result of a sequence of events in which the exposure phase is followed by a toxicokinetic and toxicodynamic phase (in which the toxic action actually occurs). Of particular significance is the fact that most substances are converted into metabolites in the body (transformation or biotransformation). These metabolites are sometimes less toxic than the parent substance (detoxication), but sometimes more so ((bio)activation). Every case of intoxication is based on a reaction at the molecular level (substance-receptor interaction). Most toxic substances are substances which react highly selectively with receptors in physiological key systems.

## 4 Quantitative Aspects of Toxic Action

*Intensity of toxic effects*

The extent to which a substance is toxic is determined primarily by the dose after which the toxic effect appears. There are, for example, various gradations of acute oral toxicity. Substances that induce toxic effects when taken orally in dosages on the order of a number of micrograms per kilogram body weight are *extremely toxic. Very toxic* substances are those that exert their acute effect when the dosage is on the order of a number of milligrams per kilogram, while *moderately toxic* substances have an acute toxic effect when administered in a dosage of some hundreds of milligrams per kilogram. Above that level, up to a few grams per kilogram, one is dealing with *slightly toxic* substances. Substances causing an acute toxic effect at 5 grams or more per kilogram are considered to be *non-toxic.* This classification is rather subjective, but it is nevertheless of practical significance in grouping poisons.

An exact quantification of the intensity of toxic effects of a substance is often impossible. In most cases, a descriptive approach has to suffice. A numerical approach to the relationship between dose and effect is possible however if one restricts oneself to an arbitrarily chosen, measurable aspect of the effect such as lethality, functional damage to an organ, or the development of tumors. In an occupational situation, for example, one can register and measure certain complaints and correlate them with data on the level of exposure to a certain substance.

The same can be done in toxicity tests using animals though this situation provides more possibilities, because at the end of the experiment, during dissection and follow-up research, a particular intensity of the toxic effect can be studied more accurately than in intact organisms.

*Humans and experimental animals display different individual reactions*

If the determination of the relationship between dose and effect is based on this principle, it rapidly becomes clear that humans as well as test animals show interindividual differences in the sensitivity to a specific dose. This is related to biological variability within a population.

*No-effect level*

For each dose or concentration, therefore, there is a specific frequency with which an effect occurs in a group of organisms or a human population, the so-called response. The higher the dose, the higher the frequency. This relationship can be presented graphically in the form of a frequency (%) curve and this procedure is regularly applied in toxicology. In this way, the relationship between dose and effect can be clearly illustrated. Next, via graphic extrapolation, the median value of the effective dose range can be determined, while via extrapolation the non-effective dose can be estimated. This latter piece of information is important in setting safety standards for potentially toxic substances (no-effect level).

Figure 1.3 is an example of a curve showing the relationship between dose and effect. It shows a dose-response relationship, as the effect is expressed in terms of the fraction of a population displaying the effect.

*Dose-response relationship*

The dose is plotted logarithmically, which is common practice because the sensitivity in a population shows approximately a normal distribution in relation to the log-dose. Transformation from dose to log-dose thus gives a symmetrical sigmoid curve. A mathematical transformation is sometimes applied in this type of graphic presentation, for example on the x-axis, by expressing the effect per-

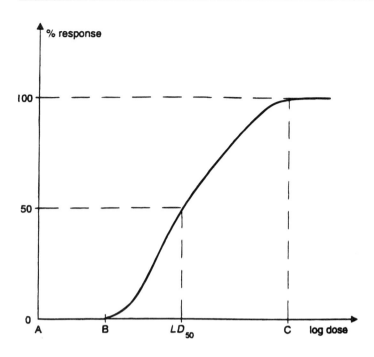

FIGURE   1.3
General shape of the relationship between dose and effect (response) plotted as a frequency (%) curve (explained in the text of this study unit).

centages in terms of different mathematical units. When this is done, the relationship between dose and response is linear. Further details on this aspect can be found in Study unit 7.

*Median lethal dose, $LD_{50}$*

Figure 1.3 shows how extrapolation can be used to estimate the $LD_{50}$ of a substance, if the curve represents the relationship between dose and percentage of deaths in an animal population. The $LD_{50}$ is the median lethal dose, i.e. the dose calculated to produce death in 50% of the population.

The range AB in Figure 1.3 represents the non-effective dose, in this case the non-lethal dose. Point B, which is in fact the $LD_0$, cannot be established exactly, since this point on the curve is determined by the presence of a small number of relatively sensitive animals in the population under study. Therefore, it can be assumed that if the experiment is repeated with a larger number of animals, point B will shift to the left. Similarly, point C, which is determined by the least sensitive animals, will move to the right. In an identical experiment, using animals from the same strain, the $LD_{50}$ will remain in approximately the same position. This explains the fact that, when the lethal effect of substances is represented numerically, use of the $LD_{50}$ is preferred to that of $LD_0$ and $LD_{100}$. Other effects can also be represented by means of a frequency (%) curve, for example inhibition of growth and certain specific types of effect (cancer, liver and kidney conditions etc.).

*See next section*

Although point B shows a tendency to move to the left as larger numbers of organisms are studied, it will never reach point A. Empirical experience and theoretical insight into the mechanisms of toxicity of chemicals justify the assumption that a certain minimum dose must first be exceeded before any significant disturbance of function (for example inhibition of enzymes or damage to membranes) will result. An exception might be made for carcinogenic substances with an initiating (mutagenic) effect, since here an extremely small dose may be sufficient to cause the transformation of a normal cell into a preneoplastic cell or cancer cell. In that case, an increase in the number of test animals or humans will cause point B to shift more and more in the direction of point A.

*Acute and chronic toxicity*

Short-term exposure of organisms (to relatively high doses of a substance) generally leads to symptoms that are different from those following long-term exposure (to relatively low doses). In the former case we are dealing with *acute toxicity* and in the latter with *chronic toxicity*. When evaluating the toxicity of a substance it is necessary to take into account both acute and chronic data.

For many substances, a connection can be demonstrated between the concentration or the level in the diet to which organisms are exposed and the exposure time that is needed before a certain effect occurs. This time period is generally referred to as the *latency period*, i.e. the period of time between the moment at which exposure to the substance starts and the moment at which a certain effect appears.

*Relationship between dose and duration of exposure*

Certain irritant gases, e.g. phosgene, follow Haber's law, which states that their effect depends on the product of concentration and duration of exposure. This relationship, which is valid to a greater or lesser extent for many substances, indicates an irreversible interaction between substance and receptor. It need not necessarily mean that the substance accumulates on or near the receptor, but may also point to cumulation of the effect (hit and run effect). Experiments have shown that for most carcinogens also, the duration of exposure (up to the moment when tumors start to develop) is approximately inversely proportional to the daily dose. In other words:

$$d(\text{daily dose}) \times t(\text{duration of exposure}) = \text{constant}$$

*Addition: synergism*

When organisms are exposed to a combination of substances, the possibility that the different substances will influence each other's action must be taken into account. This is known as *additive* if there is a proportional summation of effects. If the combined effect is greater than would be expected on the basis of the individual effects, this is known as *synergism* or *potentiation*. In the case of synergism, it is often found that one substance influences the biotransformation of the other. For example, in Pakistan some years ago, workers who had sprayed pesticides suffered from serious intoxication after working with the organophosphate ester malathion. Normally, malathion is not very toxic. However, its formulation appeared to contain isomalathion as an impurity, and this is a powerful inhibitor of the detoxication of malathion. In this case, isomalathion acted as a synergist of malathion.

*For QSAR see Study unit 8*

Increasingly, attempts are made to analyze structure-activity relationships both qualitatively and quantitatively (*QSARs or Quantitative Structure-Activity Relationships*).

For a number of acutely toxic chemicals (e.g. chlorophenols, certain solvents), it has been reported that their toxicity in fish could quantitatively be described using lipophilicity parameters like the octanol-water partition coefficient (see Study unit 8) of the substances ($P_{oct-water}$). In this case, the toxicity is apparently related to the concentration of the substances in the fish. Most mechanisms of toxicity are more complex and only a few parameters can be used in a QSAR approach.

*Summary*

The toxicity of a substance is mainly determined by the dose at which the toxic effect occurs. Toxicity is therefore not an independent characteristic of a substance but is always a function of the quantity of the substance that is absorbed by the organism. Whether or not a toxic effect appears is determined by the dose.

The toxicity of a substance is the reciprocal value of the dose necessary to cause a toxic effect, and is a function of the molecular properties of the substance. When evaluating the toxicity of substances, both acute and chronic data must be taken into account, since short-term exposure to relatively high concentrations generally causes symptoms different from those of long-term exposure to relatively low concentrations.

## 5 Interspecies and interindividual differences in sensitivity

There may be considerable differences in sensitivity to toxic substances between species and between individuals. This should be taken into consideration when evaluating the risks associated with chemicals. The most important factors involved in these differences are dealt with in the following subsections.

### 5.1 INTERSPECIES DIFFERENCES

*Anatomy and body size*

Small animals have a relatively large body surface/body volume ratio. This means that contact with a substance via the skin surface can lead to a relatively large quantity being absorbed. It also means that the metabolic rate is relatively high, so that more food is ingested. If the food happens to be contaminated, a relatively high dose of a substance will be ingested in comparison to larger species.

*Physiology*

*Selective toxicity*

An extreme example is the difference between animals and plants. The toxicity of many insecticides results from their effects on the nervous system. Plants therefore are relatively insensitive. On the other hand animals, are relatively insensitive to most herbicides, many of which affect physiological mechanisms that are characteristic of plants (e.g. photosynthesis). This is termed *selective toxicity*.

### 5.2 INTERINDIVIDUAL DIFFERENCES WITHIN A SPECIES

*Genetic differences*

*Hypersensitivity*

Hypersensitivity can be based on genetically determined variability in enzyme activity. Individuals with a G6PD (glucose-6-phosphate dehydrogenase) deficiency in their red blood cells are hypersensitive to oxidative substances such as aromatic nitro substances, chlorates, antimalarial agents and glycosides from broad beans.

*Age*

*High-risk group*

Babies are more sensitive to the toxic effect of nitrates than adults (methemoglobinemia). Their sensitivity is ascribed to a (transient) deficiency in NADH-methemoglobin reductase. Hence, in this case babies form a *high-risk group*.

*Dietary habits and lifestyle*

See also Study units 3 and 4

Diet appears to be of great significance in the development of cancer. In the body many carcinogenic substances are activated to become reactive metabolites under the influence of biotransformation enzymes. This so-called endogenous (bio)activation is influenced by factors such as the fat content of foods and the presence of particular natural substances in foods (e.g. the anti-carcinogenic indoles in cabbage).

*Disease*

*Other substances*

Individuals with a sclerotic constriction of the coronary artery in the heart, for example, are more sensitive to carbon monoxide.

*Simultaneous exposure to other substances*

*See also synergism in section 4*
*Alcohol intolerance*

Exposure to various industrial substances (for example $CS_2$) and pesticides (like dithiocarbamates) can lead to so-called *alcohol intolerance*. In other words, the sensitivity to alcohol is increased (reduced biotransformation of alcohol).

*Summary*

Differences in sensitivity between species are mainly related to differences in anatomy, body size and physiology. Differences in sensitivity between individuals within a species generally originate from factors such as heredity, age, dietary habits and lifestyle, disease and simultaneous exposure to other substances.

SELF ASSESSMENT QUESTIONS

1    Without consulting the text, draw figures which illustrate
     a   the multidisciplinary nature of toxicology
     b   the phased nature of the toxic effect of a substance
     c   the dose-response curve. Add written marginal notes.

2    Give an outline or definition of the terms and concepts which are mentioned in the section Learning objectives.

3    What does Haber's law state?

FEEDBACK

**Answers to the self assessment questions**

1 + 2 Check and correct your answers on the basis of the text of this study unit.

3    Haber's law states that the toxic effect of a substance is determined by the product of the concentration and the duration of exposure.

# Contents Study unit 2
## Exposure: qualitative and quantitative aspects

0-8493-9232-2/96/$0.00 + $.50
© 1996 by CRC Press, Inc.

# Study unit 2

# Exposure: qualitative and quantitative aspects

*A. Musch*

INTRODUCTION

The (health) risk that organisms run as a result of the presence of substances in their environment is determined by two factors:

1    the toxicity of the substances;

2    the fate of the substances in the environment and in the organism.

The toxicity of substances will be returned to in other parts of this course, for example in the study units on dose-response relationships and cytotoxicity. The fate of a substance in the environment determines the way in which and the extent to which organisms are exposed. The fate of a substance in the organism determines whether or not an effect manifests itself.

> ASSIGNMENT   2.1
> This study unit deals with exposure. How is this term interpreted in everyday life, e.g. how is it defined in dictionaries?

*Qualitative and quantitative aspects*      In toxicology, *exposure* is defined in qualitative terms as the condition in which chemicals come into contact with, and radiation penetrates, an organism. Exposure can also be quantified. In practice, this distinction between qualitative and quantitative aspects of exposure is not always consistently implemented. In this course the distinction is maintained as much as possible. The fate of a substance in the environment, as well as in the organism, depends on a large number of parameters (variables). These can be arranged into categories which correspond to the nature of the events that take place, from the moment the substance is introduced into the environment up to the moment when its effect becomes evident. Consequently, the following phases can be distinguished:

1    production phase (sources);

2    environmental-kinetic phase;

3    (quantitative) exposure phase;

4    toxicokinetic phase;

5    toxicodynamic phase.

The (quantitative) exposure phase covers the moment at which the substance comes into contact with the organism. The kinetic phases cover the fate of the substance in the environment and the organism. The interaction with the organism, which leads to harmful effects, forms the dynamic phase. Figure 2.1 shows a schematic overview of the various stages. Burdening an individual by

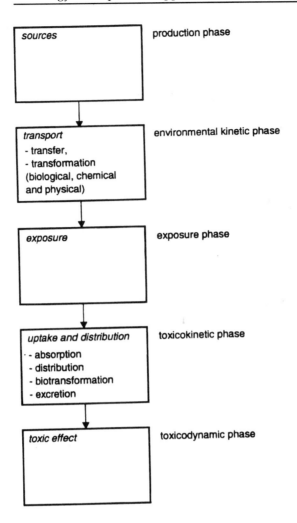

FIGURE    2.1
Different phases in the fate of a toxic substance

exposure to a substance may have certain consequences for the individual's health. The importance of this consequence, i.e. the severity of the effect, depends, on the one hand, on the magnitude of the burden and, on the other, on the sensitivity of the exposed individual. These aspects will be discussed in section 6.

This study unit deals with aspects that characterize the interface between the environment and the organism. It should be noted that the subjects covered here are not limited to just one of the phases in Figure 2.1. The qualitative and quantitative aspects of exposure will be discussed, as well as the methods used for determining the level of exposure.

LEARNING OBJECTIVES

After studying this unit, you should be able to:
— define in your own words the following concepts and apply them:
    — qualitative aspects of exposure
    — quantitative aspects of exposure
    — exposure routes
    — emission and deposition
    — body burden

- biological, chemical and environmental monitoring
- hazard and risk

— use examples to indicate whether a hazard or a risk is involved.

— give an illustrative example of the significance of the form of exposure in producing an effect.

— indicate which processes can lead to exposure and describe these processes with the help of examples.

— illustrate by means of examples how "external" factors can influence exposure.

— identify the most important factors and conditions that may be responsible for differences in sensitivity between species as well as between individuals of one species, and be able to define the concept of hypersensitivity.

— indicate which internal and external factors and processes determine which groups in a population are high-risk groups.

*Study hints*

It is useful to write down new terms as you come across them, and to check afterwards whether you still remember what they mean.

The average study load of this unit is estimated at $3\frac{1}{2}$ student learning hours. If you are familiar with the field of environmental science, many terms will already be familiar to you.

STUDY CORE

## 1 Form of exposure

The occurrence and magnitude of harmful effects and the part of the organism in which they arise depend on the form in which the organism is exposed to the toxic compound.

The form of exposure is determined by the *environmental compartment* in which the organism exists (water, soil, air), the *physical state* of the compound (gas, liquid), the *physicochemical properties* of the compound (soluble in water or not) and the *nature of the contact* (single or prolonged).

Humans and animals can come into contact with toxic substances intentionally or by accident. Intentional exposure occurs through administration or intake of a substance, which may happen in the framework of research (toxicological experiments on animals), through abuse (heroin, deliberate poisoning) or by way of therapy (anticancer drugs). Medical and pharmaceutical technology has developed many methods for the administration of drugs.

> ASSIGNMENT 2.2
> Give some examples of such methods.

Toxic compounds can also come into contact with organisms unintentionally or by accident. Chemicals may be present unintentionally in food or drinking water (nitrate in spinach, for example, or toluene that enters drinking water through plastic pipes). Unlike the situation where a substance is deliberately administered, in these cases there is usually only a poor understanding of the compounds to which an organism is exposed, both in a qualitative and a quantitative sense. The relationship between dose and response will be discussed in Study unit 7.

## 2 Exposure routes

The chance of contact with harmful substances is usually greatest in the immediate vicinity of the source of pollution. Exposure is, however, also possible over considerable distances. Humans and animals can take up pollutants in a number of ways (*exposure routes*). Exposure may take place, for example, through food or air, via solids and liquids that accidentally or deliberately come into contact with the skin, through (drinking) water, through direct or indirect contact from mother to child, or via an artificial route.

Table 2.1 shows the various routes of exposure. The table will be discussed in detail in the following subsections.

## 2.1 FOOD

Apart from nutrients, food contains numerous other organic and inorganic compounds. A great many of these are substances whose structures and effects—

TABLE 2.1
Sources and Exposure Routes of Xenobiotics

| vehicle | source | cause | physical form | route | entry point | example |
|---|---|---|---|---|---|---|
| food | natural | characteristic of a plant/animal | in solution, crystalline or bound | direct | mouth→ gastrointestinal tract | nitrate in spinach |
| | artificial | contamination, addition | ditto | direct or indirect | ditto | cadmium in cereals; coloring agents in jam |
| surface water | natural | naturally occurring minerals and organic compounds | dissolved or absorbed | direct | ditto or via gills and skin | fluoride |
| | artificial | waste water discharge | ditto | direct (waste water discharge), leaching out, washing, chemical transformation | ditto | pesticides, chloro-hydrocarbons |
| drinking water | natural | composition of mineral water | ditto | direct from rock and soil | mouth gastrointestinal tract | fluoride |
| | artificial | pollution of the source or water | dissolved | from soil pollution or pipes | ditto | nitrate, copper |
| air (traffic) | usually artificial | emissions from industries, homes exhaust gases | gas or dust particles | usually direct | lungs | $SO_2$ (combustion) Pb (traffic) |
| skin | intentional | medication | solid, dissolved or emulsion | administration | skin | ointments, creams |
| | unintentional | polluted workplace | ditto | direct | ditto | benzene |
| other | intentional | e.g. medication | dissolved (usually) | direct administration | e.g. intravenous | drugs, narcotics |
| | intentional | characteristics of the animal | | animal bite or sting | skin, sub-cutaneous, circulation | snake venom |

20

both beneficial and harmful—are unknown. Among those that are known, there are several toxic compounds which occur naturally in food, but in such minute quantities that they do not cause any adverse effects. Some edible plants contain highly toxic substances which, in the course of normal preparation, undergo degradation or disappear. For example, certain poisonous proteins present in various types of beans, are denatured by cooking.

*Contaminants*
*PCBs is an abbreviation of polychlorinated biphenyls*

Foodstuffs also contain a variety of non-natural and undesirable substances. These may be *contaminants* such as pesticide residues, heavy metals taken up from polluted soil, residues of veterinary drugs in meat, etc. Pollution of the soil can lead to the occurrence of undesirable substances in foodstuffs. In this respect cadmium, mercury and PCBs are notorious examples. One route of exposure is the consumption of crops grown in polluted soil. An indirect route of exposure is through eating beef or drinking milk from cows that have grazed on polluted grasslands.

The abundant use of nitrogen fertilizer can lead to excessive nitrate levels in green vegetables. Under certain conditions, nitrate can be converted to the much more poisonous nitrite and ultimately even to a carcinogenic nitrosamine (Figure 2.2).

*Additives*

Some substances *(additives)* are intentionally added to foodstuffs to influence their shelf-life, color and taste and this (at excessive concentrations) could cause harmful effects.

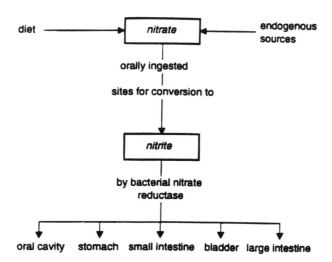

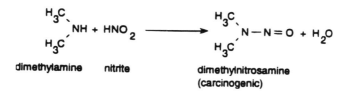

FIGURE 2.2
Conversion of nitrate, via nitrite into the carcinogen nitrosamine

Formation of nitrosamine can take place in the stomach (low pH) following consumption of food rich in nitrates, for example spinach, together with an amine-containing dietary component that can be nitrosated.

21

## 2.2 WATER

Through water, organisms become exposed to a large number of potentially harmful substances. A distinction should be made between surface water and drinking water. Aquatic animals can take up substances from the surrounding water with their food, by swallowing (suspended) particles, through the skin or via the gills. Water-dwelling mammals, such as whales and seals, are more comparable to terrestrial animals as far as exposure to poisonous substances is concerned. In general, the uptake of water-soluble substances through the skin is negligible in these animals compared to uptake in food (often fish or invertebrates which swim in the same polluted water). One of the characteristics of aquatic animals such as fish, crustaceans and mollusks is that they possess gills. Large quantities of water pass over the surfaces of these gills, which are filled with blood. The uptake of substances from the water through the thin epithelial layer into the blood is generally very efficient. For many substances an equilibrium is soon established between the substance in water and that inside the animal. The supply through food and by other means is then largely irrelevant.

> ASSIGNMENT 2.3
> Describe to what extent sea mammals and sea fish are similar with regard to food chain effects.

*Drinking water*

Water agencies are responsible for the provision of good quality drinking water to the consumer. This responsibility extends as far as the consumer's front door. Therefore, these agencies must not only oversee the quality of water in the reservoirs, but also prevent possible contamination along the way. In the past, water pipes were often made of copper and, especially in houses, of lead. As a result, the water became contaminated with these metals. Considerable concentrations of these metals may build up, particularly if the water stands in the pipes for some time. The use of plastic pipes also has its hazards. If the pipes pass through polluted soil, the pollutants sometimes permeate the pipes, again resulting in contaminated water.

*Methyl bromide is an inexpensive insect fumigant for soil, fruits, grains and warehouses.*

Organic substances are particularly notorious in causing problems. A well-known example is the pollution of drinking water with methyl bromide in areas where there are a large number of greenhouses.

## 2.3 AIR

*Air*
*Indoor air*

As a result of human activities, all kinds of irritating as well as toxic substances are found in the air. These substances can be present as gases, but also in the form of very fine particles and aerosols. In countries with a temperate climate, people spend about 70% of their time indoors, largely in their own homes. With regard to exposure time, the air inside homes should be given a good deal of attention. Indoors, the air—which may already have been polluted before it entered the house—is contaminated by substances originating from heating equipment and cookers (carbon monoxide, nitrogen oxides), cigarette smoke, paint, detergents, insulation material, etc. A well-known example is the release of formaldehyde from chipboard glued with urea formaldehyde, or from urea formaldehyde used for insulation.

*Outdoor air*

Pollution of outdoor air arises mainly from various types of industries, ranging from refineries and chemical plants to laundries, as well as from the combustion of fossil fuels ($SO_2$, $NO_x$) and traffic (CO, $NO_x$, Pb, asbestos, hydrocarbons).

22

Outdoor air has no boundaries within our atmosphere. This means that pollutants which have been released into the air can be distributed over a wide area in a relatively short time, depending on the weather. This leads to dilution of the contaminants and hence to a rapid decline in their effects. This also implies, however, that removal of pollutants from outdoor air is impossible. This can only be done at the source.

## 2.4 THE SKIN

Some lipophilic substances (substances poorly soluble in water but readily soluble in fat), such as the solvents trichloroethylene and perchloroethylene, can penetrate the body via the skin at a surprising rate. The intact skin with its sebaceous surface layer is relatively inaccessible to water-soluble substances. If the skin is damaged, this barrier to the uptake of such substances is removed. In the case of exposure to dissolved substances, the nature of the solvent (fat/oil or water) is very important. Exposure via the skin can take place more or less intentionally through the use of ointments, creams, cosmetics and the like. Most cases of exposure via the skin are occupational. Examples include workers in the chemical industry, crop dusters and office cleaners. In children, contact with polluted soil can also lead to exposure via the skin.

## 2.5 EGG, YOLK AND PLACENTA

Teratogenic substances, see
Study unit 31

*Egg*

*Yolk*
*Placenta*

Toxic substances can cause damage to the offspring via the parent animals in various ways. Some substances damage genetic material (usually DNA). Mutagenic substances can exert their effects in male as well as in female gametes. Some substances, the so-called teratogens, affect the fetus. Especially in early development, there are stages at which the developing animal is highly sensitive to damage caused by toxic substances. If the mother has ingested or been exposed to toxic substances, these may be found in the *eggs* (birds, fish) with the effects frequently developing as the embryo uses up the nutrients in the *yolk*. The toxic substances may also be passed on to the fetus through the *placenta*. In humans, for example, the concentration of lead in the fetus is about the same as that in the mother. Substances can also have an indirect teratogenic effect, if, for instance, they cause damage to the uterine wall or affect the blood supply to the fetus. This is the case for cadmium. This metal is transported by the placenta to the fetus in only small quantities, but it inhibits the development of blood vessels in the placenta, so that the blood supply to the fetus is sub-optimal. Various lipophilic substances, such as chlorinated hydrocarbons (DDT, dioxins, PCBs), are known to be present in high concentrations in the fatty yolks of fish and birds, with serious consequences for the earliest stages of development of these animals. In mammals, some toxic compounds are partially excreted, as the parent compound or as metabolite(s), in the milk (aflatoxin metabolites, PCBs). This means that infants can be orally exposed to these substances through the mother.

## 2.6 ARTIFICIAL ROUTES

Exposure to undesirable substances can also take place through injection or infusion into the bloodstream, and via treatments such as kidney dialysis, in which substances from the material used can diffuse into the plasma (for example, components of synthetic material, e.g. plastics). An important aspect of this is that in these forms of exposure a number of uptake barriers are circumvented and that, unlike in the case of uptake through the mouth or intestine, the liver with its high metabolic (often detoxicating) capacity does not have to be passed first.

## 2.7 EXPOSURE VIA MORE THAN ONE ROUTE

If a substance is present in drinking water as well as in food and air, combined exposure takes place along various routes. Depending on the substance, these routes will contribute to different extents to the total uptake. If, for example, liquid mercury is spilled in a room, people who work or live there will come into contact with it in several ways: through skin contact, swallowing or inhalation. However, only inhalation leads to uptake sufficient for poisoning.

*Direct versus systemic*

A distinction must be made between substances that have a direct effect, on specific areas of the body (locally acting substances) and substances whose effect is established after distribution throughout the body (systemically acting substances). In the latter case, uptake via the various exposure routes must be added. When this is done, the possible differences in kinetics for the various routes will have to be taken into account. This can be done by using ratios which indicate what dosages yield similar effects, assuming that the effect is the same for either route.

ASSIGNMENT 2.4
Exposure to cadmium takes place predominantly via food and drinking water. Heavy smokers, however, are also exposed via inhalation. Cadmium uptake via food (under normal circumstances) is about 6% of the amount present. From cigarette smoke, however, 40–50% is taken up. What ratio would you deduce from these data?

## 3 Chemical and Physical Speciation in Relation to Exposure

*Speciation is the molecular form in which an element is present*

When evaluating exposure to a poisonous substance, the form in which the substance is present, its physical as well as its chemical form, plays an important part.

*Medium*

The medium in which the substance is present also has a determining influence on the exposure. The mobility of a substance in soil is many times less than that in water. What influence such differences have depends on the substance itself. Also important is whether the polluted environmental compartment is the biotope of the organism under investigation. Exposure to a substance dispersed in the soil is quite different for an earthworm than for humans.

*Chelation = formation of stable complexes of metal ions with certain substances, the so-called chelators*

Substances may occur freely, but also bound to particles or proteins, as complexes or chelates. Substances enclosed in soil minerals or dust particles will only contribute to exposure once they have been released, e.g. by leaching out from fly ash. (If fly ash is in prolonged contact with water, it gradually releases certain chemicals.)

*Chemical form*

Related substances can nevertheless show considerable differences in toxicity due to differences in kinetics and dynamics. This is clearly demonstrated for metals. Quite often it is not the element as such that presents the health risk but rather the specific compound. Metals can occur in the unbound state, or in inorganic or organic compounds. Inorganic (and also some organic) compounds may or may not be ionized (depending among other factors, on pH). Insoluble salts are much less toxic than soluble salts (unless the former are converted to a soluble substance in the body). Orally administered $BaCl_2$, for example, is highly toxic, while $BaSO_4$ is used as an X-ray contrast medium. The different valencies of many metals ($Cu^+$ and $Cu^{2+}$, $As^{3+}$ and $As^{5+}$) are all capable of forming compounds. Trivalent arsenic compounds, for example, are found to be much more toxic than the pentavalent compounds. Organometal compounds are frequently widely different from the inorganic metal compounds. For example, lead, lead salts and tetraethyl lead differ greatly with regard to routes of exposure and toxicity.

*Physical form*

As far as the physical form of the substance is concerned, exposure is influenced by whether the substance is present as a gas, liquid or solid, whether the substance is dissolved or attached to particles, or whether it is present in the form of smaller or larger particles itself.

*Volatility*

Whether free metals can cause exposure of any significance depends on the volatility of the metal (metallic mercury can be inhaled), or its state of dispersion. Metallic particles in a forge can sometimes lead to severe exposure of the workers through inhalation (causing "metal fume fever") or via skin contact. Nickel is known to cause skin irritation.

*Metal fume fever = severe feverish attacks resulting from inhalation of metal vapor*

In general, little information is available about the form in which substances, particularly heavy metals, occur in the environment and in food. It is often easier to determine in what form they occur in water or in air. Usually, numerous forms are present simultaneously, and in most cases it is not known which form is (mainly) responsible for the toxicity.

## 4 Toxicological Significance of the Exposure Route

Although toxic effects are evident only after absorption, it is still important to know by which route a substance has entered the body.

Whether or not a substance is absorbed, and at what rate, is determined by the barriers which are encountered along the route of entry into the body. If the absorption rate is slow compared to the rate of excretion or detoxication, the effect can be expected to be lower than in the opposite situation. What may be a barrier for one substance can be a transport route for another (the placenta, for example).

> What is an essential difference between uptake through the lungs or the skin and uptake via the mouth→stomach→intestines?

After uptake via the lungs, the mucous membrane of the mouth, the skin or intravenous injection, the substance enters the general circulation directly (although the rate at which this occurs will vary considerably for the different routes). After oral ingestion and gastrointestinal uptake, the substance is first transported to the liver with its many biotransformation pathways. These can lead to products that are more (intoxication by reactive metabolites) or less (detoxication) toxic.

Some substances can also have local effects on skin, mucous membranes or lungs.

## 5 Quantitative Aspects of Exposure

The hazards that substances can present are determined largely by the environmental burden and the extent of the related exposure of the organisms in that environment. If adequate legislation and regulations concerning pollutants are to be achieved, there must first be a clear insight into the quantitative relationships between pollution and exposure of certain organisms in a particular environmental compartment.

### 5.1 FROM SOURCE TO EXPOSURE

*Emission*

*Emission* is the process of discharge or release of substances, organisms or energy (sound, radiation or heat). In addition, the term is also used to indicate the quantity that is discharged or released. Emission into water is usually referred to as discharge.

*Transmission*
*Dispersion*

*Dispersion* of the substance into the environment is known as *transmission*. Emission is usually expressed in terms of weight per unit time (the total emission of nitrogen oxides in certain parts of Western Europe is approximately 500 000 metric tons per year). Sometimes concentrations are given, which is important to the immediate vicinity of the source and to the prevention of acute poisoning. During the transport of the substance from the source to the exposed organism a number of processes take place, such as dispersion (dilution), physical changes (forming of droplets or breakdown of dust particles), chemical changes (hydrolysis, photolysis, oxidation). During the transport a part will stay dissolved in water or as a vapor in the air, leading to an *exposure concentration*, another part will deposit into subterranean water, soil, surfaces of plants and animals. This is called *deposition*.

> ASSIGNMENT 2.5
> Pollution of air by nitrogen oxides in a busy street is sometimes expressed in terms of the concentration at a level of 1.5 meters above the road. Why would measurements be taken at that particular level?

*Deposition*

*Deposition* is expressed in units of weight per surface area per time unit. In the US, for example, about 50 mg cadmium per $m^2$ per month is found to be deposited in homes. Deposition of air pollutants can take place as "dry deposition" (= settling by gravitation) and as "wet deposition" (through uptake in falling raindrops). There is, of course, a relationship between emission and deposition. This relationship is, however, very complicated and is determined by the height of chimneys, the velocity and direction of the wind, the presence of obstacles, temperature, rainfall, etc.

> ASSIGNMENT 2.6
> Which factors determine the relationship between emission and deposition if a substance is discharged into water?

Ambient concentration and deposition is important to current exposure, and emission to future developments. For example, in the case of "acid rain", deposition, expressed in terms of concentration, is usually less important than the total emission. The total amount of acidifying substances that have entered the environment over the years (and are still accumulating) is more important than their day-to-day concentrations in the air (provided of course that these remain below the safety limits for acute toxicity).

> ASSIGNMENT 2.7
> Study the intermezzo below, on nitrogen dioxides, and answer the following questions as accurately and completely as you can; substantiate your answers with arguments if possible.
>
> a How large is the emission of NO and $NO_2$ in the following example and what are the sources of these gases?
> b Do the standards of the Public Health Council and the upper limits mentioned in the 1986–1990 Indicative Long-Term Program for Environmental Protection refer to emission or deposition?
> c What can you say about natural and anthropogenic emission with respect to public health?

### Intermezzo

*Nitrogen oxides*

Although seven different nitrogen oxides are known, the most important ones, i.e. those occurring in significant concentrations in the atmosphere and posing a potential threat to public health, are nitrogen monoxide (NO) and nitrogen dioxide ($NO_2$). The harmful effects of nitrogen oxides for humans will be discussed in detail in the study units on respiratory toxicology. The sum of nitrogen oxides in the air is referred to as $NO_x$. The total annual $NO_x$ emission in the countries of the European continent is estimated at about 6.2 Tg $NO_x$-N.

The emission density is highest in western and central Europe (Figure 2.3).

*6.2 Tg (= teragram = $10^{12}$ g) $NO_x$-N means 6.2 Tg of N present in form of $NO_x$*

The main source of nitrogen oxides is combustion, in which oxygen and nitrogen combine to form $NO_x$ at high temperatures. Some of the nitrogen emitted in this way originates from fuel, another part from air. In the European Union, automobile traffic is the most important $NO_x$ source, accounting for 49% of the total $NO_x$ emission. A further 41% is emitted by power plants and in-

0        500 km

■ > 2.5 g (N-$NO_x$) m$^{-2}$
■ 1.0 - 2.5 g (N-$NO_x$) m$^{-2}$
▦ 0.5 - 1.0 g (N-$NO_x$) m$^{-2}$
▨ < 0.5 g (N-$NO_x$) m$^{-2}$

FIGURE   2.3
$NO_x$ emissions in Europe (Source, Iversen et al., 1989)

dustrial and domestic combustion. Emissions from agriculture and industrial processes account for 6% and 4% of the total NOx emission, respectively.

Apart from human-derived sources, NO and $NO_2$ are also produced by natural processes. Worldwide, the annual $NO_x$ emission from soils amounts to 20–80 Tg $NO_x$–N, while an additional 10–40 Tg $NO_x$–N is added annually to the atmosphere by lightning. Worldwide anthropogenic emissions amount to ca. 20 Tg $NO_x$–N, of which 85% is concentrated in latitudes between 30 and 60 °N.

The NO and $NO_2$ emitted can be converted to nitric acid ($HNO_3$) in the atmosphere and then form nitrate particles. Furthermore, NO and $NO_2$ play an important role in those photochemical processes in the atmosphere that are related to both the formation and depletion of ozone ($O_3$). Oxidized nitrogen compounds are removed from the atmosphere by incorporation into rain or snow or by direct deposition on the earth's surface in gaseous or particulate form. The residence time of NO and $NO_2$ in the air is estimated at about 3 days, implying that these compounds can be transported over long distances, i.e. 2000 km or more.

The concentrations of NO and $NO_2$, and the proportions in which these oxides are present in outdoor air, are subject to considerable fluctuations, depending on time and place. Clean air contains about 1 mg $m^{-3}$ NOx, mainly in the form of $NO_2$. In western and central Europe, mean $NO_2$ concentrations lie between 8 and 13 mg $m^{-3}$. In polluted regions, such as urban areas, NO and $NO_2$ concentrations can be as high as 1000 and 500 mg $m^{-3}$, respectively.

*OSHA = Occupational Safety and Health Administration (USA); located in the Department of Labor*

*NIOSH = National Institute for Occupational Safety and Health (USA); located in the Department of Health and Human Services*

For TWA see Study units 14 and 40

American OSHA standards for $NO_2$ and NO are 5 ppm (= 9 mg/$m^3$) ceiling and 25 ppm (30 mg/$m^3$), 8-h TWA respectively; NIOSH recommended exposure limits are 1 ppm (1.8 mg/$m^3$) ceiling (15 min.) for $NO_2$ and 25 ppm (30 mg/$m^3$) TWA for NO. Here NIOSH TWA recommendations are based on exposures as long as 10 hours.

EU (European Union) guidelines recommend a limit of 135 mg $m^{-3}$, with 98% of hourly samples showing a $NO_2$ level below this standard. The EC has also recommended that $NO_2$ levels should be below 50 mg $m^{-3}$ for 50% of the time. The latter value is frequently exceeded in large urban areas.

*OECD = Organization for Economic Cooperation and Development*

*MSC-W = Meteorological Synthesizing Center-West*

Organizations like the OECD in Paris and the MSC-W in Oslo publish annual surveys of emissions of air pollutants in Europe. The MSC-W uses mathematical models to calculate the airborne transport of sulfur and nitrogen compounds. The models are also used to estimate depositions of these substances in Europe. With these long-range transport models it is possible to calculate which emissions are the main contributors to concentrations in a particular area. These results can then be used to determine the most effective "abatement strategies". Sometimes it may be more effective to reduce emissions in a neighboring country, by supporting that country financially, rather than to invest considerable effort in achieving sizable emission reductions in one's own country. The method also allows surveys to be made of cross-border pollution. This is done, for example, by drawing up "blame matrices", which show the contributions by one country to air pollution and deposition in another country. Such matrices form an important basis for international political agreements on emission reduction.

The emission and deposition of a particular substance may show significant fluctuations with time, which means that exposure also fluctuates greatly. In the case of rapidly acting toxic substances, the momentary concentration is of the utmost importance. For substances that are not acutely toxic but tend to accumulate (lead, for example), the mean values over longer periods of time are more important.

*Accidents*

Emission of polluting substances can take place through *accidents*, but also deliberately. The first occurs if there is a technical fault in a production process. Emission may then take place through valves, leaks and so on. Contamination caused in this way is often highly concentrated.

*Deliberate emission*

*Deliberate emission* normally occurs via chimneys, pipelines, exhausts, etc. Usually, the concentration of the polluting substance is fairly low but the emission usually continues for a long time. In production processes such emissions cannot be avoided but their level is a matter of technology and economics.

## 5.2 EXPOSURE-RESPONSE RELATIONSHIP

*Extent and duration of exposure*

Since the severity of a toxic effect depends on the *extent and duration of exposure*, and on the sensitivity of the affected individual, an effect may show itself to varying extents:

- barely noticeable (nuisance);
- reversible disorder;
- irreversible disorder or disability;
- lethal.

*Quantitative exposure-response relationship*

The sensitivity to an external factor varies from one individual to another. A group of people in a contaminated environmental compartment will display a range of sensitivity distributed around a mean. In each particular case of exposure, an effect will have a certain intensity in a certain percentage of individuals. The larger the extent and the longer the duration of exposure, the greater the percentage (the response). This is called a *quantitative exposure-response relationship*. The curves in Figure 2.4 represent such a relationship. Only the parameters of the curve—mean sensitivity and the deviation from the mean—differ from one case to the other. These values can be determined experimentally.

Experimental groups will, however, always differ from groups exposed as a result of an accident. Therefore, it should be noted that risk evaluation based on experimentally established relationships only relates to idealized model situations.

ASSIGNMENT 2.8
In addition to a quantitative exposure-response relationship for an average population (A) Figure 2.4 shows two other curves. What can you deduce about the sensitivity of groups B and C with respect to the substance concerned?

## 5.3 DETERMINATION THE LEVEL OF EXPOSURE

Except for those substances that have a direct harmful effect on the skin, the mucous membranes, the eye or the inner lining of the lung (corroding and irritant

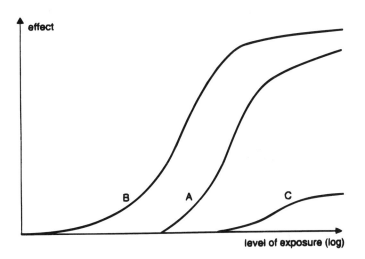

FIGURE 2.4
Some examples of level of exposure-response relationships

*Internal exposure*

substances such as phenol and formaldehyde), the crucial factor is not the external level of a substance but rather its concentration in the body, and specifically in the target organ or organs. This is the concentration to which the organism is actually *exposed* internally (*internal exposure*).

If the absorption rate of a substance exceeds the rate of excretion and biotransformation, accumulation may take place, and the total amount of the substance in the body, the *body burden*, will increase. Distribution over the body will depend on the properties of the substance and tissue (iodine accumulates in the thyroid gland, DDT mainly in adipose tissue).

### 5.3.1 Monitoring

*Body burden*

It is of vital importance to establish the (potential) level of exposure of humans and animals to toxic substances. There are a number of ways to do this. Firstly, the concentration of the substances in the environment and in food and beverages can be measured and estimates can be made of the resulting exposure.

The extent to which exposure has actually taken place can also be investigated. This can be done by measuring the level of a substance or its metabolites in one or more organs, or by determining the effects on the organism. The latter method only makes sense if the substance concerned causes sufficiently specific and observable effects.

*Monitoring*
See also Study unit 40

If the measurements mentioned above are carried out regularly over a period of time, this is called *monitoring*. A distinction can be made between environmental monitoring and biological monitoring.

Internal exposure is determined by systematic measurement of a substance or its metabolites in blood, urine or exhaled air. This method is mainly used for workers in industry, but also for other occupational groups. One important advantage of (individual) biological monitoring is that it provides information on the intake by an individual via all exposure routes together, under normal working conditions. The ambient concentrations (in the air for example) usually vary greatly with time and place, and there are also significant variations in respiration, occupational hygiene, etc. Biological limits for various substances have been proposed on the basis of internal concentrations.

## 6    Risks and risk analysis

Virtually any substance can induce toxic effects. Whether there is indeed a risk of toxic effects is determined by the circumstances.

In order to evaluate whether, in a given situation, a toxic substance will constitute a risk to certain populations, a thorough analysis of the situation is required.

### 6.1 RISK ANALYSIS

*Risk Analysis*
*Risk*

A *risk analysis* investigates the risks which humans or the environment run due to the production, presence and use of a substance. It is assumed that risk is not an implicit property of a substance, but a potential one. A distinction is made between hazard and risk. *Hazard* concerns the presence of potentially hazardous substances, for example, in the soil. A *risk* occurs when man (or another organism) absorbs the substance and there is a probability of adverse effects because of this. Hazard thus refers to potential toxicity and the actual situation; how one deals with the substance in that particular situation determines the risk. Hazard is a property of the substance and its situation and can be expressed in terms of injury. Risk, on the other hand, has to do with the circumstances of action, and can be expressed as a percentage.

ASSIGNMENT 2.9
Indicate with H and/or R whether there is a hazard (H) and/or a risk (R) in the following situations:

1 a worker in a chemical industry (pesticide plant) dealing with packaging;
2 a worker in a small galvanizing company with poor facilities;
3 children living in the neighborhood of a lead smelter;
4 a resident of a house built on the grounds of a former gasworks (the contaminated topsoil has been replaced with new soil; traces of tar are still present at a depth of 1–3 m);
5 a crop duster eating his sandwich while preparing the insecticide spray mixture.

A complete risk analysis encompasses toxicological aspects as well as aspects of environmental chemistry and health. The parameters of the analysis are determined by man, the substance and the environment.

Chlorine, a dangerous, highly toxic substance, constitutes a significant hazard. However, if the appropriate safety measures are taken, e.g. in its transportation (for example by train), there is a low risk.

6.2 RISK FACTORS

Which factors determine the risk from exposure to a toxic substance? Table 2.2 lists several factors that play a part.

6.3 HIGH-RISK GROUPS

*High-Risk groups*
*Situational risk*

Not all individuals in a population are subject to the same health risk. For this reason, the term *high-risk group* was coined. There is no strict, generally accepted definition of this term. Quite often a distinction is made between situational risks and an increased sensitivity to a certain substance. The term *situational risk* means the risk inherent to a particular situation (location, occupational activities, etc.) in which there is a considerable chance of exposure. People who live in the vicinity of an industry that pollutes the environment have a greater chance of coming into contact with the emission of that industry than others. If the same people also work in these industries, their risks are even higher.

In general, people who because of their work run a higher chance of coming into contact with chemicals, constitute a high-risk group. In many countries, institutions like OSHA have been set up especially to safeguard workers against these and other threats to their health.

TABLE 2.2
Some Important Factors which Determine the Risk of Exposure to Toxic Substances.

| nature of substance | presence of solvents and detergents | quantity | functional status of organism | genetic differences |
|---|---|---|---|---|
| physical state dispersion variation in distribution lipophilicity | emulsification in water (many pesticides contain a flow-promoting agent) | concentration duration | liver or kidney disease Shin injury caused by fire | enzyme deficiencies |

31

There are also people who belong to a high-risk group because of their higher *sensitivity* to one or more substances, compared to others in the population. An example would be *CNSLD patients*, who generally have a comparatively high sensitivity to substances that irritate the airways.

Small *children* constitute another large high-risk group. Through their behavior (from rummaging through kitchen cupboards to chewing pieces of painted wood) as well as their often higher sensitivity, they run relatively higher risks. Children are known to put objects and their fingers into their mouths while playing, which means that they ingest (or actually eat) sand, soil and dust. In this way they may be exposed to toxic substances present in the soil, a means of exposure that is far less likely for adults. Despite several studies on this subject, realistic estimate of the quantities of toxic substances and the number of children involved is still a problem.

Certain hobbies, such as soldering and swimming, can lead to increased exposure to toxic substances. Even if it does not lead to harmful effects on its own, a hobby may constitute a health risk when combined with, for example, occupational exposure. Apart from young children, pregnant women, along with their unborn children, can also be considered at higher risk from exposure to all kinds of substances. The same is true for elderly people.

Why should elderly people constitute a high-risk group?

At an advanced age, the functional capacity of various organs in the body starts to decline. This is the case, for instance, for the liver and the kidneys, which play an important part in the metabolism and excretion of foreign substances. Changes in these processes can cause significant changes in the toxicity of such substances. In addition, the reserve capacity of various organs is often severely reduced. This may mean that small toxic effects, which the organs can normally deal with, lead to severe consequences.

*Cholinesterase inhibitors are used in the treatment of glaucoma and myasthenia gravis.*

Where non-situational risks are concerned, it would be better to refer to sensitive groups rather than high-risk groups. Individuals belonging to the above-mentioned groups already can be recognized without prior toxicological evaluation. The size of these groups within a population is usually easy to estimate. The same cannot be said of situations involving hypersensitivities due to interference with the immune system or to congenital enzyme deficiencies. Thus, some people are hypersensitive to cholinesterase inhibitors, because of a shortage of the enzyme pseudocholinesterase in their blood serum. Such disorders can only be discovered by means of specific tests.

6.4 EXPOSURE AND RISK ANALYSIS

To carry out a risk analysis data are required on:

- emission (quantities, circumstances);
- deposition (including any possible variations);
- behavior of the substance in the various environmental compartments (distribution kinetics, conversion kinetics, bioaccumulation, etc.);
- toxicity, if relevant supplemented by epidemiological data.

A risk analysis can be used to set standards. Making a risk analysis for a substance requires information on the occurrence of that substance in the environmental compartments and its behavior within them.

*Environmental compartments*

Roughly speaking, four *environmental compartments* can be distinguished (each of which can be subdivided into further subcompartments):

1 *air* (from this compartment exposure can take place via the respiratory organs and, to a limited extent, through mouth and skin);

2 *water* (from which exposure can occur via the mouth and/or gills and, to a lesser extent, through the skin)

3 *soil* (in this case exposure can take place via food, direct contact, evaporation or leaching by water);

4 *biological compartment* (all organisms that are exposed to toxic substances. The concentrations of xenobiotics in living organisms can sometimes become very high. After it is digested this compartment provides exposure via food, water and air to other organisms).

## 6.5 RISK ANALYSIS AND STANDARD-SETTING

*Standards*
For the setting of standards, see Study unit 14

The government can set *standards* for chemicals, with the aim of preventing or minimizing the risk of detrimental effects from such substances. Depending on the situation, such standards may be achieved in different ways, and may be of a very different nature. Nonetheless, they are always based on toxicological as well as socio-economic interests. Risk analysis is involved in two ways. First, before a standard can be set, and measures can be designed, the exposure that takes place, or might take place, has to be assessed, together with its potential consequences. Secondly, in an actual situation, the present and future exposure need to be analyzed and compared with existing standards. Once present and future risks have been assessed, the data can be used as the basis for sound advice on the measures to be taken.

Most standards aim at reducing or preventing exposure by setting maximum levels of substances in water, food, air and soil. Restrictions with regard to use can also reduce exposure (for example, not using soil with high levels of heavy metals for a vegetable garden).

A few standards are based on effects that have been found after exposure. Thus, there are two different standards with regard to the use of alcohol by motorists. The first is based on the effect of alcohol (drunkenness), the second on the blood alcohol level (blood sample) or, consequently, the concentration in exhaled air (breathalyzer).

ASSIGNMENT 2.10
How was the former standard tested in the past?

## 7 Prevention or reduction of exposure

The health risks from toxic substances for humans and animals can be limited by reducing the exposure to these substances. To this end there are various methods, which are summarized in Table 2.3.

ASSIGNMENT 2.11
Use Figure 2.5 to deduce at what stage and how exposure of humans to pesticides might be reduced.

## SELF ASSESSMENT QUESTIONS

1. In the situations described below, indicate

   a which groups of people, animals and plants are exposed to the toxic substances concerned

TABLE 2.3
Some measures for limiting the exposure to toxic substances.

| measure | special features | example |
|---|---|---|
| 1. (governmental) intervention in production and use | withdrawal of license, admission, banning production | pesticides (DDT); PCBs |
| 2. removal | transport, removal from material | waste to the dump; flushing or burning polluted grounds |
| 3. degradation | (micro)biological, burning | biological water purification combustion plant |
| 4. reduction of bioavailability | chemical, physical | applying calcium to Cd-containing garden soil; sealing ceramic products (fly ash) |
| 5. regulations on production and use | occupational hygiene; form of application | MAC-values; herbicides in granules instead of in liquid |
| 6. behavioral change | | giving up smoking |

    b  how exposure takes place

    c  which groups run a higher risk

    d  which measures can possibly be taken to reduce the risk.

        A.  An aluminum plant emits fluorides via its chimneys. The plant is situated in an agricultural area (mainly pastures). Excessive amounts of fluorides cause defects in the bones and teeth.

        B.  Urban traffic releases exhaust gases that contain a great number of toxic compounds, such as carbon monoxide, nitrogen oxides, hydrocarbons and lead compounds.

        C.  Chipboard is used in many houses and buildings. In the production of chipboard a type of glue is used which gives off varying quantities of formaldehyde.

2    In many countries use of DDT was prohibited many years ago. Yet it is still occasionally found in cows' milk. Indicate what the exposure routes are for the relevant organisms.

3    Pig breeding farms and other bio-industries emit a certain amount of ammonia. Via deposition this finds its way into the soil, where it may be oxidized by soil organisms to, for instance, nitrate. Indicate the possible exposure routes to plants, people and animals, for ammonia as well as its metabolites. Indicate also at what points health risks may occur for these organisms.

## FEEDBACK

1    **Answers to the Assignments**

2.1    Exposure, as defined in Webster's Dictionary:

> ex-po-sure (ik spō'shər) *n.* [EXPOS(E) + -URE]  1. an exposing or being exposed  2. a location, as of a house, in relationship to the sun, winds, etc. [an eastern *exposure*]  3. appearance, esp. frequent appearance, before the public, as in the theater, on radio and TV, etc.  4. the fact of being exposed in a helpless condition to the elements  5. *Photog. a)* the subjection of a sensitized film or plate to the action of light rays, X-rays, etc. *b)* a sensatized surface or section of a film for making one picture *c)* the time during which such a surface or film is exposed

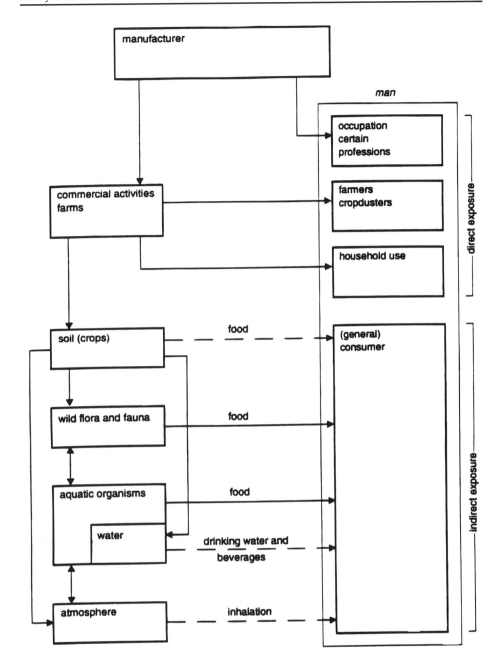

FIGURE 2.5
Schematic representation of possible routes of exposure to pesticides

2.2 The most important methods that are referred to here (pharmaceutical preparations) are:
- as a powder (orally);
- as tablet or dragée (orally, under the tongue);
- as capsule (orally);
- as a liquid (orally);
- as injected fluid (via a hypodermic needle or drip);
- as suppository (rectally);

- as ointment (on the skin, etc.);
- as drops (nose, ear, eye).

2.3    In sea mammals, just as in terrestrial animals, food chain effects occur. In other words, organisms closer to the end of the food chain contain higher levels of persistent substances than animals at the lower levels. Such effects are not found in fish, where a balance is achieved between the substance's concentration in water and its concentration in the fish (which for lipid-soluble substances depends on the fat content of the fish).

2.4    50/6, or ca. 8.

2.5    This is the mean level at which an adult inhales.

2.6    Also in water there will be a correlation between emission and deposition. Again, many factors will influence this relationship. The direction of the current and the solubility of the substance will be particularly important.

2.7    a    The natural emission is 430 million metric tons NO and 700 million metric tons $NO_2$ per year and is of vegetable origin. The anthropogenic emission of NO and $NO_2$ together is estimated at 50 million metric tons, deriving mainly from combustion processes (traffic, power stations, domestic heating, processing industries).

        b    The Public Health Councils' standard is a deposition standard, since it specifies the quantity to which a person may be exposed at a certain place and at a certain time. The ceiling that is given, however, refers to the total release, and thus to emission.

        c    The natural emission is much larger than the man-made emission, but with regard to deposition, which ultimately determines the exposure and the resultant health risks, the man-made contribution will, in certain places and at certain moments, be much larger.

2.8    The individuals in Figure 2.4B are clearly more sensitive to the toxic effects of the substance: effects are already observable at lower levels of exposure. In contrast, those in Figure 2.4C are less sensitive than the group in Figure 2.4A.

2.9    1  H
        2  H, R
        3  H, R
        4  H
        5  H, R

2.10   By subjecting the "suspect" to a physical test, for example, asking him/her to walk in a straight line, as is usually done.

2.11   The exposure of humans to pesticides can be reduced, for instance, by:

- prohibiting or limiting their production;
- measures on storage/dumping of waste;.
- limiting their use (banning them in certain areas such as water collection areas; using pesticides only against certain insects; no household use);

- safety measures for handling them (packaging, protective clothing for cropdusters)
- soil sanitation
- check foodstuffs and beverages on presence of pesticides

## 2 Answers to the Self Assessment Questions

1A a fluorides are deposited onto the grass, which is then eaten by cows

b exposure of cows through their feed

c younger animals are possibly at a higher risk (developing bones and teeth)

d reduction of emission, monitoring of the environment using fluoride-sensitive plants; in the event of a single large emission, cutting and removing the grass in the area.

B a all road users, possible dispersion of lead-containing dust in houses

b exposure via inhalation of gases and dust, contribution to general pollution of the air by nitrogen oxides and hydrocarbons (smog/acid rain)

c children (especially lead), traffic police, etc. (especially carbon monoxide), CNSLD patients

d reduction of motor traffic, cleaner combustion processes (using catalytic converters, unleaded petrol), prohibition of the use of roadside grass as cattle fodder.

C a residents and users of houses, schools, offices, etc.

b exposure via inhalation (possible direct irritation of the respiratory tract)

c certain individuals who are highly sensitive to formaldehyde, people who are regularly in closed rooms where chipboard has been used (children, elderly people), CNSLD patients

d improvement of chipboard production, reduction of release of formaldehyde by sealing off the chipboard (painting), reduction of chipboard use, ventilation.

2 Part of the DDT used in the past has found its way to the soil and has not yet completely disappeared from it. Hence, soil animals are still exposed to this compound (and its metabolites). Birds and mammals which eat these soil animals take up DDT via this route (food chain). If the soil is disturbed at deeper levels (for example, when digging up old orchards), the DDT which is still present at this depth re-enters the topsoil. If the land is then used for grazing, cows take up the DDT via grass and soil. This DDT is partially excreted through the milk. By consumption of this milk humans also become exposed to DDT (food chain). The meat from these cows will also contain higher DDT levels for some time, which can constitute yet another exposure route for humans.

3 Ammonia in the air can lead to direct damage in plants. When very high levels are emitted, toxic symptoms may also develop in humans and animals. Ammonia taken up by the soil acts as manure (which adversely affects environments poor in nutrients, such as moorlands and fens). Conversion to nitrate causes acidification of the soil. Ammonia that enters

the groundwater can render this water unsuitable for drinking by humans and animals. However, contamination of groundwater with nitrate, the oxidation product of ammonia, is more likely to produce problems for the users.

*Illustrations*

Figure 2.3 Source: Iversen, T., Saltbones, Sardes, H., Eliassen, A. and Hou, O. (1989) EMEP/MSC-W, Report 2/89, Oslo, Norway, 92pp.

# Contents Study unit 3
# Biotransformation: detoxication and bioactivation

0-8493-9232-2/96/$0.00 + $.50
© 1996 by CRC Press, Inc.

# Study unit 3

# Biotransformation: detoxication and bioactivation

*B. M. Blaauboer*

## INTRODUCTION

See also Study unit 7

Organisms are surrounded by a large number of chemical compounds, which may be harmful to their functioning. If the concentration of any substance in an organism becomes too high, this will inevitably lead to damage.

Substances are often taken in with the diet or the inspired air and may, depending on their physicochemical properties, accumulate in the body.

*xenobiotic = substance foreign to the body*

It is particularly those xenobiotics which are easily soluble in fat (lipophilic compounds) which tend to accumulate in the body. The explanation for this is found in the functions of the excretory organs, such as the kidneys, liver and lungs. These organs excrete substances into spaces filled with liquids or gases which subsequently contact the surfaces of the excretory ducts.

An example is the kidneys, which filter substances from the blood through the glomeruli. These substances are excreted in the glomerular filtrate, which is transported through the renal tubules to the bladder. In the renal tubules many substances are reabsorbed into the circulation either actively (water, salts, glucose, etc.) or passively (all lipophilic substances). Passive reabsorption of lipophilic substances takes place because these substances tend to dissolve in the lipid membranes of the epithelial cells. Since they can subsequently bind to proteins and lipoproteins in the blood, there is net transport from the glomerular filtrate to the blood. This means that, provided these substances continue to be supplied, their concentration will increase.

Hence, if nothing happened to these lipophilic substances, they would accumulate in the body.

The situation in aquatic animals is somewhat more favorable, as substances can be exchanged with a much greater quantity of water and through a much greater (skin) surface area, in particular through the gills.

The living organism can usually eliminate a xenobiotic in two ways: by direct excretion or by metabolic transformation of the parent substance. The metabolic system responsible for such transformation is called the biotransformation system. This study unit discusses the main characteristics of this system, the enzymes involved and the consequences for the toxicity of substances.

### LEARNING OBJECTIVES

After having studied these units you should be able to

— describe the concepts of biotransformation, bioinactivation and bioactivation and use these concepts actively.
— describe the principle routes for biotransformation of foreign substances in relation to the metabolism of the body's own metabolic products.

41

— describe the mechanisms underlying the biotransformation reactions.
— indicate the biological significance of biotransformation processes, in particular for the kinetics of lipophilic compounds and for the effects of substances.
— give some examples of phase I and phase II bioactivation reactions.
— explain the differences in difference spectra for various types of substrate.

*Study Hints*

Students are assumed to be familiar with the physiology of the excretory organs, the action of enzymes and enzyme kinetics and the concepts of lipophilicity, polarity and hydrophilicity. If necessary, read up on these subjects in a book on physiology and/or biochemistry. The subject matter is related to the study units dealing with kinetics, structure–activity relationships and carcinogenesis. The study load of this study unit is, depending on your previous knowledge and training, 4 student learning hours.

STUDY CORE

## 1 Conversion of substances: biotransformation

Organisms have a number of enzyme systems which are able to metabolize foreign substances and endogenous metabolic waste products to more water-soluble compounds, which are more readily excreted.

ASSIGNMENT 3.1

Vitamin $D_3$ is a lipid-soluble vitamin found in cod-liver oil, margarine and butter. For its activity (regulation of calcium absorption), vitamin D must be plasma–soluble. What biotransformation(s) should vitamin D undergo to achieve this? Refer to a physiology book if necessary.

*Biotransformation system*
*Phase I reactions*
*Phase II reactions*

The various processes involved in this are collectively termed the *biotransformation system*. Biotransformation reactions may be divided into *phase I reactions* (oxidations, reductions, hydrolyses), which introduce a polar group into the molecule, and *phase II reactions* (conjugations), which conjugate an endogenous, hydrophilic substance with a polar group in a molecule. The conjugated product is then water-soluble.

ASSIGNMENT 3.2

What would happen to these substances during a period of prolonged fasting, and what consequences might that have?

See Study unit 7

If concentrations at the site of action become sufficiently high, this will lead to toxic effects. An example is the death of Sandwich terns during the breeding seasons in the 1960s as a result of exposure to dieldrin (Table 3.1).

ASSIGNMENT 3.3

What strikes you in Table 3.1 as far as the dieldrin levels are concerned?

1.1  FROM LIPOPHILIC TO POLAR: PHASE I REACTIONS

During phase I the molecule is altered by the introduction of polar groups, such as hydroxyl (-OH), carboxyl (-COOH) and amino ($-NH_2$) groups. The alteration

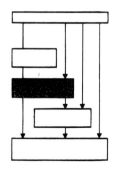

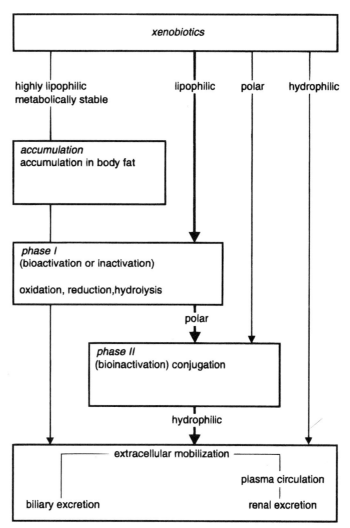

FIGURE   3.1

The various steps of biotransformation

Figure 3.1 gives a general overview of biotransformation, showing phase I and phase II reactions. The final block represents the various excretory processes. Some lipophilic substances cannot be processed by the biotransformation system, for example because they are not suitable substrates for the enzymes of the system. Examples of such substances are polychlorinated biphenyls (PCBs) and DDT. Such substances will therefore accumulate in the body, in particular in body fat.

TABLE   3.1

Comparison of dieldrin residues in the liver of Sandwich terns in the Wadden Sea, in killed animals and in animals found dead.

| Age group | Year | History | Number | Liver residue of dieldrin in ppm (wet weight) median and range |
|---|---|---|---|---|
| juvenile | 1965 | killed | 3 | 0.31 (0.20–0.42) |
| juvenile | 1965 | found dead or in convulsion | 8 | 4.6  (1.9–6.6) |
| adult | 1965 | shot | 5 | 0.84 (0.48–2.0) |
| adult | 1965 | found dead or in convulsion | 5 | 5.5  (4.7–7.2) |
| chick | 1966 | found dead after a storm | 6 | 0.63 (0.45–0.91) |
| chick | 1965 | found dead or in convulsion | 6 | 5.6  (2.4–12.0) |

---

*Oxidation*

*Reductions*

*Hydrolysis*

of the molecule may also lead to the unmasking of such groups. These changes may take place as a result of oxidation, reduction or hydrolysis. Which of these reactions a particular xenobiotic will undergo is determined by the structure of the molecule (Table 3.2).

*Reductions* are far less common. The reduction of azo and nitro compounds (f, g) yields the corresponding amines.

Decomposition by *hydrolysis* means cleavage of a foreign compound by the addition of water. An ester, for example, is hydrolyzed to an acid and an alcohol. A good example of a phase I reaction is the conversion of benzene into phenol:

TABLE   3.2
Overview of possible types of phase I biotransformation reactions

| Type of reaction | Substrate | Metabolite(s) |
| --- | --- | --- |
| **A. oxidations** | | |
| *I mixed-function oxidase-dependent reactions* | | |
| aromatic hydroxylation | R—⬡ | R—⬡—OH |
| aliphatic hydroxylation | R – CH$_3$ | R – CH$_2$OH |
| epoxidation | R – C = C – R' (H, H) | R – C – C – R' (H, O, H) |
| N-hydroxylation | ⬡—NH$_2$ | ⬡—NHOH |
| O-dealkylation | R – O – CH$_3$ | ROH + CH$_2$O |
| N-dealkylation | R – NHCH$_3$ | R – NH$_2$ + CH$_2$O |
| S-dealkylation | R – S – CH$_3$ | R – SH + CH$_2$O |
| deamination | R – CH – CH$_3$ (NH$_2$) | R – C – CH$_3$ + NH$_3$ (‖O) |
| S-oxidation | R – S – R' | R – S – R' (↓O) |
| dechlorination | CCl$_4$ | [CCl$_3$•] → CHCl$_3$ |
| oxidative desulfuration | R$_1$ – O, S \ P / R$_2$ – O, O – R$_3$ | R$_1$ – O, O \ P / R$_2$ – O, O – R$_3$ |
| II amine oxidation | R – CH$_2$ – NH$_2$ | R – CHO + NH$_3$ |
| III dehydrogenation | CH$_3$ – CH$_2$ – OH | CH$_3$CHO    CH$_3$COOH |
| **B. reductions** | | |
| azoreduction | R – N = N – R' | R – NH$_2$ + R' – NH$_2$ |
| nitroreduction | R – NO$_2$ | R – NH$_2$ |
| carbonyl reduction | R – C – R' (‖O) | R – CH – R' (OH) |
| **C. hydrolyses** | | |
| esters | R – C – O – R' (‖O) | R – C – OH – R' – OH (‖O) |
| amides | R – CONH$_2$ | R – COOH + NH$_3$ |

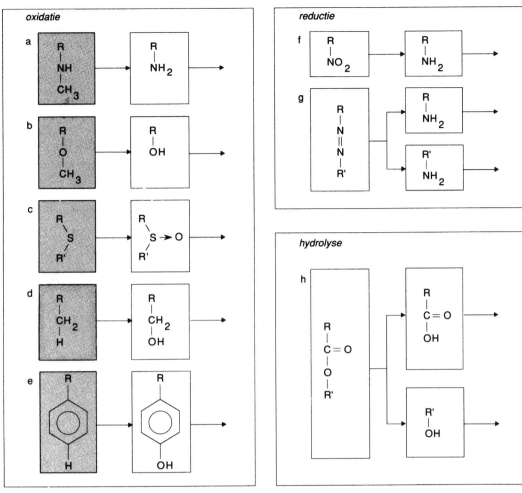

FIGURE 3.2
The most common phase I biotransformation reactions

Figure 3.2 has been included to clarify the various oxidation, reduction and hydrolysis reactions. Oxidation is the most important of the phase I reactions. Examples are the hydroxylation reactions of various aromatic and aliphatic compounds. Substrates for oxidative reactions include the alkylamino compounds (a) (e.g. nicotine, morphine). It is the N-alkyl groups in particular which can be removed by oxidative dealkylation. O-alkyl groups (b), especially methyl groups (= methoxy groups), can also be removed oxidatively. Compounds with a thioether group (c) are readily oxidized to sulfoxides. Alkyl groups (d) are also readily oxidized and undergo fairly rapid hydroxylation. Oxidation of aromatic compounds (e) leads to phenolic products.

In this example, the hydroxyl group is the polar group which has been introduced into the molecule.

ASSIGNMENT 3.4

In the following examples, indicate which type of reaction has taken place (compare Table 3.2) and which group(s) in the reaction products are responsible for the increased polarity.

Example 1:

chlorphentermine

Example 2:

amphetamine

## 1.2 BIOTRANSFORMATION ENZYME SYSTEMS: THE MIXED-FUNCTION OXIDASE SYSTEM

*Cytochrome P-450*
*Mixed-function oxidase system*
The name of the system refers to its ability to incorporate one atom of a molecule of oxygen into the substrate and reduce the other atom of oxygen to water.

In the oxidation of foreign lipophilic compounds an enzyme called *cytochrome P-450* plays an important role. This enzyme is part of an enzyme system referred to as the *mixed-function oxidase* (MFO) system.

A large number of different types of oxidative reactions are catalyzed by this system.

ASSIGNMENT  3.5

Which reactions from Table 3.2 are meant here?

The system comprises a number of components, with cytochrome P-450 occupying a key position. It also includes two flavoproteins, which play a role in providing reducing equivalents, donated by NADPH and NADH. Cytochrome $b_5$ is also involved (see Figure 3.3).

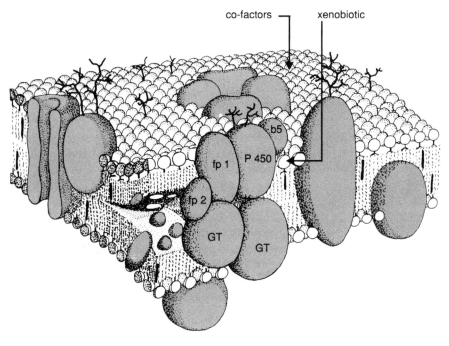

FIGURE   3.3
Localization of the mixed-function oxidase system in the membrane of the smooth endoplasmic reticulum (SER) in the cell.

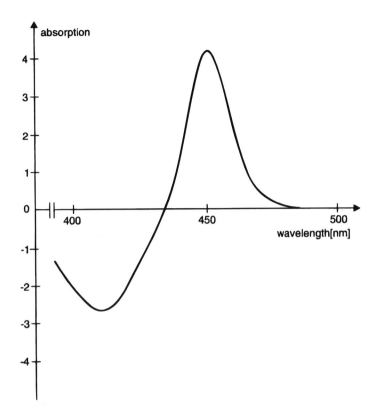

FIGURE 3.4

Absorption spectrum 400–500 nm, (carbon monoxide difference spectrum) of cytochrome P-450

Cytochrome P-450 is a hemoprotein, with Fe-protoporphyrin IX as the prosthetic group. The iron atom can be either divalent or trivalent. The name of the enzyme is derived from its ability to bind with carbon monoxide in the reduced form and form a complex which has a characteristic absorption at 450 nm (see Figure 3.4).

In the MFO reaction, cytochrome P-450 is the site where both the substrate and the oxygen bind.

The most characteristic feature of the reaction cycle catalyzed by cytochrome P-450 is the ability of the heme iron to undergo cyclic oxidation—reduction reactions in relation to substrate binding and oxygen activity.

A schematic representation of the functioning of the mixed-function oxidase system is provided in Figure 3.5.

The following steps can be distinguished:

a   A substrate (SH) binds to the oxidized ($Fe^{3+}$) form of cytochrome P-450.

b   An electron (donated by NADPH) can then be transferred to the resulting enzyme-substrate complex via a flavoprotein (= an enzyme) called NADPH cytochrome P-450 reductase ($FP_1$ in the diagram).

c   Molecular oxygen is then incorporated into the reduced ($Fe^{2+}$) enzyme-substrate complex.

d   This complex then accepts a second electron, donated by NADH and transferred via a second flavoprotein ($FP_2$ or NADH cytochrome $b_5$ reductase) and cytochrome $b_5$. This second electron may, however, also be donated via $FP_1$, as is indicated in the diagram by a dashed line. The system can thus also function using NADPH alone.

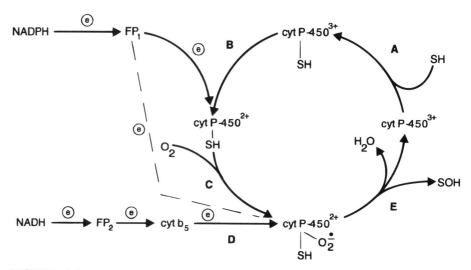

FIGURE 3.5

Schematic representation of cytochrome P-450 mono-oxygenase activity

The valence of the iron atom is indicated by a small 2 or 3. An electron is indicated by an e; SH stands for the substrate.

e   The second reduction step activates the oxygen molecule and eventually causes the enzyme-substrate-oxygen complex to split into a molecule of water, an oxidized substrate (SOH) and oxidized cytochrome P-450. The enzyme is then once more available to take part in a new cycle. It will now be clear why this enzyme system is called the mixed-function oxidase system: it has multiple functions.

Which functions are meant?

*Functions of the MFO system*

The MFO system has the following functions:

1   reduction to water of one atom from molecular oxygen
2   incorporation of the second oxygen atom into the substrate (also called oxygenation).

This leads to the following overall equation:

$$SH + NADPH + H^+ + O_2 \rightarrow SOH + NADP^+ + H_2O \qquad (3.1)$$

where SH is the substrate to be oxidized and SOH is the hydroxylation product. This equation can be applied to a wide variety of substrates, including many xenobiotics, such as drugs, pesticides and organic solvents.

Examples of the oxidation of *endogenous* substrates can be found in steroid metabolism, which also involves a number of oxidative reactions in which a cytochrome P-450-dependent system plays a role.

It has been questioned whether a uniform enzyme system would actually be capable of metabolizing such a wide variety of substrates. And indeed a number of *isozymes of cytochrome P-450* have been shown to exist, each of which has its own types of substrate for which it is to a certain extent specific. Using various separation techniques (e.g. column chromatography), immunological characterization and amino acid sequencing it has been established that there is a family of similar proteins which do display certain differences, but share the same basic architecture and the same heme group.

All organisms examined so far, microorganisms, such as bacteria, as well as higher organisms, have been shown to possess one or more isozymes of cytochrome P-450. The differences between the isozymes in various species may be small. In some cases, only one amino acid has been substituted; in others, large sections of the amino acid sequence may be different. These differences provide an indication of the extent to which the species involved are genetically related. There may also be differences between the various organs of one organism with respect to the isozymes of cytochrome P-450 present.

*Substrate-cytochrome P-450 binding*

Substrates may bind to cytochrome P-450 in at least two different ways. One group of substrates binds to the protein part of cytochrome P-450, while the other group interacts with the heme group.

*Binding to protein*

Substrate binding can be investigated by means of spectrophotometry, since binding of a substrate to cytochrome P-450 results in spectral changes. Recording the spectrum of an enzyme in the presence of a substrate, using a solution of the enzyme without the substrate as a reference, produces the so-called difference spectrum. The substrates which bind to the protein moiety of cytochrome P-450 produce a difference spectrum with a maximum at 390 nm (see Figure 3.6),

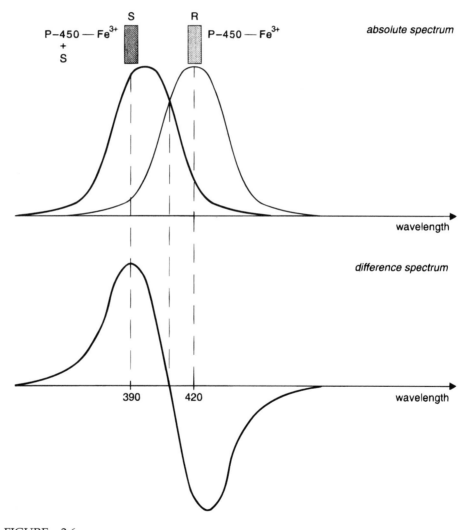

FIGURE 3.6

Difference spectrum of cytochrome P-450

The left cuvette contains the enzyme–substrate complex (S). Beneath it is the corresponding absolute spectrum (thick line). The right cuvette contains the reference (R), i.e. the cytochrome P-450 (thin line). The bottom figure shows the difference spectrum of S and R.

*Type I substrates*

caused by a shift of the spectrum towards shorter wavelengths as a result of the enzyme's binding to the substrate. These substrates are called *type I substrates*.

*Binding to heme group*
*Type II substrates*

Another group of substrates binds to the heme group of the enzyme. These substrates cause a change in the spectrum with a maximum around 420 nm. They are called *type II substrates*.

### Intermezzo

The spectral changes reflect changes in the so-called spin state of the iron atom in the heme group of cytochrome P-450 (see Figure 3.7).

The iron atom has six binding sites for ligands. Four of these ligand positions are occupied by the porphyrin ring, the fifth is occupied by a thiolate anion from an adjacent cysteine residue of the polypeptide chain, whereas the sixth can be occupied by a hydroxyl group from the protein part or from water.

*$Fe^{3+}$ has five d electrons*

Binding of a substrate to cytochrome P-450 causes changes in the characteristics of the sixth ligand position. These changes are related to shifts in the electron configuration of the iron atom. The five d electrons can be distributed in various ways. In the so-called low-spin state two electron pairs have formed, leaving one electron unpaired. In the high-spin state all five d electrons are unpaired. This is represented below:

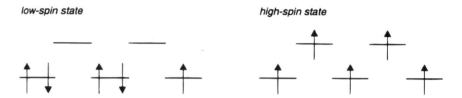

In the control situation (without substrate) most of the iron atoms of cytochrome P-450 are in the low-spin state. There is an equilibrium between the low-spin and high-spin states.

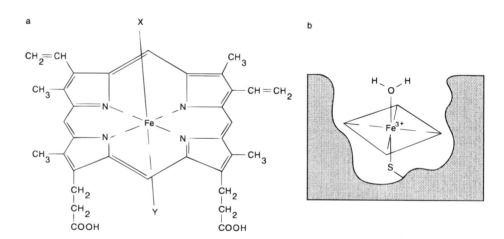

FIGURE   3.7

Schematic representation of the incorporation of Fe-protoporphyrin IX into cytochrome P-450

(a) The iron atom forms a complex with the four nitrogen atoms in the center of the tetrapyrrole ring, while the fifth ligand (x) may be a thiolate anion from an adjacent cysteine residue of the polypeptide chain and the sixth ligand is probably occupied by water (y). This water molecule can be easily substituted by oxygen or a substrate. (b) Shows the presumed three-dimensional representation of the active site of cytochrome P-450. Please note that the x-y axis has been rotated by 180° with respect to Figure a.

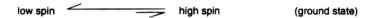

low spin       high spin       (ground state)

Binding of a type I substrate to the protein part of the enzyme causes a shift from low-spin to high-spin state. In other words: iron atoms which were previously in the low-spin state change to the high-spin state.

low spin       high spin       (type I interaction after complex formation)

This is accompanied by a spectral change with an absorption maximum at 390 nm. Binding of a type II substrate takes place at the sixth ligand position of the iron atom in the heme group, producing a shift from the high-spin to the low-spin state.

low spin       high spin       (type II interaction after complex formation)

ASSIGNMENT 3.6

Could you explain the form of a type II difference spectrum on the basis of the fact that complex formation of a type II substrate with cytochrome P-450 causes a further shift from the high-spin to the low-spin state?

*Reversed type I substrates (RI)*      In addition to type I and type II substrates, there are also the *reversed type I substrates (RI)*. Such a substrate gives a type I interaction at low concentrations and a type II interaction at high concentrations.

Binding of such a substrate to the enzyme results in a shift from the high-spin to the low-spin state.

Certain substances form stable complexes with cytochrome P-450 by binding firmly to the heme iron. This means that the enzyme is locked in the low-spin state and transformations can no longer take place; the enzyme has been inactivated. If the cycle has proceeded up to and including the point where the first

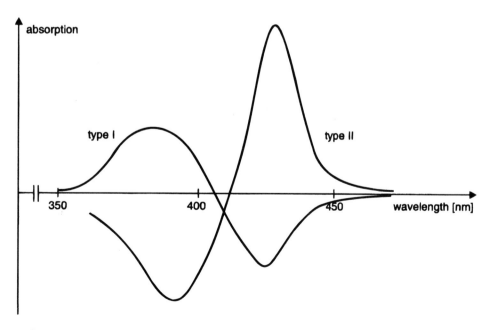

FIGURE 3.8
Example of a difference spectrum of a type II interaction

electron is transferred and/or the point where the second electron is transferred, *activated oxygen* (see Figure 3.5) may in this case be released as a *superoxide anion radical* ($O_2^{\bullet-}$) or as $H_2O_2$. The radical may damage the enzyme or other cellular components. These substances are thus capable of substrate binding with cytochrome P-450, but are metabolized only slowly or not at all. They block the transformation of other substrates, as well as causing activated oxygen to be produced, which may lead to cell damage.

### 1.3 BIOINACTIVATION AND BIOACTIVATION

See also Study unit 7

Biotransformation often leads to changes in a molecule which increase its water-solubility and improve its excretion. This generally means that such conversions shorten the duration of the toxic effect, since the original foreign substance disappears (by being converted into a different compound) and its metabolites are excreted. This means that there will be less accumulation of the substance in the organism and that its level will decrease. Since there is a general relationship between the concentration of a substance and the intensity of its toxic effect, bioinactivation means a decrease in that intensity. Moreover, the biological activity (including toxicity) of substances often turns out to be lower after conversion. Aminopyrine, for example ($LD_{50}$ in mice: 0.24 mg kg$^{-1}$) is converted into 4-aminoantipyrine ($LD_{50}$: 1.2 mg kg$^{-1}$).

*Bioinactivation or detoxication reactions*

It is for these reasons that biotransformation reactions may involve *bioinactivation reactions* or *detoxication reactions*.

There are however many exceptions. It is especially in phase I of the biotransformation system that we find many reactions which yield products with a higher intrinsic toxicity than the parent compound. This is not in itself surprising: the introduction of polar groups into a molecule not only increases its suitability to undergo conjugation reactions in phase II, but may very well also increase its reactivity towards other substances.

If a substance can react with a component of a biological system (e.g. a protein or DNA, or a substance which plays a role in the cell's own metabolism) there is a reasonable chance that the biological system will be influenced by it. If this influence is an adverse one, it means that the substance, if present in sufficiently high concentrations, is toxic.

Biotransformation reactions which yield products having a higher toxicity than the parent compound are referred to as *bioactivation reactions*. There are many examples of such reactions, one of the best-known of which is the conversion of the insecticide *parathion* into *paraoxon*.

parathion → paraoxon

See Study unit 33

Parathion belongs to the organothiophosphates, the neurotoxicity of which is based on their interaction with the enzyme *acetylcholinesterase (AChE)*. The affinity of this enzyme for paraoxon, however, is many times higher than that for the parent compound parathion. In other words, the oxidation reaction required to make the substance more water-soluble in this case leads to the formation of a bioactivation product.

In a subsequent reaction, paraoxon may be hydrolyzed, as a result of which it loses its toxic effect on AChE.

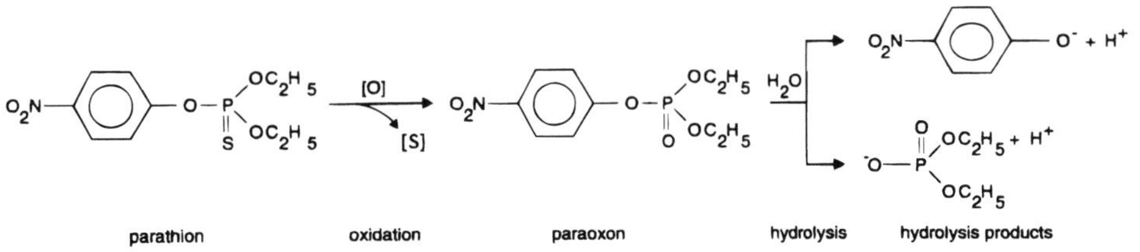

It is among the oxidation reactions of phase I in particular that many bioactivations are found. The example of the benzene metabolism given above in fact also includes a bioactivation step. The conversion of benzene to phenol involves the formation of a highly reactive intermediate, an *epoxide*. This epoxide is not stable and most of it will quickly be converted into phenol.

*Epoxide*

See also Study units 11 and 12

Because of its electrophilic character the epoxide can also react with *nucleophilic* groups in biomacromolecules such as proteins and DNA, which may lead to damage to these molecules. Reactions with DNA may result in changes which eventually lead to cancer.

For many of the well-known carcinogens bioactivation is a prerequisite for their action, which always involves the formation of an *electrophilic* reactive intermediate. Examples: benzo[*a*]pyrene is converted into a dihydrodiol epoxide; aflatoxins are active as epoxides; vinyl chloride epoxide is formed from vinyl chloride.

Table 3.3 gives some examples of the formation of reactive intermediates via phase I bioactivation reactions.

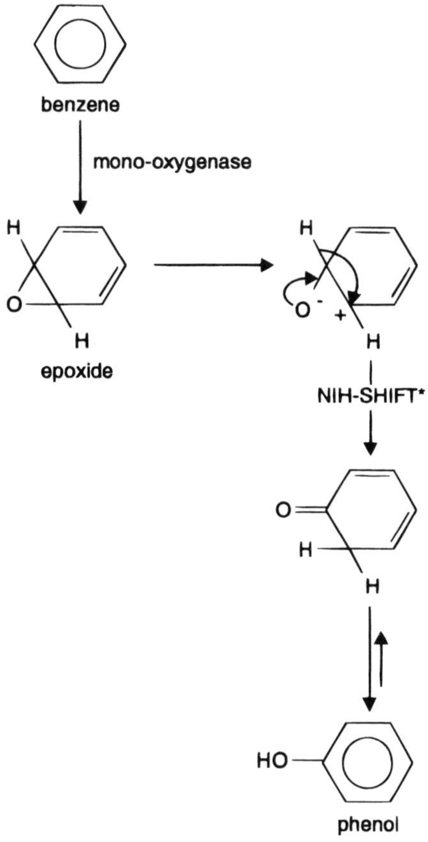

FIGURE 3.9
Hydroxylation of benzene via epoxidation
The shift of the H atom which occurs in this conversion is referred to as the NIH shift, after the National Institute of Health where the conversion was first discovered.

53

TABLE 3.3
Formation of reactive intermediates (RI) from xenobiotics, mediated by mixed-function oxidase.

| Compound | Formula | Proposed RI | Type of toxicity |
|----------|---------|-------------|------------------|
| bromobenzene | Br—⟨◯⟩ | Br—⟨⬡⟩°(epoxide) | liver necrosis |
| vinyl chloride | H,H / C=C / H,Cl | H,O,H / C—C / H,Cl | liver cancer |
| aniline | $H_2N$—⟨◯⟩ | HO—NH—⟨◯⟩ | methemoglobinemia |
| dimethylnitrosamine | $H_3C$ \ N–N=O / $H_3C$ | $H_3C^+$ | carcinogenesis |
| carbon tetrachloride | $CCl_4$ | $^\bullet CCl_3$ | liver necrosis |
| chloroform | $CHCl_3$ | | renal necrosis |

## Summary

Organisms are able to change the biological activity of foreign compounds by enzymatic conversion (biotransformation). This process usually leads to de-activation of the foreign compounds, and, as a result of the changes they have undergone, they are as a rule also more readily excreted from the body. A first step in the biotransformation process is the conversion of lipophilic substances into more polar ones. These first reactions are called phase I reactions and they often take place under the influence of enzymes which are components of the mixed-function oxidase system (MFO). The mixed-function oxidase system consists of a number of proteins which together are able to catalyze the oxidation of a great variety of substances. These proteins are: cytochrome P-450, NADPH cytochrome-P450 reductase, cytochrome $b_5$ and NADH cytochrome $b_5$ reductase. The system primarily oxidizes lipophilic compounds and is responsible for the introduction of a polar group into the substrate molecule. Molecular oxygen is used for this purpose. With the help of two electrons, donated by NADPH (or NADH) the oxygen is activated, after which one oxygen atom is incorporated into the substrate and the other is reduced to water. Cytochrome P-450 is found in a number of different forms. Each of these so-called isozymes catalyzes the oxidative conversion of a group of compounds with some degree of specificity. Substrates can bind either to the protein part of cytochrome P-450 (type I substrates) or to the iron atom in the heme group (type II substrates).

Biotransformation of foreign compounds leads to changes in their biological activity. Toxicity will in many cases be reduced (bioinactivation) but a large number of bioactivation reactions are also known to take place, especially among oxidative reactions (phase I).

## 2    Conversion of substances: from polar to hydrophilic

The introduction of a polar group into a molecule may give the substance a sufficiently hydrophilic character for rapid excretion. For most substances, however, this is not the case and a subsequent reaction is required.

## 2.1 PHASE II REACTIONS: CONJUGATIONS

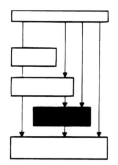

*endogenous = produced in the body*
*Conjugation reactions*

In phase II, substances are combined with hydrophilic endogenous compounds. The result is a substance with a sufficiently hydrophilic character to allow rapid excretion. Such so-called *conjugation reactions* can occur with a variety of substances, usually intermediates in the organism's metabolism. The substances most frequently involved are glucuronic acid, sulfate, glycine and glutathione. Table 3.4 gives an overview of the most common conjugation reactions.

These substances are conjugated with a polar group in the substrate. The introduction of a polar group during phase I reactions thus makes it possible for a conjugation reaction to take place in phase II.

We will again use benzene metabolism as an example:

benzene      benzene epoxide      phenol      phenylglucuronide

Organisms thus have at their disposal a system for the elimination of lipophilic substances. This enables them to metabolize lipophilic xenobiotics, but the system is also able to process endogenous degradation products, such as bilirubin, a degradation product of the red blood pigment hemoglobin.

The enzymes involved in these reactions are found in virtually all organisms: bacteria, yeasts, plants and all classes of the animal kingdom. There are, however, wide differences, both qualitative and quantitative, between organisms. This will be discussed in more detail in the next study unit. As a general rule, terrestrial animals tend to have a well-developed biotransformation system.

The influence of an organism's diet on the activity of the system is considerable. Herbivorous animals ingest a greater variety of xenobiotics than carnivorous animals. A lower activity of biotransformation enzymes is found particularly in carnivorous animals with dietary imbalance. In a sense, their prey has already done part of the work. If we compare fish with mammals and birds, the activity of the enzymes in fish is noticeably lower. This can be explained by the fact that fish can more easily eliminate lipophilic substances because of the extensive exchange with their environment.

The great majority of phase II reactions are bioinactivations. Here too, however, there are a number of exceptions, which will be discussed after the relevant enzymes have been dealt with.

TABLE 3.4

Types of conjugation reactions for a number of specific functional groups

| Conjugation reaction | Functional group |
| --- | --- |
| glucuronic acid conjugation | $-OH$; $-COOH$; $-NH_2$; $NH$; $-SH$; $-CH$ |
| sulfate conjugation | aromatic $-OH$; aromatic $-NH_2$; alcohols |
| glycine conjugation | aromatic $-NH_2$; $-COOH$ |
| acetylation | aromatic $-NH_2$; aliphatic $-NH_2$; hydrazines; $-SO_2NH_2$ |
| methylation | aromatic $-OH$; $-NH_2$; $NH$; $-SH$ |
| glutathione conjugation | epoxide, organic halides |

## 2.2 PHASE II BIOTRANSFORMATION ENZYMES: GLUCURONYL TRANSFERASE, SULFOTRANSFERASE, GLUTATHIONE S-TRANSFERASE AND EPOXIDE HYDROLASE

*Glucuronidation*

Among the phase II reactions, the *formation of glucuronides* is quantitatively the most important. Conjugation of a substrate containing a polar group with glucuronic acid can only take place after the glucuronic acid has been activated. The activated glucuronic acid consists of uridine diphosphate glucuronic acid (UDPGA), which is formed in a number of enzymatic reactions (see Figure 3.10).

*Glucuronyl transferase*
*Glucuronic acid*

UDPGA can serve as an endogenous substrate for the enzyme *glucuronyl transferase* (GT), which catalyzes the conjugation between a substance with a polar group and *glucuronic acid*. Figure 3.11 shows the glucuronidation of phenol by way of example.

Like the P-450, glucuronyl transferases are also known to be a family of isozymes. Reaction usually takes place with a hydroxyl group (–OH), but may also involve, for example, an amino group (–NH$_2$), leading to the formation of N-glucuronides.

*Sulfation*

Another common phase II reaction is *sulfate conjugation*. Again, the sulfate needs to be activated first before the reaction with the substrate can take place. Sulfate is first converted into adenosine–5'–phosphosulfate (APS):

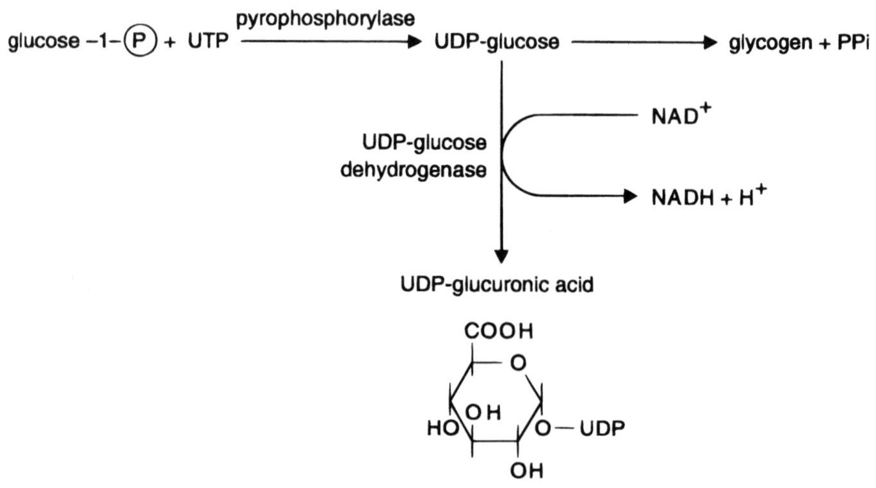

FIGURE   3.10
Synthesis of UDP-glucuronic acid
UTP=uridine triphosphate; PPi = pyrophosphate

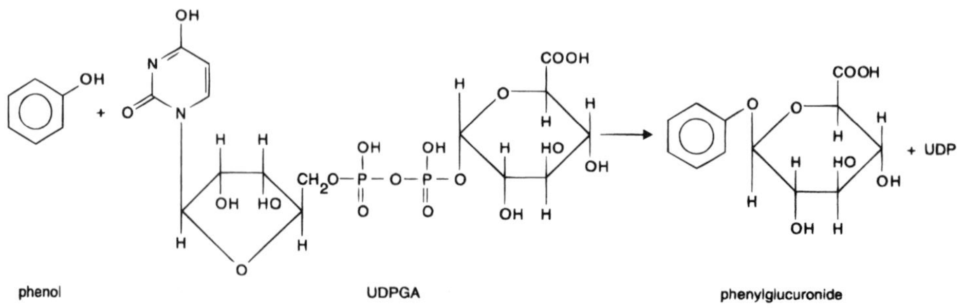

FIGURE   3.11
Glucuronidation of phenol to phenylglucuronide

56

$$SO_4^{2-} + ATP \xrightarrow{\text{sulfurylase}} APS + PPi \text{ (pyrophosphate)}$$

which is then further metabolized to 3'-phosphoadenosine-5'-phosphosulfate (PAPS):

$$APS + ATP \xrightarrow{\text{APS-phosphokinase}} PAPS + ADP$$

$$PAPS + substrate \longrightarrow PAP' + sulfate$$

(phenols, alcohols, steroids,etc)

*Sulfotransferase*

A substrate then reacts with this activated sulfate, catalyzed by the enzyme *sulfotransferase* (= sulfokinase). The conversion of phenol can again serve as an example:

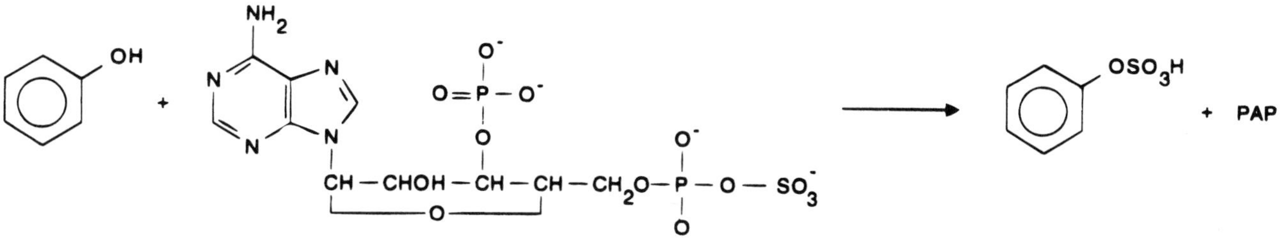

phenol                    PAPS                    phenyl sulfate

There are also a number of isozymes of this enzyme, each of which has a certain specificity for (groups of) substrates.

*Glutathione conjugation*
*Mercapturic acid formation*

*Glutathione conjugation* eventually results in the formation of so-called mercapturic acids. These reactions can also take place with a wide variety of substrates, which often have a reactive group, such as a halogen atom. Examples are the conjugations of dichloronitrobenzene and bromocyclohexane with glutathione.

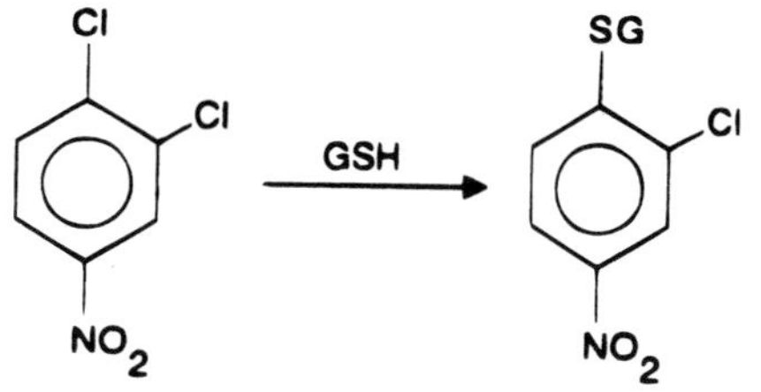

3,4-dichloro-
nitrobenzene

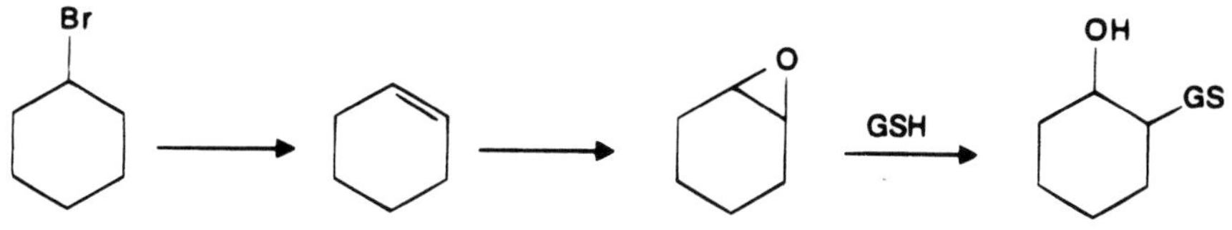

bromocyclo-          cyclo-                                    GS = glutathionyl
hexane               hexane                                    group

ASSIGNMENT 3.7

What is the difference between conjugation of a halogenated compound with glutathione and conjugation of an epoxide with glutathione?

Epoxides can be metabolized to mercapturic acids by glutathione conjugation. Mercapturic acid formation proceeds via a number of reactions. Benzene metabolism, with the reactive intermediate benzene epoxide as the substrate, again provides a suitable example:

benzene premercapturic acid            benzene mercapturic acid

As reactive (electrophilic) intermediates can undergo glutathione conjugation, the presence of mercapturic acids in the urine is an indication of exposure to substances which yield such intermediates. This test can be used in industry, for example, to establish the possible exposure of workers to hazardous substances.

*Epoxide hydrolase*

The last enzyme to be discussed is *epoxide hydrolase*. This enzyme is responsible for the detoxication of epoxides by hydration.

bromobenzene 3,4-oxide            bromobenzene 3,4-dihydrodiol

This process probably proceeds via activation of water, rather than via activation of the epoxide ring; it is assumed that the enzyme deprotonates water.

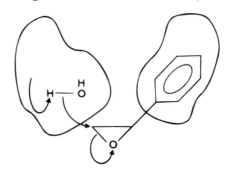

*Summary*

Examples of phase II reactions discussed above include glucuronidation, sulfation and mercapturic acid formation.

Both glucuronidation and sulfation proceed via enzymatic reactions, in which, respectively, active glucuronic acid and active sulfate are used. Mercapturic acid formation is an enzymatic process which may be the result of conjugation of reactive substances with glutathione. The conjugated product is then converted into a mercapturic acid.

## 2.3 BIOACTIVATION VIA PHASE II REACTIONS

The products of phase II reactions are usually highly water-soluble and are therefore readily excreted by the organism. Furthermore, most conjugates have a very low biological activity. Many phase II reactions are therefore bioinactivation reactions or detoxication reactions.

*Sulfation*

As with the phase I reactions, however, there are a number of exceptions. *Sulfation*, for example, may in some cases lead to the formation of unstable compounds. These are the sulfate conjugates of benzyl alcohols and hydroxamic acids.

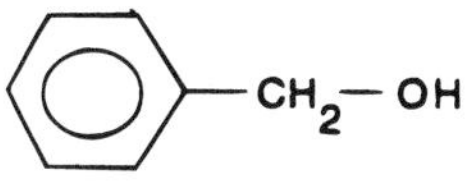

benzyl alcohol

*Benzyl alcohol*

In organic chemistry, the benzyl group often serves to protect amino groups.

*Hydroxamic acids*

*Hydroxamic acids* are functional derivatives of carbonic acids.

The hydroxylamino group is, for example, readily substituted by a nucleophile:

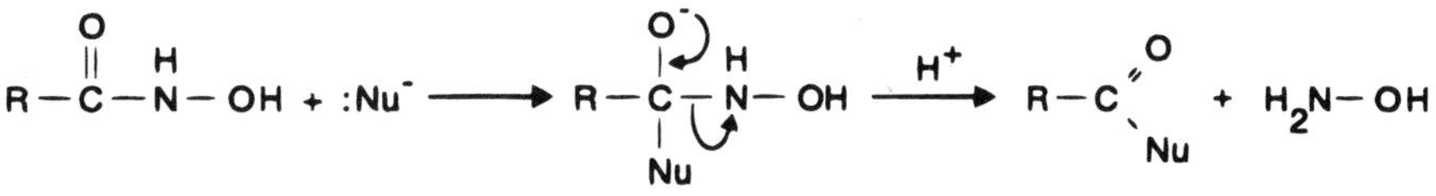

These unstable conjugates of benzyl alcohol and hydroxamic acids decompose into nitrenium or carbonium ions (see figure).

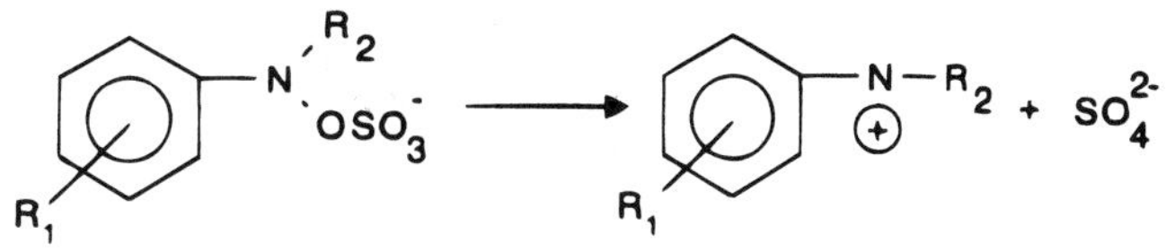

nitrenium ion

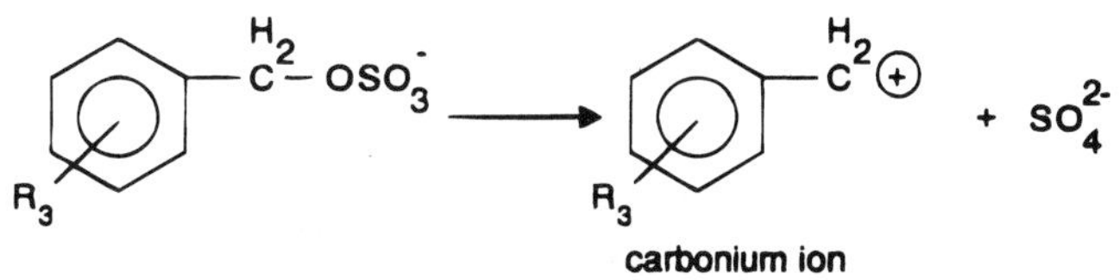

carbonium ion

*Formation of electrophilic ions*

These highly electrophilic ions react readily with proteins, RNA and DNA, which may lead to cell death or tumor formation. Some glucuronides are also unstable under certain conditions. This is true, for example, for a number of aromatic amines. These may be bioactivated, for example in the liver, to form N-hydroxyl derivatives, after which they can be bioinactivated by forming N-glucuronides (see figure).

59

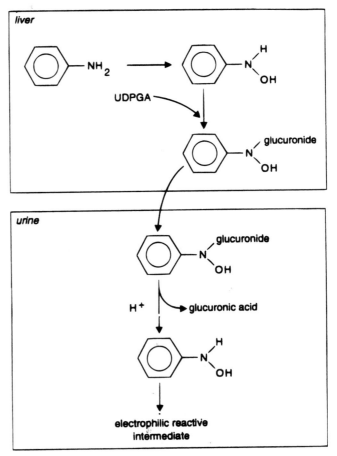

In an acid environment (e.g. in urine), the glucuronyl group acts as a good leaving group, which means that the bioinactivation is reversed, allowing the substance to exert its carcinogenic effect after all, in this case in the bladder epithelium.

*Glutathione conjugation*

Finally, a number of compounds can also be activated by *glutathione conjugation*. There are two metabolic routes for this, the first of which involves the presence of two functional groups, both of which may react with the S-atom of glutathione. An example of this is the activation of 1,2-dibromoethane, which may lead to the production of the highly reactive *thiiranium ion*.

1,2-Dibromoethane is widely used as an insecticide, fungicide and fuel additive. It is known to have a number of toxic effects: mutagenicity (demonstrated in bacteria) and carcinogenicity (demonstrated in mice and rats). The following metabolic route is probably responsible for the induction of these effects:

In the second route for bioactivation via glutathione conjugation, a thiol is formed from the intermediate cysteine conjugate (see figure).

60

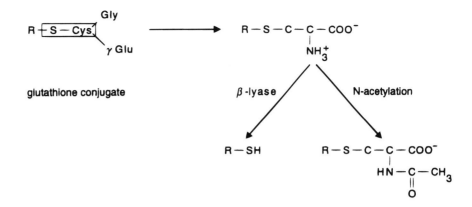

Some of the sulfhydryl compounds thus produced are reactive, for example the thiol originating from hexachlorobutadiene.

$$Cl_2C=C-C=CCl_2 \quad \rightarrow \quad \rightarrow \quad \rightarrow \quad Cl_2C=C-C=C(Cl)(SH)$$

*Summary*

A second step in the biotransformation process is the so-called phase II reactions. In these reactions, polar xenobiotics and xenobiotics which have undergone a phase I reaction are conjugated with endogenous substances.

Examples of phase II reactions discussed above include glucuronidation, sulfation and mercapturic acid formation.

Both glucuronidation and sulfation proceed via enzymatic reactions, in which, respectively, active glucuronic acid and active sulfate are used. The names of most of the enzymes which act as catalytic agents in the various conjugation reactions end in transferase, for example glucuronyl transferase, acetyltransferase and sulfotransferase.

Mercapturic acid formation is an enzymatic process which may be the result of conjugation of reactive intermediates with glutathione. The conjugated product is converted into a mercapturic acid.

Phase II reactions may also yield products which are more reactive (more toxic) than their parent compounds, although less frequently than phase I reactions. Examples are the production of nitrenium, carbonium and thiiranium ions.

## 3  Summary

Biotransformation reactions are enzymatic conversions of lipophilic foreign substances and of endogenous metabolic waste products. These reactions convert lipophilic (non-polar) compounds into polar, and therefore more water-soluble, substances. Biotransformation can be seen as divided into two steps: phase I and phase II. In the phase I reactions, the mixed-function oxidase system plays an important role. Cytochrome P-450 holds the key position in this system. Phase II consists of conjugation reactions with, for example, glucuronic acid, sulfate or glutathione. Biotransformation may lead to considerable changes in the biological activity of a foreign compound. If this activity is decreased, the process is referred to as bioinactivation or detoxication; if the toxicity is increased, it is referred to as bioactivation. Some examples of phase II bioactivations have been discussed.

SELF ASSESSMENT QUESTIONS

1   In the overall equation for processes mediated by mixed-function oxidase one molecule of oxygen ($O_2$) is used. What happens to this molecule?

2   What is the origin of the oxygen atom in the metabolite formed in the cytochrome P-450 mediated reaction?
    a.  molecular oxygen
    b.  a water molecule
    c.  both
    d.  neither

3   Like hemoglobin, cytochrome P-450 is a so-called hemoprotein.
    a.  correct
    b.  incorrect

4   At which moment in the cytochrome P-450 reaction cycle does the heme iron change from the oxidized state ($Fe^{3+}$) into the reduced state ($Fe^{2+}$)?
    a.  when the substrate binds to cytochrome P-450
    b.  when the first electron is transferred from NADPH to the cytochrome P-450-substrate complex
    c.  when one oxygen atom from molecular oxygen is introduced
    d.  when the second electron is transferred via cytochrome $b_5$

5   The MFO system can also mediate oxidative reactions in the absence of cytochrome $b_5$. Can you explain this?

6   Various types of substrate interact with cytochrome P-450.
    a.  Which types of substrate are distinguished and how can a certain substance be demonstrated to belong to a particular type?
    b.  The distinction between the various types of substrate is based on the binding of the substrate to the cytochrome P-450 complex. Indicate at which sites the various types of substrate bind to the cytochrome P-450 complex.

7   Indicate which is the most correct option.
    The oxidation of xenobiotics in the endoplasmic reticulum depends on the presence of
    a.  S-adenosylmethionine
    b.  uridine diphosphate glucuronic acid
    c.  acetyl CoA
    d.  hepatic cholinesterase
    e.  none of the above substances

8   Indicate which is the most correct option.
    The biotransformation of a substance by the microsomal oxidation system in the liver
    a.  always yields a more polar metabolite
    b.  requires the presence of NADPH and molecular oxygen
    c.  may yield products showing higher toxicity than the parent compound
    d.  options a to c are all correct

9    Indicate which of the following options is or are correct (more than one may be so!).

   a.   biotransformation of xenobiotics may yield metabolites which are as toxic as or more toxic than the parent compounds

   b.   biotransformation products tend to be more polar than their parent compounds

   c.   bioactivations are more common among phase I reactions than among phase II reactions

   d.   the most common conjugation reaction among the phase II biotransformation reactions is the glutathione conjugation

## FEEDBACK

### 1    Answers to the assignments

3.1   Vitamin D (= cholecalciferol) is taken in with the diet. It undergoes a first conversion in the liver into 25-OH-cholecalciferol, and is then converted in the kidney into 1,25-$(OH)_2$-cholecalciferol (= D-hormone) (see figure). Vitamin D thus undergoes double hydroxylation.

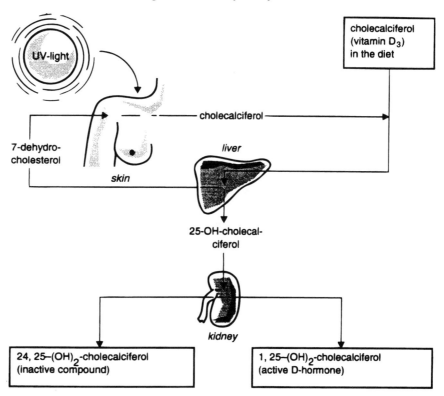

3.2   These substances would be released from the body fat as a result of the fat being consumed. Transport via the blood would make them available for interactions in other organs, where they could cause adverse effects.

3.3   The birds which were found dead without any obvious cause of death all had a very high level of dieldrin in the liver.

3.4   1   N-hydroxylation; the hydroxyl group

      2   Deamination; the keto group

3.5    All reactions mentioned under A-I in Table 3.2.

3.6    A type II difference spectrum differs from a type I difference spectrum in that its absolute maximum is to be found at long wavelengths and its minimum at short wavelengths.

As the text states, the reference cuvette primarily contains cytochrome P-450 with the electrons of the iron atoms in the low-spin state (this produces an absolute spectrum with a maximum around 420 nm). A type II interaction causes even more Fe atoms to revert to the low-spin state. The low-spin state in itself represents a lower energy level (energy is released when electrons go from the high-spin to the low-spin state), corresponding to a longer* wavelength in the absolute spectrum. Figure B shows the absolute spectra, from which Figure C, the difference spectrum, can be derived graphically.

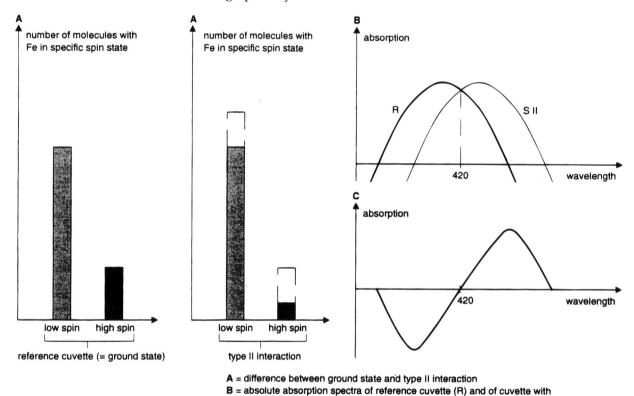

**A** = difference between ground state and type II interaction
**B** = absolute absorption spectra of reference cuvette (R) and of cuvette with
        bound type II substrate (S II)
**C** = difference spectrum

*This inverse relationship follows from Planck's law:

$$\Delta E = hf$$

where

$\Delta E$ = difference in energy content of the system
$h$ = Planck's constant
$f$ = frequency of the absorbed photon

$$f = \frac{c}{\lambda}$$

where

$c$ = velocity of light (= constant) and
$\lambda$ = wavelength of the absorbed light

3.7 Conjugation of a halogenated compound with glutathione is a substitution reaction. Conjugation of an epoxide with glutathione is an addition.

## 2 Answers to the self assessment questions

1 One oxygen atom (1) is incorporated into the substrate, the second (2) is reduced to water.

$$SH + NADPH + H^+ + O_2 \rightarrow SOH + NADP^+ + H_2O \qquad (3.1)$$

2 a

3 a

4 b

5 The role of cytochrome $b_5$, transferring the second electron to the cytochrome P-450-substrate-oxygen complex, can also be fulfilled by NADPH (see the dashed line in Figure 3.5).

6 a Type I, type II and reversed type I; the type to which a particular substance belongs can be demonstrated with the help of difference spectra.
  b Type I substrates bind to the protein part of the cytochrome P-450 complex. Type II substrates bind to the sixth ligand position of the iron atom in the heme group of cytochrome P-450.
  Reversed type I substrates bind to the protein part of cytochrome P-450 at low concentrations and to the iron atom (like type II substrates) at high concentrations.

7 e
  a to c are involved in conjugation reactions. The oxidation of xenobiotics in the ER requires NADPH, oxygen and cytochrome P-450. See also Study unit 4.

8 d

9 a, b and c are correct.
  d is incorrect.

# Contents Study unit 4
# Biotransformation: species differences and determining factors

Introduction  *67*

Study core  *68*

0-8493-9232-2/96/$0.00 + $.50
© 1996 by CRC Press, Inc.

Study unit 4

# Biotransformation: species differences and determining factors

*A. Bast*

INTRODUCTION

*Species differences*

Man is continually exposed to an increasing number of chemicals, such as insecticides, food additives, coloring agents and drugs. These xenobiotics are eliminated from the body. As discussed in Study unit 3, biotransformation plays an important role in the process of elimination. One of the main objectives of toxicology is to protect man from the harmful effects of foreign compounds. Therefore, when studying the toxic effects of such foreign compounds, it is important that toxicity studies are performed in test animals which are similar to humans, both qualitatively (types of biotransformation routes) and quantitatively (rate at which biotransformation and elimination take place, and the extent to which a xenobiotic is metabolized). If this is not the case, the toxicologist should at least know in what ways the various species differ from each other. These may be important when identifying the effects of a compound on certain specific areas of toxicology, including pathology, hematology, carcinogenesis, mutagenesis, teratogenesis and cellular toxicity. The species differences in biotransformation hamper accurate extrapolation of data from one species to another.

*Interindividual variation*
Interindividual: between individuals of one species
*Intraindividual variation*
Intraindividual: within one individual

An additional problem is that there may be significant *inter-individual variation* in the capacity for metabolizing xenobiotics. The metabolic rate of a particular individual is determined primarily by genetic factors, but also depends on age, sex and environmental factors (such as smoking, diet, etc.). In addition, environmental factors cause *intra-individual variation* in biotransformation. Much of the variation in biotransformation reactions that is observed between species, between individuals within a species, and within an individual can be traced back to the properties of enzyme systems involved in metabolism. The present study unit discusses the variability in biotransformation through several examples. It also explains the role played by cytochrome P-450, including the effects of inhibition and induction of this enzyme on bioactivation and detoxication of xenobiotics. Lastly, the localization of enzyme systems involved in biotransformation is discussed.

LEARNING OBJECTIVES

After studying this unit, you are expected to be able to:

— explain, using examples, how external factors influence metabolism describe species, interindividual and intraindividual differences in the biotransformation of xenobiotics, discuss the major causes and give examples

— explain what is meant by induction of biotransformation enzymes, and indicate its biological significance

— name various enzyme inducers and describe the differences in the mechanisms underlying induction

— describe the influence of the occurrence of cytochrome P-450 isozymes on induction phenomena, and on the substrate specificity of the enzyme system

— elucidate the use of model substrates for the *in vivo* and *in vitro* examination of biotransformation, using examples

— explain what is meant by inhibition of (biotransformation) enzymes and describe various mechanisms of inhibition with examples

— indicate, using examples, how the ultimate toxic effect depends on the balance between activation and detoxication

— indicate how transformations of endogenous compounds are related to the biotransformation of xenobiotics, and know the endogenous substrates of a number of enzymes.

*Study hints*

The present study unit is based on the knowledge you have acquired in Study unit 3. The study load for the present unit is estimated at 4 hours.

## STUDY CORE

### 1    Biotransformation: species and interindividual differences

There are many types of biotransformation reactions. They vary in type and significance from one species to another, and even between individuals of the same species. In this section, the main causes for this diversity are explained.

### 1.1    SPECIES DIFFERENCES

Significant differences have been demonstrated between different species for both phase I and phase II reactions. For the biotransformation of a particular xenobiotic, this may be quantitative (identical metabolic reactions taking place at different rates) or qualitative (different metabolic reactions). Such variation makes the extrapolation of toxicity data from test animal to man very difficult. Some general examples of qualitative differences are: dogs do not acetylate aromatic amines, cats are deficient in N-acetyl transferase and UDP-glucuronyl transferase, guinea pigs do not form mercapturic acid conjugates, and pigs are deficient in sulfate conjugation.

Many examples could be given to show that the species differences in biotransformation can be quite considerable, but three examples will be discussed here.

---

EXAMPLE

anticoagulant = a compound which prevents or retards blood coagulation

The *anticoagulant* ethylbiscoumacetate is rapidly converted by rabbits and humans, but the ultimate metabolites are different (see Figure 4.1).

ASSIGNMENT   4.1

Describe the metabolic routes by which ethylbiscoumacetate is converted in man and in rabbits.

---

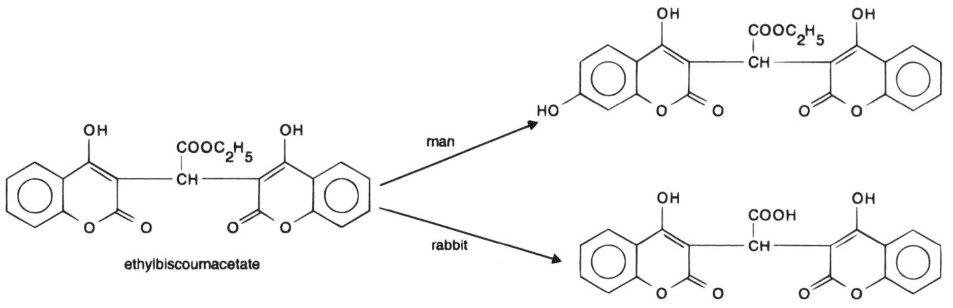

FIGURE 4.1
Biotransformation of ethylbiscoumacetate in man and in rabbits

EXAMPLE

Phenol is transformed via phase II reactions to the glucuronide and the sulfate. The relative quantity of each phenol metabolite depends on the species involved (see Table 4.1).

Matters become even more complicated if a compound undergoes both phase I and phase II reactions. Biotransformation of amphetamine is a good example of this.

EXAMPLE

In rats amphetamine undergoes aromatic hydroxylation, followed by conjugation of the resulting phenol. In rabbits and guinea pigs, oxidative deamination is the main route. Rabbits then reduce the ketone and excrete the resulting alcohol as a conjugate in the urine. Guinea pigs, in contrast, first oxidize the ketone to benzoic acid and then excrete the latter after conjugation, also by the renal route (Figure 4.2).

It should of course be remembered that non-mammals (fish, birds, reptiles, insects) and even microorganisms also carry out biotransformation reactions. Fish generally have a lower metabolic capacity for xenobiotics than birds, while birds metabolize xenobiotics less efficiently than mammals.

1.2    GENETIC DIFFERENCES

Apart from differences between species, differences between strains within one species have also been found, in man as well as in rats and mice.

antipyretic = agent which reduces fever
analgesic = painkiller

In the early literature on genetic influences on biotransformation of xenobiotics in man, experiments are described in which antipyrine was administered to monozygotic (and therefore genetically identical) twins and to dizygotic (genetically different) twins. Antipyrine used to be administered to reduce fever (as *antipyretic*) and as a pain killer (*analgesic*). It is now no longer used as such, but still finds application as a model substrate for studying metabolism. It is particularly suitable for this purpose, as it has been found that the elimination rate of antipyrine is the same in identical twins, but different in dizygotic twins. In recent years, further progress has been made in this field when a single gene was found to regulate the oxidative metabolism of a large number of compounds.

TABLE 4.1

Species variation in the conjugation of phenol with glucuronic acid and sulfate

| | Phenol conjugation (as percentage of total excretion in a species) | |
| | Glucuronide | Sulfate |
| --- | --- | --- |
| cat | 0 | 87 |
| man | 23 | 71 |
| rat | 25 | 68 |
| rabbit | 46 | 45 |
| pig | 100 | 0 |

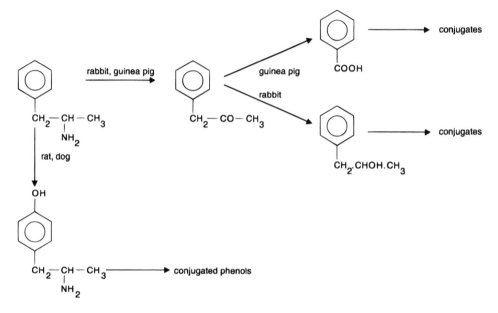

FIGURE 4.2

Biotransformation of amphetamine in rabbits, rats, guinea pigs and dogs

EXAMPLE

antihypertensive = agent which reduces high blood pressure

One of the first compounds to be studied in this connection was the antihypertensive debrisoquine. When the 4-hydroxylation of debrisoquine (Figure 4.3) is determined in a population, it is found that two phenotypes are found, in other words, the population is bimodal for the hydroxylation of debrisoquine.

*Extensive metabolizers*
*Poor metabolizers*
Toxicogenetic phenomenon = genetically determined toxic phenomenon

The largest group appears to hydroxylate efficiently at the 4 position. They are the so-called *extensive metabolizers*. In contrast, a small portion of the population, the *poor metabolizers*, show almost no 4-hydroxylation of debrisoquine. "Poor metabolizers" account for approximately 8% of the Caucasian population. As would be expected in the case of a toxicogenetic phenomenon, the percentage of poor metabolizers varies for different ethnic groups. The percentage in the Middle East (Egypt, Iraq, Saudi Arabia), for example, is 1–2%.

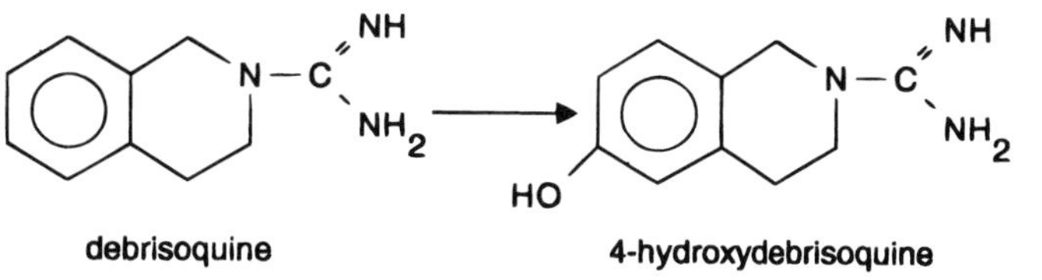

FIGURE 4.3
4-Hydroxylation of debrisoquine

ASSIGNMENT 4.2

Explain why the percentage of poor metabolizers differs for the various ethnic groups.

A number of biotransformation reactions, including dehydrogenations, O-dealkylations and aromatic hydroxylations of various compounds, are regulated by the debrisoquine hydroxylation locus. However, genetic polymorphism has now also been established for oxidation which is not brought about via the debrisoquine locus.

ASSIGNMENT 4.3

It is striking that virtually all research in this area has been performed on pharmaceuticals. Can you explain this?

*Genetic polymorphism*

For phase II reactions also, a bimodal distribution of the activity in a population can sometimes be found. A well-known example is the *genetic polymorphism* for the acetylation of xenobiotics (Figure 4.4). There are two phenotypes, termed fast acetylator and slow acetylator. The drug isoniazid, which is used to treat tuberculosis, displays such polymorphism.

The acetylation phenotype observed for isoniazid can also be seen for other compounds which undergo N-acetylation, indicating a certain correlation. Examples of other such xenobiotics are hydralazine (an antihypertensive drug) and a number of sulfonamides (compounds with a bactericidal action, so-called chemotherapeutic substances) (Figure 4.5).

neuropathy = disorder of the nerves

In most European countries, approximately 40% of the population are fast acetylators. In Asian countries, this figure is about 80%, while almost 96% of the Eskimos are fast acetylators. The acetylation phenotype determines whether, and if so, what toxic side effects a compound can be expected to have. Isoniazid, for example, may cause toxic effects in the nerves (neuropathy) of slow acetylators, but hepatic injury in fast acetylators. In the case of hydralazine, the effective dose administered for the reduction of hypertension is lower for slow than for fast acetylators. A serious side effect of hydralazine is lupus erythematosus, an auto-immune disease, which is more common in the slow than in the fast acetylation phenotype.

ASSIGNMENT 4.4

Explain why a lower dose of hydralazine is used in slow acetylators than in fast acetylators.

The acetylation phenotype can easily be established using a harmless compound which undergoes N-acetylation, by determining the quantity of N-acetyl metabolite in the urine after the substance has been administered.

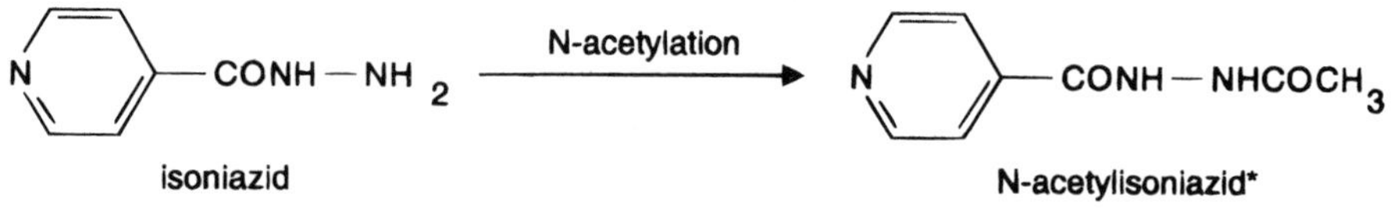

FIGURE   4.4
Acetylation of isoniazid

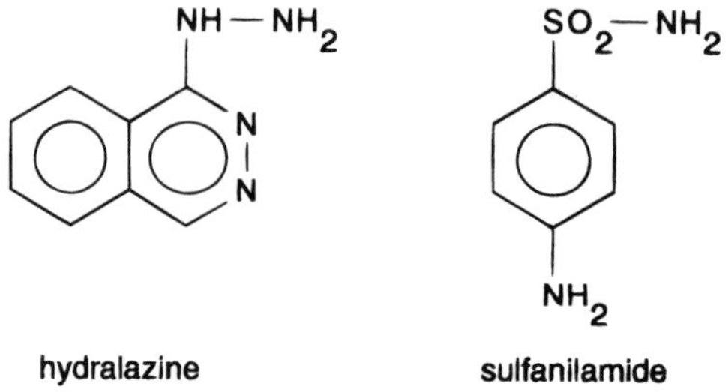

FIGURE   4.5
Structural formulae of hydralazine and sulfanilamide (a sulfonamide)

ASSIGNMENT   4.5

Draw a diagram of the bimodal distribution of N-acetylisoniazid formation. Assuming that isoniazid is administered to a large population, plot the percentage of N-acetylisoniazid present in the urine against the number of individuals.

It is important to know whether there is genetic polymorphism in the biotransformation patterns of xenobiotics which are administered to humans (e.g. medicines). A poor metabolizer may experience a strong effect (either desired or not) at a dose that has no effect on an extensive metabolizer. Also, if a metabolic oxidation route is lacking, the compound may be converted via another biotransformation reaction, which in normal circumstances is of only minor importance. Such a shift in the type of metabolic conversion can sometimes give rise to the formation of highly toxic metabolites.

EXAMPLE

The analgesic phenacetin normally undergoes O-dealkylation to acetaminophen, a phase I reaction (Figure 4.6). The latter is then glucuronidated and sulfated (phase II reactions). A poor metabolizer O-dealkylates phenacetin only slowly. As a result, secondary transformation routes become more important, i.e. the formation of 2-hydroxyphenetidin. This metabolite may give rise to the formation of methemoglobin, the oxidized form of hemoglobin, which affects the transport of oxygen by hemoglobin. This does not take place in extensive metabolizers, in whom phenacetin is transformed mainly to acetaminophen.

*Methemoglobin*

1.3   SEX DIFFERENCES

The dependence of biotransformation on the sex of the organism is a form of genetic control, but is manifested via hormonal influences. From a biochemical point of view, sex differences in the biotransformation of xenobiotics arise from

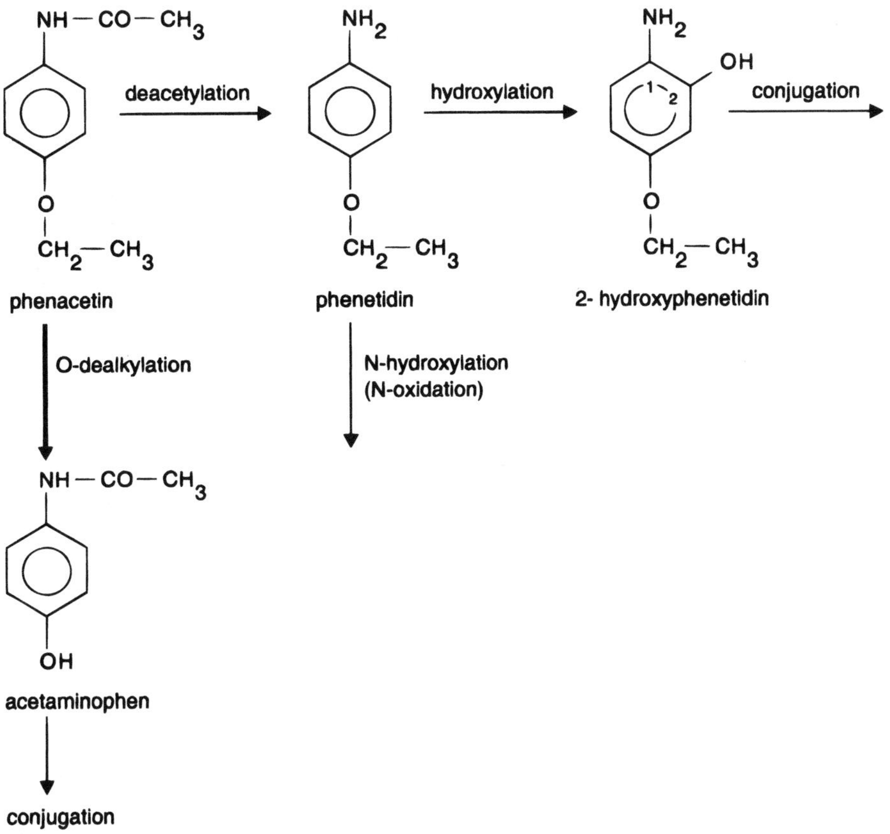

FIGURE 4.6
Metabolism of phenacetin to acetaminophen and 2-hydroxyphenetidin

a combination of various factors, including differences in enzyme concentrations and activities and changes in the lipid environment of the enzymes. Cytochrome P-450 consists of a number of isozymes. Some of these have been isolated and found to be sex-dependent. It has recently been suggested that the pituitary releases a so-called feminizing factor which causes the liver in female mammals to act as a "female" liver. The release of this factor is controlled by the hypothalamus. In males, this function of the hypothalamus is inhibited by hormones, and the pituitary consequently does not release the feminizing factor. The effect of the sex of an organism on biotransformation is often very pronounced in test animals (rats and mice), but seems to be of very little significance in humans.

## 1.4    AGE DIFFERENCES

Age plays an important role in the biotransformation of xenobiotics. The differences are particularly obvious when comparing very young, adult and very old animals. For phase I reactions, the development of enzyme activity from birth to adulthood can take various courses (Figure 4.7).

The activity may increase linearly from birth to the adult stage (curve a). In rats, this pattern is seen for many aromatic and aliphatic hydroxylations. Development according to curve b, i.e. an increase in activity from the suckling stage up to adulthood, can be observed for some N-demethylations. In addition, development according to curve c (a rapid increase in activity immediately after birth, followed by a rapid drop down to the adult level) and curve d (an increase in activity from birth to the weaning stage and then a decrease to the adult level) has been observed. The biochemical background of age-dependent biotransfor-

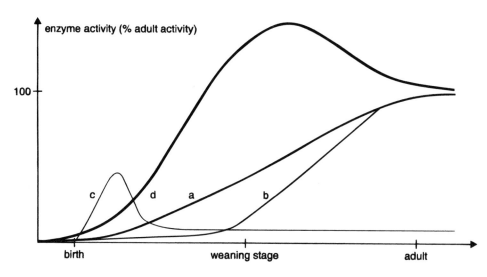

FIGURE 4.7
Age-dependent development of phase I reactions
Enzyme activity is shown as a percentage of the adult activity (100%). Further details can be found in the text.

mation can be found in cellular changes, in particular in the development of the endoplasmic reticulum, and in molecular changes such as alterations in the components of the cytochrome P-450 system.

The pattern of development of glucuronidation has also been extensively studied. Curve a in Figure 4.8 describes the glucuronidation of xenobiotics. It shows an increase in activity up to birth, after which activity decreases to the adult level. Curve b, showing low activity up to birth followed by a rapid increase, describes the development of glucuronidation activity for endogenous compounds.

ASSIGNMENT 4.6

Can you explain why some babies cannot excrete bilirubin immediately after birth?

perinatal = shortly before and
after birth

Other phase II reactions (acetylation, amino acid conjugation and glutathione conjugation) also develop *perinatally* rather than in the fetal stage. An exception is sulfotransferase activity. This is already observed during the fetal stage, probably because of the important role of sulfation in conjugations with endogenous steroids.

1.5 VARIATION DUE TO EXTERNAL FACTORS

Many interindividual differences in the metabolism of compounds can be traced back to genetic factors, age, and (to a certain extent) environmental factors. Intraindividual variation, on the other hand, is mainly determined by external factors and disease.

ASSIGNMENT 4.7

The boxes in Figure 4.9 are of different sizes. What do you think is the philosophy behind this? Can you mention a number of external factors that may be responsible for the occurrence of intra-individual variation?

Many organs have biotransformation capacity, such as the liver, intestinal wall, intestinal flora, lungs and kidneys. Changes in the physiology of these organs resulting from disease will affect metabolism. Hepatic disease will generally cause a reduction of enzymatic activity in the liver, influence the blood flow

74

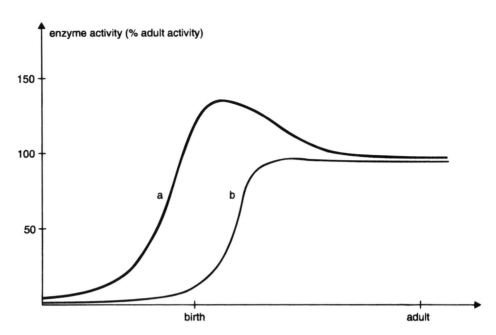

FIGURE 4.8
Age-dependent development of glucuronidation
Enzymatic activity is shown as the percentage of the activity in the adult stage (100%).

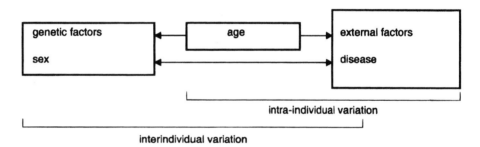

FIGURE 4.9
Factors contributing to the intra-individual and interindividual variation in the bio-transformation of xenobiotics

hypoalbuminemia = decreased quantity of albumin in the blood

through the liver (causing a change in the inflow of xenobiotics) and lead to a reduction in albumin concentration (*hypoalbuminemia*). The latter interferes with the binding of compounds to albumin in the blood. The influence of a whole range of environmental factors has been studied in great detail, and appears to depend on the species in question, the compound which is metabolized and the age of the individual. Table 4.2 lists a number of external factors such as dietary and environmental factors.

Table 4.2 can be illustrated by means of a few examples. The hepatotoxicity of aflatoxin (Figure 4.10) depends on the formation of aflatoxin epoxide. In test animals, a low-protein diet causes a decrease in the biosynthesis of many enzymes which are essential to phase I reactions, and consequently to a reduction in the hepatotoxicity of aflatoxin. Experiments have been described in which the effects of *pyrolysis* products (such as those formed during the preparation of food) on biotransformation were studied. Meat grilled on a barbecue contains large quantities of these pyrolysis products, which are mainly formed on degradation of amino acids such as tryptophan, or compounds like benzo[*a*]pyrene. These compounds *induce* (increase the concentration of) a certain isozyme of cy-

pyrolysis = chemical decomposition caused by high temperatures

*Induction*

75

TABLE 4.2
External factors influencing the biotransformation of xenobiotics

| | |
|---|---|
| *environmental factors* | insecticides, pesticides and herbicides<br>heavy metals<br>industrial pollution |
| *dietary factors* | non-nutrients in the diet:<br>—indoles<br>—tobacco components and tobacco products<br>—marihuana products<br>—alcohol consumption<br>—pyrolysis products<br><br>nutrients in the diet:<br>—trace elements<br>—essential elements (minerals, vitamins)<br>—proteins<br>—lipids<br>—carbohydrates |

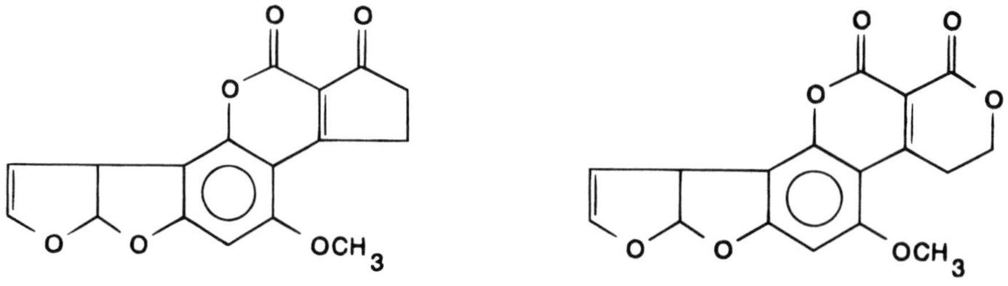

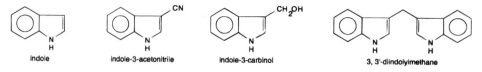

aflatoxin B$_1$          aflatoxin G$_1$

FIGURE 4.10
The mycotoxins aflatoxin B$_1$ and G$_1$

For more information on induction see the following section

tochrome P-450, referred to as cytochrome P-448. This isozyme is involved in the metabolism of polycyclic aromatic hydrocarbons, which may lead to the formation of mutagenic or carcinogenic metabolites. Components (primarily indoles) from certain types of cabbage can also lead to the induction of cytochrome P-448.

indole          indole-3-acetonitrile          indole-3-carbinol          3, 3'-diindolylmethane

FIGURE 4.11
Structural formulae of indole, and some indole derivatives found in cabbage or Brussels sprouts

Pesticides are present throughout our environment, in soil and air, in water and in food. Some of them, DDT for example, induce various enzymes that catalyze phase I reactions.

It will be evident that some factors amplify biotransformation processes, while others inhibit them. Sometimes the effects are not additive, but reinforce each other in either a negative or positive sense.

76

*Summary*

Biotransformation reactions are dependent on many internal and external factors, causing species, interindividual and intra-individual differences in the metabolism of xenobiotics.

Many factors influence metabolism, and various categories of factors may overlap. For example, genetic and sex differences in the biotransformation of xenobiotics will be similar in various respects. The same can be said of the influence of the endocrine system on the metabolism of xenobiotics.

The metabolism of xenobiotics is a complicated matter. It can be influenced by a variety of factors, which will sometimes interact with each other.

The previous section has only introduced preliminary aspects of this complex subject.

## 2    Cytochrome P-450: induction and inhibition

This section discusses induction and inhibition of enzymes involved in biotransformation, with the emphasis on cytochrome P-450. The use of model substrates to determine the total cytochrome P-450 activity, and even the activity of the individual isozymes, will also be dealt with. Inhibition of cytochrome P-450 can take place in various ways, and this will be illustrated by several examples.

### 2.1    INDUCTION AND MODEL SUBSTRATES

Many of the non-nutrients in food and many environmental factors, such as those mentioned in Table 4.2, stimulate (induce) their own metabolism or the biotransformation of other compounds. Enzyme induction can be illustrated by the action of the muscle relaxant zoxazolamine. Pretreatment of a test animal with the inducer phenobarbital causes induction of cytochrome P-450, so that the metabolism of zoxazolamine (aromatic hydroxylation) is stimulated (Figure 4.12).

> ASSIGNMENT   4.8
>
> What makes the induction of zoxazolamine metabolism easily observable *in vivo*? Think of the biological action of this compound.

Induction of cytochrome P-450 does not always lead to stimulation of the metabolism of xenobiotics, and not always to the same extent.

*Isozymes of cytochrome P-450*

Some inducers increase the metabolism of a compound, while others do not. Because of this phenomenon, and because of the ability of cytochrome P-450 to metabolize a large variety of compounds, the existence of various isozymes of cytochrome P-450 has long been suspected. Experimental findings have proved this suspicion to be correct, and isozymes with varying amino acid sequences, substrate specificity and sensitivity to inducers have been isolated.

> ASSIGNMENT   4.9
>
> Explain how the intraindividual, the interindividual and the species variation in the metabolism of xenobiotics can be explained at least in part by the existence of cytochrome P-450 isozymes. Suggest also why this was suspected on the basis of the observation that a compound which induces cytochrome P-450 does not always stimulate the biotransformation of a xenobiotic which is converted by a particular isozyme.

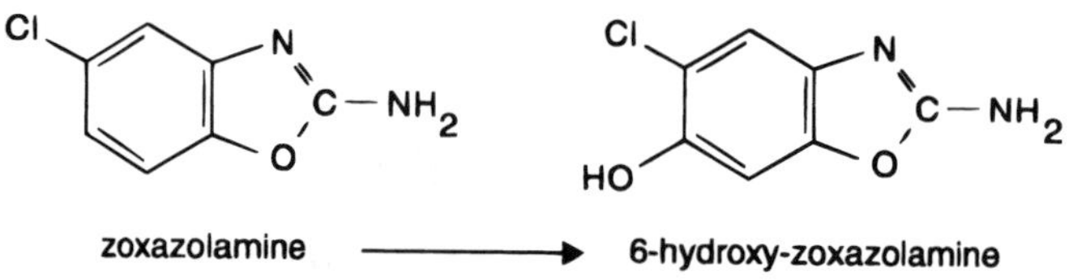

zoxazolamine ⟶ 6-hydroxy-zoxazolamine

FIGURE 4.12
Aromatic hydroxylation of zoxazolamine

In research, the enzymatic activity of cytochrome P-450 is often determined using model substrates.

---

EXAMPLE

An example of this is the substrate aminopyrine, which is demethylated by cytochrome P-450. This reaction can be carried out *in vitro* (using the microsomal fraction of the liver). After addition of the necessary co-factors, formaldehyde is formed in a two-step demethylation reaction (Figure 4.13).

*In vivo*, formaldehyde is converted, via formic acid, to carbon dioxide ($CO_2$). If aminopyrine, radioactively labelled ($^{14}C$) in the N-methyl groups, is used, radioactive formaldehyde and formic acid and, in the expired air, radioactive $^{14}CO_2$ are found. This procedure is sometimes used as a test for liver function.

---

In practice, other, often colorimetric/fluorimetric methods are also used for the determination of cytochrome P-450 activity (see Table 4.3).

## 2.2 DETERMINATION OF CYTOCHROME P-450 ISOZYMES

Various substrates can be used to establish the isozyme pattern of cytochrome P-450. *In vitro*, alkoxycoumarins are sometimes used. These are converted by O-dealkylation to hydroxycoumarin, which can easily be determined by fluorimetry.

It is primarily the alkyl substituent which appears to determine by which cytochrome P-450 isozyme O-dealkylation takes place. Especially *in vivo* (but also *in vitro*), antipyrine is used as a model substrate. The various metabolic routes of antipyrine (Figure 4.14) are mediated by different isozymes of cytochrome P-450. For example, 4-hydroxylation of antipyrine can be induced by 3-methylcholanthrene. 3-Methylcholanthrene also induces the hydroxylation of benzo[a]pyrene. It therefore seems reasonable to assume that the formation of 4-hydroxyantipyrine is related to the hydroxylation of benzo[a]pyrene. This has indeed been established in the human liver. This type of experiment can eventually result in "metabolic mapping" of an individual in certain circumstances. It should, however, be borne in mind that there will virtually always be a certain overlap between the various (immunologically distinguishable) isozymes in the mediation of the various biotransformation routes.

ASSIGNMENT 4.10

The arrows in Figure 4.14 showing the various metabolic routes for antipyrine are of different thickness. Can you give the reason for this?

*Two types of induction*

In general, *two types of induction* can be distinguished, which are mediated by representatives of the barbiturates and polycyclic aromatic hydrocarbons, respectively. Induction by barbiturates, such as phenobarbital, leads to an increase in the quan-

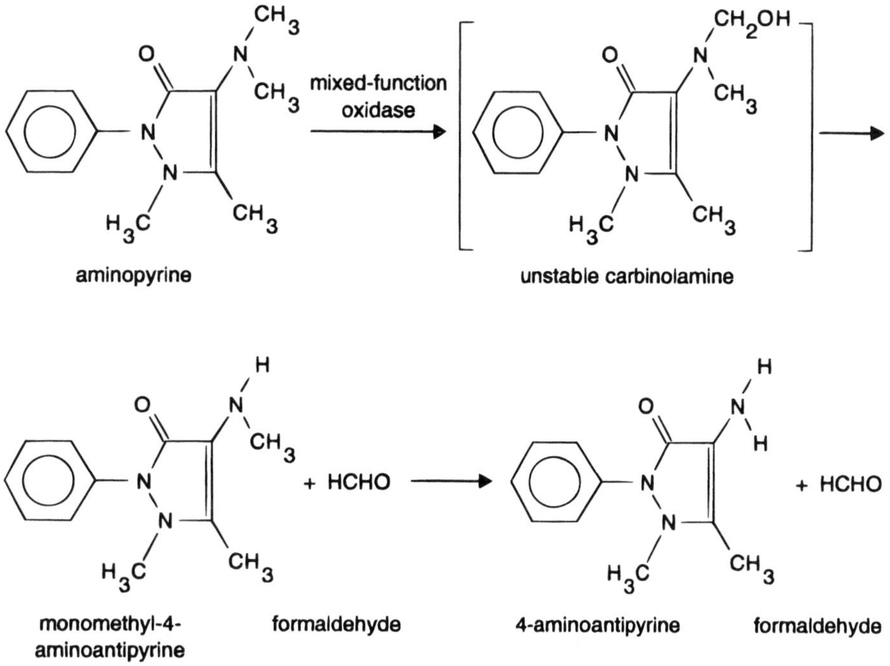

FIGURE 4.13
Two-step N-demethylation of aminopyrine

TABLE 4.3
Model substrates used for measuring the activity of cytochrome P-450

| substrate | reaction | product to be measured |
|---|---|---|
| ethylmorphine formaldehyde 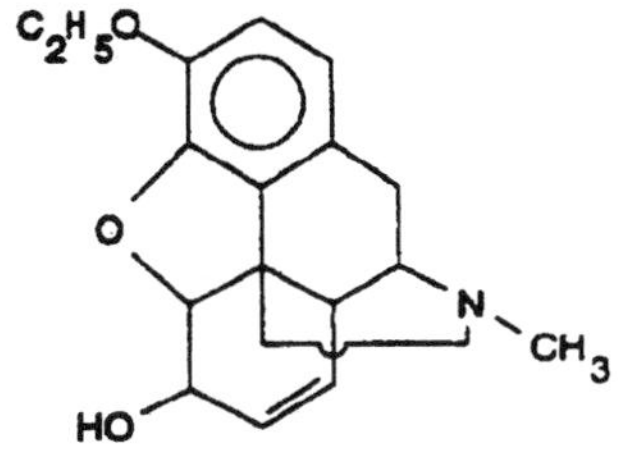 | N-demethylation | desmethylethylethylmorphine 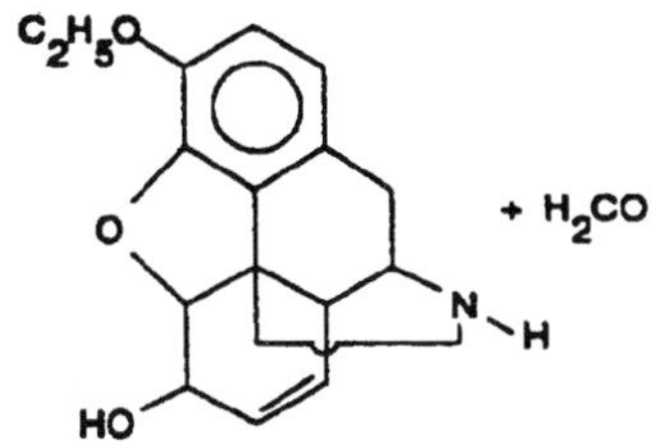 + $H_2CO$ |
| aniline 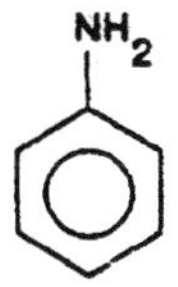 | p-hydroxylation | p-hydroxyaniline  |
| ethoxycoumarin 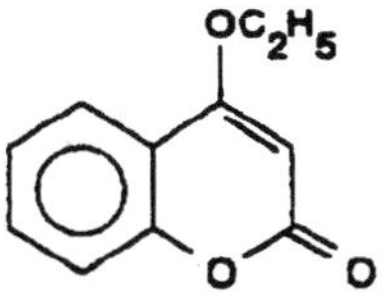 | O-deethylation | hydroxycoumarin 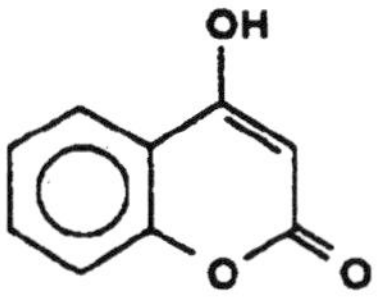 |

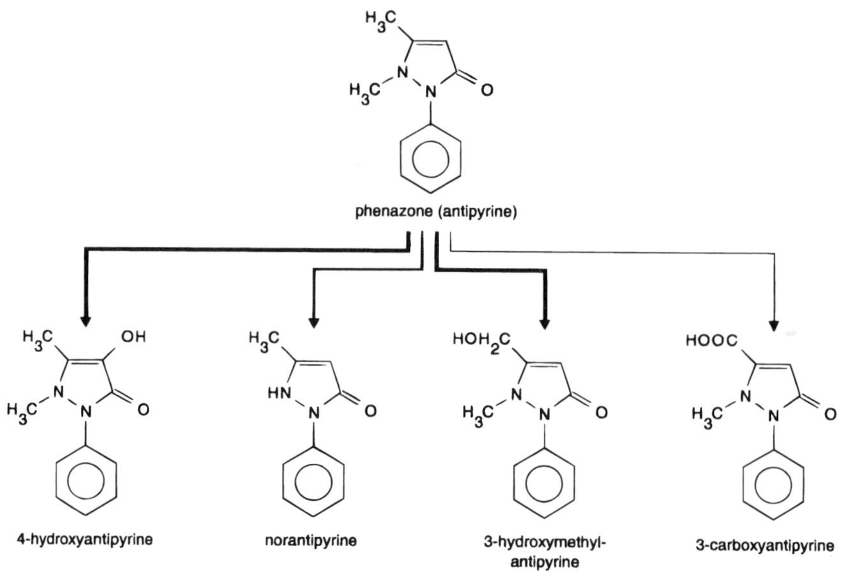

FIGURE 4.14
Antipyrine and its metabolic routes mediated by cytochrome P-450 isozymes

tity of specific messenger RNA, probably via stimulation of the transcription process. This, in turn, leads to the synthesis of NADPH-dependent cytochrome P-450 reductase and cytochrome P-450. Induction brought about by polycyclic aromatic hydrocarbons, such as benzo[a]pyrene, 3-methylcholanthrene and 2,3,7,8-tetrachlorodibenzo-p-dioxin (TCDD or dioxin, Figure 4.15), proceeds via binding of the inducer to a specific protein in the cytosol which acts as an acceptor molecule (receptor). The inducer–receptor complex gives rise to the formation of specific messenger RNA in the nucleus, after which the newly synthesized cytochrome P-450 is incorporated into the endoplasmic reticulum. It is only for this type of inducer that a relationship between structure and specific binding to the receptor can be found.

ASSIGNMENT   4.11

Try to construct a diagram of these two induction mechanisms.

Induction has also been described for other biotransformation enzymes, such as the glucuronyl transferases, the glutathione S-transferases and the epoxide hydrolases. This induction is often rather non-specific, in that proliferation of the endoplasmic reticulum or stimulation of the synthesis of many other enzymes in the liver is caused simultaneously. Some of the phase II enzymes are also present in several forms (glucuronyl transferase, glutathione S-transferase). It is not surprising, therefore, that the type of induction is often determined by the inducer that is used.

EXAMPLE

If, for example, glucuronyl transferase is induced by phenobarbital, chloramphenicol appears to be an excellent substrate for the transferase that is formed. Induction by 3-methylcholanthrene results in stimulation of the synthesis of a transferase that specifically mediates the glucuronidation of 3-hydroxybenzo[a]pyrene.

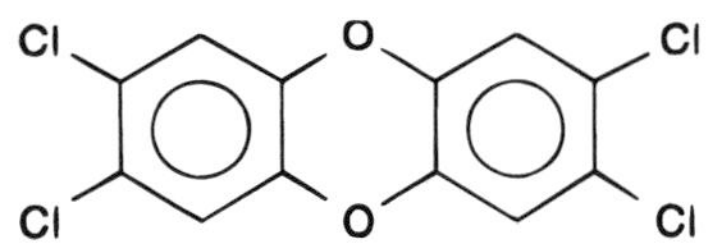

2,3,7,8-tetrachlorodibenzo-p-dioxin (TCDD)

FIGURE 4.15
2,3,7,8-tetrachlorodibenzo-p-dioxin (TCDD)

Induction of biotransformation enzymes other than cytochrome P-450 may of course also significantly influence the metabolism of a xenobiotic.

2.3    INHIBITION OF CYTOCHROME P-450

Inhibition of cytochrome P-450 by xenobiotics can take place in various ways. A compound may bind to the active sites on the *apoprotein region* of cytochrome P-450. These binding sites are located on a *hydrophobic* region of the cytochrome P-450 protein. If substrates are to bind in this way, they must be at least partially lipophilic. It will be clear that only substrates that are converted by the same cytochrome P-450 isozyme and that occupy the same binding sites on this isozyme can compete with one another. Examples of this so-called competitive inhibition have been described in detail within the field of *pharmacotherapy*, since this phenomenon can lead to drug interaction.

*Apoprotein region*

pharmacotherapy = treatment with medicines

---

EXAMPLE

Cimetidine (Figure 4.16) is used therapeutically to inhibit the secretion of gastric juices. The compound is notorious for its inhibition of cytochrome P-450. This probably involves interaction of cimetidine with the heme group of the enzyme.

---

*Interaction with $Fe^{3+}$*

Xenobiotics that interact with the $Fe^{3+}$ of the heme group of cytochrome P-450 can inhibit cytochrome P-450, as the enzyme can no longer activate oxygen, which also takes place at the heme group. Inhibition of biotransformation by xenobiotics in this way is often of a non-competitive nature.

---

EXAMPLE

An example is metyrapone, a compound which can be used to test for pituitary function. Cytochrome P-450 (Figure 4.17) has a high affinity for this substance. Binding takes place as a result of interaction between the N atoms of metyrapone and the heme iron. The apoprotein is possibly of importance for the correct orientation of metyrapone in relation to the $Fe^{3+}$ in the heme group.

ASSIGNMENT   4.12

Draw the difference spectrum for the interaction of metyrapone with cytochrome P-450.

---

*Conversion to metabolic intermediates*

Some compounds are converted to *metabolic intermediates*. As such, they may form complexes with cytochrome P-450 which leads to inactivation of the enzyme. There are numerous examples of compounds which form such complexes.

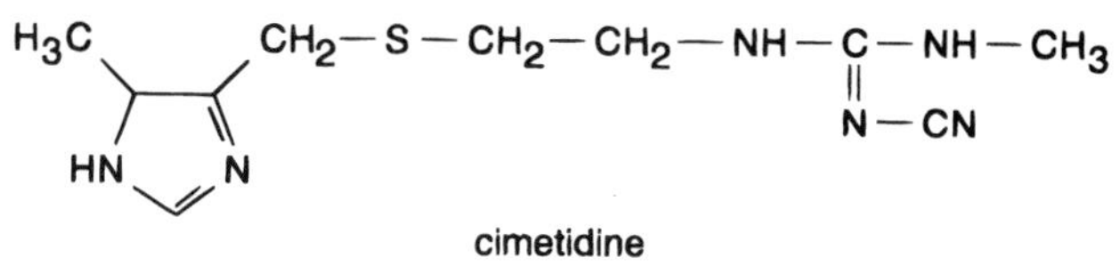

H3C
CH2—S—CH2—CH2—NH—C—NH—CH3
N—CN
HN
N
cimetidine

FIGURE 4.16
Structural formula of cimetidine

CH2
S
Fe3+
N
O
CH3
C—C
CH3
N
metyrapone

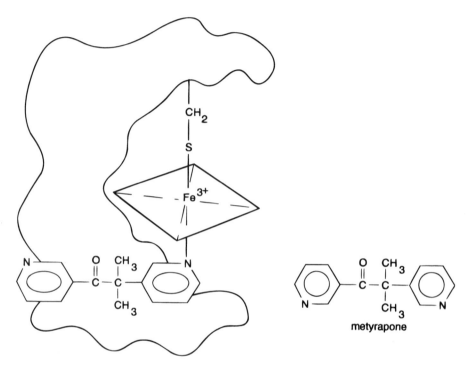

FIGURE 4.17
Interaction of metyrapone with the heme iron in cytochrome P-450

Two groups can be distinguished on the basis of whether or not biotransformation takes place at an amino group in the molecule.

---

EXAMPLE

The first category includes the anti-Parkinson drug orphenadrine (Figure 4.18). Mono-N-dealkylation leads to the formation of tophenacine. This is subsequently followed by cytochrome P-450-mediated conversion to a reactive metabolic intermediate. The latter forms a complex with the heme iron (in its reduced form, $Fe^{2+}$) of cytochrome P-450.

It is not yet clear whether it is the nitroxide radical or the nitroso metabolite which is the metabolic intermediate that forms a complex with cytochrome P-450.

The second category includes the methylenedioxybenzene derivatives. The reactive intermediate is probably a carbene. Figure 4.19 shows the formation of safrole carbene from safrole, occurring in plants. Safrole used to be applied as an additive in toothpaste, chewing gum, soap and some pharmaceutical preparations. It is a weak liver carcinogen. Complexing of the carbene with cytochrome P-450 results in non-competitive inhibition.

---

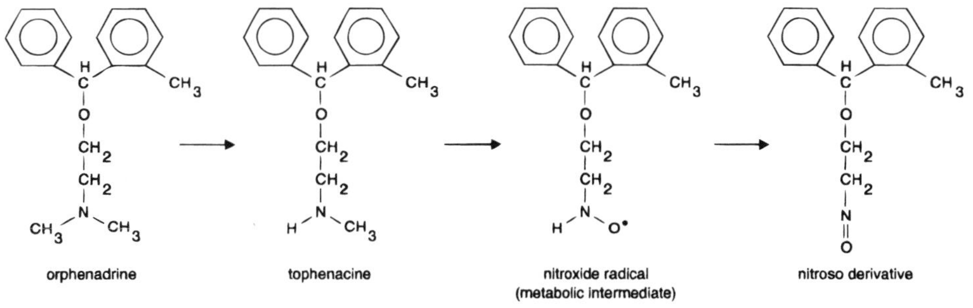

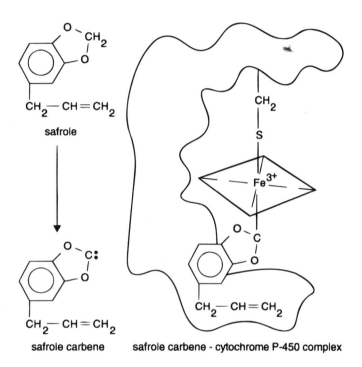

FIGURE 4.18
Biotransformation of orphenadrine to a metabolic intermediate

FIGURE 4.19
Biotransformation of safrole to safrole carbene, a potential metabolic intermediate

Porphyrin = heme group without iron pigment, colored compound

Some xenobiotics also form complexes with the porphyrin part of cytochrome P-450. These xenobiotics contain a double or a triple C-C bond.

After metabolism of the compound, alkylation leads to the formation of substrate–porphyrin adducts, which can be seen as green pigments. Since activation by metabolism is needed before adducts can be formed, the parent compounds concerned are called *suicide substrates*. These compounds, e.g. allylisopropyl-acetamide (Figure 4.20), seem to interact selectively with cytochrome P-450.

*Suicide substrates*

Cytostatic agent = agent that hinders cell development

Inhibition of cytochrome P-450 can also take place by covalent binding to the apoprotein (for example, metabolism of the antibiotic chloramphenicol) or via alkylation of sulfhydryl (SH) groups (e.g. by the cytostatic agent cyclophosphamide). Compounds that damage the membrane of the endoplasmic reticulum, the membrane in which cytochrome P-450 is embedded, can also inhibit the enzyme. Xenobiotics which block electron transfer, which plays a role in the action

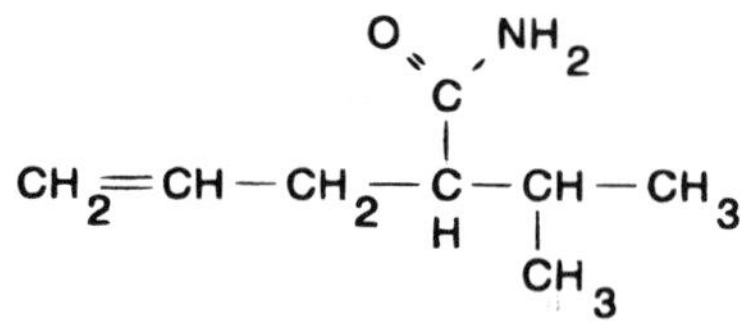

$$CH_2\!=\!CH-CH_2-\underset{\underset{\displaystyle CH_3}{|}}{\overset{\overset{\displaystyle \underset{C}{\overset{O}{\diagdown}}\,\,\overset{NH_2}{\diagup}}{|}}{\underset{H}{\overset{|}{C}}}}-CH-CH_3$$

FIGURE 4.20
Structural formula of allylisopropylacetamide

of cytochrome P-450, inhibit the total enzymatic activity. Any effects on the synthesis and degradation of heme, for example by cobalt, will also modulate cytochrome P-450 activity. Cobalt has been shown to have a significant inhibitory effect on the rate-limiting step in the biosynthesis of the heme group (by inhibiting the enzyme $\delta$-aminolevulinic acid synthetase). In addition, cobalt stimulates the degradation of the heme group (by enhancing heme oxygenase activity).

*Summary*

It is possible to induce (stimulate) various biotransformation systems. The effect of induction is determined to a large extent by the type of compound that causes it. It is also possible to inhibit biotransformation enzymes.

Induction of cytochrome P-450 is usually the result of an increase in the level of specific messenger RNA and thus of an increase in transcription capacity (e.g. by phenobarbital). Induction can also originate from interaction with specific cytosol receptors (e.g. by polycyclic aromatic hydrocarbons).

Targets for compounds which inhibit cytochrome P-450 are usually components of cytochrome P-450 itself (e.g. porphyrin region, apoprotein region, iron atom of heme group), or enzymes, involved in the cytochrome P-450 action.

## 3    Factors determining the development of toxic effects

Many toxic effects are induced by a sequence of events. The first step is usually the formation of a reactive intermediate. By interaction with a bio(macro)molecule, the reactive toxic agent then initiates a chain of disturbances of physiological and chemico-physiological processes which ultimately results in the toxic effect. The factors which determine whether or not a toxic effect will manifest itself can be classified according to the following criteria:

*Ratio of bioactivation to detoxication*

a.   *ratio of formation of reactive intermediate to detoxication*. This ratio determines the amount of intermediate that ultimately becomes *available* for interaction with a bio(macro)molecule.

EXAMPLE

This is illustrated by the following example. In an *in vitro* experiment, in the absence of detoxication systems, the 4,5-epoxide of benzo[*A*]pyrene (Figure 4.21) appeared to be one of the strongest mutagenic metabolites of benzo[*A*]pyrene, whereas after administration of the epoxide to test animals, no increase in the natural incidence of tumors was observed.

*Physiological homeostases*
*See also Study unit 11*

b.   *physiological homeostases*, such as thiol homeostasis, calcium homeostasis and glucose homeostasis. If these balances are disturbed to the extent that essential cellular functions become impaired, this may be lethal to the cell. It should therefore be possible to protect against toxic substances without influencing the ratio mentioned under a.

84

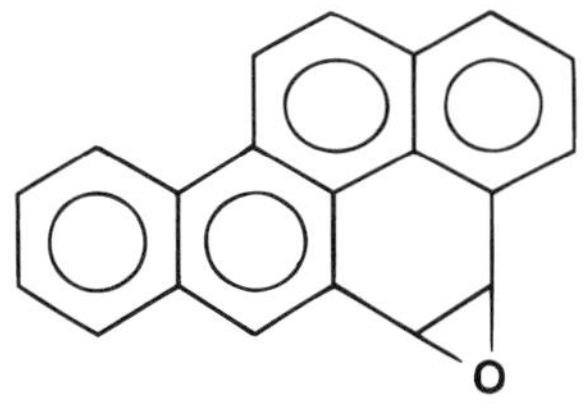

B[a]P (4S,5R)-oxide

FIGURE 4.21
4,5-epoxide of benzo[a]pyrene

EXAMPLE

Detoxication of acetaminophen
takes place via glucuronic acid
and sulfate conjugation, and
excretion in the urine

This possibility has been confirmed by research into the prevention of hepatic toxicity with the analgesic acetaminophen. In test animals, acetaminophen-induced hepatic necrosis could be prevented by administering the compound in combination with acetylsalicylic acid. The protective action of acetylsalicylic acid could not be ascribed to a direct effect on activation or detoxication, nor to inhibition of the absorption of acetaminophen. It probably results from mobilization of glucose. The increase in the blood glucose concentration (possibly) may lead to increased production of reducing equivalents (NADPH molecules). The reactive metabolite of acetaminophen (acetaminophen quinonimine) can be reduced back to the parent compound by NADPH. (Figure 4.22)

Therefore, this is not a matter of a direct effect on the activation/detoxication ratio, but of an indirect effect through influencing glucose homeostasis.

Bioactivation and detoxication are metabolic processes. The consequence of this is that whether or not a toxic effect manifests itself, they are determined by the same factors that determine biotransformation. The five recognized groups of factors are:

1   chemical factors
2   genetic factors
3   physiological factors
4   toxicokinetic factors
5   environmental factors.

To a large extent, these factors have already been mentioned in the preceding sections. An example of a chemical factor is DDT, which was discussed in section 1.5. sections 1.1 and 1.2 gave a fairly detailed account of genetic factors in relation to species and individual differences in biotransformation. Sex and age have been mentioned as examples of physiological factors. One factor determining the induction of a toxic effect via an effect on toxicokinetic behavior, is protein binding.

Protein binding will be discussed
in Study unit 5
*Differences in enzymatic activity
between organs*

In many cases, one cannot make a definite distinction between type 1, 3, 4 and 5 factors on the one hand and type 2 (genetic) factors on the other. The reason is that structure and functioning of a living organism are determined by the manner in which the genetic information of that organism is programmed. The relationship is clearly shown, for example, in the *differences in enzymatic activity between organs*. This can be explained as follows. If an enzyme is embedded in a membrane as, for example, cytochrome P-450 isozymes in the endoplasmic reticulum, the ability of the enzyme to assume the active conformation is partly determined by the structure of the membrane. In an organism, the various organs

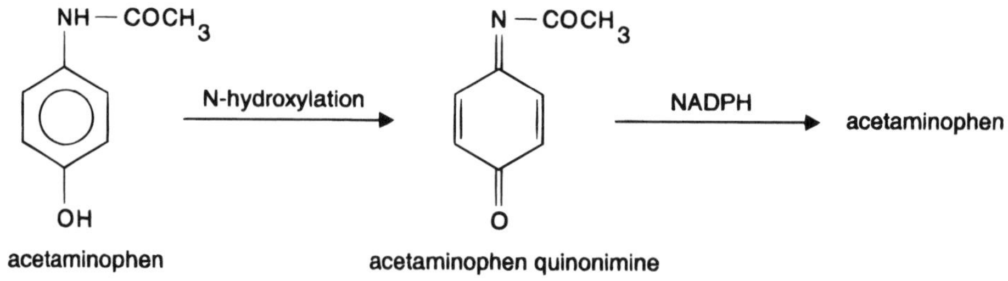

FIGURE 4.22
Formation of a reactive metabolite from acetaminophen and regeneration of the parent compound by reduction of the metabolite with NADPH

differ in the composition of their cellular components, including the membranes. Another factor that determines the activity of an enzyme is the ratio between the rate of its synthesis and degradation. This ratio is a function of cellular metabolism. Since the latter is determined by cell structure, there are also large differences between organs in this respect. Tables 4.4 and 4.5 list examples of differences in enzymatic activity between organs concerning the formation and detoxication of epoxides.

The results in the tables show that the activity of a detoxication enzyme is clearly the highest in that organ in which the bioactivation enzyme displays the highest activity. In practice, however, this does not necessarily mean that bioactivation and detoxication are always in balance, as is shown by the following examples:

- carbon tetrachloride acts selectively on the liver (via the formation of the trichloromethyl radical in the liver)
- phenacetin primarily causes renal injury (its activation mechanism has not yet been fully elucidated, but does take place in the kidney)
- ipomeanol (the toxic substance in sweet potatoes, produced by the fungus *Fusarium solani*) causes injury to pulmonary tissue (by epoxide formation in the lungs).

These examples show that in these organs bioactivation exceeds detoxication.

*For the factors which play a role in the regulation of calcium and glucose homeostasis, please refer to books on biochemistry. More information can be found in Study unit 10, on cytotoxicity.*

Thiol homeostasis is largely dependent on the reductive status of the cell. NADPH-dependent reductases keep thiols in the reduced form (Figure 4.23).

## 4    Location and endogenous substrates of enzymes

In the present section, the intracellular location of enzymes will be discussed briefly. Attention will also be paid to the fact that many endogenous substrates of biotransformation enzymes are known. Biotransformation is not only determined by enzymatic activity and substrate specificity, but also by the location of the enzymes.

The role of enzymes in the metabolism of endogenous compounds is related to their location.

*Endoplasmic reticulum*

Cytochrome P-450 is important in the conversion of a broad range of endogenous compounds, including steroids, thyroid hormones, fatty acids, arachidonic acid and its metabolites and vitamin D. It is not surprising, therefore, that this enzyme system has been demonstrated in many organs and tissues. In the liver, a high concentration of cytochrome P-450 is found in the *endoplasmic reticulum*. It is also present in the nuclear membrane and in the mitochondria. Table 4.6 lists the location and endogenous substrates of a few important phase II reactions.

TABLE 4.4

Organ and species differences in the aromatic hydroxylation*of benzo[a]pyrene

| species | liver | kidneys | lungs |
|---|---|---|---|
| rat | 5.8 | 0.37 | 0.13 |
| mouse | 11.26 | 0.03 | 1.02–0.2 |
| rhesus monkey | 2.5 | 0.38 | 0.2 |

*hydroxylase activity in pmol product $min^{-1}$ $mg^{-1}$ microsomal tissue

TABLE 4.5

Organ and species differences in the conjugation of styrene oxide with glutathione*

| species | liver | kidneys | lungs |
|---|---|---|---|
| rat | 87 | 67 | 12.3 |
| mouse | 149 | 34 | 14.7 |
| guinea pig | 356[1] | 93.0 | 24.7 |
| man | 25 | 5.9 | 6.9 |

*nmol product per min per mg protein of the 100 000 g supernatant
[1]As was described in section 1.1, guinea pigs cannot form mercapturic acids. In this species, only a GSH adduct is formed.

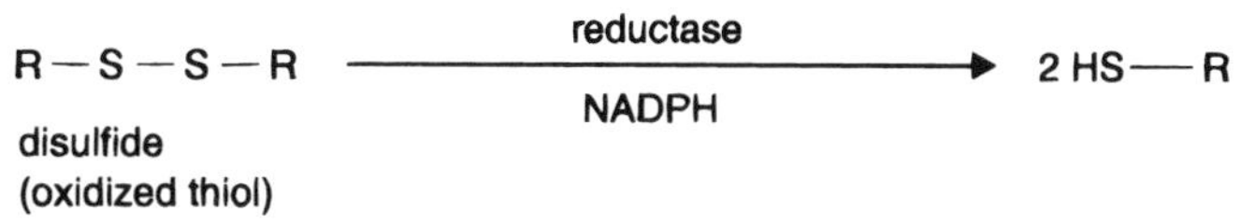

$$R-S-S-R \xrightarrow[\text{NADPH}]{\text{reductase}} 2\,HS-R$$

disulfide
(oxidized thiol)

FIGURE 4.23

*Cytoplasm*

Phase II enzymes are found mainly in the *cytoplasm*, with the exception of glucuronyl transferase, which is situated in the endoplasmic reticulum.

ASSIGNMENT 4.13

Bearing in mind the lipophilicity of the substrates, can you explain why phase I oxidizing enzymes are located in the membrane, making this the location where the phase I reactions in which they are involved take place, and why phase II reactions generally take place in the cytosol?

In addition to cytochrome P-450, many other enzymes take part in the metabolism of xenobiotics. The role of these enzymes in endogenous metabolism is often known in detail. Relatively little research, however, has been carried out into their function in the biotransformation of xenobiotics. Examples are the enzymes monoamine oxidase (substrates are several endogenous neurotransmitters, such as epinephrineline and norepinephrine), diamine oxidase (substrate histamine), xanthine oxidase (substrate xanthine) and acetylcholinesterase (substrate acetylcholine). The location of phase II enzymes and their potential role in the metabolism of endogenous substrates have also been studied fairly well (see Table 4.6). Interaction between endogenous and exogenous substrates (xenobiotics), of course, may well take place. This has been observed in induction studies.

TABLE 4.6
Some important phase II reactions, with their intracellular location and
endogenous substrates

| Phase II reaction | Location | Endogenous substrate |
| --- | --- | --- |
| glucuronidation | endoplasmic reticulum | steroids<br>thyroxine<br>catecholamines<br>bilirubin |
| sulfation | cytosol | steroids<br>carbohydrates |
| acetylation | cytosol | serotonin |
| methylation | cytosol and endoplasmic reticulum | biogenic amines |
| glutathione conjugation | cytosol and endoplasmic reticulum | metabolites of arachidonic acid |

*Summary*

The location of enzyme systems is related to the role these enzymes play in the
metabolism of endogenous compounds. For both phase I and phase II reactions
the location and role of enzymes are reasonably well understood.


SELF ASSESSMENT QUESTIONS

1  Can you explain the data obtained from the following experiment?

   a.  In a liver perfusion experiment in which the liver was perfused via the
       portal vein, the elimination of $^{14}C$–labelled acetaminophen, which was
       formed from $^{14}C$ phenacetin administered during the experiment, was
       found to proceed more slowly than the elimination of preformed $^3H$
       acetaminophen, which was added to the perfusion medium.

   b.  What would be the reason for using a radioactively labelled compound
       in this experiment?

   c.  Can you predict the outcome of an experiment similar to that described
       under a, but with retrograde perfusion (i.e. perfusion from the hepatic
       vein)?

2  A group of nine volunteers was given a control hospital diet for 4–7 days.
   The diet consisted of a hamburger for lunch and a steak for dinner, both
   of which were wrapped in aluminum foil and cooked on a barbecue. For
   the next 4 days, the meat was prepared in the same way but without being
   wrapped in foil. Finally, the first diet was given for another 7 days. When
   900 mg phenacetin was given orally to the volunteers after the control diet
   (meat in aluminum foil) as well as after the barbecue diet (meat without
   foil), a clear difference was seen in the course of the phenacetin concentration–time curve.

   The plasma concentration-time curve returned to the control situation
   when the volunteers were once more given the control diet.

   a.  Explain the results.

   b.  Why, do you think, is the experiment performed as a longitudinal study
       (subsequently giving the various diets to one group of volunteers)?

   c.  Could the experiment also be carried out with compounds other than
       phenacetin?

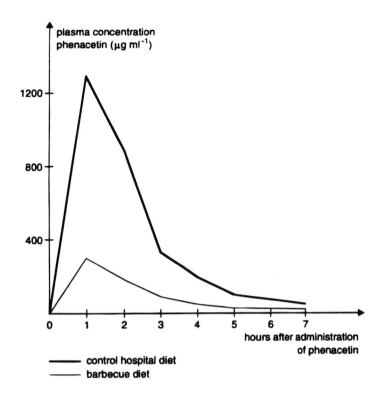

control hospital diet
barbecue diet

FEEDBACK

1    **Answers to the assignments**

4.1    The anticoagulant ethylbiscoumacetate undergoes hydrolysis in rabbits, and aromatic hydroxylation in man. Both the hydroxylated product in man and the free acid in rabbits are inactive.

4.2    Different ethnic groups are genetically different. It is therefore not surprising that there is also a difference in the percentage of poor metabolizers between ethnic groups.

4.3    Differences in biotransformation are most prominent in well-controlled studies. When new drugs are developed and tested, the biotransformation pattern is also always very carefully examined.

4.4    Slow acetylators require a lower dose of hydralazine than fast acetylators, because otherwise the blood concentration would become too high in the former group. Chronic overdosing of hydralazine in slow acetylators might lead to accumulation.

4.5    Approximately 40% of the population in European countries are fast acetylators. This is manifested in a higher percentage of N-acetylisoniazid in the urine.

4.6    Bilirubin is glucuronidated. The glucuronidation system develops around the time of birth. It sometimes happens that glucuronidation activity has not yet reached a sufficiently high level to allow conjugation of bilirubin immediately after birth.

4.7    The various sizes of the boxes in Figure 4.9 reflect the extent to which the factors shown in these boxes determine interindividual and intra-indi-

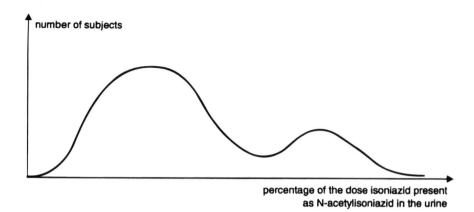

number of subjects

percentage of the dose isoniazid present
as N-acetylisoniazid in the urine

vidual variation. Factors which may be responsible for intraindividual variation are listed in Table 4.2.

4.8 Zoxazolamine is a muscle relaxant. Induction of zoxazolamine metabolism *in vivo* causes the effect of zoxazolamine to last for a shorter period of time. Hence, after induction, the duration of muscle relaxation is shorter.

4.9 If the cytochrome P-450 isozyme pattern is different (interspecies or interindividual variation) or becomes different (intraindividual variation), this may explain differences in the biotransformation of a compound if that compound is converted by a certain variable isozyme of cytochrome P-450. Induction of cytochrome P-450 does not necessarily involve all isozymes. If a xenobiotic is converted by an isozyme which is not influenced by a particular inducer, the biotransformation of that xenobiotic will not be changed.

4.10 If antipyrine is administered orally to human subjects, the urine is found to contain (as a percentage of the dose) approximately 27% 4-hydroxyantipyrine, 14% norantipyrine, 29% 3-hydroxymethylantipyrine and only 5% 3-carboxyantipyrine. The thickness of the arrows in Figure 4.14 reflects the quantitative proportions of the various metabolites formed.

4.11

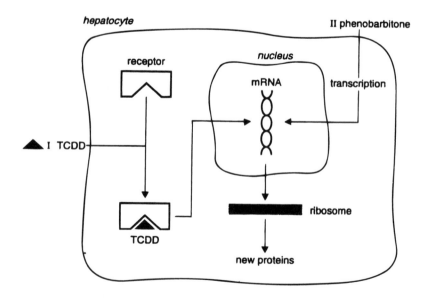

hepatocyte                                    II phenobarbitone

receptor            nucleus

mRNA          transcription

I TCDD

TCDD              ribosome

new proteins

4.12 Metyrapone will give a type II or ligand interaction with the oxidized ($Fe^{3+}$) cytochrome P-450 (see Study unit 3).

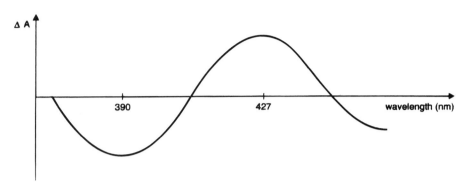

4.13 Phase I enzymes have lipophilic substances as substrates. Lipophilic substances are especially found in membranes. A phase I reaction results in the substrate becoming more hydrophilic (see Study unit 3). Phase I reactions can be followed by phase II reactions. Before phase II reactions are possible, the substrate must already be slightly more hydrophilic (and therefore perhaps available in the cytosol). Note: the glucuronidation enzymes, however, are situated in the endoplasmic reticulum.

## 2 Answers to the self assessment questions

1  a. This experiment indicates heterogeneous distribution of biotransformation enzymes in the liver. Acetaminophen formed during perfusion with phenacetin is eliminated more slowly (in the perfused liver mainly via metabolism and to a lesser extent via biliary excretion in the case of single-pass perfusion) than acetaminophen which is added to the perfusion medium as such. This indicates that phase II enzymes are reached sooner than phase I enzymes. Acetaminophen undergoes conjugation (mainly sulfation), while phenacetin undergoes O-deethylation.

   b. The advantage of using radioactive labeling is that measurement is still possible even when very low concentrations are used. It also means that, by using $^{14}C$ as well as $^{3}H$, both $^{14}C$ phenacetin and $^{3}H$ acetaminophen can be added simultaneously. In this way the elimination of $^{14}C$ acetaminophen (formed) and of $^{3}H$ acetaminophen (added) can be studied in one experiment, and biological dispersion is only slight.

   c. The elimination rate of $^{14}C$ acetaminophen (formed from $^{14}C$ phenacetin during perfusion) is now equal to that of $^{3}H$ acetaminophen. This is to be expected because, in retrograde perfusion, the phase I enzymes are reached first and the phase II enzymes next.

2  a. The grilled meat (without aluminum foil) probably causes induction as a result of the formation of pyrolysis products (see Table 4.2), so that phenacetin is transformed more rapidly.

   b. The advantage of a longitudinal study is that it excludes interindividual variation. Any intra-individual variation is probably smaller than the interindividual variation.

   c. Compounds other than phenacetin will be influenced in the same way, as long as they are converted by the induced isozymes.

# Contents Study unit 5
# Absorption, distribution and elimination of xenobiotics

0-8493-9232-2/96/$0.00 + $.50
© 1996 by CRC Press, Inc.

# Absorption, distribution and elimination of xenobiotics

*R. J. M. Niesink*

## INTRODUCTION

*kinetikos (Gr.) = relating to motion*

Toxicokinetics is the field of science which is concerned with the question of how and to what extent foreign substances are subjected to processes within an organism. In other words, it attempts to answer the question: "How does the body deal with a substance?" Toxicokinetics differs in this sense from dynamics, which is concerned with the question how and to what extent a foreign substance affects the organism. Toxicokinetics has developed from pharmacokinetics, which studies kinetic processes in order to determine the correct dosage of a drug or the best method of administration. An important parameter in toxicokinetics is the change in blood concentration of a foreign substance with time. The concentration is determined by the rate at which and the extent to which the substance is taken up by and distributed over the organism, and by the rate at which it is metabolized and/or excreted. Two processes play an important role in this:

- passage of the substance across biological membranes;
- enzymatic transformation.

Enzymatic transformations have already been dealt with in Study units 3 and 4. In the present study unit, the ways in which substances cross membranes when they are absorbed, distributed and excreted are discussed. After introducing a number of kinetic concepts and principles, this and the following study unit will describe how and to what extent the kinetic behavior of toxic substances may affect their availability in the body. The first of these two units emphasizes the qualitative, descriptive aspects of toxicokinetics, while the second deals with the quantitative, mathematical aspects.

LEARNING OBJECTIVES

After studying the two units on toxicokinetics (units 5 and 6), you should be able to:

— describe the fate of a foreign compound within the organism
— indicate the nature of the processes which a substance undergoes in the various tissues and organs:
  — enzymatic transformation (see also Study units 3 and 4 on biotransformation)
  — passage across membranes
  — binding to proteins and the relevant quantitative aspects

— indicate for the various tissues and organs how their structure and physiology determine the course of the kinetic processes:
  — nature of the tissue (lipid material, lipophilicity)
  — protein binding
  — blood perfusion
— describe the mechanisms involved in the following processes:
  — passive transport
  — active transport and the 'carrier' concept
  — facilitated transport
— define the following concepts:
  — absorption
  — distribution
  — excretion
— with the help of the knowledge gained (described in the learning objectives), predict and/or describe the fate of a substance in an organism on the basis of the physical and chemical properties of that substance.

If an objective refers to a physiological process or processes, the following should be added: "and indicate the consequences for the expression of the biological effect of the compound".

*Study hints*

Many of the terms in the present study unit were introduced in the study units on biotransformation.

It is assumed that you are familiar with the principles of enzyme kinetics, and with the physiology of the kidney. If necessary, consult books on biochemistry or physiology for structure and function of biomembranes. Despite the considerable length of this study unit, the study of this unit is estimated to take about 4 hours.

STUDY CORE

## 1     Fate of foreign compounds in the organism

As was stated in the introduction, kinetics is concerned with how and to what extent biologically active compounds are subjected to processes in living organisms.

*Amount of harmful substance reaching target organ*

From Study unit 7, it will become clear that the toxicity of foreign compounds depends partly on the dose to which the organism is exposed. This means that the higher the dose, the greater the intensity of the effects on the organism. What really matters is not the amount of the toxic compound present in the environment, in the food, etc., but the amount of the harmful substance that reaches the target organ.

The diagram in Figure 5.1 shows the possible routes a compound can take in the body.

Describe roughly how these processes take place.

In summary, the compound is absorbed (e.g. from the gastrointestinal tract, via the lungs or via the skin), distributed throughout the organism via the circulation, and eventually excreted. In addition, there may be accumulation in certain

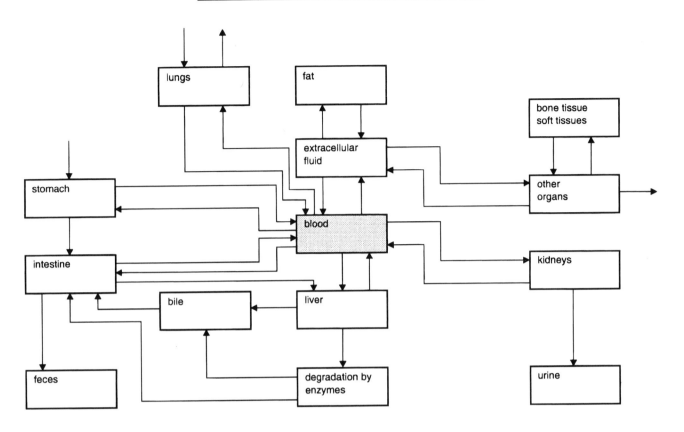

FIGURE 5.1
Schematic representation of absorption, distribution and excretion of xenobiotics

tissues and/or biotransformation. In the following sections, absorption, distribution and excretion of the compound from the organism are discussed.

## 2 Principles underlying absorption of toxic substances

*Local action*

A toxic substance can only exert its harmful effect after it has been absorbed by the organism and entered the circulation. Exceptions to this rule are compounds that act *locally* such as caustic substances, including strong acids and bases, which may have a direct effect on the skin. To cause an effect in a specific target organ, the substance first has to reach that organ.

The absorption of foreign compounds from the environment into the bloodstream is largely determined by the capacity of the xenobiotic to cross semipermeable membranes.

*Absorption into the bloodstream*

Once a compound has entered the bloodstream, it can be transported to its site of action. If a xenobiotic is administered intravenously, it will be distributed rapidly throughout the blood in the organism. This does not imply, however, that it will also be distributed rapidly in the other body fluids. The various body fluids do not form a homogeneous solution in the body, but rather are present in various compartments, separated from each other by membranes.

Describe the route that is followed by a xenobiotic from the site at which it is taken up from the intestine to the site of action in the respiratory chain of a hepatocyte. Include the passage across the various membranes.

*Intravascular space*
*Intercellular space*

After intravenous administration, or after absorption from the intestine or elsewhere in the body, a xenobiotic enters the blood, or *intravascular space*. To reach the *intercellular space* from here, it must penetrate the vascular wall. From the intercellular space, the compound will then have to pass across the membrane of the tissue cell. The last barrier to be crossed is the membrane of any corpuscular cellular component (see Figure 5.2; in the above assignment this is the membrane of the mitochondrion).

*Accessibility of extravascular space*

The intravascular space is separated from the intercellular space by the cells of the vascular wall. The composition and structure of this wall are not identical throughout the organism (see Figure 5.3). This is why the *accessibility of the extravascular space* will vary from one site to another in the organism. The blood–brain barrier, for example, can be such an effective obstacle for some substances that they will never reach the cerebral fluid.

The blood flow through an organ plays an important role in the uptake of xenobiotics from the bloodstream (see Figure 5.4).

*Lipophilic (= hydrophobic) and hydrophilic substances*

A characteristic of biological membranes is that due to their lipid nature they are readily permeable to lipophilic (= hydrophobic) substances. A purely lipid membrane would be impermeable to hydrophilic compounds. In practice, however, hydrophilic compounds can also pass biological membranes, albeit at a much slower rate than lipophilic substances. This implies that the permeability of a membrane is not only determined by its lipid content. There must also

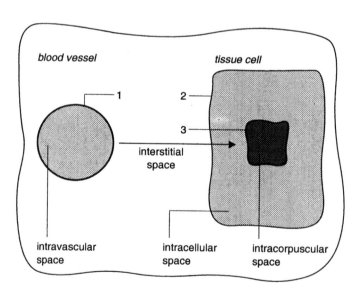

FIGURE 5.2

Diagram of the membranes and fluid compartments involved in distribution throughout the organism

A xenobiotic taken up through the intestinal wall or administered intravenously is taken as an example.
Membranes: 1 vascular wall, 2 cell membrane, 3 membrane of intracellular components.

be a passage route for hydrophilic substances in addition to that for lipophilic compounds. It is assumed that the cell membrane contains water-filled pores that enable hydrophilic substances to pass through the lipid membrane (see Figure 5.5).

*Biological barriers*

Biological barriers are not only formed by the demarcation of a single tissue cell (the cell membrane). They may also consist of larger complexes of closely associated cells, for example those formed by endothelial cells. In such complexes, not only the pores in the cell membranes, but also the so-called intercellular *junctions* play a role in the absorption of hydrophilic substances. In the capillaries in skeletal muscle tissue, these junctions make up 0.2% of the endothelial surface area. This means that the surface area available for the uptake of lipophilic substances is 500 times that for hydrophilic substances. In the case of epithelium or endothelium, a distinction will have to be made between intercellular and intracellular penetration of substances. The ratio between the lipid surface area and the pore surface area determines the difference in permeability between the blood vessels in the various organs.

## 3   Transport across membranes

*Figure 5.6 gives a summary of passing membranes by xenobiotics. A more detailed description of these processes can be found in biochemistry textbooks.*

The mechanisms by which foreign compounds can pass a membrane are as follows:

- passive diffusion
- filtration
- facilitated diffusion
- active transport
- pinocytosis

Indicate the differences between these transport mechanisms.

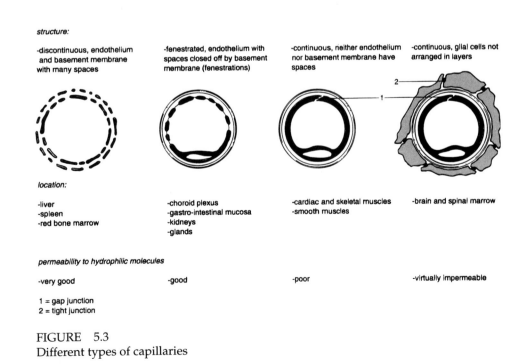

structure:

-discontinuous, endothelium and basement membrane with many spaces

-fenestrated, endothelium with spaces closed off by basement membrane (fenestrations)

-continuous, neither endothelium nor basement membrane have spaces

-continuous, glial cells not arranged in layers

location:

-liver
-spleen
-red bone marrow

-choroid plexus
-gastro-intestinal mucosa
-kidneys
-glands

-cardiac and skeletal muscles
-smooth muscles

-brain and spinal marrow

permeability to hydrophilic molecules

-very good

-good

-poor

-virtually impermeable

1 = gap junction
2 = tight junction

FIGURE   5.3
Different types of capillaries

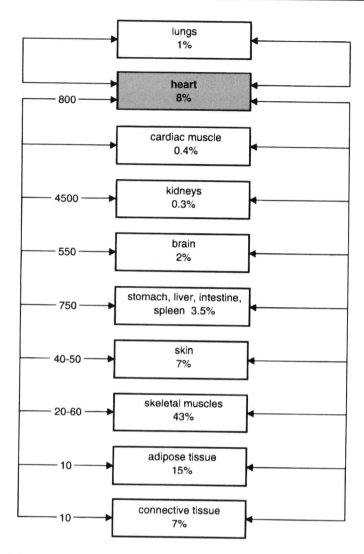

FIGURE 5.4
Perfusion of various organs (ml min.$^{-1}$ kg$^{-1}$) and the percentage of body weight (%)
More than 60% of the cardiac output is present in well-perfused organs, such as lungs and kidneys.

*Passive diffusion*
*Filtration*

*Passive diffusion* is the most common route by which xenobiotics pass through membranes. Passive diffusion is not substrate-specific and is the result of the difference in concentration on both sides of the membrane, and on the lipophilicity of the compound concerned. *Filtration*, however, is based on transport through pores and aqueous channels in the cell membrane and is restricted to hydrophilic substances with a low molecular mass. Unlike diffusion, filtration always requires a pressure gradient.

The transport of foreign substances through the aqueous channels depends on the force of the waterflow, and the size of the pores and of the molecules involved. Most pores measure only 0.7 nm in diameter, and allow only molecules with a molecular mass less than 100 to pass. The nature of the driving force behind the process of filtration may, for example, be hydrostatic or osmotic.

*Facilitated diffusion*
*Active transport*

*Facilitated diffusion* and *active transport* both involve a carrier mechanism. The difference is that the former takes place due to a difference in concentration on

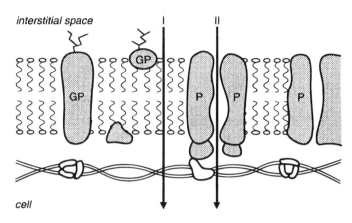

GP = glycoprotein    P = protein lining membrane pore

FIGURE   5.5
The membrane of an erythrocyte as an example of a biological membrane
I=example of a (lipophilic) substance diffusing through a lipid membrane
II= example of a (hydrophilic) substance diffusing through a pore in the membrane

both sides of the membrane, in the direction of the lowest concentration (i.e. does not require energy), whereas the latter occurs against a concentration gradient (i.e. does require energy). Both processes are substrate-specific. This implies that saturation by the substrate may occur. This is often the case for amino acids and sugars, or for xenobiotics that are chemically closely related to these compounds. *Active transport* systems may become saturated with the result that the transport kinetics become *zero-order*.

*Zero-order kinetics*
Zero-order kinetics means the rate of the process is independent of the substrate concentration.

ASSIGNMENT   5.1

What are the consequences of this for the relationship between concentration and transport rate?

*Pinocytosis*

*Pinocytosis* takes place by invagination of the cell membrane around the foreign entity. This process is of particular importance in the removal of larger particles, for example of particles from the alveoli in the lungs.

3.1   DIFFUSION THROUGH LIPID MEMBRANES

Xenobiotics usually pass across membranes by passive diffusion. Passive diffusion largely takes place across the lipid component of the cell membrane, and will, in that case, only transport the lipid-soluble, non-ionized form of the molecule.

*Factors determining the rate of transport across membranes*

The rate of transport across the membrane is directly proportional to the difference in concentration between the non-ionized molecules on either side of the membrane. In most cases, however, there will be a dynamic system, with the concentration on both sides of the membrane continuously changing. This may be the result of removal of molecules by the bloodstream, metabolism, ionization, binding to blood proteins, etc.

*Partition coefficient*

The transport rate is also dependent upon molecule size, lipid solubility of the molecule (also called hydrophobicity) and, to a lesser extent, temperature. Non-ionized molecules with a high (oil–water) *partition coefficient* ($P_{oct}$) will generally diffuse rapidly.

**Intermezzo**

See also intermezzo $P_{oct}$, Study unit 8.

The partition coefficient of a substance refers to the ratio of the amount of that substance that dissolves in an organic solvent not mixable with water and the amount that dissolves in an aqueous

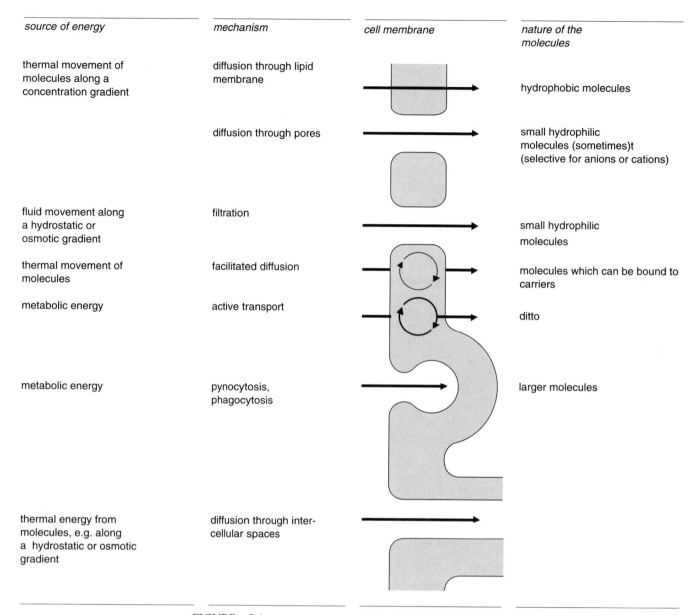

| source of energy | mechanism | cell membrane | nature of the molecules |
|---|---|---|---|
| thermal movement of molecules along a concentration gradient | diffusion through lipid membrane | | hydrophobic molecules |
| | diffusion through pores | | small hydrophilic molecules (sometimes)t (selective for anions or cations) |
| fluid movement along a hydrostatic or osmotic gradient | filtration | | small hydrophilic molecules |
| thermal movement of molecules | facilitated diffusion | | molecules which can be bound to carriers |
| metabolic energy | active transport | | ditto |
| metabolic energy | pynocytosis, phagocytosis | | larger molecules |
| thermal energy from molecules, e.g. along a hydrostatic or osmotic gradient | diffusion through inter-cellular spaces | | |

FIGURE 5.6
Characteristics of some membrane transport systems

solution. Experimentally, a partition coefficient can be determined by bringing together an aqueous phase (compartment A) and a lipid/oorganic phase (compartment B) in a vessel (e.g. a separating funnel, Figure 5.7). The compound for which the partition coefficient is to be determined is dissolved in the vessel and will then be distributed over the two compartments. The partition coefficient can be calculated from the results of a quantitative analysis of the concentrations of the compounds in both compartments.

The classic model of the lipid phase was olive oil. An ideal model liquid is to be expected to approach the properties of membrane lipids. In practice, however, not all membranes are alike. This is why different solvents are used as model for different membranes. Apolar hydrocarbons, like heptane, appear to be quite satisfactory models for e.g. the blood–brain barrier. Partition coefficients obtained from high-molecular mass alcohols (e.g. octanol) or esters (e.g. amyl acetate) have proved to be more suitable for assessing absorption in the gastrointestinal tract. One should be aware that values obtained experimentally are only approximations of the *in vivo* situation.

Molecules with a very high partition coefficient will easily penetrate into a membrane, and having done so, leave it less easily.

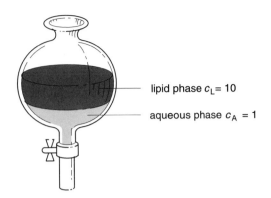

FIGURE   5.7
Compound with a high $P_{oct}$ which partitions in a separatory funnel over the lipid and the aqueous phases
$C_L$ = concentration in lipid phase
$C_A$ = concentration in aqueous phase

What could be the result of this?

The result could be that such substances accumulate in the membrane. Examples are local anesthetics, which accumulate in the membranes of nerve cells. Figure 5.8 shows the equilibrium factors which play a role in passage across membranes.

Table 5.1 shows how the percentage of a number of compounds which diffuse across the intestinal membrane is related to the lipid/water partition coefficient. The table clearly shows that a non-polar substance, like thiopentone, diffuses out of the intestine more easily than the much more polar compound mannitol.

*Concentration gradient over the membrane*

The lipid membrane in biological systems, such as that between the intravascular fluid and the *interstitial fluid*, behaves, as it were, like a lipid compartment between two aqueous compartments. The change in concentration over this lipid phase will be greater the higher the partition coefficient is. Figure 5.9 gives an

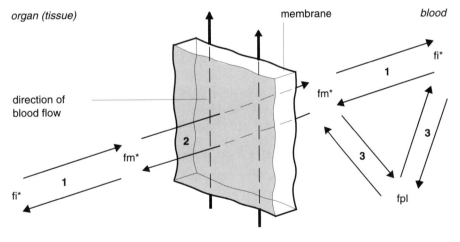

f   = fraction
i   = ionized
m   = molecular (non-ionized)
pl  = bound to plasma proteins

1 = ionization equilibrium
2 = equilibrium between uptake and release
3 = equilibrium between bound and non bound to plasma proteins

FIGURE   5.8
Equilibria playing a role in the passage of compounds through membranes

Table 5.1

Comparison of intestinal absorption with lipid/water partition coefficients of the non-dissociated forms of a number of organic acids and bases

| substance | absorption (%) | solubility in chloroform ($P_{HCCl_3}$) |
|---|---|---|
| thiopentone | 67 | 100 |
| aniline | 54 | 26.4 |
| acetanilide | 43 | 7.6 |
| acetylsalicylic acid | 21 | 2.0 |
| barbitulic acid | 5 | 0.008 |
| mannitol | <2 | <0.002 |

After Hogben et al. 1958 In: *J. Pharmacol. Exp. Ther.*, 126, 275.

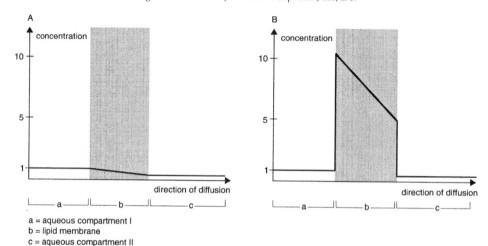

a = aqueous compartment I
b = lipid membrane
c = aqueous compartment II

FIGURE 5.9

Changes in concentration over a lipid membrane, for two compounds with different partition coefficients (1 and 10 respectively)

In both cases, the time point was selected at which the concentration in compartment I was twice as high as that in compartment II. Since the diffusion rate depends on the concentration gradient, compound B will pass through the membrane 10 times as quickly.

example of two compounds (A and B) for which the concentration is the same on both sides of the membrane. The partition coefficient of compound B, however, is ten times that of A. The figure shows that, as a result of this difference, the *concentration gradient across the membrane* is much steeper (ten fold) for compound B than it is for A. Since the diffusion rate depends on the concentration gradient, substance B will be able to cross the membrane ten times as fast.

### 3.1.1 *Effects of the degree of ionization*

Substances in the ionized form do not pass easily across membranes. This has consequences for xenobiotics that occur in the form of acids, bases or salts, as they may be present in the ionized form. The concentration of a compound present in non-ionized form is determined by its $pK_a$ and by the pH of the environment. If the pH of the environment is known, the concentration of the non-dissociated form can be calculated using the $pK_a$ of the compound in question. To do so, the Henderson–Hasselbach equations for acids or bases are used.

*Henderson–Hasselbach equation*

*For acids*:

$$pH = pK_a + \log\frac{[A^-]}{[HA]} \quad \text{where} \quad HA \rightleftharpoons H^+ + A^- \tag{5.1a}$$

*For bases:*

$$pH = pK_a + \log\frac{[A]}{[HA^+]} \quad \text{where} \quad A + H^+ \rightleftharpoons HA^+ \quad (5.1b)$$

ASSIGNMENT   5.2

a) Calculate how much of an acid with $pK_a$ 4 is present in the non-ionized form if the pH of the environment is 1.
b) Calculate how much of a base with $pK_a$ 5 is present in the ionized form at the same pH.

It will be obvious that, at pH = 4, weak acids will usually be present in the non-ionized form and hence will be readily absorbed. Under these conditions bases will usually occur in the ionized form, and will therefore not diffuse very well. In practice, however, the non-ionized form of bases will also be continuously removed from the inner side of the membrane by the bloodstream, so that eventually a large quantity of the base will still be transported across the membrane in its non-dissociated form.

Table 5.2 gives the pH values of a number of important biological compartments in the organism.

If a system is in equilibrium, the Henderson–Hasselbach equation can be used to calculate how a substance is distributed over two aqueous compartments separated from each other by a lipid membrane, provided the pH in the aqueous compartments and the $pK_a$ of the compound concerned are known.

*For a base:*

$$\frac{C_1}{C_2} = \frac{1 + 10^{(pK_a - pH_1)}}{1 + 10^{(pK_a - pH_2)}} \quad (5.2a)$$

*For an acid:*

$$\frac{C_1}{C_2} = \frac{1 + 10^{(pH_1 - pK_a)}}{1 + 10^{(pH_2 - pK_a)}} \quad (5.2b)$$

$C_1$ and $C_2$ are the concentrations (A⁻ *and* HA) on both sides of the membrane at equilibrium.

ASSIGNMENT   5.3

Show how the second formula (Equation 5.2b) can be derived from the Henderson–Hasselbach equation.

### 3.2   DIFFUSION THROUGH MEMBRANE PORES

Diffusion through pores and intercellular junctions depends on the size of the molecules, and takes place in an aqueous environment. The partition coefficient

Table   5.2
pH values in some body compartments

| | |
|---|---|
| blood | 7.35–7.45 |
| oral cavity | 6.2–7.2 |
| stomach (at rest) | 1.0–3.0 |
| duodenum | 4.8–8.2 |
| jejunum | 6.3–7.3 |
| ileum | 7.6 |
| colon | 7.8–8.0 |
| rectum | 7.8 |
| cerebral fluid | 7.3–7.4 |
| vagina | 3.4–4.2 |
| urine | 4.8–7.5 |
| sweat | 4.0–6.8 |
| milk | 6.6–7.0 |

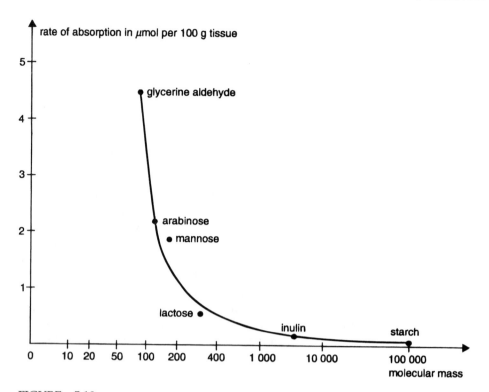

FIGURE   5.10
Relationship between molecular size and rate of absorption in the intestine following oral administration

is of no importance in this process. As an example, Figure 5.10 shows the absorption of hydrophilic particles through the pores of the small intestine. There is a clear relationship between molecular size and absorption rate.

Try to explain this phenomenon.

Since not all pores in a membrane are of the same size, but vary around a certain average, the number of molecules which will be able to pass the membrane via the pores per unit of time will decrease with increasing molecular mass. It should be noted though that, in comparison to diffusion through the lipid layer, diffusion through pores in the membrane is of only limited importance in toxicology.

## 4    Absorption of toxic compounds

In fish and aquatic invertebrates, the gills may also form a route for absorption of toxic substances.

The gastrointestinal tract, the respiratory system and the skin are the most important natural routes by which toxic substances usually enter an organism. There are also a few less natural entrance routes, such as intravenous administration of drugs, rectal (suppositories) and nasal absorption (nose drops and sprays for asthma patients and intake of cocaine, heroin etc.).

### 4.1    ABSORPTION VIA THE DIGESTIVE TRACT

*Oral intake*

After *oral intake* of toxic substances, in many cases the extent of absorption via the gastrointestinal tract is determined by their lipophilicity. The uptake of hydrophilic substances through the pores is relatively small. This explains, for example, why the South American Indians can safely eat the meat of their prey, which they have killed with the arrow poison *curare*. The hydrophilic compound

Parenteral = outside the intestine

curare, which is lethal to the animal on parenteral contact via the arrow, is not absorbed from the orally consumed meat.

Absorption of xenobiotics can take place along the entire length of the digestive tract.

*Buccal absorption*

Although the mouth usually serves only as a passage by which a substance enters the organism, occasionally it is also the site where absorption takes place. This is referred to as *buccal absorption*. Substances that enter the body in this way do not first pass the liver. This is in contrast to compounds which enter the body via the intestinal tract, with the exception of those absorbed from the rectum (see Figure 5.11).

Many substances can be absorbed rapidly through the wall of the gastrointestinal tract. Passage into the blood only requires transport across an epithelial layer. Because of its villous structure, this epithelial layer has a very large surface area. This special structure is most pronounced in the small intestine and to a lesser extent in the stomach and large intestine. The epithelial cells also have *microvilli* in the small intestine; these are responsible for even further enlargement of the surface area. Table 5.3 compares the absorptive surface areas of the various parts of the digestive tract.

*Microvilli for additional enlargement of surface area*

The table shows that by far the largest absorptive surface area is located in the small intestine. This is therefore the site where most xenobiotics are absorbed.

With a few exceptions, all blood vessels surrounding the gastrointestinal tract lead to the portal vein and via that to the liver. The exceptions are the blood vessels at the beginning and the end of the gastrointestinal tract, i.e. those of the mouth and pharynx, and those of part of the rectum. This means that substances absorbed from the gastrointestinal tract are first transported, by the venous blood, to the liver. There, in many cases, a large part of the foreign substance is

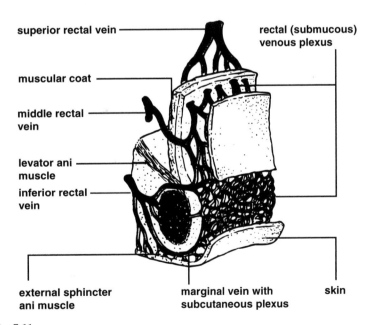

FIGURE   5.11
Blood flow from the rectum
The blood leaves the rectum via three veins. The superior vena cava leads into the portal vein and into the liver. The middle and inferior rectal veins lead directly into the inferior vena cava. Following this route xenobiotics avoid hepatic metabolism. A complication is the presence of connections (anastomoses) between the three rectal veins, which make it (theoretically) possible for substances absorbed in the lower part of the rectum to enter the liver and undergo biotransformation.

Table 5.3
Comparison of the size of the absorptive surface of the various parts of the gastrointestinal tract.

| | |
|---|---|
| oral cavity | 0.02 |
| stomach | 0.1–0.2 |
| small intestine | 100 |
| large intestine | 0.5–1.0 |
| rectum | 0.04–0.07 |

*First-pass metabolism*

either removed from the blood and excreted into the bile, converted (*first-pass metabolism*) or stored in the liver. In this way, the portal vein construction provides protection against poisons that may occur, for example, in food. Presumably, this system has developed in the evolution of the vertebrates as a protective mechanism against the many secondary (non-nutritive) substances in plants to which herbivorous animals are naturally exposed.

*Enterohepatic circulation*

If the liver excretes the unchanged substance or one of its active metabolites into the bile, the substance or metabolite may be reabsorbed when entering the intestine and be excreted once more into the bile. This process slows down the elimination of the substance from the body. It is known as *enterohepatic circulation* (see also Figure 5.12, section 6.2 and Study unit 21).

*Bucco-enteral circulation*

Another cycle is the *bucco-enteral circulation*. This takes place when toxic substances are absorbed in the intestine, subsequently taken up by the salivary glands from the blood, and then excreted again by the glands into the oral cavity.

Lipophilic xenobiotics are generally taken up by the intestinal wall by passive diffusion through the lipid membrane. Some substances of low molecular weight pass across the membrane through the pores (aqueous phase). Alcohol is an example. The absorption of weak acids and bases depends on the pH of the various regions of the gastrointestinal tract. Weak acids will be absorbed from the stomach since the low pH there (pH 1–2) suppresses their dissociation. For the same reason, alkaloids will be absorbed primarily from the more alkaline intestine (pH 5–6). In general, highly dissociated substances

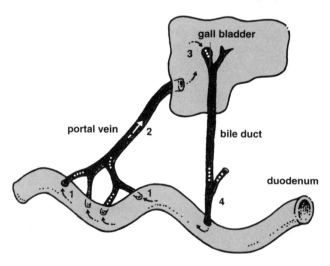

FIGURE 5.12
Diagram of the enterohepatic circulation
The direction of the circulation is indicated

and hydrophilic compounds are hardly or not at all absorbed by passive diffusion through the intestinal wall, unless the epithelium is damaged. In contrast to the absorption of nutrients through the wall of the digestive tract, the absorption of lipophilic xenobiotics through the intestinal wall is often a passive process.

ASSIGNMENT   5.4

Explain why the absorption of xenobiotics through the intestinal wall is often a passive process, in contrast to that of many nutrients.

It should be noted though that, like nutrients, xenobiotics entering the body orally are exposed to the action of digestive enzymes and the bacterial flora in the intestine. For example, the system of forestomachs in ruminants, including a very large rumen, will have a decelerating effect on the absorption of plant poisons. As a result, these poisons will be exposed longer to the destructive biochemical action of the flora in the rumen.

4.2   ABSORPTION VIA THE RESPIRATORY TRACT

*Lungs*

The *lungs* constitute an important route of entry for toxic gases, volatile solvents and occasionally aerosols (small solid or liquid particles suspended in air). Through the trachea, the inhaled air reaches the bronchi and their branches, the bronchioles, which in turn lead into the alveoli. It is via the alveoli that exchange between air and blood takes place. The alveolar epithelium is extremely thin, so that the diffusion path is relatively short. The surface area of the alveoli is very large ($100 \text{ m}^2$ in man). Both factors promote a high diffusion rate (see Figure 5.13).

The pulmonary vascular structure also promotes the absorptive function of the lung. Together, the pulmonary capillaries have a very large surface area ($80 \text{ m}^2$ in man), while the blood perfusion is very high. The combination of these factors makes the lung one of the most effective absorptive areas in the body. The rapidity with which poisoning with HCN (hydrocyanic acid), or anesthesia with nitrous oxide (laughing gas) or chloroform takes place shows that low molecular weight and lipophilic gases are quickly absorbed. The absorption rate

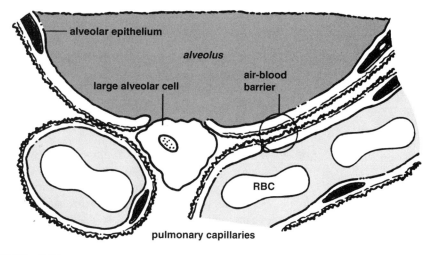

FIGURE   5.13
Cross-section through the membrane of an alveolus
RBC = red blood corpuscle

increases with increasing $P_{oct}$. Hydrophilic compounds diffuse primarily through the water-filled pores, the rate of absorption decreasing with increasing molecular size. The absorption rate in the lungs, however, is considerably higher than that in the small intestine. When the inhaled air passes through the airways, the larger particles are deposited onto the mucosa, transported to the mouth by ciliary movement of the bronchial epithelium, and either spat out or swallowed. The latter means that uptake can still take place via the gastrointestinal tract.

The size of the suspended particles determines the extent of penetration into the airways. A large portion of gases which easily dissolve in water, such as hydrochloric acid, is already removed by the bronchial part of the airways, as such substances dissolve in the mucous layer.

The smaller the diameter of particles, the deeper these will be deposited in the pulmonary system. Particles with a diameter of 10 $\mu$m or more stay behind in the nose and pharynx. Those with a diameter of 2–10 $\mu$m can reach the bronchi and bronchioles, and particles with a diameter of about 1 $\mu$m can penetrate as far as the alveoli and be absorbed or deposited there, out of reach of the ciliated epithelium. Quartz dust, for example, which is deposited in the lungs, is the cause of *silicosis*, a chronic intoxication which used to severely afflict many stonecutters and stonemasons before working on sandstone was officially banned. Extremely small particles, with a diameter on the order of 0.1 $\mu$m, are too light to settle in the airways in any significant quantity, and most of them are expired again. Breathing technique also plays an important role: slow and deep breathing and holding one's breath promote the deposition of particles with a diameter between 0.5 and 5 $\mu$m.

For inhalation of volatile compounds as a fraction of the inspired concentration, absorption can be determined by measuring the retention ($R$), which is the difference in concentration of the substance between the inspired and the expired air.

> Can you express the relationship between the difference in concentration and retention in terms of a formula? Use $C_i - C_o$ to represent the difference in concentration of a substance between the inspired and the expired air (i = in; o = out).

This relationship can be expressed as follows:

$$R = \frac{C_i - C_o}{C_i} \quad \text{or} \quad R \cdot C_i = C_i - C_o \tag{5.3}$$

It follows that the quantity absorbed per minute (mmol min$^{-1}$) is $C_i \cdot R \cdot MV$ ($MV$ being the respiratory minute volume). This means that an increase in minute volume, as may be caused by physical effort, leads to an increased absorption of the substance. This is of particular importance in relation to exposure to volatile substances in industry.

*Body burden*

When exposure to the volatile substance has stopped, the absorbed substance is almost entirely expired again. The concentration in the expired air is a useful measure of the quantity of the compound left behind in the body (= body burden). The higher the concentration of the volatile compound in the blood, the greater will be its release into the expired air.

> ASSIGNMENT 5.5
>
> What is the relationship between the body burden and the "breathalyzer" or "drunkometer" used by the police to check on drinking and driving?

ASSIGNMENT   5.6

Which factors play a role in transport via and absorption by the lungs?

*Pinocytosis*
See section 3

In addition to diffusion through the membrane, some compounds are absorbed in the lungs by *pinocytosis*. This has been demonstrated, for example, for aerosols of uranium dioxide.

*Absorption via gills*

In fish, *gills* form an important route of entry for environmental chemicals. Absorption by this route is very similar to absorption by the lungs in terrestrial animals. The gills account for more than 90% of the total body surface of fish. The gills can also absorb substances which are not or hardly at all volatile but which do dissolve in water. Lipophilic compounds can be removed from the water via the gills quite effectively. The rate constant for absorption can be determined roughly for compounds that are not rapidly metabolized by the fish. In order to do so, the ratio of the concentration of the compound in the fish to that in the water is determined shortly after exposure of the fish to the compound.

ASSIGNMENT   5.7

Why should this determination take place shortly after exposure?

### 4.3   ABSORPTION VIA THE SKIN

See also Study unit 2

Via the *skin*, people come into contact with a large number of toxic compounds. It is primarily at the workplace that individuals are confronted with a wide variety of chemicals which, when absorbed, may induce harmful effects.

In what type of work do you think this will be particularly common?

This occurs mostly in the chemical industry and agriculture. Fortunately, the skin is relatively impermeable, which makes it a reasonably good barrier. The skin protects the body against excessive dehydration. The outer stratum corneum or horny layer, which consists of keratin, allows very little water to pass and suppresses evaporation of water (except from the sweat glands). Because the stratum corneum consists of dead cells, it has no blood supply. Living cells and vascularization are found only in the deepest layer of the epidermis (see Figure 5.14).

*Percutaneous absorption*

nicotine

4,6-dinitro-O-cresol (DNOC)

Therefore compounds which are absorbed via the skin will first have to pass across the keratinized skin layer before they can reach the bloodstream. Although it is theoretically possible that substances penetrate the skin via the hair follicles, the epidermal tissue does in fact make up such a large part of the surface area that absorption via the follicles is negligible. In the case of absorption of a foreign substance through the skin, termed *percutaneous absorption*, the compound has to reach the circulation from the outer surface of the skin, through the horny layer, the epidermis and the dermis. Because these layers do not have the same overall thickness, the specific site of dermal exposure is of course very important. It has been found though that the skin can absorb lipophilic compounds of low molecular mass surprisingly quickly. It is far from rare that people are poisoned by dermal absorption of a substance. This often happens when handling highly toxic lipophilic pesticides, like *nicotine, parathion* and *dinitro-ortho-cresol (DNOC)*. This may be caused by, for example, a leak in a storage container containing pesticide which is carried on the back, or because the clothing becomes drenched in pesticide while spraying against the wind.

109

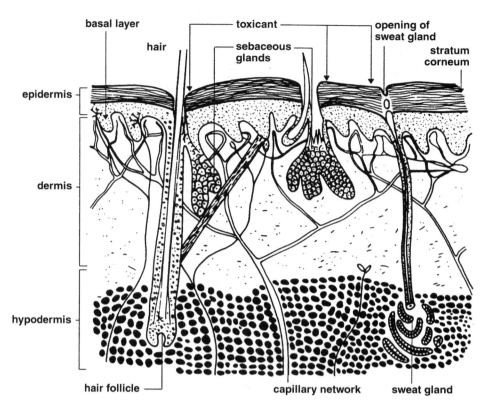

FIGURE 5.14
Cross-section of human skin

The extent of percutaneous absorption of a substance depends largely on the physical and chemical properties of the substance itself. In particular, factors like the degree of ionization, molecular size and water and lipid solubilities influence penetration through the skin. Local factors such as the pH, ambient temperature, blood perfusion and local anatomy also play a role. The palm of the hand will not absorb substances very well, in contrast to the inner side of the lower arm.

ASSIGNMENT 5.8

Explain how local factors can play a role in percutaneous absorption.

*Solvents*

There are solvents which promote passage across the skin. An example of such a substance is *dimethyl sulfoxide (DMSO)*, which may increase skin permeability through swelling of components of the stratum corneum. Such substances are sometimes applied in ointments to speed up absorption of the therapeutic substance. When a substance is administered on the skin, the solvent is of greater importance than for other routes of administration. If a lipophilic compound is added to, e.g. Vaseline®, the rate of absorption may be determined more by the rate at which the substance leaves the solvent than by its actual passage through the skin.

*Fish*

Although the skin of fish is virtually impermeable to toxic substances, chemicals may still attach to it.

## 5 Distribution over the organism

*Depot formation*

The next step in the toxicokinetic process is the distribution of a substance throughout the organism. It may, for example, accumulate near the site where it induces its toxic effect. It may also be taken to a so-called depot and be stored there for a time, or transported to organs, where the substance is activated, inactivated or excreted. The transport processes discussed in Section 3 and the various barriers do, of course, have a significant influence on the manner in which a substance is distributed in the organism.

*Inulin is a polysaccharide (M = 5500) which is used for measuring renal function.*

After a substance has been absorbed, it is distributed throughout the body via the bloodstream. Initially, distribution will take place by diffusion over the various aqueous compartments. Some substances, such as saccharose and *inulin*, will be distributed virtually exclusively over the blood and the interstitial fluid, for example after intravenous administration. They do not need to pass across cell membranes and thus fill only the extracellular fluid compartment. In adults, the total body fluid accounts for approximately 60% of the body weight. In obese individuals, this percentage is lower because a larger proportion of their body weight consists of fat. In young children, on the other hand, the percentage is higher because their bone tissue has yet not completely calcified, and hence contributes to a lesser extent to the body weight than in adults.

Table 5.4 shows the various compartments in the average individual with a normal body build. It should be borne in mind, however, that the table provides no more than an approximation. Entry of various substances into these compartments is determined by their physicochemical properties. Some substances have been found to be distributed over a volume corresponding with the *physiological volumes* given in the table.

*Physiological volumes*

Several small, hydrophilic molecules, like *urea*, *thiourea*, *aminopyrine* and *antipyrine* do pass across the cell membrane quite well. Since they bind only slightly to proteins and are practically insoluble in lipids, they are distributed more or less homogeneously over the total body water, i.e. both extracellular and intracellular. This type of compound is therefore particularly suitable for determining the volume of total body water.

*Distribution over aqueous and lipid compartments*

In most cases, mixed distribution patterns are encountered, which means that a compound is distributed over both the aqueous and the lipid compartments.

Table 5.4
True volume of distribution *V* of body compartments, over which xenobiotics may be distributed

| group | compartment | volume of the compartment in % of body weight | V, in liters (average) | physico-chemical properties | examples |
|---|---|---|---|---|---|
| 1 | blood plasma | 4 | 3 | 1 large molecular mass | heparin; dextrans |
|  | interstitial | 14–18 ⎤+ | 10–13 ⎤+ |  |  |
| 2 | extracellular volume (ECV) | 18–22 | 13–16 | 2 hydrophilic and molecular mass > 200–300; (an)ions | insulin; Br⁻; suxamethonium |
|  | intracellular volume (ICV) | 35–40 | 25–28 | 3 lipophilic | ethyl alcohol; antipyrin; $D_2O$ |
|  | transcellular fluid* | 1–3 ⎤+ | 0.7–2 ⎤+ |  |  |
| 3 | total body fluids | 54–64 | 39–46 |  |  |

The second column shows the fluid compartments to which the drug may have access, classified into three major groups. The fifth column shows the main physicochemical properties of the drug as regards distribution over these three major groups. The sixth column gives some examples of compounds whose distribution is typical for these groups.
*The transcellular fluids include the cerebrospinal fluid, secretions in the digestive tract, tears etc.

*Kinetic volume of distribution*

Compounds are also often distributed over a volume which is much larger than that which the whole organism could possibly contain. This is why the term *kinetic volume of distribution* is preferred. This kinetic distribution volume by no means always relates to a physiological or anatomical reality. It is in fact no more than an operational parameter which indicates the relationship between the total quantity of the toxic substance present in the organism at a certain moment and the plasma concentration at that particular time. This can be expressed in terms of a formula:

$$Q_t = VC_t \qquad (5.4)$$

in which:

$V$ = kinetic volume of distribution
$O_t$ = quantity of the substance present in the body at time $t$
$C_t$ = plasma concentration at time $t$.

It will be clear that $V$ for a particular substance may have different values, depending on the time ($t$) of measurement. After all, this parameter largely depends on the quantity of the substance which has left the plasma, but is still present in the body (= redistribution).

ASSIGNMENT 5.9
When will this not be the case?

The amount depends on the phase in the distribution process, and hence on time. In general, the rate at which exchange between blood and tissues takes place will be higher in comparison to the circulation rate through the capillaries.

ASSIGNMENT 5.10
What are the consequences of this relatively high exchange rate for the plasma concentration of a compound which is flowing out of a tissue?

*Accumulation*

For many substances, binding to cellular components or dissolution in lipids leads to a much higher concentration in the tissue than in the blood plasma. In such cases, the term *accumulation* or *sequestration* is used. A well-known example is the selective accumulation in body fat of highly lipophilic compounds which are difficult to metabolize (DDT, dieldrin, PCBs, PBBs). The liver and kidney have a large accumulative capacity, especially for heavy metals. This is one of the reasons why these organs in particular are subjected to toxicological examination in cases of intoxication. Table 5.5 provides a sur-

Table 5.5
Relative levels in blood and tissues after exposure to dieldrin and lead (blood = 1)

| substance | blood | liver | brain | kidneys | adipose tissue | bone |
|---|---|---|---|---|---|---|
| Dieldin (man)[1] | 1 | 26.3 | 3.32[2] <br> 4.93[3] | — | 158 | — |
| lead (rat)[4] | 1 | 1.7 | 1.1 | 6.6 | – | 77 |

[1]After data from Vlieger *et al.* (1968)
[2]Grey matter
[3]White matter
[4]Calculated on the basis of data from Azar et al (1972) on exposure to lead

112

Chronic administration means that the substance is administered for a longer period of time, in contrast to acute administration.

vey of the accumulation of dieldrin and lead in various organs after chronic administration.

Sometimes, accumulation of a compound in a tissue can take the form of a precipitate. An example of this is the deposition of fluoride in bone tissue. Fluoride replaces the hydroxyl group in the crystal lattice of apatite, leading to the formation of fluoroapatite. Lead and strontium are also precipitated in bone tissue.

The significance of the chemical structure for the degree of accumulation in tissue is clearly expressed in the differences in distribution of mercury when this is administered in the form of various organic and inorganic compounds (see Table 5.6).

It can be seen clearly from the table that the most lipid-soluble mercury compound, methylmercury hydroxide, is also that which is distributed most evenly over the various organs. Its concentration in the brain is more than half of that in most other tissues. By contrast, the concentrations of the more polar mercury compounds are relatively much higher in the liver and kidneys. Those organs which display the greatest affinity for a particular mercury compound are also the target organs of that compound. Methyl mercury hydroxide is concentrated in the brain, while other compounds are concentrated in the kidneys.

Whether or not substances accumulate in tissues can be elucidated by administering radioactively labeled compounds and subsequent autoradiography of sections taken from different parts of the body of a test animal. Quantitative determination, however, requires the measurement of concentrations.

## 5.1    PLASMA PROTEIN BINDING

*Distribution mechanism*

Many xenobiotics partly dissolve in the aqueous phase of the plasma, and are transported through the organism in that way. Nevertheless, the dissolved form is not the most important form in which most xenobiotics are distributed. An important *distribution mechanism* for toxic compounds is binding to plasma proteins. Cellular components of the blood also contribute to the transport of toxicants, but they play a much less significant role than the plasma proteins. Transport of toxic compounds by the lymph is also quantitatively of lesser importance. The blood flow through the intestines, for example, is 500–700 times greater than that of lymph. Even so, it should be noted that, in some exceptional cases, transport by both erythrocytes and lymph may be of significance.

*Reversible and irreversible binding to tissue proteins*

Many substances, including toxic ones, are bound reversibly to a variety of biological components. There are also toxic and non-toxic substances and/or metabolites that irreversibly bind to tissue proteins.

Table   5.6
Relative concentrations of mercury in a number of organs, 10 days after intravenous injection of various types of mercury compounds in a dose of one fifth $LD_{50}$ in white Leghorn cockerels (blood = 1)

| Substance | blood | liver | brain | muscle | kidneys |
|---|---|---|---|---|---|
| mercuric nitrate | 1 | 2850 | 6.7 | 37 | 3960 |
| methyl mercury hydroxide | 1 | 1.5 | 0.8 | 0.7 | 1.7 |
| phenyl mercury hydroxide | 1 | 3600 | 4.7 | 83 | 2400 |
| methoxyethyl mercury hydroxide | 1 | 100 | 7.5 | 6 | 170 |

[1]Calculated on the basis of data from Swenson and Ulfvarson (1968)

113

ASSIGNMENT 5.11

What type of chemical bond will be involved in irreversible binding?

In the majority of ligand–plasma protein bonds, binding is reversible. This reversible binding is an important means of transport for toxic compounds to the various tissues. This is in contrast to irreversible binding, which of course prevents distribution.

*Reversible plasma protein binding*

Assuming, for the sake of simplicity, that in the case of reversibility all binding sites on a protein have the same affinity for the ligand, then the following relationship is valid:

$$R + X \underset{k_2}{\overset{k_1}{\rightleftharpoons}} RX \quad \text{or} \quad \frac{[R]\ [X]}{[RX]} = K_d \tag{5.5}$$

in which $[X]$ is the concentration of the free compound in moles per liter, $[R]$ is the concentration of the binding sites that are still free, $[RX]$ is the concentration of the occupied binding sites and $K_d$ is the dissociation constant $k_2/k_1$.

ASSIGNMENT 5.12

Demonstrate that $1/K_d$ is a measure of the affinity of the protein binding site for the toxicant.

It follows from Equation 5.5 that of a group of protein binding sites, the sites with the lowest dissociation constant ($K_d$) will form the strongest bonds with the toxicant. Molecules bound to plasma proteins are carried through the body with the bloodstream. Sometimes they may interact with molecules other than plasma proteins and thus be removed from the circulation. Such dissociation will occur if the affinity of the other molecule is greater than that of the plasma protein. The binding forces must therefore be strong enough to bring about the association in the first place, but at the same time weak enough so that changes in the physical or chemical environment can lead to dissociation. Such changes may involve:

- the presence of proteins with a higher affinity (smaller $K_d$);
- the presence of proteins with lesser affinity, but which occur in a higher concentration;
- pH;
- temperature.

As long as plasma concentrations change, for example by absorption or release, there will be redistribution over the tissue and plasma proteins. Again and again the steady state is re-established.

Study unit 8, on structure–activity relationships, discusses hydrophobic binding in detail.

Many substances bind so strongly to plasma proteins that only a small fraction is present in the plasma in the free, unbound form. In general, organic anions are bound more strongly than organic cations. The affinity increases if a lipophilic group is present. Further, the longer the hydrocarbon chain—up to a certain limit—the stronger the binding is. Highly polar compounds, such as glucose and antipyrine, are bound only to a small extent, or not at all.

See also Study unit 7, on dose–response relationships.

Plasma protein binding is of major importance in toxicology. It reduces the concentration of the free compound in the blood. Because only the free compound can interact directly with the tissue cells, plasma protein binding reduces the intensity of the toxic effect. In a sense, plasma protein binding can act as a buffer, and in that way, protect tissues.

On the other hand, binding to plasma proteins also slows down elimination of a substance, and causes the blood proteins to provide a kind of reservoir of the substance from which the free substance can be mobilized. If the free concentration is still high enough to cause an effect, this means that the duration of the effect is prolonged.

*Irreversible binding*

The non-specific and irreversible nature of binding of xenobiotics causes competition for the binding sites. This will result in a physiological ligand being displaced by a xenobiotic with greater affinity. This displacement by a foreign substance can also affect the transport of a metabolite by its carrier protein, and this may have harmful effects on the organism. For example, long-term administration of the acaricide tetrasul (2,4,5,4-tetrachlorodiphenylsulfide) to rats causes the development of goiter. The hormone thyroxine (T4) is displaced from its carrier proteins, thyroxine-binding globulin (TBG) and thyroxine-binding prealbumin (TBPA). The result is accelerated degradation of thyroxine.

*See Study unit 15*

A number of proteins have a special role in the transport of heavy metals by plasma proteins. These are proteins like transferrin and ceruloplasmin, that are involved in iron and copper metabolism, but which are also capable of binding foreign heavy metals.

The binding capacity of plasma proteins for xenobiotics may vary considerably between species. The alkaloid pilocarpine, for example, has been found to engage in only a weak bond with plasma proteins in pigs, while this bond is strong in cows, horses, sheep, rabbits and other species. The differences in xenobiotic binding capacity between various species may play a role in the differences in toxicity found between these species. Before such a conclusion can be drawn, however, it should first be established whether the total plasma protein concentrations in the various species are indeed the same. It has been shown that this is by no means always so. For example, the total plasma protein content in mammals has been found to vary between 6.0 and 8.5 g per 100 ml, while that in birds may range from 2.3 to 5.3 g per 100 ml. The concentration in fish is considerably lower than that in mammals. Analysis of the kinetics of plasma protein binding is essential to gain insight into the influence of the structure of compounds on their binding to blood proteins, and (possible) species differences.

## 5.2    ANALYSIS OF THE KINETICS OF BINDING TO PLASMA PROTEINS

Studies on the reversible binding of xenobiotics to plasma proteins are usually performed by means of equilibrium dialysis or ultrafiltration. The fraction which passes through the membrane, or which is present in the ultrafiltrate, forms the unbound or free fraction. The sum of the bound and free fractions is the total quantity. The bound fraction can simply be determined by calculating the difference between the total and the free fraction.

If $n$ is the number of binding sites per molecule protein, and $P$ the concentration of the protein, then $nP$ is the total number of binding sites per liter. $nP$ also equals the sum of the concentration of occupied [RX] and of free binding sites [R] i.e.:

$$nP = [RX] + [R], \text{ or:}$$
$$[R] = nP - [RX] \tag{5.6}$$

115

Substitution of nP − [RX] for [R] in Equation (5.5) gives:

$$K_d[RX] = [X](nP - [RX])$$
$$K_d[RX] = nP[X] - [RX][X]$$
$$K_d[RX] + [X][RX] = nP[X]$$
$$P = \frac{K_d[RX] + [X][RX]}{n[X]}$$

If $r$ is the number of moles bound substance per mole protein, then:

$$r = \frac{[RX]}{P} \quad \text{and substitution of } P \text{ gives}: \quad r = \frac{n[X]}{K_d + [X]} \tag{5.7}$$

For the Michaelis–Menten equation, see Appendix A.

Equation 5.7 shows a remarkable similarity to the Michaelis–Menten equation known from enzyme kinetics. This is explained by the fact that, in the derivation of the latter equation, the rate of the enzymatic reaction is assumed to be proportional to the concentration of the substrate–enzyme complex.

Assuming that half of the total number of binding sites is occupied, i.e. $r/n$ = 1/2 in Equation 5.7., then $2[X] = K_d + [X]$, or $[X] = K_d$. That means that $K_d$ is the concentration at which 50% of the maximum binding capacity is used. Like the Michaelis–Menten equation, Equation 5.7 can be represented graphically. Figure 5.15a shows an example in which $r$ is plotted against the concentration of the free substance $[X]$. Figure 15.5b shows the same relationship semilogarithmically. The resulting sigmoid curve illustrates the relationship between ligand and receptor binding in a particularly instructive way. Study unit 7 deals with this subject in more detail.

The curve shows that the value of $1/K_d$ is an indication of the affinity of the protein for the compound.

In order to determine the value of $K_d$ and the effects of other compounds on the ligand–protein bond, transformations of Equation 5.7 are applied to obtain a straight line. The most commonly applied transformation is the reciprocal transformation, which gives a so-called *Lineweaver–Burk equation*:

*Lineweaver–Burk equation*

$$\frac{1}{r} = \frac{1}{n} + \frac{K_d}{n[X]} \tag{5.8}$$

In the Lineweaver–Burk plot, $1/r$ is plotted against $1/[X]$.

The intercepts with the abscissa and the ordinate represent $-1/K_d$ and $1/n$, respectively. An example of a Lineweaver–Burk plot is shown in Figure 5.16a.

*Scatchard plot*

Binding of xenobiotics to plasma proteins is often studied with the help of a *Scatchard plot*. This plot shows the ratio of the bound and free ligand concentrations ($r/[X]$) on the y axis and the concentration of bound ligand ($r$) on the x axis (see Figure 5.16b).

The Scatchard equation can also be derived from Equation 5.7.

$$r K_d + r[X] = n[X], \quad \text{or} \quad r K_d = n[X] - r[X] \text{ and}$$
$$\frac{r K_d}{[X]} = n - r, \quad \text{or} \quad \frac{r}{[X]} = \frac{n}{K_d} - \frac{r}{K_d} \tag{5.9}$$

$r/[X]$ is now plotted against $r$. The intercepts then give the values of $n$ and $n/K_d$. Scatchard plots are often used to test whether all binding sites have the same

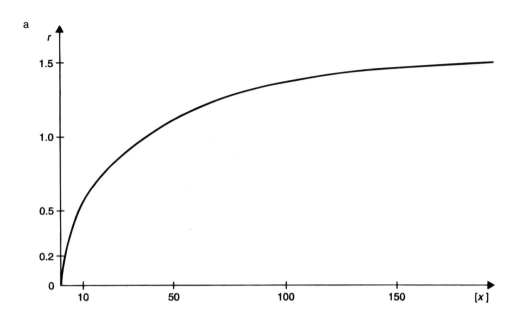

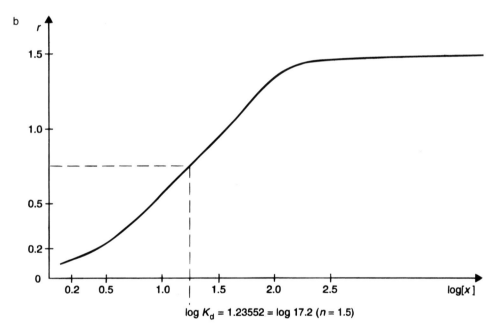

log $K_d$ = 1.23552 = log 17.2 (n = 1.5)

FIGURE   5.15
Binding of 4-sulfanilamido-5,6-dimethoxypyrimidine to blood albumin

[X] = molar concentration of the free compound

$r$   = number of moles bound compound per mole protein

$K_d$ = dissociation constant

$n$   = number of binding sites per protein molecule

From: Spring, P. (1968), *Arzneimittelforschung* 16, 346–354.

affinity. If the Scatchard plot is not a straight line, this means that there are different types of binding sites. Each linear part has its own $-1/K_d$, representing the affinity of the binding site concerned. Figure 5.17 gives an example.

With the help of Scatchard plots, it has been possible to demonstrate that many plasma proteins do indeed have several types of binding site. On the basis of

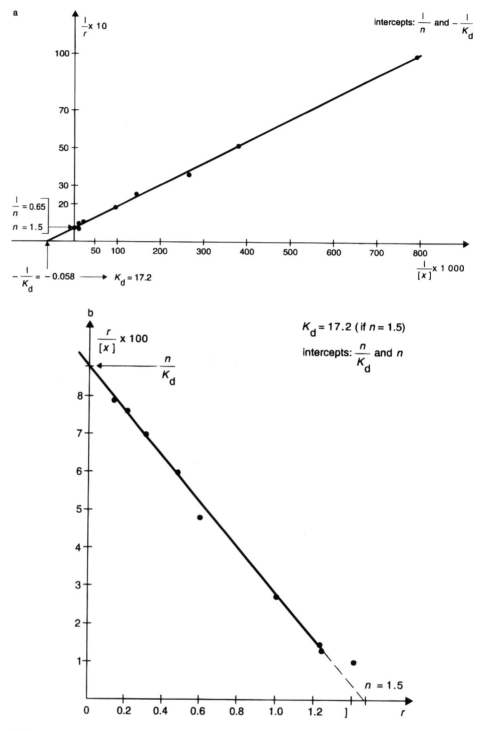

FIGURE 5.16
Lineweaver–Burk plot (a) and Scatchard plot (b)

studies on the binding behavior of azo dyes to blood proteins, it has been established that the affinity increases with increasing molecular size. This is true in particular of aromatic hydrocarbons, which, by means of Van der Waals forces, can contribute to the strength of binding. A flat ring structure assists the approach to the protein surface, and the approach should not be hampered by steric hindrance. Any polar groups should be positioned in such a way that the affinity of the hydrophobic sites on the protein for the molecule is higher than that of water.

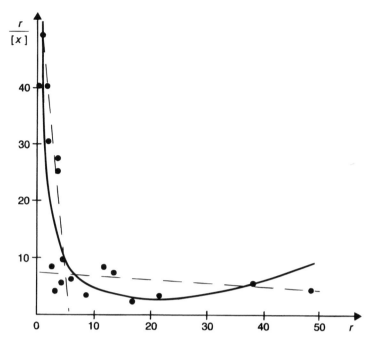

FIGURE 5.17
Scatchard plot for more than one type of protein binding site

So far, little is known about species differences with respect to $K_d$ values.

## 6    Elimination

Once a substance has been absorbed by the organism and distributed throughout the various tissues and organs, it will usually also be removed from the body again. The term *elimination* includes all the processes in the body which lead to a decrease in the amount of a foreign substance in the organism. Elimination will eventually also reduce the quantity of a substance at its site of action, and may thus put an end to the biological effect. The main elimination processes are excretion and biotransformation. The total elimination of a foreign substance is the resultant of:

- biotransformation
- renal excretion
- fecal excretion
- excretion via the lungs
- excretion via milk, placenta, eggs
- excretion via nails, hair, sweat, etc.

ASSIGNMENT 5.13

Which process discussed earlier on in this study unit should also be considered as a form of elimination?

*Extrahepatic metabolism*    It often occurs that compounds are no longer present in their original form, but have been altered by metabolic processes. The transformation takes place primarily in the liver, but *extrahepatic metabolism* (e.g. in the lungs or kidneys) may also be the main route via which a substance is transformed. A foreign substance

119

or its metabolite may also be conjugated to an endogenous compound. Such a conjugated compound is usually more water soluble than the parent compound, so that renal excretion is facilitated.

*Excretion*

*Excretion* is the removal from the organism of a foreign substance or one of its metabolites. Excretion mechanisms are responsible for most of the elimination processes. The most important excretion routes are via the kidneys into the urine (renal excretion) and via the bile into the feces (biliary excretion). Less important routes are direct excretion via the feces and excretion via saliva, sweat, tears, nasal mucus and milk. Excretion of volatile substances mainly takes place via the lungs. In previous study units it has already been mentioned that in most cases hydrophilic compounds can be excreted unchanged, whereas lipophilic substances can usually not be removed until they have first been converted to more hydrophilic metabolites.

## 6.1   RENAL EXCRETION

Renal excretion is one of the most important excretion routes for xenobiotics and their metabolites. Three processes are important in this respect: glomerular filtration, tubular secretion and tubular reabsorption (Figure 5.18).

*Glomerular filtration*
1 Da = 1 u = unit of mass (1/16 of oxygen atom)

Glomerular filtration involves ultrafiltration. The structure of the glomerular membrane complex allows, at least in man, virtually complete passage of compounds with a molecular weight up to 5000 Da (daltons). Therefore the concentration in the glomerular filtrate of compounds up to 5000 Da will be the same as that in the plasma. This is true for both the ionized and the non-ionized form. However, also heavier molecules (up to ± 40 000 Da) can pass the glomerular membrane. In rats the limit is even higher (up to 60 000 Da). This explains why, even under normal physiological circumstances, a small amount of glucose is found in the urine of rats. The selectivity of the glomerular membrane is related only to the molecular mass of compounds. This means that substances that are bound to plasma proteins, and thus form part of a high-molecular weight complex, cannot be filtered by the glomerulus. The concentration of these substances in the glomerular filtrate will be equal to their free plasma concentration. Since the glomerular filtration rate is proportional to the free plasma concentration, the former is reduced by binding to plasma proteins.

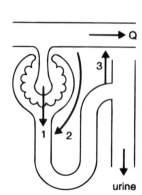

FIGURE   5.18
Diagram of the processes involved in renal excretion of xenobiotics
$Q$ = renal plasma flow, ±700 ml plasma per min, 1 = glomerular filtration; 2 = tubular secretion, ±0–650 ml per min.; 3 = reabsorption. Net excretion = 1 + 2 – 3; the rate at which urine is formed in man is about 1 ml per min.

120

*Tubular secretion*

There are various active transport systems in the proximal tubules. Specific systems that mediate tubular reabsorption (e.g. glucose, amino acids) transport but hardly any xenobiotics, because of their high specificity. Apart from these specific systems, there are also two separate systems with a low degree of specificity that are responsible for *tubular secretion* (from the plasma into the tubule). These two tubular secretion systems transport acids (anions) and bases (cations), respectively. As they are of low specificity, a large number of different compounds can be transported actively into the tubule. The anionic system transports, among others, organic acids (aminosalicylic acid, penicillins), sulfonic acids and acidic metabolites (sulfate conjugates, glucuronides, glycine conjugates). The cationic system transports compounds like organic bases (morphine, histamine) and quaternary ammonium compounds. Because of the low degree of specificity and the finite capacity of both systems there is a certain degree of competition between substances which are transported by the same system. The affinity of the active transport systems of the proximal tubular cells for the various compounds is usually considerably higher than the affinity of plasma proteins. This means that plasma protein binding is not necessarily a limiting factor.

Why not?

On passing through the kidney, even substances of which a large proportion is bound to plasma proteins can be secreted entirely by tubular secretion. The amount of a foreign compound excreted by active transport is replenished due to dissociation of the plasma protein complexes so rapidly that its elimination rate is not noticeably decreased.

*Active reabsorption*

As stated above, active reabsorption is mediated by specific transport mechanisms which primarily transport endogenous compounds such as glucose and amino acids. Because of this specificity, xenobiotics hardly qualify for active reabsorption, unless they are closely structurally related to the relevant endogenous compound. Therefore, most xenobiotics are reabsorbed by passive diffusion driven by a concentration gradient. The ultrafiltrate is concentrated in the tubular part of the nephron, resulting in a higher concentration of the substances taken along. The resulting concentration gradient will cause a large proportion of these substances to diffuse back into the blood via the tubular cells. This applies in particular to lipophilic substances. Because lipophilic substances can diffuse rapidly through the membranes of the tubular cells, the higher concentration in the tubular urine will cause them to return almost completely to the blood. The result is that the body can excrete nonvolatile, lipophilic compounds only with great difficulty, unless the organism has a biotransformation mechanism which converts them to more polar metabolites. Well-known examples of lipophilic substances that are difficult to remove from the body, are DDT and polychlorinated biphenyls (PCBs). With chronic exposure, these will accumulate in the body.

What factor or factors will determine the reabsorption of organic acids and bases in the nephron?

The reabsorption of organic acids and bases in the nephron mainly depends on the ionization constant of the compound concerned and the pH of the environment. This pH dependence is occasionally put to use in clinical practice. An example is the administration of sodium bicarbonate in the case of aspirin poisoning ($pK_a = 3.5$), which renders the urine alkaline and thus promotes the excretion of the aspirin in the urine.

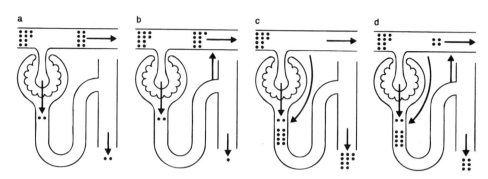

FIGURE 5.19

Examples of renal excretion of xenobiotics

• = relative quantities of a compound in plasma, tubular urine, or urine

a. glomerular filtration only; $Cl_r \approx 125$ ml min.$^{-1}$. Hydrophilic compounds with a molecular weight $\leq 5000$ Da, ionized at pH [symbol] 6.

b. glomerular filtration and reabsorption: $0 \leq Cl_r \leq 125$ ml min.$^{-1}$. Lipophilic compounds with a molecular weight $\leq 5000$ Da, non-ionized at pH $\approx 6$.

c. glomerular filtration and tubular secretion: $125 \leq Cl_r, \leq 625$ ml min.$^{-1}$. Hydrophilic organic acids and bases, ionized at pH $< 6$.

d. glomerular filtration, tubular secretion and reabsorption: $0 \leq Cl_r \approx 625$ min.$^{-1}$. Lipophilic organic acids and bases, little ionized at pH $\approx 6$.

*Net renal excretion of xenobiotics*

It can be seen from the above that the *net renal excretion of xenobiotics* is determined by the difference in transport mechanism between the systems leading to the tubular urine and those leading away from it.

ASSIGNMENT 5.14

Which are the afferent and which the efferent systems referred to here?

*Species differences*

There are large differences between the various species as regards active excretion and reabsorption. This is not really surprising if one considers the wide variety of ways in which different animals excrete their degradation products. Examples are the excretion of uric acid by birds, the secretion of urea by amphibians and the active reabsorption of urea by sharks. So far, the significance of these differences in excretion for the toxicity of substances in different animal species has little been studied.

The net renal excretion depends on the physico-chemical properties of the foreign substance concerned, and on the functioning of the systems involved. The ability to demonstrate and determine quantitatively the presence of compounds in the urine has an important diagnostic function in cases of intoxication. In addition, the quantitative determination of compounds in the urine provides a measure of the occupational exposure to substances that are excreted neither too rapidly nor too slowly. The metabolite trichloro-acetic acid, for example, can be detected in the urine of individuals who are working or have worked with *trichloroethylene*.

## 6.2   BILIARY EXCRETION

As stated in the previous section, many xenobiotics can be excreted via the kidney, usually only after biotransformation. Besides renal excretion (clearance), the body can excrete certain xenobiotics via the intestine. For excretion of xenobiotics from the liver into the intestine, previous biotransformation is virtually always an essential precondition. The most important route by which xenobiotics present in the circulation can leave the body through the intestine, is via the bile. The liver secretes bile almost continuously. On its way to the intestine and in the gall bladder, water is removed from the bile. Not all vertebrates have a gall bladder; rats, horses, whales and deer, for example, do not. Birds have a double bile duct, one of which has a gall bladder.

*Route complementary to renal excretion*

Excretion of xenobiotics via the bile can be regarded as a complementary route to renal excretion. Smaller molecules are eliminated via the urine; larger ones via the bile. This means that the bile constitutes an important route of excretion for many conjugated compounds. For compounds such as proteins, sugars, ions and many non-metabolized xenobiotics, excretion via the bile is of little importance in comparison to that by other elimination mechanisms. For a number of compounds, however, biliary clearance can reach values of 500 ml min$^{-1}$, and thus make quite a significant contribution to their total elimination.

> ASSIGNMENT 5.15
>
> Assuming you are familiar with the concept of renal clearance, what do you think is meant by biliary clearance?

The transfer from blood to bile is an active process, in which, in the case of organic xenobiotics, three separate transport systems are involved: one for acids, one for bases (quaternary ammonium compounds) and one for polar substances that cannot dissociate. Many substances occurring in blood and tissue fluids in the ionized form, are subjected to both renal and biliary excretion. It is not known which factors determine whether a compound is excreted via the urine or via the bile. Table 5.7 shows the effect of the molecular mass of a number of biphenyls on their route of excretion in rats.

It has been possible to demonstrate that there is a threshold value for the molecular mass of polar compounds, above which biliary excretion becomes important. Above this threshold (250–300 Da), biliary excretion increases with increasing molecular mass, while renal excretion is correspondingly reduced. This threshold value varies according to species. Threshold values have been found for certain compounds and their metabolites of $325 \pm 50$ in rats, of $440 \pm 50$ in guinea pigs, and of $475 \pm 50$ in rabbits. In general, however, it can be said that there is a rather large variation between the various species as far as the quantity of a compound which is excreted in the bile is concerned. This often also results in differences in the biological half-life and the toxicity of the compounds.

Species differences make it very difficult to extrapolate data obtained in experimental animals to the human situation. Table 5.8 shows the differences in

Table 5.7
Relationship between the molecular weight of a number of biphenyls and their route of excretion in rats.

| substance | molecular mass | percentage of excretion | |
| --- | --- | --- | --- |
| | | urine | feces |
| biphenyl | 154 | 80 | 20 |
| 4- monochlorobiphenyl | 188 | 50 | 50 |
| 4,4′-dichlorobiphenyl | 223 | 34 | 66 |
| 2,4,5,2′,5′-pentachlorobiphenyl | 326 | 11 | 89 |
| 2,3,6,2′,3′,6′-hexachlorobiphenyl | 361 | 1 | 99 |

[1]After Mattheus, H.B. (1960) In: Introduction to Biochemical Toxicology

Table 5.8
Species differences in rates of excretion of phenolphthalein glucuronide and indocyanine green. Both compounds are excreted mainly via the bile

| species | dosage (mg kg⁻¹) | rate of excretion (dose/h) |
|---|---|---|
| *phenolphthalein* | | |
| *glucuronide* | | |
| rat | 10 ip | 75/24 |
| rat | 10 ip | 54/3 |
| rat | 81.5 ip | 62/2 |
| rat | 25 iv | 82/3 |
| rat | 40 iv | 45/0.5 |
| rat | 10 iv | 73/3 |
| guinea pig | 25 iv | 44/3 |
| guinea pig | 10 iv | 6/3 |
| rabbit | 25 iv | 22/3 |
| rabbit | 10 iv | 13/3 |
| dog | 10 iv | 81/3 |
| chicken | 10 iv | 71/3 |
| cat | 10 iv | 34/3 |
| sheep | 10 iv | 38/3 |
| monkey | 10 iv | 9/3 |
| *indocyanine* | | |
| *green* | | |
| rat | 2.5 iv | 60/1 |
| rat | 2.4 iv | 82/3 |
| rat | 5 iv | 28/1 |
| dog | 1 iv | 97/5 |
| guinea pig | 2.4 iv | 97/3 |
| rabbit | 2.4 iv | 94/3 |
| monkey | 0.5 iv | 95/5 |

The table shows species, dose and route of administration (iv = intravenous; ip = intraperitoneal, in mg kg⁻¹ and rate of excretion (dose per h).

excretion rate via the bile in several species for the dye indocyanine green and the glucuronide of phenolphthalein. In addition to the minimum molecular mass mentioned above, polarity is another precondition for active excretion via the bile. This is why many xenobiotics are not available for active biliary excretion until they have first been metabolized. Glucuronidation reactions are especially important in this respect, because the resulting conjugates have the properties necessary for active transport. As a result, glucuronides are usually cleared to a large extent in the bile.

ASSIGNMENT 5.16

Explain why glucuronides are cleared to a large extent via the bile.

*Active transport*

The transport systems involved in biliary excretion have all the characteristics of *active transport*. It has, for example, been demonstrated that there is competitive inhibition of excretion of substances via the bile by other compounds which are excreted via the same transport system. Since this form of excretion of xenobiotics involves an active transport process, the binding sites on the transport proteins may become saturated, which explains the existence of a threshold dose for the toxicity in some cases. Once arrived in the intestine, there are three possibilities for substances that are excreted via the bile:

- excretion of the unchanged molecule via the feces;
- reabsorption of the unchanged molecule from the intestine;
- enzymatic conversion in the intestine, followed by reabsorption into the blood.

In general, reabsorption of the unchanged molecule is rather uncommon, because the structural conditions for reabsorption (lipophilicity) are the opposite of those for biliary excretion (polarity).

On the other hand, the third possibility, that of reabsorption after enzymatic conversion in the intestine, is quite common, in particular for certain drugs. This is related to the fact that conjugates form good substrates for certain enzymes occurring in the intestine. One example is the hydrolysis of glucuronides, by β-glucuronidase from *E. coli* in the large intestine.

*Enterohepatic circulation*

The products formed in this enzymatic reaction (parent xenobiotics or possible metabolites) can be excreted directly with the feces or reabsorbed from the intestine. The result of these events may be *enterohepatic circulation* (see Figure 5.12). Enterohepatic circulation may have toxicological consequences. This is certainly so if there is reabsorption of a metabolite which is more toxic than its parent compound. The half-life of the foreign substance in the body may also increase.

Some substances are removed from the body almost exclusively by biliary excretion, so that reduced bile secretion, resulting from, e.g. some hepatic disorders, prolongs and/or intensifies their effects. If the liver is inactivated, e.g. by ligation of the bile ducts, the acute toxicity of digoxin and indocyanine green appears to increase by a factor of 4–5; in the case of diethylstilbestrol (DES) the toxicity increased 130 times.

Besides these active transport mechanisms for the excretion of organic compounds, the liver has at least one more transport mechanism for the excretion of heavy metals. Lead, for example, is excreted into the bile in a concentration that is 100 times higher than that in the plasma. Moreover, the transport capacity for lead can become saturated. It is not yet known whether other metals are excreted by the same or similar mechanisms, nor whether there is competition between the various metals for excretion via the bile.

In the newborn, elimination by the liver is only poorly developed. This is one of the reasons why some compounds are more toxic in neonates than in adults. Ouabain, a drug used in cardiac insufficiency, is 40 times more toxic in newly-born than in adult rats.

## 6.3 OTHER EXCRETORY PROCESSES

The removal of xenobiotics from the body by processes other than renal or biliary excretion is quantitatively of little importance.

*Lungs*

The most important factors determining the excretion of gaseous and volatile compounds via the *lungs* are the same as those involved in absorption. This means that the concentration of the compound in plasma and alveolar air, and the blood–gas partition coefficient are particularly significant. There is no special transport mechanism for the excretion of foreign substances from the lungs. Elimination simply takes place by diffusion. The elimination rate of foreign gases appears to be almost inversely proportional to the rate at which they are absorbed. Gases which do not dissolve well in blood, such as ethylene, are excreted rapidly, while a compound like chloroform, which dissolves in the blood much more easily, is excreted much more slowly by the lungs.

*Excretion via the feces*

*Excretion via the feces* may be direct if the absorption of a substance after oral ingestion is incomplete or has not taken place at all. In general, however, elimination via the feces is rather the result of biliary excretion, as discussed in the previous section. Substances found in the feces also may have been secreted via saliva, gastric and/or intestinal juices or via the pancreatic juice. They may also be substances that have been inhaled, and subsequently been swallowed following return from the respiratory tract. The human stomach and intestine together secrete approximately 3 liters of fluid a day. Originally, it was thought that active excretion of xenobiotics would take place via this gastrointestinal fluid. It is now assumed that passive diffusion into the gastrointestinal tract is more likely to occur. Recent studies have shown that *direct excretion* from the circulation via the intestinal tract constitutes an important route of elimination for highly lipophilic compounds, such as organochlorine insecticides, dioxin (TCDD) and polychlorinated biphenyls.

*Sweat and saliva*

Excretion via *sweat and saliva* depends on the diffusion of the non-ionized, lipid-soluble form of the substance. Toxic substances that are excreted via sweat can sometimes cause dermatological disorders. Substances that are excreted via the saliva enter the mouth, where they are usually swallowed. The process of absorption can then start all over again, though the lipophilicity of such substances is usually lower, and hence their uptake from the gastrointestinal tract is more difficult.

*Milk*

The problem of foreign substances excreted in *milk* became acute when the use of chlorinated hydrocarbon pesticides was greatly increased and antibiotics were added to cattle feed. In the meantime, research has shown that many foreign compounds, including drugs, are excreted via the milk and may even reach higher concentrations in milk than in the maternal plasma.

Research on the excretion of toxic substances in milk is important for two reasons. First, toxic substances can be transferred from the mother to the infant via breast feeding. Second, toxic compounds excreted in cow's milk can be ingested by man. Transport to the mother's milk primarily takes place by passive diffusion of the non-ionized compound. This means that transport depends on the $pK_a$ of the foreign substance, the difference in pH between milk and plasma, the plasma concentration of the substance and its lipophilicity. Since the pH of human milk (6.6) is lower than that of plasma (7.4), higher concentrations of organic bases and lower concentrations of organic acids will occur in milk than in the plasma. Although the bond between foreign compounds and milk proteins generally is weaker than that between a foreign substance and albumin, significant amounts of foreign substances can still be transported.

ASSIGNMENT 5.17

Why do some compounds, like DDT and chlorinated biphenyls, so readily accumulate in milk?

*Hair, nails and skin*

The excretion of xenobiotics via *the hair, nails and skin* is negligible in a quantitative sense. It is possible, however, to determine whether individuals have been exposed to toxic metals (like arsenic and mercury), which are frequently stored in these tissues. Ultrasensitive detection methods for these metals have been developed which are used in forensic medicine.

*Eggs*

The factors playing a part in the elimination of xenobiotics via *eggs* are roughly the same as those that are important in the elimination via milk. An important difference is the clear demarcation between the lipid-containing part of the egg, the yolk, and the aqueous part in which proteins are dissolved, the egg white. The color of the yolk of a chicken's egg depends on the level of carotenoids in the feed. This demonstrates that a considerable portion of the body burden of lipophilic compounds in oviparous mammals is passed on to the offspring. Far less is known about the excretion of xenobiotics via eggs than via milk. The few studies carried out so far mostly concerned research on chickens and quails.

The few available data show that xenobiotics, in particular lipophilic xenobiotics and mercury, can be excreted via the eggs of all oviparous animals. Polar xenobiotics eliminated via eggs accumulate in the egg white. However, the elimination via the egg of lipophilic xenobiotics, which accumulate in the yolk, is of greater quantitative importance. Oviparous animals generally do not convert toxic xenobiotics into less toxic compounds very well. Compounds such as certain polybrominated biphenyls are not metabolized by birds and therefore are not excreted by the liver or the kidneys. It has been found that in chickens and quails these compounds are excreted mainly via the eggs. This explains why, at identical exposure levels, the tissue levels of these compounds are considerably lower in female than in male animals. Although the elimination of toxic xenobiotics via the eggs is often of little importance to the mother animal, it may greatly endanger the chances of survival of the young. If the (environmental) pollution reaches serious levels, this may even lead to the extinction of an entire species.

Accumulation of xenobiotics in and their "excretion" via the fetus may result from maternal exposure during pregnancy or from redistribution of an already existing depot of xenobiotics from maternal tissue to the developing fetus. In order to reach the fetus, however, xenobiotics must first pass across the placenta. The *placenta* functions as an intermediary organ between the mother and the fetus. Oxygen and nutrients (amino acids, glucose, lipids, vitamins) pass from the mother to the fetus, while carbon dioxide and fetal metabolites (urea, uric acid, creatinine) pass across the placenta in the opposite direction.

*Placenta*

Histologically, the placenta differs among mammals with regard to the number of cell layers between the maternal and the fetal blood (Table 5.9). In man (hemochorial placenta), the maternal blood is in direct contact with the basement membrane of the fetal trophoblast, which in turn is directly connected with the endothelium of the fetal vascular system. In the cat (endotheliohemochorial placenta), on the other hand, the placental barrier also contains maternal endothelium.

Passage of nutrients and metabolites across the placenta takes place by passive diffusion and facilitated diffusion as well as active transport. Larger molecules may be transported by pinocytosis. Xenobiotics pass across the placenta

Table 5.9
Tissues separating the fetal and maternal blood

| | maternal tissue | | | fetal tissue | | | species |
|---|---|---|---|---|---|---|---|
| | endo-thelium | connec-tive tissue | epithelium | tropho-blast | connec-tive tissue | endothelium | |
| epitheliochorial | + | + | + | + | + | + | pig, horse, donkey |
| syndesmochorial | + | + | − | + | + | + | sheep, goat, cow |
| endotheliochorial | + | − | − | + | + | + | cat, dog |
| hemochorial | − | − | − | + | + | + | man, monkey |
| hemo-endothelial | − | − | − | − | − | + | rat, rabbit, guinea pig |

127

mostly by passive diffusion. Again, low-molecular-weight molecules (<500) and lipophilic compounds of medium molecular weight appear to pass readily. There is nothing to indicate that differences in placental structure have a significant influence on the transport of foreign compounds. In this respect, the placenta does not provide any protection to the embryo; its main purpose is to allow an optimal exchange of compounds. Hence, the concentrations of lipophilic compounds in fetal tissues are almost the same as those in the maternal tissues. The selectivity of the placenta is restricted to the more polar xenobiotics. Experiments have shown that lipophilic halogenated hydrocarbons accumulate in the fetal liver, adipose tissue and intestinal tract of rats. In man, the surface area of the placental interface at the end of a pregnancy is estimated as 12 m². Tragic examples of serious consequences which may result from placental transport of toxic xenobiotics to the fetus from mothers exposed to the toxic compounds are the thalidomide disaster, postnatal tumor induction by diethylstilbestrol (DES), and mercury poisoning.

The possible consequences of the passage of toxic compounds to the fetus via the placenta are discussed in the study units on reproductive toxicology.

## APPENDIX A

Michaelis–Menten equation:

$$v = \frac{V_{max}\,[S]}{K_m + [S]}$$

where:

$v$ = initial reaction rate

$V_{max}$ = maximum reaction rate

$K_m$ = Michaelis–Menten constant

[S] = concentration of substrate

The Michaelis–Menten equation describes the relationship between the concentration of the substrate and the rate of an enzyme-mediated reaction.

## SELF ASSESSMENT QUESTIONS

1 Which of the following alternatives is/are correct? Passage of xenobiotics from the blood to extravascular tissue,

   a. like skeletal muscle, takes place very slowly if the compounds are highly ionized at pH = 7.4.

   b. like the brain, can only take place in the case of highly lipophilic compounds.

   c. is as difficult from extravascular tissue to the blood, when passing across the blood–brain barrier.

2 Which of the following alternatives is/are correct? If in the case of a certain compound the volume of distribution is large, it implies:

   a. a large quantity of (total) body water

   b. many sites of action ("receptors") available to the molecule

c. a low rate of excretion

d. high lipophilicity.

3 Which of the following alternatives is/are correct?

a. Ionized compounds will hardly be able to diffuse into a cell.

b. The bioavailability of a compound indicates to the quantity of the compound that is not bound to plasma proteins.

c. Ordinary diffusion depends on the absorptive surface area.

d. Ordinary diffusion is a process that can become saturated.

4 Which of the following alternatives is/are correct? The absorption (uptake) of a xenobiotic from the gastrointestinal tract is influenced by:

a. the dietary habits of the person concerned

b. the plasma half-life of the compound

c. the pH in the gastrointes tinal tract

d. stress.

5 Which of the following statements is/are correct?

a. Injury to the horny layer of the skin may increase the absorption of xenobiotics.

b. Aerosols are absorbed mainly by the lungs.

c. Under steady state conditions, the quantity of a xenobiotic in the extracellular fluid is in equilibrium with the concentration of the compound bound to plasma proteins.

d. The distribution volume of a compound is the quotient of dose and plasma concentration.

e. In particular, large lipid-soluble molecules undergo biliary excretion.

6 What would be the stomach–plasma ratio of a weak base with a $pK_a$ in the steady state, if the pH in the stomach is 2 and that of plasma 7?

a. $10^{-3}$: 1

b. $10^{-1}$: 1

c. $10^{1}$: 1

d. $10^{3}$: 1.

7 A compound that undergoes glomerular excretion is found in the fluid in the renal tubule. This means that:

a. the compound was present in the free form, i.e. not bound to plasma proteins

b. the compound does not undergo biotransformation

c. the compound is a quaternary ammonium compound

d. the compound has a volume of distribution $\geq$ 50 liters.

8 Elimination of a weak base via the urine is high if:

a. the urine is acidic

b. the urine is alkaline

c. the pH of the urine approaches the $pK_a$ of the compound

d. the pH of plasma approaches the $pK_a$ of the compound.

9   The occurrence of a toxic effect in an organism always depends on:
    a.  the route of intake
    b.  the dose, duration of exposure and nature of the compound
    c.  the quantity of a compound that reaches a susceptible site in the organism.

10  Which of the following statements is/are correct? Diffusion into the cell
    a.  of large foreign water-soluble molecules requires that they first "dissolve" in the membrane lipids
    b.  is easier for the ionized form of a compound than for the non-ionized form
    c.  of weak electrolytes does not depend on the pH of the medium
    d.  is a relatively slow process for lipid-soluble compounds if they cannot pass through the pores in the cell membrane.

11  Which of the following alternatives is/are correct? Conjugation of xenobiotics with glucuronic acid
    a.  is increased in the newborn
    b.  produces compounds that are more lipid-soluble
    c.  in most cases leads to prolongation of the duration of the (biological) effects of the compounds concerned
    d.  leads to accelerated excretion via the urine
    e.  leads to reduced biliary excretion.

12  Figure 5.20 shows the relationship between the total plasma concentration of the compound ($C_p$) and the plasma concentration $d$ of a compound in the free form.

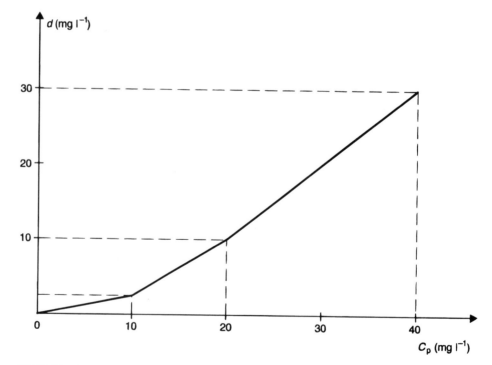

FIGURE   5.20

I    If $C_p$ is smaller than 10 mg l$^{-1}$, the proportion of the compound bound to plasma proteins is:

    a.   25%

    b.   50%

    c.   75%

II   The binding sites with the highest affinity are nearly all saturated if $C_p$ is approximately:

    a.   10 mg l$^{-1}$

    b.   20 mg l$^{-1}$

    c.   30 mg l$^{-1}$

    d.   40 mg l$^{-1}$.

13   Ethanol (molecular weight 46) is rapidly taken up from the intestine because:

    a.   it is a non-polar compound, and, moreover, very lipid-soluble

    b.   it is a polar, water-soluble compound and small enough to diffuse through water-filled pores in the membrane

    c.   it is transported by facilitated diffusion

    d.   it is taken up by so-called uphill transport (against the concentration gradient).

14   Figure 5.21 shows the relationship between the pH of the urine and the urinary concentration of a compound ($C_u$) as a ratio of the plasma concentration of the unbound compound ($C_p$).

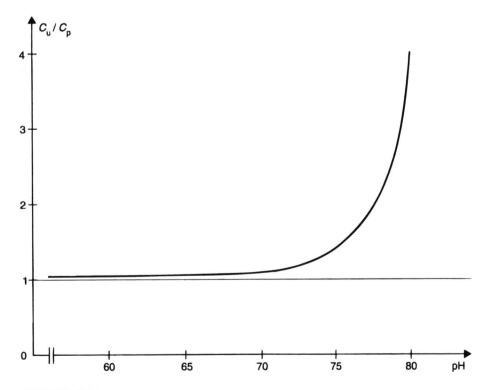

FIGURE   5.21

I This compound is

   a. a weak acid

   b. a weak base

   c. completely ionized at this pH range.

II The $pK_a$ of this compound

   a. cannot be estimated from this information

   b. is lower than 8

   c. is higher than 8.

## FEEDBACK

### 1 Answers to the assignments

5.1 Zero-order kinetics mean that the reaction (in this case binding to the carrier protein) is independent of the concentration of the substrate, here of the concentration of the compound to be transported. Therefore, an increase in concentration does not result in an increase in the rate of transport.

5.2 a. The following applies to an acid with $pK_a$ 4 in an environment with pH 1:

$$\text{antilog } 1 - 4 = [A^-/[HA]$$
$$\text{antilog } 3 = [A^-]/[HA] = 0.001$$

This means that $[A^-] : [HA] = 1 : 1000$, or 99.9% of the acid is in the non-ionized form.

   b. The following applies to a base with $pK_a$ 5 in an environment with pH 1:

$$1\text{-}5 = \log [A]/[HA^+]$$
$$\text{antilog} - 4 = [A]/[HA^+] = 0.0001$$

Therefore, $[A] : [HA^+] = 1 : 10,000$, or 99.99% of the base is in the ionized form.

5.3 These equations are derived as follows:

— for acids (see equation 5.1a)

$pH = pK_a + \log [A^{[-]}]/[HA]$, i.e.

$\log [A^-]/[HA] = pH\text{-} pK_a$, therefore:

$[A^-]/[HA] = 10^{(pH\text{-} pK_a)}$, and therefore:

$[A^-] = [HA] \cdot 10^{(pH\text{-} pK_a)}$

The quantities of the compound in both compartments are related as follows:

$$\frac{C_1}{C_2} = \frac{[HA]+[A_1^-]}{[HA]+[A_2^-]} = \frac{[HA]+[HA]\cdot 10^{(pH_1-pKa)}}{[HA]+[HA]\cdot 10^{(pH_2-pK_a)}}$$

$$\frac{C_1}{C_2} = \frac{[HA]*[1+10^{(pH_1-pKa)}]}{[HA][1+10^{(pH_2-pK_a)}]} = \frac{1+10^{(pH_1-pK_a)}}{1+10^{(pH_2-pK_a)}}$$

Where $C = [A^-] + [HA]$ is the total concentration in a compartment.

*[HA] is the same in both compartments, because at equilibrium the concentration of non-ionized compound is the same on both sides of the membrane.

5.4 Carrier proteins are highly substrate-specific. Quite often many non-nutrients will not be complementary to the physiological carrier proteins which transport nutrients etc. across the membrane.

5.5 Because alcohol is a volatile compound, it is expired to a certain degree after cessation of exposure. Hence, its concentration in the expired air is a measure of the quantity still present in the body.

5.6 Factors which are important in transport in and absorption by the lungs are: permeability of the alveolar membrane, solubility in blood and the rate of the blood flow.

5.7 After a longer period of time, the compound is released again from the blood via the gills into the water. There is a net inward or outward flow, depending on the concentration ratios involved.

5.8 It goes without saying that damage to the skin, in which the stratum corneum is no longer intact, may give rise to a greater permeability to foreign compounds. An increase in the ambient temperature may also cause an increase in the permeability of the horny layer, resulting from hyperemia and hydration of the skin.

5.9 This will not be the case if the compound is no longer present in its original form or quantity. It may take place if the substance has been metabolized or excreted.

5.10 The plasma concentration will be approximately in equilibrium with that in the tissue.

5.11 Covalent bonds.

5.12 It follows from formula 5.5 that:

$$\frac{1}{K_d} = \frac{[RX]}{[R][X]} = \frac{[\text{occupied binding sites}]}{[\text{free binding sites}][\text{free compound}]}$$

In words, this is the number of occupied binding sites in relation to the number of free binding sites ($1/K_d$), which is a measure of the affinity of the binding sites for the compound.

5.13 Irreversible binding to tissue proteins (provided it does not affect normal functioning) can in fact also be considered as an elimination process, as it reduces the availability of the compound to the body.

5.14 The affluent systems are the blood flow through the glomerulus, glomerular filtration and tubular secretion. The effluent systems are removal to the urine and reabsorption.

5.15 Renal clearance is defined as the volume of blood or plasma from which the kidney completely removes the compound in a given time period. It is expressed in units of volume per unit of time. Biliary clearance, by analogy, is the volume of blood or plasma from which the liver completely removes a compound via the bile in a unit of time.

5.16 Glucuronides have the properties required for active transport. They are polar, ionized compounds (acids with $pK_a = 3$) with a molecular weight > 300 Da.

5.17 Because milk contains a large quantity of lipids (3–5%), highly lipophilic xenobiotics such as DDT, polychlorinated and polybrominated biphenyls will readily accumulate in milk. Indeed, these compounds can be found in milk in high concentrations. Considerable quantities of heavy metals like cadmium and lead, and of chelating agents which form complexes with $Ca^{++}$, may also be found in milk.

## 2 Answers to the self assessment questions

1   a   is correct; in particular non-ionized (lipid-soluble) compounds are able to pass across biological membranes.
    b   is correct.
    c   is correct. The uptake of compounds from the blood into the brain is as difficult as their passage from the brain to the plasma. Neither the pH nor the ionic composition of the cerebrospinal fluid differs greatly from that of the plasma. The differences are determined mainly by the cellular composition and protein content of the two fluids.

2   b and d are correct. In a one-compartment model, a large volume of distribution indicates that a compound is highly lipophilic and/or has many receptors at its disposal.

Fick's law see Study unit 6

3   a and c are correct. Ionized compounds cannot diffuse through membranes. Diffusion is a process which cannot become saturated, as it does not involve transport enzymes. Diffusion follows Fick's law, and therefore depends on the size of the absorptive surface. Biological availability is a measure of the relative rate at which a compound reaches the circulation.

4   a and c are correct. The plasma half-life of a compound does not influence its uptake from the gastrointestinal tract. Stress has never been shown to have any effect on the absorption of xenobiotics from the gastrointestinal tract.

5   a, b, d and e are correct.

6   Calculation of the steady state distribution of the total concentration of a compound in two compartments at different pH's (use formulae 5.2):

$$C_1 : C_2 = \frac{1 + 10^{pK_a - pH_1}}{1 + 10^{pK_a - pH_2}} \text{(for base)}$$

$$= \frac{1 + 10^{5-2}}{1 + 10^{5-7}} = \frac{1 + 10^3}{1 + 10^{-2}} = \frac{1001}{1.01} = 10^3 : 1$$

Alternative d is correct.

7    a is correct. Only compounds not bound to plasma proteins can be excreted and/or metabolized.

8    a is correct.

9    b is (the most) correct.

10    None of the alternatives is correct.

11    Alternative d is correct. At birth, the activities of cytochrome P-450 and glucuronidation enzymes usually are still low. Alternative b is incorrect because conjugation with glucuronic acid in fact results in the formation of more water-soluble products. Glucuronidation generally leads to a reduced binding capacity. The duration of (biological) effects tends to last shorter rather than longer (although there are exceptions). Many xenobiotics are more easily excreted into the bile as a result of glucuronidation. Alternative a is also correct (see section 1.4 of Study unit 4).

12    I: c is correct.      II: a is correct.

13    Alternative b is correct.

14    I: a. is correct.      II: b. is correct.

# Contents Study unit 6
## Toxicokinetics: quantitative aspects

0-8493-9232-2/96/$0.00 + $.50

Study unit 6

# Toxicokinetics—quantitative aspects

*J. de Vries*

## INTRODUCTION

Cimetidine is already dealt with in Study unit 4

The majority of drugs used in medicine combine very loosely with their receptors, e.g. the interaction of cimetidine with the histamine receptor. Usually, the substances can be easily washed off their receptors, which then cease to trigger the effects of the substance concerned.

The mode of action of organophosphates will be described in Study unit 33

However, some xenobiotics form covalent bonds with the receptors and in this way they bring about a change that is difficult to reverse. Examples of the latter are the organophosphates, many of which are used as insecticides.

Thus, the manifestation of a toxic effect in the body may result from:

1.  a reversible reaction between an active agent and a target molecule or
2.  an irreversible interaction between these two entities.

In the first case, the intensity of the toxic effect depends on the extent to which binding to the target molecule has taken place, and hence, indirectly on the *concentration* of the active agent (A):

$$A + T \rightleftharpoons A\text{-}T \rightarrow \text{toxic effect}$$

The concentration of A determines the position of the equilibrium and hence the extent to which binding to T has proceeded.

Since the concentration of A at the site of action is in turn determined by the *blood concentration*, the changes with time in the intensity of the effect can be substituted by the changes in the blood concentration with time.

ASSIGNMENT  6.1

What is the advantage of this simplifying substitution?

*adduct molecule = molecule resulting from combination of precursor molecules*

If a toxic effect results from an irreversible interaction, then the intensity of the effect is determined by the number of adduct molecules formed and hence by the *amount* of active agent. The way in which a chemical reaches a particular blood concentration or level in the body is difficult to describe. It depends on the disposition of the substance concerned, i.e. its absorption, distribution, biotransformation and excretion. Experience shows that the body can often be represented schematically by a so-called compartment model, which lends itself well to mathematical description.

*In pharmacokinetics a compartment is a mathematical entity that can be*

The (toxicokinetic) concept of *compartment* relates to all tissues, organs and fluids in the body that do not differ from each other in terms of kinetics.

*described by a volume (not necessarily physiological) and its drug concentration; see also Study-unit 5, section 5*

If a substance, after having entered the circulation, is quickly distributed over the entire organism and if it is readily exchanged between the circulation and the rest of the body except for, for example, the adipose tissue, then the organism can be described as a *two-compartment model*. In this case the compartments are the adipose tissue (often referred to as the peripheral or tissue compartment, T) and the circulation plus the other organs and tissues (referred to as the central compartment, C). Whether a number of organs, tissues and body fluids constitute a compartment, depends on the perfusion of the tissues and organs and on the physicochemical properties of the substance concerned (lipophilicity, binding affinity, etc.).

ASSIGNMENT  6.2

What can you say about the physicochemical properties of substances whose kinetic behavior can be described by means of a two-compartment model?

This study unit describes the time course of the absorption, distribution, metabolism and excretion of xenobiotics, based on measurements of concentrations and quantities of substances and metabolites in biological matrices. It implies the use of mathematics for a quantitative description of the kinetic processes.

Toxicokinetics as described here is largely based on pharmacokinetics. This means that this unit mainly deals with reversible interactions of substances. Toxicology, however, often involves irreversible interactions of substances, such as covalent binding. As the kinetics of irreversible interactions differ from those of reversible interactions in several respects, these are discussed separately in section 5.

LEARNING OBJECTIVES

After having studied this unit, you should be able to

— translate some important physiological aspects into formulae and, conversely, indicate the physiological meaning of the most important mathematical parameters
— indicate when the intensity of a biological effect is determined by the concentration of the active agent and when by the amount
— describe the model-independent processes of absorption and clearance, and apply the corresponding formulae
— describe the compartment model concept
— give a mathematical description of a one-compartment model, after both intravenous and oral administration
— indicate two ways of determining clearance in the case of a one-compartment model
— give a description of a two-compartment model after intravenous administration
— describe the terms below and determine the corresponding parameters (for instance graphically):
    — absorption (rate constant)
    — *F* (bioavailability)
    — metabolism (rate constant)
    — excretion (rate constant)
    — elimination (rate constant)
    — apparent volume of distribution

> — half-life
> — *AUC* (area under the curve)
> — rate constants for the transfer between compartments
> — the hybride constants $\alpha$ and $\beta$
> — the coefficients: *A*, *B* and *D*
— use the mathematical description of the blood concentration-time curve after repeated administration, and the related concepts of minimum blood concentration, maximum blood concentration and mean blood concentration
— describe the concept of saturation kinetics
— use the mathematical equation of the concept of saturation kinetics
— explain the special position of the kinetics of covalent binding

*Study hints*

A good understanding of this unit requires a certain knowledge of mathematics, in particular of algebra (logarithms, natural logarithms), differentiation and integration. It may be necessary to review these subjects using a book or course on mathematics. Although the deduction of the formulae used in kinetics may seem rather complicated at first, in practice it is enough to know how to use the deduced formulae or simplified versions of them. You are not expected to be able to deduce these formulae yourself at the end of the textbook, but you should be able to understand how they are used. You are therefore advised to try to find out for yourself the significance of the individual components of each formula.

This study unit deals mainly with the theoretical aspects of kinetics, such as the deduction and significance of some important formulae. The study load for this unit is estimated at 6 student learning hours.

*Computer program Toxkin*

In addition to the present study unit and to Study unit 5, there is a computer simulation program on kinetics available (Toxkin). You may use this program to revise the various aspects of kinetics once more. The program consists of a number of (simulated) quantitative examples. In principle, you should be able to work out these assignments in Toxkin after or during studying this unit.

STUDY CORE

1    **Model-independent parameters**

In order to describe the changes in plasma levels of xenobiotics adequately, it is necessary to design a suitable mathematical model that accurately predicts the slope of the plasma concentration-time curve. However, some kinetic parameters can be determined without the use of such a compartment model. The absorption and clearance of substances, for example, can be measured directly with appropriate analytical methods. Such parameters are referred to in this unit as *model-independent*.

1.1    ABSORPTION

*absorption*

In toxicology absorption mainly refers to the transport of a chemical from its "administration" site into the venous blood. More specifically, absorption involves the diffusion of a chemical across the gastrointestinal wall into the blood. This absorption usually takes place by passive diffusion, which proceeds in accordance with Fick's law.

*Fick's law*

D stands for dose, GI for gastrointestinal, A for Absorption

If the factors for the permeability and the membrane surface over which absorption takes place are substituted by one factor $k_A$, and the concentration gradient is substituted by the amount of substance in the gastrointestinal tract ($D_{GI}$), then the disappearance rate from the gastrointestinal tract can be described by a simple differential equation.

$$\frac{dD_{GI}}{dt} = -k_A \cdot D_{GI} \qquad (6.1)$$

where:

$D_{GI}$ = the amount of substance still present in the gastrointestinal tract at time $t$ after administration (expressed in, for example, mg)

$k_A$ = the rate constant for absorption (expressed in, for example, $min^{-1}$)

$dD_{GI}/dt$ = the rate (for example in mg $min^{-1}$) at which the substance disappears from the gastrointestinal tract

The minus sign indicates that the absorption rate decreases with time because the amount of substance left to be absorbed decreases.

*First order process*

Equation 6.1 shows that the rate at which the substance disappears from the gastrointestinal tract is linearly dependent on the quantity of the substance left behind at time t, i.e. a first order process. In mathematical terms, the exponent of the function is 1.

Some processes are independent of the quantity of the drug. Examples are the absorption of a drug from a slow-release preparation, or a slow intravenous infusion of a drug. These processes are described as *zero order* (see also Study unit 5, section 3). The term zero-order is used because in mathematical terms the exponent of the function is zero; that is to say, the change in quantity of the drug with time is independent of the quantity.

*Zero order process*

Thus, a process for which the rate is proportional to the amount present follows first-order kinetics.

It is physically impossible to determine the *change in the amount of a substance* at a certain time ($dD_{GI}/dt$), but it is possible to determine the amount of the substance at a certain time($D_{GI}$). Integration of Equation 6.1 ($t$ between $t = 0$ and $t$) gives:

$$D_{GI} = D_0\, e^{-k_A \cdot t} \qquad (6.2)$$

where $D_0$ = the dose administered (expressed in, for example, mg).

The paramaters $D_{GI}$ and $D_0$ can be measured. If $D_A$ is the amount of the substance taken up into the body at time $t$ after the administration of $D_0$, $D_{GI}$ can be replaced by $D_0 - D_A$. In words: the amount present in the gastrointestinal tract at time $t$ is the difference between the original amount ($D_0$) and the amount that has been absorbed ($D_A$).

Substituting $D_{GI}$ in equation 6.2 by $D_0 - D_A$ yields:

$$D_A = D_0\,(1 - e^{-k_A \cdot t}) \qquad (6.3)$$

Whereas absorption is usually fast for substances administered parenterally, there can be considerable delays for orally administered chemicals. Food interferes with absorption, probably by a combination of binding, increased enzyme activity and competition for uptake sites. A major problem with orally administered drugs is their metabolism by the (gastro)intestinal microflora, and in the gastrointestinal mucosa and the liver.

The derivation of Equations 6.2 and 6.3 is based on the assumption that all of the substance administered ($D_0$) is taken up and that the absorption process starts immediately at $t = 0$. As stated earlier, in reality, this is never the case.

*Lag time*

A more accurate approach can be achieved by adding two other parameters: the *bioavailability*, $F$ (the fraction of the dose that has actually entered the circulation), and the *lag time*, $t_0$ (the time between the moment of administration and the moment at which absorption starts).

If Equation 6.1 is integrated between $FD_0$ and $D_{GI}$ on the one hand and $t_0$ and $t$ on the other, instead of between $D_0$ and $D_{GI}$ and 0 and $t$, then Equation 6.2 becomes:

$$D_{GI} = FD_0 \, e^{-k_A(t-t_0)} \qquad (6.4)$$

while 6.3 becomes:

$$D_A = FD_0 \, (1 - e^{-k_A(t-t_0)}) \qquad (6.5)$$

Section 3 of Study unit 5 describes various factors that determine the efficiency of absorption. The relationships represented by Equations 6.4 and 6.5 clearly show via which parameters these factors exert their influence. The absorption rate, and hence $k_A$, is determined by the rate at which a substance is released from the form in which it was ingested, by the extent to which it is adsorbed to the food, and by the motility of the gastrointestinal tract.

*First-pass effect*

The bioavailability $F$ is determined by, among other factors, the *first-pass effect*. There is a first-pass effect if a substance undergoes metabolic elimination during its first passage through the liver, before it reaches the blood circulation.

ASSIGNMENT   6.3

How could a first-pass effect be detected, assuming that all of the substance is taken up into the portal vein?

## 1.2   CLEARANCE

Elimination (see Study unit 5) is the removal of xenobiotics from the body, including excretion and biotransformation. The two organs that are particularly important in the elimination of drugs are the liver and the kidney.

*Elimination rate*

The *elimination rate* is the amount of a substance removed (from the circulation) per unit of time. Elimination also has a model-independent aspect, the so-called clearance ($Cl$).

*Clearance has the dimension volume per unit of time*

Clearance is the volume of plasma ($V_{C(irculation)}$) from which all of the (toxic) substance is removed within a specific period via excretion, metabolism or a combination of these processes. The amount of a substance removed from the circulation per unit of time, the elimination rate, is reduced in each successive unit of time. As a consequence also the concentration of the substance in the plasma is reduced proportionally. The clearance ($Cl$), however, is constant and formulated as follows:

$$\frac{\text{elimination rate}\,(\mu g\ min^{-1})}{\text{plasma concentration}\,(\mu g\ ml^{-1})} = Cl\,(ml\ min^{-1}) \qquad (6.6)$$

EXAMPLE 6-1

The following example may illustrate the concept of clearance: Imagine an organism with a volume of 100 ml in which there is initially 100 mg of a substance X. Suppose the elimination processes in the organs through which the plasma circulates completely remove the substance from 10 ml of this volume every minute. The following table shows the minute-by-minute changes that occur:

TABLE 6.1
Effect of a constant clearance on substance elimination rate

| Time | Concentration | Clearance | Drug eliminated |
|------|--------------|-----------|-----------------|
| $t = 0$ | 100 mg 100 ml$^{-1}$ | 10 ml min$^{-1}$ | 10 mg |
| $t = 1$ min | 90 mg 100 ml$^{-1}$ | 10 ml min$^{-1}$ | 9 mg |
| $t = 2$ min | 81 mg 100 ml$^{-1}$ | 10 ml min$^{-1}$ | 8.1 mg |
| $t = 3$ min | 72.9 mg 100 ml$^{-1}$ | 10 ml min$^{-1}$ | 7.29 mg |
| etcetera | | | |

In this example the clearance is constant (10 ml min$^{-1}$), whereas the amount of the substance eliminated is reduced in each successive minute. In reality, the drug is not removed discretely from part of the volume but the kinetics can be described as though it were.

Because biotransformation mainly occurs in the liver, metabolic clearance is often referred to as hepatic clearance

Clearance is an additive parameter: the total clearance ($Cl_{tot}$) is the sum of the renal ($Cl_r$), metabolic ($Cl_m$) and other possible routes. This can be explained as follows. Elimination is the resultant of a number of processes: renal excretion, biotransformation, fecal excretion (usually resulting from excretion in the bile), excretion via the lungs, etc. This yields:

$$Cl_{tot} = \frac{\text{elimination rate}}{\text{plasma concentration}} = \frac{\text{rate of elimination by renal excretion}}{\text{plasma concentration}}(Cl_r)$$
$$+ \frac{\text{rate of elimination by hepatic metabolism}}{\text{plasma concentration}}(Cl_m) + \cdots \quad (6.7)$$

Needless to say, it is crucial for the protection of an organism against toxic substances that the eliminating (clearing) organs function as efficiently as possible. For instance, toxic substances that can only be excreted via the kidneys will induce their effects more readily in patients with reduced renal function than in healthy patients.

## 2 Model-dependent approach to toxicokinetic behavior

The compartment model can be used to describe the changes in blood concentration, in the amounts excreted in the urine and feces, and in tissue concentrations.

Often it is difficult to grasp the concept of a compartment. In reality, the body is composed of a very large number of compartments. In a sense, each cell is a small compartment. However, in kinetics, a compartment refers to those organs and tissues for which the rates of uptake and subsequent clearance of a drug are similar. Once more, it should be emphasized that the number and size of the compartments are determined by the perfusion of the tissues and the organs and by the physicochemical properties of the toxic substance concerned. Usually, number and size of compartments do not relate to functional structures of the organism. It is important to realize that the concept of a compartment does not imply that the concentration of the toxic substance concerned is the same throughout the compartment.

**Constant ratios between the concentrations of a substance in the various parts of the same compartment**

The various parts of a compartment should meet the following criterion: the *ratios between the concentrations* in the various parts have to be constant, that is, they should not be affected by increases (as a result of administration) or decreases (as a result of elimination) in the total content.

The description of toxicokinetic models in this study unit is restricted to one-compartment and two-compartment models. These are widely used. Unless explicitly stated otherwise, the processes concerned are linear. Non-linear kinetics and the kinetics of irreversible interactions are discussed in sections 4 and 5.

## 2.1 ONE-COMPARTMENT MODEL

The one-compartment model in pharmacokinetics is characterized by the underlying assumption that the substance is distributed instantaneously over the body and subsequently readily exchanged between the circulation and the tissues and organs. The classification used in the following description is based on intravenous or oral administration of a drug.

### 2.1.1 Intravenous administration

Intravenous administration means direct introduction of a dose ($D_0$) into the circulation (the single compartment). In that situation, the toxicokinetic calculations assume the amount of a substance in the circulation at $t = 0$ to be $D_0$. Elimination of the substance starts with excretion and metabolism right from the moment of administration. This is represented schematically in Figure 6.1.

In what respect does $D_B$ in Figure 6.1 differ from the parameter $D_A$ mentioned in section 1.1?

Parameter $D_A$ mentioned in section 1.1 represents the total amount of substance that has been absorbed at time $t$; $D_B$, is the amount of substance that is (still) present in the body at time $t$. In the latter situation it is possible that some of the injected drug has already been eliminated. The rate at which a substance disappears from the (one) compartment, the *elimination rate*, $dD_B / dt$, can be described as the rate of a chemical process with first-order kinetics:

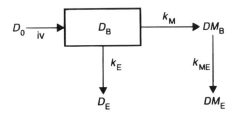

FIGURE   6.1

Graphical representation of the fate of a substance after intravenous administration in the case of a one-compartment model

$D_B$ = amount of the toxic substance present in the body (B) at time $t$ after administration

$D_E$ = amount of intact toxic substance excreted in the urine (Excretion) at time $t$ after administration

$DM_B$ = amount of metabolite (M) of a toxic substance at time $t$ after administration

$DM_E$ = amount of metabolite excreted in the urine

$k_E$ = excretion rate constant

$k_M$ = metabolic rate constant

$k_{ME}$ = rate constant for the excretion of the metabolite

$$\frac{dD_B}{dt} = -(k_E + k_M)D_B = -kD_B \tag{6.8}$$

where $k$ = elimination rate constant (= $k_E + k_M$)

The negative sign indicates that $D_B$ decreases with time. It is physically impossible to determine the elimination rate. Integration of Equation 6.8 between $D = D_0$ for $t = 0$ and $D = D_B$ for $t = t$, yields:

$$D_B = D_0\, e^{-k \cdot t} \tag{6.9}$$

*Volume of distribution*

Usually, a plasma, serum, or whole blood concentration of the drug is measured, while the above equation describes the total amount of drug in the body. Therefore, the concept of *volume of distribution* ($V_D$) has to be introduced to account for this.

Since in a one-compartment model the ratio between tissue concentration and blood concentration is constant for each tissue (see Assignment 6.4, section 2), the amount in the body will be proportional to the blood concentration ($C_C$):

$$D_B = V_D\, C_C \tag{6.10}$$

*Factor* $V_D$ can be regarded as the volume of body fluids over which $D_B$ should have been distributed in order to achieve concentration $C_C$. It should be appreciated that this volume of distribution is an *apparent volume*, i.e. it does not necessarily literally reflect a volume of fluid in which the drug is dissolved. It includes, for example, tissues in which the drug, although in equilibrium with plasma, is more highly concentrated than in the plasma. If the substance readily binds to protein, $C_C$ will only represent a small fraction of $D_B$, and $V_D$ will then be relatively large. This explains why the reported volume of distribution often exceeds the total volume of the body. Nevertheless, the volume of distribution of a drug often provides interesting information.

Substitution of $D_B$ by $V_D \cdot C_C$ in Equation 6.9 results in a description of the blood concentration as a function of time:

$$C_C = \frac{D_0}{V_D} e^{-k \cdot t} \tag{6.11}$$

*A bolus is a single dose; i.v. = intravenous*

where $D_0 / V_D$ is the blood concentration at $t = 0$ ($C_0$) and $C_0$ is the theoretical initial plasma concentration at time $t_0$ after a bolus i.v. dose.

When $C_C$ is plotted against time, as in Figure 6.2, the resulting curve is exponential. This is because the rate of removal is proportional to the concentration remaining. This is a first-order process and hence a constant fraction of the substance is excreted at any given time.

*The conversion from natural logarithms to logarithms to the base of 10 in Equation 6.12 is obtained from the simple relationship that $\ln X = 2.303 \log X$.*

If, instead of $C_C \ln C_C$ is plotted against time, the curve changes to a straight line. Because logarithmic graph paper is printed to base 10, it is more convenient to use logarithms to base 10. Equation 6.11 can be rewritten as:

$$\ln C_C = \ln C_0 - k.t$$

or

$$\log C_C = \log C_0 - k.t \log e = \log C_0 - \frac{k.t}{2.303} \tag{6.12}$$

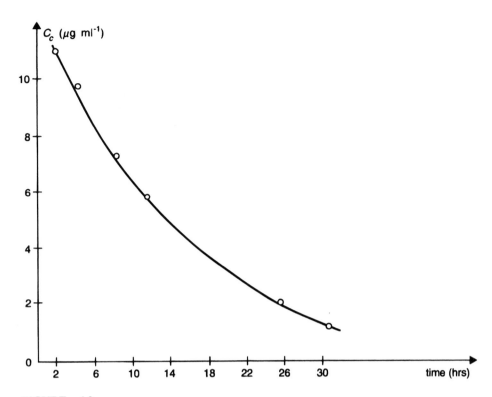

FIGURE 6.2
Blood concentration-time curve after intravenous administration of 600 mg of the antipyretic agent antipyrine, in a linear plot

where $C_C$ is plasma concentration, $t$ is time, $C_0$ is the intercept on the $y$-axis and $-k.t/2.303$ the gradient or slope.

ASSIGNMENT 6.4

Determine $C_0$ and $V_D$ for Figure 6.2 as well as for Figure 6.3. Assume that $D_0 = 600$ mg.
Which figure allows the most accurate calculation of the parameters? Explain your answer.

The linear plot in Figure 6.3 allows easy extrapolation of the straight line to obtain the concentration at time zero ($C_0$). This theoretical concentration can not be measured by sampling. Although it is theoretically assumed, in practice mixing of the drug is not instantaneous.

The kinetics of the overall process of elimination are first order because the processes governing it (excretion by various routes and metabolism) are irreversible processes and are first order themselves. The elimination process is represented by the *elimination rate constant k*, which may be determined from the slope of the plasma profile. The elimination rate constant represents the fractional loss of drug from the body.

This equation may be deduced from Equation 6.8 by dividing by $V_D$
The elimination rate constant can be calculated by using Equation 6.13 and measuring the drug blood concentrations at various times.

$$k = \frac{\text{amount of drug eliminated in unit time}}{\text{amount of drug in the body}}$$

$$\text{Mathematically}: k = \left(\frac{dC}{dt}\right)/C \tag{6.13}$$

145

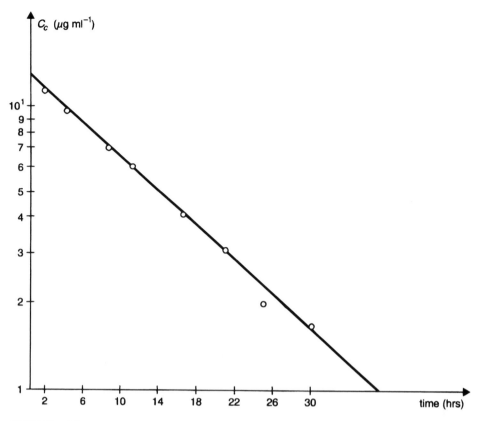

FIGURE 6.3
Blood concentration-time curve after intravenous administration of 600 mg of the antipyretic agent antipyrine, in a semi-logarithmic plot

It is clear from Figure 6.1 that the elimination rate constant $k$ is a composite parameter. In fact, it encompasses all routes of elimination (excretion in urine, feces, biotransformation and sequestration in tissues not sampled). $k$ in Equations 6.12 and 6.13 represents the first-order constants of different processes. When elimination involves several routes, including various pathways of metabolism, $k$ includes the first-order constant of each process ($k_{E1}$, $k_{M1}$ + $k_{M2}$. . . .).

Theoretically, exponential elimination is never complete. Therefore, it is more convenient to measure the biological half-life of the substance ($t_{1/2}$).

*half-life; half-time*    The *half-time*, or *half-life*, is the time interval during which the concentration of a substance is reduced by half. From Equation 6.12 it follows that:

$$\log (C_C / C_0) = -k t_{1/2} / 2.303$$

At $t_{1/2}$ : $C = C_0 / 2$

Thus : $\log (1/2) = -0.301 = -k\, t_{1/2} / 2.303$ and $k = 0.693 / t_{1/2}$    (6.14)

Starting from Equation 6.14, the following equation can be deduced for $t_{1/2}$:

146

$$t_{1/2} = \frac{0.693}{k} \hspace{3cm} (6.15)$$

EXAMPLE 6-2

100 mg of a substance is injected intravenously and the plasma concentration (in mg l$^{-1}$) is determined repeatedly. The logarithms of the concentrations are plotted against time. This results in a straight line with a slope of –0.0751 and, after extrapolation, an intercept of 1.30.

The shape of the graph shows that the processes involved fit a one-compartment model. This is important for chosing the formulae to be used. Hence:

$$k = -2.303(-0.0751) = 0.173h^{-1} \text{ and}$$
$$C_0 = 10^{1.30}(= \text{antilog } 1.30) = 20 \text{ mg l}^{-1}$$

This allows calculation of the half-life of elimination:

$$t_{1/2} = \frac{0.693}{0.173} = 4.0 \text{ h,}$$

as well as the distribution volume

$$V_D = \frac{100}{20} = 5.0 \text{ l.}$$

A half-life of 4 hours means that 4 hours after the injection of 100 mg of the substance, 50 mg is still present in the plasma (and in the tissues that are in equilibrium with the plasma). For a distribution volume of 5 litres, this means that concentrations of 20, 10, 5 and 2.5 mg l$^{-1}$ are found at, respectively, 0, 4, 8 and 12 hours after the injection.

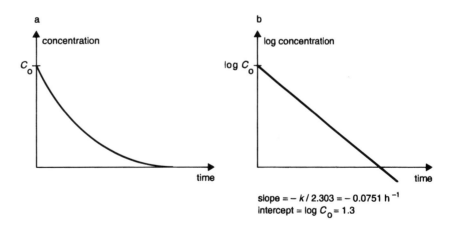

FIGURE   6.4
Time dependence of the blood concentration of a substance after intravenous administration
*a* linear representation
*b* logarithmic representation

ASSIGNMENT 6.5

Calculate $t_{1/2}$ in the antipyrine example both on the basis of the definition of half-life (Figure 6.2) and on the basis of the relationship with the elimination rate constant (Figure 6.3). Compare the results.

*Clearance*

The *clearance*, as defined in section 1.2 (Equation 6.6) can be calculated in two ways:

a   by using the elimination rate constant $k$ and the apparent volume of distribution $V_D$;

b   by using the so-called area under the curve, without knowing the values of $k$ and $V_D$.

Method $a$ can easily be demonstrated by combining the equation for the definition of clearance (Equation 6.6), the equation for the rate at which a substance disappears from the compartment (Equation 6.8) and the equation for the relationship between the amount in the body tissues and in the blood (Equation 6.10):

$$Cl = \frac{-\dfrac{dD_B}{dt}}{C_c} = \frac{kD_B}{C_c} = kV_D \qquad (6.16)$$

ASSIGNMENT 6.6

Calculate the clearance for antipyrine in Figure 6.3 using Equation 6.16. You can make use of the data obtained in Assignments 6.4 and 6.5.

*Area under the curve*

Consider a typical plasma concentration-time curve like the one in Figure 6.2. It is to be expected that clearance of the substance is closely related to the size or area of the concentration against time plot. The hatched areas in Figure 6.5 are known as the *areas under the curves* or AUCs. The greater the clearance, the smaller the area. Measurement of the AUC can be used for estimating the clearance of the substance involved.

The mathematical method $b$ involves solving the differential Equation 6.16:

$$D_0 = Cl \int_0^\infty C_c \, dt = Cl \cdot \text{area under the blood concentration-time curve}$$
$$(Area\ Under\ the\ Curve) = Cl \cdot AUC$$

or

$$Cl = \frac{D_0}{AUC} \qquad (6.17)$$

Method $b$ determines the amount of substance removed from the body over a certain period of time by integrating the plasma concentration over that period. This boils down to determine the area under the plasma concentration-time curve. The curve used for this purpose is the linear and not the semilogarithmic plot.

Appendix A briefly describes how the AUC can be calculated

The $AUC$ is expressed in mg h$^{-1}$ and can be determined in various ways, for example by means of the trapezoidal rule.

ASSIGNMENT 6.7

Calculate the clearance for antipyrine in Figure 6.2 using Equation 6.17.

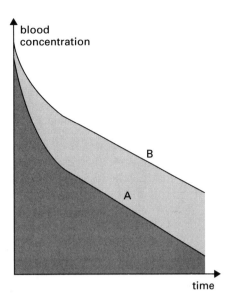

FIGURE   6.5
Plasma concentration curves of two intravenously injected substances A and B with different plasma clearance values ($Cl_A > Cl_B$)
The injected doses of both substances were the same. Note that the area under the curve of substance B is bigger than that of substance A.

Determining $k$ and $t_{1/2}$ requires a series of *blood* concentration data. Determining separate elemination rate constants (e.g. $k_E$ and $k_M$) requires samples of the *excreta* to be taken.

### 2.1.2 Oral administration

The absorption of many substances after oral administration follows first-order kinetics, and the toxicokinetic behavior can be described by a one-compartment model.

As was already discussed in Study unit 5, a wide variety of factors can influence the absorption of substances from the gastrointestinal tract (dissociation of the substance, the amount of food in the stomach, etc.). It is therefore surprising that in most cases this first-order approach provides a good approximation of the absorption process and that it often allows quite an accurate description of the facts. Figure 6.6 shows a schematic representation of the model.

The changes in the amount of substance in the body ($D_B$) are given by the following equation:

$$\frac{dD_B}{dt} = k_A D_{GI} - k D_B \tag{6.18}$$

At the same time, however, the bioavailability must be taken into account. $D_{GI}$ is therefore substituted by $FD_0 e^{-k_A(t - t_0)}$ (see Equation 6.4).

If, furthermore, $V_D \cdot C_C$ (see equation 6.10) is substituted for $D_B$, then Equation 6.18 becomes:

$$\frac{dC_c}{dt} = \frac{FD_0}{V_D} k_A e^{-k_A(t-t_0)} - kC_c \tag{6.19}$$

Integration yields:

$$C_c = \frac{FD_0}{V_D} \cdot \frac{k_A}{k_A - k} (e^{-k(t-t_0)} - e^{-k_A(t-t_0)}) \tag{6.20}$$

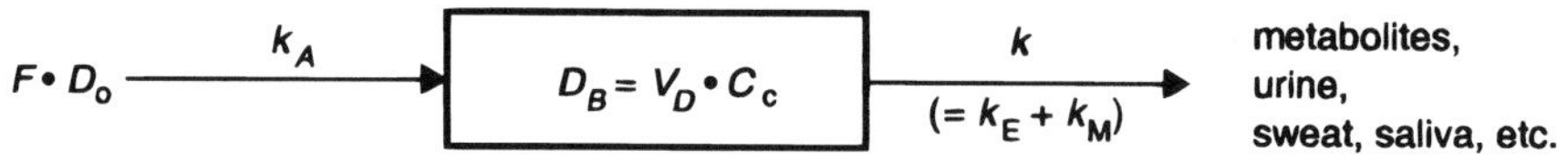

FIGURE 6.6

One-compartment model with first-order absorption

$F$ is the fraction of the amount administered ($D_0$) which has been absorbed, $k_A$ the rate constant for absorption, $D_B$ the amount of the toxic substance in the body at time $t$ after administration, $V_D$ the apparent volume of distribution, $C_C$ the plasma concentration at time $t$ and $k$ the elimination rate constant.

*For the integration of Equation 6.19 into 6.20 see Appendix B*

Equation 6.20 gives the changes in plasma concentration for a one-compartment model, after oral administration.

If the concentration is plotted logarithmically against time, the following curve is obtained:

Now that the kinetic parameters for a one-compartment model with first-order absorption have been introduced, the next step is to determine how the numerical values of these parameters can influence the concentration profiles. For that purpose, a closer look will be taken at the ratio of the *absorption rate constant $k_A$* and the *elimination rate constant $k$*. There are three possible situations:

1  $k_A > k$

2  $k_A < k$

3  $k_A = k$.

For most substances situation 1 applies. In the case of substances with a biological half-life of $\leq 1$ hour, the elimination rate constant may sometimes be larger than the absorption rate constant. If the drug is detectable in the blood after oral administration, then $k_A > k$. In this study unit, only the latter situation will be discussed. The difference between $e^{-k(t-t_0)}$ and $e^{-k_A(t-t_0)}$ will increase as $t$ increases, with the ultimate result that $e^{-k_A(t-t_0)}$ becomes negligible with respect to $e^{-k(t-t_0)}$. For high values of $t$, the relationship between concentration and time will therefore be:

$$C_c = \frac{F D_0}{V_D} \cdot \frac{k_A}{k_A - k} e^{-k(t-t_0)} \tag{6.21}$$

Taking the logarithm of both sides of Equation 6.21 yields the following equation for the final part of the curve (Figure 6.7), for $t_0 = 0$:

$$\log C_c = \log \frac{F D_0}{V_D} \cdot \frac{k_A}{k_A - k} - \frac{k}{2.3} \cdot t \tag{6.22}$$

Equation 6.22 represents the linear relationship between the logarithm of $C_C$ and time. The slope of the line is $-k/2.3$ and the intercept is:

$$\log \frac{F D_0}{V_D} \cdot \frac{k_A}{k_A - k}$$

This line is drawn in Figure 6.7.

*Method of residuals*

The absorption rate constant $k_A$ is calculated by means of the so-called *method of residuals*. In this method, the concentrations found by applying Equation 6.20 are subtracted from those found using Equation 6.21, and the 'residual' concentrations are plotted logarithmically against time. This is represented by equation 6.23 and graphically in Figure 6.8.

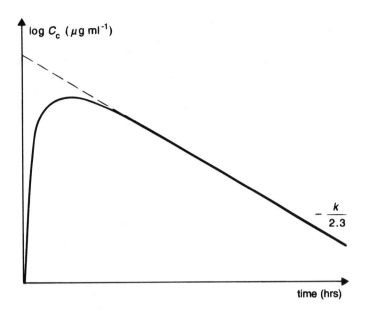

FIGURE   6.7
Blood concentration-time curve for a one-compartment model, after oral administration, in a semilogarithmic plot

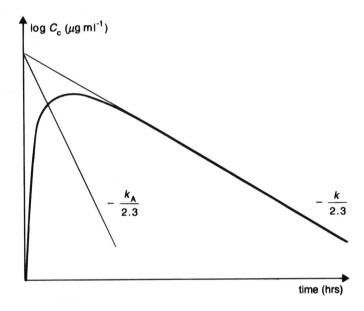

FIGURE   6.8
Result of the application of the method of residuals for calculating the absorption rate constant $k_A$
The thin line on the left connects the residual values.

The straight line with slope $-k_A/2.3$ in Figure 6.8 is given by:

$$\log C_c = \log \frac{F D_0}{V_D} \cdot \frac{k_A}{k_A - k} - \frac{k_A}{2.3} \cdot t \tag{6.23}$$

Equation 6.23 clearly shows great similarity to Equation 6.22: the two lines have the same intercept. In Equation 6.23, however, the slope of the line is $-k_A/2.3$, while it is $-k/2.3$ in Equation 6.22.

Toxicologically, there are a number of other important kinetic parameters: the maximum plasma concentration ($C_{max}$) and the point in time at which this peak concentration is achieved ($t_{max}$). The slope of the tangent line changes direction at that point. The formulae for $t_{max}$ and $C_{max}$ are, respectively:

$$t_{max} = 2.3 \frac{\log k_A - \log k}{k_A - k} \tag{6.24}$$

and:

$$C_{max} = \frac{F D_0}{V_D} \left( \frac{k_A}{k} \right)^{k/k - k_A} \tag{6.25}$$

### ASSIGNMENT 6.8

From a toxicological point of view, it may be important to know at what time after the entry of a substance the maximum concentration is reached and what the magnitude of this concentration is. Indicate how the formulae for both parameters can be deduced.

For the deduction of Equations 6.24 and 6.25, see the answer to Assignment 6.8. Equation 6.25 clearly differs from Equation 6.24. The main difference is that Equation 6.25 contains a concentration factor $F D_0 / V_D$ in addition to the rate constants. From a practical point of view, this means that $t_{max}$, unlike $C_{max}$, does not depend on the plasma concentration. The value of $t_{max}$ is reciprocally proportional to the absorption and elimination rate constants, while the value of $C_{max}$ is proportional to $k_A$ and reciprocally proportional to $k$.

Intuitively, this can be explained as follows: a lower absorption rate constant results in a flatter curve and hence in a lower value for $C_{max}$. A lower elimination rate constant, however, allows high plasma concentrations to be achieved during the absorption phase, which leads to a higher $C_{max}$.

If $k$, $k_A$ and the biological availability $F$ are known, then the distribution volume $V_D$ can be calculated from the intercept ($\log F D_0 / V_D \cdot k_A / k_A - k$) in Equation 6.23.

$F$ can be determined by comparing oral administration with intravenous administration. $Cl$ being a constant, Equation 6.17 can be rewritten as follows:

$$Cl = \frac{D_{0\ i.v.}}{AUC_{i.v.}} = \frac{D_{0\ p.o.}}{AUC_{p.o.}} \cdot F \tag{6.26}$$

in which i.v. refers to intravenous administration and p.o. (= per os) to oral administration.

Rearrangement of Equation 6.26 yields:

$$F = \frac{D_{0\ i.v.}}{AUC_{i.v.}} \cdot \frac{AUC_{p.o.}}{D_{0\ p.o.}} \tag{6.27}$$

### ASSIGNMENT 6.9

When does this relationship not apply? Explain your answer.

### ASSIGNMENT 6.10

Deduce the following equation for $F$ without using the equations for $Cl$:

$$F = \frac{k V_D}{D_0} AUC \qquad (6.28)$$

Sometimes, a substance or its metabolites are *exclusively* excreted in the urine. In that case the bioavailability of the substance after oral administration can also be determined by comparing the amounts of the substance excreted in the urine after oral and intravenous administration. This is only true, however, for linear kinetics (see Assignment 6.9).

*Summary*

In kinetics, the body is assumed to consist of one or more compartments over which a substance is distributed simultaneously. The simplest model is the one-compartment model. In this model, the body is considered as a single, kinetically homogenous unit. This model assumes that an equilibrium is rapidly established between the accessible tissues and organs, which means that the distribution is relatively rapid with respect to absorption and elimination processes.

After an intravenous bolus injection, the plasma profile (changes in the concentration with time) can be used to calculate the elimination rate constant, the half-life, the volume of distribution and the clearance. The area under the plasma concentration-time curve (*AUC*) can be determined analytically or calculated by means of the trapezoidal rule. This *AUC* can (if necessary after correction for the elimination rate constant) be used to determine the efficiency of the absorption. Although the gastrointestinal absorption of substances into the circulation is a complicated process, it can often be treated as a first-order process for practical purposes. For a correct interpretation of the concentration-time profiles, it is important to know the relative value of the absorption rate constant, which may be larger than, smaller than, or equal to the elimination rate constant. The absorption rate constant can be estimated by means of the method of the residuals.

### 2.2 TWO-COMPARTMENT MODEL

When the body is considered as a single compartment, the toxicokinetics are relatively simple. When considering distribution, elimination and effect of substances, there are situations when it is more appropriate to conceptualize the body as two, and, occasionally, more than two compartments.

*More-compartment models*

*More-compartment models* help to illustrate non-uniform rates of distribution of chemicals throughout the body. The majority of exogenous substances, when administered by rapid intravenous injection, behave as though the body consisted of at least two compartments.

*Two-compartment models*

The *two-compartment model* is useful in situations in which the body can be described as being composed of two compartments, one in which the substance spreads instantaneously, and the other over which the substance is distributed more slowly.

*Central and peripheral compartment*

According to this model, the body consists of a *"central"* and a *"peripheral"* compartment, each with its own apparent volume of distribution. The total volume of distribution of the substance is equal to the sum of the individual volumes. The compartments are often given anatomic designations, such as the "plasma" and "tissue" compartments, respectively. In many cases, the central compartment may roughly correspond to the vascular system together with rapidly perfused lean tissues such as the liver, lung, heart, kidneys and the endocrine organs, while the peripheral compartment comprises body fat together with poorly perfused lean tissues like skin and muscle. However, these anatomic and physiologic correlations should be accepted only with caution.

Figure 6.9 gives a schematic representation of the two-compartment model in the case of intravenous administration of a dose $D_0$ with elimination from the central compartment.

In this model it is assumed that substances enter, and are eliminated from, the central compartment. Elimination occurs from the central compartment only, so that substances in the peripheral compartment must be transported back to the central compartment to be eliminated.

The sequence of events in a two-compartment model can be described as follows. After the substance is initially introduced into the central compartment by intravenous bolus injection, initial, rapid distribution over the first compartment takes place. Simultaneously, the substance starts to disperse into the less accessible and more slowly equilibrating tissues and fluids that constitute the second compartment. Of course, at the same time a proportion of the substance has already been eliminated from the central compartment. During the early postdose period, there is a rapid net loss of the substance from the central compartment and a rapid decline in plasma concentration. Figure 6.10 gives a graphical representation of the course of the concentration of an intravenously injected substance in the central compartment (I) as well as in the peripheral compartment (II). For purposes of clarity and for the reasons discussed in section 2.1.1 the (vertical) concentration axis is logarithmic.

> Which processes contribute to the rapid decline in plasma concentration during the early period?

The processes that contribute to the rapid decline in plasma concentration in the phase directly following the intravenous bolus injection are: irreversible elimination from the central compartment (mainly excretion and metabolism) and uptake by the tissues and fluids in the second compartment. This period of rapidly falling plasma concentrations due to the combined effects of tissue uptake and elimination is called the $\alpha$-phase. After a certain period of time, depending on the magnitude of the rate constants between the central and peripheral compartments, $k_{CT}$ and $k_{TC}$ in Figure 6.9, a steady state is reached in the distribution of the substance over the various tissues and fluids. Net loss of the substance from the central compartment due to distribution will no longer occur.

Once a steady state is reached between the central and peripheral compartments, the rate of loss from the bloodstream is reduced. This period of slowly declining blood levels is known as the $\beta$-phase. Figure 6.10 I shows the rapid

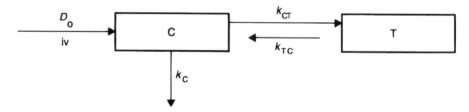

FIGURE 6.9

Schematic representation of the fate of an intravenously administered substance, after distribution over two compartments

C = central compartment (circulation and, for example, well-perfused organs such as the liver and the kidney)
T = peripheral compartment (less well-perfused tissues, such as adipose tissue and muscles)
$k_{CT}$ = the rate constant for the transport from C to T
$k_{TC}$ = the rate constant for the transport from T to C
$k_C$ = the rate constant for elimination from the central compartment C

154

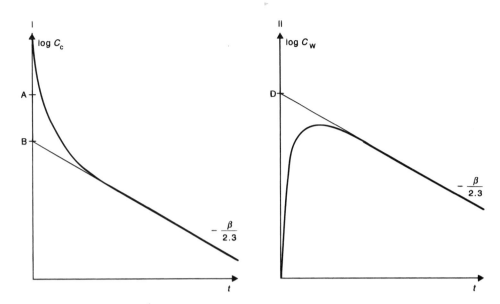

FIGURE   6.10
Biphasic decay pattern of a substance intravenously administered into the central compartment, both in the central compartment (I) and in the tissue compartment (II).

decline of the concentrations during the $\alpha$-phase and the relatively slow decline during the $\beta$–phase.

After a single intravenous bolus dose into a two-compartment system, the plasma concentration ($C_C$) at time $t$ may be described by:

$$C_C = Ae^{-\alpha t} + Be^{-\beta t} \tag{6.29}$$

where $A$ and $B$ may be regarded as analogous to $C_0$ for each compartment, so $A + B = C_0$. In the equation $\alpha$ and $\beta$ are hybrid constants, each influenced by all the individual distribution, redistribution, and elimination rate constants, i.e. $k_{CT}$, $k_{TC}$ and $k_C$, such that $\alpha$ mainly refers to distribution and $\beta$ to elimination.

The concentration-time curve for the second compartment may be described by Equation 6.30:

$$C_T = D(e^{-\beta t} - e^{-\alpha t}) \tag{6.30}$$

A semilogarithmic representation of this relationship is shown in Figure 6.10 II.

*Important parameters in a two-compartment model*

Using the plasma concentration-time curve in Figure 6.10 I, it is possible to calculate several important kinetic variables, e.g. the volumes of the mathematical compartments, half-life of elimination and clearance. In Figure 6.10 I two slopes can be distinguished: the first slope is mainly related to the distribution of the drug from the central to the peripheral compartment, and the second slope largely represents the elimination of the substance from the central compartment. The hybrid rate constant $\beta$ can be calculated from the slope of the linear terminal part of the curve.

*Apparent volumes of distribution*

The zero-time intercept $B$ represents the apparent concentration if the drug has been distributed instantaneously throughout the central and peripheral compartments. Therefore, an apparent volume of distribution ($V_D$) can be calculated.

$$V_D = D_0 / B \tag{6.31}$$

155

$V_D$ represents the total apparent volume of distribution, which is the sum of the volumes of the central ($V_C$) and peripheral ($V_{T(issue)}$) compartment together!

Similar to the determination of absorption rate constants (Figure 6.8), the method of the residuals may be used to determine another hybrid rate constant, $\alpha$ (see Figure 6.11).

The hybrid rate constant $\alpha$ may be calculated from the slope of the line, obtained by applying the method of the residuals.

$$\text{slope} = -\alpha / 2.303 \quad \text{or} \quad \alpha = -2.303 \times \text{slope} \qquad (6.32)$$

The intercept value of the calculated line gives $A$. If intercept $A$ is added to intercept $B$, $C_0$ is obtained; $(A + B = C_0)$. $C_0$ is the theoretical concentration of the substance in plasma at time zero. If $A$ and $B$ are known, the volume of the central compartment, i.e. the volume into which the drug is initially introduced can be calculated:

$$V_C = \frac{D_0}{A + B} \qquad (6.33)$$

*Biological half-life*

In the same way as for the one-compartment model (see section 2.1.1) the *biological half-life* ($t_{1/2}$ or $t_{1/2\beta}$) of the substance can be calculated using the following equation:

$$\textit{Biological half-life } (t_{1/2\beta}) = \ln 2\beta = 0.693 / \beta \qquad (6.34)$$

*Clearance*

Plasma clearance is an important parameter to measure an animal's ability to excrete and eliminate a xenobiotic. In the discussion on the one-compartment model, it was found that plasma clearance equals the (intravenous) dose divided by the area under the drug concentration-time curve from zero to infinity. The same situation occurs in the two-compartment model. Thus the equation for clearance is:

$$Cl = D_0 / AUC_{0 \to \infty} \qquad (6.35)$$

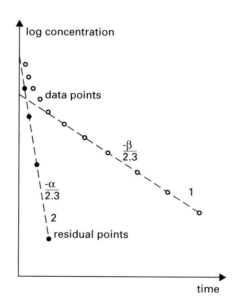

FIGURE 6.11
Log plasma concentration versus time plot after applying the method of residuals.

The area under the curve from zero to infinity can be expressed in mathematical terms by integrating Equation 6.29 between the limits of zero and infinite time. As far as clearance is concerned, this can be calculated from Equation 6.17. The $AUC$ can be obtained by:

$$AUC_{0 \to \infty} = D_0 / V_C \qquad (6.36)$$

In a two-compartment model, the substance concerned undergoes three important disappearance processes, as is shown in Figure 6.9:

- disappearance from the body ($k_C$) (elimination);

- disappearance from the central compartment into the peripheral compartment ($k_{CT}$) and

- disappearance from the peripheral compartment into the central compartment ($k_{TC}$).

The rate constants $\alpha$ and $\beta$ are hybrid rate constants, from which it is possible to derive $k_C$, $k_{CT}$ and $k_{TC}$ using Equations 6.37–6.40

$$\alpha + \beta = k_C + k_{CT} + k_{TC} \qquad (6.37)$$

$$k_{TC} = (A\beta + B\alpha)/(A + B) \qquad (6.38)$$

$$k_C = \alpha \times \beta / k_{TC} \qquad (6.39)$$

$$k_{CT} = \alpha + \beta - k_{TC} - k_C \qquad (6.40)$$

---

EXAMPLE 6-3

*Orbital puncture is a blood sample taken from the blood vessels in the orbit; the orbit is the bony cavity in which the eye is situated.*

To study the kinetic pattern of hexobarbital, a rat was given an intravenous bolus injection of 75 mg.kg$^{-1}$ body weight. The blood concentrations were determined at several time intervals after taking small blood samples by orbital puncture. The following data were obtained:

TABLE 6.2
Plasma concentrations of hexobarbital after an intravenous injection in a rat

| Time (min after i.v. injection) | Plasma concentration (mg ml$^{-1}$) |
|---|---|
| 1 | 130 |
| 3 | 86 |
| 6 | 60 |
| 10 | 44 |
| 20 | 27 |
| 30 | 18 |
| 40 | 11 |
| 50 | 8 |
| 60 | 5 |

To determine whether the kinetic behavior of hexobarbital can be described by a one- or a two-compartment model, the data were plotted semilogarithmically (see Figure 6.12).

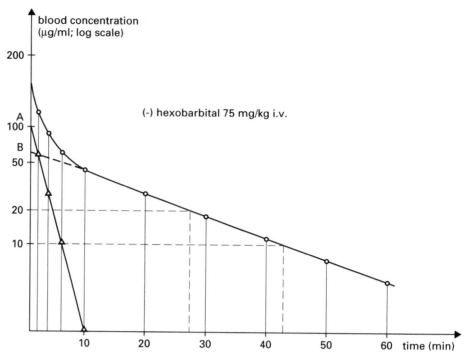

FIGURE 6.12
Graphical representation of the data in Table 6.2

The course of the curve suggests that the pharmacokinetic behavior of hexobarbital can be described by a two-compartment model. The first part of the line is (log-)exponential and the terminal part of the plot is log-linear. From the slope of this straight line, $\beta$ can be calculated:

$$t_{1/2\beta} = 0.693 / \beta$$

Calculation from the graph (linear terminal part) gives $t_{1/2\beta} = 16$ min, and $\beta$.
Extrapolating the terminal part of the plot back to zero time gives: $B = 70$ $\mu g.ml^{-1}$.

The values of $A$ and $\alpha$ are obtained by the method of the residuals. Application of this method gives the values listed in Table 6.3.

The corresponding line is drawn in Figure 6.12 (left).

Extrapolation of this line back to zero gives:

$$A = 100 \; \mu g.ml^{-1}$$

$\alpha$ can be obtained from the slope of the line:

$$t_{1/2\alpha} = -0.693 / \alpha.$$

Calculation gives: $t_{1/2\alpha} = 2$ min (graphical extrapolation), and $\alpha = 0.347$.
The kinetic behavior of hexobarbital can be described completely using Equations 6.37 – 6.40.

By applying the method of residuals, a biexponential curve can be divided into two separate exponential processes. Each of these (corresponding to lines 1

TABLE 6.3

Hypothetic plasma concentrations obtained by the method of the residuals

| Time (min⁻¹) | Plasma concentration μg.ml⁻¹ |
|:---:|:---:|
| 1 | 71 (130 – 59) |
| 3 | 30 (86 – 56) |
| 6 | 12 (60 – 48) |
| 10 | 2 (44 – 423) |

and 2 in Figure 6.11) is represented by a log-linear plot. The area under the curve is:

$$\text{AUC} = \int_0^\infty C_c\,dt = \int_0^\infty Ae^{-\alpha t}dt + \int_0^\infty Be^{-\beta t}dt = \frac{A}{\alpha} + \frac{B}{\beta} \qquad (6.41)$$

This means that in the case of a two-compartment model the $AUC$ is the sum of the individual $AUC$s of the two exponential curves.

For the above example:

$$A/\alpha + B/\beta = 100/2 + 70/0.0433 = 50 + 1628 = 1678 \text{ ml}$$

*Summary*

The one-compartment model does not suffice for a kinetic analysis if the rate at which a chemical spreads from the plasma to another compartment determines the rate at which equilibrium is achieved. Here, the log plasma concentration-time plot is not a straight line. The simplest case is the two-compartment model, in which the plasma concentration ($C_c$)-time curve is represented by the equation:

$$C_C = Ae^{-\alpha t} + Be^{-\beta t}$$

The significance of $A$ and $B$ can be compared to that of $C_0$ for the entire system: $A + B = C_0$. $\alpha$ and $\beta$ are rate constants. Although $\alpha$ relates to the distribution phase and $\beta$ to the elimination phase, they cannot be considered as a true distribution rate constant and a true elimination rate constant, respectively. $A$ and $\alpha$ can be obtained by using the method of the residuals, $B$ by extrapolation of the terminal part of the log concentration-time plot and $\beta$ from the slope of this part of the plot.

## 3    Repeated administration/chronic exposure

Toxic effects resulting from environmental pollutants and substances occurring in the food are often the result of chronic exposure to small amounts. If a substance is repeatedly taken up at intervals shorter than the time necessary for its complete elimination, it will accumulate in the body. Chronic exposure in toxicology resembles the simplest form of drug accumulation in pharmacokinetics: continuous intravenous infusion. Figure 6.13 shows that the situation in which the substance is taken up in very small amounts but at frequent intervals is an approximation to the situation of continuous intravenous infusion.

In both cases, the plasma concentration will rise to a plateau, at which the rate of elimination equals the rate of absorption. In repeated exposure, the rate of accumulation is governed entirely by the size of these very small amounts and their frequency.

In pharmacotherapy continuous intravenous infusion is very rare. More often, drugs are given as discrete doses repeated at specified times. What is the

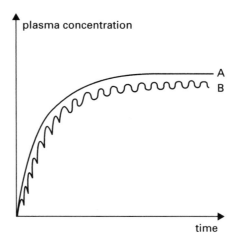

FIGURE   6.13
Plasma-concentration versus time curves of continuous intravenous infusion (graph A) and frequent administration of extremely small amounts (graph B)

resulting shape of the plasma concentration versus time curve in this case? Provided the oral doses are taken up at sufficiently long intervals, they will behave independently, since each dose will have been eliminated by the time the next one is taken up. In reality, the second and subsequent doses of the substance are taken up before the substance already present has been cleared completely (see Figure 6.14).

*Steady state*    At the *steady state*, the rate of entry of a substance into the body exactly equals the rate at which it is being removed by metabolism and excretion. Toxicologically, it is important to be able to recognize accumulation and to indicate how long the consequences of accumulation will last. It is also important to be able to predict when and to what extent accumulation will occur. In principle, it is possible to make such predictions if the toxicokinetic behavior after administration of a single dose of the toxic substance has been fully characterized.

ASSIGNMENT   6.11

Give some examples of accumulation of substances in the body.

The following questions are pertinent to the understanding of the behavior of a toxic substance after repeated uptake:

- what is the extent of accumulation; that is, how much of the substance accumulates in the body and in the blood?
- how long does it take for a steady state to be attained?
- how much interdose fluctuation in blood levels is there, once a steady state is reached?

In chronic exposure, the toxic substance often enters the body via the mouth. Hence, in the following, the kinetic behavior of a toxic substance in chronic exposure will be described on the basis of repeated oral administration of a substance for which the toxicokinetic behavior fits a one-compartment model (Figure 6.14).

Figures 6.13 and 6.14 show that, unless a substance is administered by continuous intravenous infusion, no single plasma concentration value characterizes the steady state condition. This is because plasma levels fluctuate upwards

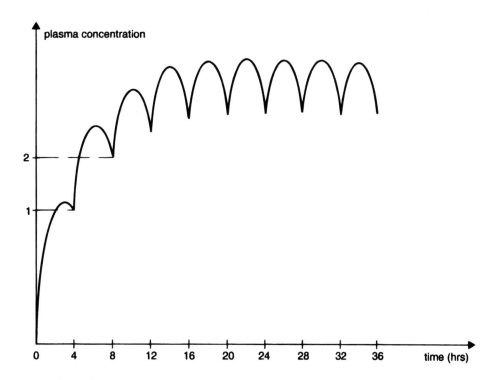

FIGURE   6.14
Blood concentration versus time plot for a one-compartment system, after oral administration of a dose $D_0$ every 4 hours.

After the initiation of treatment with a fixed dose per unit time, accumulation of a substance in the body proceeds until a steady state is reached, at which no further accumulation occurs.

and downwards during the administration interval. The magnitudes of the rise and fall, which are superimposed upon the mean overall increase, depend on the size and frequency of the doses, and on the elimination rate. Nevertheless, after repeated dosing, a plateau concentration, the steady state level, will be reached. The concentration of a substance at any time during an interval in between dosing at steady state ($C_{\infty(t)}$) can be described as:

$$C_{\infty(t)} = De^{-kt}/V_D\left(1-e^{-kT}\right) \qquad (6.42)$$

Where:

> $D$ = maintenance 'dose' at fixed interval
> $T$ = interval time
> $V_D$ = distribution volume
> $k$ = elimination rate constant

It should be emphasized that $D$ is not the amount administered but rather, the amount that is actually absorbed (body burden) and actually reaches the systemic circulation.

Equation 6.42 describes the concentration at any time $t$ during a dosage interval at steady state. If this expression is integrated between the limits $t = 0$ and $t = T$ during a dosage interval at steady state, Equation 6.43 is obtained:

$$\int_0^\tau \frac{De^{-kt}}{V_D(1-e^{-kt})}\,dt = \frac{D}{V_D(1-e^{-kt})}\int_0^\tau e^{-kt}\,dt = \frac{D}{V_Dk} = AUC_{0\to\infty} \qquad (6.43)$$

This expression describes the area under the drug concentration curve during a dosage interval $T$. The equation is identical to the expression for the area under the drug concentration time-curve from zero to infinity following a single dose, provided that the same dose is administered and the kinetics are unchanged during multiple doses. From the size of the single dose and the area under the curve at steady state, the plasma clearance, $Cl$, can readily be calculated from multiple dose data as well as from single dose data, by dividing the dose by the appropriate area under the (plasma) curve:

$$AUC_{0 \to \infty} = D/Cl = D/V_D.k \qquad (6.44)$$

*Mean steady-state plasma concentration ($C_{SS}$)*

The plateau has maximum and minimum values; however, it is useful to consider a single value, termed the *mean steady-state plasma concentration ($C_{SS}$)*. The mean steady-state plasma concentration ($C_{SS}$) is readily obtained by dividing Equation 6.44 by the dosing interval $T$:

$$C_{SS} = D/Cl.T = AUC_{SS}/T \qquad (6.45)$$

Note that $C_{SS}$ contains no information on the extent of interdose fluctuation.

*Factors influencing the mean steady state concentration*

Thus, $C_{SS}$ for a particular substance depends on the balance between entry into and exit from the body. If the rate of administration is changed, the average plateau concentration will settle at a new level. For example, if the size of each amount is doubled or, if the frequency at which the body is exposed to the substance is increased twofold, a twofold increase in average steady state level can be seen.

From Equation 6.45 it may be concluded that the extent of accumulation during multiple-dose administration, i.e. the mean steady-state plasma concentration ($C_{SS}$), depends on the size of each dose ($D$), the interval between doses ($T$), and the total clearance of the substance.

Table 6.4 gives an overview of the effect of changes in amount ($D$), interval time ($T$) and clearance on mean steady state plasma concentrations.

*Rate of accumulation*

Another important characteristic in toxicokinetics is the *rate of accumulation*, which is the time following initiation of administration that is required for the steady state condition to be reached, and after which there is no further accumulation. Estimation of the accumulation rate is more straightforward and generally more accurate than the prediction of the extent of accumulation. This is because the rate of accumulation depends almost entirely on $t_{1/2}$ and is inde-

TABLE 6.4
Effect of changes in amount ($D$), interval time ($T$) and clearance ($Cl$) on mean steady state plasma concentrations ($C_{SS}$)

| Change | Effect on $C_{ss}$ |
| --- | --- |
| D increased | increase |
| D decreased | decrease |
| T increased | decrease |
| T decreased | increase |
| Cl increased | decrease |
| Cl decreased | increase |

pendent of $D$ and $T$. In fact, the plateau concentration of a multiply administered substance is reached in little more than four half-lives.

Consider a substance with an elimination half-life $t_{1/2}$, administered in equal amounts at fixed dosage intervals. Each time an interval equal to $t_{1/2}$ elapses following the start of treatment, accumulation proceeds towards steady state by another 50%. That is, accumulation is 50% complete after 1 time $t_{1/2}$, 75% after 2 times $t_{1/2}$, 87.5% after 3 times $t_{1/2}$ and 93.8% after 4 times $t_{1/2}$. In other words, in four half-lives a concentration of about 94% of the maximum is reached. The time required to reach this plateau depends only on the elimination half-life. Regardless of that value $C_{SS}$, the rate at which it is attained is always the same.

Equations 6.46 and 6.47 describe the maximum ($C_{\infty\,max}$) and the minimum ($C_{\infty\,min}$) concentration of a substance at steady state for a certain dose ($D$), distribution volume ($V_D$), elimination rate constant ($k$) and dosage interval ($T$).

$$C_{\infty\,max} = D/V_D\left(1-e^{-kT}\right) \tag{6.46}$$

$$C_{\infty\,min} = De^{-kT}/V_D\left(1-e^{-kT}\right) \tag{6.47}$$

Equations 6.46 and 6.47 give information on the interdose fluctuation in blood levels once steady state is attained. This fluctuation is the difference between the maximum and minimum concentrations. Subtracting Equation 6.47 from 6.46 gives:

$$C_{\infty\,max} - C_{\infty\,min} = \left\{D/V_D(1-e^{-kT})\right\} - \left\{De^{-kT}/V_D(1-e^{-kT}\right.$$

$$= \left\{V_D(1-e^{-kT})\right\}/\left\{V_D(1-e^{-kT}\right\} = D/V_D = \tag{6.48}$$

*Note that the plasma concentration in Figure 6.14 is logarithmically plotted!*

Equation 6.48 shows that the difference between the maximum and the minimum concentrations at steady state is identical to the maximum concentration obtained after the initial dose, $C_0$.

### Summary

In this section relevant aspects of repeated exposure to a toxic substance were discussed. If the substance absorbed has not yet been completely eliminated at the time the subsequent dose is administered, accumulation will occur. A steady state will be achieved, in which the concentration in the body fluctuates around a certain plateau level. The point in time at which the plateau level is reached is determined by both the elimination rate and absorption rate. The mean amount of substance present in the body during steady state does not depend on the absorption rate constant. This amount may exceed that which can be taken up with one dose.

### 4    Capacity-limited kinetics, saturation kinetics, non-linear kinetics

Many of the processes that are studied within the framework of toxicokinetic research are interactions of xenobiotics with binding sites on proteins. If the concentration of ligand exceeds a certain value, all binding sites will be occupied; in other words, saturation will be reached. If the protein is a carrier (transport protein), then saturation will lead to decreased elimination rate and prolonged effect. The same is true for saturation of a metabolic detoxication route. In both cases, the result of saturation may also be that a subordinate metabolic route assumes such proportions that it becomes an (additional) activation route. The following description of saturation kinetics is restricted to the one-compartment model and to intravenous administration. As regards the mode of elimination, a distinction is made between elimination via hepatic metabolism only, and elimination via a combination of excretion and hepatic metabolism.

## 4.1   ELIMINATION VIA HEPATIC METABOLISM ONLY

The order of metabolic elimination can be determined by means of enzyme kinetics. This type of elimination is described by a Michaelis-Menten equation:

$$\frac{dC}{dt} = -\frac{V_{max} \cdot C}{K_M + C} \tag{6.49}$$

where:

$\dfrac{dC}{dt}$ = elimination rate

$V_{max}$ = maximum rate of the metabolic process

$K_M$   = Michaelis-Menten constant for that process

$C$    = plasma concentration after intravenous administration

Solution of the differential equation (6.49) yields:

$$\ln C = \ln C_0 + \frac{C_0 - C}{K_M} - \frac{V_{max}}{K_M} \cdot t \tag{6.50}$$

At saturation, which means that $C \gg K_M$, the elimination rate can be expressed as follows:

$$\frac{dC}{dt} = -V_{max} \tag{6.51}$$

In other words, the elimination rate at saturation approaches the maximum biotransformation rate. The maximum elimination rate has a constant value, which means that the reaction follows zero-order kinetics. (In zero-order processes the reaction rate is independent of the concentration!)

ASSIGNMENT   6.12

Deduce Equation 6.51 from Equation 6.49.

If no saturation occurs, in other words, if the concentration is low or $C \ll K_M$, then in Equation 6.49 $V_{max}/K_M$ may be substituted by $k_M$, the rate constant for metabolic elimination.

ASSIGNMENT   6.13

Explain why $V_{max}/K_M = k_M$ if no saturation occurs. Make use of Equation 6.8.

This leads to the following equation:

$$\frac{dC}{dt} = -C \cdot k_M \tag{6.52}$$

According to enzyme kinetics this equation represents a first-order process (since the rate is determined by the concentration!).

EXAMPLE 6-4

Figure 6.15 compares the plasma concentration-time curves of a substance with first-order elimination (a) and a substance with saturable elimination (b). In the figures on the left, the concentration is plotted on a linear scale, in those on the right on a semilogarithmic scale. The linear plot for substance b shows a straight line which changes to a concave curve. The semilogarithmic plot shows a convex curve changing to a straight line. The arrows in the figure indicate the point at which the transition from zero-order to first-order kinetics takes place.

EXAMPLE 6-5

Oxidation to acetaldehyde is the rate-determining step in the elimination of alcohol

The value of $K_M$ for the oxidation of alcohol (ethanol) to acetaldehyde in the liver is circa 80 mg l$^{-1}$. After the amounts many people are accustomed to consume, the plasma concentration is often much higher. The (metabolic) elimination of alcohol at these dosages can therefore be regarded as a process that initially follows zero-order kinetics (Figure 6.15b). The elimination rate of alcohol is about 7 g per hour (= $V_{max}$).

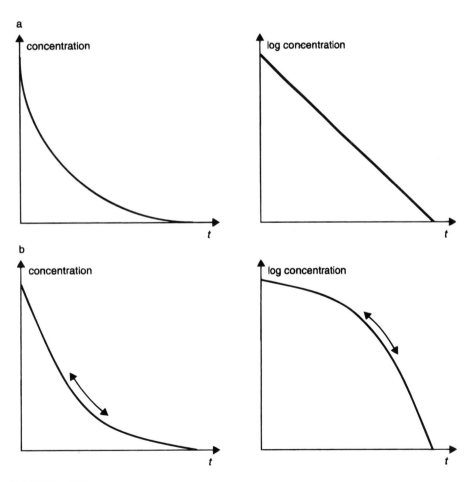

FIGURE    6.15
Plasma concentration-time profiles of a) a substance eliminated via a first-order process (a) and a substance showing Michaelis-Menten kinetics (b)

The following graphic procedure is used for the calculation of the toxicokinetic parameters (Figure 6.16).

The linear part of the plot in Figure 6.16 can also be represented by:

$$\ln C = \ln C_0^* - \frac{V_{max}}{K_M} \cdot t \tag{6.53}$$

where (approximately)

$$\ln C_0^* = \ln C_0 + \frac{C_0}{K_M} \tag{6.54}$$

ASSIGNMENT   6.14

What approximation has been used for the formulation of Equation 6.54? Is that approximation justified? Check this by means of curve C in Figure 6.16.

If $C$ is subsequently plotted logarithmically against time, $K_M$ can be calculated from the intercept (Equation 6.54) and $V_{max}$ from the slope.

EXAMPLE 6-6

The elimination of alcohol (ethyl alcohol), which is more than 95% in the liver and mainly through biotransformation, illustrates the course of non-linear kinetics. Alcohol biotransformation is catalyzed by the enzyme alcohol dehydrogenase and takes place in the cytoplasm; also alcohol is metabolized

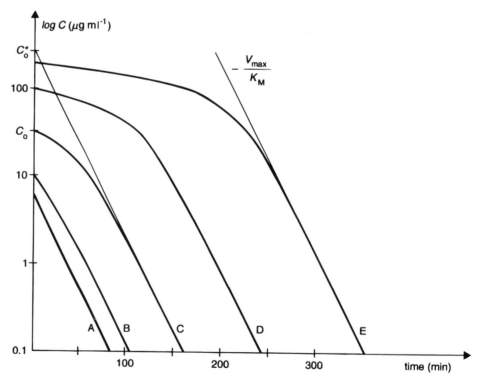

FIGURE   6.16

Plasma concentration-time curves for a substance showing capacity-limited kinetics
The initial concentrations ($C_0$) are 5(A), 10(B), 40(C), 100(D) and 200(E) $\mu$g ml$^{-1}$. The values of the metabolic parameters $V_{max}$ and $K_M$ are 1 $\mu$g min$^{-1}$ and 20 $\mu$g ml$^{-1}$, respectively.

(<25%) by a microsomal oxidation system. The enzyme-NADH complex slowly dissociates, so that the enzyme system becomes saturated at relatively low plasma alcohol concentrations.

The time necessary to reduce a plasma alcohol concentration of 0.01 mol l$^{-1}$ to 0.001 mol l$^{-1}$ in a healthy adult man is about 4.4 hours. This is a consequence of the non-linear, combined zero-order kinetics of alcohol. If the enzyme system that catalyzes the oxidation of alcohol were to follow first-order kinetics from 0.01 mol l$^{-1}$ onwards, the time interval to reach a plasma concentration of 0.001 mol l$^{-1}$ would be 1.6 hours. The delaying action of the high saturation of the enzyme system on the elimination is even more pronounced at higher initial concentrations. Plasma concentrations of 0.1% ($\approx$ 0.02 mol l$^{-1}$) are slightly to moderately toxic. It takes about 3 hours before a threshold level of 0.5% ($\approx$ 0.01 mol l$^{-1}$) is reached. With pure first-order kinetics, this would be less than a quarter of an hour. To sober up from 0.1 mol l$^{-1}$ ($\approx$ 5%; dead drunk) to an acceptable plasma concentration of 0.5% takes about 30 hours; with strict first-order kinetics, this would already have been reached within one hour. Needless to say, it is most unpleasant to take 24 hours to sober up after such a drinking bout.

These calculations apply roughly for an average individual; a relatively large biological variation should be born in mind.

> Which physiological conditions should be reckoned with especially?

Generally speaking, one should take into consideration hepatic disturbances and enzyme induction (higher $V_{max}$). Genetic and age differences and drug-interactions can also be of importance. Very young children in particular have a low hepatic alcohol dehydrogenase activity. The effect of enzyme induction in alcoholics is often nullified by hepatic lesions.

---

### 4.2 ELIMINATION VIA EXCRETION IN COMBINATION WITH METABOLIC ELIMINATION

Many substances are not excreted exclusively in the urine, or eliminated by means of metabolic transformation. Elimination will often take place through a combination of these processes.

In such cases, the elimination rate can be described as follows:

$$\frac{dC}{dt} = -\left(\frac{V_{max} \cdot C}{K_M + C} + k_E \cdot C\right) \tag{6.55}$$

The first term $-(V_{max} \cdot C) / (K_M + C)$ relates to metabolic elimination, the second $(-k_E \cdot C)$ to excretion in the urine.

If the approximation given in Equation 6.52 is applied and the rate constant for metabolic elimination ($k_M$) is expressed as a fraction ($f$) of the rate constant for the total elimination ($k$):

$$\frac{k_M}{k_E + k_M} = \frac{k_M}{k} = f \tag{6.56}$$

then Equation 6.55 can be rewritten as:

$$\frac{dC}{dt} = -\left(1 - f + \frac{f \cdot K_M}{K_M + C}\right) k \cdot C \tag{6.57}$$

Integration of 6.57 yields:

$$\ln C = \ln C_0 + \frac{f}{1-f} \ln \frac{\left\{ 1 + (1-f) \dfrac{C_0}{K_M} \right\}}{\left\{ 1 + (1-f) \dfrac{C}{K_M} \right\}} - kt \qquad (6.58)$$

If $k$ is determined by plotting $C$ logarithmically against $t$, and $k_E$ has been determined on the basis of urine concentration data, then $k_M$ is known and $f$ can be calculated by using Equation 6.56.

The determination of $K_M$ and $V_{max}$ follows the same procedure as that used in the case of elimination via hepatic metabolism.

The following equation should then be used:

$$\ln C_0^* = \ln C_0 + \frac{f}{1-f} \ln \left\{ 1 + (1-f) \frac{C_0}{K_M} \right\} \qquad (6.59)$$

---

EXAMPLE 6-7

A substance that is eliminated by excretion as well as by metabolism was intravenously administered at two dose levels: 1000 mg (A) and 2500 mg (B). In case A, no saturation occurred (see fig. 6.17, curve A). In that case, blood and urine samples were collected.

In case B, saturation was apparent (see Fig 6.17, curve B). In the latter case, only blood was sampled. $k$ and $k_E$ were obtained by plotting the blood and urine data after 100 mg semilogarithmically. $k$ was calculated from the slope of the blood concentration-time curve (Fig 6.17, curve A), and $k_E$ from the intercept of the excretion rate-time curve (Fig 6.18). k was 0.2059 h$^{-1}$ and $k_E$ 0.1530h$^{-1}$.

If $k$ and $k_E$ are known, then $k_M$ and $f$ are also known: $k_M$ ($= k - k_E$) = 0.0529 h$^{-1}$, and $f$ ($= k_M/k$) = 0.26 (equation 6.56). $k_M$ was calculated from the intercept (equation 6.59) of the semilogarithmic plot of the blood data after 2500 mg (Figure 6.17, curve B): $k_M$ = 0.0435.

---

*Summary*

Many substances are removed from the body by means of mechanisms that are potentially saturable. True first-order elimination is in fact only seen for substances excreted in the urine via passive glomerular filtration. Elimination via hepatic metabolism is usually characterized by capacity-limited kinetics as well. Although there are many other saturable processes, for example the binding of a substance to plasma proteins, this section focussed on the quantitative aspects of the saturation kinetics of the above-mentioned processes. It also discussed a method of calculating the toxicokinetic parameters of these two non-linear processes.

5    **Kinetics of covalent binding**

For dose-response relationships, see Study unit 7

If the action of a substance is based on *reversible* binding to active sites -resulting in a stable structure- then the intensity of the effect is usually related to the plasma concentration of that substance. This is because the intensity of the effect depends on the concentration at the site of action. In other words, the extent to which the substance is bound to the receptors corresponds to a particular concentration.

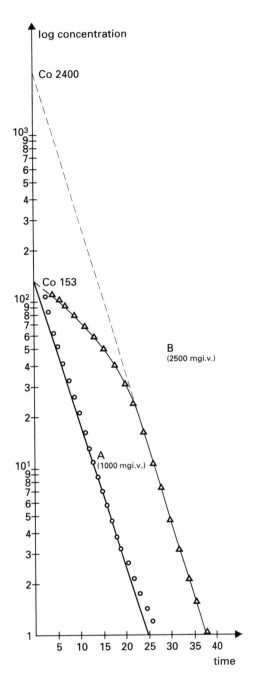

FIGURE 6.17
Blood concentration-time curves

The concept of reactive
intermediates is discussed in
Study unit 3

If the intermediates are highly reactive, the action is based on irrevesible binding. These intermediates will scarcely reach the blood circulation. Even if a reactive intermediate, e.g the 3,4-epoxide of bromobenzene, does reach the blood circulation, then there is still *no point* in using the concept blood concentration, as the concentration decreases gradually on the way to the 'target' organ (the lung) as a result of binding to proteins.

In such cases the intensity of the toxic effect is proportional to the number of target molecule-reactive intermediate adducts, and often -generally speaking- to

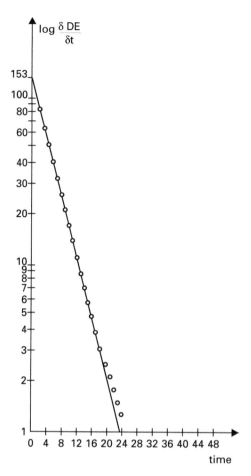

FIGURE 6.18
Excretion rate-time curve

the total amount of covalently bound reactive intermediate (i.e. including specific and non-specific binding). The amount of reactive intermediate that is made available for binding to active sites can only be determined by measuring the amount that is actually bound to the active sites. The amount of covalently bound metabolite will increase as long as the substance that has entered the body undergoes metabolic transformation.

The toxicokinetic equation corresponding to Figure 6.19 is:

$$C = \frac{k_2}{a} \cdot \frac{k_4}{c} \cdot A_0 \left( 1 - \frac{c}{c-a} e^{-a \cdot t} + \frac{a}{c-a} e^{-c \cdot t} \right) \qquad (6.60)$$

where:

| | |
|---|---|
| $C$ | = amount of covalently bound reactive intermediate B |
| $A_0$ | = the dose of the biologically active substance |
| $k_1, k_2, k_3$ and $k_4$ | = the rate constants |
| $a$ | = $k_1 + k_2$ |
| $c$ | = $k_3 + k_4$ |
| $\dfrac{k_4}{a}$ | = the fraction of $A_0$ that is converted into the reactive intermediate |

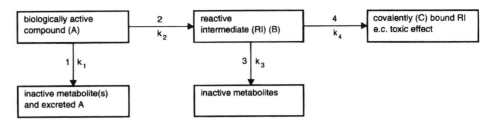

FIGURE 6.19

Diagram of the kinetics of covalent binding of reactive intermediates to macromolecules

This diagram is based on the assumption that: 1 All processes involved follow first-order kinetics, that is, the elimination (biotransformation and excretion) of the parent substance (A), the formation of the reactive metabolite (B), the covalent binding of the reactive metabolite to macromolecules (C), and the conversion of the reactive intermediate to inactive metabolites; 2 Elimination of A can be described by a one-compartment model.

$$\frac{k_4}{a}$$ = the fraction of reactive intermediate that is covalently bound

If $t \to \infty$ the amount that is covalently bound depends on the product of the two fractions:

$$C = \frac{k_2}{a} \cdot \frac{k_4}{c} \cdot A_0 \qquad (6.61)$$

The value of $k_2/a$ is determined directly by the relative importance of routes 1 (elimination) and 2 (bioactivation), and indirectly by the chemical reactivity of the parent substance, by the activities of the enzymes involved and (in certain cases) by the availability of an endogenous substrate. This last factor may play a role in a state of saturation (resulting from a high dose or from decreased protein binding, for example as a result of interaction or a low-protein diet).

See for the toxicity of acetaminophen Study unit 23

When, for example in the case of acetaminophen (Figure 6.20), the dose exceeds a certain level, the active sulfate (the co-substrate for sulfate conjugation) will become depleted. This will result in a decreased $k_1$ and (as a result) a decreased $a$. This in turn, will cause an increase in $k_2/a$, and ultimately an increase in covalent binding.

$k_4/c$ is determined directly by the ratio between routes 3 and 4. Indirectly, it is also influenced by the (electrophilic) reactivity of the reactive intermediate, the activities of the enzymes involved, the availability of the endogenous substrates and the reactivity of the nucleophilic sites on macromolecules. This can again be illustrated by the example of acetaminophen overdosing. Route 3 (conjugation with glutathione) is in that case a major route, while route 4 is a minor route. After administration of a particular dose, the glutathione pools are depleted, resulting in a decreased $k_3$, an increased $k_4/c$, etc.

SELF ASSESSMENT QUESTIONS

1   What is the most striking difference between the log drug concentration-time plot of a chemical that is distributed over the body, according to a one-compartment model and that of a substance that fits a two-compartment model?

2   Name the rate constants that are related to the hybrid constant $\beta$ in a two-compartment model.

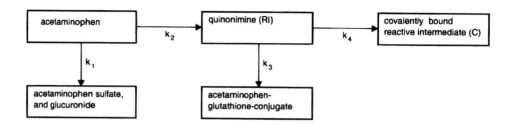

FIGURE 6.20
Metabolism of acetaminophen
This process involves the formation of a reactive intermediate and covalent binding. The latter is probably not the cause of the toxicity of acetaminophen.

3   What happens to the value of $C_{ss}$ when a dosage schedule of 250 mg every 6 hours is changed in a dosage schedule of 500 mg every 12 hours?

4   After oral administration of 500 mg of the analgesic acetaminophen the following changes in the blood concentration with time were found:

TABLE 6.5

| t (minutes after administration) | Blood concentration ($C_c$ mg $l^{-1}$) |
|---|---|
| 14 | 4.45 |
| 36 | 6.98 |
| 66 | 7.16 |
| 130 | 4.83 |
| 195 | 3.08 |
| 310 | 1.42 |

The availability $F$ was 1 and $t_0$ could be set at 0. Calculate $k$, $k_a$ and the distribution volume $V_D$ by means of the method of the residuals.

5   After intravenous administration of a substance the blood concentration was found to change with time as follows:

TABLE 6.6

| t (hours after administration) | Blood concentration ($C_c$ µg $l^{-1}$) |
|---|---|
| .5 | 1345 |
| 1 | 864 |
| 1.5 | 593 |
| 2 | 438 |
| 2.5 | 346 |
| 3 | 290 |
| 4 | 228 |
| 5 | 193 |
| 6 | 168 |
| 8 | 131 |
| 12 | 81 |
| 16 | 50 |

a. Plot the blood concentration logarithmically against time. On the basis of the shape of the curve thus obtained, determine which compartment model applies here.

b. Calculate $B$, $\beta$, $A$ and $\alpha$.

6 In order to protect pigs in pig farms against bacterial infections, the animals receive a daily treatment with furazolidone via their feed. Calculate the mean amount of substance present in the animals after the plateau level has been reached, assuming that each animal receives a daily dose of 75 mg and that in pigs furazolidone has an elimination half-life of 1 hour.

Note: the amount of a compound present at steady state, expressed as fraction of the total amount that is taken up with each dose ($FD_0$) is: ($1/Tk$). Use this equation.

7 As long as a dose has not been completely absorbed after oral administration, absorption and elimination occur simultaneously. Explain why the constant $k_A$ obtained by means of the method of residuals is a true absorption rate constant and not a hybrid constant.

FEEDBACK

1 **Answers to the assignments**

6.1 The substitution allows direct determination of a parameter in a homogenous environment, for example in plasma. In addition, a parameter like concentration can be determined far more accurately than a biological effect.

6.2 The substance accumulates in the (adipose) tissue. The lipophilicity of the substance concerned must therefore be high.

6.3 By comparing the amount of substance present in the circulation after oral administration with the amount present after intravenous administration. (By means of the parameter 'area under the curve', which is discussed in section 2.1.1.)

6.4 Figure 6.2:

$C_0$ = circa $12.7\,\mu g\ ml^{-1}$ (extrapolation)

$$V_D = \frac{D_0}{C_0} = \frac{600\ 000}{12.7} = 47.2\ l$$

Figure 6.3:

$C_0 = 13\ \mu g\ ml^{-1}$ (to be read from the graph)

$$V_D = \frac{600\ 000}{13} = 46.2\ l$$

Figure 6.3 allows the most accurate determination of these parameters. Extrapolation (Figure 6.2) can never yield more than an estimate.

6.5 $\quad \log \dfrac{C_0}{2} = \log C_0 - \dfrac{k}{2.3} \cdot t_{1/2}$ (compare Equation 6.12)

$$\log C_0 - \log 2 = \log C_0 - \dfrac{k}{2.3} \cdot t_{1/2}$$

$$0.3010 = \dfrac{k}{2.3} \cdot t_{1/2}$$

$$t_{1/2} = \dfrac{0.6g3}{k}$$

Figure 6.2:

$C_C = 10\ \mu g\ ml^{-1}$ at 3 h and 15 min.
$C_C = 5\ \mu g\ ml^{-1}$ at 13 h and 30 min.
Hence, $t_{1/2} = 10$ h and 15 min.

Figure 6.3

$$\dfrac{\Delta \log C_c}{\Delta t} = -\dfrac{k}{2.3}$$

$$\dfrac{\log 10 - \log 4}{3.25 - 16.75} = \dfrac{1 - 2 \times 0.3010}{-13.5} = \dfrac{0.3980}{-13.5} = -\dfrac{k}{2.3}$$

$k = 0.068\ h^{-1}$

$$t_{1/2} = t_{1/2} = \dfrac{0.693}{0.068} = 10.19\ h$$

6.6 $\quad Cl = k \cdot V_D = 0.068 \times 46.2 = 3.1\ lh^{-1}$

6.7 $\quad Cl = \dfrac{D_0}{AUC} = \dfrac{600\ 000}{142.2^*} = 4.2\ lh^{-1}$

$^*AUC = 142.2\ \mu g\ ml^{-1} \times h$, calculated by means of the trapezoidal rule: area of trapezium $A = 1/2\ a\ (b + c)$

6.8 $\quad$ At the peak of the blood concentration time curve:

$$\dfrac{dC_c}{dt} = 0$$

(The change in the plasma concentration per unit of time is zero at the maximum!)

Starting from Equation 6.20 (the formula for the plasma concentration-time curve after oral administration) and setting $t_0 = 0$, the following equation is obtained:

$$\dfrac{dC_c}{dt} = -k\dfrac{F D_0}{V_D}\dfrac{k_A}{k_A - k}e^{-k \cdot t_{max}} + k_A \dfrac{F D_0}{V_D}\dfrac{k_A}{k_A - k}e^{-k_A \cdot t_{max}} = 0$$

where $t_{max}$ is the point in time at which the maximum blood concentration is reached.

This equation can be reduced to:

$$\frac{F\,D_0}{V_D} \cdot \frac{k_A}{k_A - k}(-k\,e^{-k\cdot t_{max}} + k_A\,e^{-k_A\cdot t_{max}}) = 0$$

The first part of this equation, $(F\,D_0/V_D) \cdot (k_A/k_A - k)$, can never be equal to zero as it is made up of constants. If one of these constants were zero, then the plasma concentration would be zero at each time $t$. Hence, the factor between brackets in the equation must be equal to zero, yielding the following equation:

$$k\,e^{-k\cdot t_{max}} = k_A\,e^{-k_A\cdot t_{max}}$$

Rearranging this formula and using logarithms the following equation is obtained:

$$t_{max} = 1/(k_A - k)\ln(k_A/k)$$

or

$$k\,e^{-k\cdot t_{max}} = k_A\,e^{-k_A\cdot t_{max}}$$

or, if $^{10}$log is used:

$$\log k - \frac{k}{2.3}\cdot t_{max} = \log k_A - \frac{k_A}{2.3}\cdot t_{max}$$

$$t_{max} = 2.3\,\frac{\log k_A - \log k}{k_A - k}$$

If $k$ and $k_A$ are known, then $t_{max}$ can be calculated. The maximum blood concentration can be calculated by substituting $k$, $k_A$ and $t_{max}$ in the equation for $C_C$.

6.9  If the ratio $AUC/D_0$ is not constant. This is the case in saturated absorption (if absorption is saturated, the $AUC$ no longer increases after administration of another dose) and in saturated elimination.

6.10  Suppose a fraction $D_T$ of $D_0$ has been taken up at $t = T$.
$D_T$ is equal to the sum of the amount that is still present in the body at $t = T$, the amount that has already been metabolized ($D_M$) and the amount of (intact) substance that has already been excreted ($D_E$):

$$D_T = D_B + D_M + D_E$$

Differentiation over time leads to:

$$\frac{dD_T}{dt} = \frac{dD_L}{dt} + \frac{dD_M}{dt} + \frac{dD_E}{dt}$$

Using Equations 6.8, 6.10 and 6.13 yields:

$$dD_T = V_D\,dC_c + k\,V_D\,C_c\,dt$$

Integration gives the following solution:

$$D_T = V_D\,C_{cT} + k\,V_D\int_0^t C_c\,dt$$

where $C_{c,T}$ = the blood concentration at $t = T$.

If all of the substance has been absorbed and the elimination process has been completed, the following equation applies:

$$D_\infty = F D_0 = k V_D \int_0^\infty C_c \, dt = k V_D \, AUC$$

(At $t = \infty$ the blood concentration = 0, which implies that the term $VC_{c,T}$ disappears). Rearrangement of this equation finally gives Equation 6.28.

6.11 Examples of substances that accumulate in the body are: halogenated hydrocarbons (in the adipose tissue of living organisms) and antibiotics in animal tissues intended for consumption. Study units 3 and 5 also provide some examples of accumulation.

6.12 If $C \gg K_M$, then $K_M$ can be disregarded in the denominator on the right side of Equation 6.49, the equation becomes:

$$\frac{dC}{dt} = -\frac{V_{max} \cdot C}{C} = -V_{max}$$

6.13 If no saturation occurs, which means that $C \ll K_M$, then $C_c$ can be disregarded in the denominator on the right side of equation 6.49, resulting in:

$$\frac{dC}{dt} = -\frac{V_{max} \cdot C}{K_M}$$

Multiplying both sides of this equation by the apparent volume of distribution $V_D$ gives:

$$\frac{dV_D \cdot C}{dt} = -\frac{V_{max} \cdot V_D C}{K_M}$$

Substitution of $D_B$ for $V_D \cdot C$ yields Equation 6.8, in other words $V_{max}/K_M = k_M$ This means that if no saturation occurs, $k_M$ can be calculated from the slope of the line represented by equation 6.50.

6.14 In Equation 6.54 the term $-C/K_M$ on the right hand side of Equation 6.50 has been disregarded.

This approximation is only used for the determination of the metabolic parameters $V_{max}$ and $K_M$. These parameters are determined on the basis of the final (linear) part of the curve concerned. Since for high values of $t$ $C$ becomes so small in relation to $K_M$ that $C/K_M \cdot t$ can be disregarded, this equation can be rewritten as follows:

$$\ln C = \ln C_0 + \frac{C_0}{K_M} - \frac{V_{max}}{K_M} \cdot t$$

$K_M$ can be calculated from the intercept and $V_{max}$ from the slope $(-V_{max}/K_M)$:

*intercept*:

$$\ln C_0^* = \ln C_0 + \frac{C_0}{K_M}$$

$$\ln\frac{C_0^*}{C_0} = \frac{C_0}{K_M}$$

$$\log\frac{C_0^*}{C_0} = \frac{C_0}{K_M} \cdot \log e = 0.434\frac{C_0}{K_M} \rightarrow K_M$$

### 2    Answers to the self assessment questions

1    The log drug concentration versus time plot of the one-compartment model is a straight line, while the log drug concentration-time plot in a two-compartment model is not.

2    The rate constants that are related to the hybrid constant $\beta$ in a two-compartment model are:
$k_{CT}$ = the rate constant for the transport from C to T
$k_{TC}$ = the rate constant for the transport from T to C
$k_C$  = the rate constant for elimination from the central compartment C.

3    When $D$ and $T$ are both changed by the same factor, $C_{SS}$ will stay exactly the same. See also the following figure.

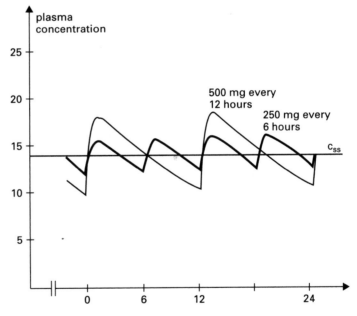

FIGURE   6.21

4    In order to calculate the three parameters, the blood concentration data are plotted logarithmically against time.
Application of Equations 6.22 and 6.23 yields:

•    Calculation of $k$:

$$\frac{\log 2 - \log 10}{260 - 22} = -\frac{0.6990}{238} = -\frac{k}{2.3} \rightarrow k = \frac{1.6077}{238} = 0.4\ \text{h}^{-1}$$

•    Method of residuals:

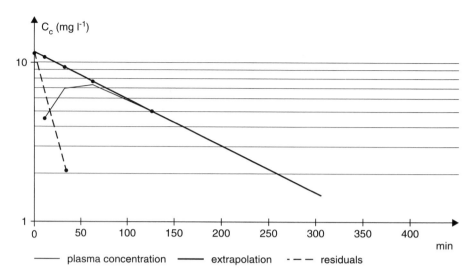

FIGURE 6.22

| at t = 14 min: | 10.62 |
| | 4.45 |
| | ——— |
| | 6.17 |

| at t = 36 min: | 9.10 |
| | 6.98 |
| | ——— |
| | 2.12 |

| at t = 66 min: | 7.45 |
| | 7.16 |
| | ——— |
| | 0.29 (this cannot be plotted) |

- Calculation of $k_a$:

$$\frac{\log 3.1 - \log 8}{28 - 8} = -\frac{0.4117}{20} = -\frac{k_a}{2.3} \rightarrow k_a = \frac{0.9469}{20} = 2.8 \text{ h}^{-1}$$

- Calculation of $V_D$:

$$\frac{FD_0}{V_D} = \frac{k_a}{k_a - k} = 11.65 = \frac{1 \times 500}{V_D} \times \frac{2.8}{2.8 - 0.4}$$

$$V_D = \frac{583.3}{11.65} = 501$$

5    a    The *disappearance* of a substance from the circulation clearly proceeds in two phases, which means that a *two*-compartment model is involved.

      b    Calculation of $B$, $\beta$, $A$ and $\alpha$.
          $B$ and $A$ can be obtained directly from the blood concentration-time curve (see Figure 6.23):

- Determination of $B$: 343 µg l$^{-1}$
- Determination of $A$:

| at t = 0.5 | 1345 |
| | 325 |
| | ——— |
| | 1022 |

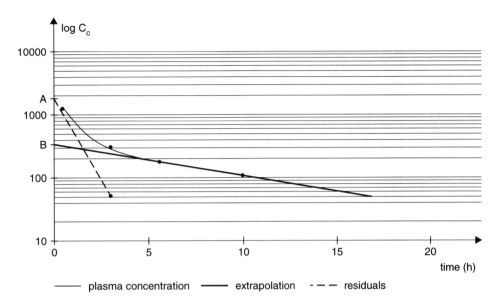

plasma concentration — extrapolation - - - residuals

FIGURE 6.23

$$at\ t = 3 \qquad \begin{array}{r} 290 \\ 238 \\ \hline 52 \end{array}$$

$$A = 1800\ \mu g\ l^{-1}$$

Application of Equation 6.29 and of the methods illustrated in Figure 6.11 yields $\beta$ and $\alpha$.

- Calculation of $\beta$:

$$-\frac{\beta}{2.3} = \frac{\log 100 - \log 240}{10.23 - 3} = -0.0526$$

$$\beta = 0.12\ h^{-1}$$

- Calculation of $\alpha$:

$$-\frac{\alpha}{2.3} = \frac{\log 52 - \log 1022}{3 - 0.5} = -0.5174$$

$$\alpha = 1.19\ h^{-1}$$

Make use of equation $1/t \cdot k$; this provides the percentage of accumulation:

$$\frac{100}{t \cdot k} = \frac{100}{24 \times 0.693} = 6\%$$

This means that after the plateau level has been reached a mean amount of 4.5 mg of the substance is present in the animal. $k$ can be calculated by means of Equation 6.15.

7　　Use the curve obtained by plotting the blood concentration logarithmically against time for a substance whose kinetic behavior fits a one-compartment model after oral administration. The final part of the curve concerns *elimination* exclusively. The changes in the blood concentration with time during that phase can be described as follows:

$$C = \frac{F D_0}{V_D} \cdot \frac{k_A}{k_A - k} \, e^{-k \cdot t}$$

By subtracting this equation from that for absorption and elimination:

$$C = \left[ \frac{F D_0}{V_D} \cdot \frac{k_A}{k_A - k} \, e^{-k \cdot t} \right] - \left[ \frac{F D_0}{V_D} \cdot \frac{k_A}{k_A - k} \, e^{-k_A \cdot t} \right]$$

(this is Equation 6.20, written in a different way), an equation is obtained which only relates to absorption:

$$C = \frac{F D_0}{V_D} \cdot \frac{k_A}{k_A - k} \, e^{-k_A \cdot t}$$

## APPENDIX A

*Determination of the area under the plasma concentration-time curve (AUC)*

Equation 6.17 represents the area under the plasma concentration-time curve (AUC) after an intravenous bolus injection. This area can often be calculated directly from the results, for example in the case of model-independent kinetics. There are several methods, of which two will be described here.

*Trapezoidal rule*

One of the most common methods uses the *trapezoidal rule*, which is quick and accurate. The accuracy of the method is determined by the number of experimental measurements used.

A trapezium is a quadrilateral figure with two parallel sides and two non-parallel sides. If the plasma concentrations are plotted on normal graph paper, then the surface under the plasma profile can be divided into a series of trapezia, whose areas can be calculated and added up to yield the area under the curve.

The data in Table 6.I represent a typical plasma profile of a substance with a half-life of 1 hour, administered by intravenous bolus injection. If these data are

TABLE 6.I
Plasma profile of a substance with a half-life of 1 hour, administered by intravenous bolus injection

| Time (hours) | Concentration ($\mu g \, ml^{-1}$) | Cumulative AUC ($\mu g$ hour $ml^{-1}$) |
|---|---|---|
| 0.0 | 25.0 | |
| 0.25 | 21.0 | 5.75 |
| 0.50 | 17.6 | 10.58 |
| 1.0 | 12.5 | 18.11 |
| 2.0 | 6.25 | 27.49 |
| 3.0 | 3.13 | 32.18 |
| 4.0 | 1.56 | 34.53 |
| 6.0 | 0.40 | 36.49 |
| 8.0 | 0.10 | 36.99 |
| 12.0 | 0.0 | 37.19 |

plotted on normal graph paper and the points in the graph connected by straight lines, this will result in a series of trapezia and a triangle for the time interval from 8 to 12 hours. Calculating the area of each segment and adding them yield the *AUC* values shown in the third column of this table. The area of a trapezium is given by $1/2h(B + b)$, in which $h$ stands for the height and $B$ and $b$ for the lengths of the two parallel sides.

*Rectangle method*

An equally useful method for determining the AUC is the so-called *rectangle method*. In this method, each concentration is multiplied by the difference between the mid-times of the intervals on either side of the time corresponding to that concentration. The final concentration, if not negligible, is multiplied by the difference between the concentration-time and the mid-time before it. Finally an extrapolation term is added to allow estimation of the area under the curve. The extrapolation term is given by:

final concentration / final elimination rate constant

The final elimination rate constant can be calculated from the slope of the log concentration-time plot.

Table 6.II below shows an example of the rectangle method.

TABLE   6.II
Example of the calculation of the AUC using the rectangle method

| Time | | Plasma concentration (mg $l^{-1}$) | Interval | Average time before, after | $\Delta$ Average times (h) | $\Sigma$ plasma concentration factor (mg h$^{-1}$ $l^{-1}$) |
|---|---|---|---|---|---|---|
| hours | min | | | | | |
| 0 | 0 | 0.0 | | | | |
|  | 15 | 0.093 | | | | |
|  | 30 | 0.1730 | | | | |
|  | 45 | 0.2358 | | | | |
| 1 | 0 | 0.2898 | 0.25 | 0.125 | 0.25 | $1.78 \times 0.25 = 0.444$ |
|  | 15 | 0.3168 | | | | |
|  | 30 | 0.3322 | | | | |
|  | 45 | 0.3389 | | | | |
| 2 | | 0.3385 | | 0.125, 0.5 | 0.625 | $0.339 \times 0.625 = 0.212$ |
| 3 | | 0.3044 | | | | |
| 4 | | 0.2556 | | | | |
| 5 | | 0.2141 | 1.0 | 0.5 | 1.0 | $1.099 \times 1.0 = 1.099$ |
| 6 | | 0.1791 | | | | |
| 7 | | 0.1454 | | | | |
| 8 | | 0.1240 | | 0.5, 2.0 | 2.5 | $0.1240 \times 2.5 = 0.310$ |
| 12 | | 0.0699 | | | | |
| 16 | | 0.0500 | | | | |
| 20 | | 0.0416 | | | | |
| 24 | | 0.0370 | | | | |
| 28 | | 0.0339 | 4.0 | | 4.0 | $0.345 \times 4.0 = 1.380$ |
| 32 | | 0.0316 | | | | |
| 36 | | 0.0291 | | | | |
| 40 | | 0.0272 | | | | |
| 44 | | 0.0253 | | | | |
| 48 | | 0.0238 | | | 2.0 | $0.0238 \times 2.0 = 0.048$ |

Last time elimination rate constant is 0.0167 h$^{-1}$, so the extrapolation factor is: 0.0238/0.0167 = 1.425 mg h l$^{-1}$.
Summation gives: AUC = 4.91 mg h l$^{-1}$.
An extra detection of the plasma concentration for 48 hours could give a more exact result. In that case, the AUC is less defined by the extrapolation factor.

## APPENDIX B

Equation 6.19 is a linear, first-order differential equation with a second term which can be written in the more general form:

$$\frac{dy}{dx} + P(x) \cdot y = Q(x) \tag{B1}$$

The solution of this type of equation, is as follows.

In the general equation above, the variables $x$ and $y$ cannot be separated. In order to allow a separation of variables, the equation is modified in such a way that the left side of the equation becomes a differential of the product of $y$ and a factor which also occurs in the right part, so that it can eventually be solved through integration:

$$dI\, y = I\, Q(x)\, dx \tag{B2}$$

$$I\, y = \int I\, Q(x)\, dx + C \tag{B3}$$

$$y = \frac{1}{I} \int I\, Q(x)\, dx + \frac{C}{I} \tag{B4}$$

where $I$ represents the above-mentioned factor. $I$ is assumed to be a function of $x$. This can be accomplished as follows. First, Equation B1 is multiplied by $I\, dx$:

$$I\, dy + I\, P(x) \cdot y\, dx = I\, Q(x)\, dx \tag{B5}$$

If the left side of this equation is to be the differential of $I \cdot y$, then necessarily becomes:

$$I\, P(x) \cdot y\, dx = y\, dI$$

or

$$\frac{dI}{I} = P(x)\, dx$$

The solution of the latter equation is:

$$I = e^{\int P(x)\, dx + C_1} = C_2 e^{\int P(x)\, dx} \tag{B6}$$

Since:

$$dI\, y = I\, dy + y\, dI = I\, dy + y\, C_2 e^{\int P(x)\, dx}\, d\int P(x)\, dx = I\, dy + y\, I\, P(x)\, dx$$
$$= I\, Q(x)\, dx$$

Equation B5 can be replaced by Equation B2.

Application of this method to Equation 6.19 yields:

$$\frac{dC_c}{dt} + k\, C_c = \frac{F\, D_0}{V_D}\, k_A e^{-k_A t} \tag{B7}$$

$$I = C_2 e^{\int k\, dt} = C_2 e^{k\, t}$$

Multiplying B7 by $I\, dt$ gives:

$$C_2 e^{kt} dC_c + k C_2 e^{kt} C_c\, dt = \frac{F D_0}{V_D} k_A C_2 e^{-(k_A - k)t} dt$$

$$dC_2 e^{kt} C_c = \frac{F D_0}{V_D} k_A C_2 e^{-(k_A - k)t} dt$$

$$C_2 e^{kt} C_c = -\frac{F D_0}{V_D} \frac{k_A}{k_A - k} C_2 e^{-(k_A - k)t} + C_3$$

$$\text{at } t = 0 : 0 = -\frac{F D_0}{V_D} \frac{k_A}{k_A - k} C_2 + C_3$$

$$C_2 e^{kt} C_c = -\frac{F D_0}{V_D} \frac{k_A}{k_A - k} C_2\, e^{-(k_A - k)t} + \frac{F D_0}{V_D} \frac{k_A}{k_A - k} C_2$$

$$C_c = -\frac{F D_0}{V_D} \frac{k_A}{k_A - k} e^{-k_A t} + \frac{F D_0}{V_D} \frac{k_A}{k_A - k} e^{-kt}$$

$$C_c = -\frac{F D_0}{V_D} \frac{k_A}{k_A - k} (e^{-kt} e^{-k_A t}) \tag{B8}$$

Equation B8 is Equation 6.20.

The solution of the equation is also possible using the Laplace transformation. However, this is beyond the scope of this textbook.

## APPENDIX C

*Fick's law* describes the movement or flux of a substance through a membrane by passive diffusion. It is expressed as:

$$\frac{m}{t} = P_k A (C_0 - C_i)$$

where:

| | |
|---|---|
| $m$ | = the amount of substance passing through an area or interface ($A$) |
| $t$ | = time |
| $C_o$ and $C_i$ | = the concentrations of the substance outside and inside the membrane respectively |
| $P_k$ | = the permeability constant. |

*First pass effect* means that a proportion of the absorbed substance is removed before it can enter the circulation. The blood flow from the gastrointestinal tract moves directly to the liver before returning to the heart and systemic circulation. Thus, a substantional fraction of a drug that is absorbed from the gastrointestinal tract may be metabolized by the liver or excreted into the bile without ever reaching the rest of the body.

# Contents Study unit 7
# Dose-time-effect relationships

0-8493-9232-2/96/$0.00 + $.50
© 1996 by CRC Press, Inc.

# Study unit 7

# Dose-time-effect relationships

*A. Musch*

INTRODUCTION

As is commonly known, the intensity of the effect of any substance that is ingested or administered depends on the quantity of the substance involved and the frequency with which ingestion or administration takes place. A drug taken in too small a dose usually does not work. If, however, too much of it is taken, symptoms of intoxication may manifest themselves. This principle is in fact true for virtually every substance that enters the body. The effects of alcoholic beverages are determined by the number of glasses consumed, and range from feeling rather merry to severe intoxication or possibly even death (Figure 7.1).

The effect of time is apparent from the fact that the hangover after excessive drinking lasts longer, the larger the amount of alcohol ingested. Daily alcohol consumption over a long period of time leads to other effects, such as liver damage and neurological disturbances.

*alcohol per ml in blood

FIGURE 7.1
Effects of various blood alcohol concentrations

187

In toxicology these relationships are described in terms of *dose*, *time* and *response*. Toxicologists try to establish these relationships.

*Dose–response, time-response-relationship*

In this study unit the relationships between dose and response and between time and response are discussed on the basis of several examples. The difference between graded and quantal responses will be dealt with. Some basic concepts in receptor theory will be explained, such as receptor, agonist and antagonist, and affinity. The mathematics of dose–response relationships and the statistical analysis of experimental results will also be discussed. In addition to the calculation of $LD_{50}$, the significance of this concept will also be given attention. The role of time in toxicology will be discussed, and to conclude the extrapolation of certain quantitative toxicological data will be dealt with.

LEARNING OBJECTIVES

After having studied this unit, you should be able to:

— explain the concepts quantal response and graded response, threshold dose, agonist and antagonist, affinity for a receptor, probit and logit analysis, $LD_{50}$, and other toxicity parameters, and latency period
— indicate how the variables dose (or concentration) and time influence the toxicity of a substance
— calculate various parameters, such as $LD_{50}$, affinity, logit and probit
— predict the effect of a competitive and a non-competitive antagonist, and conversely, draw conclusions on the type of antagonist from the changes in a dose–response relationship.

*Study hint*

While studying the present unit, you will need graph paper, a pencil and eraser, a ruler and a pocket calculator. Many of the terms in the present unit were introduced in previous units. Before you start studying this unit, you may find it helpful to read the margin texts in Study units 1, 2 and 5 once more. The study load for this unit is estimated at 6 study learning hours.

## STUDY CORE

### 1 Explanation of Some Concepts

This section explains the following concepts: dose and concentration, graded and quantal response, and dose–time–response relationship. Subsequent sections will deal with these concepts in greater detail.

### 1.1 DOSE AND CONCENTRATION

The intensity of an effect of a substance depends on the dose. What is meant by this?

*Dose*

The *dose* is the mass quantity of a substance administered to a subject or which in some way enters the subject's body. This quantity is sometimes expressed in absolute terms (mg, g, etc.), but often relative to body weight (mg kg$^{-1}$, etc.). For some purposes, e.g. for extrapolation to other species, the dose is expressed relative to the body surface area or to energy consumption. Body surface area and energy consumption decrease in relation to weight with increasing body size (Table 7.1).

TABLE 7.1
Relationship between body weight and body surface area in a number of vertebrates

| Species | Weight (g) | Surface area (cm²) |
|---------|-----------|--------------------|
| mouse | 20 | 46 |
| rat | 200 | 325 |
| guinea pig | 400 | 565 |
| rabbit | 1500 | 1270 |
| cat | 2000 | 1380 |
| monkey | 4000 | 2980 |
| dog | 12000 | 5770 |
| man | 70000 | 18000 |

If series of substances are to be compared with one another, the quantities are, if possible, expressed in molar units (e.g., $\mu$mole, mmole, mole).

*Concentration*

ppm = parts per million
See note in addendum on possible confusion

In many cases, certainly in the case of exposure to environmental contaminants, the dose is not known. At the most, the concentration of the substance in the compartment concerned may be known, for example in drinking water or in the air. The concentration of the substance can, for example, be expressed in g per l water, mg per kg feed and g per m³ air. Often dimensions such as ppm (= parts per million) and ppb (= parts per billion) are also used.

ASSIGNMENT 7.1
What is the daily dose of copper ingested by an individual via the drinking water, if the concentration in the water is 80 mg l⁻¹, and the daily consumption of water is 1.5 l? What proportion does this dose bear to the total oral dose of copper ingested daily?

1.2   GRADED AND QUANTAL RESPONSES

The effects induced by a substance usually do not occur until a certain dose is exceeded. With increasing dosage, the effects often not only become more severe, but also manifest themselves sooner. This is the case for alcohol (see Figure 7.2).

*Response*

There are two types of response to toxic substances. For many types of effect, the extent to which they occur—the *response*—can be measured on a continuous scale. In these cases, the response is of the *graded*, or *gradual* type (see Figure 7.3) and is distinguished from the "all or nothing" response. In the latter type, the response can be measured only by counting the number of individuals who do respond in a group of identically treated subjects. This type of response is called a *quantal response* (see Figure 7.4).

*Graded response*

*Quantal response*

An effect which is measured as a graded response can be converted to a quantal response by the introduction of a standard. For example, in some cases, one may want to establish whether a substance is toxic or not, without being interested in the extent of its toxicity. This may be compared with an individual wanting to know whether his blood pressure is too high, without being interested in the exact number of mm Hg. If, for example in the case of growth inhibition (graded response), the standard effect is defined as inhibition of 25% or more, all individuals in the group who display at least that inhibition are counted as responding, and all those who do not as non-responding subjects.

189

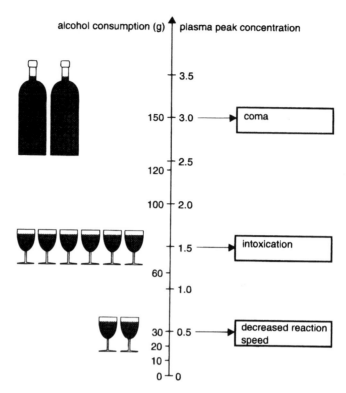

FIGURE 7.2

Relationship between the consumption of a single dose of alcohol (in grams) and its effects
The peak concentration in the blood plasma is also shown (per mille).

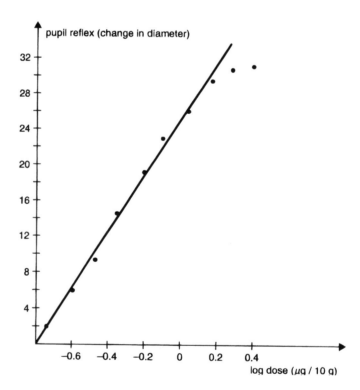

FIGURE 7.3

Graded response: relationship between the dose of atropine administered subcutaneously
and its effect on the diameter of the pupil of the eye in mice

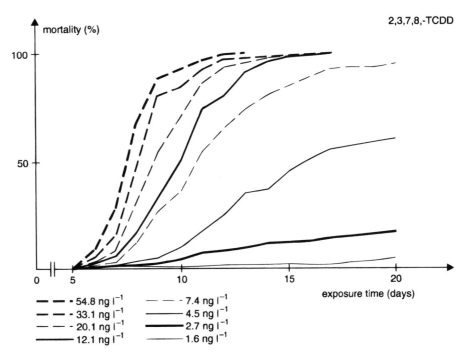

FIGURE 7.4
Quantal response: mortality in young trout (at the yolk sac stage) after 4 days of exposure to various concentrations of TCDD
The cumulative mortalities in the concentration series of standard 2,3,7,8-tetrachlorodibenzo-p-dioxin (TCDD) varied from 2% at the lowest concentration of 1.6 ng l$^{-1}$ to 100% at 12.2 ng l$^{-1}$ and higher.


ASSIGNMENT   7.2

Can the reverse also be true, i.e. can a quantal response be converted to a graded one?

### 1.3   DOSE-TIME RESPONSE RELATIONSHIPS

The magnitude of an effect induced by a substance (i.e. the intensity of the effect = graded response, or the number of responding subjects = quantal response) generally depends on the quantity or concentration in which the substance is administered or taken in. The relationships between the dose or concentration and the intensity of the effect or response (the dose–response and concentration–response relationships) will be discussed separately. The role of time in the development of the effect will also be dealt with.


## 2   Graded response

In the preceding section a distinction is made between two types of response, namely graded (gradual) and quantal. The present section discusses the gradual responses (graded response) as they appear in toxicological research using isolated organs or tissue preparations. The graded response in the intact animal will also be discussed.

*Isolated organs versus intact animal*

### 2.1   GRADED RESPONSE IN ISOLATED ORGANS/TISSUES

Graded responses can be observed in organ or tissue preparations as well as in intact animals. There are, however, major practical differences between the situations. Analysis and description of what exactly takes place is much simpler

191

The use of organ preparations in toxicology is extensively discussed in Study unit 25

for a preparation than for an intact animal. This is due to the absence of a whole range of interfering mechanisms, such as nervous and endocrine regulation and transport processes in the whole animal.

### 2.1.1 Receptors

*Specific*
*Affinity*

*Receptors*

Molecular toxicologists try to explain toxic effects of a substance on the basis of interactions between the molecules of the substance and certain structures or (macro)molecules within the organism. In some cases this interaction may be highly *specific*, which means that the molecular sites of action and the toxic substance concerned have a particular *affinity* for one another. Analogous to the terminology used in pharmacology, these sites of action are referred to as *receptors*. On the whole, little or nothing is known about the nature of such receptors although our knowledge is increasing rapidly. They sometimes consist of active sites (or binding sites) or allosteric sites of enzymes. Receptors may be, for example, thiol (-SH) groups of enzymes, or membrane proteins with which certain metal ions can react specifically. This is assumed to lead to certain changes in the conformation of the receptor molecule or of the surrounding membrane molecules These changes in turn will give rise to a particular biological effect.

*Substance–receptor interaction*

The specific character of the interaction suggests that a certain chemical complementarity may be involved. There are various ways in which such interactions between substance and receptor may occur. These are as follows:

*Electrostatic interaction*

- *electrostatic interaction*; this is based on the attraction of two oppositely charged molecules. Examples are ionic bonds and hydrogen bonds;

*Van der Waal's forces*

- *van der Waals' forces*; these are weak attraction forces between apolar molecules, which decrease rapidly as the distance between the molecules increases. They only play a role if the molecules are very close to each other, i.e. if the spatial structures of the two partners are fully complementary. Van der Waals' forces (unlike electrostatic interaction) lead to highly specific interaction;

*Covalent binding*

- *covalent binding*; in this type of interaction the two reactants fuse together to form one molecule. The bonds involved have a very high energy content, which means that they are very strong and virtually irreversible. Examples are the interactions between electrophilic metabolites and nucleophilic centers in DNA bases, and that between organophosphates and acetylcholinesterase. In toxicology, unlike in pharmacology, this type of binding plays a more important role;

*Hydrophobic bonding*

- *hydrophobic bonding*; some receptors consist of large lipophilic groups of molecules which form part of cellular membranes. Apolar molecules are, as it were, pushed in the direction of the hydrophobic (= lipophilic) receptor. These hydrophobic interactions are mostly non-specific. They do, however, make a distinct contribution to the affinity between receptor and toxic substance. Because of this type of interaction, receptor and toxicant can approach each other very closely so that van der Waals' forces may also come into play. The uptake of apolar molecules into, for example, cell membranes will cause changes in the functioning of these membranes due to thermodynamic changes. Examples are substances with an anesthetic effect, like ether and chloroform.

*Interactions without mediation of receptors*

In addition to the interactions mentioned so far, there are also interactions in which *no specific receptors* are involved. By no means all poisons act through interaction with specific sites of action. The toxic effects of many xenobiotics can be explained by certain non-specific chemical or physical properties. This is the case, for example, for strong acids or bases (damage to epithelial tissue or disturbance of the acid–base homeostasis) and chelating agents (binding of metal ions, and thus withdrawing certain essential elements from the organism).

### 2.1.2 Receptor theory

*Receptor*

Around 1900, the concept *receptor* was introduced to explain the effects of biologically active substances, which were often found to be effective at very low concentrations.

*Receptor sites*

The classic receptor theory developed at that time, assumes certain (macro)molecules to have binding sites (*receptor sites*) to which certain substances can bind more or less specifically, causing a biological effect.

*agonist = active substance*

The physiologist Langley was the first to observe that an active substance (in his case nicotine) could only bind to particular sites (on striated muscle tissue) and exert its effects there (muscular contraction). A specific complex must therefore be formed between the active substance, called the *agonist*, and the receptor, which leads to the induction of an effect (Figure 7.5). This concept of the combination of agonist and receptor site was developed by Langley in 1906, and later formulated in a quantitative form by Clark.

*Antagonist*

Clark assumed that the percentage of the maximum effect produced by a certain agonist concentration corresponds to the percentage of the receptor sites occupied by the agonist. This percentage is determined by the concentration of the agonist at the receptor site, and by the *affinity* of the receptor for the agonist. Occupation of a particular type of receptor was thought to give rise to identical effects, irrespective of the agonist's identity. This assumption, however, was found to be false. There are substances for which a particular receptor site does have an affinity, but whose binding to that site causes a smaller effect than binding of the agonist, or no effect. A substance is called an *antagonist*, if it reacts with the receptor or with other components of the effector system, resulting in inhibition of the action of the agonist, while the antagonist itself does not have any effect. Section 2.1.5 deals with the action of antagonists in greater detail.

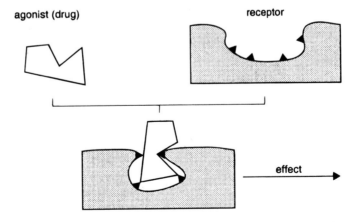

FIGURE 7.5

Diagram of the interaction between an agonist (drug) and a receptor
The figure shows the change in the conformation of the receptor and the resulting manifestation of a biological effect, e.g. an electric impulse.

It is assumed that the binding between agonist and receptor site is *reversible*, and that an *equilibrium* is reached:

agonist + receptors $\rightleftarrows$ agonist-receptor complex

### 2.1.3 Derivation of dose–response curves

Studies on the biological activity or toxicity of a substance often make use of isolated organs. Working with these organs avoids a number of complications that occur when experimenting on intact animals. Figure 7.6a shows a diagram of the experimental set-up using an isolated organ, in this case a piece of intestine.

If an isolated organ is exposed to various concentrations of the substance under investigation, a characteristic relationship is often found between the concentration used and the intensity of the effect (Figure 7.6b).

With the help of the receptor theory described above, a formula can be derived with which the results can be described mathematically.

The interaction between agonist and receptor is as an association–dissociation equilibrium, of which the position is determined by the dissociation constant $K_d$. Expressed mathematically:

$$\frac{[P][X]}{[PX]} = K_d \tag{7.1}$$

a

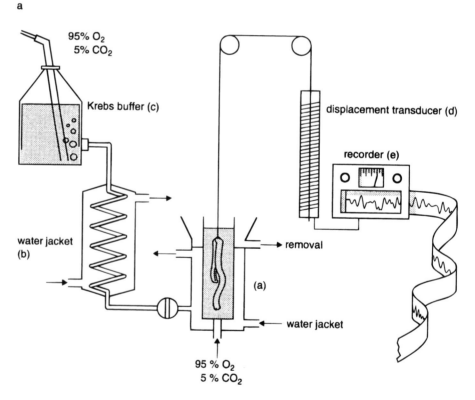

**FIGURE 7.6a**

Diagram of the experimental set-up of an isolated intestine

A piece of colon or duodenum is suspended in vessel (a). This portion is connected to a transducer (d), which transforms the contraction into an electric signal that is passed on to recorder (e). Vessel (a) also holds a special saline solution (Krebs buffer or other solution) which is supplied from vessel (c). A mixture of oxygen and carbon dioxide is led through this solution and is brought to the correct temperature in (b).

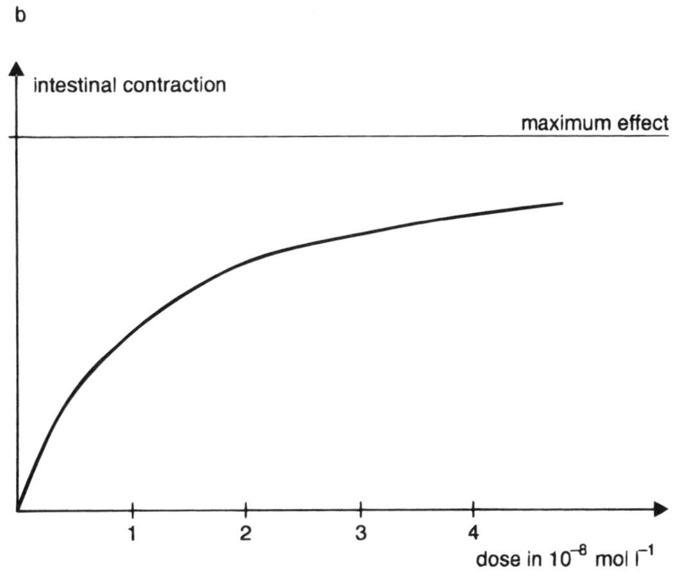

b

FIGURE 7.6b
Relationship between dose (moles of acetylcholine, x-axis) and biological effect (intestinal contraction, y-axis)

where:

$[P]$ = concentration of non-occupied receptor sites

$[X]$ = concentration of free effector (agonist) molecules

$[PX]$ = concentration of occupied receptor sites

ASSIGNMENT 7.3

Describe mathematically the concentration of the total number of receptor sites and the concentration of the total number of effector molecules.

*Note that $[X_{tot}]$ is in fact the only known concentration.*

Nearly always, only a very small proportion of the effector molecules is bound to the receptor ($[PX] \ll [X]$), so that the concentration of free effector molecules can be equated with the total concentration of effector molecules. In formula: $[X] = [X_{tot}]$.

The degree of occupation of the receptors as such is in most cases very difficult or impossible to measure. However, occupation of the receptor molecules provides a so-called *stimulus*, which in its turn causes a *measurable effect* (e.g. muscle contraction):

occupation receptor → stimulus → measurable effect (= response)

*The measurable effect is proportional to the number of recepors occupied by the agonist*

In general, the measurable effect is directly proportional to the number of receptor sites occupied by the agonist. Occupation of all receptors causes the maximum effect. If the effect $E$ is expressed as a fraction of the maximum effect $E_{max}$, then this fraction is equal to the occupied fraction (or percentage) of the receptor sites. This is described in the following equation:

*E is the relative effect (= effect/maximum effect)*

$$E = \frac{[PX]}{[P_{tot}]} = \frac{[PX]}{[P] + [PX]} = \frac{1}{\dfrac{[P]}{[PX]} + 1} = \frac{[X]}{\dfrac{[P][X]}{[PX]} + [X]} = \frac{[X]}{K_d + [X]} \qquad (7.2)$$

Graphically, the *log dose–response curve* is nearly always used in order to make the curve usable for very high and very low doses on the one hand, and on the other to transform it to a sigmoid curve with an approximately straight segment in the middle (Figure 7.7). The S-shaped curve is symmetrical in relation to point ([X],E) at which [X] = $K_d$ and E = 0.5. The position of the curve is determined by $K_d$ only.

ASSIGNMENT 7.4

Replot Figure 7.6b, now with the concentration on logaritmic scale.

As can be seen, Equation 7.2 has the same mathematical form as the *Michaelis–Menten equation* in enzyme kinetics. As in enzyme kinetics, the non-linear relationship between the concentration of free effector molecules [X] and the effect E can be transformed to a linear one, a *Lineweaver-Burk plot*, if 1/E is plotted against 1/[X]:

$$1/E = 1 + K_d/[X]$$

The Lineweaver-Burk plot is discussed in Study unit 5

ASSIGNMENT 7.5

Does this straight line always pass through the point (0,1)?

*2.1.4 Calculation of $K_d$*

The dissociation constant can be calculated in several ways. Both graphic and mathematical techniques can be used. It is possible, using mathematical transformations, to convert the dose–response relationship to a more manageable relationship. More specifically, $K_d$ can be determined:

- *directly from the dose–response relationship* (see Figure 7.7)
  If the dose ([X]) is plotted logarithmically, the central part of the sigmoid curve can be regarded as virtually linear. Using statistical linear regres-

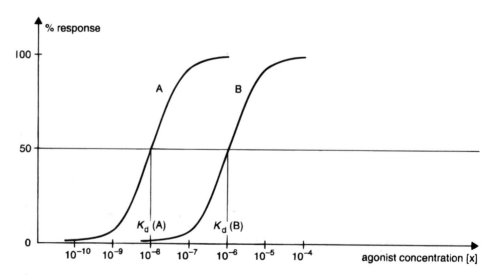

FIGURE 7.7

Relationship between dose and response for two agonists (A and B) with different $K_d$
The dose (in moles) has been plotted logarithmically.

sion techniques, the line best fitting the experimental values can be calculated. The intercept with $y = 50\%$ then gives $K_d$. Curve-fitting techniques can also be used to calculate the entire curve;

- *after transformation*

  There are various ways to transform the relationship between dose and
  response such that a linear relationship results. After such a transformation, it is possible to calculate $K_d$ from the experimental data using linear
  regression techniques. The *Lineweaver–Burk transformation* is most commonly used. $1/E$ is plotted against $1/[X]$. In a formula:

$$\frac{1}{E} = 1 + \frac{K_d}{[X]} \tag{7.3}$$

which is a linear relationship of the form: $y = a + b \times x$

If $a$ and $b$ have been determined on the basis of the experimental data, $K_d$ can
be calculated directly from this equation. Comparison with Equation 7.3 shows
that $a = 1$. In practice, $E_{max}$ is not given, but must be derived from the results.
(See Figure 7.8)

Other options are, for example, to plot $E$ against $E/[X]$, or $[X]/E$ against $[X]$.
This gives:

$$E = 1 - K_d \cdot \frac{E}{[X]} \tag{7.4}$$

and

$$\frac{[X]}{E} = K_d + [X] \tag{7.5}$$

respectively, and Figures 7.9a and b.

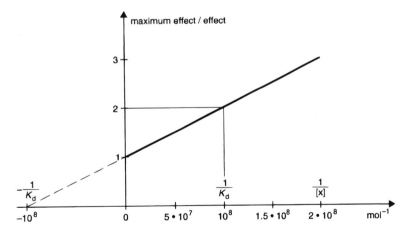

FIGURE   7.8
Double-reciprocal representation of the dose–response relationship (Lineweaver–Burk
plot)
$E_{max}/E$ has been plotted against $1/[X]$ for an agonist $x$ with $K_d = 10^{-8}$.

197

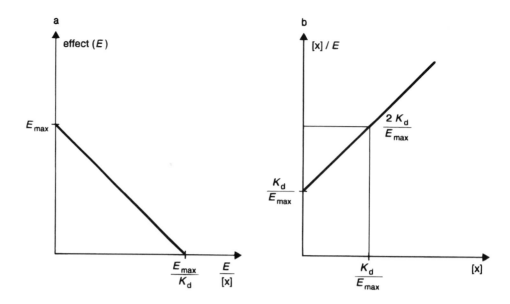

FIGURE   7.9a and b
Dose–response relationships plotted after two different transformations

### 2.1.5 Effect of an antagonist on the dose–response relationship

Antagonists are substances which in some way reduce the effect of an agonist. In (clinical) toxicology, antagonists can often be put to good use as antidotes. Four types of antagonists can be distinguished:

- *Competitive antagonism*

    firstly, there are substances that bind to the receptor in the same reversible manner as the agonist, but initiate no effect or a smaller effect than the agonist. The same intensity of effect can then be obtained by increasing the concentration of the agonist. The maximum effect has remained the same. This type of antagonist is called *competitive*.

    A substance that binds to a different site from that of the agonist and thus reduces the affinity of the receptor for the agonist also acts as a competitive antagonist. Here too, the inhibitory effect can be overcome by increasing the concentration of the agonist. The log dose–response curve then shows a parallel shift to the right (see Figure 7.10).

- *Non-competitive antagonism*

    secondly, there are substances which bind to the receptor system in such a way that their effect cannot be overcome by administering more of the agonist. This may be the case, for example, when the antagonist does not prevent binding of the agonist to the receptor, but does prevent the resulting effect. This type of substance is called a *non-competitive antagonist* (Figure 7.11).

- *Chemical antagonism*
  *Functional antagonism*

    in addition to these two types of antagonism, chemical and functional antagonism can be distinguished. In the case of *chemical antagonism*, the agonist is bound by the antagonist and thus made inactive. In *functional antagonism*, the antagonist acts in fact as an agonist, but then on a different system, causing an opposite effect.

The various forms of antagonism can be expressed mathematically as follows:

*Competitive antagonism:*

$$P + X \leftrightarrows PX \longrightarrow \text{effect}$$

$$P + Y \leftrightarrows PY \longrightarrow \text{no effect}$$

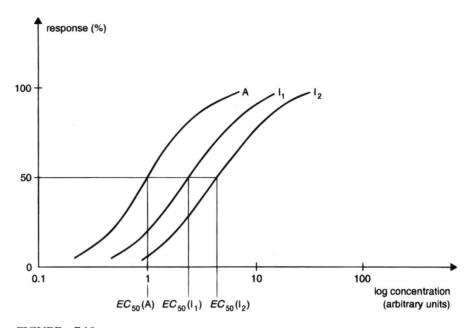

FIGURE   7.10
Dose–response curves of adrenaline (A) in the presence of the antagonist dihydroergot-amine in increasing concentrations ($I_1$ and $I_2$)

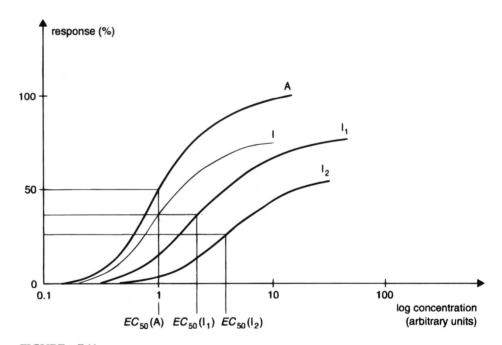

FIGURE   7.11
Effect of a non-competitive antagonist on the dose–response relationship
A is the curve for the agonist alone, I is the curve for the agonist in the presence of the antagonist, and $I_1$ and $I_2$ are curves for a mixed-type antagonist. In practice, mixed competitive/ non-competitive antagonists are quite common.

$$K_X = [X] \times [P]/[PX] \text{ and effect} \approx [PX]$$

$$K_X = [Y] \times [P]/[PY] \text{ and PY gives no effect or a smaller effect}$$

*Non-competitive antagonism:*

$$P + X \leftrightarrows PX; PX \text{ gives effect}$$

$$P + Y \leftrightarrows PY; PY \text{ gives no effect}$$

PY + X ⇆ PXY; PXY gives no effect

PX + Y ⇆ PXY

*Chemical antagonism:*

P + X ⇆ PX; PX gives effect

A + X⟶ AX; AX is an inactive product.

An example of a chemical antagonist is a substance which, by chelation, removes metal ions which play a role as a co-factor in enzymatic action.

*Functional antagonism:*

X + P$_1$ ⇆ P$_1$X; P$_1$X gives an effect

Y + P$_2$ ⇆ P$_2$Y; P$_2$Y gives the same effect as P$_1$X, but negative.

If P$_1$ and P$_2$ occur in the same cell, this is known as functional antagonism in the stricter sense. An example is the antagonism between histamine and $\beta$-adrenergic substances (e.g. isoproteronol) with respect to smooth muscle tissue in the bronchus.

*Physiological antagonism*

If the two substances act on different cell systems or organ systems and induce opposite effects, this is known as *physiological antagonism*.

Lack of insight into the biochemical modes of action of most toxic substances and drugs generally renders it impossible to make an unambiguous classification into various types of antagonism. For a competitive antagonist, the following equation for the dose–response relationship can be set up:

$$E = \frac{[X]}{[X] + K_X \left(1 + \dfrac{[Y]}{K_Y}\right)} \tag{7.6}$$

and in Lineweaver–Burk form:

$$\frac{1}{E} = 1 + K_X \left(1 + \frac{[Y]}{K_Y}\right) \cdot \frac{1}{[X]} \tag{7.7}$$

(This means that the intercept with the *y*-axis has not changed, but that the slope and the intercept with the *x*-axis have.) In Equation 7.7, $K_X$ and $K_Y$ are the reciprocals of the affinities of the receptor for X and Y, respectively. It is assumed that PY does not initiate any effect. If the effect is plotted against the log dose of the agonist, it is found that a competitive antagonist shifts the S curve to the right. If formulas are developed for non-competitive antagonism, one can see that the intercept of the Lineweaver–Burk line with the *y*-axis changes. Instead of 1, this is then:

$$\left(1 + \frac{[Y]}{[K'_Y]}\right)$$

In this formula, $K'_Y$ is the reciprocal of the affinity of PX for Y. In a normal log dose–response graph (e.g. Figure 7.11, curve I), there is not only a shift to the right, but also the maximum effect is no longer reached.

### 2.1.6 Other receptor theories

In many cases, the *classical theory* (occupation of receptors, mass action), as applied above, provides a satisfactory explanation of the facts observed. Sometimes, however, modifications or additions are necessary to give a satisfactory explanation. Such additions/modifications include:

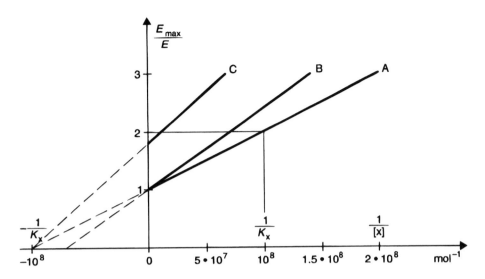

FIGURE   7.12
Double-reciprocal presentation of a dose–response relationship for an agonist alone (A), and in combination with a competitive antagonist (B) or a non-competitive antagonist (C)
$E_{max}$ is the maximum effect of the agonist

*Intrinsic activity*
Intrinsic activity means the extent to which a substance–receptor complex induces a biological effect (as percentage of the maximum effect)

*Minimum degree of receptor occupation*

- agonists may differ not only in affinity, but also in *intrinsic activity*;
- a biological effect is not observed until a certain *minimal extent of receptor occupation* has been reached. Only when a sufficient number of receptors have been occupied further occupation will lead to a biological effect.
- the maximum effect is sometimes reached before all receptor sites are occupied. This is in fact the reverse of the previous point. Further occupation of receptors does not lead to a greater effect because a different process in the chain of events determines the maximum effect.

In addition to the receptor theory discussed in this section, other theories have also been developed, which might be better able to explain some properties of agonists, antagonists and receptors. This will not, however, be discussed any further here.

The concepts of agonist and receptor and the corresponding theory described above, are used in pharmacology as well as in toxicology. In toxicology, however, the receptor theory and its consequences occupy a far less important position. This is because the specificity of toxicity is often very low, and because many reactions of toxic substances with endogenous substances or structures are irreversible (covalent binding is important in toxicology). Sometimes, however, long-term reversible binding to enzymes may give rise to a progressive pathological situation.

2.2   GRADED RESPONSE IN THE INTACT ANIMAL

Preceding sections have concentrated on relationships between substance and effect in isolated parts of an organism. This is of considerable significance for the study of, for example, the mechanism of action of substances. In order to examine the toxicity of a substance, however, it is necessary to focus (again) on what actually happens when a human, animal, or other organism, with its complex, interrelated systems, is exposed to a toxic substance. Numerous types of effects can be expressed as graded responses, for example changes in growth rate, organ weight, rise or drop in blood pressure and glucose level.

Generally, parameters are used which, in a healthy animal, are kept within certain limits by special regulatory mechanisms (homeostasis). External interferences will be compensated for as long as possible. Only when a certain *threshold* is exceeded deviations from the normal situation do occur. This may be compared to a heated room, in which the temperature is maintained despite changes in the outside temperature by a thermostatically controlled heating system. Only when the outside temperature rises or drops by extreme values will the temperature in the room also rise or drop.

*Threshold dose*

Exposure to toxic substances can also be regarded as an external factor. One may therefore expect a noticeable effect to take place only when a certain *threshold dose* has been exceeded. In the case of chronic or long term exposure to relatively low doses, the organism has the opportunity to put compensating mechanisms into action. Once the threshold is exceeded, however, these often rather slow mechanisms can no longer cope and a (toxic) effect develops. It can be seen that the relationship between dose and response in intact animals is rather a complex one. This is why it is not possible to draw up a generally applicable mathematical model for such a situation.

The graded response can be measured in a single individual. If the effect is fully reversible (within a practically reasonable period of time), a dose–response relationship can be established. Such effects are rare in toxicology, however. For more reliable results, groups of individuals are used for each dose. The dose–response relationship then consists of the average response per group (with standard deviation or any other measure of variation) for the various doses. From the dose–response relationship, one can, for example, calculate the threshold dose. This is of practical importance in determining the no-effect level of a substance and for admission of substances in foodstuffs, drinking water, etc. Various problems may rise when dealing with such matters, as will be obvious from the following examples.

EXAMPLE 1

Many substances cause enlargement of the liver on long-term exposure. A toxicity experiment with the fungicide hexachlorobenzene (HCB) showed that this substance caused a dose-dependent enlargement of the liver in female quails, along with other effects. The results of the experiment are shown in Figure 7.13. At dosages of 5 mg HCB per kg feed and higher, the relative weight of the liver was found to be significantly increased. This experiment would point to a no-effect level (only insofar as the weight of the liver is concerned) of 1 mg per kg feed. Figure 7.13 suggests a linear relationship between the log dose and the relative weight of the liver (in which case this line would lead to a threshold dose of approximately 1 mg kg$^{-1}$), but, considering the wide dispersion of the results, non-linear relationships cannot be excluded.

EXAMPLE 2

An experiment in which Japanese quails were given a daily dose of a particular type of polychlorinated biphenyl (PCB) for 7 days, showed a very large increase in the activity of the enzyme ALA synthetase ($\delta$-aminolevulinic acid synthetase). This enzyme plays an extremely important role in the synthesis of hemoglobin. It is not surprising, therefore, that this particular PCB causes disturbed heme synthesis and porphyria. The results are presented in Figure 7.14 (graph A). The

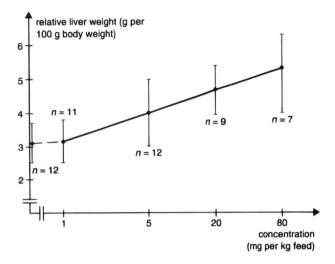

FIGURE 7.13
Effects of hexachlorobenzene (HCB) on the relative weight of the liver in female Japanese quails, administered in various concentrations in the feed for a period of 90 days
The figure shows mean values ±SD

lowest dosage of PCB used in this experiment (50 mg kg$^{-1}$) was still found to have quite a considerable effect. It can be seen from the figure whether this downward line will start bending away sooner or later at lower dosages. In a follow-up experiment (see graph B), much lower dosages were used. The results of this experiment show that there is at first a gradual, dose-dependent increase in activity, which bends upwards sharply between the dosage levels of 10 and 50 mg kg$^{-1}$, after which the dose–response curve has a considerably steeper slope. An explanation of this finding might be that the PCB affects enzyme synthesis and the regulation of that synthesis in two very different ways.

It is often impossible to draw any definite conclusions on the course of dose–response curves at very low dosages from toxicity data. The same can be said for the effects seen with such low dosages. It is therefore often impossible to determine whether there really is a threshold dose and, if so, how high it is. What usually can be determined is the dose at which the response exceeds a certain value (e.g. greater than the normal physiological variation) or the dose at which a statistically significant difference from the control group becomes observable.

*Summary*

This section discussed a number of aspects of the graded response, both in isolated organ preparations and in intact animals. The receptor theory provides insight, both qualitative and quantitative, into the action of substances at cell and organ level. The occurrence of a graded response in intact animals, however, appears to be rather different from this.

## 3 Quantal response

As stated earlier, many toxicological studies are not concerned with gradual responses, but with effects which *may or may not occur* at a particular dose. Examples are death, or the induction of a tumor. In these cases, the intensity of the effect is measured by *counting the number of responding individuals* in a group of equally exposed individuals.

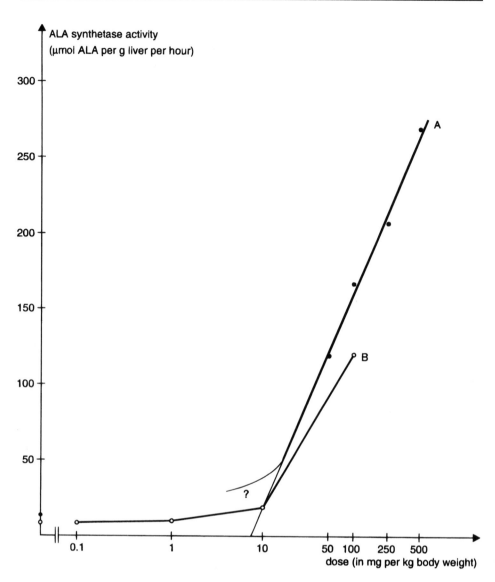

FIGURE 7.14

δ-ALA (δ-aminolevulinic acid) formed by hepatic mitochondria of Japanese quails exposed to various daily doses of PCB (Aroclor 1260) for a period of 7 days
A results of first experiment
B results of second experiment
Experiment 2 shows that A cannot be extrapolated linearly downwards, but bends away rather abruptly.

## 3.1   DEFINITIONS

The best-known application is the determination of the toxicity of a substance from the relationship between dose (or concentration) and lethality. To this end, animals are randomly distributed over a number of groups. All animals in one group receive the same dose of the substance under investigation, and for each group the dosage is gradually increased. The number of animals which die within a particular period of time (24 hours, 1 week, etc.) are counted.

*Threshold dose*

If all animals were equally sensitive, there would be a *threshold dose* below which all animals would remain alive, and above which all would die (Figure 7.15).

If toxicity experiments are carried out with a series of dosages, it appears that in practice this is not the case, provided the differences between subsequent dosages are not too large. This observation is based on the variation in sensitivity within a population. The more sensitive individuals die at a lower dose than the more resistant ones. In a homogeneous population, many individuals have an average sensitivity, while the percentage of animals which are much more or much less sensitive decreases as one moves away further from the mean. This can be plotted in a *frequency diagram* as shown in Figure 7.16.

A bell-shaped curve can be drawn through the diagram. The diagram is not symmetrical but is skewed towards the left. This is usually the case if the dose as such is plotted on the *x*-axis. This phenomenon will be discussed in more detail at a later stage.

If a dose $d_i$ is administered to a population of animals or a sample from it, all the animals sensitive to this dose as well as all animals with higher sensitivity will actually die. This means that the total number of deaths is the sum of all an-

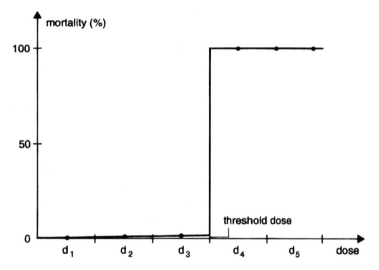

FIGURE 7.15

Graph showing mortality caused by substance x if all animals within an experimental group were to be equally sensitive

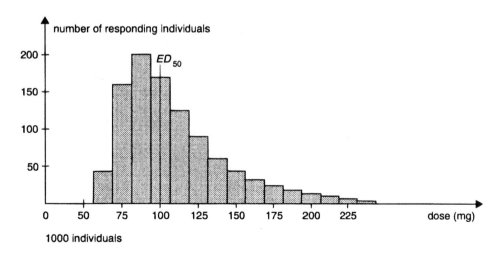

FIGURE 7.16

Relationship between dose and number of individuals responding by displaying a certain effect

**NB**: the distribution in this figure is asymmetrical. The $ED_{50}$ (median), which divides the surface area of the diagram into two equal parts, does not coincide with the top of the diagram (the mode).

imals under the curve to the left of $d_i$. Plotting this for various dosages results in the S-shaped curve in Figure 7.17.

*$LD_{50}$, $ED_{50}$*
*Definition*

When toxicity is described in quantitative terms, the concepts $LD_{50}$ (lethal dose 50%) and $ED_{50}$ (effective dose 50%) are often used. $ED_{50}$ is the dose which, according to the *dose–response relationship*, would cause the effect in 50% of the population. The dose–response relationship is the curve (according to the statistical or mathematical model applied) that fits the experimental data most satisfactorily.

*$LC_{50}$, $EC_{50}$*

If the *concentration* is used instead of the dose to express the extent of exposure, the concepts $LC_{50}$ and $EC_{50}$ are applied.

ASSIGNMENT 7.6

Define the concepts $ED_{10}$ and $ED_{99}$.

The term "median dose" or "median effective dose" means the same as $ED_{50}$.
In addition to this toxicity measure, the variation in sensitivity within a population is also important. The slope of the log dose–response relationship is a direct measure of this variation. The smaller the variation, the steeper the curve. In other words: standard deviation $(\sigma) \approx (\text{slope})^{-1}$.

*Logarithm of the dose*

Experience has shown that if lethality is plotted against the *logarithm of the dose* (or concentration) the result is a curve which is indistinguishable from the *cumulative Gaussian curve* corresponding to a statistical *log normal distribution*. The distribution of the sensitivity to a particular substance over a (homogeneous) group thus appears to be log normal (Figure 7.18). This enables statistical analysis of the results of a toxicity experiment.

ASSIGNMENT 7.7

Combine the 24–hour lethality data of the two replications shown in Table 7.2, and plot the results obtained against the log concentration.

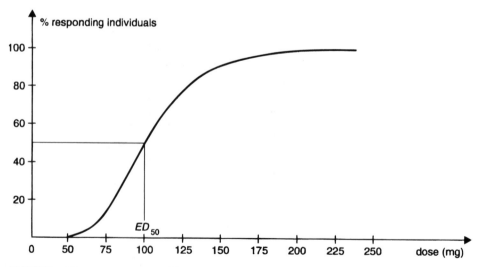

FIGURE 7.17
Relationship between dose and percentage of animals which responded at a certain dose
This is a cumulative representation of the responding individuals shown in Figure 7.16.

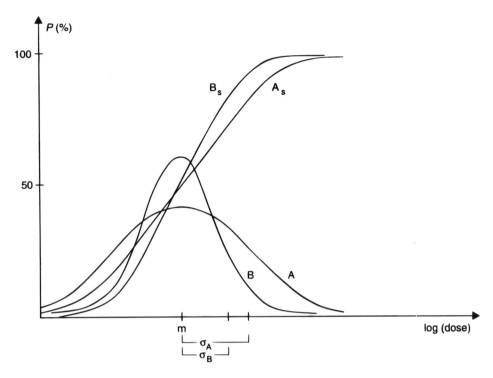

FIGURE 7.18
Frequency distribution of the sensitivity (curves A and B) and the cumulative dose-response curves ($A_s$ and $B_s$)
$\sigma_A = 1$
$\sigma_B = 0.67$

TABLE 7.2
Results of an acute toxicity experiment in prawns exposed to a series of dilutions of an effluent from a refinery

| | | | Number of animals dead | |
| --- | --- | --- | --- | --- |
| Concentration | Replication | n | 24 hours | 48 hours |
| control | 1 | 10 | 0 | 0 |
| | 2 | 10 | 0 | 0 |
| 10% | 1 | 10 | 0 | 2 |
| | 2 | 10 | 1 | 1 |
| 18% | 1 | 10 | 1 | 3 |
| | 2 | 10 | 1 | 3 |
| 25% | 1 | 10 | 2 | 5 |
| | 2 | 10 | 3 | 4 |
| 32% | 1 | 10 | 5 | 9 |
| | 2 | 10 | 7 | 7 |
| 56% | 1 | 10 | 10 | 10 |
| | 2 | 10 | 10 | 10 |
| 100% | 1 | 10 | 10 | 10 |
| | 2 | 10 | 10 | 10 |

The experiment was repeated a second time (* replication 2). n gives the number of animals in the test group. (Buikema *et al.* 1982, Table 2, p. 243.)

The sensitivity of an organism to a toxic substance will depend on a large number of randomly distributed factors, so that a statistical distribution according to the log normal model is not unlikely. Nevertheless, other distributions are possible, which (in the range usually applied in experiments, i.e. 5–95% response) would also give a satisfactory description of the results of toxicity experiments (See Table 7.2).

## 3.2    DOSE–RESPONSE CURVES

Mathematical relationships between dose and response have been established from theoretical models (e.g. the normal distribution as a statistical model). In addition, researchers are interested in summarizing experimental observations in a mathematical formula, so that more generally applicable statements can be made. To this end, transformation of the experimentally obtained values is often necessary, for example logit and probit transformations, which will be dealt with in the following sections.

As was mentioned earlier, in homogeneous populations the dose–response curve is S-shaped and can be described as a cumulative Gaussian curve. If the mean and the standard deviation are known, the sensitivity curve is completely defined. The mathematical expressions for the sensitivity distribution and the dose–response relationship are included in the Addendum as Equations 7.8 and 7.9. From these equations it follows that:

- the frequency distribution is symmetrical around the mean $m$, the highest frequency at $x = m$;
- $P(m) = 0.5$, i.e. $m = \log (ED_{50})$;
- $P$ (the responding fraction of the group) becomes very small at low doses, but will never be zero (in other words, in this model there is no threshold dose below which there is no effect).

The use of this model for the statistical description of toxicity experiments will be elaborated on in the following section. It should be noted that there is no need to use the normal distribution. There are also other suitable distributions available.

*Logistic growth curve*

The S-shaped dose–response relationship is often described using a so-called logistic curve. This curve is also used to describe the growth of populations, and is for this reason referred to as the *logistic growth curve*.
Formula for the dose–response relationship:

$$P(D) = (1 + e^{\log(a)-b\cdot\log(D)})^{-1} = \frac{D^b}{a + D^b} \tag{7.10}$$

where $D$ stands for dose, and $a$ and $b$ are parameters determining the curve. The position of the dose–response relationship is determined by $a$, while the slope is determined by $b$. Like the normal distribution, this formula gives a symmetrical sensitivity distribution, which approaches zero rather more slowly at both extremes. Here, the mean value is at $D = a^{1/b}$. Within the range which is generally relevant in experiments (5–95% response), the two curves cannot really be distinguished from each other. They can only be distinguished if experiments are performed with thousands of individuals per group (megamouse experiments), and provided there are no interfering factors such as a lack of homogeneity. If, however, one extrapolates to very low dosages and therefore also to very low response frequencies, the differences become significant. Differences in response frequency of, for example, $10^{-5}$ and $10^{-6}$ may be small in an absolute sense, but may still mean the difference between 600 and 60 victims if applied to, e.g. a large population. As an example, Table 7.3 compares a log normal model and a log-logistic model. The results are shown graphically in Figure 7.19.

ASSIGNMENT 7.8

What would be the number of victims in a population of 15 million people, according to the log normal model and according to the log-logistic model, if everyone were to be exposed to 1/1000 of the $LD_{50}$ of the substance in Table 7.3?

$$P(D) = \frac{D^b}{a + D^b} \qquad (7.10)$$

TABLE 7.3

Expected response percentage (percentage of victims) in a fictitious situation for the log normal and the log-logistic model over a range of dosages

| Dose (arbitrary units) | Log normal (%) | Log logistic (%) |
|---|---|---|
| 16 | 98 | 96 |
| 8 | 93 | 92 |
| 4 | 84 | 84 |
| 2 | 69 | 70 |
| 1 | 50 | 50 |
| 1/2 | 31 | 30 |
| 1/4 | 16 | 16 |
| 1/8 | 7 | 8 |
| 1/18 | 2 | 4 |
| 0.01 | 0.05 | 0.4 |
| 0.001 | 0.00035 | 0.026 |
| 0.0001 | 0.0000001 | 0.0016 |

Values chosen were: the mean D = 1 and SD/$SC$ = log(4).

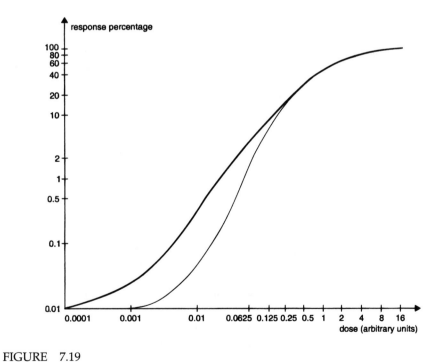

FIGURE 7.19

Graphic representation of the figures in Table 7.3

The bold line shows the (expected) response percentages for a log normal distribution, while the light line shows the logistic distribution. As can be seen the lines hardly differ from each other in the range between 5 and 95% response, but the deviations at response percentages < 5% are considerable.

NB: If, in Equation 7.10 $b = 1$, the formula becomes similar to that for the graded response of isolated organ systems (see Equation 7.2). However, in virtually all toxicity experiments $b > 1$.

*Hit theory*

Certain statistical models have been developed which are not based on a sensitivity distribution but on what are known as hit theories. A *hit theory* assumes that if an essential structure receives one or more "hits" from the substance, there will be an effect. The chance that a hit will occur depends on the concentration of the substance. Section 5.1 discusses this in somewhat greater detail with regard to carcinogenic substances.

### 3.3 STATISTICAL ANALYSIS: CALCULATION OF $LD_{50}$

The results of toxicity experiments provide data on the response intensity at various dosages. To make a general statement on the toxicity of a substance for the entire population on the basis of these results, obtained from a population sample, requires statistical analysis.

In the following, three different analytical methods will be described, namely:

- analysis using *logit transformation*
- analysis using *probit transformation*
- a *graphical method*.

### 3.3.1 Analysis using logit transformation

The analysis of the results of a toxicity experiment can be based on a logistic dose–response relationship. This can be done by logits.

A logit is no more than a mathematical transformation which serves to make the dose–response curve linear. The mathematical definition of a logit is:

$$\text{logit}(P) = \ln \frac{P}{1 - P}$$

where $P$ = the fraction of responders in the group exposed to dose $D$.

The formula for the dose–response relationship is then:

$$\text{logit}(P) = a + b \cdot \ln(D) \tag{7.11}$$

in which:

$b$ = slope of the line

$a$ = intercept with the $y$-axis (= logit $(P)$-axis)

If $\log D$ is plotted on the $x$-axis, and the corresponding logit $P$ on the $y$-axis, the result is a straight line. Using linear regression methods (for example the principle of least squares; see Study unit 8, section 3.1.2), the straight line best fitting the experimental data can be found.

When the principle of least squares is applied, a number of complications arise. First, not all points are equally valuable for the analysis. Points close to the 50% response carry more weight than those around high and low percentages. To be able to correct for this, a weighting factor is introduced. From statistical theory, it follows that the weighting factor is:

NB: $(1 - P)$ is often written as $Q$.

$$W = n P(1 - P) \tag{7.12}$$

where:

> $W$ = weighting factor
>
> $n$ = number of individuals in the group

All values for log dose ($x$ values) and logit $P$ ($z$ values) must be multiplied by the weighting factor.

A problem with weighting factors is that for $P$ one should really use the value derived from the best-fitting dose–response relationship, but that is exactly what one is trying to find!

*Iterative method*

As a first approximation, the value for $P$ found experimentally is used to calculate $W$, and this is then used to calculate the line. For a second approximation $W$ and $P$ values are used that correspond to the log dose values used, according to the calculated line. With these values, a new line is calculated. One can continue doing so until there are no longer any differences between subsequent lines. From the resulting line, the data required, for example the $LD_{50}$, can then be derived. This method is called an *iterative method*. Instead of $P = 0$ and $P = 1$ (0 and 100%, respectively), approximations frequently used are $P = 1/2n$ and $P = 1 - 1/2n$ respectively. The best estimates for $a$ and $b$ ($\hat{a}$ and $\hat{b}$), the corresponding variances $V_a$ and $V_b$, the $LC_{50}$ and the variance in the $LC_{50}$ ($VLC_{50}$) are obtained by applying the method of least squares from Equations 7.13 to 7.19. These are included in the Addendum.

---

EXAMPLE

Water fleas (*Daphnia magna*) were exposed to various concentrations of dichlorobenzene in the water for a period of 48 hours. The results were as follows:

TABLE

| $C$ | $x$ | $n$ | $m$ | $P$ | $Z$ | $W$ |
|-----|------|-----|-----|------|-------|--------|
| 10 | 2.30 | 51 | 0 | 0.00 | −4.62 | 0.50* |
| 16 | 2.77 | 54 | 6 | 0.11 | −2.08 | 5.33 |
| 25 | 3.22 | 54 | 8 | 0.15 | −1.75 | 6.81 |
| 40 | 3.69 | 51 | 12 | 0.24 | −1.18 | 9.18 |
| 64 | 4.16 | 59 | 40 | 0.68 | +0.74 | 12.84 |

$C$ = concentration in mg $l^{-1}$, $x$ = ln (concentration), $n$ = number of animals in the group, $m$ = number of dead animals, $P$ = fraction of animals that died, $Z$ = logit ($P$), $W$ = weighting factor.
Calculating according to the formula e gives:
$LC_{50} = 51.41$
$\hat{b} = 2.29$
$\hat{a} = -8.78$
* for $P$ the following approximation was chosen: $P = \dfrac{1}{2n} = 0.0098$

---

A complete calculation is provided in Appendix A.

---

ASSIGNMENT   7.9

Calculate the $LD_{50}$ and the slope of the logit line for the data provided in Table 7.2 (48 hours, both replications together).

### 3.3.2 Probit analysis

If the results of a quantal response experiment are plotted with the percentage of responding individuals on the *y*-axis and the log dose on the *x*-axis, the result is, as stated before, an S-shaped curve.

*Application of the probit method*

This curve can be transformed to a straight line by rescaling of the *y*-axis. To that end, the percentage of responding subjects for each dosage is expressed in a new unit which is known as the *probit*. A regression line through the points thus obtained can be calculated from the probits corresponding to the percentage of responding subjects and the logarithm of the administered dose. Figure 7.20 shows the results of this procedure, applied to the data in Table 7.4.

*Theoretical derivation of the probit method*

The probit method uses transformation of the response percentages found on the basis of the log normal distribution. The normal distribution can be described by a standard normal curve, in which the mean $\mu = 0$ and the standard deviation $\sigma = 1$. In a population with normal distribution, 68.3% are within the limits of the mean ($\mu$) $\pm 1$ standard deviation (*SD*, $\sigma$), while 95.5% are within $\mu \pm 2\sigma$, and 99.7% within $\mu \pm 3\sigma$. As was stated before, quantal response phenomena generally have a log normal distribution. Therefore, the response percentage from an experiment can be transformed to units of standard deviation of the mean.

TABLE 7.4

Data from a quantal response toxicity experiment

| Dosage (mg kg⁻¹) | Log dose | Response (dead versus living animals) | % dead animals | Probit value |
|---|---|---|---|---|
| 1.6 | 0.20 | 0/15 | 0 | – |
| 2.0 | 0.30 | 1/15 | 7 | 3.52 |
| 2.5 | 0.40 | 2/15 | 13 | 3.87 |
| 3.2 | 0.51 | 7/15 | 46 | 4.90 |
| 4.0 | 0.60 | 10/15 | 67 | 5.44 |
| 5.0 | 0.70 | 12/15 | 80 | 5.84 |
| 6.3 | 0.80 | 14/15 | 93 | 6.48 |
| 8.0 | 0.90 | 15/15 | 100 | – |

The table shows the relationship between does and response (i.e. the death of the experimental animal). The probit values have been derived from Table 7.5B.

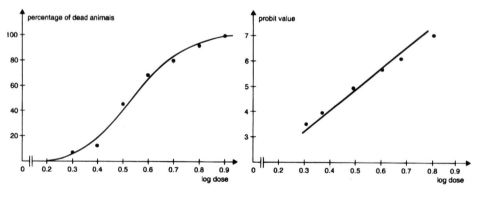

FIGURE 7.20

Graphic representation of the probit transformation using the numerical example in Table 7.4

*Normal equivalent deviations*

*Probability unit*

This is shown in Figure 7.21. This unit is referred to as *normal equivalent deviation (NED)*. In such a transformation the NED for 50% is 0, while an NED of +1 corresponds to 84.1% and a NED of −1 to 15.9%. In practice, however, negative figures are avoided, which is why NEDs are not used as such, but only after the number 5 has been added. The latter unit (NED + 5) is called the *probability unit*, or *probit*. A 50% response thus corresponds to a probit of 5, a response of 84.1% to a probit of 6, etc. If the log dose (or log concentration) is plotted on the *x*-axis, and the corresponding response percentage in probits on the *y*-axis, and if the data obtained do indeed comply with the log normal model, the result is a straight line. This line has a slope of $1/\sigma$, and passes through the point $(\mu, 5)$. This procedure has been followed for the data in Table 7.4.

For experimental results, the best-fitting line will have to be calculated. The straight line constructed using probits can be described mathematically as follows:

$$pr = \frac{1}{\sigma}(x - \mu) + 5 = a + b \cdot \log(D) \qquad (7.20)$$

where:

$pr$ = number of probits corresponding to the percentage of responding subjects

$\sigma$ = standard deviation

$x$ = ln (concentration)

$\mu$ = mean number of dead animals

The coefficients *a* and *b* have the same meaning as in Equation 7.11, but have different numerical values here.

As is the case for logits (see Table 7.5A), there are also probit tables from which for each response percentage the corresponding probit can be read directly. See, for example, Table 7.5B.

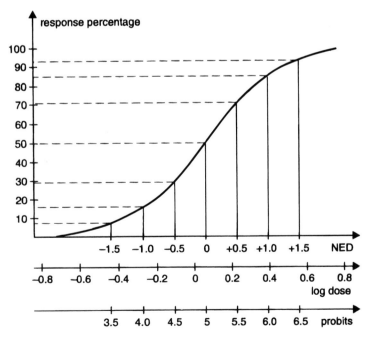

FIGURE   7.21
Graphic representation of the response percentage in *NED* and probits

213

By way of illustration, the response percentages from the dichlorobenzene experiment from the preceding sections are shown below, now using probits.

EXAMPLE (SEE THE DATA IN THE EXAMPLE OF LOGIT ANALYSIS, SECTION 3.3.1)

TABLE

| C (mg l⁻¹) | n | P(%) | Probits | In C |
|---|---|---|---|---|
| 10 | 51 | 0 | 2.67* | 2.30 |
| 16 | 54 | 11 | 3.77 | 2.77 |
| 25 | 54 | 15 | 3.96 | 3.22 |
| 40 | 51 | 24 | 4.29 | 3.69 |
| 64 | 59 | 68 | 5.47 | 4.16 |

*profit determined for $P = 1/2n$.
Calculation using the principle of least squares gives the line:
$pr = 1.32 \ln(D) - 0.214$. For $LC_{50}$ the pr(obit) = 5.
Substitution gives: in $LC_{50} = 3.94$, so that $LC_{50} = 51.9$ mg l⁻¹

TABLE   7.5A
Table for transformation of percentages into logits

| Percentage | 0 | 1 | 2 | 3 | 4 | 5 | 6 | 7 | 8 | 9 |
|---|---|---|---|---|---|---|---|---|---|---|
| 50 | 0 | 0.04 | 0.08 | 0.12 | 0.16 | 0.20 | 0.24 | 0.28 | 0.32 | 0.36 |
| 60 | 0.41 | 0.45 | 0.49 | 0.53 | 0.58 | 0.62 | 0.66 | 0.71 | 0.75 | 0.80 |
| 70 | 0.85 | 0.90 | 0.94 | 0.99 | 1.05 | 1.10 | 1.15 | 1.21 | 1.27 | 1.32 |
| 80 | 1.38 | 1.45 | 1.52 | 1.59 | 1.66 | 1.73 | 1.82 | 1.90 | 1.99 | 2.09 |
| 90 | 2.20 | 2.31 | 2.44 | 2.59 | 2.75 | 2.94 | 3.18 | 3.48 | 3.89 | 4.60 |
| 99 | 4.60 | 4.70 | 4.82 | 4.95 | 5.11 | 5.29 | 5.52 | 5.81 | 6.21 | 6.91 |

The table only shows the percentages $p > 50\%$. Because the logit of percentages $p < 50\%$ equals the negative value of $100 - p$, the values for percentages < 50% can also be read from the table.
Example 1: Find the logit of 68%. Sixty is second in the first column, while 8 is in the horizontal row above the table. The two rows intersect at the value 0.75. The logit of 68% is therefore 0.75. Example 2: Find the logit of 42%. This equals –logit (100 – 42%), i.e. –logit 58%, which is –0.32.

TABLE   7.5B
Table for transformation of percentages into probits

| Percentage | 0 | 1 | 2 | 3 | 4 | 5 | 6 | 7 | 8 | 9 |
|---|---|---|---|---|---|---|---|---|---|---|
| 0 | – | 2.67 | 2.95 | 3.12 | 3.25 | 3.36 | 3.45 | 3.52 | 3.59 | 3.66 |
| 10 | 3.72 | 3.77 | 3.82 | 3.87 | 3.92 | 3.96 | 4.01 | 4.05 | 4.08 | 4.12 |
| 20 | 4.16 | 4.19 | 4.23 | 4.26 | 4.29 | 4.33 | 4.36 | 4.39 | 4.42 | 4.45 |
| 30 | 4.48 | 4.50 | 4.53 | 4.56 | 4.59 | 4.61 | 4.64 | 4.67 | 4.69 | 4.72 |
| 40 | 4.75 | 4.77 | 4.80 | 4.82 | 4.85 | 4.87 | 4.90 | 4.92 | 4.95 | 4.97 |
| 50 | 5.00 | 5.03 | 5.05 | 5.08 | 5.10 | 5.13 | 5.15 | 5.18 | 5.20 | 5.23 |
| 60 | 5.25 | 5.28 | 5.31 | 5.33 | 5.36 | 5.39 | 5.41 | 5.44 | 5.47 | 5.50 |
| 70 | 5.52 | 5.55 | 5.58 | 5.61 | 5.64 | 5.67 | 5.71 | 5.74 | 5.77 | 5.81 |
| 80 | 5.84 | 5.88 | 5.92 | 5.95 | 5.99 | 6.04 | 6.08 | 6.13 | 6.18 | 6.23 |
| 90 | 6.28 | 6.34 | 6.41 | 6.48 | 6.55 | 6.64 | 6.75 | 6.88 | 7.05 | 7.33 |
| 99 | 7.33 | 7.37 | 7.41 | 7.46 | 7.51 | 7.58 | 7.65 | 7.75 | 7.88 | 8.09 |

### 3.3.3 Analysis using graphic methods

A special type of graph paper has been developed which makes it relatively easy to present the results of toxicity experiments graphically. This paper is based on the log normal distribution. Percentages are plotted along the $y$-axis, at distances that correspond to probits (the distance between 50 and 60%, for example, is much smaller than that between 80 and 90%), while the $x$-axis is divided logarithmically. If the results of a toxicity experiment match the log normal distribution, the experimental values will lie on a straight line. Often a straight line can be drawn through the measured points, just by eye. The point of intercept of that line with the line $y = 50\%$ is $LD_{50}$. It is often also possible to get a first impression of the correspondence to the assumed model. For example, if a population is not homogeneous but consists of a mixture of two populations with sufficiently different sensitivity distributions, the resulting line is curved rather than straight.

Using the $\chi^2$ test (chi squared test), it is possible to check whether the drawn line corresponds to the points given, by calculating:

$$\chi^2 = \sum \frac{(\text{observed} - \text{expected})^2}{\text{expected}} \tag{7.21}$$

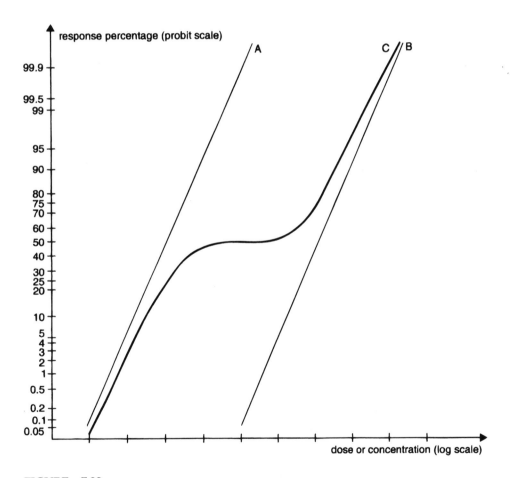

FIGURE 7.22

Dose–response relationships for three populations A, B and C (C is a 1 : 1 combination of A and B)

Along the $x$-axis, the doses are plotted logarithmically, while the $y$-axis shows the response percentages according to the probit model.

For the type of experiment under discussion, this is:

$$\chi^2 = \sum_i \left\{ \frac{n_i}{P_i \cdot (1 - P_i)} (p_i - P_i)^2 \right\} \qquad (7.22)$$

where:

$p_i$ = observed response frequency in dose group $i$

$n_i$ = number of animals in group $i$

$P_i$ = response frequency according to the drawn line

The number of degrees of freedom is the number of dose groups minus 2.

If the value found for $\chi^2$ is too large, there are two possibilities: $a$ the line was not selected properly (select new line and repeat test) $b$ the observations do not match the model used (e.g. non-homogeneous population of test animals, significant lethality due to other factors).

For a long time, a method of estimating $LD_{50}$ and its standard deviation has been followed for which graph paper (referred to as log probability paper) was used together with tables and nomograms. Now that calculators and computers are widely available, this method (of Litchfield and Wilcoxon) is rather outdated. Figure 7.23 shows graphically how a concentration–response relationship is transformed to a probit versus concentration graph.

### 3.3.4 Effect of interfering factors

*Spontaneous effects*

A common interfering factor in the analysis of dose-response data is the occurrence of *spontaneous effects* in the non-exposed control group, for example death in the control group. If this effect occurs, part of the lethality in the exposed groups will have to be attributed to other (unknown) causes. When determining the dose–response relationship, this will have to be corrected for. If the spon-

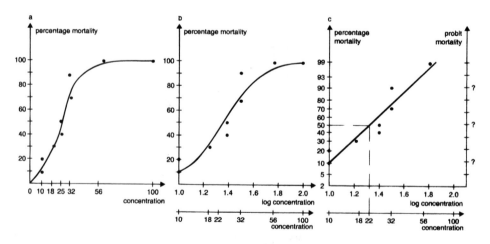

FIGURE   7.23

Transformation of a mortality curve

$a$ non-transformed plot of concentration versus mortality percentage (x-axis linear, y-axis linear)

$b$ logarithmic representation of the same figure as in a (x-axis logarithmic, y-axis linear)

$c$ plot of log concentration versus the probit value of the mortality (x-axis logarithmic, y-axis in probits)

216

taneous death can be assumed to occur independent of death caused by the administered substance (if this is not the case, matters become very complicated indeed), *Abbott's correction formula* can be applied.

If a fraction $c$ of the individuals were to respond in the absence of the substance, the response frequency $P^*$ for dose $D$ would be:

$$P^*(D) = c + (1-c) \cdot P(D) \qquad (7.23)$$

From this it follows that the response frequency resulting from exposure to the substance is:

$$P(D) = \frac{P^*(D) - c}{1 - c} \qquad (7.24)$$

If $c$ is known, the analysis can then proceed as has been described above. In practice, however, $c$ can only be estimated more or less accurately from the results of the control group.

---

EXAMPLE

Experiment in which water fleas were exposed to various concentrations of an algae killer in the water for a period of 50 hours

---

ASSIGNMENT 7.10

Using the logit method, calculate the $LC_{50}$ for the corrected $P$ values presented in the above example.

### 3.4 SIGNIFICANCE OF $LD_{50}$

*Definition of $LD_{50}$*

$LD_{50}$ is often considered to be a constant that indicates how toxic a substance is. It is, however, merely a statistical expression to describe the lethal effect of a substance on a particular population under certain circumstances, and not a fundamental property of a substance. $LD_{50}$ is only a statistically determined parameter which is a measure of the lethality of a substance under the experimental circumstances. It is used, for example, to compare the toxicities of substances with each other and to classify the substances according to their potential hazard (Table 7.6).

The extent to which $LD_{50}$ has been used in the past for assessing the safety of substances could almost be termed as abuse. Although determination of the $LD_{50}$ under well-described circumstances provides valuable information on the toxicity of a substance, this information only concerns one aspect of the toxicity,

TABLE

| $C$ (concentration mg $l^{-1}$) | $n$ (number of animals) | $m$ (number of dead animals) | $P^*$ (response) | $P$ (corrected) |
|---|---|---|---|---|
| 0 | 50 | 3 | 0.06 | — |
| 16 | 54 | 6 | 0.11 | 0.05 |
| 25 | 54 | 8 | 0.15 | 0.10 |
| 40 | 51 | 12 | 0.24 | 0.19 |
| 64 | 59 | 40 | 0.68 | 0.66 |

The corrected $P$ was calculated using Equation 7.24. In this example $c = 0.06$.

TABLE 7.6
The $LD_{50}$ and $LC_{50}$ used as a basis for the toxic risk phrases in the EU Classification, Packaging and Labeling Regulations

| | | |
|---|---|---|
| *very toxic substances* | | |
| - if swallowed | $LD_{50} < 25$ mg/kg | (acute oral rat) |
| - in contact with skin | $LD_{50} < 50$ mg/kg | (acute dermal rat/rabbit) |
| - by inhalation | $LC_{50} < 50$ mg/l/4h | (acute inhalation rat) |
| *toxic substances* | | |
| - if swallowed | 25 mg/kg $< LD_{50} < 200$ mg/kg | (acute oral rat) |
| - in contact with skin | 50 mg/kg $< LD_{50} < 400$ mg/kg | (acute dermal rat/rabbit) |
| - by inhalation | 0.5 mg/l/4h $< LC_{50} < 2$ mg/l/4h | (acute inhalation rat) |
| *harmful substances* | | |
| - if swallowed | 200 mg/kg $< LD_{50} < 2000$ mg/kg | (acute oral rat) |
| - in contact with skin | 400 mg/kg $< LD_{50} < 2000$ mg/kg | (acute dermal rat/rabbit) |
| - by inhalation | 2 mg/l/4h $< LC_{50} < 20$ mg/l/4h | (acute inhalation rat) |

namely lethality. Of much greater importance are, for example, the slope of the dose–response curve, the effects and the rate at which they occur, the pathological symptoms, etc.

*Extrapolation*

It is dangerous to evaluate the toxicity of a substance exclusively on the basis of an $LD_{50}$ value. It should also be born in mind that it is difficult to *extrapolate* the $LD_{50}$ of a substance for a particular population of an animal species to other populations of that species, under slightly different conditions. Extrapolation to a different species, for example man, gives extremely uncertain results. Also, from the viewpoint of reducing the use of experimental animals, fewer $LD_{50}$ determinations are carried out. Comparison of $LD_{50}$ values determined in various laboratories often shows that there are large differences. In a *round robin study* (a large-scale interlaboratory study) in which the $LD_{50}$ of a substance in male rats was determined in 65 laboratories simultaneously, the variation in the measured $LD_{50}$ value appeared to be more than tenfold. This means that there is often no point whatsoever in attempting to determine $LD_{50}$ very accurately.

*Summary*

Quantal response relationships can be represented as a sigmoid curve. In order to draw more general conclusions from the results of a random sample survey, it is necessary to be able to describe the population in which the survey was carried out. Empirically, in many cases the normal distribution (Gaussian distribution) has proven to be an adequate description of the frequency distribution of a large number of substances. The Gaussian curve can be plotted cumulatively, causing it to become S-shaped (Figure 7.18). With the aid of a mathematical transformation, the experimental response percentages corresponding to certain log dose values can be plotted as logits. The graph thus obtained is a straight line, provided the population has a homogeneous distribution and originates from a normal distribution.

Plotting the cumulative normal distribution on a probability scale also results in a straight line. The deviations from the mean in units of standard deviation corresponding to the percentage of responding subjects can be read from tables. Increasing these figures by five gives the so-called probits. In practice, probits are always positive. A probit of 5 corresponds to the mean, i.e. 50% response.

In addition to transformation methods, there is also a graphic method which makes use of log normal paper. Because of the introduction of computers, however, this method is hardly ever used.

Sometimes, spontaneous effects occur in an experimental animal population. In that case, it is necessary to correct the experimental values. This can be done, for example, by applying Abbott's correction formula.

In toxicology, the $LD_{50}$ (or $LC_{50}$) has often been (and in fact still is) determined. As long as there is no suitable substitute for this parameter, it will no doubt continue to be used, although there are many objections attached to its use. To start with, the $LD_{50}$ gives information on only one toxic effect, namely death. In addition, the resulting value can only be applied to the actual test animal and depends strongly on the experimental conditions.

## 4 Time factor

In addition to dose-response relationships, relationships between time and dose (or concentration) are also important. In toxicology, the factor time may play a role in various ways, for example in *bringing about the effect*, but time may also be a *part of the effect*. This statement will probably become more clear in the discussion on the classification of the various ways in which the word 'time' is used in toxicology.

### 4.1 CLASSIFICATION

In toxicology, the factor time has two clearly distinguishable aspects, namely:

*Time versus duration*

a.  time *until* the effect

- the time after administration of a single dose until an effective concentration is reached in or near the target organ by distribution throughout the body;
- the time until an effective concentration is reached in or near the target organ through accumulation during long-term exposure;
- the time required for the accumulation of effects (e.g. primary biochemical lesions) which eventually lead to a pathological effect.

b.  *duration* of the effect

Point a. also includes the latency period between exposure to a carcinogenic substance and the development of a tumor (see section 4.4).

### 4.2 ONSET AND DURATION OF THE EFFECT IN A SIMPLE REVERSIBLE PROCESS

The concept of duration of effect is of course only useful if the effect disappears again, in other words if the effect is reversible. Although this is not very common in toxicology, it is still useful to consider such a case.

An example is *narcosis* (anesthesia) induced by barbiturates (Figure 7.24). If the narcosis is unintentional, this can be regarded as a toxic effect.

*Minimum effective concentration, $C_{eff}$*

*Narcosis* occurs if the concentration of the barbiturate in the central nervous system exceeds a certain limit (*minimum effective concentration, $C_{eff}$*). An important factor here is the kinetics of the barbiturate. If it is administered intravenously, the blood concentration will reach a high level almost immediately. The blood transports the substance to the brain. In general, this takes some time, but for many barbiturates only little time is needed so that—provided the dose was sufficient—the threshold concentration in the brain is soon exceeded and narcosis sets in. Meanwhile, the substance is distributed further through the body (e.g. into body fat), followed by metabolism and excretion. The rate at which these

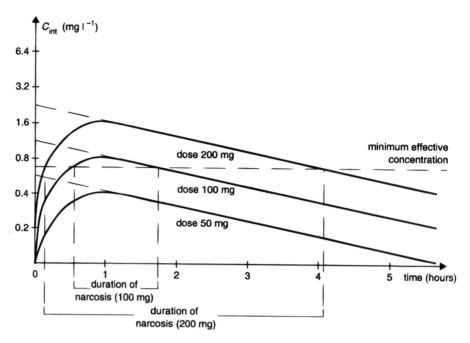

FIGURE   7.24
Hypothetical internal concentration curves for three different doses of an anesthetic
The effect of the dose on the duration of narcosis is shown.

processes take place is determined by the barbiturate concerned and by the organism. In this respect the following relationship exists:

$$C_{int,t} = D(e^{-\beta \cdot t} - e^{-\alpha \cdot t}) \tag{7.25}$$

where

$C_{int,t}$ = internal concentration (in the nervous system) at time $t$

$\beta$ and $\alpha$ = two parameters related to the transport to and from the organ concerned (in this case the central nervous system)

$D$ = constant determined by the initial concentrations and the rate constant for transport from plasma to central nervous tissue

$C_{eff}$ = internal concentration above which the effect sets in.

There is an effect if $C_{int} \geq C_{eff}$

4.3   EFFECT OF EXPOSURE TIME

Often, exposure to a toxic substance does not result from intake or administration of a single dose but of a series of doses for a *longer period of time*. This is certainly true from environmental pollutants in water and air, but also from substances present in food.

*Cumulative dose*

If a substance is present at a constant concentration ($C$), the quantity absorbed will be proportional to that concentration times the time passed since the beginning of the exposure. In other words, the *cumulative dose* is proportional to $C \cdot t$. If the effect occurs at the time when the effective dose is absorbed, i.e. when the cumulative dose equals the effective dose, then $C \cdot t = K$ (a constant). This relationship has indeed been found in a number of cases, e.g. for the toxic effect of certain nerve gases.

$C \cdot t = K$ can also be written as:

$$\log(C) + \log(t) = k, \text{ or} :$$

$$\log(t) = k - \log(C) \qquad (7.26)$$

In many cases, however, this relationship does not entirely hold true. One then applies the following formula:

$$\log(t) = k - a \cdot \log(C) \qquad (7.27)$$

This means that a log-log plot is a straight line, not with a slope of 45°, but either less or more steep (see Figure 7.25).

It often appears that, at high concentrations, the time required for the effect to manifest itself does not become any shorter. Apparently a minimum period of time is needed for the effect to become manifest. Further, even with a very long exposure time, below a certain concentration no effect occurs. The latter concentration is known as the *incipient effective concentration*. If the response is 50% lethality, this is known as the *incipient $LC_{50}$* (see Figure 7.26). This can be expressed as follows

*Incipient effective concentration*

$$(C - C_{inc}) \cdot (t - t_{min}) = \text{constant} \qquad (7.28)$$

The above considerations are only relevant as long as metabolism and excretion of the substance do not play a dominant role. If this is the case, the internal concentration may remain so low that no effect will occur (see also Study unit 6).

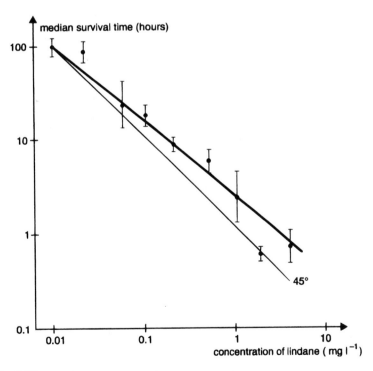

FIGURE 7.25
Log-log plot representing the toxicity curve for the survival time of *Daphnia pulex* after continuous exposure to lindane
The thin line has a slope of precisely 45°.

221

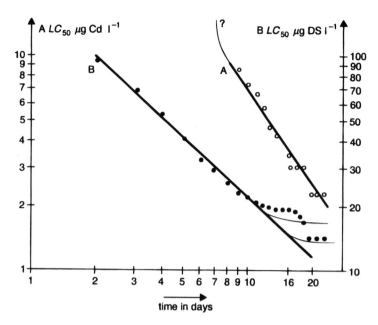

FIGURE 7.26
Relationship between $LC_{50}$ and time before manifestation of effects, for cadmium (A) and disulfiram (B) in water fleas (*Daphnia pulex*)

ASSIGNMENT 7.11

Give a (potential) incipient $LC_{50}$ and a minimum time until the effect manifests itself in Figure 7.26.

ASSIGNMENT 7.12

Can an incipient $LC_{50}$ be regarded as a threshold concentration, comparable to the threshold dose discussed in the preceding section?

## 4.4 LATENCY PERIOD

It takes some time after single-dose or short-term exposure to a carcinogenic substance before the first clinical symptoms (tumor) become manifest. The time between exposure and effect, the *latency period*, depends on the dose to which one is exposed. Sometimes, the latency period may be as long as several decades. A mesothelioma, for example, does not develop until about 5 years and sometimes even 30–40 years after exposure to asbestos fibers.

Mesothelioma is a malignant tumor of the pleura.

As was described by Druckrey in 1967, the following generally applies:

$$t \cdot D^n = \text{constant} \tag{7.29}$$

where:

$t$ = median latency period (= time after exposure until a tumor has developed in 50% of the population).

$D$ = dose or concentration and

$n$ = exponent that is usually greater than 1 and that depends on the substance, on the organism and on the test conditions. If, for example, $n = 3$, the latency period becomes eight times as long if the dose is halved.

4.5   DELAYED EFFECT

The effect of some substances is evident only after a long exposure time. This is not because the substance first needs to accumulate in the organism, but because cumulation of (primary) effects has to take place before the actual toxic effect manifests itself.

*Anticoagulants are agents which inhibit blood clotting.*

Examples of such substances can be found among the anticoagulants, which are used, for example, as rat poison.

EXAMPLE

The rodenticide Endocid® inhibits prothrombin synthesis. As long as there is sufficient prothrombin in the blood, coagulation proceeds normally. It is not until after exposure for a number of days (e.g. in the form of bait) that the prothrombin reserve becomes depleted and severe internal hemorrhages occur, causing the rat to die. If the dose is high enough to cause sufficient inhibition of synthesis, after about 5 days virtually all exposed animals die in a relatively short time (Table 7.7).

*Summary*

In this section, the role of the time factor in toxicology was briefly discussed. This role is particularly important in the case of chronic exposure to toxic substances, as may occur in everyday life. Finally, exposure to high doses of toxic substances with severe acute effects is (fortunately) rare. Some special aspects have also been dealt with, as they may arise in the case of carcinogenic substances and substances with delayed effect.

5   **Extrapolation models**

*Low dose-extrapolation*

The effects of low concentrations expected in the environment or in food are often predicted from results of tests in animals using high dose levels. The extrapolation from high doses is complicated by many factors. It is difficult to predict the shape of the dose–response curve at lower doses with certainty. Models used for low-dose extrapolation fall into the following classes: tolerance distri-

TABLE   7.7
Median mortality time of brown rats, after administration of the anticoagulant Endocid® in the feed

| Concentration in the feed (mg kg⁻¹) | Median mortality time (in days) |
|---|---|
| 0.8 | >40* |
| 1.6 | 30 |
| 3.2 | 6 |
| 6.5 | 5 |
| 12 | 7 |
| 25 | 5 |
| 50 | 5 |
| 100 | 6 |
| 200 | 5 |
| 400 | 6 |

*all rats were still alive after 40 days

223

bution simple linear extrapolation, hit models like one-hit and multiple-hit and time-to-tumor models.

*Threshold dose*

It is generally assumed that toxic substances do not cause a harmful effect below a certain dose. This implies the existence of a *threshold dose*. Exposure below this dose would then not pose a risk to health.

*Acceptable daily intake*
ADI = amount of a chemical, usually restricted to pesticides and food additives, that can be ingested daily, by humans, for an entire life-time without causing appreciable adverse effects.

*Tolerance distribution model*

The assumption of a threshold is adopted when the *ADI (acceptable daily intake)* is established. Applying safety factors, the no observed-adverse effect levels found in toxicity experiments in animals are extrapolated to (most probably) safe exposure standards in man.

The tolerance distribution model assumes a threshold for each individual below which they would not be affected. The key assumption is that the *variation among individual threshold levels* can be described by a probability distribution function. Commonly used distributions are the normal or the logistic distribution.

## 5.1 CARCINOGENIC SUBSTANCES

The extremely high doses used in carcinogenesis testing are unrealistic for extrapolating low dose effects. High doses may cause metabolic and pharmacokinetic effects not seen at lower doses. Therefore they may not even lie on an upward extrapolation from intermediate doses. High doses are valuable for demonstrating carcinogenic potential, but may not be appropriate for use in extrapolations for risk assessment.

See Study unit 13

For carcinogenic substances, the assumption of a threshold is generally not accepted (in most cases there is no evidence for the existence of an absolute threshold dose). Instead, it is assumed that every exposure to a carcinogenic substance increases the risk of developing cancer. For certain groups of substances, however, which are involved in carcinogenesis but do not themselves initiate the process, the assumption of a threshold dose is believed to be correct.

*The $ED_{01}$ or megamouse study*

Data from dose–effect relationships in carcinogenity using low doses are scarce. An exception is the National Center for Toxicological Research low dose carcinogenity study from 1980. This so-called *megamouse* or $ED_{01}$ study was designed to study the low end of the dose–response curve for the well-known carcinogen 2-acetylaminofluorene (2-AAF). A total of almost 25,000 mice were dosed with the compound. Only urinary bladder and liver tumors were found to be related to the administration of 2-AAF. This study showed that there was no reason to believe that a threshold existed below which no cases of tumor would result from exposure to a chemical carcinogen. Furthermore, this study clearly showed the twin effects of increasing the dose of a carcinogen reducing the induction time and increasing the total tumor yield. It is self evident that the precise study of low-dose effects is so resource intensive that comparable experiments will be extremely rare in the future.

### 5.1.1 Single and multiple hit models

*Single hit*

As an argument against the existence of a threshold dose, it has been postulated that one single "attack" on DNA may lead to uncontrolled growth of a somatic cell, which may eventually result in the formation of a tumor. Averaged out over the tissue, the relationship between the response ($p$) and (low) daily doses ($d$) will be approximately linear if the following assumptions are made: the single cell is the risk-determining unit, there is a threshold for initiation and there is a random distribution of these cell initiation thresholds.

Expressed in a formula:

$$p = 1 - e^{-k \cdot d}$$

If $k \cdot d$ is very small, this becomes:

$$p \approx k \cdot d \tag{7.30}$$

At low doses, the chance of an effect may, of course, become so small (in relation to the size of the population and the natural incidence of tumors) that there is in fact a threshold dose.

The results of carcinogenicity tests in animals that have a low natural (spontaneous) tumor incidence indicate that not one but *several hits* are required, or that there should be hits in several phases of the carcinogenic process (tumorigenesis).

*Single-hit versus multiple-hit model*
*The multi stage model is dealt with in Study unit 13.*

There are indeed, apart from the *single-hit model*, two more models: the *multiple-hit* and the *multi-stage model*.

In the *single-hit* model, also known as the one-hit model, the tumor response ($I$) is proportional to the dose $(d)$:

$$I \approx k \cdot d$$

In the *multiple-hit* model the tumor response is proportional to a power of the dose:

$$I \approx (k \cdot d)^m \tag{7.31}$$

In addition to tumorigenesis as a result of exposure to the carcinogen, spontaneous tumor incidence ($I_0$) should also be taken into account. Assuming that the spontaneous incidence arises as a response to background stimuli of which the "dose" is equivalent to a dose $a$ of the carcinogen, then:

$$I \approx (k \cdot d + a)^m \quad \text{and} \quad I_0 \approx a^m$$

*Increase in tumor frequency*

The *increase in tumor frequency* caused by the carcinogen ($\Delta I$) is thus:

$$\Delta I \approx I - I_0 = (k \cdot d + a)^m - (k \cdot d)^m \tag{7.32}$$

If the relative increase in tumor frequency, $\Delta I/I_0$, and the relative daily dose, $k \cdot d/a$ (i.e. the dose causing $\Delta I$ relative to the dose causing $I_0$) are plotted logarithmically against each other in the case of $m = 3$, Figure 7.27 is obtained.

The course of the different lines may be explained by the following equations:

$$\frac{\Delta I}{I_0} = \left(\frac{k \cdot d}{a}\right)^3 + 3\left(\frac{k \cdot d}{a}\right)^2 + 3\left(\frac{k \cdot d}{a}\right) \tag{7.33}$$

Equation 7.33 explains why $\Delta I/I_0$ and $k \cdot d/a$ are plotted against each other. For relatively high values of $d$ the total equation (7.33) holds true. In Figure 7.27 this is indicated by $\approx d^3$. If $d$ decreases, first $(k \cdot d/a)^3$ can be neglected, and sub-

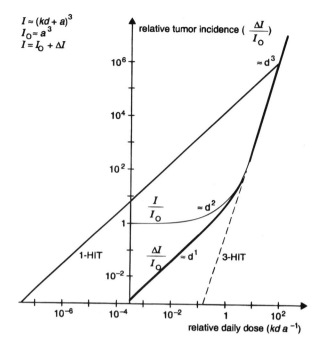

FIGURE 7.27
Relative increase in tumor incidence plotted against the relative daily dose

sequently the term $3(k{\cdot}d/a)^2$. This means that if $k{\cdot}d << a$; $\Delta I/I_0$ is proportional to the dose, as in the case of the single-hit model:

$$\frac{\Delta I}{I_0} = 3\left(\frac{k \cdot d}{a}\right) \quad \text{or} \quad \Delta I = 3(k \cdot d)\,a^2$$

The intercept for the curve when $I/I_0$ and $k{\cdot}d/a$ are plotted logarithmically against each other, may be explained by the following equation:

$$\frac{I}{I_0} = \left(\frac{k \cdot d}{a}\right)^3 + 3\left(\frac{k \cdot d}{a}\right)^2 + 3\left(\frac{k \cdot d}{a}\right) + 1 = \frac{\Delta I}{I_0} + 1 \qquad (7.34)$$

If the spontaneous tumor incidence is relatively high (as is often the case in man), the single-hit model constitutes a reasonably workable approach, as is indicated above ($k{\cdot}d << a$).

### 5.1.2 Mantel–Bryan model

Various methods are used, all of which attempt to extrapolate to low response frequencies on the basis of data obtained experimentally or otherwise. The dose or concentration which, in the particular model used, leads to a certain, previously agreed, very low response frequency (sometimes $P = 10^{-8}$, but also $10^{-6}$) is then believed to be acceptable from a health risk point of view.

*Mantel–Bryan procedure*

An example is the *Mantel–Bryan procedure*. This method is based on the probit (log normal) model (Figure 7.28). Extrapolation is from the *observed* dose–response points downwards to $10^{-8}$ by means of a straight line with a slope of 1 (the probit line through the measured points virtually always has a slope > 1). A second "conservative" element (i.e. an element leading to a low, definitely safe value) which has been introduced is the use of the upper limit of the 99% confidence interval rather than the actual response percentage.

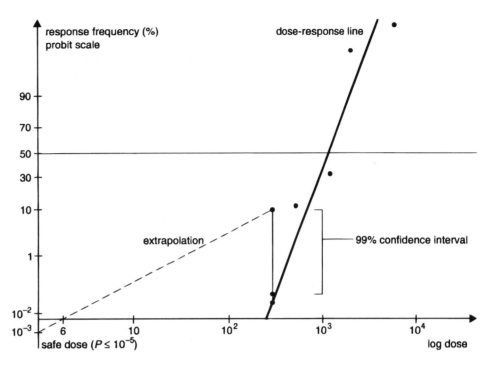

FIGURE 7.28
Extrapolation to find the safe dose according to the Mantel-Bryan procedure (dashed line)

The Mantel–Bryan model has been criticized in that it often does not fit even the observed values. Various correction factors have been proposed. Despite the attempted corrections, this type of simple extrapolation is still subject to criticism, and most risk assessment involves more complex models.

## Summary

The present study unit discussed how the intensity of the effect of a substance and the quantity of that substance to which the organism has been exposed, are related in a number of situations. The graphical relationship between the dose of a substance and the response is called the dose–response curve. It assumes a causal relationship between the substance and the effect being measured. It implies that there is an active site for the substance (*receptor*) and that the manifestation of the response is related to the concentration of the substance at that site. Furthermore it is assumed that the concentration of the substance at the active site is related to the dose administered or to the time and concentration of exposure. Both the relationship between the log dose and the relative effect in the case of a graded response, and the relationship between the log dose and the cumulative fraction of responding individuals show a sigmoid curve. Apart from this superficial similarity in shape, there are many differences. The most important properties of both relationships are summarized in the table below.

Despite the simplicity of the arbitrary rule "the more of a substance (or the longer the exposure), the greater the effect" (Paracelsus), it requires rather complicated operations to transform the obtained data to a (quantitatively) manageable form. Non-linear plots of dose–response are not easily extrapolated, and various mathematical transformations are used to provide straight or extrapolatable lines. Dose is almost always expressed on a logarithmic scale, whereas response is often expressed in probability units (probits).

## SELF-ASSESSMENT QUESTIONS

1   Epinephrine causes an increase in blood pressure in dogs. Cheng and Russel studied the influence of yohimbine on this effect. The results of their experiments are shown in the table below. Is yohimbine a competitive or a non-competitive antagonist of epinephrine? Calculate $E_{max}$ and $K_X$ (for adrenaline) and $K_Y$ (for yohimbine).

2   Two groups of trout of different origin were exposed to various concentrations of fluoride in the water during 3 weeks. Calculate the $LC_{50}$ for both groups and draw the log concentration–response lines. What would be the consequences if the results of both groups were added up? Each concentration group consisted of ten fish.

### TABLE IN SAMENVATTING

| Curve | Application | Basis | Slope at point of infection | Position on dose axis |
|---|---|---|---|---|
| log dose, graded response (fraction of maximum effect) | in individual or isolated systems | receptor theory | equal for similar mechanisms (mass action law) | individual sensitivities or $K_d$ |
| log dose, quantal response (cumulative fraction responders) | in populations | empirical (statistical-theoretical) | sd of sensitivity distribution | median sensitivity of population |

Increase in blood pressure (in mm Hg) in dogs caused by epinephrine as affected by yohimbine

| Epinephrine (μg kg⁻¹) | Yohimbine-HCl (μg kg⁻¹) | | | | | | |
|---|---|---|---|---|---|---|---|
| | 0 | 2 | 8 | 32 | 64 | 128 | 256 |
| 1 | 70 | 46 | 30 | 16 | 14 | 10 | 6 |
| 2 | 110 | 74 | 58 | 28 | 20 | 12 | 8 |
| 4 | 148 | 110 | 90 | 58 | 42 | 24 | 14 |
| 8 | 180 | 152 | 132 | 96 | 80 | 58 | 34 |
| 16 | 194 | 188 | 178 | 134 | 116 | 96 | 72 |

| Concentration fluoride mg l⁻¹ | Number of dead fish | |
|---|---|---|
| | Group A | Group B |
| 22 | 10 | 10 |
| 9 | 6 | 10 |
| 6 | 3 | 8 |
| 4 | 0 | 6 |
| 2.5 | 1 | 5 |
| 1 | 0 | 1 |

3   Indicate for the examples below whether there is a graded or a quantal response:

- standing on a busy traffic junction leads to an increase in the % CO-hemoglobin in the blood;
- staying in a room with 300 ppm CO for 3 hours caused severe headache in 80% of the subjects in a test group;
- during a period of severe smog in London in 1952, 2484 persons died in 1 week, while the average weekly mortality before the smog period was 850;
- in a toxicity experiment in fish, the activity of the enzyme acetylcholinesterase in the brain was determined after 8 weeks of exposure to parathion. The results were as follows:

  control   = $0.43 \pm 0.08$ mol AChE per mg per hour (mean $\pm SD$)
  11 gl$^{-1}$   = $0.24 \pm 0.05$ mol AChE per mg per hour (mean $\pm SD$)
  110 gl$^{-1}$ = $0.18 \pm 0.12$ mol AChE per mg per hour (mean $\pm SD$)

- fish exposed to DDT recovered earlier from MSS 222 narcosis than control fish, namely after 4 and 6 minutes, respectively.

4   Transform the data below from a graded response to a quantal response. Take a 25% reduction as a standard for the quantal response. Determine $ED_{50}$.

5   On the basis of Figure 7.29, calculate the time until effect of three different concentrations of methylmercury:
   a.   for the effect on "head maintenance"
   b.   for the effect on "tail position".

FEEDBACK

1   **Answers to the assignments**

7.1   The daily dose is $1.5 \cdot 80 = 120$ $\mu$g per day. The total uptake of copper will be many times larger. The copper content of liver is about 50 mg kg$^{-1}$, so that someone who consumes 100 g of liver already ingests 5 mg copper.

7.2   No, the conversion of a quantal response to a graded one is basically impossible. If, however, the number of exposed individuals is very large, counting is sometimes replaced by measuring. An example of this is the measurement of the hemoglobin that dissolves on hemolysis of red blood cells due to the action of certain substances. The hemoglobin plasma concentration (= graded response) is then determined, rather than the percentage of lysed cells (= quantal response).

| Dose | Effect (reduction in hemoglobin content in %) per animal | | | | | |
|------|-----|----|----|----|----|----|
| 1    | −5  | 0  | 5  | 5  | 15 | 20 |
| 1.3  | 0   | 5  | 5  | 15 | 25 | 30 |
| 1.7  | 10  | 10 | 10 | 25 | 25 | 30 |
| 2.2  | 20  | 25 | 30 | 30 | 30 | 40 |
| 2.9  | 25  | 30 | 30 | 35 | 40 | 40 |

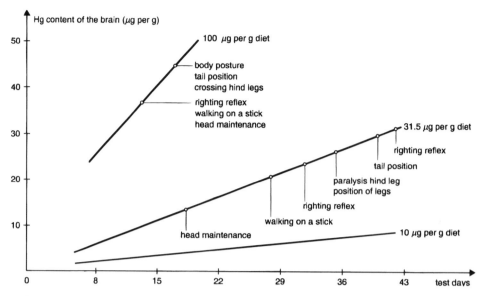

FIGURE 7.29
Concentrations of mercury in the brain of mice and the manifestation of neurological symptoms after exposure to methylmercury through the feed

7.3 The concentration of the total number of receptor sites $[P_{tot}] = [P] + [PX]$, and the concentration of the total number of effector molecules $[X_{tot}] = [X] + [PX]$.

7.4 See figure.

7.5 By definition, the line passes through point $P(0,1)$, because for this point: effect = maximum effect.

7.6 $ED_{10}$ ($ED_{99}$) is the dose at which the effect is found in 10% (99%) of the individuals in a population.

7.7 Recalculation for two replications taken together gives:

| Concentration | N | 24 hours | 48 hours |
|---|---|---|---|
| control | 20 | 0 | 0 |
| 10% | 20 | 1 | 3 |
| 18% | 20 | 2 | 6 |
| 25% | 20 | 5 | 9 |
| 32% | 20 | 12 | 16 |
| 58% | 20 | 20 | 20 |
| 100% | 20 | 20 | 20 |

The results have been plotted linearly in Figure a and semilogarithmically in Figure b.

7.8 $LD_{50}$, the dose at which 50% of persons will die, equals the average here, i.e. is a dose of $1 \cdot 1/1000$ of the $LD_{50}$ is therefore 0.001 in Table 7.2. In a log normal model, this corresponds to 0.00035%, and in the log-logistic model to 0.026%. Out of 15 million people the following numbers of victims can thus be expected :

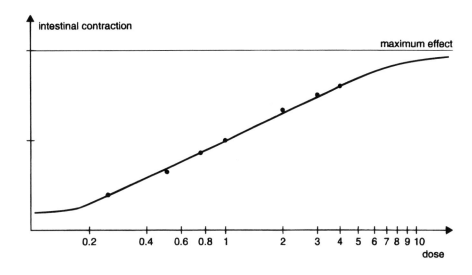

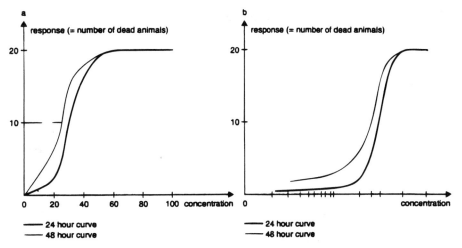

log normal model: $35 \cdot 10^{-5} \cdot 10^{-2} \cdot 15 \cdot 10^{6} = 52.5$
log-logistic model: $26 \cdot 10^{-3} \cdot 10^{-2} \cdot 15 \cdot 10^{6} = 3900$

7.9   $LC_{50} = 22.8\%$, $\hat{b} = 2.65$

First, make a table similar to that in the example in section 3.3.1 (see also answer 7.7).

The slope of the logit line is $\hat{b}$, and according to Equation 7.14 this is:

$$\frac{\sum W \cdot x \cdot z \cdot \sum W - \sum W \cdot x \cdot \sum W \cdot z}{\sum W \cdot x^{2} \Sigma - \left(\sum W \cdot x\right)^{2}} = \frac{(7.12 \cdot 15.88) - 49.24 \cdot (-0.97)}{(156.57 \cdot 15.88) - (49.24)^{2}} = 2.65$$

$$\ln LC_{50} = -\frac{\hat{a}}{\hat{b}}$$

Calculation according to Equation 7.13 gives $\hat{a} = -8.27$
In $LC_{50} = 3.125$, so that $LC_{50} = $ antilog $3.125 = 22.76$.

Depending on whether you have calculated the logits or have read them from Table 7.5a, you will find small deviations in the various values.

| C concentration | n number of animals | m (48 hrs) number effect | P percentage | z logit (P)* | W n· P(1 – P) | x ln C |
|---|---|---|---|---|---|---|
| 0 | 20 | 0 | 0.00 | –3.66 | 0.48 | – |
| 10 | 20 | 3 | 0.15 | –1.73 | 2.55 | 2.30 |
| 18 | 20 | 6 | 0.30 | –0.85 | 4.20 | 2.89 |
| 25 | 20 | 9 | 0.45 | –0.20 | 4.95 | 3.22 |
| 32 | 20 | 16 | 0.80 | 1.39 | 3.20 | 3.47 |
| 56 | 20 | 20 | 1.00 | 3.66** | 0.48 | 4.03 |
| 100 | 20 | 20 | 1.00 | 3.66** | 0.48 | 4.61 |

\* The approximation $P = 1/2n$ (= 0.025) is used.
\*\* The approximation $P = (1 – 1/2n)$ (= 0.975) is used.

7.10  $LC_{50} = 54.8$ mg $l^{-1}$

Using Equations 7.13, 7.14 and 7.17 in the Addendum, and using the corrected $P$ values, â and b̂ are first calculated, and from these the corrected $LC_{50}$ is calculated.

Intermediate values: $\Sigma W = 28.5$; $\Sigma W z = -20.87$; $\Sigma W x = 106.74$; $\Sigma W x^2 = 405.87$; $\Sigma W x z = -60.95$.

Substitution gives:
â = –11.3; b̂ = 2.82 and $LC_{50} = 54.98$ mg $l^{-1}$.

7.11  Line B in Figure 7.26 clearly bends away on longer exposure times. If the experiment had been terminated after 16 days, one would have concluded that the incipient $LC_{50} = 20$ mg $l^{-1}$. However, one must conclude that it is somewhat lower. Line A in the figure seems to indicate that it takes at least 10 days before 50% lethality is reached. For this length of the experiment, there are still no indications of an incipient $LC_{50}$.

7.12  No. At or below a threshold dose, the effect no longer manifests itself. At the incipient $LC_{50}$, 49% lethality may still be observed (quite apart from any other effects).

2    **Answers to the self assessment questions**

1    If the results are plotted (see Figure 7.32), the maximum effect appears not to change for the low doses of yohimbine (2 and 8 $\mu$g kg$^{-1}$). This means that this is a competitive antagonist. For the higher doses, the data do not allow a sufficiently reliable conclusion on whether $E_{max}$ changes or remains the same.

Using linear calculation, the Lineweaver–Burk plot (Figure 7.33) shows $E_{max} = 229$ and $K_X = 2.25$ $\mu$g kg$^{-1}$.

If Equation 7.7 is used, then one finds that for $D_{yohimbine} = 2$ $\mu$g kg$^{-1}$, $K_Y = 2$ mg kg$^{-1}$.

2    $LC_{50}$ A     : 7.9 mg $l^{-1}$
$LC_{50}$ B     : 2.8 mg $l^{-1}$
$LC_{50}$ A + B : 4.9 mg $l^{-1}$

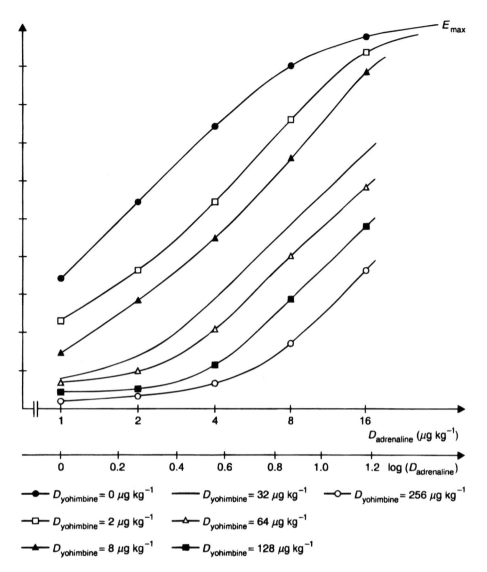

FIGURE 7.32

Although there is a significant difference in sensitivity between both groups, in this case combination still gives a more accurate (or in fact an apparently more accurate) result.

A perfect dose-response relationship is no evidence of homogeneity.

3  Graded, quantal, graded, graded, graded.

4  $EC_{50} = 1.6$
See also Figure 7.35.

5  Table

|  | $10\,\mu g\,g^{-1}$ | $31.5\,\mu g\,g^{-1}$ | $100\,\mu g\,g^{-1}$ |
|---|---|---|---|
| head maintenance | > 43 d | 18 d | 14 d |
| tail position | > 43 d | 40 d | 17 d |

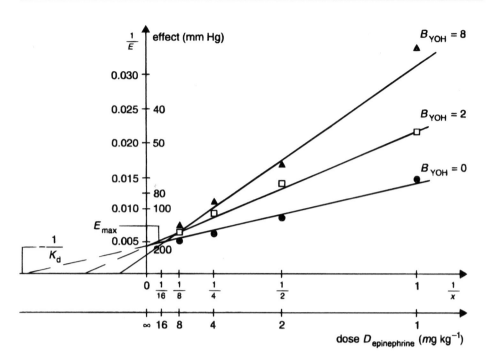

FIGURE 7.33

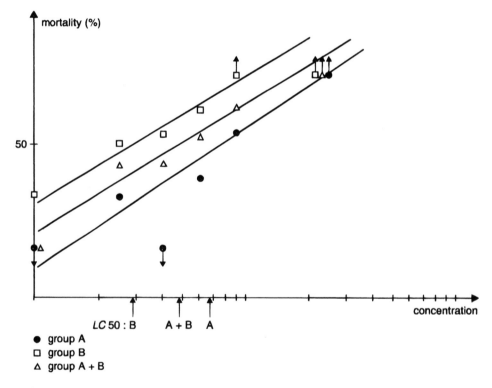

FIGURE 7.34

## Addendum

This addendum contains a number of formulae which accompany sections 7.2 and 7.3.

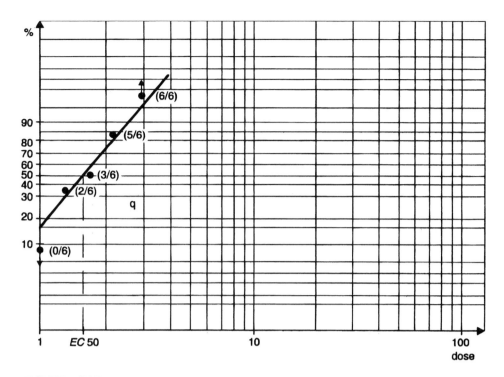

FIGURE   7.35

*Log normal distribution:*
Formula for the sensitivity distribution:

$$f(x) = \frac{1}{\sigma \cdot \sqrt{2\pi}} \cdot \exp\left[-\frac{1}{2}\left(\frac{x-m}{\sigma}\right)^2\right] \tag{7.8}$$

Formula for the dose–response relationship:

$$P(x_i) = \int_{-\infty}^{(x_i-m)/\sigma} \sqrt{2\pi} \cdot \exp\left(-\frac{1}{2}x^2\right)dx \tag{7.9}$$

where:

$x_i$  = specific log dose for $P$,

$m$   = mean log dose,

$\sigma$   = standard deviation in the log dose,

$f(x)$  = frequency distribution of the various sensitivities and

$P(x)$  = responding fraction of the group receiving log dose = x

*Calculation of $LC_{50}$ according to the logit model*

$$\hat{a} = \frac{\sum W \cdot x^2 \cdot \sum W \cdot z - \sum W \cdot x \cdot \sum W \cdot x \cdot z}{\sum W \cdot x^2 \cdot \sum W - (\sum W \cdot x)^2} \tag{7.13}$$

$$\hat{b} = \frac{\sum W \cdot x \cdot z \cdot \sum W - \sum W \cdot x \cdot \sum W \cdot z}{\sum W \cdot x^2 \cdot \sum W - (\sum W \cdot x)^2} \tag{7.14}$$

$$V_a = \frac{\sum W \cdot x^2}{\sum W \cdot x^2 \cdot \sum W - (\sum W \cdot x)^2} \qquad (7.15)$$

$$V_b = \frac{\sum W}{\sum W \cdot x^2 \cdot \sum W - (\sum W \cdot x)^2} \qquad (7.16)$$

$$\ln(LC_{50}) = -\frac{\hat{a}}{\hat{b}} \qquad (7.17)$$

$$\ln(LC_P) = \left\{ \log\left(\frac{P}{Q}\right) - \hat{a} \right\} - \hat{b} \qquad (7.18)$$

$$V(\ln(LC_{50})) = \left(\frac{1}{b}\right)^2 \cdot \left\{ \frac{1}{\sum W} + \frac{[\ln(LC_{50}) - m]^2}{\sum W \cdot (x - m)^2} \right\} \qquad (7.19)$$

The standard deviations can be derived from the calculated variances ($V_a$, $V_b$ and $V_{LC_{50}}$):

$$\sigma_a = \sqrt{V_a}, \text{ etcetera.}$$

The standard deviations can be used to determine the confidence intervals for the estimated parameters.

For example the 95% confidence interval for a is:

$$\hat{a} - 1.96 \cdot \sigma_a \leq a \leq \hat{a} + 1.96 \cdot \sigma_a$$

In the above formulae:

$x$ = ln (dose) or ln (concentration)
$z$ = logit P (corresponding to x)
$W$ = $n \cdot P \cdot (1 - P)$
$n$ = number of subjects per dosage
$V_x$ = variance in $x$
$LC_P$ = lethal concentration for $P$% instead of 50%
$Q$ = $1 - P$
$m$ = $\sum W \cdot x / \sigma W$

In many cases, the natural logarithms ($^e$log or ln) are used.

## Appendix A

Calculation of the example in section 3.3.1. The formulae used are formulae 7.13, 7.14 and 7.17.

$\sum W = 0.50 + 5.33 + \ldots + 12.84 = 34.66$
$\sum W \cdot x^2 = 0.50 \, (2.30)^2 + \ldots + 12.84 \, (4.16)^2 = 461.35$
$\sum W \cdot z = 0.50 \, (-4.62) + \ldots + 12.84 \, (0.75) = -26.64$

$\Sigma W \cdot x = 0.50\ (2.30) + \ldots + 12.84\ (4.16) = 125.13$

$\Sigma W \cdot x \cdot z = 0.50\ (2.30)\ (-4.62) + \ldots + 12.84\ (4.16)\ (0.75) = -74.84$

$$\hat{a} = \frac{\Sigma W \cdot x^2 \cdot \Sigma W \cdot z - \Sigma W \cdot x \cdot \Sigma W \cdot x \cdot z}{\Sigma W \cdot x^2 \cdot \Sigma W - (\Sigma W \cdot x)^2}$$

$$= \frac{(461.35)\ (-26.64) - (125.13)\ (-74.84)}{(461.35)\ (34.66) - (125.13)^2} = \frac{-2925}{333} = -8.78$$

$$\hat{b} = \frac{\Sigma W \cdot x \cdot z \cdot \Sigma W - \Sigma W \cdot x \cdot \Sigma W \cdot z}{\Sigma W \cdot x^2 \cdot \Sigma W - (\Sigma W \cdot x)^2}$$

$$= \frac{(-74.84)\ (34.66) - (125.13)\ (-26.64)}{(461.35)\ (34.66) - (125.13)^2} = \frac{-739}{332} = 2.23$$

$$\ln LC_{50} = -\frac{\hat{a}}{\hat{b}} = -\frac{-8.78}{2.23} = 3.94 \rightarrow \text{dus } LC_{50} = \text{antilog} = 51.28$$

**Note**

The concept "ppm" may lead to confusion. For example, 1 ppm toluene in water corresponds to 1 mg l$^{-1}$, but 1 ppm in air means 1 particle (molecule) of toluene per million particles (molecules) of air (at normal temperature and pressure this is 3.75 mg m$^{-3}$). This means that for solvents (water) and foodstuffs, 1 unit of weight per million units of weight is meant, whereas in the case of gases, 1 molecule per million molecules is meant. The dose per unit of time is proportional to the concentration, the level of which is determined by factors such as breathing frequency and daily water consumption.

# Contents Study unit 8
## Structure–activity relationships

Introduction   239

Study core   240

0-8493-9232-2/96/$0.00 + $.50

# Study unit 8

# Structure-activity relationships

*J. L. M. Hermens*

INTRODUCTION

A biological effect is the ultimate result of an interaction between a substance and a target molecule in the body. It is therefore not surprising that the biological as well as toxic effects of a compound can be linked to certain of its structural properties. However, due to the complexity of biological systems, the exact molecular mechanisms underlying the effects of most toxic substances are not known. For a number of compounds it is possible to identify the structural properties responsible for their effects. This explains why one substance is carcinogenic and another one not, or why one inhibits an enzyme while the other one does not.

The $LC_{50}$ doses (14 days) of pentachlorobenzene and monochlorobenzene in guppies are 0.71 and 170 $\mu$mole 1⁻¹, respectively. Why is the toxicity of pentachlorobenzene so much higher? Differences in intensity between compounds with the same type of toxic effect are due to differences in toxicokinetic behavior and differences in affinity of the target molecule. Such differences can often be attributed to differences in physico-chemical properties. When a relationship exists between physico-chemical properties ($x$) and toxicity ($y$), it raises the question whether the toxicities of substances can be predicted based on their physico-chemical properties. These properties can usually be measured more accurately, faster and more cheaply, than the biological effects. It is also an attractive alternative to animal testing. In short, can animal experiments be replaced by computer models?

Various techniques have been devised to study the relationships between physico-chemical properties and biological activities. These techniques are known by the acronym QSAR, short for *quantitative structure–activity relationships*.

*Quantitative structure–activity relationships*

In this study unit these techniques will be discussed and illustrated using some practical examples. Whether these techniques can have a useful place in decision making about toxic substances will be considered.

LEARNING OBJECTIVES

On completing this unit, you should be able to

— indicate the relationship between structural properties and toxicity of chemicals
— explain which processes underlie the differences in toxicity
— explain why physico-chemical properties are important in interpreting differences in biological activity; specifically in terms of toxicokinetics

239

(transport, metabolism and binding to blood proteins) and the substance–target molecule interaction
— give a brief explanation of the following:
  — substituent constant
  — octanol–water partition coefficient ($K_{ow}$)
  — $\pi$ constant
  — Hammett $\sigma$-constant
  — Taft constant ($E_s$)
  — Hansch equation
  — Free–Wilson and pattern-recognition techniques
— derive the Hansch equation
— calculate $K_{ow}$, $\pi$, $\sigma$ and $E_s$ values for simple examples and apply them to the Hansch equation
— calculate $K_{ow}$ for a molecule using Rekker's method
— indicate the practical uses and respective limitations of the different QSAR techniques.

*Study hints*

This study unit deals with concepts that have been covered in preceding units, especially those seen in units 1 and 7. It might be useful to refresh the essential concepts from those units before proceeding with this one.

In addition, it is helpful to have read about the concepts of induction and mesomerism and nucleophilic substitution from a chemistry book. This unit will briefly cover the toxicity mechanisms for a few groups of substances. Later in the textbook these are dealt with more comprehensively. At this stage, you are advised not to dwell on these too long, as a complete understanding is not yet essential. A basic calculator and millimeter graph paper are required for the exercises.

The estimated study load of this unit is six hours.


STUDY CORE

## 1 Relationship between chemical structure and type of effect

*Target molecule*

The toxic effect of a substance is ultimately based on the interaction between the substance, or one of its metabolites, and a molecule in the body: the *target molecule*. It is therefore not surprising that the type of effect and the intensity of the toxicity are related to the chemical properties or structure of a substance.

---

EXAMPLE 8–1

Compare the compounds $\alpha$-chlorotoluene (benzyl chloride) and 3-chlorotoluene in terms of their mutagenicity (see Figure 8.1).
The Ames test shows that benzyl chloride is mutagenic, whereas 3-chlorotoluene is not. *Mutagenicity* means that a substance is capable of changing genetic material by altering the structure of the DNA. The Ames test is a simple means for testing substances for mutagenicity.

*Mutagenicity*
More information about mutagenicity and the Ames test can be found in Study unit 11.

---

Why should one substance be mutagenic and another not?

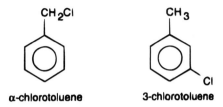

FIGURE 8.1
Chemical structures of $\alpha$-chlorotoluene (benzyl chloride) and 3-chlorotoluene

*Nucleophilic groups*
*Electrophiles*
electrophilic = electron-seeking
(a lack of surrounding electrons)
nucleophilic = nucleus-seeking
(a surplus of surrounding
electrons)
*Alkylating compounds*

DNA consists of pyrimidine and purine bases. These bases contain *nucleophilic groups*, such as $NH_2$ and NH and the O atom, and therefore have a strong affinity for electrophiles. For this reason, many *electrophilic compounds* are mutagenic and often also carcinogenic, because they can react with DNA and change its properties.

An important group of electrophiles is the *alkylating compounds*, with the general structure R-X, where R is an alkyl group and X is a good "leaving" group (for example, a halogen atom). Alkylating compounds can react with nucleophilic groups (*Nu*), forming a covalent bond:

$$R\text{-}X + Nu \rightarrow R\text{-}Nu + X$$

*Nucleophilic substitution*

This type of reaction is known as *nucleophilic substitution*. A carbonium ion ($R^+$) is formed in one of the reaction mechanisms.

Looking more closely at the structures of the two compounds mentioned, it can be seen that for benzyl chloride carbonium ion formation takes place more readily than for 3-chlorotoluene because for benzyl chloride the carbonium ion is stabilized through *mesomerism*, while for 3-chlorotoluene it is not (see Figure 8.2).

*Mesomerism*

A large number of compounds, like benzyl chloride, are able to react directly with nucleophilic groups. Table 8.1 provides an overview of some of these substances.

These compounds are mutagenic because of their reactivity towards nucleophilic groups. The effects of these substances are thus clearly related to their structures.

ASSIGNMENT 8.1

Show the reaction (including structural formulae) between a sulfhydryl group (-SH) and an epoxide.

ASSIGNMENT 8.2

Although benzene is not an electrophilic compound, it is a well-known carcinogen. How can the carcinogenicity of this compound be explained?

DNA is not unique in containing nucleophilic groups. Proteins are especially rich in these groups, with which electrophiles can form covalent bonds. If an electrophile reacts with the active site of an enzyme, the enzyme may lose its activity. The ultimate effect of a substance, mutagenicity or *enzyme inhibition*, depends among other things, on the fate of the substance in the body. Since the toxic effect of a substance rests ultimately on its interaction with a target molecule in the body, the relationship between structure and toxic effect is hardly surprising. However, because of the complexity of biological systems, there are

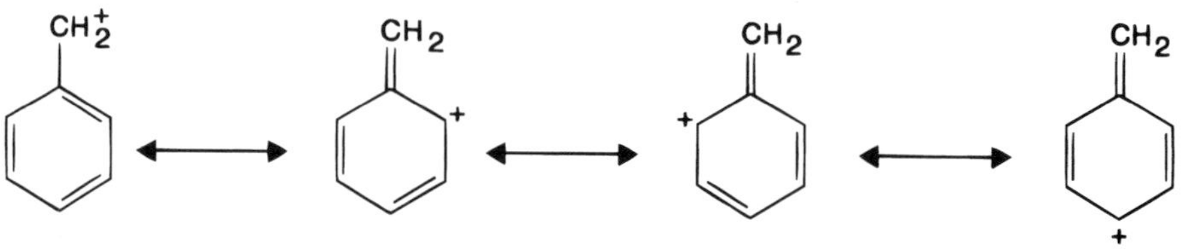

FIGURE 8.2
Resonance structures of the carbonium ion of $\alpha$-chlorotoluene (benzyl chloride)

TABLE 8.1
Some groups of compounds that can react directly with nucleophilic groups

| Class | General structure | Example | Name |
|---|---|---|---|
| Imines | 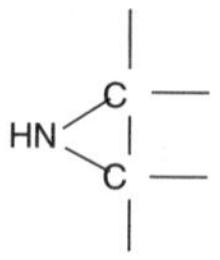 HN C—C (ring) | 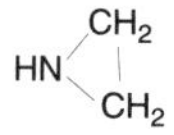 HN CH$_2$—CH$_2$ (ring) | ethyleneimine |
| epoxides | 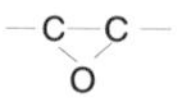 C—C with O | 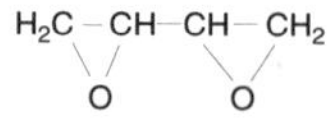 H$_2$C—CH—CH—CH$_2$ with O, O | diepoxybutane |
| lactones | 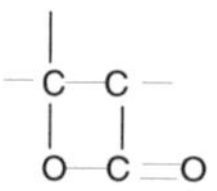 C—C, O—C=O | 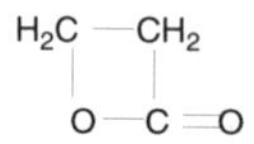 H$_2$C—CH$_2$, O—C=O | $\beta$-propiolactone |
| sulfate esters | $(RO)_2SO_2$ | $CH_3OSO_2OCH_3$ | dimethyl sulfate |
| mustards | — | $ClCH_2CH_2$ \ S / $ClCH_2CH_2$ | mustard gas |
| halogenated hydrocarbons | — | $CH_2 = CH - CH_2Cl$ | allyl chloride |

few compounds for which the mode of action is known at a molecular level. Consequently, it is not easy to identify such relationships.

## 2 Relationship between physico-chemical properties of chemicals and the intensity of their toxic effects

Section 1 has shown how the mechanisms underlying the effects of a substance are brought about by particular structural properties of the compound. However, compounds that have the same type of effect frequently differ in the intensity of their effect, i.e., in their *biological activity*.

*Biological activity*

---

EXAMPLES 8–2

The toxicity of chlorobenzenes in guppies ($LC_{50}$) is found to increase considerably with the number of chlorine atoms contained in the compounds (see Table 8.2).

Within a series of organophosphate insecticides, the concentrations which reduce the activity of the enzyme acetylcholinesterase (AChE) by 50% differ widely. In the common housefly the $LD_{50}$ doses also show wide variation (see Table 8.3).

---

What reasons might there be for this difference in activity?

TABLE 8.2
$LC_{50}$ values for some chlorobenzenes in guppies

| Compound | 14-day $LC_{50}$ in guppies ($\mu$mol l$^{-1}$) |
|---|---|
| monochlorobenzene | 170 |
| 1,2-dichlorobenzene | 40 |
| 1,2,3-trichlorobenzene | 13 |
| 1,2,3,4-tetrachlorobenzene | 3.7 |
| pentachlorobenzene | 0.71 |

TABLE 8.3
Concentrations which reduce the activity of acetylcholinesterase by 50% ($EC_{50}$), and $LD_{50}$ values in the common housefly for some insecticidal diethylphosphates

| Substituents* | $EC_{50}$ AChE (mol l$^{-1}$) | $LD_{50}$ in the housefly ($\mu$g kg$^{-1}$) |
|---|---|---|
| meta-nitro | $5.0 \times 10^{-8}$ | 9.8 |
| 2,4,5-trichloro | $6.0 \times 10^{-9}$ | 8.0 |
| 2,4,6-trichloro | $3.3 \times 10^{-6}$ | 175 |
| 2,4-dichloro | $5.0 \times 10^{-7}$ | 15.0 |
| ortho-chloro | $2.0 \times 10^{-5}$ | 250 |
| 2,4-dinitro | $3.0 \times 10^{-9}$ | 155 |
| para-nitro | $2.6 \times 10^{-8}$ | 0.5 |
| ortho-nitro | $5.0 \times 10^{-8}$ | 7.0 |
| para-chloro | $3.0 \times 10^{-5}$ | 150 |

*derivatives of diethylphenylphosphate [$(C_2H_5O)_2(PO)OC_6H_5$]: substituents on aromatic ring.
Source: Fukuto and Metcaff (1956)

To explain these differences it would make sense to look again more closely at the processes that underlie the induction of an effect.

When an effect is established two important processes may be distinguished, each of which determines the biological activity of a substance:

*Toxicokinetic behavior*
See also Study units 5 and 6

- the *toxicokinetic behavior* of the substance. The extent to which or the rate at which processes such as transport, binding to blood proteins and metabolism proceed, determines the ultimate concentration or quantity of a substance in its active form at the site of action (the target);

*Toxicodynamic behavior*
See also Study unit 7

- the *toxicodynamic behavior* of the substance (what the substance does to the body).

Both types of behavior greatly influence the *biological activity*. Differences in biological activity between compounds are largely determined by *differences in equilibrium constants or reaction rate constants*.

The biological activity thus depends on the toxicokinetic as well as the toxicodynamic properties of a substance. The starting point here is that if, for substances with the same effect, the number of "molecular events" is constant, than the intensity of the biological effect is the same. In other words, at a particular intensity, the number of target molecules changed on interaction with the toxic substance is the same.

Differences in toxicokinetic behavior (transport, binding to blood proteins and metabolism) of substances, as well as differences in affinity of the target molecule, are in turn based on differences in physico-chemical properties.

243

## 2.1 INFLUENCE OF PHYSICO-CHEMICAL PROPERTIES ON TRANSPORT OF SUBSTANCES

For most substances, *absorption, distribution and elimination processes* are based on diffusion. After oral administration, absorption proceeds via passage across the membrane of the stomach or the intestine wall. After inhalation, diffusion takes place across the alveolar membranes. In fish, the absorption of toxic compounds from water takes place via diffusion across the gill membrane. In the distribution of substances through the body, diffusion processes across membranes also play a crucial role.

*Permeability constant*
See also Study unit 5

The rate of transport via the lipid phase of a membrane depends on the one hand on the *concentration gradient* across the membrane, and on the other hand on the *properties of the membrane and the substance* itself. These properties are incorporated in the so-called *permeability constant (P)*. This constant, $P$, is a parameter for the distribution of a substance over the water phase and the membrane and for the diffusion within the membrane. Compounds with a strong preference for lipid-like media (*hydrophobic or lipophilic compounds*) will pass through the membrane more easily than substances with a strong preference for water (*hydrophilic compounds*). For hydrophiles the membrane acts as a barrier. Hydrophobic solvents (such as ether, heptane and octanol) are often used as models for a lipid (hydrophobic phase) of biomaterial (especially membranes). Table 8.4 gives examples of the relationship between the hydrophobic nature of substances and membrane permeability.

In Table 8.4 olive oil was used as a model of the lipid phase of the membrane. From these data, it can be seen that if the partition coefficient (i.e. hydrophobicity or lipophilicity) is low, then so is the membrane permeability for organic compounds.

> Try to express the relationship between the hydrophobic nature of substances and membrane permeability in your own words.

*Octanol–water partition coefficient*

Nowadays, octanol is widely used as solvent, since in practice membrane permeability matches the octanol–water partition coefficient. The *octanol–water partition coefficient* is most commonly denoted by $K_{ow}$, but $P_{oct}$ is also used. The properties of octanol strongly resemble those of membrane lipids.

TABLE 8.4

Relationship between hydrophobicity and membrane permeability for a number of compounds

| Compound | Partition coefficient olive oil-water | Permeability for algae |
|---|---|---|
| 1,2-dihydroxypropane | 570 | 24 000 |
| propionamide | 360 | 36 000 |
| acetamide | 83 | 15 000 |
| glycol | 50 | 12 000 |
| N-methylurea | 44 | 1 900 |
| urea | 15 | 1 000 |
| glycerol | 7 | 210 |
| erythreitol | 3 | 13 |
| sucrose | 3 | 4 |

$\mu m^{-2}$ molar concentration difference$^{-1}$
Source: Albert (1979), p. 60.

**Intermezzo**

*Determination of the octanol–water partition coefficient ($K_{ow}$ or $P_{oct}$)*

$K_{ow}$ is derived as follows:

$$K_{ow} = \frac{\text{concentration of substance } X \text{ in octanol}}{\text{concentration of substance } X \text{ in water}}$$

See also Study unit 5

This $K_{ow}$ can be experimentally determined by allowing a substance to distribute itself over an octanol layer and a water layer in a separation funnel. The concentrations in the two phases are then determined by chemical analysis and the ratio of the two concentrations gives the $K_{ow}$.

*Degree of ionization*

In passive diffusion, it is the non-ionized form that passes through the membrane, depending on a concentration gradient. So, the *degree of ionization* is important for those compounds which may in principle be present in the ionized form. The degree to which an acid or base is ionized depends on the pH of the medium and the strength of the acid or base. For an acid, the ratio of the concentration of the substance in the ionized form (A⁻) and that in the non-ionized form (HA) may be calculated from the pH and the dissociation constant ($K_a$) as follows:

$$\log\frac{[\text{A}^-]}{[\text{HA}]} = \text{pH} - pK_a \tag{8.1}$$

where $pK_a = -\log K_a$ and $\text{pH} = -\log [\text{H}^+]$

ASSIGNMENT   8.3

Derive equation 8.1

ASSIGNMENT   8.4

Table 8.5 lists data on the bioconcentration factor (BCF) in guppies for some chlorobenzenes. Plot the logarithm of the BCF against the logarithm of the octanol–water partition coefficient ($K_{ow}$).
Explain the shape of the curve.

TABLE   8.5
Relationship between hydrophobicity (log $K_{ow}$) of a number of chlorobenzenes and their concentrations (*BCF*) in guppies

| Compound | log $K_{ow}$ | BCF* |
|---|---|---|
| 1,4-dichlorobenzene | 3.53 | 1 800 |
| 1,2,3-trichlorobenzene | 4.20 | 13 000 |
| 1,3,5-trichlorobenzene | 4.20 | 14 000 |
| 1,2,3,5-tetrachlorobenzene | 4.94 | 72 000 |
| pentachlorobenzene | 5.69 | 260 000 |

*BCF: bioconcentration factor (ratio of concentration in fish to concentration in surrounding water)

ASSIGNMENT   8.5

Table 8.6 shows data on the effect of pH on the $LC_{50}$ for two chlorophenols (4-chlorophenol and pentachlorophenol) in guppies. Explain why the $LC_{50}$ values for 4-chlorophenol at pH 6 and pH 8 are about equal and why the $LC_{50}$ for pentachlorophenol is much lower at pH 6 than at pH 8.

TABLE 8.6
The effect of the pH of aquarium water on the $LC_{50}$ of chlorophenols in the guppy

| Compound | $LC_{50}$ µmol l⁻¹ | |
|---|---|---|
| | pH = 6 | pH = 8 |
| 4-chlorophenol ($pK_a$ = 9.37) | 60.00 | 71.0 |
| pentachlorophenol ($pK_a$ = 6.69) | 0.44 | 3.4 |

## 2.2 EFFECTS OF PHYSICO-CHEMICAL PROPERTIES ON BINDING TO BLOOD PROTEINS, METABOLISM AND INTERACTIONS WITH THE TARGET MOLECULE

*Binding to blood proteins*

*Binding to blood proteins* has an important influence on the toxicity of a substance, as it can lower the free concentration of the substance and thus its activity. Albumin is the most abundant protein in plasma. It predominantly binds organic bases and acids, because at pH 7.4 (the pH of blood) it possesses positive as well as negative charges. Binding will be largely based on *electrostatic interactions*.

Plasma proteins usually have a high affinity for hydrophobic compounds. In this case (*hydrophobic*) *interactions* take place with the non-charged elements of the protein structure.

*Metabolism*

The presence of a particular structural feature is essential for the *metabolism* of a substance. Which interactions play a role in this depends on the enzyme concerned and on the substrate. The degree to which a compound is metabolized is highly dependent on the intrinsic activity of the enzyme, and the reactivity of the substance.

*steric = spatial*
*repulsion = action of bodies that repel each other*
*Interactions between a toxic substance and its target molecule*

If the active site of an enzyme is hydrophobic, hydrophobic interactions will dominate. In contrast, if the active site of the enzyme is more polar, electrostatic and van der Waals interactions as well as hydrogen bonding can take place. Metabolism proceeds at a slower rate if there is steric hindrance or repulsion. *Interactions between a toxic substance and its target molecule* may, just as for protein binding, involve hydrophobic, electrostatic and van der Waals forces. Steric hindrance may also be a factor. In addition, a compound may covalently bind to a target molecule. An example is the reaction between electrophiles and nucleophilic groups.

Table 8.7 summarizes the different *types of interaction* and the *physico-chemical properties* that influence the strength of these interactions. The table also shows which parameters are used to compare the strength of these interactions. A few of these parameters will be discussed in more detail in section 3.

The biological activity is thus dependent on:

- the probability that a molecule reaches its site of action ($Pr_1$) (transport),
- the probability of that molecule entering into an interaction with the target molecule ($Pr_2$) (binding).
  The total probability ($Pr$) of a molecule entering an interaction with the target equals the product $Pr_1 \cdot Pr_2$. The concentration ($C_t$) of the target molecules that undergo interaction with a substance is proportional (proportionality constant $a$) to $Pr_1$, $Pr_2$ and the exposure concentration ($C$), i.e.:

$$C_t = a \cdot Pr_1 \cdot Pr_2 \cdot C \tag{8.2}$$

Since a particular intensity of an effect is related to a particular $C_t$, Equation 8.2 can be rewritten as:

*Basic equation for QSAR*

$$\log \frac{1}{C} = \log Pr_1 + \log Pr_2 + \text{constant} \tag{8.3}$$

246

TABLE 8.7
Overview of the various types of interaction, relevant physico-chemical properties and parameters used in the description of the interactions

| Interaction (reaction)* | Physico-chemical property* | Parameter** |
|---|---|---|
| hydrophobic interaction | hydrophobicity | octanol-water partition coefficient ($K_{ow}$ or $P_{oct}$) |
| electrostatic interaction | | |
| -ion-ion | charge on the atoms | charge/Hammett |
| -ion-dipole | charge on the atoms | $\sigma$ constant |
| -dipole-dipole | charge on the atoms | |
| hydrogen-bonding | charge on the atoms | charge/Hammett $\sigma$ constant |
| van der Waals interaction | polarizability | molar refraction |
| steric hindrance | size | van der Waals radius/ Taft constant |
| covalent binding | a.o. induction and mesomerism | Hammett $\sigma$ constant/ reaction rate constants |

*See unit 7
**These parameters are discussed in more detail in subsection 3.1.1.

constant = log a/Ct

Equation 8.3 forms the basis for *quantitative structure–activity relationships*.

## 3  (Quantitative) structure–activity relationships: (Q)SAR

Studies on relationships between physico-chemical properties and biological activity of compounds originate from pharmacology and the chemical industry. The development of a new drug or pesticide takes many years of research. If a particular compound is known to have a particular effect, attempts will be made to enhance its activity and to minimize its toxicity by suitable alteration of its structure. Economically it would be preferable to predict the effect of structural changes on activity before animal testing.

EXAMPLE 8–3

A hypothetical example:

The action of a well-known group of insecticides, the organophosphate esters (OP esters), is based on the *irreversible* inhibition of the enzyme acetylcholinesterase (AChE), specifically by phosphorylation of the alcoholic hydroxyl group in the serine moieties of AChE (Figure 8.3b). The nucleophilic OH group reacts with the electrophilic phosphorus atom. The structure of a particular OP ester is shown in Figure 8.3a.

A researcher at the bench could arrive at the following conclusion. If halogen atoms (Cl or Br) are introduced into the phenyl ring ($C_6H_5$), this will increase the hydrophobicity ($K_{ow}$) and, hence presumably also the availability at the site of action. An additional advantage is that the positive charge on the phosphorus atom increases, as halogen atoms are electron withdrawing substituents. One such compound, bromophosphine (which has Cl substituents at the 2- and 5-positions and a Br atom at the 4-position), has been synthesized and indeed shows a high activity (Figure 8.3c). Similarly, the introduction of a nitro group ($NO_2$) will have a positive effect on the strength of the interaction with the target molecule, since this group also increases the positive charge on the phosphorus atom through mesomerism. Methyl parathion, a well-known OP ester, has in fact a nitro group at the 4-position

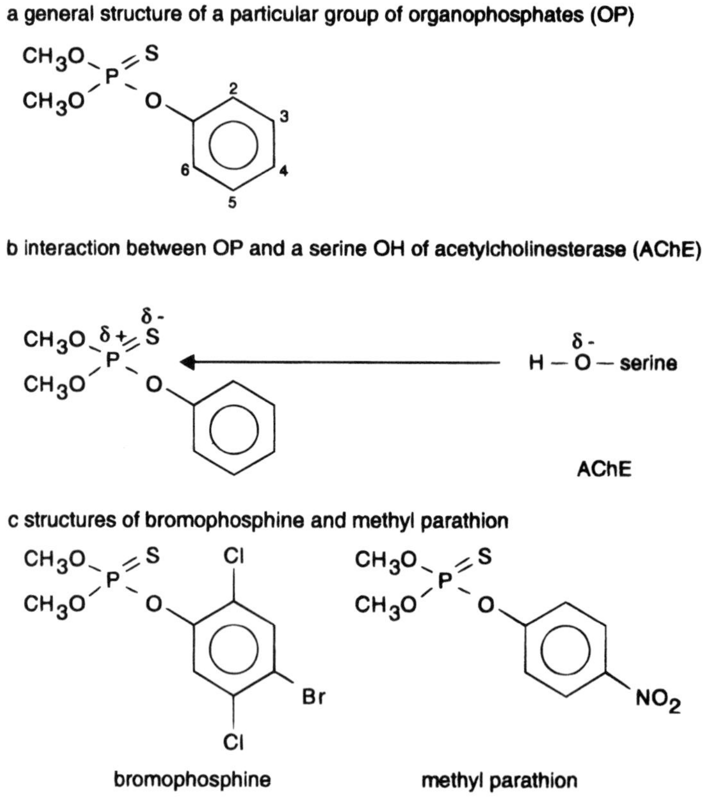

**a general structure of a particular group of organophosphates (OP)**

**b interaction between OP and a serine OH of acetylcholinesterase (AChE)**

**c structures of bromophosphine and methyl parathion**

bromophosphine                    methyl parathion

FIGURE   8.3
Organophosphates
a. general structure of a particular group of organophosphates (OP)
b. interaction between OP and a serine OH of acetylcholinesterase (AChE)
c. structures of bromophosphine and methyl parathion

---

(Figure 8.3c). In contrast, the introduction of a methyl group ($CH_3$), decreases the positive charge on the phosphorus atom. Synthesis and testing of such compounds is therefore probably not worth trying.

---

*Qualitative/quantitative*

It is possible to influence the activity of compounds by changing their physico-chemical properties, such as the $K_{ow}$ or the charge on the atoms. The above example is a *qualitative* one. A quantitative approach, however, would be preferable in order to make quantitative predictions.

Three types of QSAR techniques have been developed to establish relationships between physico-chemical properties and biological activity:

1.  Hansch analysis
2.  Free–Wilson technique
3.  pattern-recognition techniques.

The first two techniques can be applied if one is interested in *quantitative relationships,* while the last technique is particularly appropriate for establishing relationships in terms of the *type of effect.* The ultimate goal remains the prediction of biological activity.

The above example concerned the development of pesticides. These techniques can, of course, also be applied in predicting toxic effects.

### 3.1 HANSCH ANALYSIS

The *Hansch technique* is based on Equation 8.3. This equation states that the concentration of a substance required for a particular intensity of the effect depends, for a series of compounds, on two probability parameters, $Pr_1$ and $Pr_2$:

For $Pr_1$ and $Pr_2$, see section 2.2 above

$$\log \frac{1}{C} = \log Pr_1 + \log Pr_2 + \text{constant} \qquad (8.3)$$

See section 3 above

It has already been seen that $Pr_1$ (the probability that a molecule reaches its site of action (transport)) is strongly dependent upon the hydrophobicity of a substance. This may be expressed in terms of the octanol–water partition coefficient ($K_{ow}$) as follows:

$$\log Pr_1 = a \log K_{ow} + \text{constant} \qquad (8.4)$$

Sometimes the introduction of a quadratic $\log K_{ow}$ term results in a better fit with the experimental data. In those situations, Equation 8.4 is extended using the term $(\log K_{ow})^2$.

Equation 8.4 assumes that the fate of a substance in the body (kinetics) is simple: the substance diffuses directly to the target molecule. In many situations, the kinetics prove to be more complex, for example, when the substance binds to blood proteins, or is metabolized to a reactive compound that in turn can be scavenged before it reaches its site of action. In such cases, the probability of the reactive intermediate of the compound reaching the target molecule ($Pr_2$) cannot be expressed simply by equation 8.4.

In a reversible interaction, $Pr_2$ (the probability of a molecule entering an interaction with the target molecule) is proportional to the equilibrium constant ($K$) for the interaction with the target molecule, i.e.:

$$\log Pr_2 = \log K + \text{constant} \qquad (8.5)$$

Combining equations 8.3, 8.4 and 8.5 yields:

$$\log 1/C = a \log K_{ow} + \log K + \text{constant} \qquad (8.6)$$

If equation 8.6 is to be applied to hypothetical compounds, it will be necessary to have methods for the determination of $K_{ow}$ and $K$. Without these methods, it would be a purely hypothetical exercise. This approach has therefore only emerged after new techniques had been developed for the calculation or estimation of $K_{ow}$ and $K$ for structurally related *aromatic* compounds, using substituent parameters.

#### 3.1.1 Substituent constants

*Estimation of $K_{ow}$ values*
*Substituent constant for $K_{ow}$ ($\pi$)*

The octanol–water partition coefficient ($K_{ow}$) for compounds that are structurally related may be calculated using a *substituent constant for $K_{ow}$ ($\pi$)*, developed by Fujita and Hansch (1964). This constant is defined as:

$$\pi(X) = \log K_{ow}(C_6H_5X) - \log K_{ow}(C_6H_6) \qquad (8.7)$$

where $C_6H_6$ is benzene and $C_6H_5X$ a benzene derivative with one H atom replaced by a substituent, $X$ (for example, chlorine).

The $\pi$ value of a chlorine atom can thus be determined from the difference in $K_{ow}$ value between chlorobenzene and benzene. The $\pi$ constants for all kinds of substituents can be calculated in this way from the experimental $K_{ow}$ values. Table 8.8 lists the $\pi$ constants for some common substituents. This shows that Cl, Br, and I as well as $CH_3$ groups, raise the $K_{ow}$ values (positive $\pi$ values), while substituents such as $NO_2$, $NH_2$ and OH lower the $K_{ow}$ values (negative $\pi$ values). The effect of the latter category of substituents is not surprising, as these groups are much more polar in character and thus have a strong preference for the water phase. *The constant $\pi$ is additive*, which means that if more H atoms in a particular structure (R) are replaced by substituents ($X_1$, $X_2$), log $K_{ow}$ can be obtained from:

$$\log K_{ow}(RX_1 X_2 \ldots) = \log K_{ow}(RHH \ldots) + \pi X_1 + \pi X_2 + \ldots \qquad (8.8)$$

The $\pi$ constants in Table 8.8 have been calculated from $K_{ow}$ values for benzene derivatives. It has been found, however, that the contribution of a particular substituent to the $K_{ow}$ value is roughly the same for many other structures. This makes it possible to arrive at a reasonable estimate for log $K_{ow}$ for all kinds of structures.

---

EXAMPLE 8–4

Calculation of $K_{ow}$ from $\pi$ constants.

The log $K_{ow}$ for 2-chloronitrobenzene ($C_6H_4ClNO_2$) can be calculated from the log $K_{ow}$ for benzene ($C_6H_6$) and the $\pi$ constants for Cl and $NO_2$ in the following way:

$$\log K_{ow}(C_6H_4ClNO_2) = \log K_{ow}(C_6H_6) + \pi Cl + \pi NO_2$$
$$= 2.13 + 0.71 + (-0.28)$$
$$= 2.56$$

---

TABLE 8.8

Substituent constraints for a number of aromatic compounds ($C_6H5X$).

| Substituent(X) | $\pi$ | $f$ | $\sigma$ (meta) | $\sigma$ (para) | $E_s$ |
|---|---|---|---|---|---|
| H | 0.00 | 0.175 | 0.00 | 0.00 | 1.24 |
| F | 0.14 | 0.399 | 0.34 | 0.06 | 0.78 |
| Cl | 0.71 | 0.922 | 0.37 | 0.23 | 0.27 |
| Br | 0.86 | 1.131 | 0.39 | 0.23 | 0.08 |
| I | 1.12 | 1.448 | 0.35 | 0.18 | −0.16 |
| $NO_2$ | −0.28 | −0.078 | 0.71 | 0.78 | −1.28 |
| $NH_2$ | −1.23 | −0.854 | −0.16 | −0.16 | 0.63 |
| OH | −0.67 | −0.343 | 0.12 | −0.37 | 0.69 |
| CN | −0.57 | −0.205 | 0.56 | 0.66 | 0.73 |
| $CH_3$ | 0.56 | 0.702 | −0.07 | −0.17 | 0.00 |
| $CH_2$ | — | 0.533 | — | — | — |
| $CH_2CH_2CH_3$ | 1.55 | — | 0.07 | −0.13 | −0.36 |
| $C_6H_5$ | 1.96 | 1.886 | 0.06 | −0.01 | — |
| $C_6H_4$ | — | 1.688 | — | — | — |
| $C_6H_3$ | — | 1.431 | — | — | — |

Log $K_{ow}$ Benzene = 2.13

$\pi$ = substituent constant for hydrophobicity

$f$ = fragmental constant for hydrophobicity

$\sigma$ = Hammett constant for the effect of substitution on electron distribution

$E_s$ = Taft constant for steric hindrance

See Hansch and Leo (1979) and Rekker (1977) for comprehensive overviews of substituent constants.

In addition, there are various systems for determining $\pi$ and $\sigma$ constants, depending on the parent compound (see Hansch and Leo, 1979).

Substituent constants calculated for benzene derivatives are not applicable to phenols and anilines. Hence, other substituent constants have been calculated for those structures besides the usual $\pi$ constants. These constants, designated as $\pi^-$, are found to depend also on the position (ortho, meta or para) of the substituent.

> ASSIGNMENT 8.6
>
> Using the log $K_{ow}$ for toluene (2.69) and the $\pi$ values from Table 8.8, calculate the log $K_{ow}$ for:
>
> 2-nitrotoluene
>
> 4-bromotoluene
>
> 2-methyltoluene (o-xylene)
>
> 2-chloro-3-bromotoluene

This method can obviously be used only for compounds that are structurally related (in this example, toluene derivatives). The method developed by Rekker (1977) does not have this limitation.

*Rekker's method*
*Fragmental values*

*Rekker's method* is based on *fragmental values*. A molecule is split up into several fragments and the $K_{ow}$ may be calculated from the fragmental values ($f_i$) as follows:

$$\log K_{ow} = \Sigma f_i \tag{8.9}$$

Rekker calculated the fragmental values for numerous fragments. Values for some of these are shown in Table 8.8. Sometimes the values need to be adjusted.

---

EXAMPLE 8–5

Calculation of $K_{ow}$ according to Rekker's method:

The log $K_{ow}$ for 2-chloronitrobenzene ($C_6H_4ClNO_2$) can be calculated from the fragmental values for $C_6H_4$, Cl and $NO_2$ as follows:

| | |
|---|---|
| fragmental value for $C_6H_4$: | 1.688 |
| fragmental value for Cl: | 0.922 |
| fragmental value for $NO_2$: | –0.078 |
| | ----- + |
| log $K_{ow}$ | 2.53 |

---

> ASSIGNMENT 8.7
>
> Using Rekker's method, calculate the log $K_{ow}$ for the same compounds as in assignment 8.6.

*Estimation of K values*

By analogy with the $\pi$ constants, other substituent constants have been introduced for estimating the strength of interaction with the target molecule (or $K$ in Equation 8.6).

$$\log 1/C = a \log K_{ow} + \log K + \text{constant} \tag{8.6}$$

$K_{ow}$ and $\pi$ are good parameters for *hydrophobic interactions*. For *electrostatic interactions* and *hydrogen bonding*, however, it is the charge on the atoms that is important. Substituents influence the distribution of charge in a molecule through *induction* and *mesomerism* (as is shown by the example of OP esters in Figure 8.3).

To describe the effects of substituents on charge distribution, Hammett in the 1940s introduced a *substituent constant for charge distribution* ($\sigma$) which is based on the ionization equilibrium for benzoic acid (e.g. see Hammett, 1970, and other references):

$$C_6H_5CO_2H \rightleftarrows C_6H_5CO_2^- + H^+$$

Substituents on the phenyl ring influence the negative charge of the anion and hence the affinity of this anion for protons.

This *Hammett constant*, $\sigma$, is defined as:

$$\sigma(X) = pK_a(C_6H_4XCO_2H) - pK_a(C_6H_5CO_2H) \qquad (8.10)$$

where $C_6H_5CO_2H$ is benzoic acid and $C_6H_4XCO_2H$ is benzoic acid in which one of the hydrogen atoms has been replaced by a substituent, $X$ ($pK_a = -\log K_a$ ($K_a$ is the ionization constant of the acid)).

The $\sigma$ values for some substituents are given in Table 8.8. A positive value indicates that the substituent is a stronger electron attractor than hydrogen (for example, Cl); substituents with negative $\sigma$ values are weaker electron attractors than hydrogen.

In principle, $\sigma$ constants are also additive. If more than one substituent is present, their respective $\sigma$ constants may be summed. Like the $\pi$ constant, the $\sigma$ constant cannot be applied to all classes of compounds. Besides the standard $\sigma$ constant, other $\sigma$ constants ($\sigma^+$, $\sigma^-$) have been introduced for special types of compounds, e.g. phenols and anilines.

$\sigma$ constants also depend on the position (ortho, meta, para) of the substituent.

The Taft constant, $E_s$, has frequently been used as a *substituent constant for steric hindrance* (see Taft, 1956). This *constant* is related to the rate constant ($k$) for the hydrolysis of methyl acetate ($CH_3(CO)OCH_3$):

$$CH_3(CO)OCH_3 + H_2O \rightleftarrows CH_3CO_2H + CH_3OH$$

$E_s$ is defined as follows:

$$E_s(X) = \log k(XCH_2(CO)OCH_3) - \log k(CH_3(CO)OCH_3) \qquad (8.11)$$

where $CH_3(CO)OCH_3$ is methyl acetate and $XCH_2(CO)OCH_3$ is methyl acetate in which one H atom has been replaced by a substituent, $X$ in the acetate moiety.

Table 8.8 lists $E_s$ values for various substituents. The larger the substituent is (for instance, going from Cl to Br to I), the lower is the $E_s$ value.

### 3.1.2 The Hansch approach

With the substituent constants $\pi$, $\sigma$ and $E_s$ the parameters are available to provide information on the effects of substituents on $K_{ow}$, the charge distribution and steric hindrance in a molecule for a series of structural analogs. These parameters can be used to estimate values for $K_{ow}$ and $K$ in Equation 8.6. In addition, $K_{ow}$ can be calculated using Rekker's fragmental values. The value of log $K$ from Equation 8.6 can be replaced by:

$$\log K = b\sigma + cE_s \tag{8.12}$$

Equation 8.12 holds true if steric repulsion as well as electrostatic effects determine the affinity of the target molecule for a substance. Naturally, it is also possible that only one of the two parameters is important. Substitution of 8.12 for $\log K$ in 8.6 yields:

$$\log 1/C = a\log K_{ow} + b\,\sigma + c\,E_s + d \tag{8.13}$$

d in Equation 8.13 is the "constant" in Equation 8.6

*Hansch equation*

Equation 8.13 is called the *Hansch equation*, after the scientist who developed it (Hansch, 1973).

If Equation 8.13 is applied to a series of structural analogs, then $K_{ow}$ may be replaced by $\pi$. In addition, in principle, the equation can be extended by incorporating other parameters, such as the ones given in Table 8.7. Of course, not all the parameters need to be relevant. The relevance of each one is decided by the type of interaction between the active agent and the target molecule.

If experimental values of $\log 1/C$ are known for a limited number of compounds, Equation 8.13 can be solved by substituting the corresponding values of $K_{ow}$, $\sigma$ and $E_s$. This provides values for the coefficients $a$ to $d$. Thus, it becomes possible to calculate $\log 1/C$ for compounds by substituting the corresponding values for $K_{ow}$, $\sigma$ and $E_s$, respectively. The advantage of this approach is that it can be used to *predict the biological activity* of as yet unstudied or unsynthesized compounds.

Equation 8.13 can be solved by multiple linear regression.

### Intermezzo

*Multiple linear regression*

Multiple linear regression is a mathematical technique that strongly resembles normal linear regression, except for the number of parameters in the equation. Linear regression:

$$y(i) = a\,x(i) + C \tag{8.14}$$

Multiple linear regression:

$$y(i) = a\,x_1(i) + b\,x_2(i) + c\,x_3(i) + \ldots + C \tag{8.15}$$

*Least-squares method*

If the values of $y(i)$, $x_1(i)$, $x_2(i)$, etc. are available for a set of data for $n$ compounds, Equations 8.14 and 8.15 can be solved by the *least-squares method*. This method enables calculation of the coefficients $a, b, c, \ldots$ and of the constant, $C$, by minimizing the differences between the calculated $y$ values ($\hat{y}$) and the experimental $y$ values.

As an example, take a random set of data (Table 8.9). The data set in Table 8.9 comprises 9 points and 2 different parameters ($x_1$ and $x_2$). Numerical values for $y$, $x_1$ and $x_2$ are given for each of the 9 points.

TABLE 8.9
Values of $y(i)$, $x_1(i)$ and $x_2(i)$

| Number | $y$ | $x_1$ | $x_2$ |
|--------|------|------|-------|
| 1 | 0.61 | 2.89 | −4.36 |
| 2 | 0.09 | 5.33 | −4.11 |
| 3 | 1.00 | 3.49 | −4.59 |
| 4 | 1.68 | 2.84 | −5.52 |
| 5 | 0.89 | 4.22 | −5.05 |
| 6 | 1.40 | 3.68 | −5.31 |
| 7 | 0.23 | 3.32 | −4.04 |
| 8 | 0.00 | 5.24 | −4.23 |
| 9 | 0.63 | 3.70 | −4.00 |

By using the least-squares method, the following equation is obtained:

$$y(i) = 0.23\, x_1(i) + 0.76\, x_2(i) + 1.88 \tag{8.16}$$

*Correlation coefficient (r) and standard deviation (s)*

The quality of the equation is expressed by the *correlation coefficient* (*r*) and the *standard deviation* (*s*). If the calculated values of $y(i)$ match the experimental values of $y(i)$, then $r = 1$ and $s = 0$. This state is never achieved in practice, because of the ever present lack of accuracy in measurements of $x$ and $y$ (for example, as a result of experimental error). The closer the parameter $r$ approaches 1, and the lower the value of $s$, the better the correlation between $x(i)$ and $y(i)$. If $r = 0$, there is no apparent correlation between $x(i)$ and $y(i)$. Tables have been published that allow verification of whether the $r$ values found are significant.

Numerical values for $r$ and $s$ can be calculated as follows:

$$r = \sqrt{\frac{SS_1 - SS_2}{SS_1}} \tag{8.17}$$

$$s = \sqrt{\frac{SS_2}{n - k - 1}} \tag{8.18}$$

SS = sum of squares

where:

$$SS_1 = \Sigma \left\{ y(i) - y_m \right\}^2$$
$$SS_2 = \Sigma \left\{ y(i) - \hat{y} \right\}^2$$

| | |
|---|---|
| $y(i)$: | experimental value of $y$ |
| $\hat{y}(i)$: | calculated value of $y$ |
| $y_m$: | mean value of $y$ |
| $n$: | number of data |
| $k$: | number of parameters (different $x$ values) in the equation. |

The least-squares method can be used if the number of different parameters ($x$) is not too large regarding the number of data ($n$). In general, the number of data ($n$) must be 4 to 5 times the number of different parameters ($k$).

A correlation is considered good if the correlation coefficient ($r$) is greater than 0.95.

ASSIGNMENT   8.8

What happens to $r$ as the fit between the equation and the experimental findings becomes better? Explain this.

Applying Equations 8.17 and 8.18 to the data set given in Table 8.9 yields values of 0.953 and 0.20, respectively, for the correlation coefficient ($r$) and the standard deviation ($s$).

The data from Table 8.9 thus fit the following equation:

$$y(i) = 0.23\, x_1(i) + 0.76\, x_2(i) + 1.88 \tag{8.16}$$

$$n = 9 \quad r = 0.953 \quad s = 0.20$$

The extent to which the experimental $y$ values and the $y$ values calculated from Equation 8.16 agree may be seen from Figure 8.4. In this figure the calculated values of $y$ (y axis) are plotted against the experimental values for $y$ (on the x axis). The straight line corresponds to the situation in which the calculated $y$ values are equal to the experimental $y$ values. The closer the points are to the line, the better the equation and the higher the value of $r$ and the lower the value of $s$.

Some examples of the application of multiple linear regression analysis to biological data, using the Hansch equation, are given below.

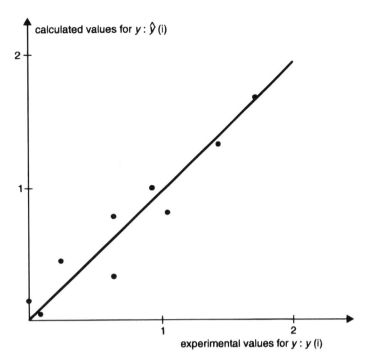

FIGURE   8.4
Experimental values $y(i)$ for $y$ plotted against calculated values $\hat{y}(i)$ for y. The values of $\hat{y}(i)$ were calculated from Equation 8.16 and the data in Table 8.9. The plotted line corresponds with $y(i) = \hat{y}(i)$

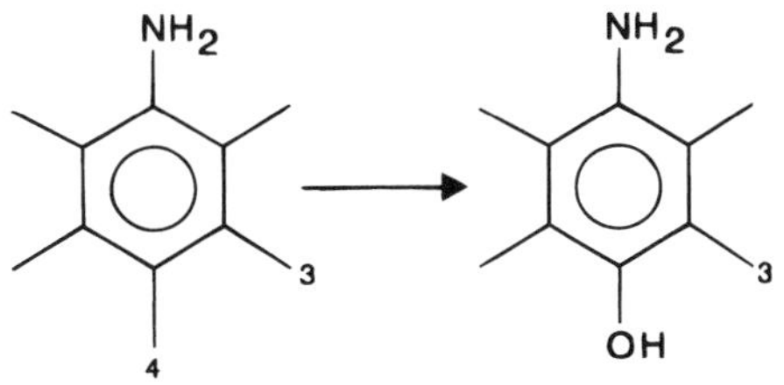

FIGURE   8.5
Microsomal hydroxylation of anilines

### 3.1.3 Some examples of the Hansch analysis

*Hydroxylation of aniline derivatives*   Anilines readily undergo hydroxylation at the 4-position (Figure 8.5). Data on hydroxylation are given in Table 8.10A.

The group of substances consists of eleven aniline derivatives that differ in the substituents at the nitrogen atom on the one hand, and, in the substituents at position 3 of the aromatic ring on the other. Log $K_{ow}$ ranges from 0.90 for aniline to 3.16 for N-butylaniline (N-$C_4H_9$). Clearly, halogen atoms as well as alkyl groups increase log $K_{ow}$. The longer the alkyl chain, the higher log $K_{ow}$.

Table 8.10A shows $\sigma$ and $E_s$ values for the substituent at position 3 of the aromatic ring. The first five compounds all have a hydrogen atom at this position ($\sigma = 0$ and $E_s = 1.24$). For the remaining six compounds $\sigma$ and $E_s$ vary. To summarize, there are data for:

- the biological activity (*BR*), i.e. hydroxylation by microsomal fractions
- $K_{ow}$, $\sigma$ and $E_s$ as parameters for the hydrophobicity, electronic effects and steric hindrance. By applying multiple linear regression to these data, Equation 8.13 can now be solved.

TABLE 8.10A

Physico–chemical properties and aromatic hydroxylation[a] (biological response, BR) of aniline derivatives

| Compound | log $K_{ow}$ | $\sigma$ | $E_s$ | log BR[b] | |
|---|---|---|---|---|---|
| | | | | experimental | calculated** |
| H (aniline) | 0.90 | 0.00 | 1.24 | 1.72 | 1.67 |
| N-C$_4$H$_9$ | 3.16 | 0.00 | 1.24 | 2.31 | 2.33 |
| N-C$_3$H$_7$ | 2.66 | 0.00 | 1.24 | 2.21 | 2.20 |
| N-C$_2$H$_5$ | 2.16 | 0.00 | 1.24 | 2.14 | 2.06 |
| N-CH$_3$ | 1.66 | 0.00 | 1.24 | 1.76 | 1.93 |
| 3-Cl | 1.88 | 0.37 | 0.27 | 1.71 | 1.64 |
| 3-F | 1.30 | 0.34 | 0.78 | 1.69 | 1.66 |
| 3-Br | 2.07 | 0.39 | 0.08 | 1.64 | 1.62 |
| 3-I | 2.37 | 0.35 | −0.16 | 1.58 | 1.62 |
| 3-CH$_3$ | 1.40 | −0.07 | 0.00 | 1.50 | 1.41 |
| 3-NO$_2$ | 1.37 | 0.71 | −1.28 | 0.88 | 0.94 |
| 3-OCH$_3$* | 0.93 | 0.12 | 0.69 | 0.57 | 1.53 |

[a]Microsomal fractions of the liver, lung and kidneys of the rabbit.
[b]BR: biological response as amount of substrate converted (expressed as the % relative to o-chloroaniline).
*This compound was not included in the QSAR equations (see text)
**Calculated from Equation 8.24.

In this case, the parameter of biological activity, indicated as BR, is not expressed as the intensity of a particular effect at a particular concentration (C), but as the amount of product formed. In principle, that makes no difference. The first step is to *calculate the relationship* between the various physico-chemical properties available (log $K_{ow}$, $\sigma$ and $E_s$) and the biological effect (in this case the hydroxylation). If multiple linear regression is applied to the data set in Table 8.10A, seven equations can in principle be derived:

- equations with only one parameter (log $K_{ow}$, $\sigma$ or $E_s$);
- equations with two parameters (log $K_{ow}$, $\sigma$; log $K_{ow}$, $E_s$ and $\sigma$, $E_s$) and
- an equation with all three parameters (log $K_{ow}$, $\sigma$ and $E_s$).

The various equations are shown in Table 8.10B.

*Quality of the equations*

The next step is the *inspection of the quality* of these equations with the help of the correlation coefficient $r$. Looking only at the quality of the equations, it appears that Equations 8.23 and 8.25 show the best correlations ($r = 0.98$). Equation 8.25, however, is no better than Equation 8.23 (SD values are the same). It can be concluded from this that the introduction of the $\sigma$ parameter has not led to a better equation. In other words, differences in electron distribution between aniline derivatives caused by substitution at position 3 appear to have no influence on the extent of hydroxylation. Thus, only Equation 8.23 is left, which has both log $K_{ow}$ and $E_s$ as parameters. An adequate description of the experimental data appears to require both parameters; equations with only log $K_{ow}$ (8.19) or $E_s$ (8.21) are of considerably lower quality ($r = 0.65$ and 0.88, respectively).

*Interpretation of the equations*

The last step is the *interpretation* of the equations. Both hydrophobicity (log $K_{ow}$) and steric factors ($E_s$) apparently influence the hydroxylation. The values of the coefficients in equation 8.23 also show that hydroxylation decreases if the size of the substituent increases, since BR decreases if $E_s$ decreases. An explanation for this could be that the presence of bulky substituents at position 3 hinders the approach to the enzyme, resulting in less extensive conversion of the substrate.

TABLE 8.10B
QSAR equations, obtained by applying multiple linear regression analysis to the
data set given in Table 8.10A

| log BR = (n = 11) | r | sd | Equation-number |
|---|---|---|---|
| $0.39 \log K_{ow} + 1.01$ | 0.65 | 0.31 | 8.19 |
| $-1.12\sigma + 1.95$ | 0.72 | 0.29 | 8.20 |
| $0.41 E_a + 1.52$ | 0.88 | 0.20 | 8.21 |
| $0.31 \log K_{ow} + 0.96\sigma + 1.32$ | 0.89 | 0.20 | 8.22 |
| $0.27 \log K_{ow} + 0.36 E_a + 1.03$ | 0.98 | 0.08 | 8.23 |
| $-0.07\sigma + 0.40 E_a + 1.54$ | 0.88 | 0.21 | 8.24 |
| $0.27 \log K_{ow} - 0.106\sigma + 0.34 E_s + 1.06$ | 0.98 | 0.08 | 8.25 |

ASSIGNMENT 8.9

Calculate log BR for 3-chloroaniline using Equation 8.23
(Table 8.10B) and the data for log $K_{ow}$ and $E_s$ (Table 8.10).
Compare the results with the experimental values for log BR.

The last two columns of Table 8.10A compare the experimental log BR values
with those calculated using Equation 8.23. In general, these show very close
agreement. In deriving Equation 8.23, one compound (3-methoxyaniline) has
been omitted, because it falls outside the relationship expressed by the Equation (experimental log BR and calculated log BR are 0.57 and 1.53, respectively).

The above example illustrates several aspects of the Hansch approach:

- it appears that a process such as the metabolism of a series of aniline derivatives may be described adequately by QSAR;
- the effects of the parameters (log $K_{ow}$ and $E_s$) indicate that hydrophobic
  interactions as well as steric repulsion play a role in the interaction with
  the enzyme;
- the QSAR equation (equation 8.23) can in principle be used for the prediction of the extent to which untested aniline derivatives are metabolized. Since the experimental and calculated log BR values for a compound
  such as 3-methoxyaniline differ widely, while an explanation is lacking,
  it will be clear, however, that difficulties are attached to the prediction of
  biological activity.

*Organophosphate insecticides*

Several QSAR studies have been carried out for organophosphate esters (OP esters). In one of these studies, the Hansch equation was applied to a series of OP
esters that differed in the substituents at the para position on the phenyl ring
(see Figure 8.6).
The parameters examined were:

- hydrolysis rate constant, $k_{hydr}$;
- concentration causing 50% inhibition of acetylcholinesterase (AChE);
  $EC_{50}$;
- $LD_{50}$ (in the common housefly).

Without going into the actual experimental data, look at the equations with
the highest correlation coefficients (Equations 8.26–8.28, from: Hansch, 1973,
p. 111).

$$\log k_{hydr} = 1.96\,\sigma^- - 6.62$$
$$n = 4 \quad r = 0.969 \tag{8.26}$$

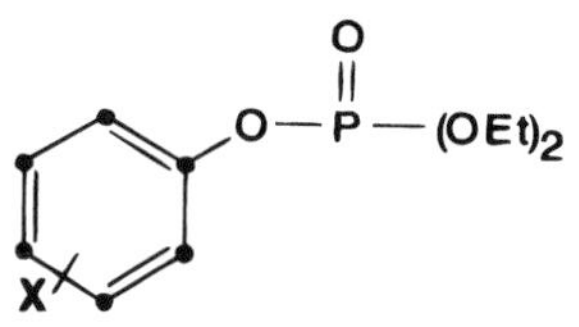

FIGURE 8.6
General structure of organophosphates in a QSAR study

$$\log 1 / EC_{50} \ (\text{AChE}) = 2.49\,\sigma^- + 4.18$$
$$n = 8 \quad r = 0.985 \tag{8.27}$$

$$\log 1 / LD_{50} = 2.42\,\sigma^- + 0.26\,\pi - 0.60$$
$$n = 8 \quad r = 0.987 \tag{8.28}$$

The QSAR equations show that the hydrolysis rate constant (Equation 8.26) as well as the inhibition of AChE (Equation 8.27) are clearly related to the $\sigma$ constant. The parameter $\sigma^-$ is used in the QSARs because it leads to better correlation than the normal $\sigma$ constants.

The effects of $\sigma$ are not surprising; the substituents on the phenyl ring influence the positive charge of the P atom and, consequently, the affinity for the OH groups in water and serine. The correlation with $LD_{50}$ values in the common housefly shows that, apart from $\sigma$, a hydrophobicity term ($\pi$) is also important. That $\sigma$ alone is insufficient to account for the $LD_{50}$ can be explained by the fact that lethality, in contrast to hydrolysis and enzyme inhibition, also involves transport phenomena.

*A QSAR study in aquatic toxicology* The last decades have seen considerable QSAR research in the area of aquatic toxicology. Equation 8.29 shows the results of a QSAR study by Könemann (1981). The data set concerned a group of 50 non-reactive, non-ionized organic compounds, such as aliphatic and aromatic hydrocarbons and chlorinated hydrocarbons, alcohols, ethers and similar compounds. A good correlation was found between the $K_{ow}$ and the 14-day $LC_{50}$ in guppies (see equation 8.29).

$$\log 1 / LC_{50} = 0.871 \ \log K_{ow} - 4.87$$
$$n = 50 \quad r = 0.987 \tag{8.29}$$

Figure 8.7 shows the relationship between $\log K_{ow}$ and $\log LC_{50}$. The higher the value of $K_{ow}$, the higher the lethality (lower $LC_{50}$). This increase in toxicity with rising $K_{ow}$ is related to the fact that more hydrophobic substances are more readily taken up.

The distinguishing feature of this QSAR study is that the data set is not restricted to structure analogs. It also appears that the differences in $LC_{50}$ can be fully explained by the differences in $K_{ow}$, as the equation can scarcely be improved by introducing other parameters.

The fact that the 50 substances can be described by this one equation indicates that these substances could have similar actions. It is assumed that in these $LC_{50}$ experiments the effect is comparable with that of volatile anesthetics. The effect is therefore relatively insensitive to particular structural characteristics, but is simply related to hydrophobicity. In other words, the mechanisms underlying these effects of these particular substances is not very specific.

258

*Minimum LC₅₀*

An interesting aspect is that with this QSAR equation the *minimum LC₅₀* for organic compounds can be predicted. Every organic substance has at least this non-specific action and is thus at least as toxic as calculation from this QSAR forecasts.

The experimental $LC_{50}$ and the calculated minimum $LC_{50}$ for a number of substances are compared in Table 8.11 and Figure 8.7.

The first two compounds in this series, methanol and 3-chlorotoluene, belong to the group of non-reactive, non-ionized organic compounds. The minimum $LC_{50}$ has been calculated based on their $K_{ow}$, which is given in the second column and in equation 8.29. For these two substances, the calculated minimum $LC_{50}$ is in good agreement with the observed $LC_{50}$. The values for methanol are identical, while for 3-chlorotoluene the calculated minimum $LC_{50}$ differs from the experimental $LC_{50}$ by a factor of 1.5. This difference is within the normal inaccuracy in determining $LC_{50}$ values.

Equation 8.29 is, however, not applicable to all compounds, as shown in the following examples:

- a compound such as dieldrin has an experimentally determined $LC_{50}$ value that is considerably lower (by a factor of 100) than the calculated minimum $LC_{50}$ (see Table 8.11 and Figure 8.7). This is also true for other pesticides, such as malathion and lindane, as well as for substances like dichloroaniline and dinitrobenzene. The higher toxicity (lower $LC_{50}$ compared to minimum $LC_{50}$) of these substances is probably due to a more specific action;

- the last substance in this table, $\alpha$-chlorotoluene (or benzyl chloride), is at first glance structurally closely related to 3-chlorotoluene. Yet this compound, unlike 3-chlorotoluene, is considerably more toxic than its calculated minimum $LC_{50}$ value indicates. This can be explained by the fact that unlike 3-chlorotoluene, $\alpha$-chlorotoluene is a reactive compound. This higher reactivity produces a clearly different type of action (see also section 1). At the same time, this example illustrates the risks involved in predicting toxicity. The greatest problem is in classifying a particular substance in the right group.

The Hansch equation has been, and continues to be, applied to various effects and substances.

## 3.2  FREE–WILSON APPROACH

*Free–Wilson approach*

Unlike the Hansch approach, the *Free–Wilson* approach is not based on physico-chemical properties but entirely on the *structure of a compound*.

TABLE   8.11
Comparison of calculated minimum $LC_{50}$ and experimental $LC_{50}$ in guppies for a number compounds

| Compound | log $K_{ow}$ | $LC_{50}$ (min)* μmol 1⁻¹ | $LC_{50}$(exp.) μmol 1⁻¹ |
|---|---|---|---|
| methanol | −0.79 | $3.6 \times 10^5$ | $3.6 \times 10^5$ |
| 3-chlorotoluene | 3.31 | 97 | 145 |
| dieldrin | 5.30 | 1.8 | 0.017 |
| malathion | 2.82 | 257 | 4.0 |
| lindane | 3.53 | 63 | 0.20 |
| 1,3-dinitrobenzene | 1.53 | 3467 | 56 |
| 3,5-dichloroanitine | 2.42 | 578 | 24 |
| $\alpha$-chlorotoluene | 2.48 | 513 | 3.1 |

*Calculated minimum $LC_{50}$ for guppies (Equation 8.23) data from: Hermens et al. (1985)

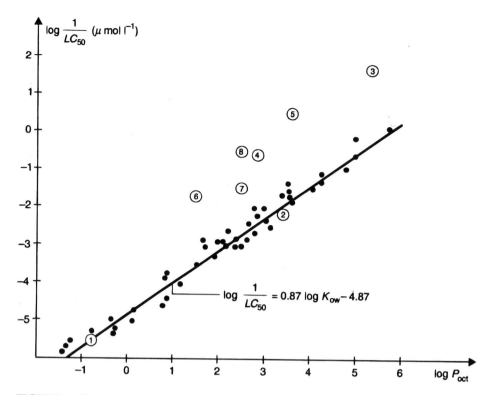

FIGURE 8.7

Relationship between log $K_{ow}$ and log $(1/LC_{50})$ for 50 non-reactive compounds
The 50 non-reactive compounds are indicated by •.
The plotted line corresponds with equation 8.28
Compounds 1 (methanol) and 2(3-chlorotoluene) belong to this group of non-reactive compounds.
Compounds 3 to 8 (dieldrin, malathion, lindane, 1,3-dinitrobenzene, 3,5-dichloroaniline and $\alpha$-chlorotoluene)
have a markedly lower $LC_{50}$ compared with the other 50 substances.
For more information, see also Table 8.11 and the text.

*Only applicable to structural analogs*

The starting point here is that the effect of a substituent on the biological activity is additive and independent of the presence of other substituents. This approach is only applicable to compounds that are structural analogs. The Free–Wilson approach is based on the following general equation:

$$BR = \sum (A_{ij} S_{ij}) + k \tag{8.30}$$

where:

$BR$ = biological response

$A_{ij}$ = contribution of a substituent ($i$) at position ($j$) in a molecule to $BR$

$S_{ij}$ = indicates whether this substituent $i$ is present at position $j$ ($S = 1$) or not ($S = 0$).

*Combination of the Free–Wilson and Hansch approaches*

One approach that has made use of a combination of the Free–Wilson and Hansch approaches has been described in a QSAR study, concerning the prediction of $LD_{50}$ values in rats. The authors proposed a method to calculate the $LD_{50}$ values of 425 compounds by using one QSAR equation. Their final equation has the form:

$$\log 1/LD_{50} = a \log K_{ow} + b\,MW + c_1 X_1(i) + c_2 X_2(i) + \ldots +$$
$$c_{27} X_{27}(i) + d \tag{8.31}$$

where:

$K_{ow}$ = octanol–water partition coefficient

$MW$ = molecular weight

$X_1, X_2 \ldots X_{27}$ = factors corresponding to particular structural characteristics

Depending on whether or not a structural fragment is present in a particular compound, $X$ equals 1 or 0, respectively.

Examples of these structural fragments include nitro groups and carbonyl groups. This equation was solved by multiple linear regression analysis, which provides numerical values for the coefficients $a$, $b$, $c_1$–$c_{27}$ and d; the correlation coefficient finally obtained was 0.702.

See also Study unit 7

This approach has been much criticized. First, the $LD_{50}$ values are based on a data set that was not previously critically evaluated. The data have been obtained from all sorts of experiments, each with their own experimental conditions, which means that the data are not really comparable.

*Criticism of the use of QSAR*

In addition, the use of QSAR is also criticized at a more fundamental level, particularly because so many different compounds with varying structures and actions are included in one equation. Further, the application of QSAR analysis to $LD_{50}$ values as such is criticized, on the grounds that there is no unambiguous mechanism of action as far as lethality is concerned. Part of this criticism seems to be justified, except for the view that QSAR analyses should not be applied to $LD_{50}$ or $LC_{50}$ values. A more important criterion is whether the observed correlations can be applied in practice to provide reasonably accurate predictions.

The above method for the prediction of $LD_{50}$s in the rat is not frequently used in practice. It does not provide insight into which properties of substances affect a compounds biological activity or toxicity. The Hansch approach is much more frequently applied and, in principle, the form of the Hansch equation (i.e. which properties are found to be important) can provide indications about the mechanism of action.

3.3 PATTERN RECOGNITION TECHNIQUES

The use of various *pattern recognition techniques* in QSAR studies is a very recent development. The term QSAR is not really justified here, as these techniques are used to find relationships between the structure of a substance and the presence or absence of a particular effect, without paying attention to quantitative aspects. It would be better to refer to them as to *structure–activity relationships* (SAR). Here is a brief description of the background to these techniques.

*Structure–activity relationships (SAR)*

Pattern recognition techniques are used to identify *qualitative relationships* between a set of *molecular descriptors* and the presence or absence of a particular biological effect (such as carcinogenicity). These molecular descriptors can be parameters indicating the presence of particular structural fragments, possibly complemented by other parameters, such as physico-chemical properties. Each molecule is thus characterized by a number of molecular descriptors ($N$). This leads to a data set for a number of compounds ($n$). Subsequently, statistical analysis decides which of these molecular descriptors determines the presence or absence of the effect. These techniques have been applied to data on the carcinogenicity of aromatic amines and polycyclic aromatic hydrocarbons. It is often found that about 90% of the compounds can be correctly classified.

## 3.4 APPLICATIONS OF QSAR TECHNIQUES

In the previous sections, attention was focused on the various QSAR techniques. An all-important question is whether these techniques can be used in practice, for example in policy-making. In principle, the replacement of animal experiments by calculations of toxicity or qualitative estimates of, for example, the potential carcinogenicity of a chemical is attractive. Nevertheless, it is not likely that such calculations will replace animal experiments in the near future. The Hansch approach as well as pattern recognition techniques, retains an element of uncertainty, and it would be irresponsible to set standards or make decisions (such as whether or not to admit a new substance to the market) based on uncertainties. The European *policy for the registration of new substances* rightly insists, therefore, that data on toxicity are obtained by animal research. The United States takes a different view: the American Environmental Protection Agency (EPA) uses QSAR data in its policy regarding the approval of new substances. On the basis of these data, it is decided whether additional experimental data are required.

*Policies for the registration of new substances*

How can QSAR be applied?

Nevertheless, there are a number of possible applications of QSAR techniques. To mention a few:

- QSARs can be applied in risk evaluation of a large number of existing substances (around 60 000) for which little toxicity information is available. Using structure–activity relationships, it is possible to select substances which are suspected to pose a greater risk than other substances, before testing them (priority setting);

*Priority setting*

- a predicted toxicity can amongst other things replace a *range-finding experiment*. Prior to a $LC_{50}$ experiment, the range of concentrations that includes the $LC_{50}$ needs to be determined (range finding). If one supposes that a reasonably sound prediction can be made, one can run the risk of omitting such a range-finding experiment;

- predictions of toxicity can already play a role in the development of new substances. If it is reasonable to expect, based on its structure, that a substance will be carcinogenic or that it will be bioconcentrated in aquatic organisms, this could be a reason not to synthesize it;

- parameters that appear to be relevant in a QSAR may provide indications about the mechanism of action.

## 4    Summary

The toxicity of a substance is clearly related to its chemical structure. Relevant structural parameters are hydrophobicity, electron distribution and steric hindrance. The influence substituents have on these parameters can be calculated by using substituent constants.

The contribution of these parameters is related to their influence on the toxicokinetic behavior of the substance on the one hand, and on the intrinsic activity of the active agent towards the target molecule on the other. Various techniques for predicting the activity of compounds have been developed on the basis of this relationship between particular structural characteristics or physico-chemical properties and biological activity (Hansch, Free–Wilson and pattern recognition). These techniques can be used to predict the activity of substances, and such predictions can play a role in policies regarding environmental contaminants.

## SELF ASSESSMENT QUESTIONS

1   Which biological process can explain the differences in biological activity that exist between the members of a series of compounds with the same mode of action?

2   Which types of chemical interactions may take place between a substance and its target molecule?
    Which physico-chemical properties determine the intensity of these interactions?

3   The iso-electric point for albumin is 4.80. What can be said about the ratio of negative to positive charges at pH 7.4?

4   Why is the possibility of using substituent constants essential when making QSAR calculations?
    Which substituent constants have been introduced? Define each of these constants.

5   Write down the Hansch equation. Express in your own words the meaning of this equation.

6   Calculate $\log K_{ow}$ for 1-chloro-2,4-dimethylbenzene using the $\pi$ method ($\log K_{ow}$ of benzene = 2.13) and using Rekker's method.

7   Why is it that for ionized compounds $K_{ow}$ is often determined in a buffer of pH = 7.4?

8   Equation 8.27 shows that the concentration causing a 50% inhibition of acetylcholinesterase (AChE) correlates with the Hammett $\sigma$ constant for a series of organophosphate insecticides with different substituents at the para position (see Figure 8.6). It was also found that for this data set, $LD_{50}$ values in the common housefly correlate both with the Hammett $\sigma$ constant and the $\pi$ constant (equation 8.28). Comparing the para-chloro and para-amino analogs, which of the two compounds would be:

    •   the more effective inhibitor of AChE?

    •   the more toxic in the common housefly?

    Explain your answers in terms of the influence these substituents have on the physico-chemical properties of the compound.

## FEEDBACK

1   **Answers to the assignments**

8.1   Reaction between an epoxide and a sulfhydryl group (-SH)
      A free electron pair from the -SH group attacks the slightly positive C atom.

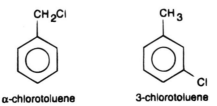

α-chlorotoluene          3-chlorotoluene

8.2 Benzene does not react with nucleophilic groups. It is metabolized in the body to an epoxide and this compound does have alkylating properties. The epoxidation is mediated by the so-called mixed-function oxidase system (see also units 3 and 4).

This is an example of bioactivation.

Alkylation of DNA by the epoxide underlies the carcinogenity of benzene.

8.3 The dissociation of an acid proceeds as follows:

$$\text{HA} \rightleftharpoons \text{H}^+ + \text{A}^-$$

The equilibrium constant for this reaction (the ionization constant of the acid ($K_a$)) is thus:

$$K_a = \frac{[\text{A}^-][\text{H}^+]}{[\text{HA}]}$$

If this is converted to logarithmic form, then:

$$\log K_a = \log \frac{[\text{A}^-][\text{H}^+]}{[\text{HA}]}$$

This equation can be rewritten:

$$\log K_a = \log[\text{A}^-] + \log[\text{H}^+] - \log[\text{HA}]$$

Substituting $pK_a = -\log K_a$ and $pH = -\log[\text{H}^+]$ yields:

$$-pK_a = \log[\text{A}^-] - \log[\text{HA}] - pH$$

or:

$$\log \frac{[\text{A}^-]}{[\text{HA}]} = pH - pK_a$$

8.4 The relationship between $\log K_{ow}$ and $\log BCF$ (from Table 8.5) is shown in Figure 8.8.

It can be clearly seen that the bioconcentration factor ($BCF$) increases with the octanol–water partition coefficient ($K_{ow}$). This increase is related to the fact that hydrophobic compounds are absorbed more rapidly and are eliminated less rapidly.

8.5 Phenols can occur in an ionized ($A^-$) or in a non-ionized form ($HA$). The degree of ionization of a phenol naturally depends on the $pK_a$ as well as the pH.

Using the $pK_a$ values for the two compounds and the pH, the ratio $[A^-]/[HA]$ can be calculated with the help of equation 8.1. This ratio is shown in the table below.

TABLE 8.12

| | | $pH - pK_a$ | $\dfrac{[\text{A}^-]}{[\text{HA}]}$ |
|---|---|---|---|
| 4-chlorophenol | pH 6 | −3.37 | 0.00 |
| $pK_a = 9.37$) | pH 8 | −1.37 | 0.04 |
| pentachlorophenol | pH 6 | −0.69 | 0.20 |
| $pK_a = 6.69$) | pH 8 | 1.31 | 20.4 |

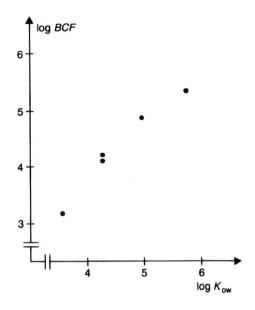

FIGURE 8.8

4-Chlorophenol is virtually 100% non-ionized at both pH 6 and 8. There is thus a negligible difference in the degree of ionization at the two different pH values. The situation is clearly different for pentachlorophenol, which has a $[A^-]/[HA]$ ratio of 0.2 at pH 6, while at pH 8 this ratio is 20. This means that at pH 8 a much larger proportion of the compound is present in the ionized form. Since only the non-ionized form is taken up, the absorption at pH 8 will clearly be less than at pH 6, which means that the toxicity at pH 8 is also lower (and hence $LC_{50}$ is higher).

8.6 $\log K_{ow}$ of 2-nitrotoluene is calculated by using $\pi$ constants from Table 8.8 as follows:

$$\log K_{ow} = \log K_{ow} \text{ (toluene)} + \pi NO_2$$
$$= 2.69 + (-0.28)$$
$$= 2.41$$

In the same way $\log K_{ow}$ for the remaining compounds can be calculated:

| | |
|---|---|
| 4-bromotoluene | $\log K_{ow} = 3.55$ |
| 2-methyltoluene | $\log K_{ow} = 4.26$ |
| 2-chloro-3-bromotoluene | $\log K_{ow} = 4.26$ |

8.7 Log $K_{ow}$ of 2-nitrotoluene is calculated using $f$ values from Table 8.8 as follows:

$$\log K_{ow} = f C_6 H_4 + f CH_3 + f NO_2$$
$$= 1.688 + 0.702 + (-0.078)$$
$$= 2.31$$

For the other compounds $\log K_{ow}$ can be calculated in the same way:

| | |
|---|---|
| 4-bromotoluene | $\log K_{ow} = 3.521$ |
| 2-methyltoluene | $\log K_{ow} = 3.092$ |
| 2-chloro-3-bromotoluene | $\log K_{ow} = 4.186$ |

Comparing the results of these two methods ($\pi$ constant and Rekker's fragmental constant), small differences are found. For more complex structures the discrepancies may be larger. The only reliable value is then the experimentally determined $K_{ow}$.

8.8 If an equation gives a better description of the experimental values, the differences between the calculated $y$ values ($\hat{y}$) and the experimental $y$ values are smaller, i.e. $SS_2$ from Equations 8.17 and 8.18 is smaller.
In that situation, $r = 1$ and $s = 0$.

8.9 For 3-chloroaniline $K_{ow}$ is 1.88 and $E_s$ is 0.27.
Substituting these values in Equation 8.23 yields:

$$\log BR = (0.27 \times 1.88) + (0.36 \times 0.27) + 1.03 = 1.63$$

The experimental log $BR$ value is 1.71, so there is a difference of 0.08 from the calculated log $BR$. This difference is small enough to be considered insignificant, given the experimental error in such measurements.

## 2 Answers to the self assessment questions

1 Two important processes influence the biological activity: transport to the site of action and interaction with the target molecule.
The amount or concentration at which a substance can reach the site of action is determined by processes such as absorption, binding to blood proteins, metabolism and transport in the body.
The affinity of the target molecule depends on the structural characteristics of both biologically active compound and the target molecule (see assignment 8.2).

2 There are several types of chemical interactions between a substance and its target molecule (see first column). Type as well as intensity of the interactions depends on the physico-chemical properties of the compound (see second column).

TABLE 8.13

| type of interaction | physico-chemical property |
| --- | --- |
| hydrophobic interaction | hydrophobicity |
| electrostatic interaction | |
| -ion-ion | charge on the atoms |
| -ion-dipole | ditto |
| -dipole-dipole | ditto |
| hydrogen-bonding | charge on the atoms |
| vander Waals interaction | polarizability |
| steric hindrance | size |
| covalent binding | a.o. induction and mesomerism |

The intensity of these interactions has a direct effect on the biological activity of a substance. Since such physico-chemical properties are not easy to measure (and in fact impossible to measure if the compound has not yet been synthesized), parameters have been introduced that provide information on such properties (see assignment 8.4).

3    At this pH, the majority of charges are negative, so the number of negative charges is much larger than the number of positive charges.

4    QSARs may be particularly useful in the development of new drugs. In this way, attempts can be made to predict the activity of a substance before synthesizing it. It is of course impossible to determine experimentally the properties of these, as yet unsynthesized compounds (such as $K_{ow}$ and dipole moment). It is therefore essential that parameters that provide information on the properties of the substance are available. Thus, $\pi$ constants can be used to estimate a property such as hydrophobicity for a series of structural analogs. In principle, it is not necessary to know the $K_{ow}$ for the whole molecule, because this information can be obtained simply from the $\pi$ constants.

The following three important substituent constants are available:

*   *substituent constant $\pi$*, parameter for hydrophobicity:

$$\pi(X) = \log K_{ow}\,(C_6H_5X) - \log K_{ow}\,(C_6H_6)$$

where $C_6H_6$ = benzene and $C_6H_5X$ = a benzene derivative, in which one H atom has been replaced by a substituent $X$ (for example, chlorine).

*   *substituent constant $\sigma$ (Hammett)*, parameter for electron distribution:

$$\sigma(X) = pK_a\,(C_6H_4XCO_2H) - pK_a\,(C_6H_5CO_2H)$$

where $C_6H_5CO_2H$ = benzoic acid and $C_6H_4XCO_2H$ = benzoic acid in which one of the H atoms has been replaced by a substituent $X$ ($pK_a$ = $-\log K_a$; $K_a$ is the ionization constant of the acid).

*   *substituent constant $E_s$ (Taft)*, parameter for steric hindrance:

$$E_s(X) = \log k(XCH_2 - (CO)OCH_3) - \log k(CH_3(CO)OCH_3)$$

where: $CH_3(CO)OCH_3$ = methyl acetate, $XCH_2 - (CO)OCH_3$ is methyl acetate in which one H atom has been replaced by a substituent $X$ ($k$ is the rate constant of hydrolysis).

5    The Hansch equation is rewritten:

$$\log \frac{1}{C} = a \log K_{ow}\ (\textit{or } a\,\pi) + b\,\sigma + cE_s + d$$

where $C$ is the concentration responsible for the intensity of the effect (for example, 50% enzyme inhibition).

In other words, this equation can be used to describe the relationship of the biological activity of a series of substances with parameters that provide information on hydrophobicity, electron distribution and steric hindrance. Hardly ever are all of these parameters relevant: which ones are is determined by the fate of the compound in the body. Both toxicokinetics and toxicodynamics may be so complex that the preconditions on which the equation is based are not met. In addition, the parameters chosen may be unsuitable for describing the interaction with the target molecule.

6    Log $K_{ow}$ of 1-chloro-2,4-dimethylbenzene:

*π method*:

$$\begin{aligned}
\log K_{ow} &= \log K_{ow} \text{ (benzene)} + \pi \text{Cl} + (2 \times \pi \text{CH}_3) \\
&= 2.13 + 0.71 + (2 \times 0.702) \\
&= 3.96
\end{aligned}$$

*Fragmental constant method*:

$$\begin{aligned}
\log K_{ow} &= f\text{C}_6\text{H}_3 + f\text{Cl} + (2 \times f\text{CH}_3) \\
&= 1.431 + 0.922 + (2 \times 0.702) \\
&= 3.76
\end{aligned}$$

7   Since the absorption of substances that may ionize is strongly influenced by their degree of ionization, it is important to know the value of $K_{ow}$ at the pH which is biologically relevant (pH usually about 7.4). In this way, it is possible to make proper comparisons of the biological activities of these compounds based on $K_{ow}$ values corresponding to that pH.

8   For the common housefly, both the concentrations that cause a 50% inhibition of AChE and the $LD_{50}$ appear to fit the following QSAR equations:

$$\log \frac{1}{EC_{50}} (AChE) = 2.49 \, \sigma + 4.18$$
$$n = 8 \quad r = 0.985$$

$$\log \frac{1}{LD_{50}} = 2.42 \, \sigma^- + 0.26 \, \pi - 0.60$$
$$n = 8 \quad r = 0.987$$

These equations use $\sigma^-$ values. It may be assumed that $\sigma$ and $\sigma^-$ show the same tendencies.

The substituent constants for chlorine (Cl) and amino groups ($NH_2$) are:

|         | $\pi$  | $\sigma$ |
|---------|--------|----------|
| Cl      | 0.71   | 0.23     |
| $NH_2$  | −1.23  | −0.16    |

From the $\sigma$ constants for both substituents and the equation for AChE inhibition, it appears that for the chlorinated compound $\log 1/EC_{50}$ (AChE) is higher, and hence the $EC_{50}$ lower, than for the amino compound. The chloro-analog is thus more effective as an enzyme inhibitor.

The explanation for this is that chlorine has electron-attracting properties, as a result of which the positive charge on the phosphorus atom increases. A higher positive charge means a higher affinity for the nucleophilic OH group of the serine in AChE (see Figure 8.3b).

The $\pi$ constant as well as the $\sigma$ constant is greater for Cl than for $NH_2$. This means that in the equation for $LD_{50}$, $\log 1/LD_{50}$ is higher, and hence the $LD_{50}$ lower, for the chlorinated compound than for the amino compound.

Therefore the Cl analog causes death at lower concentrations. In addition to the fact that this chloro-analog is a more effective inhibitor of AChE, it should be remembered that the Cl compound is also absorbed more readily because of its higher hydrophobicity.

# Contents Study unit 9
## Toxicity of mixtures

0-8493-9232-2/96/$0.00 + $.50

# Study unit 9

# Toxicity of mixtures

*A. Musch*

## INTRODUCTION

Toxicological investigations are generally carried out to study the effect of a single substance on a certain type of organism. From this, conclusions can be drawn regarding the risks to such organisms from exposure to that particular substance. Our environment and food, however, include huge numbers of substances. Based on toxicological knowledge of these substances, it is possible to determine more or less successfully the intake, concentration or exposure time for each individual substance at which the health risk exceeds a certain standard.

However, this does not preclude the possibility that exposure to more than one substance at a time could lead to qualitatively and/or quantitatively different effects. In medical science it is well-known that the combined administration of drugs sometimes leads to results that are not characteristic of the individual drugs.

> ASSIGNMENT 9.1
>
> Can you suggest examples of substances which enhance the effect of other substances?

Much pharmacological and toxicological research has therefore been carried out on the action of mixtures consisting of two or three substances. The interaction between two substances sometimes proves to be so complex and difficult to interpret that studies on mixtures of more than two substances would seem to be a hopeless task. Nonetheless, well-founded statements will have to be made, for example, on the risk to aquatic organisms posed by the presence of thousands of chemicals in polluted surface water (where each individual substance occurs in such a low concentration that it is not expected to be harmful). This study unit discusses the interaction between a few substances and the consequences for toxicity, as well as the action of mixtures of large numbers of substances.

> LEARNING OBJECTIVES
>
> After studying this unit, you will be expected to
>
> — be familiar with the various aspects of exposure to combinations of toxic substances;
> — be able to indicate how combined effects can play a part in the different phases (exposure, toxicokinetic and toxicodynamic phase);
> — be familiar with the various manifestations of combined action:
>   — antagonism
>   — concentration additivity

271

— partial additivity
— no additivity
— potentiation;
— be able to indicate in which situations the above phenomena can arise;
— be able to explain the quantitative aspects of various combined actions;
— be able to give some examples of combined effects.

*Study hints*

Before beginning this study unit, it is necessary to have mastered the topics discussed in previous study units. In particular, reference will be made to topics covered in Study units 2, 5 and 8. The study load for this unit is about 3 student learning hours. To work out the assignments you will need an electronic calculator and (millimeter) graph paper.

STUDY CORE

1    **Theoretical considerations and models**

Various problems arise when studying the consequences for an organism of exposure to several substances simultaneously. First of all, there is the question whether the substances influence one another and, if so, in what way and with what effects. Secondly, the question of the extent of the effects needs to be answered. The first problem refers to the *mode of action* and the *qualitative aspects*, while the second seeks insight into the *quantitative aspects* of the toxicity of mixtures.

2    **Qualitative aspects of combined action**

The combined action of two or more substances can become evident at various points in the toxic process and in various ways. It can arise:

a.    in the exposure phase
b.    in the kinetic phase
c.    in the dynamic phase (including physiological interactions), or by
d.    chemical and/or physical interactions.

*Interactions in the environment*    a.    In the environment and in food, chemical or physical interactions between two substances can lead to new substances, which have an entirely different toxicity to that of the original substances. A well-known example is the formation of carcinogenic nitrosamines from the reaction between nitrite and secondary amines in the acidic environment of the stomach.

ASSIGNMENT  9.2

In which types of food can one expect to find a high level of nitrite? Why would eating a combination of fish and, for example, spinach not be advisable?

Nitrite occurs, for instance, in meat and vegetables (after conversion from nitrate). Secondary amines can be found in drugs, for example, but also in many natural products. This means that in the exposure phase highly carcinogenic substances can be formed. Another example of interaction in the environment is that of inorganic mercury with microbial enzymes. As a result, inorganic mercury is converted to the organic mercury compounds methyl and dimethyl mercury, which are far more harmful.

*Influence on kinetics*

b. Substances may greatly affect each other's kinetics (absorption, distribution, metabolism and excretion). For example, the nature of the solvent often determines to a large extent the absorption of a substance via the skin. Absorption of a lipophilic substance in oil proceeds much more slowly than when the substance is dissolved (or suspended) in water. An entirely different type of interaction takes place when the solvent changes the physiological state of the skin, for example, by hydrating the stratum corneum. Two substances will also interact if they both require the same carrier for their transport. The change in toxicity of some heavy metals in cases of deficient, or excessive absorption of, for example, Ca, Fe or Zn may be based on this phenomenon.

*Biotransformation*

Many enzyme systems play a part in the *biotransformation* of foreign substances. Inhibition or stimulation of such a system causes changes in the elimination of substances, but also in whether or not (reactive) metabolites are present. This may be illustrated by the dithiocarbamates (which are used in the rubber industry and as fungicides) which inhibit acetaldehyde dehydrogenase, an enzyme involved in, for instance, alcohol metabolism. Dithiocarbamates thus cause severe toxic symptoms following the consumption of alcohol because very high concentrations of acetaldehyde accumulate in the blood. The use of disulfiram (Antabuse® or Refusal®) in treating alcoholism is based on this.

*Influence on the dynamic phase*

c. Two substances with opposite effects on an organ system cause a combined action, of which the outcome is determined by the precise ratio (in time and dosage) of the substances. For example, DDT causes excitation of the nervous system (convulsions), while barbiturates attenuate the activity of the nervous system. Administration of barbiturate after DDT intoxication reduces the symptoms.

ASSIGNMENT 9.3

Could the reverse treatment, administration of DDT after poisoning by barbiturate, also be applied?

*Chemical interaction*
BAL = British Anti Lewisite, a substance developed to treat the consequences of exposure to the arsenic-containing poison gas Lewisite.

Antidotes are discussed in Study unit 38

d. Some substances react with each other in the body to produce another toxic substance or a harmless substance.
The action of many *antidotes* is based on their interaction with toxic substances circulating in the blood. This is true for chelators such as $CaNa_2$-EDTA and dimercaprol (BAL), which can be used to reduce the concentration of free metal ions and to enhance their excretion (of lead and arsenic, respectively). This means that the kinetics of these metals are affected.

The use of amylnitrite to treat cyanide intoxication is based on the induction of methemoglobinemia, that is, oxidation of the iron atom in hemoglobin from the ferrous to the ferric state. Ferrihemoglobin binds to cyanide, thus preventing the latter from reaching the redox system of the cell (the last step in the cytochrome oxidase chain).

Substances that change the electrolyte balance in the blood or urine influence the availability and excretion of other substances and consequently the action of these substances. This phenomenon can sometimes be applied therapeutically in cases of poisoning (for example, administration of bicarbonate solution after phenobarbital poisoning).

ASSIGNMENT 9.4

How do you explain the administration of bicarbonate in phenobarbital poisoning?

# 3 Quantitative models

## 3.1 SOME CONCEPTS

Before discussing the quantitative aspects of the toxicity of mixtures, some relevant terms will be introduced.

*Toxic unit*

The dose or concentration of a substance A in a mixture is often expressed in *toxic units* ($T_A$). The dose ($D_A$) is then related to the effective dose ($ED_A$) of the substance, hence:

$$T_A = D_A / ED_A \text{ toxic units}$$

*M is the sum of toxic units*

In mixture toxicity models and in experimental results, the mixture dose is expressed as the sum of the numbers of toxic units of the constituent substances. For the mixture dose which causes the same effect as the *ED* of the individual substances, this sum is often referred to as *M*.

In order to determine the effect, 50% mortality is often used, which means that *ED* is actually an $LD_{50}$.

## 3.2 PRESENTATION OF RESULTS

*Mixture of two substances*

For a mixture of two substances, it is relatively simple to present the quantitative effects of the combination.

For a number of combinations of the two substances the dose causing the standard effect (for example, 50% mortality) is determined.

The results can be presented in a graph in which the quantity of substance A in the mixture is plotted against the quantity of substance B. The easiest way to compare the results is by expressing both quantities as effective doses (concentrations) or toxic units:

$$T_A = D_A / ED_A \text{ and } T_B = D_B / ED_B$$

*isobole = line connecting points of equal strength*

Figure 9.1 shows a number of possible outcomes of a mixture. This representation is known as an *isobologram*.

*Additivity*

*Additivity* refers to the situation where the combined effect, i.e. the effect of substances A and B together, is equal to the sum of the individual effects of A and B.

*Antagonism*
*Antagonism has been discussed in Study unit 7*

If two substances, administered simultaneously, counteract each other's actions, this is known as *antagonism*. The term antagonism is also used if one substance, which is in itself non-toxic, suppresses the effect of another substance that is toxic. This can be written as: "effect of A" + "effect of B" = "effect of (A + B)"; numerically: 2 + 3 = 4; 4 + (–4) = 0; 4 + 0 = 1.

*Potentiation*

*Potentiation* is the phenomenon by which one substance that does not cause a toxic effect on its own strengthens the action of another, toxic, substance. Effect of "(A + B)" > "effect of A" + "effect of B"; numerically: 0 + 2 = 10.

*Synergism*

The use of the term *synergism* may lead to confusion, as this phenomenon is not unambiguously defined in the literature. Some authors equate synergism with potentiation, while others also include partial additivity under the term. Some refer to synergism only if an inactive substance enhances the action of another substance in that mixture.

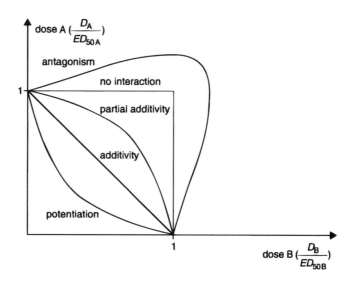

FIGURE   9.1
Isoboles for several possible combined actions of two substances
(quantities of the substances A and B are plotted in toxic units)

In this text book, the term synergism will be used exclusively for those cases where substances that are individually capable of causing a toxic effect produce a greater effect in a mixture than the sum of the effects of the individual substances. Effect of "(A + B)" > "effect of A" + "effect of B"; numerically: 2 + 3 > 5.

The mode of action of monoamine oxidase (MAO) inhibitors is described in Study unit 33.

An example of synergism is the combination of monoamine oxidase inhibitors (MAO inhibitors) and certain amines. In the 1950s and 1960s, various MAO inhibitors were used in the treatment of depression. Before the synergistic properties of these substances were discovered, they had already caused many deaths as a result of simultaneous use of amines. These amines could be ingested as drugs, such as amphetamine or the antidepressant drug amitriptyline, but also with food, which might contain amines in quantities which would be perfectly safe under normal circumstances. Such amines occur, for example, in red wine, certain varieties of cheese and in meat and yeast extracts. The synergistic effect of MAO inhibitors is based on their ability to inhibit the action of the enzymes that convert amines in the body, the monoamine oxidases.

Another example of synergism, the combination of thiocarbamate and alcohol, has already been discussed in section 2.1.

*Mixtures of three substances*

For mixtures of three substances, a spatial diagram with three axes might be set up, but for most cases this will not provide a clear picture. Mixtures of more than two substances defy the powers of imagination. The toxicologist can then only resort to mathematical representations.

ASSIGNMENT   9.5

Use the data from Table 9.1 to construct an isobologram.
What is your conclusion about the combined action of these two substances? Refer to Figure 9.1 in your answer.

Figure 9.2 shows an isobologram presenting the possible combined actions of an active substance A and a substance B which in itself is inactive.

TABLE 9.1

Mixtures of 1-octanol (OC) and hexanol (HEX) which cause 50% mortality in young fathead minnows (*Pimelometopon pulcher*), a fish species found off the Californian coast

| [OC] in mol | [HEX] in µmol |
|---|---|
| 0 | 0.104 |
| 0.020 | 0.076 |
| 0.038 | 0.069 |
| 0.045 | 0.054 |
| 0.061 | 0.031 |
| 0.078 | 0.020 |
| 0.103 | 0 |

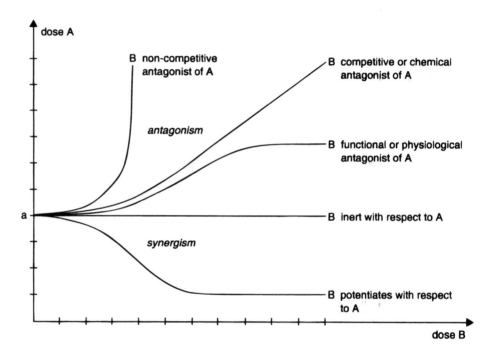

FIGURE 9.2

Isoboles for combinations of an active substance (A) and an inactive substance (B)
B influences the effectiveness of A. A distinction can be made between potentiation (potentiation of A by B) and antagonism. Various types of antagonism are shown.

*Purpose of an isobologram*

Once the results of a toxicity experiment have been plotted in an isobologram, it is easy to see whether the combined action is additive or otherwise (although only for two-substance mixtures). Unfortunately, little is revealed about the processes involved. Several researchers have tried to construct a theoretical framework that would allow a better understanding of the toxicity of mixtures in a qualitative sense and a better evaluation of the experimental results. The theoretically successful model by Hewlett and Plackett, the model by Chou and, especially, the practical elaborations by Könemann will be discussed in the following sections.

### 3.3 HEWLETT AND PLACKETT MODEL

In their studies of the action of mixtures of substances, Hewlett and Plackett distinguish four types of combined action (Table 9.2).

TABLE 9.2
Types of combined action according to Hewlett and Plackett

| action | similar | dissimilar |
|---|---|---|
| non-interactive | SSA | IA |
| interactive | CSA | DA |

SSA = simple similar action
IA = independent action
CSA = complex similar action
DA = dependent action

A combined action is defined as "similar" or "dissimilar" when the primary action of the components is the same or different, respectively, and as "interactive" or "non-interactive" if one compound, respectively, influences or does not influence the biological activity of the other.

The four possibilities in Table 9.2 will now be discussed in more detail. Although the Hewlett–Plackett model is strictly theoretical, where possible, examples will be given of the different types of combined action.

*Simple Similar Action*

*Concentration additivity*

*Simple similar action* describes the situation in which components of the mixture have the same mode of action and do not influence each other's activity. The toxic effect on which the evaluation is based (e.g. 50% mortality) occurs at a dose of the mixture which is determined by *concentration additivity*. Concentration additivity is often referred to simply as additivity.

For a two-substance mixture, 50% mortality occurs when the sum of the doses or concentrations of the individual substances ($M$, expressed in toxic units) equals 1. In other words, $M = D_1/LD_{50-1} + D_2/LD_{50-2} = 1$. For a mixture of $n$ substances:

$$M = \sum_{i=1}^{n} \frac{D_i}{LD_{50-i}} = 1$$

In a mixture of different cyanide salts, these substances act in a concentration-additive manner. The collective toxicity is determined by the total amount of cyanide ions ($CN^-$) and not by the different cations.

*Independent action*

*Independent action* implies that the substances in the mixture have a different mode of action and do not influence each other. Various situations can be distinguished, depending on the individual susceptibility in the population to the different components of the mixture.

Three cases will be discussed here. The first shows a completely positive correlation, the second a completely negative correlation, and the third no correlation at all.

*Completely positive correlation*
Equitoxic mixtures are mixtures in which the concentrations of the individual components, expressed as fractions of the $LC_{50}$, are equal

In the case of a *completely positive correlation* ($r = 1$), an individual who is highly sensitive to substance A is also highly sensitive to substance B. The toxicity is determined entirely by the component that is present in the highest concentration. If the mixture is equitoxic and consists of $n$ substances, then 50% mortality will occur if *one* substance is present in the mixture at its $LC_{50}$. In that situation $M = 1$. In other words, the sum of the concentrations ($M$) is equal to that of the most toxic substance in the mixture. In fact, there is no combined effect at all; the toxicity of the mixture is not greater than that of the decisive ingredient. For this reason, this type of combined action is sometimes not included in the category of additivity.

EXAMPLE

For a mixture of three insecticides, A, B and C, the number of dead flies in a population of 100 flies is taken as a measure of the effect. If a number of toxic units of A are administered sufficient to kill 40% of the flies, administering a number of toxic units of B and/or C as well will make no difference, provided $T_B$ and $T_C$ are both below 40. ($T_B$ and $T_C$ are the numbers of toxic units of B and C; respectively). The 40 most susceptible flies out of 100 will be killed, whether this is caused by substance A, B or C. Of the remaining 60 flies, none will be killed by substance B or C since they are not susceptible to A and the sensitivity correlation = 1, so they are not sensitive to B or C either.

*Completely negative correlation*

A *completely negative correlation* ($r = -1$) is only possible for a mixture of two substances. 50% mortality will occur if the mortality percentages for both substances together are 50 ($p_1 + p_2 = 0.5$). The value of $M$ depends on the slope of the concentration-response relationship, but will always exceed 1.

EXAMPLE

A group of 100 flies are exposed to insecticides P and Q. A completely negative correlation exists, that is, the flies that are sensitive to substance P are not sensitive to substance Q and vice-versa. If the number of toxic units of P administered is such that 40% of the flies are killed, then these are all flies that would not have been killed by the same number of toxic units of Q. The surviving flies are not sensitive to substance P but are sensitive to substance Q. Any amount of Q will therefore kill a proportion of the remaining flies. Combinations of substances with a negative correlation are particularly sought after for combined antibiotics and for insecticides.

*No correlation*

There may also be *no correlation* between the various sensitivities ($r = 0$). The effect of exposure to a mixture can be calculated from the mortality risks at exposure to the same concentrations of individual components, using the following equation:

$$1 - P = (1 - p_1) \cdot (1 - p_2)...(1 - p_n)$$
$$P = 1 - (1 - p_1) \cdot (1 - p_2)...(1 - p_n) \tag{9.1}$$

ASSIGNMENT 9.6

Calculate the mortality risks in this situation for each substance of an equitoxic mixture of three substances, if this mixture causes 50% mortality.

The value of $M$ can only be calculated if the dose–response relationships are known (especially in the area of low response frequencies), but it always lies between 1 and $n$. This is known as *partial additivity*.

EXAMPLE

Again, a group of 100 flies and two insecticides, A and B, will serve as an example. The 40 flies killed by A are, in fact, randomly 'selected' from the population of 100. In other words, they are neither more nor less sensitive to B than the surviving flies. If the fraction of flies killed by A is put at $p_1$, then the number killed by B can only be a fraction of the remaining flies $(1 - p_1)$. If the fraction killed by B is $p_2$, then the total fraction of flies killed is:

$$P = p_1 + p_2 (1 - p_1) = p_1 + p_2 - p_1 \cdot p_2$$

The correlations between the sensitivities to the various substances in the mixture will in practice vary from –1 to +1. Many combinations of substances are known to have different actions, such as cyanide (blocking of oxidative processes in the cell) and parathion (inhibition of the enzyme acetylcholinesterase) or pyrethrin (effect on nerve membranes) and carbon monoxide (inhibition of oxygen transport by hemoglobin), etc. Quite often, it is not known beforehand whether there are any complicating interactions between such substances. Sometimes, substances have different main effects, but similar side-effects.

*Complex Similar Action*
*Dependent Action*

When there are interactions between the different components in a mixture, it is no longer possible to predict the mixture's toxicity. Interaction of substances in a mixture means that the substances do not exert their effects independently from each other. The combined toxicity of the mixture can take various forms from partially additive to potentiating to antagonism.

*Supra-additivity*
*Potentiation*

*Antagonism*

If one component in a mixture enhances the activity of another component, but does not have a toxic effect of its own, this is known as *supra-additivity* or *potentiation* ($M < 1.0$). If one component reduces the action of the other, this is called *antagonism* ($M > n$). A process such as potentiation is based on a specific interaction between the substances, for example, in the kinetic phase. In general, this will only happen at dosages which are individually effective as well. Potentiation rarely occurs with environmental pollutants, which are usually present in concentrations below their no effect levels. An exception are substances which induce or inhibit the same enzyme system. In this case, concentration additivity may well take place.

ASSIGNMENT 9.7

Can you give some examples of this?

### 3.4 CHOU MODEL

Chou and co-workers have developed a model for the action of mixtures based on the enzyme kinetics according to Michaelis–Menten (first-order kinetics) and comparable kinetics of higher ($m^{th}$) order.

*Mutually exclusive*
*Mutually nonexclusive*

Chou distinguishes two situations, one in which substances are termed *mutually exclusive* and another where they are termed *mutually nonexclusive*. In these cases, the substances have different modes of action or work independently of one another. If the action of one substance is entirely independent of that of another substance in the mixture, these substances are referred to as *mutually exclusive*. As soon as there is any mutual influence, this is referred to as *mutually nonexclusive*.

According to Chou and Talalay, the dose–effect relationship in the case of additivity is:

$$\text{logit}\,(x) = m \cdot \left[\log(T_1 + T_2) + \alpha \cdot T_1 \cdot T_2\right] \tag{9.2}$$

where

$x$ = the percentage of effect

$m$ = the slope of the log dose-effect curves

$T$ = the dose of substance 1 ($T_1$) or substance 2 ($T_2$) in toxic units

$T_1$ = $D_1/D(x)_1$

$T_2$ = $D_2/D(x)_2$

$D_1$ = the dose of substance 1 in the mixture that has $x\%$ effect

$D_2$ = ditto for substance 2

$D(x)_1$ = the dose of substance 1 which (on its own) induces $x\%$ effect

$D(x)_2$ = ditto for substance 2

$\alpha$ = 0 or 1.

For $x = 0.5$, $D(x) = LD_{50}$

*Combination Index*

Whether additivity, antagonism or synergism is the case is assessed on the basis of the so-called *Combination Index* (CI, Chou's Combination Index). In equation form:

$$CI = D_1/D(x)_1 + D_2/D(x)_2 + \alpha \cdot D_1 \cdot D_2 / D(x)_1 \cdot D(x)_2 \qquad (9.3)$$

where:

$\alpha = 0$ for mutually exclusive substances

$\alpha = 1$ for mutually nonexclusive substances.

Chou calculates the *CI* for all values of the effect of the mixture ($x = 0$ to 1).

*Significance of the Combination Index*

From the *CI* values, calculated from an experiment, the following conclusions can be drawn:

$CI = 1$ means additivity (summation) of effects

$CI < 1$ means synergism

$CI > 1$ means antagonism.

According to Chou, substances are mutually exclusive if both substances in a mixture (with a fixed ratio between $D_1$ and $D_2$) have parallel dose–response curves (Chou uses the logit model). In the model, substances are called nonexclusive if the line for the mixture shows a concavely upward curve (line D in the right-hand panel of Figure 9.3)

The designation of summation of effects in this model corresponds to concentration additivity (for $\alpha = 0$).

---

EXAMPLE

A study on the toxicity in a population of houseflies of a mixture of two insecticides, pyrethrin and rotenone, in a weight by weight (w/w) ratio of 5 : 1 gave the following results:

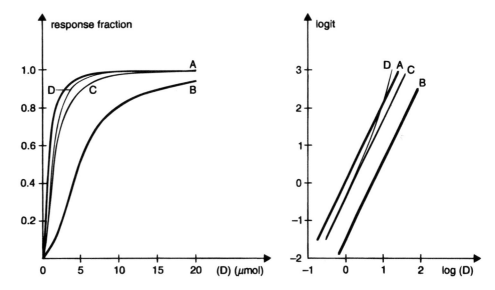

FIGURE 9.3

Dose–response curves for two substances (A and B) and for mixtures of these two (C and D)

Curve C represents mutually exclusive substances and curve D mutually nonexclusive substances.

The left-hand panel shows a dose–response curve, while the right-hand panel shows the log dose–logit curves.

$$LD_{50} \text{ rotenone } = 0.16 \text{ mg ml}^{-1}$$
$$LD_{50} \text{ pyrethrin } = 0.94 \text{ mg ml}^{-1}$$
$$LD_{50} \text{ mixture } = 0.43 \text{ mg ml}^{-1}$$

The three dose–response curves are parallel.

### 3.5    MIXTURE TOXICITY INDEX

The problem with the two models discussed above is that they only apply for the evaluation of two-substance mixtures. Summing the numbers of toxic units ($M$) yields a range of values from 0 (maximal synergism) through 1 (concentration additivity) and $n$ (no additivity) to $\infty$ (complete antagonism). Comparing the results of experiments with mixtures containing different numbers of substances then becomes difficult.

*Mixture Toxicity Index*

For his research into the action of mixtures containing large numbers of substances Könemann developed the *Mixture Toxicity Index* (*MTI*, for short). This index can be applied to any combination of substances.

*Definition*
First study the explanation of the different symbols, which is given beneath the equation, to see what they represent

$$MTI = (\log M_O - \log M)/\log M_O \tag{9.4}$$

where:

| | |
|---|---|
| $n$ | = the number of substances |
| $C_i$ | = the concentration of substance $i$ in the mixture |
| $L_i$ | = the $LC_{50}$ of substance $i$ in a mixture of $n$ substances |
| $f$ | = the response fraction |
| $f_i$ | = $C_i/L_i$ |
| $f_{max}$ | = highest value of $f_i$ in the mixture |

281

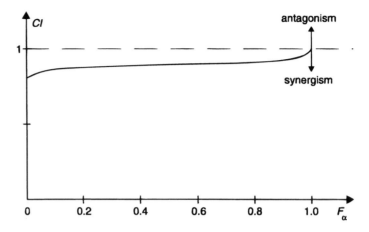

FIGURE 9.4

Combination Index ($CI$) is plotted against the effect of the mixture ($F_a$ = response fraction)

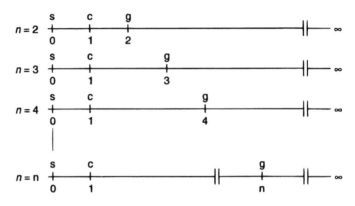

FIGURE 9.5

The sum of toxic units of two or more substances in a mixture which causes the standard effect

s = maximum synergism; c = concentration additivity; g = no additivity ($r$ = 1); ∞ = complete antagonism; between c and g lies the area of partial additivity.

$$M = \sum f_i \; (= \text{sum of all the toxic units})$$
$$M_0 = M/f_{max}$$

In equitoxic mixtures all $f$ values are equal, so that $f_{max} = f$. The equation for such mixtures thus becomes:

$$MTI = 1 - (\log M / \log n) \tag{9.5}$$

The significance of the value of $MTI$ is given in Table 9.3.

With the aid of $MTI$ a confident estimation can be made of the nature of the combined action observed in a particular situation. The results of mixtures of different numbers of components can also be compared using $MTI$.

## 4 Examples and experimental results

Aquatic toxicity research has shown that the toxicity of mixtures (in this case for guppies) is often in good or virtually complete agreement with concentration additivity. In order to test the concentration additivity model, Könemann selected mixtures of substances that would probably fit Hewlett and Plackett's de-

TABLE 9.3

Toxicity of mixtures on the basis of their *MTI* values

| MTI | terminology for the combined action |
|---|---|
| < 0 | antagonism |
| = 0 | no additivity ($r = 1$) |
| 0 – 1 | partial additivity |
| = 1 | concentration additivity |
| > 1 | supra-additivity (potentiation) |

For QSAR see Study unit 8

scription of simple similar action. Groups of substances for which the toxicity can be described by a good structure-activity relationship (QSAR) probably have similar modes of action.

Könemann selected, for example, a group of 50 lipophilic compounds that do not have any specific action. Equitoxic mixtures of these 50 substances caused mortality in fish. 50% mortality was found for a mixture in which each individual substance was present at 0.02 times its $LC_{50}$, i.e.:

$$\Sigma(C_i / LC_{50_i} = M = 0.9$$

Other groups of substances yielded similar results. For example, within a mixture of 11 chlorophenols $M$ was found to equal 1.0.

Is this what you would have expected?

The above results are of course to be expected for those substances that were selected for their similar action. An experiment with a mixture of nine substances, selected for the opposite reason, i.e. for the greatest possible variety in action, yielded an *MTI* of 0.6.

The conclusion is that such substances also show additivity, albeit partial. Later experiments with larger groups of substances and with other aquatic animals have confirmed this additivity.

## 5    Pratical implications

From experiments with mixtures containing many different substances it appears that–at least in aquatic environments–additivity or partial additivity usually occurs, but also that low concentrations ($< 0.02 \cdot LC_{50}$; this is mostly below the no observed effect level) still contribute to the total toxicity of the mixture.

It has also been found that partial additivity not only occurs when the observed effect is mortality, but that it is also found for sublethal effects. The degree of additivity will then probably be somewhat lower.

Although mixtures of two or three substances can show very different types of combined action, a mixture of many substances thus seems to lead to a kind of statistical mean effect, *viz.* partial additivity. An important consequence of this finding is that in cases of simultaneous exposure to many substances it is not enough to merely use the standards which have been established for the individual substances. Besides individual standards, such as *MAC* values and *NTEL*s (= no toxic effect level), *summation standards* can be applied in the protection of human beings and the environment:

$$\Sigma \frac{C_i}{MAC_i} < 1$$

or

TABLE 9.4
Composition of a mixture of substances with different mechanisms of action

| | |
|---|---|
| KCl | 1,2,4-trichlorobenzene |
| CuCl$_2$ | $\alpha,\alpha'$-dichloro-m-xylene |
| decamethrin | 2,4-dichloroaniline |
| triphenyltin chloride | hexachlorobutadiene |
| 3,4,5-trichlorophenol | |

$$\sum \frac{C_i}{NTEL_i} < 1$$

The summation standard will probably lead to an overestimation of the combined effects of substances with different modes of action. Further research is needed to demonstrate if this is indeed the case and, if so, to what extent.

## 6 Summary

Interactions between chemicals can take place at different moments and in different ways. For example, substances can influence the absorption, protein binding, biotransformation and excretion of other substances. Substances may also increase or decrease each other's activity at their site of action (target molecule or target organ). The influence can ultimately manifest itself as an increased or decreased toxic response of the organism.

Hewlett and Plackett distinguish between similar and dissimilar actions and between interaction and no interaction. Their model defines similar actions to those of two (or more) substances which bind to the same target (target molecule, receptor). The term interaction is used when the presence of a substance can influence the quantity of another substance at the site of action and/or can influence the action of the quantity present. Chou and co-workers distinguish between "mutually exclusive" and "mutually nonexclusive" substances, by which they indicate whether the action of a substance is dependent on that of another. In addition to these two more theoretical models, there is also the practical approach of Könemann, who introduced a mixture toxicity index. Research using this model has shown that, in practice, the overall effect of mixtures of large numbers of substances often leads to partial additivity. On the basis of his experimental findings, Könemann suggests that, in cases where standards have to be set for substances in mixtures, a summation standard should be used.

SELF ASSESSMENT QUESTIONS

1.  If two substances interact in the exposure phase, resulting in a third, new substance, as in the case of nitrosamine formation from nitrite and secondary amines, should a combined action (carcinogenesis) that is additive, antagonistic or synergistic be expected?

2.  In this study unit, quantal responses have been used in the quantitative analysis of the effects of mixtures. Similar analyses, however, can be carried out with graded responses, for example by expressing the effects in terms of fractions of the maximal effect. Suppose two substances (A and B) cause similar graded effects, the extent of which can be calculated from the equation:

$$E_A = E_{max} \cdot \frac{[A]}{K_A + [A]}$$  (analogous for B)

In this equation, $K_A$ is a constant and $[A]$ is the concentration of A. $E_{max}$ is identical for A and B.

a. What will the equation be, if the concentration of the substance is expressed in terms of toxic units $T$ (assuming the toxic effect $E$ to be $0.5 \cdot E_{max}$)?

b. What will the effect be, if A and B show concentration additivity and the mixture consists of 1 toxic unit of each substance, or of 0.5 toxic units of each substance?

c. What will the result be if there is (response) additivity? (hint: substitute $E/E_{max}$ by $P$).

d. What is striking when comparing the answers of question 2b with those of 2c?

FEEDBACK

1 **Answers to the assignments**

9.1 There are many substances which enhance the (biological) activity of other substances. Previous study units have mentioned substances which facilitate the absorption of other substances. Other examples are:

- alcohol exaggerates the effects of many drugs such as antihistamics;

- organic solvents may increase the dermal absorption of several substances;

- milk can increase the absorption of lead from the gastrointestinal tract;

- chelators can increase the absorption of metal ions, as the chelator–metal ion complexes are less polar than the metal ions involved;

- inhibitors of intestinal peristalsis can also increase the absorption of other substances, as they prolong the time during which these substances are present in the gastrointestinal tract;

- many medicines interact with other medicines.

Some substances enhance the bioactivation of other substances (for example, DDT and phenobarbital; see Study unit 3).

9.2 Nitrite occurs, for example, in meat products and vegetables (as a reduction product of nitrate). Secondary amines can be found in drugs, but also in various natural products such as fish. Highly carcinogenic substances can therefore be formed during the exposure phase. See also Study unit 2.

9.3 No. Apart from other harmful (side) effects of DDT, it is not advisable to administer this lipophilic substance, in the high concentrations that are required, as it has a long biological half-life.

9.4 The explanation is as follows. The $pK_a$ of phenobarbital is 7.2. Increasing the pH of urine with bicarbonate results in increased ionization of phenobarbital. This leads to a reduction of reabsorption in the distal renal tubules, and ultimately to an increase in the excretion rate.

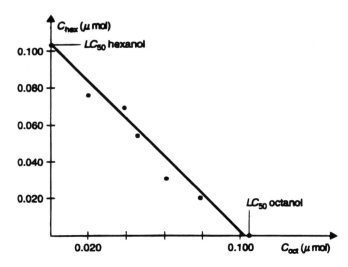

FIGURE 9.6
Isobologram of the data from Table 9.1

9.5    The conclusion is that in mixtures octanol and hexanol behave in a completely additive way.

9.6    In an equitoxic mixture, the mortality risks for individual components are equal:

$$p_1 = p_2 = p_3 = P$$

Hence: $P = 1 - (1 - p)(1 - p)(1 - p)$.
50% mortality means that $P = 0.5$, so $(1 - p)^3 = 0.5$ or $p = 0.21$.

9.7    All organophosphate insecticides inhibit the enzyme acetylcholinesterase. Different groups of (chlorinated) aromatic hydrocarbons induce the mixed-function oxidase system.

2      **Answers to the self assessment questions**

1.     Synergistic. The reactants themselves are not carcinogenic. Their reaction products induce tumors. This is called synergism. The term potentiation might also be used here, but in practice the distinction between potentiation and synergism is not quite clear.

2.     a.    $E = 0.5\,E_{max}$ for $[A] = K_A$ and for $[B] = K_B$, respectively.

       Hence $T = [A]/K_A$ and $T = [B]/K_B$ respectively.
       Substitution for A and B in the equation yields:

       $$E = E_{max} \cdot \left\{ T / (T + 1) \right\}$$

       b.    Mixture of 1 toxic unit of each substance:

       $$E / E_{max} = 1 + 1 / (1 + (1 + 1)) = 2/3 = 0.67$$

       Mixture of 0.5 toxic unit of each substance:

       $$E / E_{max} = 0.5 + 0.5 / (1 + (0.5 + 0.5)) = 1/2 = 0.5$$

c.  Mixture of 1 toxic unit of each substance:

$$E/E_{max} = 1/2 + 1/2 - 1/2 \cdot 1/2 = 0.75$$

Mixture of 0.5 toxic unit of each substance:

$$E/E_{max} = 1/3 + 1/3 - 1/3 \cdot 1/3 = 0.56$$

d.  The effects are greater in response additivity than in concentration additivity. This happens only if the dose–response relationship curves of the components are as flat as they are in this case. In practice, the dose–response relationship curve will be much steeper and the proportions are reversed.

N.B. The logit model yields $p = D^b/(1 + D^b)$ where the exponent $b$ usually has a value greater than 1.

# Contents Study unit 10
# Cytotoxicity: molecular mechanisms of cell death

0-8493-9232-2/96/$0.00 + $.50
© 1996 by CRC Press, Inc.

# Cytotoxicity: molecular mechanisms of cell death

*J. de Vries*

## INTRODUCTION

*Cytotoxicity = cell toxicity*

Not only has the development of auxiliary disciplines in the field of chemistry (biochemistry, analytical chemistry and organic chemistry) and biology (physiology and cell biology) contributed to the development of toxicology, but also to that of the various subdisciplines of toxicology itself. The latter is particularly true of *cytotoxicology*. Cytotoxicology is concerned with the study of cell toxicity and its underlying mechanisms.

The contribution made by the development of cytotoxicology is obvious for a number of reasons. First of all, many toxic substances that cause organ or tissue damage injure individual cells of these organs and tissues. Secondly, in cytotoxicological studies there are no problems with complex toxicokinetic behavior, and no involvement of systemic regulatory mechanisms. Thirdly, the effects of substances in cell cultures can often be assessed within a very short time, which may greatly reduce the duration of the investigation. The use of cells for toxicological research enables the direct study of the mechanisms of cell-specific or organ-specific effects. This is particularly important as it provides the scientific basis for a more rational approach to risk assessment. It should be noted, however, that in certain cases extrapolation, from cell to organism will be difficult.

> ASSIGNMENT   10.1
>
> When assessing the risks for humans on the basis of cytotoxicity data, with what problem might one be faced in the first place?

Common subjects of research within cytotoxicology are mutagenesis, carcinogenesis and cell death. The cytotoxicological aspects of mutagenesis and carcinogenesis are dealt with in Study units 11, 12 and 13. This unit focuses on the mechanisms of cell death.

### LEARNING OBJECTIVES

— After studying this unit, you should be able to describe the major mechanisms of cell injury and cell death, and the mechanisms by which the cell protects itself against these phenomena, using examples.

*Study hints*

Since this study unit deals mainly with the ways in which chemicals can induce toxic effects in cells, it contains a considerable number of structural formulas and equations. It is therefore advisable to keep a handbook of (organic) chemistry ready for consultation. The study load is estimated at 5 student learning hours.

## STUDY CORE

### 1   Mechanisms of cell death

The main factors determining the occurrence of cell death are:

1   the nature of the (ultimate) active toxic agent—in many cases a reactive intermediate—and the availability of that agent at the site of the target molecules;

2   the role of the target molecules in the functioning of the cell;

> ASSIGNMENT 10.2
> Briefly clarify factor 2!

3   the effectiveness of the cellular defense mechanisms in detoxicating and eliminating the active agents and in repairing (primary) damage;

4   the nature and availability of toxic products released from dead cells.

The first factor has already been extensively dealt with in Study units 4 and 6. Here, the types of reactive intermediates that have been the subject of research into the mechanisms of cell death will be highlighted.

Concerning the second factor, it can be generally stated that the functioning of the cell depends primarily on the energy supply to the cell and the integrity of the enzymes and membranes. The cell needs to have sufficient ATP at its disposal to guarantee transport, synthesis and repair to proceed adequately. A reduction in ATP synthesis, for example as a result of uncoupling of the oxidative phosphorylation, may lead to cell death. The importance of the maintenance of enzyme and membrane integrity will be dealt with in section 3.

The third factor, processes of detoxication and elimination, have been extensively dealt with in Study units 3 and 4. Detoxication of reactive oxygen species is discussed in this study unit. The repair of (primary) DNA damage is one of the topics in Study unit 11. Section 3.2 discusses the fourth factor.

Reactive oxygen species (= oxygen intermediates, oxygen metabolites) are products from molecular oxygen via one-electron reduction steps; they readily interact with other molecules.

### 2   Reactive intermediates: formation and detoxication

The past two decades have seen great progress in research on the role of reactive intermediates in the induction of toxicity. Formation and detoxication of reactive intermediates and the enzyme systems involved have been studied. The following reactive intermediates have been identified as causes of toxicity:

- *electrophilic structures*, such as epoxides, quinones and nitrenium ions;
- *radicals*, other than reduced forms of oxygen;
- *reactive oxygen species*.

### 2.1   ELECTROPHILIC STRUCTURES

The processes leading to the formation of this type of intermediate are usually catalyzed by cytochrome P-450 isozymes.

*Epoxide*

A well-known example of a cytotoxic epoxide is the 3,4-epoxide of bromobenzene:

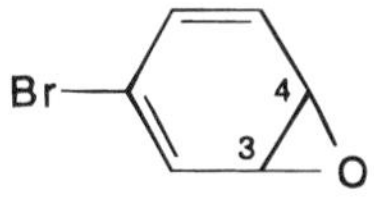

Phenobarbital, see Study units 3 and 4

Administration of bromobenzene to test animals pretreated with phenobarbital showed an increased (metabolic) elimination of bromobenzene. The increase concerned excretion in the urine of the following metabolites:

- 4-hydroxybromophenyl glucuronide
- 4-hydroxybromophenyl sulfate
- bromobenzene 3,4-dihydrodiol
- bromobenzene 3,4-dihydrodiol glucuronide
- 4-bromophenyl mercapturic acid

Pretreatment with phenobarbital also resulted in an increase in liver necrosis by bromobenzene.

ASSIGNMENT   10.3

Summarize the various detoxication pathways of the 3,4-epoxide of bromobenzene in a diagram.

A quinone is a conjugated cyclic diketone, for example:

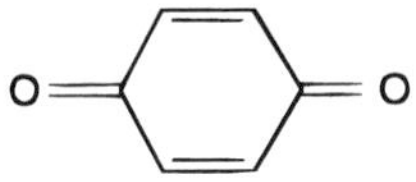

**para-benzoquinone**

There are indications that bromobenzene is a xenobiotic that can also induce its toxicity through a reactive intermediate in the form of a quinoid structure, the *ortho*-quinone of 4-bromobenzene:

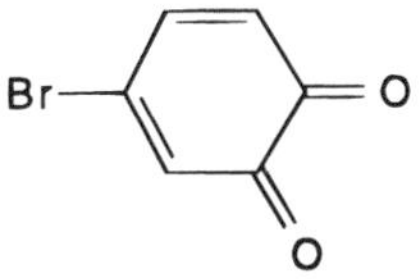

**ortho-quinone of 4-bromobenzene**

This substance might be the product of oxidation of the catechol 3,4-dihydroxybromobenzene, which has been identified as a metabolite of bromobenzene:

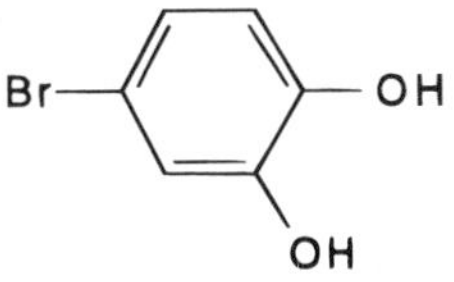

3,4-dihydroxybromobenzene

The oxygenation of bromobenzene to the epoxide is known as primary metabolism, while the processes leading to the formation of the *ortho*-quinone are termed secondary metabolism. Quinones can be detoxicated by glutathione in two ways. This can be explained by the fact that quinones are not only electrophilic agents but also oxidants:

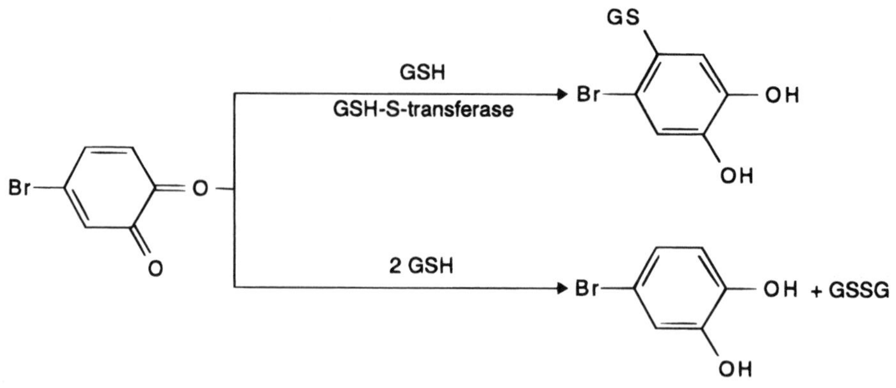

FIGURE 10.1
Detoxication pathways of 4-bromo-*o*-benzoquinone by glutathione (GSH) resulting in the formation of glutathione conjugate or the catechol dihydroxybromobenzene

*Nitrenium ion*

*Carbene*
A carbene is an organic intermediate with the structure $\overset{R}{\underset{R}{>}}C\!:$ i.e. a carbon atom bound to two R groups and possessing one free electron pair.

Nitrenium ions are nitrogen compounds in which the nitrogen atom is surrounded by a ring of six electrons instead of the normal eight. This implies that nitrenium ions are reactive electrophiles. Compare their structure with that of carbene.

Evidence for the role of nitrenium ion formation in toxicity has been obtained from research into the mechanism of liver cancer induction by 2-acetylaminofluorene (AAF):

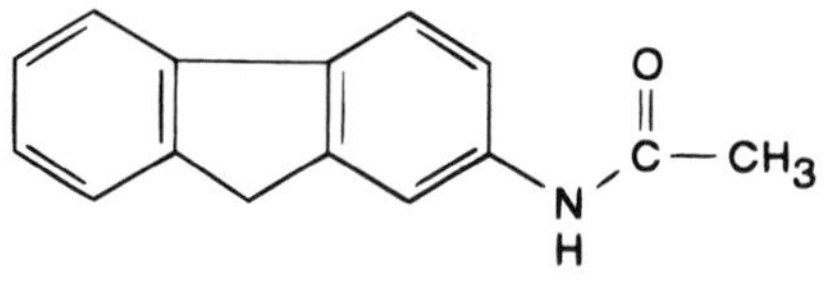

2-acetylaminofluorene; AAF

Acetylaminofluorene was originally developed as a pesticide. However, the development was stopped when chronic toxicity studies revealed that the substance could cause liver cancer in rodents.

Research aimed at finding the primary target molecule showed that the acetylaminofluorene group binds to the C-8 site of a guanine nucleotide:

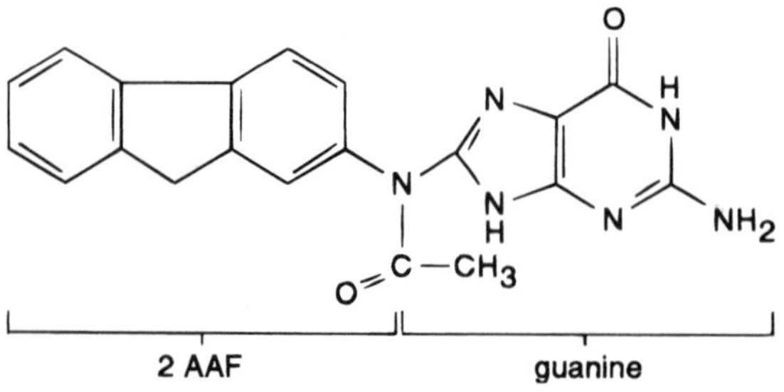

This binding of acetylaminofluorene to DNA appeared to depend on oxygenation by a cytochrome P-448 isozyme, followed by sulfation. Based on these observations the following reaction scheme for the bioactivation of acetylaminofluorene is now commonly accepted:

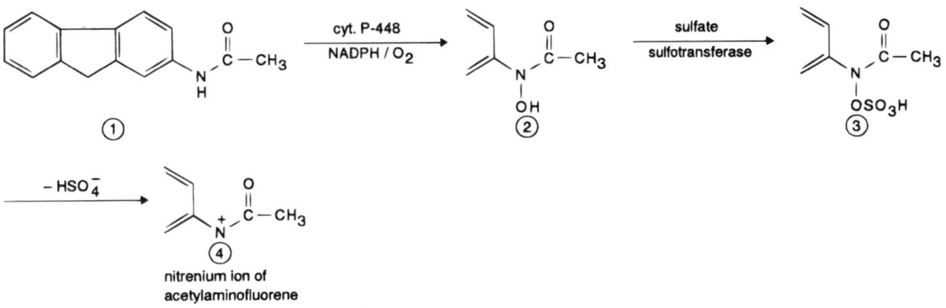

FIGURE 10.2
Metabolic activation of acetylaminofluorene: nitrenium ion formation

Conjugation with sulfate leads to the formation of a nitrenium ion (4), the final mutagenic carcinogen. Conjugation of hydroxylamine (2) with glucuronic acid is one possible detoxication pathway. Detoxication of acetylaminofluorene can also take place through aromatic hydroxylation followed by conjugation:

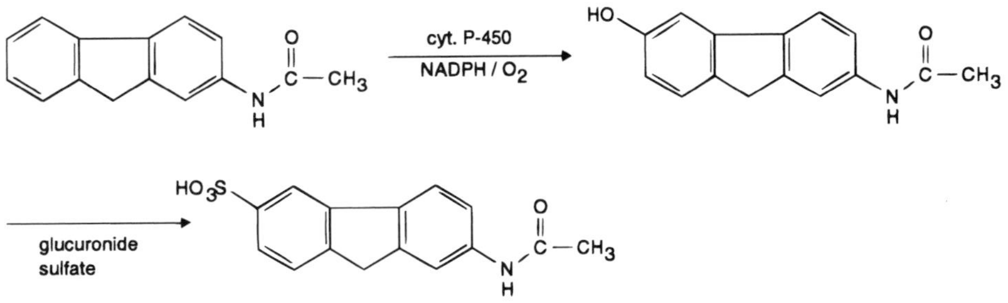

FIGURE 10.3
Detoxication of acetylaminofluorene through aromatic hydroxylation, followed by glucuronidation and/or sulfation

## 2.2 RADICALS

A very important group of reactive intermediates are the free radicals. Free radicals are molecules or atoms with an unpaired electron. They may be either organic or inorganic.

Free radicals can be formed via addition or release of an electron, or by homolytic cleavage of a covalent bond. The one-electron reduction by which many chemicals yield free radicals is catalyzed by the microsomal NADPH cytochrome P-450 reductase. Free radicals can induce a wide range of effects: membrane damage, inactivation of enzymes, cell death and cancer. The role of radical formation in causing toxic effects has been extensively studied for the induction of liver necrosis by halogenated methanes, such as the solvents chloroform ($CHCl_3$), carbon tetrachloride ($CCl_4$) and bromotrichloromethane ($BrCCl_3$). In these studies, bioactivation of carbon tetrachloride has received most of the attention.

*Trichloromethyl radical* $^\bullet CCl_3$

*In vivo* studies of the molecular mechanism underlying the hepatotoxicity of $CCl_4$ have indeed provided evidence for the formation of a radical, *viz.* the trichloromethyl radical $^\bullet CCl_3$. The results of these studies can be summarized as follows:

- after administration of radiolabelled carbon tetrachloride ($^{14}CCl_4$) to rats, the lipid fraction of the liver was found to contain chlorinated fatty acids. These chlorinated fatty acids were also found in reaction mixtures produced by direct exposure of liver lipids to the trichloromethyl radical. This trichloromethyl radical can be obtained in the following way (starting from dibenzoyl peroxide):

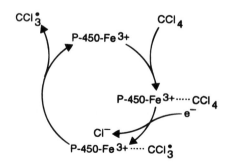

dibenzoylperoxide

phenyl radical

$$C_6H_5{}^\bullet + {}^{14}CCl_4 \longrightarrow C_6H_5Cl + {}^{14}CCl_3{}^\bullet$$

chlorobenzene

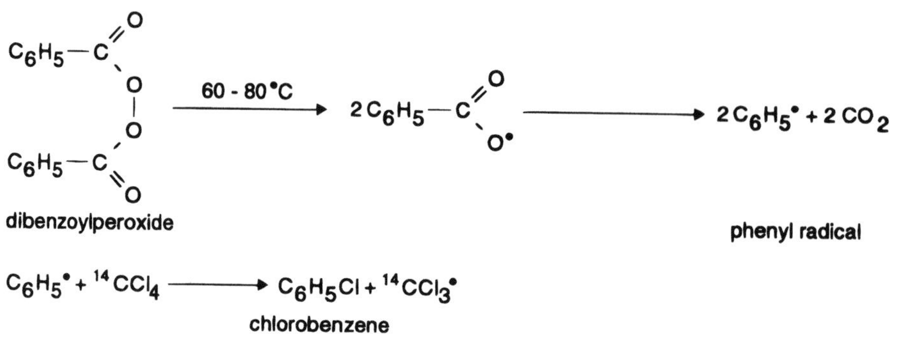

FIGURE 10.4

Schematic representation of the formation of the trichloromethyl radical from dibenzoylperoxide

- gas chromatographic analysis of the air exhaled by rats pretreated with $CCl_4$, showed that a small portion of $CCl_4$ had been converted to hexachloroethane and chloroform.

ASSIGNMENT 10.4

The above experiment showed that the air exhaled by rats treated with carbon tetrachloride contains hexachloroethane and chloroform. Try to retrace the line of reasoning that leads to the conclusion that the trichloromethyl radical must have been generated.

Incubation of liver microsomes with $CCl_4$ in the presence of NADPH confirmed on the basis of physicochemical methods that the trichloromethyl radical was indeed formed. The metabolic activation of $CCl_4$ was shown to depend on NADPH and not on $O_2$. This illustrates that cytochrome P-450 activity only manifests itself via a reduction. The reductive removal of halogen from halogenated alkanes under the influence of cytochrome P-450, is assumed to take place as follows:

FIGURE 10.5

Possible mechanism of the cytochrome P-450-mediated dehalogenation of carbon tetrachloride

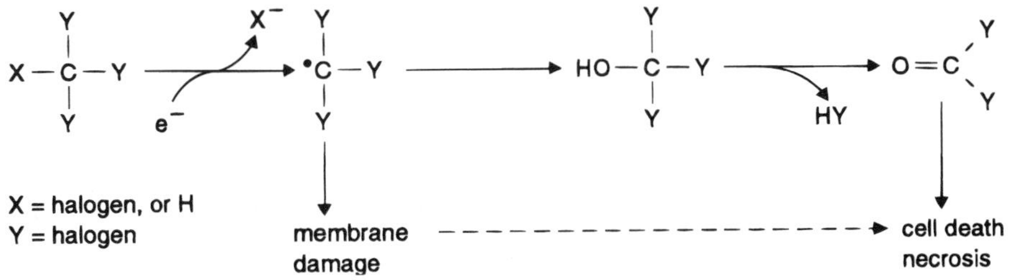

$$X-\underset{\underset{Y}{|}}{\overset{\overset{Y}{|}}{C}}-Y \quad \xrightarrow[e^-]{X^-} \quad {}^\bullet\underset{\underset{Y}{|}}{\overset{\overset{Y}{|}}{C}}-Y \quad \longrightarrow \quad HO-\underset{\underset{Y}{|}}{\overset{\overset{Y}{|}}{C}}-Y \quad \xrightarrow[HY]{} \quad O=C\overset{Y}{\underset{Y}{\diagdown}}$$

X = halogen, or H
Y = halogen

membrane damage  - - - - - - - - - - - - - - →  cell death necrosis

FIGURE   10.6
Possible role of bioactivation in the development of toxic effects by halogenated methanes

TABLE   10.1
Reactive forms of oxygen, and the way in which they are formed

| reactive oxygen species | mode of formation |
|---|---|
| singlet oxygen ($^1O_2$) | excitation of $O_2$ |
| superoxide anion radical ($O_2^{\bullet-}$) | one-electron reduction of $O_2$ |
| perhydroxyl radical ($^\bullet O-OH$) | protonation of superoxide anion radical |
| peroxide anion ($O_2^{2-}$) | one-electron reduction of $O_2^{\bullet-}$ |
| hydroxyl radical ($OH^\bullet$) | from $H_2O$ under the influence of ionizing radiation and from $H_2O_2$ through metal-catalyzed disintegration |
| ozone ($O_3$) | from $O_2$ through photolysis |

$$\overset{Cl}{\underset{Cl}{\diagup}}C=O$$

*Phosgene*

$$\overset{GS}{\underset{GS}{\diagup}}C=O$$

*Glutathionylcarbonate*

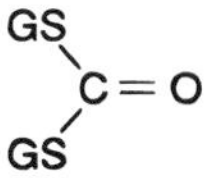

ASSIGNMENT   10.5

Extend the circle in Figure 10.5 by adding a second electron.

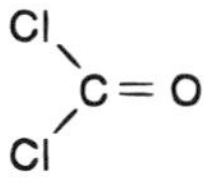

The formation of the trichloromethyl radical appears to be responsible for the damage to lipid membranes. It is thought that a secondary metabolite causes cell death. Microsomal oxidation of chloroform ($HCCl_3$) was found to involve the formation of phosgene. Incubation of $HCCl_3$, $CCl_4$ and $BrCCl_3$ with rat liver microsomes in the presence of glutathione (GSH) resulted in the formation of glutathionylcarbonate. Furthermore, after administration of $HCCl_3$ the availability of GSH appeared to be an important factor in the prevention of liver necrosis.

The nearest approach to the role of bioactivation in the induction of hepatotoxic effects by halogenated methanes is presented schematically in Figure 10.6.

2.3   REACTIVE OXYGEN SPECIES

Besides molecular oxygen, which is found in nature and is essential to all heterotrophic cells, there are also reactive forms of oxygen. Table 10.1 provides an overview of the various reactive forms of oxygen, and the way in which they are formed.

Reactive oxygen species have been shown to play a part in the induction of membrane damage, cardiotoxicity and neurotoxicity, oxidative stress in cells and cancer.

The existence of reactive forms of oxygen has its origin in the physicochemical properties of the oxygen molecule (in the ground state, i.e. as it occurs in the atmosphere). Because of its electron configuration, oxygen can act as an electron acceptor:

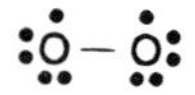

$$:\overset{..}{\underset{..}{O}} - \overset{..}{\underset{..}{O}}:$$

The outer molecular orbitals of oxygen each contain one electron; the spins of these electrons are parallel. According to the Pauli exclusion principle, oxygen (in the ground state) can only undergo univalent reductions. As a consequence, the complete reduction of oxygen to water consists of four successive one-electron steps:

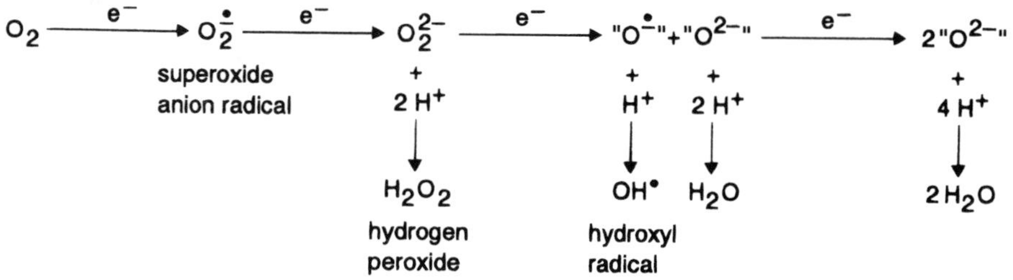

$$O_2 \xrightarrow{\ e^-\ } O_2^{\cdot} \xrightarrow{\ e^-\ } O_2^{2-} \xrightarrow{\ e^-\ } "O^{\cdot-}" + "O^{2-}" \xrightarrow{\ e^-\ } 2"O^{2-}"$$

superoxide
anion radical

$$O_2^{2-} \quad + \quad 2\,H^+ \quad \downarrow \quad H_2O_2$$
hydrogen
peroxide

$$+ H^+ \quad + 2\,H^+ \quad \downarrow \quad \downarrow \quad OH^{\cdot} \quad H_2O$$
hydroxyl
radical

$$+ 4\,H^+ \quad \downarrow \quad 2\,H_2O$$

FIGURE 10.7
Reduction of oxygen to water by addition of four electrons

Well-known examples of reactive oxygen intermediates are the *superoxide anion radical, hydrogen peroxide* and the *hydroxyl radical.*

*Superoxide anion radical $O_2^{\cdot}$*

### 2.3.1 Intracellular formation of reactive oxygen species

The superoxide anion radical is formed when one electron is taken up by one of the $\pi^*2p$-orbitals of molecular oxygen.

The formation of this species may involve endogenous substances and chemical-physiological processes as well as xenobiotics.

*Reduction of oxygen*

75% of all superoxide anion radicals that are formed in the liver derive from *reduction of oxygen* by the semiquinone of ubiquinone (coenzyme Q). Out of every 25 molecules of oxygen that are reduced at the end of the respiratory chain, one "picks up" an electron from ubisemiquinone (which corresponds to a production of 24 nmol $O_2^{\cdot}$ per g liver).

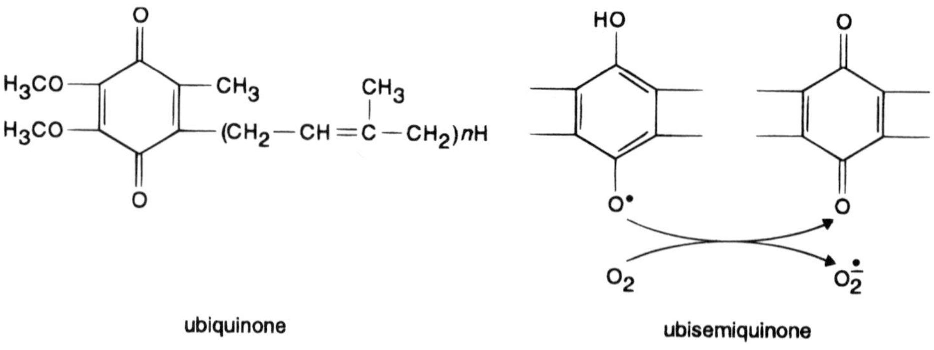

ubiquinone

ubisemiquinone

FIGURE 10.8
Reduction of oxygen by ubisemiquinone
a Molecular structure of coenzyme Q (ubiquinone; n = 1–10). b Reduction of $O_2$ by the semiquinone of coenzyme Q.

296

Auto-oxidations of reduced
hemoproteins

A second endogenous source of superoxide anion radicals is the auto-oxidation of reduced heme proteins. It is known, for example, that oxiferrocytochrome P-450 substrate complexes may undergo auto-oxidation and subsequently split into (ferri)cytochrome P-450, a superoxide anion radical and the substrate:

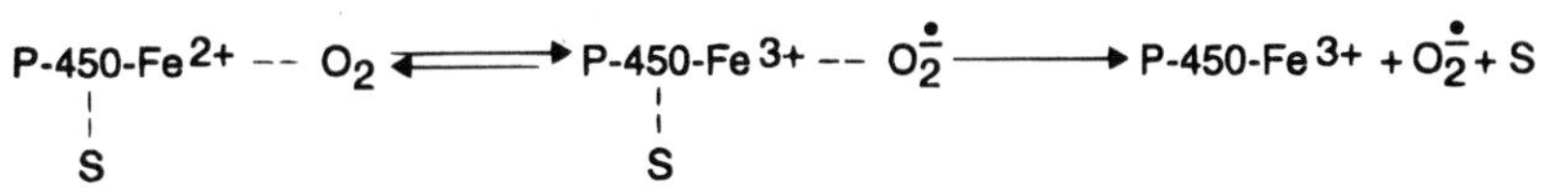

$$\text{P-450-Fe}^{2+} -- \text{O}_2 \rightleftarrows \text{P-450-Fe}^{3+} -- \text{O}_2^{\bullet -} \longrightarrow \text{P-450-Fe}^{3+} + \text{O}_2^{\bullet -} + \text{S}$$
$$\underset{\text{S}}{|} \qquad\qquad \underset{\text{S}}{|}$$

FIGURE   10.9
Schematic representation of the uncoupling of the cytochrome P-450 cycle

This process is known as the uncoupling of the cytochrome P-450 cycle. It is also referred to as the *oxidase activity* of cytochrome P-450.

Oxyhemoglobin may serve as a source of superoxide anion radicals in a similar way:

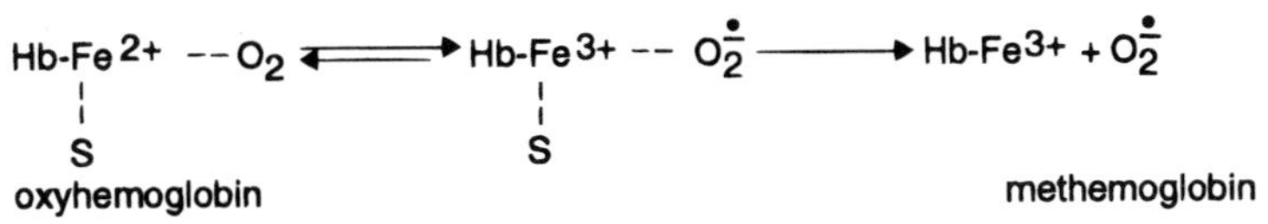

$$\text{Hb-Fe}^{2+} -- \text{O}_2 \rightleftarrows \text{Hb-Fe}^{3+} -- \text{O}_2^{\bullet -} \longrightarrow \text{Hb-Fe}^{3+} + \text{O}_2^{\bullet -}$$
$$\underset{\underset{\text{oxyhemoglobin}}{\text{S}}}{|} \qquad\qquad \underset{\text{S}}{|} \qquad\qquad\qquad\qquad \text{methemoglobin}$$

FIGURE   10.10
Superoxide anion radical formation through auto-oxidation of oxyhemoglobin

*Redox cycle*

Xenobiotics involved in the formation of the superoxide anion radical are substances that can be taken up in so-called redox cycles. These include quinones and hydroquinones in particular. In the case of quinones the redox cycle starts with a one-electron reduction step, just as in the case of ubiquinone. The resulting semiquinone subsequently passes the electron received on to molecular oxygen. The reduction of quinones is catalyzed by the NADPH-dependent cytochrome P-450 reductase (Figure 10.11).

Obviously, hydroquinones can enter a redox cycle via an oxidative step. This step may be catalyzed by enzymes, for example prostaglandin biosynthetase. Another type of xenobiotic that can be taken up in a redox cycle, is the bipyridyl derivatives. A well-known example is the herbicide *paraquat*, which causes injury to lung tissue in humans and animals. Figure 10.12 schematically shows its bioactivation.

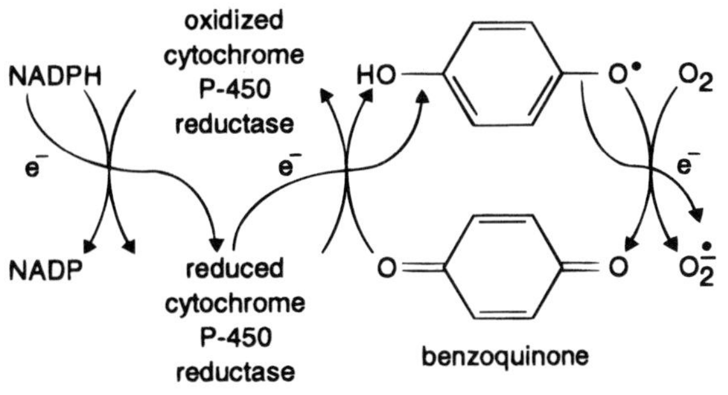

FIGURE   10.11
Redox cycle of benzoquinone

297

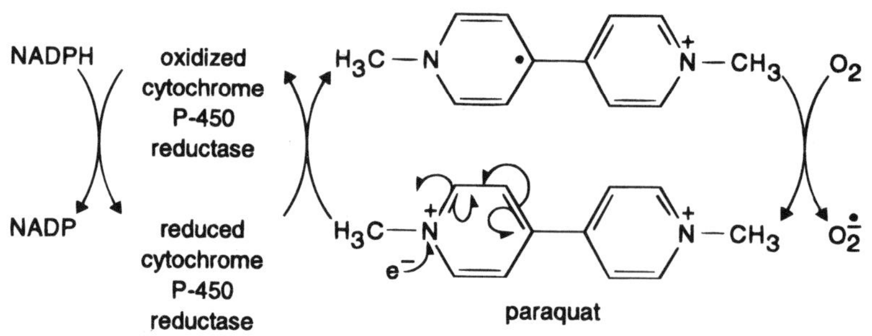

FIGURE 10.12
Schematic representation of the redox cycle of paraquat

Some studies suggest that this redox cycle and the released active oxygen radical are responsible for the injurious effect of paraquat on the lung.

*Hydrogen peroxide*

*Hydrogen peroxide*, an intermediate of the reduction of oxygen, is formed through so-called *dismutation* of the superoxide anion radical:

$$O_2^{\bullet-} + O_2^{\bullet-} + 2\,H^+ \longrightarrow H_2O_2 + O_2$$

FIGURE 10.13
Dismutation of the superoxide anion radical

This process may proceed via enzymatic action (catalyzed by *superoxide dismutase*, SOD) or spontaneously. In the first case, the oxygen formed is in the ground state. In the second case, *singlet oxygen* ($^1O_2$) is formed, which is very reactive. This is because the two electrons that were unpaired in the ground state are now paired. The result is an "empty" molecular orbital, i.e. a free electron pair can be taken up.

*Hydroxyl radical (OH$^\bullet$)*

The hydroxyl radical is one of the most powerful and most reactive oxidants that exist. It reacts immediately with any available biological substance. The hydroxyl radical is thought to be produced via the so-called *Haber–Weiss reaction*, a reaction of the superoxide anion radical with hydrogen peroxide, which is presumably catalyzed by iron ions (Figure 10.14).

$$\text{a } O_2^{\bullet-} + H_2O_2 \longrightarrow OH^- + OH^\bullet + {}^1O_2$$

this reaction is probably catalyzed by iron ions:

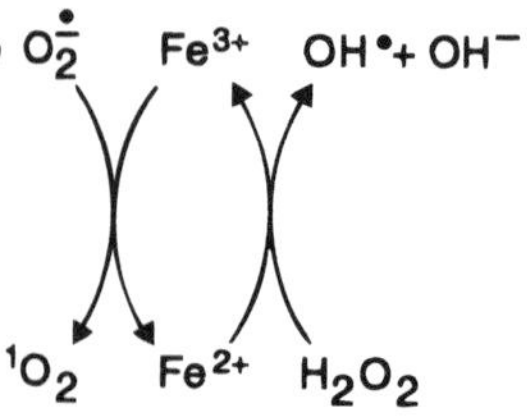

FIGURE 10.14
Hydroxyl radical formation
a Haber–Weiss reaction.
b Catalytic action of iron ions in the Haber–Weiss reaction.

TABLE 10.2
Classification of the superoxide dismutases into three categories on the basis of the metal ions they contain and the organisms and organs in which they occur

| type | occurring in |
|---|---|
| copper-zink-SOD | erythrocytes, yeasts, plants and animals |
| manganese-SOD | bacteria, plant tissues and liver tissue |
| iron-SOD | bacteria and algae |

### 2.3.2 Defense mechanisms against the injurious effects of reactive oxygen species

Over the past 25–30 years it has become clear that the living cell disposes of a number of enzymatic and non-enzymatic defense mechanisms against reactive oxygen species.

#### a. Enzymatic defense against reactive oxygen species

There are three classes of enzymes known to provide protection against reactive oxygen species: the catalases and peroxidases, that react specifically with hydrogen peroxide, and the superoxide dismutases.

*Superoxide dismutases (SOD)*

The *superoxide dismutases (SOD)* are metal-containing proteins that catalyze the conversion of the superoxide anion radical to molecular oxygen in the ground state and hydrogen peroxide. Based on the metal ions they contain, the superoxide anion radicals can be divided into three categories (see Table 10.2).

Superoxide dismutase is almost exclusively found to be an intracellular enzyme. It can only be demonstrated in very small amounts in the plasma or the lymph. This is of great importance, since any metabolic disorder involving the release of the superoxide anion radical, or any increase in the concentration of the superoxide anion radical in an extracellular fluid may be very harmful to the organism. The dismutation of superoxide anion radicals proceeds as follows (Figure 10.15):

$$\text{a} \quad O_2^{\bullet -} + \text{SOD-Cu}^{2+} \longrightarrow O_2 + \text{SOD-Cu}^{+}$$

$$\text{b} \quad O_2^{\bullet -} + \text{SOD-Cu}^{+} + 2\,H^{+} \longrightarrow H_2O_2 + \text{SOD-Cu}^{2+}$$

FIGURE 10.15
Dismutation of superoxide anion radicals as an example of enzymatic protection against reactive oxygen intermediates
In the first part of the reaction (a) the superoxide anion radical acts as a reducing agent, in the second part (b) as an oxidant.

To detoxicate hydrogen peroxide the cell has two enzymes at its disposal: *catalase*, a heme-containing enzyme, and *glutathione peroxidase*, which contains selenium.

*Catalase*

*Catalase* converts hydrogen peroxide to water and oxygen. In fact, catalase cooperates with superoxide dismutase in the removal of the hydrogen peroxide resulting from the dismutation reaction.

Catalase occurs in most tissues, encapsulated in subcellular organelles, the so-called *peroxisomes*. Maximum catalase activity requires very high concentrations of hydrogen peroxide. This distinguishes catalase from other peroxide-transforming enzymes. Catalase acts only on hydrogen peroxide, not on organic hydroperoxides.

*Glutathione peroxidase* catalyzes not only the conversion of hydrogen peroxide, but also that of organic peroxides. The enzyme is specific for glutathione (GSH), but not for the substrates to be detoxicated. It can transform various peroxides, e.g. the hydroperoxides of lipids. Glutathione peroxidase is found in most tissues, both in the cytosol and in the mitochondria. In the cytosol, the enzyme is present in special vesicles. The highest levels of this enzyme are found in the erythrocytes and in the liver, although levels in the heart and lungs may be considerable as well.

ASSIGNMENT 10.6

Give the equations for the detoxication process of $H_2O_2$ by glutathione peroxidase.

Superoxide dismutase (SOD) and glutathione peroxidase depend on metal ions (e.g. Cu) and metalloids (e.g. Se) as cofactors. This means that compounds that can interact with the metabolism of trace elements may partly or completely remove the control over cell toxication. Silver has been shown to inhibit glutathione peroxidase in rats.

ASSIGNMENT 10.7

What are the chances of hydroxyl radicals being formed inside the cell? On what factors does such formation depend?

b. *Non-enzymatic defense against reactive oxygen species*
The antioxidant enzymes discussed above can be seen as a first-line defense. After all, they prevent the conversion of the less reactive oxygen species, superoxide anion radical and hydrogen peroxide, to more reactive species such as the hydroxyl radical. The second line of defense largely consists of substances that eliminate radicals. The major radical scavengers of the cell are the vitamins E and C. *Vitamin E* ($\alpha$-tocopherol) is lipophilic and is incorporated in membranes. *Vitamin C* (ascorbic acid) is water-soluble and occurs in the cytosol. Ascorbic acid reacts quite rapidly with the superoxide anion radical and with hydrogen peroxide, but even faster with hydroxyl radicals. Furthermore, it can eliminate singlet oxygen. This antioxidant exerts its protective effect, for example, in the lens of the eye (which does not contain any superoxide dismutases) and in the fluid surrounding the pulmonary alveoli, where it complements the action of SOD and catalase. The mechanisms of the detoxication of lipid radicals by vitamin C are schematically shown in Figure 10.16.

Fatty acid chains in biological membranes are mostly unsaturated. They are therefore highly sensitive to oxidation by singlet oxygen or hydroxyl radicals. The oxidation consists of a chain of reactions which is known as *lipid peroxidation* (see section 3.2). Lipid peroxidation causes serious membrane damage and may therefore lead to cell death. Membrane components with an antioxidant effect may block the injurious chain reaction. A well-known example is $\alpha$-tocopherol. This compound reacts with a lipid radical to yield the $\alpha$-tocopherol radical and a harmless fatty acid. The $\alpha$-tocopherol radical can then be reduced to $\alpha$-tocopherol by glutathione (GSH). $\alpha$-Tocopherol is present in high concentrations in the membranes of the human eye and is probably the only lipid-soluble antioxidant occurring in human blood plasma. Figure 10.17 schematically represents the reaction of $\alpha$-tocopherol with lipid radicals.

The radicals that evolve from vitamins E and C during detoxication reactions are less reactive, because they are stabilized by resonance. Moreover, they are

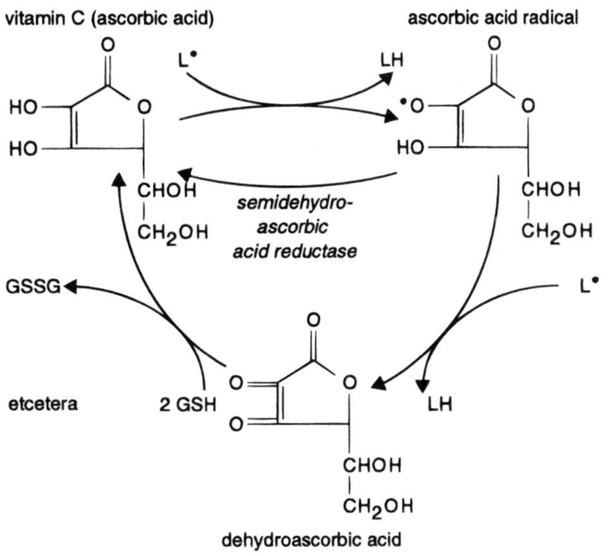

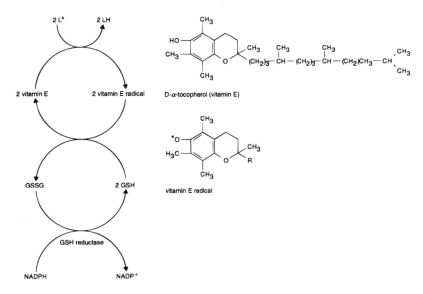

FIGURE 10.16
Detoxication of lipid radicals (L•) by vitamin C and subsequent regeneration of vitamin C

FIGURE 10.17
Detoxication of lipid radicals (L•) by vitamin E and subsequent regeneration of vitamin E

transformed back into the original vitamins by glutathione-dependent systems.

## 3 Interactions of reactive intermediates with cellular molecules and their toxic implications

The preceding sections have explained how reactive substances may be generated in biological systems and how the body is equipped to protect itself against the possible harmful effects of these intermediates. This section takes a closer look at some of the processes by which intermediates formed in the body may cause damage to the cell.

The major types of interaction of reactive intermediates are (1) covalent binding and (2) oxidative interactions, which may include oxidative stress or lipid peroxidation. The dividing line between these two types of interaction is not always clear. A reactive intermediate may, for example, cause cell death through covalent binding. The dead cells may subsequently release toxic products that induce their effects via oxidative processes. The reverse process has also been described.

## 3.1   COVALENT BINDING AND ITS TOXIC IMPLICATIONS

Reactive intermediates may bind covalently to cellular molecules such as nucleic acids, proteins, cofactors, lipids and polysaccharides. The potential effects are manifold: decreased energy production, changes in membrane permeability, inhibition of the synthesis of macromolecules etc. The connection between binding to nucleic acids on the one hand and mutagenesis and carcinogenesis on the other will be discussed in Study units 11, 12 and 13. So far, little is known about the implications of covalent binding to cofactors, lipids and polysaccharides. Because of this, the present section restricts itself to the link between covalent binding to proteins and cell death.

The role of covalent binding in the induction of toxicity has been clearly demonstrated for a number of compounds (see Table 10.3).

> ASSIGNMENT   10.8
>
> Outline how the various types of reactive intermediates listed in Table 10.3 (epoxides, quinonimines, radicals and phosgene) may react with nucleophilic groups.

The conclusion on the role of covalent binding is based on data obtained from experiments with radiolabeled xenobiotics. In these experiments, the criterion for binding to protein is thus the binding of the radioisotope to proteins. This implies the risk that most of these findings concern binding to cell proteins that are not essential to the survival of the cell.

TABLE   10.3
Examples of compounds for which the role of covalent binding in the induction of toxicity has been demonstrated

| xenobiotic | proposed reactive metabolite | target organ and binding site |
|---|---|---|
| bromobenzene | 3,4-epoxide and/or *ortho*-quinone | liver |
| acetaminophen | quinonimine | liver |
| carbon tetrachloride | trichloromethyl radical and/or phosgene | liver |
| p-aminophenol | quinonimine | kidney |
| ipomeanol | epoxide | lung |

*Glutathione depletion*

For *bromobenzene* and *acetaminophen* it has been shown that substances preventing cell death did not have any effect on (total) covalent binding.

An early effect of overdosage with bromobenzene and acetaminophen *in vivo* is *glutathione depletion* in the liver cells. A similar effect can be achieved *in vitro* by incubation of isolated liver cells with high concentrations of these xenobiotics. The glutathione system plays an important role in the detoxication of the reactive intermediates of both substances. This has been described for the reactive intermediates of bromobenzene in section 2.1. The detoxication of the quinonimine of acetaminophen proceeds in exactly the same way as that of the *ortho*-quinone of bromobenzene. For both cases, studies on isolated liver cells have provided evidence for the assumption that glutathione protects the thiol groups of proteins against the attacks of the toxic metabolites.

*Increase in cytosolic Ca²⁺ concentration*

When incubating hepatocytes with high concentrations of acetaminophen and bromobenzene thiol depletion was found to be followed by an increase in $Ca^{2+}$ concentration in the cytosol. In the cell $Ca^{2+}$ is distributed between the endoplasmic reticulum, the mitochondria, the cytosol ($10^{-7}$ mole $l^{-1}$) and proteins (see also Figure 15.15). The thiol group-dependent $Ca^{2+}/Mg^{2+}$-ATPase plays an important part in the transport of $Ca^{2+}$ between the cellular compartments. This suggests that disturbance of $Ca^{2+}$ homeostasis is connected with the disturbance of the thiol homeostasis.

ASSIGNMENT   10.9

Outline how the 3,4-epoxide of bromobenzene might inactivate $Ca^{2+}/Mg^{2+}$-ATPase

Disturbance of $Ca^{2+}$ homeostasis has also been observed in liver cells incubated with carbon tetrachloride.

*Phospholipase activity*

An increase in cytosolic $Ca^{2+}$ level may have harmful consequences for the cell, since the membrane-bound phospholipases (lipid-hydrolyzing enzymes) are $Ca^{2+}$-dependent. An increased cytosolic $Ca^{2+}$ concentration will therefore result in increased phospholipase activity.

Disturbance of $Ca^{2+}$ homeostasis may ultimately lead to changes in the composition and permeability of the cellular membranes, which in turn will have serious consequences:

- damage to the protective barrier between the cell and its environment;
- release of hydrolyzing lysosomal enzymes;
- increased peroxidation of polyunsaturated fatty acids.

Activation of lipases has been demonstrated in hepatocytes incubated with carbon tetrachloride.

*Blebbing*

Effects on membranes have also been observed. Bromobenzene and acetaminophen appeared to cause "blebbing" (vesicle formation) of the cell membrane of isolated liver cells (Figures 15.16 and 10.18).

In summary, the sequence of processes leading to cell death is believed to be:

bioactivation → interaction with endogenous cell molecules (covalent binding?) → disturbance of thiol homeostasis → a disturbance of $Ca^{2+}$ homeostasis → activation of lipases → cytomorphological changes (blebbing) → cell death.

303

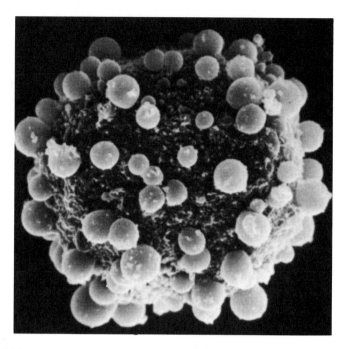

menadione

FIGURE 10.18
Electron micrograph of a hepatocyte showing bleb formation after incubation for 30 min. with menadione (200 μM)

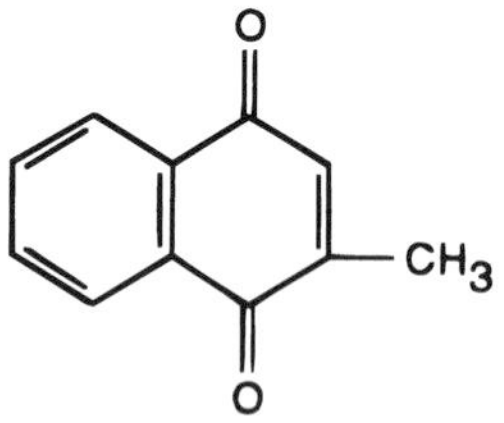

### 3.2 OXIDATIVE INTERACTIONS: OXIDATIVE STRESS AND LIPID PEROXIDATION

*a. Oxidative stress*

The situation in which there is a continuous interaction with oxidizing agents inside the organism, in other words, the state in which consistently more reducing equivalents are used than would be the case for the normal functioning of the cell, is referred to as *oxidative stress*.

The preceding sections have dealt with the types of reducing equivalents stored in the cell: NADPH, glutathione, protein thiols and vitamins C and E. The central role of glutathione in the storage system of reducing agents was highlighted. Well-known primary causes of oxidative stress are reactive oxygen species and quinoid structures.

The superoxide anion radical can interact directly with thiol groups:

$$\text{(reducer)} \quad \text{(oxidant)}$$
$$R-SH + O_2^{\bullet-} + R'-SH \longrightarrow R-S^{\bullet} + H_2O_2 + R'-S^-$$
$$R-S^{\bullet} + {}^{\bullet}S-R \longrightarrow R-S-S-R$$

FIGURE 10.19
Reaction of the superoxide anion radical with a thiol group

The superoxide anion radical may also dismutate and form hydrogen peroxide. Hydrogen peroxide formation leads to utilization of reducing equivalents as a result of its detoxication by glutathione peroxidase. If the protective capacity of superoxide dismutase and catalase is insufficient, hydroxyl radicals and singlet oxygen may be formed. The superoxide anion radical and hydrogen peroxide are not very reactive in aqueous solution. They can therefore interact with

*oxidative stress*

304

each other, in other words, they can form hydroxyl radicals and singlet oxygen via the Haber–Weiss reaction. Hydrogen peroxide can be scavenged by vitamin C and by glutathione peroxidase. Both the hydroxyl radical and singlet oxygen can oxidize thiol groups.

The production of reactive oxygen species, and hence the utilization of reducing equivalents, may be considerably enhanced by substances that are taken up in redox cycles. When considering the utilization of reducing equivalents in the case of quinones, however, one should take into account that these compounds can also interact directly with the components of the reductive defense system: reduction by NADPH and thiols, and conjugation with thiols.

---

EXAMPLE 10–1

The quinonimine of acetaminophen undergoes both reduction and conjugation, whereas that of 3,5-dimethylacetaminophen only undergoes reduction. The cytotoxicity of the acetaminophen quinonimine is comparable to that of the parent compound: glutathione depletion followed by cell death. The substituted acetaminophen and the quinonimine derived from it are not cytotoxic.

---

ASSIGNMENT  10.10

Explain, on the basis of the above data, why the substituted acetaminophen and the corresponding quinonimine do not cause toxic effects in liver cells.

Although these data again emphasize the important role of covalent binding in the induction of cell death, it does seem that oxidative stress, followed by depletion of reducing equivalents, may have disastrous effects on the cell: addition of the antioxidant *catechin* to an incubation of hepatocytes with acetaminophen prevented cell death but had hardly any effect on covalent binding. Apparently, the glutathione depletion creates the right conditions for oxidative stress in the cells. This would imply that in the sequence of events proposed in section 3.1 "interaction with cellular constituents" would have to be replaced by "glutathione depletion" and "disturbance of thiol homeostasis" by "oxidative stress", followed by "depletion of reducing equivalents". Depletion of reducing equivalents may result in increased $Ca^{2+}$ concentrations in several ways. First of all, as was pointed out before, the $Ca^{2+}/Mg^{2+}$-ATPase may be inactivated by oxidation of the thiol groups. Mitochondrial damage resulting from the oxidation of the pyridine nucleotides, NADH and NADPH, may also be a cause of the increase in cytosolic $Ca^{2+}$ concentration.

Reactive oxygen species are also thought to be involved in the cytotoxic effects of polyhydric phenols on catecholamine neurons and myocardial cells. Polyhydric phenols are probably taken up in redox cycles via auto-oxidation.

*Depletion of reducing equivalents*

catechin

catechol

6-hydroxydopamine

---

EXAMPLE 10-2

One of the aspects of a study on the mechanism of the neurotoxicity of 6-hydroxydopamine was to establish whether the toxicity could be attributed to auto-oxidation (to an *ortho*-quinone) or to interaction with thiol groups. The study was carried out on neuroblastoma cells. Inhibition of thymidine incorporation into DNA was used as a measure of cytotoxicity.

6-Hydroxydopamine was compared with a number of structurally related compounds, such as epinephrine, norepinephrine and 2,4,5-trihydroxyphenylalanine. 6-Hydroxydopamine appeared to be the most toxic substance, and to undergo auto-oxidation most intensively.

The *ortho*-quinone of 6-hydroxydopamine interacted only very slightly with thiols.

---

ASSIGNMENT  10.11

What can be concluded from this with regard to the mechanisms underlying the cytotoxicity of 6-hydroxydopamine?

---

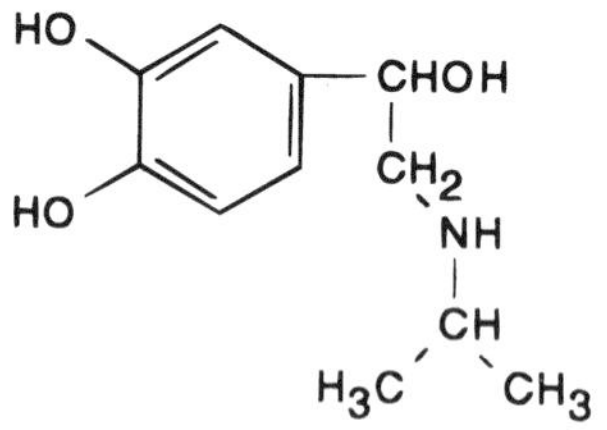

isoproterenol (a catecholamine)

EXAMPLE 10-3

Incubation of myocardial cells with the β-adrenergic sympathomimetic isoproterenol resulted in an increased cytosolic $Ca^{2+}$ concentration, followed by cell damage. The damage could be prevented if the incubation took place in the presence of vitamin C.

---

### b. Lipid peroxidation

In addition to disturbances in $Ca^{2+}$ homeostasis, oxidative stress followed by depletion of reducing equivalents may also lead to another cause of membrane damage, namely *lipid peroxidation.*

Lipid peroxidation and cell death often go hand in hand. The preceding sections have discussed how reactive compounds may be produced in biological systems and how the body is equipped to resist possible injurious effects by these intermediates. The present section elaborates on some of the processes through which the intermediates produced in the body may cause damage to the cell:

I.    abstraction of a hydrogen atom from a polyunsaturated fatty acid chain by singlet oxygen and hydroxyl radicals (*radical formation, initiation*);

II.   reaction of the resulting fatty acid radical with molecular oxygen (*oxygenation* or, more specifically, *peroxidation*);

III.  as stated in the preceding section, these events may be followed by a *detoxication* process, in which the reaction chain is stopped. This process, which may proceed in several steps, is sometimes referred to as *termination*.

Figure 10.20 summarizes these stages in lipid peroxidation.

*Abstraction of hydrogen atoms*

I.    *Abstraction of hydrogen atoms* occurs at the sites where two allyl groups meet. In arachidonic acid, for example, these are the positions 7, 10 and 13:

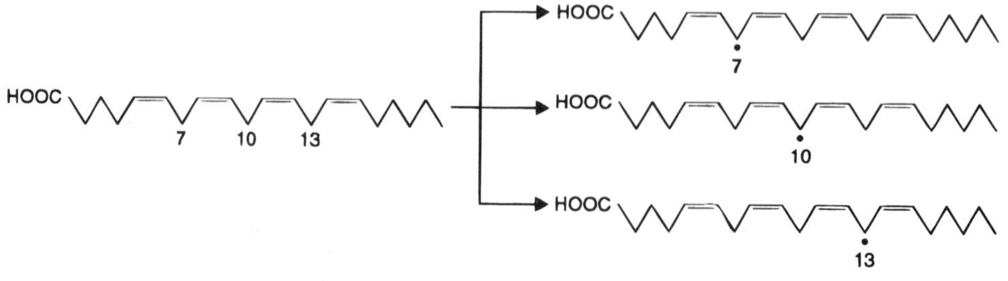

306

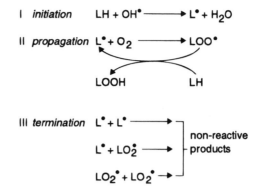

FIGURE 10.20
Stages in lipid peroxidation
LH = polyunsaturated fatty acid
L• = lipid radical

The radicals that are formed rearrange to the more stable *conjugated dienes*:

HOOC ⌇⌇=⌄= /  ⟶  HOOC ⌇⌇⌃=⌄ /
(conjugated diene)

*Oxygenation*

II. Next, *oxygenation* takes place:

HOOC ⌇⌇•⌄= /  —$O_2$→  HOOC ⌇⌇⌄= /
(peroxy radical)

*Peroxy moiety*
*Adjacent to double bond*

If the *peroxy moiety* is situated immediately *adjacent to a double bond* in the arachidonic acid skeleton, for example at position 15, a hydroperoxide is produced:

/⌄⌃⌇ —$O_2$→ /⌄⌃⌇ ⟶ /⌄⌃⌇
(hydroperoxide)

From hydroperoxides radicals may be formed under the influence of $Fe^{2+}$ ions, (cf. the Haber–Weiss reaction summarized in Figure 10.14). The radicals thus produced may split into alkanes and polyunsaturated semi-aldehydes:

⌄⌃⌇  ⟶  ⌄ + ⌃ + L•
(semi-aldehyde) (pentane)

*Endoperoxide formation*

If the peroxy moiety is situated in the α position with respect to a double bond in arachidonic acid, for example at position 11, then ring formation produces a so-called endoperoxide.

*rearrangement to conjugated dienes*

The double bound is situated in the α,β-position with respect to the carbon atom with the unpaired electron. This results in a *hydroperoxide:*

The double bound is situated in the β,γ-position with respect to the carbon atom with the unpaired electron. This results in an *endoperoxide:*

Endoperoxides disintegrate to yield *malondialdehyde* and other products. If the processes described above involve biological membranes (cell membrane, endoplasmic reticulum, mitochondrial membrane, lysosomal membrane etc.), this will ultimately lead to the destruction of these membranes, with all its consequences.

*Fluorescent cross-linking*

Singlet oxygen and the hydroxyl radical may also affect the structure of membranes indirectly, i.e. via a product of lipid peroxidation, such as malondialdehyde. Cross-linking (condensation of malondialdehyde with the primary amino groups of proteins and phospholipids) then results in high-molecular-weight, fluorescent products (fluorescence maximum at 470 nm after excitation at 360–380 nm), the so-called Schiff bases:

(condensation product of malondialdehyde
with primary amino groups)

The degree of cross-linking is clearly related to age. For example, the lung tissue of older people appears to contain more high-molecular-weight products and to fluoresce more strongly than that of younger persons (Tappel: "The older you grow, the more you glow"). The reason is in all probability that with increasing age the capacity to eliminate reactive oxygen species decreases.

As was stated above, lipid peroxidation and cell death often go hand in hand. It is not always clear, however, whether cell death results from lipid peroxidation or vice versa.

A study of the toxicity of acetaminophen in isolated liver cells, for example, revealed that the disulfide-reducing agent dithiothreitol provides protection against toxic effects, but not against lipid peroxidation.

## 4    Methods for determining necrosis, covalent binding and lipid peroxidation

It will be clear from the above that a large part of the cytotoxicological research into cell death has been carried out on liver cells. This section therefore focuses on the liver cell.

### 4.1    ESTABLISHING THE LEVEL OF NECROSIS

Since the methods for determining necrosis will be extensively dealt with in Study unit 16 (Necrosis and apoptosis), this section only covers a few aspects. Necrosis is an advanced and usually irreversible stage of degeneration of cells and cell components such as mitochondria, lysosomes, and rough and smooth endoplasmic reticulum. It is characterized by the presence of cell fragments (e.g. mitochondrial, lysosomal and cell membranes, degranulated rough endoplasmic reticulum and cell nuclei) and dead cells.

*Morphological parameters in mechanistic studies*

An important part of cytotoxicological research is the study of morphological changes, usually by electron microscopy. There are recent indications that the results of morphological research may contribute to mechanistic research. For example, hepatotoxic substances cause blebbing of the cell membrane of hepatocytes (see Figure 10.18).

A study on the possible causes of bleb formation compared tertiary butyl hydroperoxide $((H_3C)_3C\text{-OOH})$ and allyl isothiocyanate $(H_2C=CH\text{-}CH_2N=C=S)$. In the case of the former, bleb formation appeared to be preceded by damage to the mitochondria. This was not the case for allyl isothiocyanate. As a result of the destruction of cells and cell components, enzymes are released, including β-glucuronidase from the lysosomes, and acid phosphatase, alkaline phosphatase, lactic dehydrogenase (LDH), alanine aminotransferase (ALT), aspartate amino tansferase (APT) and isocitrate dehydrogenase from the cytosol. The release of enzymes is accompanied by an increase in their activity in the incubation medium. This increase is generally used as an index of cytotoxicity. It is a very sensitive measure.

### 4.2    DETERMINATION COVALENT BINDING AND LIPID PEROXIDATION

In order to determine *covalent binding* of a substance to protein, the substance concerned is radioactively labeled. After incubation with the substance, the cells are isolated and homogenized. Differentiated centrifugation of the homogenate then yields the fraction that consists of the proteins to which the radioactive isotope is bound.

Various methods are applied for the determination of *lipid peroxidation*. A generally accepted method is the thiobarbituric acid test. In it, lipid peroxidation products, such as malondialdehyde (MDA), are condensed with 2-thiobarbituric acid in the following way:

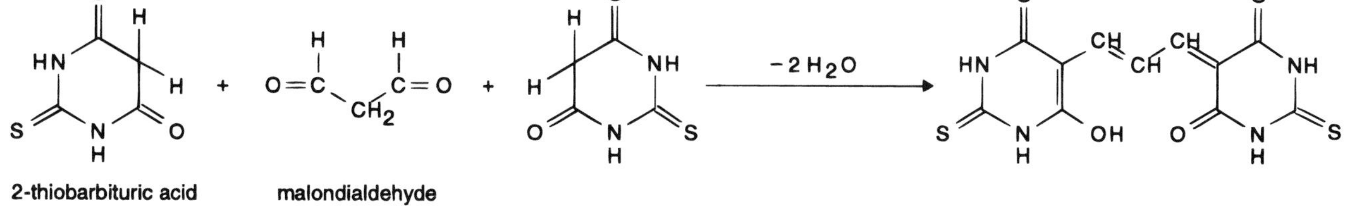

2-thiobarbituric acid            malondialdehyde

FIGURE    10.21
Condensation reaction of malon(di)aldehyde with 2-thiobarbituric acid

The resulting condensation products have an absorption maximum at 535 nm. This method is not specific for MDA. Another disadvantage is that malondialdehyde undergoes metabolic transformations inside the cell.

A second method consists of the spectrophotometric determination of the conjugated dienes produced by peroxidation (absorption maximum at 233 nm).

There is yet another method, in which the high-molecular-weight products resulting from cross-linking with malondialdehyde are determined fluorimetrically.

## 5 Summary

The focal point of the present study unit was the mechanism of cell death. The role of the following types of reactive intermediates in the induction of cell death has been discussed:

- electrophilic structures: epoxides, quinones and nitrenium ions;
- radicals, other than reduced forms of oxygen;
- reactive oxygen species.

For each type of intermediate, the way in which it is formed is described, how it can be detoxicated, with which primary target molecules it can react and what sequence of disturbances is initiated by the reaction with the primary target molecule.

As far as the formation of reactive intermediates is concerned, the following processes have been individually mentioned:

- formation of nitrenium ions: an example of bioactivation by conjugation;
- formation of radicals: reduction (of carbon tetrachloride) by cytochrome P-450;
- formation of reactive oxygen species: the role of redox cycles in the induction of toxic effects.

For the detoxication of reactive intermediates the cell compartment in which they are formed is important. The detoxication systems are distributed over the various cell compartments: glucuronyl transferase and epoxide hydrolase occur (mainly) in the endoplasmic reticulum, glutathione transferases (mainly) in the cytosol, superoxide dismutases in the mitochondria and the cytosol, catalase in the peroxisomes, glutathione peroxidase in the cytosol and the mitochondria, vitamin E in the membranes and vitamin C in the cytosol. The central role of the glutathione system in detoxication has been pointed out.

The interaction of reactive intermediates with primary target molecules was illustrated by two examples: (1) the abstraction of hydrogen atoms from the polyunsaturated fatty acid arachidonic acid by the trichloromethyl radical and (2) the covalent binding of the 3,4-epoxide of bromobenzene to thiol groups of $Ca^{2+}/Mg^{2+}$-ATPase. Both types of target molecule perform functions that are vital to the survival of the cell: construction of membranes and maintenance of $Ca^{2+}$ homeostasis, respectively. In this context, it should be noted that cell death appears not always to be related to the chain of processes initiated by hydrogen atom abstraction (lipid peroxidation) and covalent binding.

SELF ASSESSMENT QUESTIONS

1    On what does the functioning of the cell primarily depend?

2    Give some causes of membrane damage.

adriamycin

3　What may be the cause of an increase in the cytosolic $Ca^{2+}$ concentration?

4　What is the double role of iron in the physiology of the cell with regard to detoxication and intoxication?

5　Give a complete overview of the detoxicating functions of glutathione.

6　The cytostatic drug adriamycin is cardiotoxic in man. How could this toxicity be explained?

## FEEDBACK

### 1　Answers to the assignments

10.1　At present, the cells used in cytotoxicological research are rarely human cells. This means that there will be species-related differences at the cellular level as well as in toxicokinetic behavior, and this will have to be taken into account.

10.2　Not all molecules with which an active toxic agent interacts have vital functions in the cell.

10.3

10.4　Hexachloroethane ($C_2Cl_6$) can be imagined as being produced by dimerization of the trichloromethyl radical.

dimerization: $^{\bullet}CCl_3 + {}^{\bullet}CCl_3 \longrightarrow CCl_3 - CCl_3$

Chloroform could be formed by the addition of one hydrogen atom to the trichloromethyl radical. This hydrogen atom could be derived from, for example, a lipid.

hydrogen atom abstraction: $^{\bullet}CCl_3 + LH \longrightarrow HCCl_3 + L^{\bullet}$

10.5

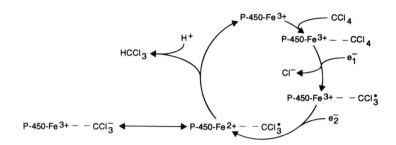

10.6

10.7 The chances of hydroxyl radicals being formed in the cell are very slim. The formation of OH˙ depends on the availability of the superoxide anion radical (is SOD effective?), $H_2O_2$ (are catalase and GSH peroxidase effective?), as well as on the ratio $Fe^{2+}:Fe^{3+}$.

If the enzymatic defense systems are sufficiently effective, OH˙ will not constitute a real threat to the cell.

10.8 Assume GSH to be the nucleophile.

| | | |
|---|---|---|
| epoxide | quinonimine | |
| | radical | $CCl_3^˙ + GSH \longrightarrow GS^˙ + HCCl_3$ |
| | | $GS^˙ + ^˙SG \longrightarrow GS-SG$ |
| | halogenide | |

10.9 $Ca^{2+}/Mg^{2+}$-ATPase is a thiol group-dependent enzyme. The interaction of the enzyme (represented by Enz-SH) with the 3,4-epoxide of bromobenzene can be represented as follows:

312

10.10 The quinonimine of 3,5-dimethylacetaminophen is detoxicated through reduction by GSH:

As long as there is a supply of reducing equivalents, glutathione disulfide is reduced to glutathione again:

$$GSSG \xrightarrow[\text{NADPH}]{\text{GSH reductase}} 2\,GSH$$

10.11 The cytotoxicity of this substance could be attributed to either auto-oxidation or interaction with thiol groups. Since the *ortho*quinone of 6-hydroxydopamine hardly interacts with thiols, it is more likely that the mechanisms of the cytotoxicity of 6-hydroxydopamine are connected with the high capacity for auto-oxidation of this substance.

## 2 Answers to the self assessment questions

1 The energy supply and the integrity of membranes and enzymes.

2 Covalent binding, an increased cytosolic $Ca^{2+}$ concentration, lipid peroxidation.

3 Blockage of the transport of $Ca^{2+}$ (out of the cell) by covalent binding or by depletion of reducing equivalents; mitochondrial damage as a result of the depletion of reducing equivalents.

4 As part of the cytochrome P-450 complex, iron is responsible for the detoxication of many xenobiotics. Also as part of the cytochrome P-450 complex, iron may give rise to the formation of reactive oxygen species through uncoupling from the cytochrome P-450 cycle. Finally, it may generate oxidizing species via the Haber–Weiss reaction and the cleavage of hydroperoxides.

5 Conjugation with electrophiles, reduction of oxidants, scavenging of radicals, detoxication of hydrogen peroxide and hydroperoxides, regeneration of the vitamins C and E from their respective radicals, protection of thiol groups in (essential) proteins.

6 Adriamycin is a quinone. Hence it can enter redox cycles.

# Contents Study unit 11
# Genetic toxicology

0-8493-9232-2/96/$0.00 + $.50

Study unit 11

# Genetic toxicology

*Ph. Vanparys, Th. M. C. M. de Kok and F.-J. van Schooten*

## INTRODUCTION

Life and the propagation of life are determined by the information stored in the genes. Except in certain viruses (RNA viruses), this information is carried by deoxyribonucleic acid (DNA). Chemically, this DNA is universal which means that it is identical in all living organisms.

### What are mutations?

*Mutation*

Mutations are unexpected and undirected changes in the composition of genetic information. The term *mutation* encompasses both qualitative and quantitative changes in the information structure of the individual genes and the genome. Mutations can occur at the level of the bases, the structure of individual genes, the chromosomes and the total genome. They can arise spontaneously or under the influence of external factors, such as temperature, chemical substances, ultraviolet light and ionizing radiation. It has gradually been recognized that the introduction of thousands of new chemicals into the environment leads to an increased mutation rate. Because of the increased incidence of cancer and genetic diseases, it has fairly recently come to be realized that the high mutation pressure exerts an unfavorable influence on the physical and mental well-being of humans. Monitoring of the release of mutagenic substances into the environment is therefore necessary. Essential steps in such control are identification of the mutagens and evaluation of their influence on human well-being. As a

*Genetic toxicology*

discipline of toxicological research, one of the tasks of *genetic toxicology* is to detect mutagenic chemicals. How mutations arise will be explained with the help of some simple examples. Genetic toxicology has a large array of tests for detecting mutations at its disposal, of which the most important ones will be briefly discussed. Furthermore, research on the mechanisms underlying the induction of DNA damage as well as the cellular capacity to repair this damage, is another aim of this field of toxicology. Some molecular mechanisms of both induction and repair of DNA damage will be described in this unit. Finally, the analysis of biological effects at the cellular and organ level as a result of DNA-modifications can be indicated as a point of interest in genetic toxicology.

LEARNING OBJECTIVES

After studying this unit on genetic toxicology you are expected to

— have some knowledge of the evolution of genetic toxicology as a toxicological discipline
— know what mutations are and what their biological relevance is

— be able to differentiate between the various types of mutations and to describe them

— be able to describe the conversion of mutations into changed proteins

— be able to explain the absence of a threshold value for the effect of mutagenic substances

— be able to describe the mechanisms of DNA repair

— be able to describe possible relationships between mutagenesis, teratogenesis and carcinogenesis

— be able to point out the basic aspects of structure–activity relationships in mutagenesis

— be able to describe mutagenicity tests and categorize them according to the type of genetic abnormalities they detect.

*Study hints*

This unit makes use of the contents of preceding study units. If necessary, look up the cross-references. Since you are assumed to be familiar with the basics of (molecular) genetics, it is advisable to have a genetics book at hand. The study load for this unit is estimated at 4 hours.

## STUDY CORE

### 1 History of mutagenicity research

The notion that there exists something like heredity is older than recorded history. Scientific knowledge on the subject, however, is only quite young and does not reach back any further than Mendel's discoveries in the second half of the 19th century. The general pattern found by Mendel (1822–1884) was initially ignored, and rediscovered independently by De Vries, Correns and Tschermak in 1900. The hereditary factors discovered by Mendel are contained in what De Vries called genes. In his mutation theory (1901), De Vries was the first to propose the concept *Genetic toxicology* of *mutation*, thereby laying down the foundations of *genetic toxicology*. Since that time, it has become clear that the stability of the gene is not absolute and that permanent changes can take place in genetic material. The new gene is then known as a mutant and the process which has preceded it, is called a mutation. Based on De Vries' mutation theory and experiments on the fruit fly *Drosophila melanogaster*, Thomas Hunt Morgan and his pupils demonstrated that genes are located on chro-*Experimental induction of* mosomes. Muller was the first one to induce experimental mutations by irradiat-*mutations* ing fruit flies with X-rays. With the discovery of the three-dimensional structure of DNA by Crick and Watson in 1953, a golden age began for molecular genetics during which the structure of DNA, DNA replication, the genetic code and mechanisms of protein synthesis, and mutation were unraveled. It is now realized that the key to natural selection and evolution is to be found in the DNA molecule, which can replicate itself and change itself via mutations.

*For more on teratogenesis, see* Unlike teratology, where the case of thalidomide was the incentive which led *Study units 31 and 32* to the inclusion of this new discipline in toxicological research programs, *genetic toxicology* has evolved more gradually as a toxicological discipline. Where classic toxicological disciplines could build on observations of toxicological effects, genetic toxicology required insight into genetic information (DNA) and its mechanism before it could develop any further.

Towards the end of the 1960s, it was realized that people were increasingly being exposed to mutagenic agents which could cause inheritable changes, and thus are transferred to the next generation of daughter cells. Using the bacterial reversion test with *Salmonella typhimurium*, known as the *Ames test*, it was shown in 1975 that 60–90% of carcinogenic chemicals are also mutagenic. As a result, mutagenesis has acquired a firm place in toxicological research.

*Summary*

Mutagenesis or genetic toxicology has grown from the increasing awareness that human beings and animals are continuously exposed to mutagenic agents which induce changes in inheritable properties.

## 2  Biological relevance of mutations

Thanks to molecular genetics, it is now understood that human and animal life are under the ultimate control of the DNA molecule, which replicates itself and undergoes mutation. This mechanism is the key to natural selection and evolution. The gene pool of human beings has evolved over millions of years, through mutations and recombinations, to its present composition. Without mutations, the evolution of species would have stopped at a very primitive stage. It can thus be argued that mutations have had a favorable rather than an unfavorable effect on the evolution of species, and have been essential for the origin of mankind. This statement, however, only applies for the time when the natural environment was the sole source of physical or chemical mutagens. The system of natural selection determines whether mutations are preserved, or are eliminated from a population because they are harmful. Some unfavorable mutations that are not too drastic may be retained and only have serious effects on the well-being of human beings in the long term. There are also mutations which are neutral (that is, neither advantageous nor harmful) or even favorable. Unfortunately, the last category is relatively small.

Mutations can occur in somatic cells as well as in reproductive cells. If they arise in somatic cells, they may lead to the development of cancer in adults, while in fetuses they may cause teratogenic effects (malformations in the fetus, spontaneous abortions, etc.). If mutations take place in the *reproductive cells*, they are transmitted to the offspring. If they are dominant they are immediately expressed in the form of lethality or genetic diseases. Recessive mutations may be transmitted from generation to generation before they are expressed. Ten percent of diseases in man have their origins in genetic abnormalities. Diseases that are definitely caused by gene mutations include sickle-cell anemia and phenylketonuria.

It is assumed that 9 out of every 1000 living newborn babies suffer from a disease resulting from gene mutations. The frequency of chromosomal aberrations in spontaneous abortions within 12 weeks is 614 per 1000, whereas in living newborns this is 6 or 7 per 1000. Examples of genetic diseases resulting from chromosomal aberrations will be discussed in section 3.3.

*Induction of mutations*

Mutations can arise spontaneously but they can also be induced by physical and chemical factors. The massive increase in number and amount of chemicals in the environment has led to an enormous rise in the mutation pressure. *Mutagenic pressure* indicates the contribution of newly mutated gametes in the haploid genome during one generation. It should be indicated that until now, not one human inheritable disease has been correlated with a specific mutation in gametes induced by either chemicals or radiation. However, there is no doubt that this mutagenic pressure may not be underestimated, since chemicals that appear capable of inducing mutations in gametes of other species, certainly impose a genetic risk for man.

Why is it difficult to determine mutagenic pressure?

Mutations are difficult to determine quantitatively because small changes often go unrecognized. The human mutagenic rate is estimated at 28 new mutations for albinism, 32 for hemophilia, 42 for dwarfism and 30 for microencephaly per one million male and female gametes.

Mutagenic pressure greatly depends on the moment of action of mutation inducing factors. This is clear from the increased incidence of Down's syndrome among children of older mothers. It is very rare for mothers younger than 25 years to have children with Down's syndrome. In mothers aged 40 or over, however, the incidence of children with this syndrome is 1% (see Figure 11.1).

*Mutagenesis and carcinogenesis*     The high correlation between the mutagenic effect of chemical substances in bacterial tests and the carcinogenic effect of the same chemicals in mammals demonstrates that mutations form the basis of the development of neoplasia.

### Summary

The combination of mutations and natural selection is the key to the evolution of species. The origin of many diseases can be found in genetic abnormalities in somatic or reproductive cells.

## 3    Types of mutations

As far as the classification of types of mutation is concerned, there is no general consensus among genetic toxicologists, and different classifications are employed. Further discussion on this subject is beyond the scope of this study unit and the present account will restrict itself to the various types of mutations that can take place in genetic material—using the term "mutation" in its broadest sense. Three groups of mutations can be distinguished:

*Single-point or gene mutations*    
- *single-point mutations* or *gene mutations*: these are small changes in the DNA at the level of the bases and genes, which are invisible under a light mi-

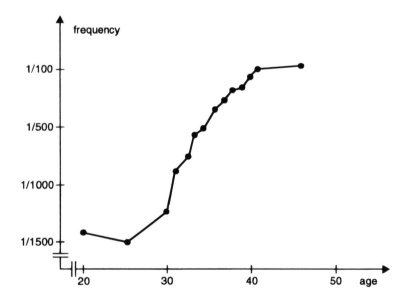

FIGURE   11.1
Frequency of Down's syndrome as a function of the mother's age

croscope. These point mutations can be based on changes in the sequence of nitrogen bases as a result of base-pair substitution, or due to addition or deletion of bases.

*Structural chromosomal aberrations*
*Clastogenes*

- *structural chromosomal aberrations*: these consist of major changes in the structure of the chromosome which are visible under a light microscope. Chemicals which cause structural chromosomal aberrations are also known as clastogenes.

*Genome mutations*

- *genomic mutations or aneuploidy*: abnormalities in the numbers of chromosomes. Chemical substances which cause aneuploidy are also called *aneugenes*.

*Aneugenes*

Little is known about modes of action, except for that of gene mutations. The theory that chromosome mutations are always the result of a great many minor mutations is still unproven. Moreover, no relationship has yet been demonstrated between the two groups of mutations.

## 3.1  GENE MUTATIONS

### 3.1.1  Base-pair substitutions

Base-pair substitution means that one or more bases somewhere along the DNA strand are replaced by other bases. Two types of mutation can be distinguished in this respect, viz. *transition* and *transversion*. In the case of *transition*, purines, i.e. adenine (A) and guanine (G), are replaced by other purines, or pyrimidines, i.e. cytosine (C) and thymine (T), are replaced by other pyrimidines (for example, A by G, T by C) (Figure 11.2). In the case of *transversion*, purines are replaced by pyrimidines and vice versa (for example, A by C, G by C). Molecular mechanisms causing the exchange of bases include:

*Transition*

*Transversion*

a.  incorporation of base analogs;
b.  chemical alteration of normal bases;
c.  binding of chemicals to bases;
d.  spontaneous base modifications.

ASSIGNMENT  11.1

Valine is coded for by four codons (GUU, GUC, GUA and GUG). Which substitutions of the third base of the GUU codon of valine represent a transition and which a transversion?

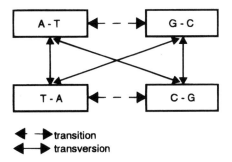

FIGURE  11.2
Transition and transversion

### a. Incorporation of base analogs

During the replication of DNA, base analogs can be incorporated at the site of the correct bases. Whereas the bases adenine (A), thymine (T), guanine (G) and cytosine (C) are highly stable in their chemical composition, base analogs are usually unstable, particularly at the site of contact with their complementary partner. A good example of this is 5-bromouracil (5-BU), which, in the case of a shortage of free thymine at the moment of DNA replication, can easily bind to the DNA strand instead of thymine. 5-BU takes part in the typical Watson–Crick base-pair formation, just like thymine, and thus binds to adenine. However, 5-BU readily changes from the keto form to the enol form (*keto–enol tautomerism*) after which it no longer binds to adenine but to guanine (Figure 11.3 and 11.4). If this transition from the keto to the enol form coincides with the moment of replication, then guanine will be incorporated instead of adenine. At the next DNA duplication, the guanine will bind to its complementary base, i.e. cytosine. In other words, a transition of an A-T base pair to a G-C base pair has taken place in the DNA strand. The premutagenic mutation (incorporation of 5-BU) has thus become permanent (*mutation fixation*) after two successive DNA syntheses. One of the two daughter cells has thus acquired a fixed point mutation which can no longer be restored by the *DNA repair mechanism* (see Section 5). Whether this genotypic mutation is expressed phenotypically, depends on the nature of the mutation.

Another base analog often used to induce mutations is 2-aminopurine, an analog of adenine.

### b. Chemical changes in (normal) bases

Bases can be altered, for example by hydroxylamine and nitrous acid. Treatment of adenine with nitrous acid causes deamination of the former, that is, the amino group (-NH$_2$) is replaced by a hydroxyl group (-OH), so that a hypoxanthine is formed (Figure 11.5). In DNA replication the hypoxanthine behaves like guanine and will thus bind to cytosine. At the following replication the cytosine

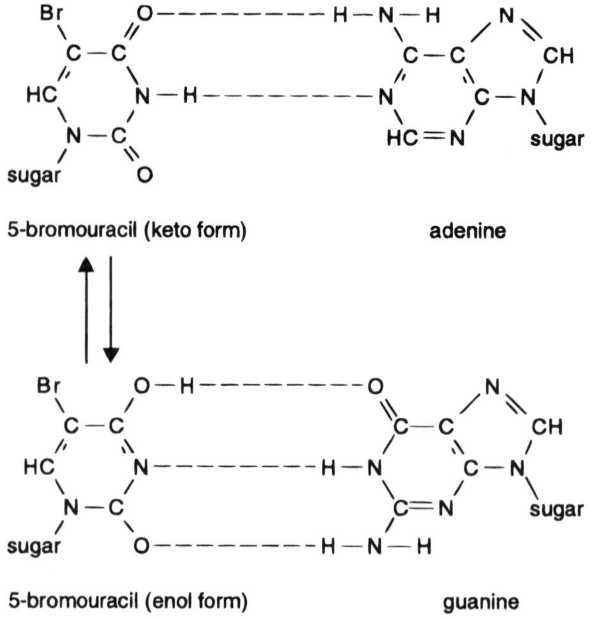

*Keto–enol tautomerism*

FIGURE   11.3
Keto–enol tautomerism of 5-bromouracil

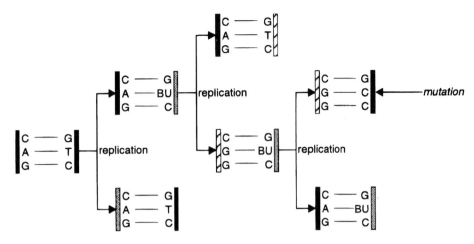

FIGURE 11.4
Mechanism of base-substitution by incorporation of 5-bromouracil

will bind to guanine, which means that here too a transition will take place, of an A-T base pair to a G-C base pair. Treatment with nitrous acid converts cytosine to uracil (a base of RNA). The uracil will bind to adenine, which makes this an example of the transition of a C-G base pair to a T-A base pair. Hydroxylamine only reacts with the pyrimidines in the DNA. It attacks the amino group of cytosine, thereby transforming the amino group to hydroxylimine (= N-OH) (Figure 11.6). This modified base ($N_4$-hydroxycytosine) preferentially binds to adenine, resulting in a transition of the C-G base pair to a T-A base pair.

ASSIGNMENT 11.2

Arrange in a diagram (using the model in Figure 11.4) the various steps necessary to arrive at a fixed mutation by modification of cytosine by hydroxylamine.

c. *Binding of chemicals to bases*

*Alkylation of bases*

Base-pair substitutions can also be achieved by *alkylation* of the bases. Alkylating chemical substances constitute the largest group of mutagenic agents. Highly potent alkylating agents are: mustard gas, dimethylsulfonic acid, diethylsulfonic acid, methylmethanesulfonic acid (MMS), ethylmethane sulfonic acid (EMS), N–methyl–N–nitro–N–nitrosoguanidine (MNNG) and epoxides. These mutagens usually alkylate at the $N^7$ position of guanine and, to a lesser extent, at the $N^3$ position of adenine and the $O^6$ position of guanine (see Figure 11.7). Figure 11.8 shows the ethylation of guanine at the 6 position by EMS. As a result, the alkylated guanine binds to thymine instead of to cytosine. A further example of this type of mutation is found in mustard gas.

Mustard gas causes alkylation of G so that it will no longer bind exclusively to its specific partner C, but also bind to T (Figure 11.9). In the next DNA replication, T will join up with A, so that a transition has taken place from G–C to A–T.

Mutations may also be induced by binding of relatively large compounds to the DNA bases resulting in so-called 'bulky adducts'. A good example of this type of compound is given by the polycyclic aromatic hydrocarbons (PAH), of which benz[a]pyrene (BP) is the most extensively studied representative. Studies on the metabolism of BP have demonstrated that a specific metabolite of BP, 7,8-dihydrodiol-9,10-epoxide (BPDE), is the major mutagenic and carcinogenic

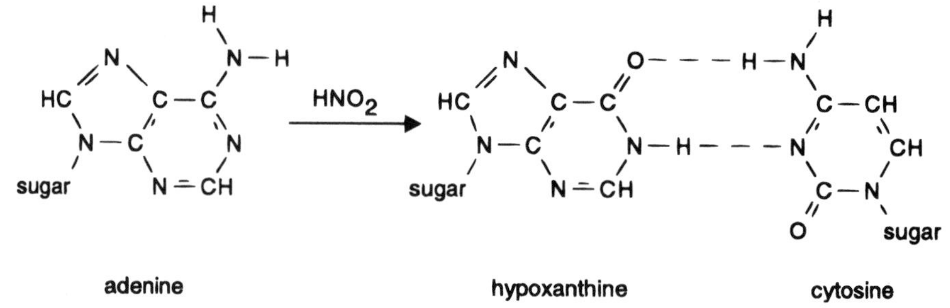

FIGURE 11.5
Chemical modification of a base (adenine) by nitrous acid

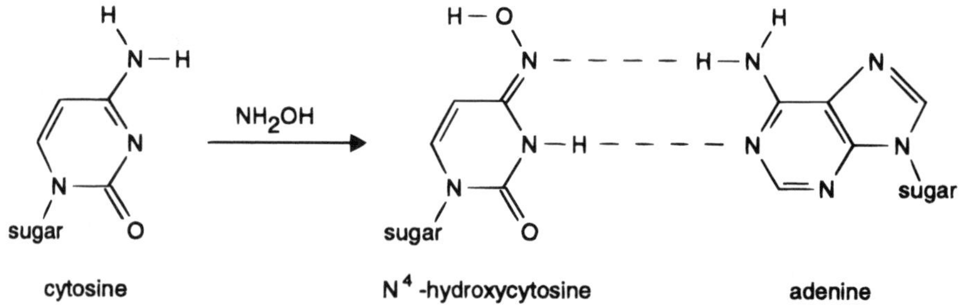

FIGURE 11.6
Chemical modification of a base (cytosine) by hydroxylamine

product. This reactive intermediate reacts mainly with the amino group of G, resulting in a covalent bond between C-atom 10 of BP and the N-atom of G (Figure 11.10). The single-point mutations that arise this way are mainly G-C to T-A transversions.

### d. Spontaneous base modification

Although the DNA bases are chemically stable, it is possible that under physiological conditions certain spontaneous modifications occur. Comparable to the keto–enol tautomerism of 5-bromouracil, which eventually results in a transition of an A–T to a G–C base pair (Figure 11.3), it is possible that base pairs are formed between enol-T and G, or between imino-C and A (Figure 11.6). This results in a transversion from T–A to C–G and from C–G to T–A base pairs respectively. Apart from deamination by nitrous acid, spontaneous deamination of C may also result in the formation of U and thereby a U-A base pair. Spontaneous loss of purine or pyrimidine bases may result in mutations (usually A is automatically incorporated at these sites) and DNA strand breaks.

### 3.1.2 Addition and deletion of bases

There is another mutation mechanism, by which a base is either removed (*deletion*) (Figure 11.11b) or inserted between two bases (*addition*) (Figure 11.11c). Deletion or addition of bases during DNA replication may arise spontaneously or may be caused by mutagenesis. It is also possible that during the repair of DNA damage, which is theoretically error-free, deletion or addition of bases occurs. This would completely alter the genetic information from the point of mutation onward (Figure 11.11). Such mutations are also known as *frameshift mutations*.

*Frameshift mutation*

Deletions or additions of bases usually have more drastic consequences for the gene and its translation to a protein than base-pair substitutions. When a

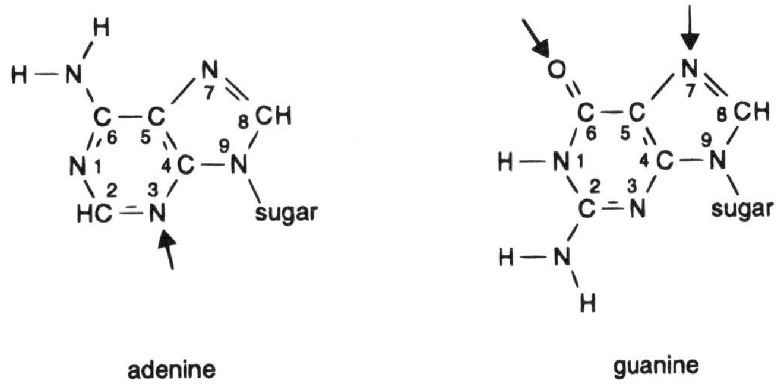

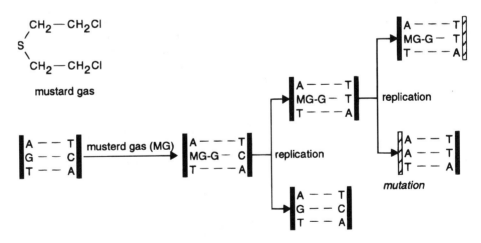

adenine

guanine

FIGURE 11.7
Alkylation sites in guanine and adenine for ethylmethane sulfonic acid (EMS), methylmethane sulfonic acid (MMS) and N-methyl-N-nitro-N-nitrosoguanidine (MNNG)

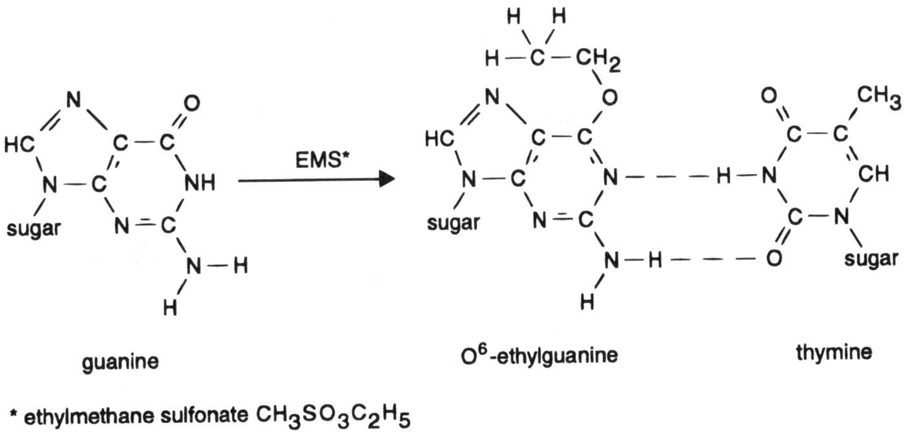

guanine

EMS*

$O^6$-ethylguanine

thymine

\* ethylmethane sulfonate $CH_3SO_3C_2H_5$

FIGURE 11.8
Binding of an ethyl group originating from EMS to guanine

mustard gas

mustard gas (MG)

replication

replication

mutation

FIGURE 11.9
Mechanism of base-substitution by alkylation with mustard gas

substitution affects a single codon, deletion or addition changes all codons following the site of mutation. *Deletion* of a base causes a base of the next codon to be incorporated when the new codon is transcribed. In the case of *addition* of a base, one of the codon's own bases is incorporated in the following codon. Such

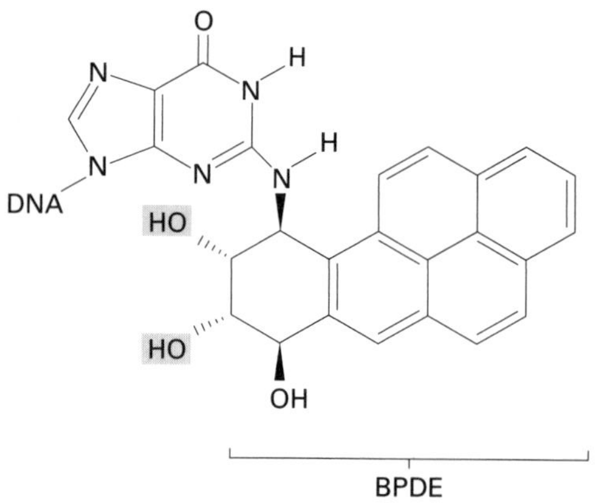

FIGURE  11.10
Benzo[a]pyrene DNA adduct
[(benzo[a]pyrene-desoxy-guanosine (BP-dG)]

mutations usually lead to substantially altered or even inactive proteins. The chemical substances which cause frameshift mutations are usually characterized by large molecules.

> ASSIGNMENT  11.3
>
> Why would molecules causing frameshift mutations usually be characterized by a large molecular structure?

Acridines, which are antibacterial agents, are the best-known frameshift mutagens. They intercalate between the bases of the DNA helix. Proflavin (Figure 11.12) is commonly used for the experimental induction of frameshift mutations.

*Phenylketonuria*

A classic example of a gene mutation (in this case a frameshift mutation) is *phenylketonuria*. This disease consists of a congenital disorder in the metabolism of the amino acid phenylalanine. Phenylketonuria is attributable to the inactivity or absence of an enzyme which, in normal individuals, converts phenylalanine to tyrosine. Due to the absence of this enzyme, progressively larger quantities of phenylalanine and phenylpyruvic acid (a derivative of phenylalanine) accumulate in the body of the infant. This causes severe disorders in the central nervous system.

> ASSIGNMENT  11.4
>
> Figure 11.11 shows a deletion (b) and an addition (c) of a base. Explain what happens if the deletion (b) and addition (c) are incorporated in the same sequence of bases.

### 3.2  STRUCTURAL CHROMOSOMAL ABERRATIONS

*Definition*

Structural chromosomal aberrations arise from breakages, deletions, exchanges and rearrangements of the chromosomal material during the cell cycle. In most cases, interaction with DNA is required to produce a clastogenic (or chromosome-damaging) effect. *Chromosomal aberration* means that a piece of chromosomal material (i.e. genetic information) ends up at a different location in the same or in a different chromosome, is lost or, conversely, is present in excess (amplification). Many chromosomal aberrations are therefore lethal to the cell. The places where breaks or exchanges occur are usually not randomly distributed over the chromosome. At the break point, fusion can take place between

| codon | reading direction of the DNA | | | | | | | | |
|---|---|---|---|---|---|---|---|---|---|
| | 1 | 2 | 3 | 4 | 5 | 6 | 7 | 8 | 9 |
| a | ATG<br>TAC | AGC<br>TCG | CGC<br>GCG | ACG<br>TGC | TCT<br>AGA | GAT<br>CTA | ATG<br>TAC | CTA<br>GAT | CGT<br>GCA |
| b | ATG<br>TAC | AGC<br>TCG | CGA ↓<br>GCT | CGT<br>GCA | CTG<br>GAC | ATA<br>TAT | TGC<br>ACG | TAC<br>ATG | GT<br>CA |
| c | ATG<br>TAC | AGC<br>TCG | CGC<br>GCG | ACG<br>TGC | TCT<br>AGA | GAT<br>CTA | AAT ↓<br>TTA | GCT<br>CGA | ACG T<br>TGC A |

FIGURE  11.11
Mechanism of frameshift mutation by deletion (b) or addition (c) of bases as compared to the original DNA (a)

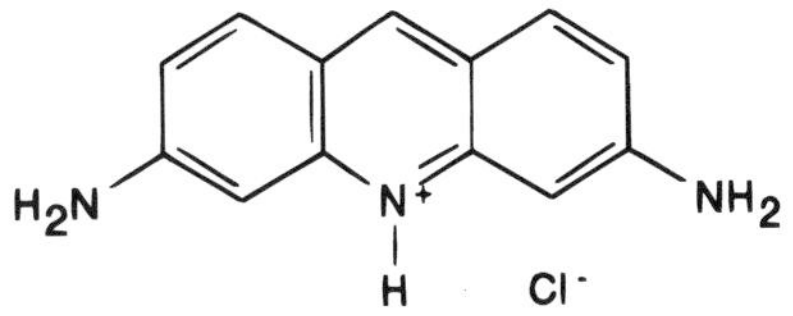

FIGURE  11.12
Chemical structure of proflavin

the separated fragments; the break points are, as it were, sticky, so that they stick to nearby chromosome fragments. Consequently, most breaks pass unnoticed. If the breaks are not repaired, the cell can only stay alive until the next cell division. The fused chromosome parts or fragments may contain a centromere or may be acentric.

Acentric chromosomes cannot be transported along the tubulin fibers, and this inevitably leads to the loss of genes that are necessary for the cell's survival. Fusion of two centric fragments from two chromosomes causes formation of bicentric chromosomes, which also results in cell death. Structural chromosomal aberrations can be further divided into two types: the *chromatid* type (one of the two chromatids showing aberration) and the *chromosome* type (both chromatids of a chromosome showing aberration).

### 3.2.1 Chromatid type abnormalities

The following abnormalities may be distinguished in this category (see Figure 11.13).

*Chromatid gap*

Isochromatid gap: a gap exists in both chromatids.
*Chromatid breakage*
*Chromatid deletion*

a. *Chromatid gap*; the non-stained part of the chromatid is no larger than the diameter of the chromatid and does, in fact, simply consists of an achromatic portion of the chromatid.

b. *Chromatid breakage and chromatid deletion*; the chromatid breakage can be distinguished from the chromatid gap in that the non-stained part of the chromatid is larger than the diameter of the chromatid. The piece of chromatid may still lie parallel to the other chromatid or be dispersed among the chromosomes.

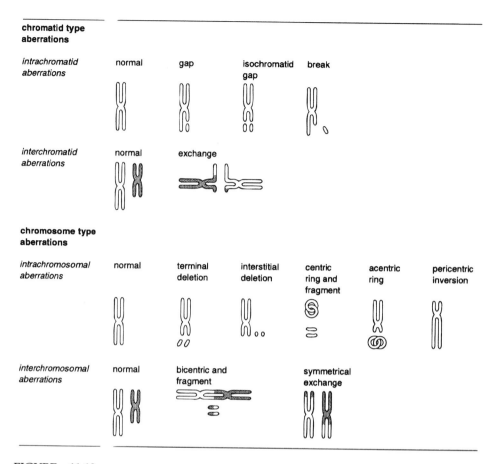

FIGURE   11.13
Schematic representation of chromosome type and chromatid type aberrations

*Chromatid exchanges*

    c.   *Chromatid exchanges*; breaks, and exchanges between chromatids can give rise to symmetrical and asymmetrical shapes.

### 3.2.2 Chromosome type aberrations

This group includes the following (see Figure 11.13)

*Terminal deletions*

    a.   *Terminal deletions'*: chromosomal material is split off at the end of both chromatids at homologous places resulting in the formation of two chromatid fragments.

*Interstitial deletions*

    b.   *Interstitial deletions*: paired acentric chromatid fragments which are smaller than the fragments in terminal deletions.

*Centric ring chromosomes*

    c.   *Centric ring chromosomes*: chromatid segments with centromeres which have joined to form a ring.

*Acentric ring chromosomes*

    d.   *Acentric chromosomes*: ring chromosomes without a centromere.

*Pericentric inversions*

    e.   *Pericentric inversions*: splitting of chromosomes with reunion of the separated chromosome fragments at the other end of the chromosome.

*Asymmetrical exchange*

    f.   *Asymmetrical exchange*: fusion of two or more chromosome fragments resulting in the formation of acentric chromosome fragments and bicentric or polycentric chromosomes.

*Symmetrical exchange*

    g.   *Symmetrical exchange*: fusion of a centric chromosome fragment with an acentric fragment from another chromosome. These exchanges are also referred to as *reciprocal translocations* and cannot be distinguished from normal chromosomes with conventional cytological staining techniques.

ASSIGNMENT  11.5

Draw a figure illustrating an asymmetrical interchromatid exchange between two chromosomes.

ASSIGNMENT  11.6

How can an interstitial deletion be distinguished from a terminal deletion?

Structural chromosomal aberrations can be observed after fixation and staining of the chromosomes during the metaphase stage of the cell cycle. Minor chromosomal aberrations are only visible after banding. Chromosomes of a particular karyotype have a banding pattern which is specific for each chromosome (Figure 11.14). Hence, small-scale exchanges of portions of the chromosome (such as translocations) can be detected.

## Intermezzo

*Banding of chromosomes*
Using cytological staining techniques, the chromatin pattern that is specific for each chromosome type can be made visible. To this end, the microscopic cell preparation is stained, after pretreatment with salt and heating, by the so-called Romanowsky–Giemsa stain. This method originates from hematology but is also widely applied in cytology and histology. The Romanowsky–Giemsa stain contains two dyes: Azure B and Eosin Y. The former binds to the phosphate groups of the DNA in the chromosomes. The stained portions show up as bands, which are specific for each chromosome. Bands can also be obtained using Azure B on its own, i.e. without Eosin. In that case the bands are stained purple instead of red. Based on these specific staining patterns, chromatids or fragments

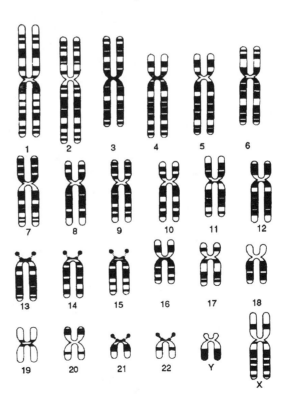

FIGURE  11.14
Chromosomal typing using stained bands
The cell is in metaphase

can be identified, and may indicate whether and where exchanges have occurred and where certain transposed fragments originate from.

Examples of genetic diseases resulting from structural chromosomal aberrations include the Philadelphia chromosome and the "cri du chat" syndrome. In the case of the Philadelphia chromosome (the name derives from the city where it was first found), a portion of the long arm of chromosome 22 is translocated to chromosome 9. This aberration is seen in the bone-marrow cells of about 90% of the patients with chronic myeloid leukemia. Children with 'cri du chat' syndrome have malformations, suffer from impeded growth and emit a cat-like cry (which explains the French name 'cri du chat'). This syndrome is due to the absence of a portion of the short arm of chromosome 5.

## 3.3    GENOME MUTATIONS

*Euploidy*

Genome mutations (also known as numerical chromosomal aberrations) involve a change in the number of chromosomes. The term *euploidy* refers to a multiple of the complete set of chromosomes (monoploid or haploid: $n$; diploid: $2n$; triploid: $3n$; etc.). If numerical changes only occur in some chromosomes and the total number of chromosomes is not changed, this is known as *aneuploidy*. Aneuploidy is the result of the loss of a damaged chromosome during cell division (i.e. the primary cause is a chromosomal aberration) or of irregular distribution (nondisjunction) of the chromatids over the two daughter cells during cell division (Figure 11.15). Under normal circumstances, the two homologues of a chromosome pair separate during meiosis in such a way that each daughter cell acquires half the number of chromosomes from the mother cell. However, if both homologues of a chromosome pair go to the same cell, this cell receives 24 chromosomes instead of the usual 23. If this abnormal gamete acquires 23 chromosomes at fertilization, its total number of chromosomes will be 47. Although the mechanisms which cause aneuploidy in mitotic and meiotic cells may be different, yet, in either case, the aneuploidy is caused by a fault in the cell-division mechanism. Potential targets for aneuploidy induction are the nuclear spindle microtubules, centromeres, regulating proteins, cytoplasmic membranes, DNA, centrioles and centrosomes. Well-known inhibitors of nuclear spindles are *colchicine, vinblastine, vincristine* and *taxol*, which means that these substances are potentially mutagenic.

*Aneuploidy*

Humans appear to have an unnaturally high aneuploidy frequency, which is considerably increased by several environmental factors. 0.5% of all newborns display aneuploidy, in which chromosomes 13, 18, 21 and the sex chromosomes are particularly involved. At conception, the aneuploidy frequency is even higher: about 16%. At that stage, other chromosomes than those mentioned above can also be involved. Three weeks after fertilization, the frequency drops to between 5 and 10%, as a result of spontaneous abortion of non-viable embryos. The carriers of genome mutations usually show obvious physical, intellectual and behavioral abnormalities. The most important genome abnormalities will be discussed below.

*Down's syndrome*

### 3.3.1 Autosomal abnormalities

*Down's syndrome*: this abnormality arises from a *trisomy of chromosome 21*. Characteristics associated with Down's syndrome are physical abnormalities as well as physical and mental growth retardation. In living newborns, Down's syndrome is the most common autosomal abnormality, occurring in 1 out of 600 children.

*Patau syndrome*
congenital = existing at birth

*Patau syndrome or trisomy of chromosome 13*: carriers of this syndrome show various congenital abnormalities, including deafness, serious eye problems, harelip

a
*normal distribution of chromosomes*

b
*unequal distribution of chromosomes*

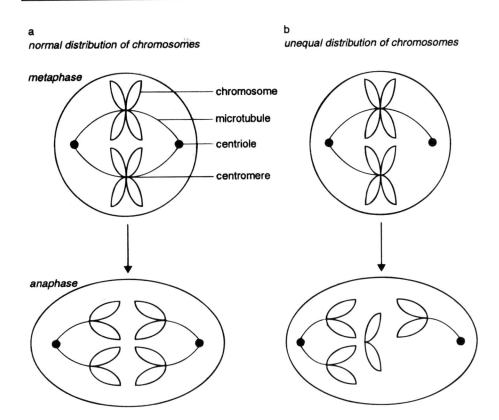

FIGURE   11.15
Schematic representation of nondisjunction by disruption of the microtubulin function

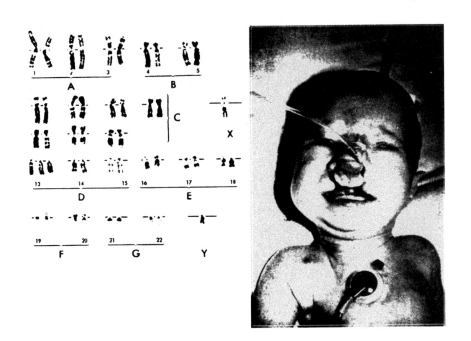

FIGURE   11.16
Patau syndrome
The karyotype of trisomy for chromosome 13 is shown on the left. On the right, a child suffering from trisomy of chromosome 13.

*Edward's syndrome*

and polydactyly. The babies usually die within 6 months (see Figure 11.16). In those few who survive for more than 1 year, mental retardation has been observed. *Edward's syndrome or trisomy of chromosome 18*: this syndrome is also characterized by manifold congenital abnormalities, including frequent cardiac defects. 30% of the children with this syndrome die during the first month after birth and 50% during the second, while 10% survive to the age of 1. Those who do reach their first birthday are severely mentally handicapped.

*Turner's syndrome*

### 3.3.2 Sex chromosome aberrations

*Turner's syndrome*; the number of chromosomes in females with this syndrome is 45, consisting of 44 autosomes and one X chromosome (sex chromosomes in karyotype XO instead of XX). This syndrome is characterized by the absence, or very poor development, of gonads in females. The excretory ducts and external genitals are female.

*Klinefelter's syndrome*

*Klinefelter's syndrome*; the number of chromosomes is 47 instead of 46, which is attributable to an extra X chromosome (karyotype XXY instead of XY). The gonad is a testis, in which the seminiferous tubules are incompletely developed. The excretory ducts and external sex organs are male.

### Summary

The three main classes of genetic changes that can be distinguished are gene mutations, structural chromosomal aberrations and numerical chromosomal aberrations. Given the major influence of each of these genetic abnormalities on human well-being, it is important for chemical substances to be investigated for their mutagenicity. Although this can often not be shown directly, it appears that an increased mutagenic pressure may be the result of the presence of a larger number of mutagens in the environment.

## 4    Conversion of mutations to altered proteins

Figure 11.17 shows how a base-pair substitution is translated to become a mutant. Protein synthesis proceeds in two major steps. First, a sequence of codons from one of the two DNA strands is transcribed to single-stranded messenger RNA (mRNA). The information carried by the mRNA is then decoded on the ribosomes per codon and translated into an amino acid. At the same time, the amino acids are linked to each other, thus forming a protein.

Supposing the transition GC to AT has taken place in the DNA, and this change is then transcribed to the RNA. Thus the mRNA contains a CAU codon instead of a CGU codon. This CAU codon of the mRNA binds to the transfer RNA which carries GTA as anticodon. The CAU codon codes for histidine instead of arginine, a mutation which changes the configuration of the protein. Usually, as a result of this, the enzymatic function of the protein is altered as well. Examples of gene mutations include the different variations in hemoglobin, such as sickle-cell anemia.

## 5    DNA repair

*DNA repair*

All modifications in DNA can be considered as potential mutations. Some of these modifications can lead to cell death or loss of the ability to divide, which puts the mutated cell at a disadvantage. They can lead to the formation of tumors which is harmful to the individual whose body contains the mutated cell. Fortunately, not all abnormalities are expressed. The cells dispose of *DNA repair mechanisms* that will attempt to repair the modifications in the DNA. They do so either in an error-free or a nearly error-free way, or in a mutation-inducing way. It can be stated that DNA modifications, for example induced by mutagens

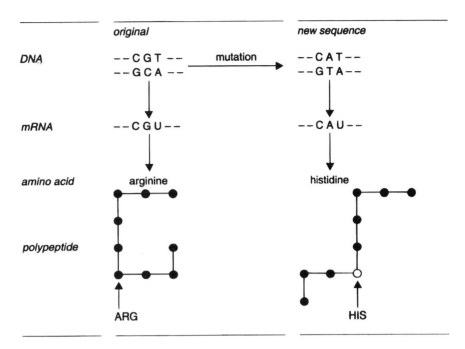

FIGURE   11.17
Consequences of a point mutation

*Error-free repair*

that alter DNA coding by alkylation, can usually be repaired without error via mechanisms that involve reconstructing enzymes (*error-free repair*).

ASSIGNMENT   11.7

Why is it initially more appropriate to refer to premutagenic modifications rather than mutations?

*Excision repair mechanisms*

Of the many types of DNA-repair mechanism, only the excision repair mechanism will be discussed here. Premutagenic modifications in mammals as well as in bacteria are repaired either by removal of the modified nucleotides, or by the removal of the modified bases. This will prevent the induction of single point mutations. The repair mechanisms described below are in essence the same for mammals as for microorganisms, but there are differences between both groups with regard to the enzymes involved.

### 5.1   REMOVAL OF MODIFIED NUCLEOTIDES

This type of DNA repair is the least specific, and is primarily involved in the repair of structural defects, such as the occurrence of thymidine dimers and bulky adducts. The modified nucleotide is first recognized, after which an endonuclease makes an incision in the vicinity of or next to the modified nucleotide (Figure 11.18a). Subsequently, a number of nucleotides are cut loose from their *Excision* phosphodiester bonds (*excision*) by an exonuclease. In the first instance, the repair synthesis of the excised DNA is the work of a polymerase which inserts new nucleotides; a ligase then closes the strand. The new nucleotides are complementary to the intact part of the other strand.

The larger the capacity for DNA repair and the more time there is available for the repair of the DNA modifications, the lower the number of *premutagenic* *Premutagenic modifications* *modifications* (modifications that are not fixed yet) will be at the moment of the next DNA replication. Some repair mechanisms tend to repair the larger DNA

331

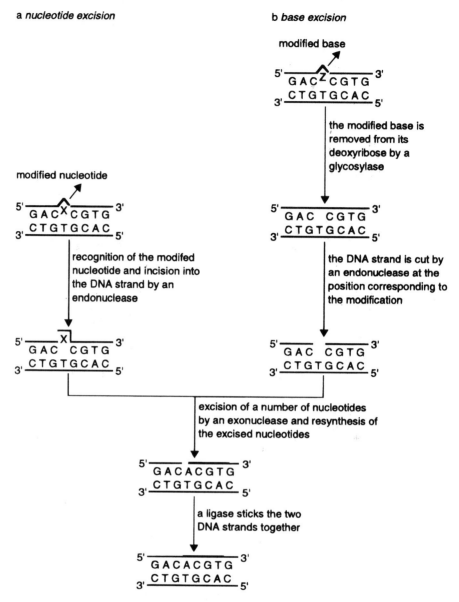

FIGURE 11.18
DNA repair mechanism by removal of modified nucleotides (a) and bases (b)

*Error-prone repair*

modifications in an error-inducing way (*error-prone repair*). These newly induced mutations can be considered as the price the cell has to pay for its survival. Survival thus takes priority over the prevention of mutations. All known repair mechanisms have been studied in microorganisms. This does not necessarily mean that the same repair mechanisms are also available to higher organisms. Nonetheless, there are several arguments which allow the assumption that identical or similar systems exist in higher organisms.

A strong argument for an important role of DNA repair in the prevention of tumors is found in individuals suffering from xeroderma pigmentosum. These patients show a severe deficiency in the DNA repair system and have a high incidence of skin tumors as a result of exposure to UV radiation which is part of the spectrum of sunlight. One of the major photoproducts induced in the DNA after absorption of UV radiation is the cyclobutane pyrimidine dimer. This dimer will be formed between two neighboring pyrimidines (primarily thymine) in the same strand by formation of a new bond between the 5 and 6 position of the pyrimidine rings (see figure 11.19). In healthy individuals, these dimers will be removed by nucleotide excision repair (see figure 11.18). Xeroderma pigmentosum patients, however, have a defect in the first steps of the excision repair, resulting in the persistence of the dimers, ultimately resulting in mutations and induction of tumors.

## 5.2  REMOVAL OF MODIFIED BASES

This system only removes the modified base from the DNA, and is primarily found for the removal of small alkyl adducts and uracil. First, the modified base is detached from its deoxyribose by a highly specific N-glycosylase (Figure 11.18b). This leaves an apurine or apyrimidine site (AP site). Next, the modified DNA strand is cut at the site of the modification by an endonuclease specific for AP sites (AP endonuclease). Subsequently, the repair synthesis proceeds in the same way as described for nucleotide excision.

DNA modifications can also be rectified by a direct repair mechanism. This implies that during repair, the DNA base or nucleotide itself will not be removed. An example is given by the action of the enzyme $O^6$-alkylguanine alkyltransferase, which is present in high concentrations in mammalian cells. This enzyme repairs damage to the DNA which has been induced by alkylating agents, by removal of the alkyl group at the $O^6$ position of guanine and the $O^4$ position of thymine. During dealkylation, the alkyl group is transferred to the cysteine acceptor site of the enzyme. As indicated above, if unrepaired, the $O^6$ methylguanine will form a base pair with thymine during the next replication cycle.

*Error-prevention systems*

In addition to repair mechanisms, there are also *error-prevention systems*. These systems do not repair DNA damage (induced by mutagens) but check on the replication DNA. As a result, bases that are incorrectly paired during replication can be removed and replaced by the correct bases.

### Summary

A cell will always try to repair damage to its DNA. Some repair mechanisms repair the damage in an error-free manner while other mechanisms induce errors in the process. DNA damage is repaired by removing modified nucleotides or bases.

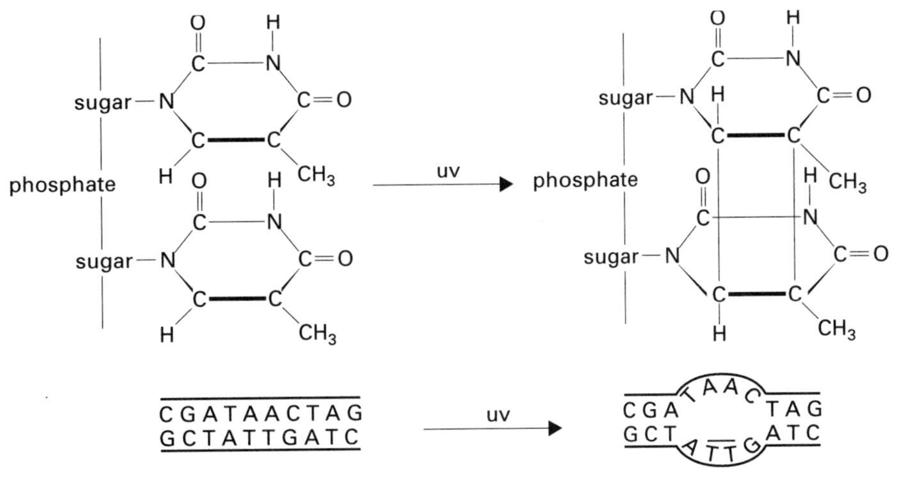

FIGURE   11.19
Structure of a thymidine dimer (upper part) and disturbance of the DNA helix (lower part) as a result of the presence of a dimer

## 6    Mutagenicity tests

Since the human gene pool is our most precious heritage, it is vital to keep the mutagenic pressure as low as possible. The high correlation between mutagenic and carcinogenic properties of chemical substances and our inability to cure mutations urgently cause scientists to detect mutagenic chemicals. Various scientific disciplines, such as genetics, biochemistry and cell biology, have started to develop short-term tests to detect mutagens and carcinogens. More than 100 tests are currently available, using a wide range of organisms. *In vitro* tests are carried out employing bacteria, bacteriophages, mammalian cells and human cells. Fruit flies, mammals and human beings themselves are being used in *in vivo* tests.

For some tests (including the bacterial reversion test), enough experience and reproducibility of results have been reached, so that they are now generally accepted as being reliable. But there is (still) no question of there being one single test that can detect all mutagenic effects with a high degree of sensitivity. Each test system, *in vitro* as well as *in vivo*, has its weaknesses and often its specific sensitivities (or even hypersensitivities), which are only partly known yet. This entails the risk of false-positive or false-negative results. This risk of erroneous results and conclusions will have to be reduced as much as possible and this can only be achieved by employing a combination of different tests in a test battery. Nowadays a number of very rapid and well-evaluated *in vitro* test systems is also used as screening tests for the detection of carcinogenic potency. The value of mutagenicity tests in detecting carcinogenic substances is determined on the basis of three criteria:

*Sensitivity, specificity and predictive value*

$$\text{sensitivity} = \frac{\text{number of carcinogens positive in the test}}{\text{total number of carcinogens in the test}}$$

$$\text{specificity} = \frac{\text{number of non-carcinogens negative in the test}}{\text{total number of non-carcinogens in the test}}$$

$$\text{predictive value} = \frac{\text{number of carcinogens positive in the test}}{\text{total number of positive carcinogens in the test}}$$

In those cases where the sensitivity indicates the actual *positive* fraction (correctly detected carcinogens), the specificity indicates the actual *negative* fraction (correctly detected non-carcinogens). The predictive value strongly depends on the number of carcinogens in the series of substances tested. In using these criteria, it is very important to consider how carcinogenicity is defined. Also, the quality of the data on which the classification of carcinogenic and non-carcinogenic is based, is important.

Probably the best-known mutagenicity test is the 'Ames test', in which certain bacterial strains of *Salmonella typhimurium* are used. These strains have been selected by Ames, and due to a specific mutation, require histidine in their culture media for normal growth. However, when by addition of a mutagenic substance to the medium the DNA is mutated at the same locus, these bacteria regain the capability to produce histidine. Therefore called *back-mutations* or *reversions*. The revertants will form visible colonies on histidine-deficient agar plates within a few days. The number of colonies per plate is a measure for the mutagenic potential of the test compound. The choice of a specific strain will determine the sensitivity of the test. For instance, some strains are more sensitive to the induction of single point mutations (e.g. strain TA 100), while others are more sensitive to frameshift mutations (TA 98). Furthermore, strains have been selected with diminished DNA repair capacity, showing a low repair rate. The sensitivity of these strains is therefore relatively high.

*Indirect mutagens and carcinogens*

Many chemical agents are not mutagenic or carcinogenic themselves, but are activated through metabolic processes to become mutagenic or carcinogenic agents. Such substances are known as *indirect mutagens* and *carcinogens*. Since test systems using microorganisms or mammalian cells *in vitro* do not, or insufficiently, possess the necessary enzyme systems (except for rat hepatocytes), enzyme extracts (the so-called *S9 fraction*) have to be added to these test systems.

*S9 fraction*
The S9 fraction is an extract

This S9 fraction mainly consists of enzymes from liver microsomes, and is prepared by collecting the supernatant after centrifugation at 9,000 g of homogenized (rat) liver. This S9 fraction is not 100% representative of the intact liver and can only attempt to imitate *in vivo* processes as close as possible. These enzyme extracts are prepared from rat, mouse or hamster liver. The metabolic activity of the S9 fractions is enhanced by strongly increasing the liver activity of the animals. This is achieved by treating the animals beforehand with enzyme-inducing substances such as phenobarbital or a mixture of polychlorobiphenyls, of which Aroclor 1254 is the most commonly used.

It must be borne in mind that:

1. the S9 fraction is not fully representative of the intact liver;

2. not all chemicals are converted in the liver; conversion may also occur in the lung or kidney;

3. in the liver, chemicals can also be converted into inactive metabolites;

4. there are differences between various animal species and human beings as far as metabolic transformation is concerned;

5. activation or deactivation can also be the work of non-microsomal enzymes.

In order to come to a useful and convenient classification of tests, the four large groups are defined here according to the genetic effects that can be measured. Table 11.1 provides an overview and a concise description of the most common mutagenicity tests.

*Primary damage to DNA*

The first group of tests detects *primary damage to DNA*. These tests indirectly measure whether any DNA damage has occurred in the cell. In principle, such damage can lead to mutations. As an example, the *sister chromatid exchange test* (SCE-test) will be described. This test is based on the detection of reciprocal exchanges between the sister chromatids of chromosomes. The mechanism underlying the exchange has not yet been elucidated. The exchange is thought to require a chromosome break, possibly with DNA repair processes playing a role. The aberrations associated with chromosome breaks may differ from each other. The exchange of chromatids can only be observed if the two sister chromatids can be distinguished from each other by differential staining. Theoretically, the test can be carried out with a wide variety of different cell types. In practice, however, Chinese hamster ovary cells and human lymphocytes are the most frequently used. The cells are allowed to grow for some time in the presence of the thymidine analog bromodeoxyuridine (BrdU). BrdU is then incorporated into the newly synthesized DNA instead of thymidine. In cells which have passed through two cycles of DNA synthesis in the presence of BrdU, exchanges can be observed, because the chromatids of one chromosome have incorporated different amounts of BrdU. Extinction of the fluorescence of the chromium dye by bromine enables detection. Preparations are then scanned for chromosomes with different amounts of BrdU in both chromatids. An impression of the sensitivity of the test technique can be obtained by staining preparations of the same cell culture for conventional chromosome analysis as well as detection of sister chromatid exchanges (see also Figure 11.20).

*Gene mutation tests*

The second group is also the largest, and consists of the *gene mutation tests*. The above described Ames test belongs to this category. With tests of the third

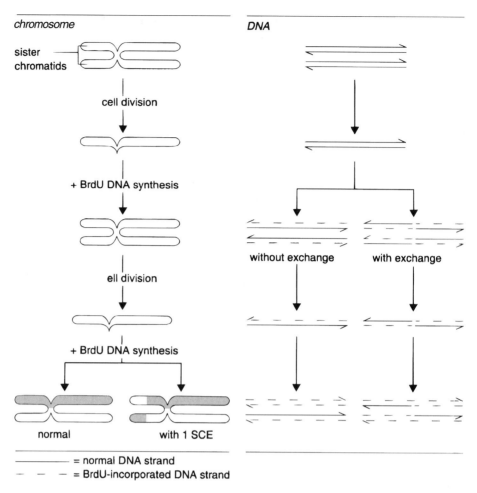

chromosome

DNA

sister
chromatids

cell division

+ BrdU DNA synthesis

ell division

without exchange          with exchange

+ BrdU DNA synthesis

normal          with 1 SCE

———— = normal DNA strand
– – – – = BrdU-incorporated DNA strand

FIGURE 11.20
Visualization of sister chromatid exchange

*Chromosomal aberrations*

group *chromosomal aberrations* are detected in eukaryotes. This group includes tests for both structural and numerical chromosomal aberrations.

An example of this category of mutagenicity test is the micronucleus assay. In contrast to the SCE test, in this assay the chromosomes are not studied in the metaphase but in interphase nuclei. Chromosome fragments without centromere, which may arise from chromosome breaks, are sometimes found outside of the nucleus in one of the daughter cells since these fragments lack an attachment site for the microtubules. After the cell cycle is completed, the extranuclear DNA fragment will decondensate and form a so-called micronucleus. The number of these micronuclei per (for instance) 1,000 binucleated interphase cells is a measure for the induced genotoxic damage.

*Potential for proliferation*

This last group of tests do not measure effects on DNA directly, but investigate the *potential* of chemical substances to induce *proliferation* in normal mammalian cells. Despite the fact that *in vitro* transformation tests have to be considered as short-term carcinogenicity tests rather than an indication of mutagenicity of chemicals, these tests have nevertheless been included in the table, since they form a link between mutagenesis and carcinogenesis. The poor reproducibility of these tests, however, has reduced their practical application quite considerably.

## Intermezzo

So far, short term mutagenicity tests have been discussed that do not always reflect the correct mutagenic or carcinogenic potential of a certain compound. Although these tests have been of great value for fundamental mutation research, it is impossible to compare the induction of mutations in different organs and tissues of intact organisms. Therefore it is often necessary to use laboratory animals to investigate the induction of tumors. These experiments require large numbers of animals, are time consuming and expensive, and thus not suitable for fast routine screening of large numbers of substances.

A new research method in this field applies *transgenic mice*. These mice possess a small part of foreign DNA in their genome. This DNA was inserted in the genome by micro-injection into the nucleus of a fertilized egg, which was subsequently implanted into a pseudo-pregnant mouse (a female mouse which has mated with a sterile male). Part of the offspring will possess the inserted DNA in all somatic and germ cells. This extra genetic information will therefore be transmitted to future generations, these mouse strains are called transgenic. In order to be used in mutagenicity research, transgenic mouse strains have been developed, which contain a bacterial gene as a mutation target. The inserted DNA is a shuttle vector containing the lac Z gene of *Escherichia coli*. This vector can easily be retained from the genomic DNA by *in vitro* packaging, and can again be transferred to *E. coli*. One of the properties of the lac Z gene is the conversion of a specific substrate, X-gal, to a blue colored compound. Mutants can be selected based on the color of the bacterial colonies, since bacteria with the intact gene will be blue when grown on media containing X-gal, while bacteria containing the mutated lac Z gene remain colorless. Using this method, it is possible to expose transgenic mice to a (suspected) carcinogenic agent, which results in mutations in the genetic material of the mouse and therefore also in the lac-Z gene. After exposure, DNA can be isolated from various organs of the mouse, and transferred to *E. coli*. The mutation frequency can be determined by counting the colorless colonies. Analysis of the DNA sequence of the lac Z gene, enables the determination of the type of mutation that was induced (see Figure 11.21)

The development of transgenic mice offers great advances for carcinogenicity research. Using this method, factors which may affect the induction of mutations, like bioavailability, metabolic (in)activation, DNA-repair or cell

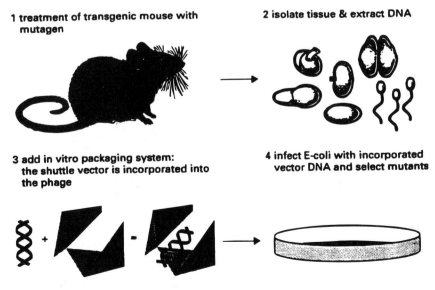

FIGURE   11.21
Mutagenicity test with transgenic mice

proliferation are all taken into account. Additionally, large numbers of animals and/or extreme high doses are no longer required for the *in vivo* determination of precarcinogenic lesions.

### Summary

So far, no single test has been developed which detects all genetic end points. It is thus necessary to investigate chemicals with a test battery which can detect all different genetic end points. Although *in vitro* tests are usually more sensitive than *in vivo* tests, it is important to include a number of *in vivo* tests in the battery, since these will reflect reality more accurately.

### 7    Is there a threshold level for mutagens?

Theoretically, there is no threshold level or no-effect level for mutagenic action. It is to be assumed that even at the lowest dose one molecule of the mutagenic substance can bind to DNA and, if this is not repaired, can cause irreversible damage. In practice, however, an experimental threshold level will be found. Only when the detoxication reactions and the repair systems are saturated, will

TABLE  11.1

Overview of some important mutagenic tests

| End point | Organism/cell | Test system | Target |
|---|---|---|---|
| | | | DNA strand |
| 1. Gene mutations | prokaryotic microbes | *Escherichia coli* | |
| —point mutation | (bacteria) | *Salmonelia typhimurium* | |
| with locus | eukaryotic microbes | *Saccharomyces cerevisiae* | |
| —multilocus deletions | (yeast/fungi) | *Neurospora crassa* | |
| | | *Aspergillus nidulans* | |
| | insects | *Drosophila melanogaster* | |
| | mammalian cells | germ cells | |
| | | somatic cells | |
| | | cell lines | |
| | | human fibroblasts | |
| | | human lymphocytes | |
| | | | Gene |
| 2. Chromosomal mutations | bacteria | *Bacillus subtilis* | |
| —numerical | | *E. coli* | |
| —structural aberrations | yeasts/fungi | *S. cerevisiae* | |
| —translocations | | *A. nidulans* | |
| —DNA damage/repair | mammalian cells *in vitro* | various cells and cell lines | |
| | | human lymphocytes | |
| | *in vivo* systems | bone marrow cells | |
| | (mouse, hamster, rat) | lymphocytes | |
| | | tissues | |
| | | | Chromosome |
| 3. Cell biology | mammalian cells *in vitro* | various cells | |
| —morphology | | cell lines | |
| —transformation | | human fibroblasts | |
| | | | Cell |
| 4. Organ neoplasia | *in vivo* systems | skin, lungs, liver, | |
| —initiation-promotion- | | bladder, mammary | |
| progression | | gland, gastro-intestinal | |
| | | tract | Organ |

Modified from De la Iglesia *et al.*, 1980

*Experimental threshold level*

there be a measurable effect (*experimental threshold level*). This effect increases proportionally to the dose (dose–response) up to a certain level, after which the effect decreases owing to complete cytotoxicity. This experimental threshold level is highly dependent on experimental conditions. Of these factors such as genetic end point, dimension of the experiment, level of the spontaneous mutation rate, whether or not repair processes are in operation, and sensitivity of the test system play an important role.

The lowest level at which an effect can be measured can hardly be regarded as a threshold level, since at that point the cellular processes will already have been disrupted to such an extent that the concept of non-toxic dose no longer applies.

### Summary

On theoretical grounds, it must be assumed that a single molecule of a mutagen is enough to induce a mutation. For that reason no non-toxic dose can be said to exist.

## 8    Relationship between mutagenicity, carcinogenicity and teratogenicity

*Teratogenicity is extensively discussed in Study units 31 and 32*

*Mutagenicity and teratogenicity*

As genes play a fundamental part in all aspects of living organisms, the concept that altered genes can lead to different diseases is becoming ever more important. It might be that toxicological end points such as *teratogenicity* and *sterility* are also controlled genetically, but there is as yet no direct evidence for this. Sometimes a relationship can be seen between mutagenic action and teratogenic effects. Spontaneous abortion is often the consequence of genetic abnormalities in the fetus. Although it is known that genotoxic substances can interfere with cell differentiation and thereby produce teratogenic effects, most teratogenic substances are not mutagenic and vice versa.

Chemicals which have a mutagenic as well as teratogenic effect include: cyclophosphamide, ethylmethane sulfonic acid, methylmethane sulfonic acid, busulfan, $NH_2$ and triethylenemelamine. The weak correlation between mutagenicity and teratogenicity is probably attributable to the fact that mutagens exert their effect in a single cell, whereas teratogenic effects require simultaneous chemical action on the differentiation of many cells during organogenesis. Contrary to mutagenicity and carcinogenicity, which are affected by genetic mechanisms (for example, point mutations and chromosomal aberrations), teratogenic effects are usually brought about by non-genetic mechanisms, such as enzyme inhibition and altered osmolarity. Interference with DNA replication, transcription, normal base incorporation, RNA transcription, and protein synthesis, none of which involve inheritable DNA alterations, can also give rise to teratogenic effects. It is thus clear that current mutagenicity tests cannot be used to detect teratogenic substances. However, tests are now being developed which use *in vitro* embryo cultures to detect, for example, molecular alterations in protein synthesis. Whether such tests can detect teratogenic substances is a question which can only be answered in the future.

*Carcinogenicity and teratogenicity*

*Carcinogenesis is discussed in detail in Study units 12 and 13*

Not much is known about the relationship between *carcinogenicity and teratogenicity*.

Administration of carcinogenic substances to a mother can cause teratogenic effects in the fetus. In some cases, the effects are not observed until much later. The teratogenic effect of the carcinogen diethylstilbestrol (DES), administered to pregnant women, only showed itself in their daughters at the age of 11.

*Mutagenicity and carcinogenicity*

As was mentioned in the introduction, the primary task of genetic toxicology is to detect mutagenic agents. But, in the second place, this branch of toxicology has an important part to play in the detection of carcinogenic substances. Factors that have contributed to using mutagenicity tests as short-term tests for carcinogenesis, are the very high costs and the extreme length of time required for long-term carcinogenicity studies. Hence the rise in the application of mutagenicity tests may render cancer studies with mutagens superfluous. When in 1973 Ames and his colleagues developed their mutagenicity test which could also detect carcinogens, the correlation between mutagens and carcinogens became apparent. The high correlation rate between mutagens and carcinogens has lent considerable support to the hypothesis that a genotoxic action underlies the oncogenic effect (somatic mutation theory).

Chemical groups such as aromatic amines, polycyclic aromatic hydrocarbons, nitrosamines and alkylating chemicals show a high correlation, while metal carcinogens, hormones and chlorinated organic molecules show a low correlation. But, although most carcinogens are also mutagenic, the reverse does not necessarily hold true. Besides large numbers of mutagenic carcinogens, there are also mutagenic non-carcinogens, such as $NaN_3$ and dichlorvos, an organophosphate. The reverse of mutagenic non-carcinogens are non-mutagenic carcinogens. This group includes many hormones or chemicals which disturb the hormonal balance. Some classification systems for carcinogens propose a distinction between genotoxic carcinogens and non-genotoxic carcinogens.

To conclude this section, Table 11.2 gives a survey in which the processes of mutagenesis, teratogenesis and carcinogenesis are compared.

## Summary

Although there is only a weak correlation between mutagenicity and teratogenicity, there is a strong correlation between mutagenic effect and carcino-

TABLE 11.2
Comparison of mutagenesis, teratogenesis and carcinogenesis (from Wilson, 1972)

| | Mutagenesis | Carcinogenesis | Teratogenesis |
|---|---|---|---|
| *time between induction and diagnosis* | next generation up to several generations or perhaps never (rare recessive mutations) | several months to many years | several weeks to months; rarely several years |
| *reversibility* | irreversible (unless immediate repair) | irreversible except in some cases by surgery or therapy | irreversible except for some cases by surgery or therapy (metabolic disorders) |
| *sensitivity* | no apparent difference between mature and immature tissue | some cancer types seem to affect especially younger individuals, in other types the opposite applies | per definition only immature tissue is sensitive; the sensitivity decreases with development |
| *characterization* | changes in amount or quality of genetic material (molecular level) | uncontrolled proliferation at cellular level | change in pattern of development at tissue and organ level |
| *target* | genetic material is usually affected at random | usually there are specific targets (e.g. bladder tumor by aromatic amines) | often with a high degree of specificity between nature of teratogen and type of malformation |
| *basic toxicological characteristics* | can be induced instantaneously (e.g. X-rays) or be caused by repeated exposure; probably no no-effect level | chronic toxicity; probably no no-effect level | acute toxicological phenomenon (only brief or immediate exposure is needed; rapid expression); apparently no no-effect level |

genicity. Little is known about the correlation between teratogenicity and carcinogenicity.

## 9    Summary

Genetic toxicology is a discipline of toxicological research, whose main objective is to safeguard the human gene pool as much as possible against the genotoxic action of chemicals. The gene pool is in fact the most precious heritage of any species and its deterioration would endanger both physical and mental well-being of the present and subsequent generations. In order to achieve the posed objective, it is necessary to identify mutagenic agents. To this end, a wide variety of genetic toxicity tests have been developed which detect primary DNA damage, gene mutations, structural chromosomal aberrations, genome mutations and transformations. Furthermore, genetic toxicology plays an important role in the analysis of biological effects of DNA modifications and cellular DNA repair capacity.

## SELF ASSESSMENT QUESTIONS

1    What are mutations and where do they occur?

2    What is the basis of natural selection and evolution?

3    Why can the occurrence of mutagenic activity in prokaryotes as well as in eukaryotes be assumed to indicate that the chemical substance is most probably mutagenic in man?

4    Why are the words 'most probably' used in question 3?

5    Why are recessive mutations a threat to the physical and mental well-being of man?

6    Is the base-pair substitution of A–T to C–G a transition or a transversion? Why?

7    How can a gap be distinguished from a break?

8    What does the following figure represent?

9    When does the incorporation of 5-BU have a drastic effect on the information encoded in DNA?

10    How do numerical chromosome aberrations arise?

11    Why is it difficult to refer to threshold levels in relation to mutagenic action?

12    Why are transformation tests considered to be atypical with regard to mutagenesis?

FEEDBACK

## 1   Answers to the assignments

11.1

11.2 Hydroxylamine.

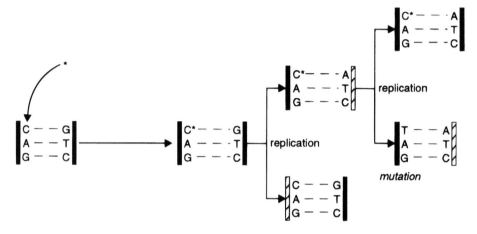

11.3 Because their large molecular structure occupies a considerable amount of space between the bases, the base which is 'pushed aside' is not read in its normal codon during the transcription of DNA. Small molecules affect the spatial arrangement to a lesser extent and the base following the intruding chemical is still read.

11.4 The deletion of a base in codon 3 causes a frameshift mutation in the subsequent codons. The addition of a base in codon 7 restores the spatial arrangement of the bases so that the subsequent codons once again correspond to the original codons.

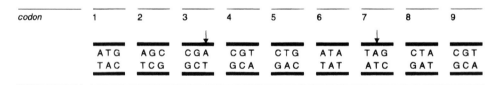

| codon | 1 | 2 | 3 | 4 | 5 | 6 | 7 | 8 | 9 |
|---|---|---|---|---|---|---|---|---|---|
| | ATG | AGC | CGA | CGT | CTG | ATA | TAG | CTA | CGT |
| | TAC | TCG | GCT | GCA | GAC | TAT | ATC | GAT | GCA |

11.5 Example of an asymmetrical interchromatid exchange:

11.6 Interstitial deletions give rise to spherical chromosome fragments, while terminal deletions yield bar-shaped chromosome fragments.

11.7 Because mutations can be repaired as long as they are not fixed by DNA replication.

11.8

    a.  If no chemically related chemicals have yet been tested for possible mutagenicity, the substance must be subjected to a battery of tests which is as comprehensive as possible, so that all genetic end points are tested.

    b.  If chemicals that are closely related have been investigated for mutagenicity, those tests can be selected which detect the mutagenic effect of that specific group of chemicals.

## 2    Answers to the self assessment questions

1    Mutations are the inheritable changes which occur unexpectedly in the carrier of the genetic material, the DNA. Changes in the genetic material can occur at the level of bases, genes, chromosomes or the total genome.

2    The key to natural selection and evolution is the DNA model, which replicates itself and changes by mutations.

3    Because the site of action of the mutagenic chemicals is the DNA. This DNA is universal, which means that it is essentially the same in all prokaryotes and eukaryotes. Moreover, the mechanisms of duplication, transcription and translation are fundamentally the same in all eukaryotes. All these similarities imply that mutagenic action in prokaryotes or eukaryotes can be extrapolated to human beings.

4    The metabolic properties of the various organisms need to be taken into account as well. Not only the differences between prokaryotes and eukaryotes, but also between the various eukaryotes there are large differences in metabolic capacities.

5    An increased frequency of recessive mutations results in inheritable genetic diseases, recessive lethal mutations and an increase in miscarriages. Since recessive mutations are only expressed in a homozygous individual, an increase in recessive mutations in a population can be carried over several generations before it becomes apparent. Many generations can thus be exposed to mutation-inducing chemicals before the effects are detected and the chemicals are banned.

6    Transversion. A purine base (A) has been substituted by a pyrimidine base (C).

7    In a gap, the unstained part of the chromatid is not larger than the diameter of the chromatid, whereas in a break, the diameter of the unstained part of the chromatid is larger than the diameter of the chromatid.

8    Symmetrical interchromatid exchange between two chromosomes without the formation of a bicentric chromosome with fragment.

9    If the premutagenic damage, in other words the incorporation of 5-BU, is not repaired by means of repair synthesis, and this is followed by two successive DNA replications, then the premutagenic damage is fixed as a mutation.

10 Numerical chromosomal aberrations generally arise due to nondisjunction, which means that the chromosomes are not equally distributed over the daughter cells.

11 Because it has to be assumed that a single molecule of a mutagenic substance can evoke a mutation.

12 Because they are considered as indication tests for carcinogenicity rather than for mutagenicity.

# Contents Study unit 12
# Introduction to carcinogenesis

0-8493-9232-2/96/$0.00 + $.50
© 1996 by CRC Press, Inc.

# Study unit 12

# Introduction to carcinogenesis

*H. Van Cauteren, Th. M. C. M. de Kok and F.-J. van Schooten*

INTRODUCTION

The history of cancer

In the history of man a number of diseases have inspired great fear. In Old Testament times leprosy was such a disease. The Middle Ages and Renaissance saw the Plague, also known as the "black death". In the nineteenth century, the most frequent cause of death in humans was tuberculosis. The twentieth century meant great breakthroughs in microbiology, in hygiene and in the development of new drugs. As a result, certain infectious diseases have been largely suppressed and nearly eradicated. Cancer has probably existed as long as multicellular organisms have. Paleontologists have shown the presence of tumors in the bones of dinosaurs, long before the advent of *Homo sapiens*. The Ancient Egyptians knew of the existence of cancer in man. There is a papyrus with a hieroglyph showing a clinical tumor. Autopsies of mummies have shown bone tumors in Egyptians. The first real descriptions of various tumors were those by Hippocrates in the 4th century B.C. He used the term "*carcinoma*", by which he meant a tumor which spreads and kills the patient. He suggested that cancer was an illness caused by too much black bile, produced by the spleen and the stomach (and not by the liver). This concept of the origin of cancer persisted for the next 200 years. Hippocrates also formulated one of the principles of cancer treatment: *primum non nocere* (first and foremost, do not cause damage). In the first century before Christ, Galen made the distinction between "*natural tumors*", such as the development of the breasts in female adolescence and "*tumors which go beyond the bounds of nature*", such as bone healing following a fracture. Finally, he described "*unnatural tumors*", which nowadays can be defined as neoplastic growth of tissue. This classification, introduced 1800 years ago, is still valid today. The views of Hippocrates and Galen have dominated medicine for many centuries. In the nineteenth century, understanding of cancer expanded enormously, primarily through intensified studies on anatomy and histology. Bichat, and later Müller, confirmed Galen's theory. They postulated the hypothesis that cancer arises from accidental tissue formation. This in turn prompted Pasteur to propose his theory of *omnis cellula et cellula*; every cell originates from another cell. Virchow demonstrated a relationship between chronic irritation and cancer. Further study led to the emergence in the nineteenth century of three hypotheses for the origin of cancer, the irritation hypothesis, the embryonic hypothesis and the parasitic hypothesis.

*Irritation hypothesis*

The *irritation hypothesis* arose from the discovery that irritation by unpurified chemicals or by radiation can cause cancer. The presence of certain ulcerations in some cases of cancer further supported this hypothesis.

347

*Embryonic hypothesis*

The second hypothesis, the *embryonic hypothesis*, was based on the argument that in rare cases birthmarks can lead to cancer, and that embryonic tumors, so-called teratomas, may occur in adults.

*Parasitic hypothesis*

The third hypothesis, the *parasitic hypothesis*, originated largely during the time of Pasteur and many other researchers. This period saw great progress in the understanding of infectious diseases. Not un-naturally, some physicians and scientists sought the origin of cancer in this direction. For example, Doven proposed the hypothesis that a bacterium, *Micrococcus neoformans*, was responsible for cancer. He reached this conclusion after isolating this organism from different types of cancer.

During the twentieth century the principal causes of cancer have been identified: chemical carcinogens and ionizing radiation. Following the discovery in the eighteenth and nineteenth centuries that coal tar causes skin cancer in humans, Yamagiwa and Ishikawa were the first to reproduce this effect in rabbits in 1915. They did this by repeatedly rubbing coal tar on the inside of rabbits' ears. A few years later, Kennaway and Hieger managed to synthesize aromatic hydrocarbons and with the first of these, dibenzo[*a,h*]anthracene, to induce skin cancer in mice. In 1933, Cook, Hewitt and Hieger identified benzo[*a*]pyrene as the carcinogenic agent in coal tar.

An analogous account can be given for the carcinogenic aromatic amines. Just before the end of the last century, in 1895, Rehn found an increased incidence of urinary bladder cancer in workers who handled particular aniline dyes. Three years later, Leichtenstern put forward his hypothesis that this bladder cancer was caused by 2-naphthylamine. In 1933, Yoshida succeeded in inducing an internal tumor in rats by oral administration of *ortho*-amino-azotoluene. Before the Second World War, several more chemical carcinogens were identified in this way. Just before, during and after the war, the mechanism underlying chemical carcinogenesis began to be understood. Berenblum, Shubik, Rous and Mottram, among others, distinguished between initiation and promotion in the development of skin cancer. Thus we arrive at recent decades. The development of oncology during this period is the main topic of the following sections.

LEARNING OBJECTIVES

After studying this unit you should be able to:

— describe the following concepts in your own words and know how to use them:
  — carcinogenicity
  — cancer
  — tumor
  — tumor initiation
  — tumor promotion
  — co-carcinogenesis
— use the standard oncological terminology for tumors correctly
— describe the processes involved in bioactivation and in interaction with DNA
— describe how endogenous and exogenous factors can influence the initiation, promotion and/or progression phases, through the use of examples.
— illustrate the role of oncogenes and tumor-suppressor genes in carcinogenesis

*Study hints*

Many medical terms are used throughout this study unit. As these may be unfamiliar to you, most are in the glossary. It is nevertheless advisable to look up these terms in a medical dictionary as well, in order to see them explained in different words. You are expected to have studied the preceding study units thoroughly. This unit links with mutagenesis (Study unit 11). The estimated study load of this unit is 4 hours.

STUDY CORE

## 1     Concepts in oncology

*Oncology*

*Oncology* is the science of the study and treatment of tumors. It is a medical specialization, and in practice, most attention is focused on the study and treatment of "malignant" tumors.

*Neoplasm or neoplasia*

A *neoplasm or neoplasia* is a relatively autonomous growth of tissue. This definition comprises several elements. The first is that of *relative autonomy*. Autonomy means that the neoplasm is no longer subject to the rules governing the interaction between *individual cells* or the intercellular tissue interactions in a living organism. The adjective "relative" denotes that a neoplasm is not fully autonomous. Normally, an intercellular signal in a particular tissue determines in an as yet unknown manner whether cells should divide or not. For example, in a skin wound, the epidermal cells will display an increased rate of division, in order to close the wound. After the wound has been sealed, this unknown signal ceases and the stimulus to cell division is switched off. The second essential element of the definition of a neoplasm is the term *growth*. Growth here means the rate of cell division. This rate may be low, which makes it difficult to distinguish the neoplasm from the surrounding tissue. Alternatively, the rate of cell division may be very high, so that the neoplasm grows to a massive size.

The third and final element of the definition is the term *tissue*. This term implies that cancer or neoplasia can, by definition, only occur in multicellular organisms, and not in unicellular organisms, such as protozoa and bacteria. Instead of neoplasia or neoplasm, the related terms cancer and tumor are also used. Some confusion may exist between the latter two terms, as the word *cancer* is widely used in medical jargon, and then usually refers to malignant neoplasms. The term *tumor* may also be confusing, because in its broad sense it only means a tissue growth, which is not necessarily malignant. For example, one might equally well be referring to an abscess, a granuloma or a parasitic cyst.

*Cancer*

*Tumor*

> ASSIGNMENT   12.1
>
> What are the three key concepts in the definition of a neoplasm?

*Hyperplasia*
*Hypertrophy*

*Hyperplasia* refers to an increase in the number of cells. *Hypertrophy*, in the context of cellular hypertrophy, signifies an increase in cell dimensions, and not in numbers. It is obvious that hyperplasia can occur in a neoplasm. It is also possible that hyperplasia may manifest itself in normal tissues without a neoplasm being found. Examples of hyperplasia in normal organisms include the rapid proliferation of cells in bone marrow, in the crypts of the small intestine or in the skin. This hyperplasia may also be stimulated, as in wound healing or callus formation.

*Metaplasia*

*Metaplasia* is the reversible process whereby particular types of cells from a certain tissue or organ change into other cell types. The best example of epithelial metaplasia is the conversion of pseudo stratified columnar epithelium from the respiratory tract into squamous epithelium. This phenomenon is referred to as squamous metaplasia. It can arise as a result of various stimulating factors, such as chronic irritation and inflammation. The mechanism of metaplasia is not a genuine transformation from one cell type into another, but rather a certain shift in the differentiation of the stem cell. One well-known example of squamous metaplasia of the respiratory epithelium is that caused by vitamin A deficiency. Upon administration of vitamin A, the epithelium reverts to its original columnar or cylindrical structure.

*Anaplasia*

*Positional anaplasia*

*Cytological anaplasia*

*Anaplasia* is the term used to refer to a change in cellular organization. Two types can be distinguished: positional anaplasia and cytological anaplasia. By *positional anaplasia* it is meant that the relationship between cells in a particular tissue has changed. *Cytological anaplasia* is mainly caused by an increase, or change, in the synthesis of macromolecules in cells.

Ploidy = the multiple of the chromosome pairs present; compare haploid–diploid

This usually concerns an alteration in nucleic acid synthesis, resulting in a morphological change in the relation between the nucleus and the cytoplasm. This is why cytological anaplasia may also be a function of the "ploidy" of a cell. Physiologically, it may be found in the placenta, in a bone callus or a healing wound. Cytological anaplasia may be seen prominently in malignant neoplasms, though it is not an essential characteristic of neoplasia.

The most common classification of neoplasia is based on their biological behavior. In this respect, two groups of neoplasms can be distinguished: benign and malignant.

*Benign tumors*

*Benign neoplasms* are well defined (i.e., clearly delimited), often encapsulated, non invasive and well differentiated. They grow relatively slowly, display relatively few mitoses, show little anaplasia in histological sections, and are not metastatic.

*Malignant tumors*

*Malignant tumors* are less well defined, and usually not well encapsulated, or they may have outgrown their capsule. They are invasive and relatively undifferentiated; they grow rapidly, display abundant mitosis, are anaplastic and finally undergo metastasis.

*Invasion*

*Metastasis*

The main conclusive criterion is the invasive and metastatic character of the malignant tumor. By definition this is absent in the case of benign tumors. By *invasion* is meant spreading into the surrounding tissue, and by *metastasis*, dissemination or secondary growth of the neoplasm at a site away from the primary tumor.

There are several systems for naming benign and malignant tumors. The suffix 'oma' indicates a tumor. With some exceptions, such as granuloma (a focus of inflammatory cells) or hematoma (accumulation of blood), this suffix refers to neoplasms. Benign neoplasms are usually given this suffix. For example, a benign tumor of glandular tissue is an adenoma, of connective tissue a fibroma. Malignant neoplasms are given a name which refers to their embryonic origin. If they originate from the cells of the ectoderm and endoderm, such as skin, throat, respiratory tract or gastrointestinal tract, they are labeled as *carcinomas*. If malignant neoplasms originate from the mesoderm (such as fat, muscle, bone and blood), they are referred to as *sarcomas*. Table 12.1 shows a few examples of these types of tumors.

TABLE   12.1
Nomenclature of neoplasms, some examples

| Tissue type | Benign | Malignant |
| --- | --- | --- |
| epithelial | adenoma | adenocarcinoma |
| | papilloma (polyp) | carcinoma |
| | | |
| mesodermal | | |
| -connective tissue | fibroma | fibrosarcoma |
| -myxomatous* tissue | myxoma | myxosarcoma |
| -fatty tissue | lipoma | liposarcoma |
| -cartilage | chondroma | chondrosarcoma |
| -bone | osteoma | osteosarcoma |
| -blood vessel | hemangioma | hemangiosarcoma |
| -lymph vessel | lymphangioma | lymphangiosarcoma |
| -striated muscle tissue | rhabdomyoma | rhabdomyosarcoma |
| -smooth muscle tissue | leiomyoma | leiomyosarcoma |

*myxomatous = slimy

### What is a liposarcoma?

A liposarcoma is a malignant tumor (sarcoma) originating from fat tissue (lipos).

Compare blastula

There are also some specialized terms. The suffix "blastoma", for example, is used if the neoplasm shows little differentiation and resembles embryonic tissue.

An example is the neuroblastoma, an embryonic tumor of the nervous system. If the embryonic origin includes all three embryonic cell types, it is called a *teratoma*.

*Teratoma*

*Carcinosarcoma*

A malignant tumor may also have similarities to both a carcinoma and a sarcoma. In that case it is called a *carcinosarcoma*.

Before discussing the pathogenesis of carcinogenesis, let us briefly define a few individual concepts.

*Carcinogenesis*

*Carcinogenesis* itself is the development of cancer starting from the very first phase, called the initiation phase, followed by the promotion phase and ending in the final phase of the disease, the progression phase.

*Initiation*

*Initiation* is the first phase of carcinogenesis, in which cells are exposed to a carcinogenic agent. During this phase, an irrevocable step is taken by which daughter cells of the exposed cell may later acquire relative autonomy with regard to cell division.

*Promotion*

*Promotion* is the next phase in the carcinogenesis process, in which initiated, but not yet recognizable, cells are stimulated to divide and become clinically or pathologically detectable neoplasms.

*Progression*

*Progression* is the phase following initiation and promotion, in which the clinically detectable tumor increasingly damages the host and finally destroys it. Widespread invasion and metastasis, with destruction of the original normal tissue, are predominant in this phase.

*Carcinogen*

A *carcinogen* is an agent that causes cancer and hence is mainly active during the initiation phase and possibly also during the promotion phase.

*Definition*

This relatively simple definition should also be seen in the context of an experimental animal population. A carcinogen is an agent, that when administered to previously unexposed animals leads to a higher incidence of malignant neoplasms. This increase is statistically significant compared to the incidence in controls. The

*Genotoxic carcinogens*

*Epigenetic carcinogens*

majority of agents do this by affecting the genetic material during the initiation phase and are hence referred to as *genotoxic carcinogens*. Other agents can raise the incidence of cancer by action in a later phase through non-genotoxic mechanisms on cell populations which have been previously exposed to initiating doses of other carcinogens. These are called *epigenetic carcinogens*. They are quite different from "genotoxic" or "genuine" carcinogens. They are frequently promoters or they may stimulate carcinogenesis by suppressing immunity, for example.

What is the difference between a proximate and an ultimate carcinogen?

*Pro-carcinogen*

A *pro-carcinogen* is an agent from which by one or more biotransformation steps in the organism the ultimate carcinogen is formed (Figure 12.1).

*Proximate carcinogen*

The *proximate carcinogen* is the stage which immediately precedes the ultimate carcinogen; the proximate carcinogen is often the substrate for the final enzymatic or non-enzymatic reaction leading to the formation of the ultimate carcinogen (Figure 12.1).

*Ultimate carcinogen*

An *ultimate carcinogen* is a reactive molecule that enters into a reaction with cellular macromolecules, resulting in initiation as the first step in carcinogenesis (Figure 12.1).

*Synergistic carcinogen*

*Co-carcinogen*

*Anti-carcinogen*

A *synergistic carcinogen* is a carcinogen which, when administered in combination with another carcinogen, enhances the activity of the latter. If this enhancing substance is not carcinogenic itself, it is referred to as a *co-carcinogen*. If an agent (either a carcinogen or a non-carcinogen) reduces the activity of another carcinogen, it is called an *anti-carcinogen*.

*Latency period*

The *latency period* is the interval between exposure to a carcinogen and the clinical manifestation of cancer.

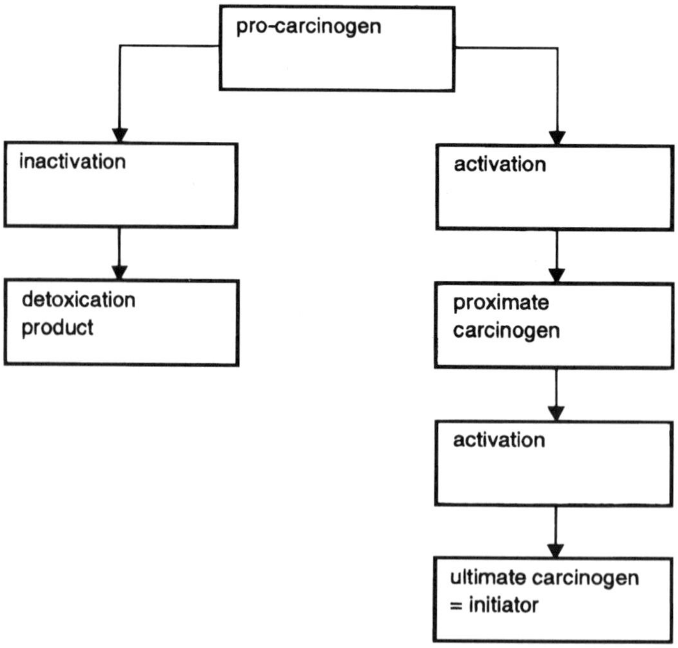

FIGURE    12.1
Initiation by chemical carcinogens

ASSIGNMENT   12.2

A carcinogen can act via a genotoxic or a non-genotoxic, epigenetic mechanism. Of the two phases of carcinogenesis, initiation and promotion, which is more closely linked to each of these two mechanisms?

## 2   Pathogenesis of cancer

It is generally accepted that carcinogenesis is a multiphase process, in which the genome is involved directly as well as indirectly. Further, this process is strongly influenced by a number of variables such as age, diet, hormonal balance, animal species and strain. The complexity of this process makes the extrapolation of experimental animal studies to humans difficult.

Although the actual number of phases in carcinogenesis is not precisely known, the hypothesis on the induction of cancer due to carcinogens can be summarized as follows (inhibiting factors are not included).

| | |
|---|---|
| Step 1 (if necessary) | Biotransformation of a pro-carcinogenic substance to a DNA-reactive compound. |
| Step 2 (initiation) | Covalent binding to DNA. |
| Step 3 (initiation) | Stabilization of the mutation in DNA. |
| Step 4 (promotion) | Expression of the mutation, change in cellular function (gene expression, receptor functions). |
| Step 5 (promotion) | Neoplastic growth, clinically or pathologically detectable. |
| Step 6 (progression) | Qualitative and quantitative manifestation of tumor growth; neoplasm develops into terminal malignant form. |
| Step 7 (metastasis) | Spreading of transformed cells to other parts of the body, where they develop secondary tumors. |

In the following sections, the three phases initiation promotion and progression will be dealt with, discussing the processes which are (or may be) involved.

### 2.1   INITIATION: THE GENOTOXIC PROCESS

Initiation takes place at the level of DNA. The genotoxic carcinogen, here called the *initiator*, alters the genetic information in the cells. As a result, the cells somehow escape the normal control of cell division and acquire relative autonomy with regard to cell division.

This genotoxic effect is established by an interaction of the compound with the cellular macromolecules which make up the genome. Although carcinogens also interact with macromolecules such as RNA, proteins and lipids (which may be important in the later phases of carcinogenesis), it is generally accepted that DNA is the primary target in the induction of cancer. The most important evidence for this is the finding that both physical (ionizing radiation) and chemical carcinogens alter DNA and that a large part of all carcinogens are also mutagenic. The biological carcinogens also interfere with DNA, but their molecular mechanism is less clear. Like the physical carcinogens, this group will be dealt with separately in the next study unit (Study unit 13, sections 1 and 2).

*Chemical carcinogens*

The *chemical carcinogens* are perhaps the most important and best studied group. For this reason, their initiation mechanism will be discussed in some more detail. The majority of chemical carcinogens are metabolically activated in a sequence of events, eventually leading to the formation of reactive electrophiles, the ultimate carcinogens. The electrophiles bind covalently to the various nucleophilic binding sites of macromolecules in the cell, including DNA. In theory, the original, "normal" cells, with the carcinogen covalently bound to macromolecules, may develop in four major directions.

What are these four possibilities?

First, "repair" mechanisms can cut out the damaged, DNA adduct and can replace it with undamaged DNA. The covalent bonds are destroyed by this process, so that the resultant cell population remains "normal" (see Study unit 11, section 5 for DNA-repair). A second possibility is that the covalent bonds remain, but at sites in the DNA not important for tumor initiation. Consequently, the resultant cell population again remains non-initiated. Thirdly, carcinogens may be cytotoxic. The cells may have been initiated, but they die because the viability of the cell is impaired by too massive an interaction with the carcinogen, consequently a possible initiation effect will not come to expression. Finally, the fourth possibility is the development of initiated daughter cells following fixation of the covalently bound DNA. These four possibilities are largely working hypotheses. However, they are supported by a variety of experimental findings (Figure 12.2).

### 2.1.1 *Initiation by chemical carcinogens*

*a.* *Metabolism*

–Activation and inactivation-

Nearly all carcinogens are pro-carcinogens and hence must be metabolically activated in the organism to the ultimate carcinogen. This metabolism involves enzymes predominantly located in the access routes to the body: the respiratory tract and the gastrointestinal tract, and the next filtering organ, the liver, in particular.

Give a brief description of this process.

The phase 1 and phase 2 reactions involved (see Study units 3 and 4) are highly complex and a particular carcinogen may undergo several biotransformations. For

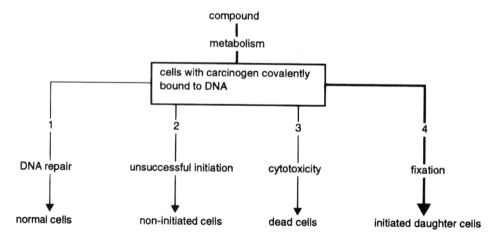

FIGURE 12.2

Possible consequences for the cell or its descendants after covalent binding of the carcinogen to DNA

example, conjugation in a particular body compartment may lead to inactivation, while a subsequent reaction in another compartment may result in the formation of the ultimate carcinogen. This process is known as reactivation. Further information will be given later, when the various chemical carcinogens are discussed.

–Altered metabolism–

*Factors influencing the metabolism of a carcinogen*

Activation, inactivation and reactivation of a chemical carcinogen can be affected by many factors.

> Can you indicate what types of factors could be mentioned here?

The predominant factors are enzyme induction, enzyme inhibition and scavenging of metabolites. Other factors include age, sex, nutritional state, dietary components and stress.

*Enzyme induction* is the process of increasing the amount of a phase 1 or phase 2 enzyme due to *de novo* protein synthesis following exposure to an inducing chemical. Enzyme induction can result in an increase as well as a decrease in the formation of the ultimate carcinogen. The same is true of enzyme inhibition, usually leading to a reduction of metabolic activation. Metabolite scavenging systems are often nucleophiles, such as glutathione or enzymes like superoxide dismutase, which detoxify reactive metabolites.

The final result of the initiation depends on the combined action of the above factors.

–Organ specificity and species differences–

The activity and substrate specificity of both phase 1 and phase 2 enzymes vary greatly from organ to organ, from individual to individual and from species to species. As a result, the carcinogenic potency of a chemical may also vary greatly with the organ, individual and species.

In particular, the presence of different isoenzymes and their sensitivity to the above factors make it nearly impossible to use *in vitro* research to predict quantitatively the effect *in vivo*. The same problem arises on extrapolation from experimental animals to man.

### b.   Covalent binding

The ultimate carcinogen is usually an electrophile that binds covalently to nucleophilic groups in the cell. Electrophiles possess relatively electron-deficient atoms (especially carbon, and to a lesser extent, nitrogen). If one electron is lacking, the electrophile is referred to as a *radical*. If a pair of electrons is missing, the term cation is used, e.g. carbocation. These electrophiles form adducts with cellular (macro)molecules, by covalent binding to electron-rich or nucleophilic sites (often sulfur, nitrogen, oxygen).

If this occurs selectively at the genetic material level, initiation of carcinogenesis may occur.

There are many nucleophilic binding sites in the living cell (Figure 12.3):

- water ($H_2O$) is the most common nucleophile and constitutes an important form of inactivation;

- protein structures contain many nucleophilic groups, like the thiol group in, e.g. cystiene moieties;

- the bases of nucleic acids also have such sites: for guanine at the $C^8$, $N^2$, $N^3$, $N^7$ and $O^6$ positions, for thymidine and uracil at the $O^2$, $O^4$ and $N^3$ positions and for cytosine at the $O^3$ and $N^2$ positions.

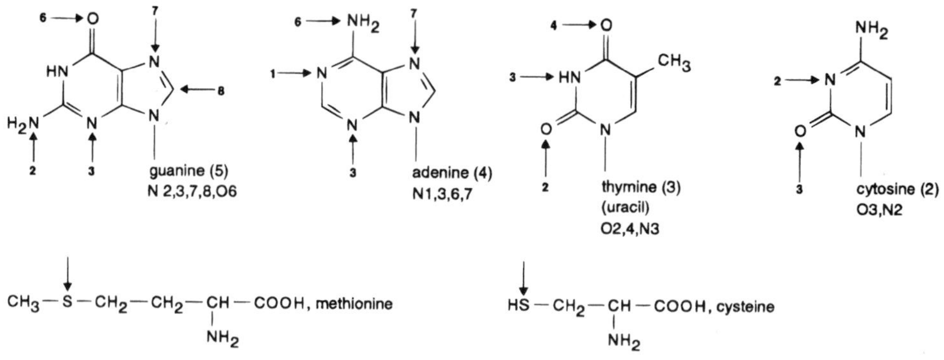

FIGURE 12.3

Nucleophilic binding sites on nucleotides in DNA and on amino acids in proteins (indicated by arrow)

The number of nucleophilic binding sites is given in brackets. The positions within a molecule are indicated by the numbers in the figure

### c.   Critical DNA binding sites in the DNA bases

DNA is generally accepted to be the primary target for chemical carcinogens. Covalent binding of electrophilic metabolites of the carcinogens to nucleophilic groups in DNA is believed to play an essential role in initiation. It is also assumed that the specific binding sites on the nucleotides of DNA are essential for the initiation to succeed. This hypothesis has been particularly supported by studies on the alkylation of nucleic acids by N-nitroso compounds, such as N-alkyl-N-nitrosoureas, and the dialkylnitrosamines.

Electrophiles easily bind to the $N^7$-position of guanine. However, there is no relationship between this adduct formation and tumorigenesis. By contrast, alkylation of the $O^6$ position of guanine clearly plays a role in the initiation of carcinogenesis. The more $O^6$ and the less $N^7$ is alkylated, the higher the carcinogenic potency of a particular N-nitroso compound is. The reason is that the $O^6$-alkylated guanine is "wrongly" coded by the DNA polymerase, resulting in base pair substitution, which is not the case for $N^7$-alkylated guanine.

*In vitro*, the same has been shown for other nucleophilic binding sites of nucleic acids. For instance, $O^6$-methylated guanine and $O^4$-methylated thymine are "miscoded" by DNA polymerase, whereas this does not occur following methylation of guanine and adenine on the 1, 3 or 7 positions and of thymine on the $O^2$ position. For *in vivo* correlations it is necessary to consider other factors such as DNA repair as well. This process mainly determines the organ-specificity of tumors.

Can you suggest what this organ specificity is based on?

Particular organs are capable of preventing accumulation of DNA, alkylated at the $O^6$ position in guanine. Other organs and tissues cannot do this and accumulate $O^6$-alkylated DNA. As can be seen from Figure 12.4, it is precisely in these tissues and organs that neoplasia is induced.

The effect of covalent binding on DNA also depends on the carcinogen itself. Methylation of guanine at the $O^6$ position results in a miscoding of guanine. Guanine will be transcribed as adenine. If benzo[*a*]pyrene is bound to guanine, the latter will be transcribed as cytosine or thymidine. Alkylation of DNA may also change the control of genetic expression of DNA. Further, the carcinogen may interfere with DNA polymerase (as in the case of certain carcinogenic metals), which may also lead to miscoding of DNA bases.

356

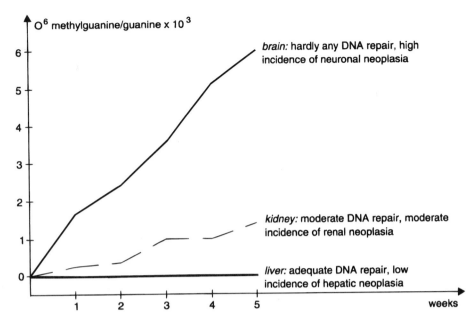

FIGURE 12.4
Accumulation of O⁶ methylguanine in the DNA of rat tissue during treatment with [³H]-MNU (N-methylnitrosourea)
Groups of rats were injected intravenously with 10 mg kg–1 once a week over a 5-week period

### d. Critical DNA binding sites in the genome

DNA adducts may damage the human genome by inducing point mutations, deletions or chromosomal translocations. When this damage is induced in relatively unimportant parts of the genome, there will be little effect. However, when these genetic changes are induced in genes which are involved in the regulation of cell growth and in cell differentiation, this might result in cell transformation. These critical genes, *oncogenes* and tumor-suppressor genes, will be discussed in section 3 of this chapter.

*Oncogenes*

### e. Fixation

As was mentioned previously, cells affected by a carcinogen need to divide into daughter cells in order to render the genotoxic process of initiation irreversible. This is called *fixation*. Cell division at the moment of initiation is thus essential. The fixation process, itself, however, cannot be directly observed, as the initiated daughter cells are not recognizable. Indirect evidence is provided by the importance of cell division and modulating factors such as DNA repair and accuracy of DNA replication.

*Fixation*

ASSIGNMENT 12.3

Why is cell division essential for the initiation process of carcinogenesis?

It has already been discussed that loss of viability due to massive interaction of carcinogens with cellular macromolecules may prevent the expression of initiating effects. On the other hand, cell necrotic effects in organs and tissues may activate division of the remaining cells. Since cell proliferation is essential for the initiation process, cytotoxicity may thus stimulate the carcinogenesis.

Genetic damage can be fixed by DNA replication or fixation. In both cases, the accuracy with which the DNA is synthesized is as important as the structure of the DNA. It is possible that some carcinogens are capable of interfering with only the process of DNA synthesis. Certain carcinogenic metals are suspected of interacting with DNA polymerase.

### 2.1.2 Initiation by physical carcinogens

#### a. Radiation

Radiation can be classified as ionizing or non-ionizing. Ionizing radiation can be caused by $\alpha$ and $\beta$ particles and neutrons, as well as by electromagnetic waves, including X-and $\gamma$ rays. All these types of radiation cause neoplasms through a genotoxic effect which is the result of their ionizing properties. By releasing energy, free radicals, ions or excited molecules are formed. Free radicals in particular are considered important in this context. The result is that ionizing radiation induces chromosomal aberrations as well as mutations. Other important effects, especially in the induction of leukemia, include interference with oncogenic viruses, effects on thymus hormone secretion and certainly also an immunosuppressive effect. Radical-scavenging molecules, for instance vitamin E and the selenium-dependent glutathione peroxidase, can antagonize *in vitro* cell transformation following radiation. The principal sources of ionizing radiation are summarized in Table 12.2.

> What examples of specific cancers can you mention that are caused by radiation?

Some examples of specific cancers caused in humans by certain sources of radiation are listed in Table 12.3.

In addition, as the consequences of the atomic bomb explosions in Japan the incidence of leukemia in the exposed inhabitants has doubled.

Of the non-ionizing types of radiation ultraviolet (UV) light also causes cancer in humans and animals. This light is omnipresent, particularly as a component of sunlight. A certain wavelength (between 280 and 320 nm) is particularly ac-

TABLE 12.2
Main sources of ionizing radiation

| Natural radiation | Man-made radiation |
| --- | --- |
| in the environment: <br> - cosmic radiation <br> - terrestrial radiation (mainly arising from metal ores) | in the environment: <br> -global fall-out (nuclear energy, fossil fuels) <br><br> medical radiation: <br> -diagnostic (X-rays) |
| radionuclides in the body: natural radioactive elements in the food chain | -radiopharmaceuticals occupational exposure |

TABLE 12.3
Causes of specific cancers in humans caused by radiation sources

| Radiation from | Source | Cancer |
| --- | --- | --- |
| radium ($^{228}$Ra) | luminescent paint (oral intake) | bone |
| thorotrast ($^{228}$Th) | diagnostic | liver (blood vessels) |
| iodine ($^{131}$I) | diagnostic drug for the thyroid | thyroid |
| X-rays | diagnostic (inadequate protection) | skin |

tive since it affects DNA. Although it is not directly ionizing, UV light can still induce DNA aberrations.

There are several indications for this. The most important is that people with xeroderma pigmentosum show increased susceptibility to sunlight-induced malignant skin neoplasms. In addition, specific irradiation-induced damage to DNA can be measured. The induction of malignant tumors in the skin of mice appears to be related to the formation of pyrimidine dimers (also see Study unit 11).

### b. Asbestos

Asbestos can be regarded as a physical carcinogen, since the physical shape and dimensions of asbestos particles are the principal factors in its carcinogenesis. However, these cannot be the only factors, since glass fibers of the same shape and dimensions are also carcinogenic, albeit to a lesser degree. Chronic exposure to asbestos results in an increased incidence of bronchogenic lung carcinoma and especially of mesothelioma, a neoplasm of phagocytic cells in the mesothelium (pleura or peritoneum). Asbestos is not genotoxic at the usual exposure levels, and an epigenetic mode of action is assumed to be involved that resembles a solid-state reaction.

The first reaction is a pleural reaction with fibroblast proliferation. It takes many years (20 to 40) before a mesothelioma can develop. This explains how an increased incidence of cancer could be found in the 1980s in people who, in the 1940s, had worked in asbestos mines or on shipyards where large quantities of asbestos were used. Cigarette smoking greatly increases the risk of asbestos-related lung cancer. This is a genuine case of *syncarcinogenesis*. However, the incidence of mesothelioma, is not influenced by smoking.

### c. Foreign-body reactions

Polymers like plastic can, if implanted subcutaneously in rodents, lead to sarcoma after a long latency period. The chemical composition is of minor importance, since even metallic objects can cause this effect. The main factors are the shape and exterior surface of the object; smooth materials are more effective than rough or perforated materials. Thicker discs are more effective in inducing sarcomas than thin ones. The actual interaction between these carcinogens and the genome is not known. The main hypothesis implies that initiation is not induced by a foreign-body reaction itself. The neoplasm is caused by continuous promotion (i.e., an epigenetic process) of spontaneous initiation or initiation by other carcinogens.

Another, less well substantiated hypothesis suggests that the macrophages form free radicals during the process of inflammation. The free radical formation would lead to damage to DNA.

It might also be that during the stimulation of cell proliferation mutations arise from the inaccuracies in DNA replication, or combinations of these three alternatives.

### d. Chronic irritation

Chronic inflammation can be a predisposing (epigenetic) factor for neoplasia, through a mechanism which may be closely related to solid-state reactions. One example of chronic irritation associated with an increased incidence of neoplasia is that of the lower lip of pipe smokers. In addition, various forms of chronic skin irritation (chemical irritation, incision) constitute a well-known promoter of skin neoplasia after exposure to an initiating dose of a carcinogen. This has led to the generally accepted view that these types of physical carcinogens act mainly via an epigenetic mechanism.

ASSIGNMENT 12.4

Which physical carcinogens are mainly active genotoxically and which exercise this effect mainly through an epigenetic mechanism?

### 2.1.3 Initiation by biological carcinogens

Biological carcinogenic agents are those organisms which colonize or infect humans and animals and thereby cause neoplasia. They include viruses, bacteria and fungi, as well as endoparasitic worms. Viruses are perhaps the most important, since they can be directly carcinogenic. Bacteria are mainly important for their part in the endogenous formation of chemical carcinogens, especially nitrosamines. Few fungi are known that can cause infections in humans and animals with carcinogenic consequences. They are chiefly pathogenic in the food resources for humans and animals and may thus contaminate the food with carcinogenic products. Accordingly, yeasts and fungi will be discussed in the context of chemical carcinogens. Various species of endoparasitic worms can affect humans and animals and induce neoplasia.

#### a.  Endoparasites

Although less well-known than the oncogenic viruses, certain worm species generated interest as early as 1913, when Fibiger discovered that gastric papillomas occurred in rats infected with *Spiroptera*, a roundworm. This worm uses the cockroach as its intermediate host and in the mature state lives in the stomach of the rat. Fibiger succeeded in inducing this papilloma after experimental infection with the worm, which was therefore called carcinogenic. In 1927 he was awarded the Nobel Prize for this achievement. Later, however, it was demonstrated that on its own the worm could not cause neoplasia, but that Fibiger's rat food had been deficient in vitamin A, which had led to hyperplasia and metaplasia in the stomach walls. It was the combination of the two factors which was responsible for the occurrence of stomach lesions. Some other species of worm can also promote certain neoplasms; Table 12.4 provides a short list.

TABLE 12.4
Worm species promoting the development of neoplasms

| Species of worm | Species of mammal | Neoplasia |
| --- | --- | --- |
| Spirocerca lupis | dog | esophageal sarcoma |
| Cysticercus | rat | liver sarcoma |
| Schistosoma mansoni | man | liver carcinoma |
| Schistosoma haematobium | man | urinary bladder carcinoma |

The worm *Schistosoma haematobium* causes chronic inflammation of the urinary tract in humans in certain East African countries. This inflammation is contaminated by bacteria which, in turn, nitrosate amines that are present to nitrosamines, which are carcinogenic. This interaction of worm infestation, bacterial infection and nitrosamine formation can be regarded as a typical example of multifactorial carcinogenesis in an area with a very high incidence of a particular type of cancer. In countries like Egypt, the eradication of *Schistosoma haematobium* might greatly reduce the high incidence of cancer of the urinary tract.

#### b.  Bacteria

Opportunistic bacteria may take advantage of a favorable growth situation to colonize particular parts of the body. These bacteria may then synthesize products which may become carcinogenic activation in the organism. Well-known examples of such products are nitrosamines. Examples of parts of the body apt to become infected are the urinary bladder, following *Schistosoma haematobium* infection, and the stomach after vagotomy. This surgical procedure causes a substantially reduced secretion of gastric acid, which renders bacterial colonization possible. The presence of the bacterial flora in the small and large intestines can also have important consequences for carcinogenesis.

### c.    Carcinogenic viruses

Certain viruses induce cancer in certain organs of one or more animal species. The precise mechanism of viral carcinogenesis is not known, but recent findings have shed some light on the subject. Studies using RNA tumor viruses, the so-called *retroviruses*, have shown that these viruses possess an onc gene (onc stands for oncogenic) or *oncogene*. These viruses have apparently acquired this onc gene through recombination of the viral genome with cellular genes. Viruses which possess this oncogene are the most pathogenic in evoking neoplasia in newborns. They are often also capable of eliciting *in vitro* transformation of cells. Normal cells, including human cells, usually possess genes which closely resemble viral oncogenes. These cellular oncogenes are expressed at a very low level. If, however, an oncogene is expressed strongly, this is correlated with the transformation potency of the virus involved.

Recently, the interest in the HTLV (Human T-cell Lymphotropic) viruses, to which one or several AIDS viruses (now renamed HIV-1 and HIV-2) are related, is very much alive. These viruses are classified as *Lentivirinae*, a group of viruses inducing chronic, progressive illness. The cellular immune system is especially prone to attacks by these viruses. This may lead to immunodeficiency, as in AIDS (mainly HIV-1), but also to the induction of certain neoplasms, including T-cell leukemia (mainly HTLV-1). Kaposi's sarcoma, a rare, malignant type of tumor, has been observed in patients infected with the AIDS virus. This type of tumor also occurs in patients in other immunosuppressive situations (kidney transplant patients, lymphoma patients).

The relationship between oncogenes and the carcinogenic process will be discussed in section 3.1 .

### Summary

Initiation is the first step in carcinogenesis. It is a genotoxic process in which the chemical carcinogen is usually covalently bound to critical binding sites of the DNA. If the DNA repair mechanism is inadequate and the affected cell continues to divide, daughter cells may develop which have fixed the changed DNA and are hence irreversibly altered. This initiation leads, in an as yet unknown manner, to relatively autonomy with regard to cell division. The metabolic activation of chemical carcinogens resulting in the formation of the ultimate carcinogens plays a key role in the initiation. In addition, initiation may be organ directed and species dependent. Physical carcinogenesis (by radiation) is similar to that of chemical carcinogenesis. So far, the mechanism of initiation by foreign-bodies and asbestos is not well understood. The same goes for viral carcinogenesis, though the activation of oncogenes could play a key role here.

### 2.2    PROMOTION: THE EPIGENETIC PROCESS

*Promoter*

A *promoter* of carcinogenesis is an agent that on long-term, repeated administration increases cancer induction following previous exposure to an initiator.

*Initiation–promotion studies*

The concept of promotion arose from a study on the latency period of cancer, particularly after exposure of experimental animals to initiator doses of the car-

361

cinogen. This type of study was first carried out by Berenblum and Shubik in the late 1940s. Figure 12.5 shows the results of their experiments.

ASSIGNMENT 12.5

On the basis of Figure 12.5, try to indicate the possible combinations of initiation (I) and promotion (P) which will or will not induce neoplasia.

A single dose of an initiator alone does not result in neoplasia within a specified experimental period (line 1 in Figure 12.5). If the initiator is followed by repeated administration of a promoter, neoplasia will be observed within the specified experimental period (line 2 in Figure 12.5). Skin neoplasia arises even if there is a certain time interval between administration of the initiator and that of the promoter (line 3 in Figure 12.5). By itself, the promoter does not have any effect (line 5 in Figure 12.5), not even if it is administered before the initiator (line 4 in Figure 12.5). Finally, the promoter requires a particular dosage scheme. If its administration is spread out over too long a period it does not sufficiently stimulate carcinogenesis (line 6 in Figure 12.5). In its pure form, this concept only applies when dealing with a promoter that does not have any initiating properties itself.

*Complete carcinogen*
*Incomplete carcinogen*

If a carcinogen has both properties, i.e. initiation as well as promotion, it is usually referred to as a "*complete carcinogen*". If it only initiates, it is called an "*incomplete carcinogen*".

If a carcinogen is repeatedly administered, it is difficult to distinguish between initiation and promotion. However, experimental studies on the consequences of repeated administration have led to a better understanding of non-genotoxic interactions in carcinogenesis. This has resulted in the characterization of initiation and promotion as listed in Table 12.5.

The initial studies on experimental skin cancer have been extended to various organ systems (Table 12.6). These studies show that promoters belong to a wide variety of types of agents.

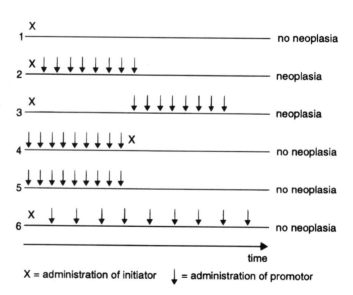

FIGURE 12.5

Initiation—promotion studies as first carried out in the mouse skin neoplasia model

TABLE 12.5

Characteristics of initiation and promotion in carcinogenesis

| Initiation | Promotion |
|---|---|
| irremovable | removable |
| irreversible with a "memory" | reversible |
| invisible cell population | at least microscopically visible cell population |
| genotoxic process | non-genotoxic, epigenetic process |
| DNA synthesis and cell division are necessary for fixation | stimulation of cell division is a key mechanism |
| dose-dependent but without a threshold | dose-dependent but with a theoretical threshold value (and hence a non-effective dosage) |

TABLE 12.6

Initiators, promoters and "pre-neoplastic" changes in various organ systems for a few experimental animals

| Tissue | Initiator | Promotor |
|---|---|---|
| urinary bladder (dog) | 2-naphthylamine | D, L-tryptophan |
| urinary bladder (rat) | methylnitrosourea | saccharin |
| urinary bladder (rat) | N-[4]-(5-nitro-2-furyl)-2-thiazolylformamide | allopurinol |
| large intestine (rat) | N-methyl-N'-nitro-N-nitroso-guanosine | lithocholic acid |
| bone marrow (rat) (leukemia) | N, N'-2,7-fluorenylbisacetamide | blood loss |
| embryonic (mouse) | 2-methylcholanthrene | tetradecanoyl(phorbol)acetate (TPA) |
| fibroblasts (in culture) | UV radiation | TPA |
| | ionizing radiation | TPA |
| forestomach (mouse) | 3-methylcholanthrene, benzo[a]pyrene, dimethyl-benzo[a]anthracene | croton oil |
| liver (rat) | 2-acetylaminofluorene diethylnitrosamine azo dyes | phenobarbital, DDT, PCBs, butylated hydroxytoluene (BHT), estrogens, 2,3,7,8-tetrachlorodibenzo-p-dioxin (TCDD) |
| lung (mouse) | urethane | BHT |
| mammary gland (rat) | 7,12-dimethylbenzo[a]anthracene | phorbol, prolactin |
| thyroid gland (rat) | 2-acetylaminofluorene | methylthiouracil |

*Pre-neoplastic lesions*

The interesting thing with regard to particular initiation–promotion models is that they show microscopically detectable changes which are called *pre-neoplastic lesions*. Understanding of these has come mainly from studies of these models in the liver. Many promoters of liver cancer are enzyme-inducing agents and may even be anti-carcinogens if they are administered together with or immediately before the carcinogen.

If administered after the initiator, however, they stimulate carcinogenesis. This can be seen from the increase in the number of islets of pre-neoplastic cells. These islets (*foci*) are not easily distinguished with the usual histological staining techniques. Special histochemical techniques, however, make them stand out quite clearly from the normal cells. Histochemically, they are distinct from the surrounding liver cells. Otherwise, they are completely identical and the

363

transition to normal cells is hardly noticeable. Hence, it is best to refer to these islets as "pre-neoplastic", rather than benign neoplastic, as benign tumors are clearly distinct from their immediate surroundings.

An initiator followed by a promoter may give rise to thousands of *foci*. Only a few of these will be followed by neoplasia. This once again shows the low "efficiency" of the process of carcinogenesis. The sensitivity to different enzymes varies greatly and may fluctuate with time. This could be explained by the phenotypical heterogeneity of neoplasia. A promoter changes the expression of genetic information to such an extent that initiated cell populations become visible. This manifestation implies that the tumor promoter induces an increase in the numbers of initiated daughter cells, i.e. selectively stimulates cell division. Theoretically, this stimulation of cell division can take place through two mechanisms, viz. positive and negative selection pressure (Figure 12.6).

*Positive selection pressure*

The promoter can exert *positive selection* pressure on initiated cells by directly stimulating cell division of initiated cells. Since the initiated cell population is more susceptible to this stimulation than the normal cell population, this stimulus results in a selective increase in the numbers of initiated cells. Such pro-

*Mitogens*

moters are called *mitogens* because they specifically stimulate mitosis and exert their effects at non-cytotoxic doses. Because the cell division stimulus can be regarded as an adaptation to a new situation, this tissue reaction is also referred

*Adaptive growth*

to as *adaptive growth*.

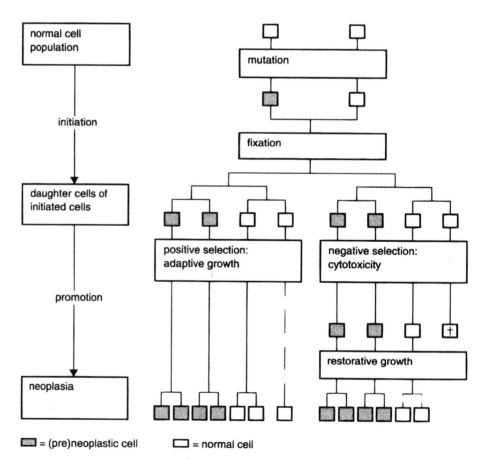

FIGURE 12.6

The concept of positive and negative selection pressure during the promotion of carcinogenesis

*Negative selection*

Another way of promotion is *negative selection* pressure by cytotoxicity. The agents involved cause cell toxicity and cell death particularly in the normal cell population. Various mechanisms render the initiated cell population more resistant to cell toxicity. The uptake of the agent by the cell and its transformation to a cell-toxic metabolite are less extensive in initiated cells. In a tissue, cell death subsequently evokes *restorative cell division*. The initiated cells react more rapidly to this than normal cells, which again gives them a growth advantage. The oldest and best-known examples of cytotoxic promoters which cause restorative cell division are those of skin cancer. As long as 40 years ago, Berenblum investigated a whole range of simple promoters, e.g. repeated administration of turpentine oil and repeated frost injuries or skin incisions (Table 12.7).

In the case of liver cancer, the toxic carbon tetrachloride is a well-known example.

> ASSIGNMENT   12.6
> Explain the promotion of liver cancer by repeated administration of carbon tetrachloride after the liver has been initiated by a single dose of diethylnitrosamine.

In this respect, foreign bodies might be mentioned, which are also suspected of requiring chronic stimulation of cell division to produce neoplastic growth. Removal of the foreign body prevents development of a sarcoma.

*Endogenous mitogens*

Mitogens include endogenous as well as exogenous agents. Hormones are *endogenous* substances, the typical functions of which may be stimulation of cell division. Therefore, many hormones can act as promoters in a particular carcinogenesis model. Examples include prolactin as a promoter of mammary gland cancer in rodents, thyroid hormone as a promoter of thyroid cancer and estrogen as a promoter of liver cancer.

*Exogenous mitogens*

*Exogenous mitogens* are also known. A much studied group of substances in experimental skin cancer in mice is that of TPA (12-O-tetradecanoylphorbol-13-acetate) and other phorbol esters.

The phorbol esters have other specific effects, but that on cell division is probably the most important. Another well-known mitogen is phenobarbital, which is involved in liver cancer in rats and mice.

These mitogens are all believed to act by binding to a cell receptor, in a manner similar to hormones. It is clear that promotion does not primarily have a genotoxic site of attack, but an epigenetic site. There are hypotheses suggesting that chromosomal effects are induced by particular promoters, but at present their significance is unclear. The real problem with epigenetic promoters is that

cauterize = to burn body tissue in order to destroy it

TABLE   12.7

Effect of promotion by irritation on the development of neoplasia in the skin of mice

| Carcinogen as initiator | Irritant as promoter | Result |
| --- | --- | --- |
| aromatic hydrocarbons | aromatic hydrocarbons | +++ |
| 3,4,5,6-dibenzacridine | slight cauterization | + |
| tar | frost injuries from $CO_2$ ice | ++ |
| tar | surgical incision | ++ |
| benzo[*a*]pyrene | turpentine | + |
| benzo[*a*]pyrene | croton oil | +++ |

in a classical cancer study it is difficult or impossible to distinguish them from genotoxic promoters or carcinogens. This problem will be discussed in more detail later. Apart from chemical factors, physical factors, like chronic irritation, and biological agents may play a role in the promotion phase of carcinogenesis. This may also be the case with the DNA-virus that causes *viral hepatitis B*. The risk of liver cancer increases especially after chronic hepatitis, leading to hepatic cirrhosis. This suggests that induction of neoplasia is an important epigenetic process for this virus. This hypothesis may well be verified in future decades, when, hopefully, sufficiently large human populations will have been treated with the new vaccine against hepatitis B. Owing to this vaccine, the incidence of hepatitis and cirrhosis, and consequently that of liver carcinoma, could drop dramatically.

### Summary

A promoter of carcinogenesis stimulates the development of neoplasia after the tissue has been previously exposed to an initiator. Long-term, repeated exposure to a promoter results in a cell division stimulus which selectively favors growth of the initiated cell population. Mechanisms of promotion are mainly based on restorative growth via cytotoxicity and on adaptive growth if the promoter is a mitogen. Hormones in particular can be considered to belong to the last group.

## 2.3 PROGRESSION: THE CLINICAL PROCESS

Progression is the phase following initiation and promotion. During progression, a clinically detectable neoplasia develops into its terminal, often malignant form, which ultimately overwhelms the host, mainly by invasion and metastasis. It is quite likely that there are still other steps in this final process. There is a transition from benign to malignant cells, from initiated, invisible cells to a cell population which is extremely anaplastic. It is assumed that during this transition the cancer cell undergoes important changes and that the host also plays an important role through interaction with the tumor cells, and especially through the immunological defense system. The changes in the cell are often accompanied by karyotypical changes. After years of absence of clinical symptoms, tumor cells may suddenly flare up in patients who were apparently cured.

What could be the cause of this sudden flare-up?

Dormancy of tumor cells is caused by inhibition of cell division and/or by a disturbance of the balance between cell division and cytolysis. Mitosis can be controlled by macrophages, factors such as lymphokines, nutrient depletion or certain hormones involved in tissue growth.

*Angiogenesis factor*

Another aspect of progression is that of tumor vascularization and invasion. This vascularization is controlled by a so-called *angiogenesis factor* and is accompanied by invasion into surrounding tissue and lymph and blood vessels. Invasion takes place with the help of enzymes, such as collagenase and cathepsin B, and possibly also by means of increased cell motility. *Metastases* can develop through dissemination of cancer cells through lymph and blood vessels. During their dispersion via lymph vessels, the cancer cells enter the local lymphatic node, so that the local immune response of the host plays an important part.

*Metastases*

The term embolus usually refers to blood clots

If cancer cells enter the bloodstream in the form of small emboli, vast numbers of them are destroyed by the interaction with various blood components. If the

366

emboli become stuck in a particular tissue or organ and survive thrombus formation, the cancer cells divide again and micrometastases develop. These metastases can continue to grow in the new tissue and subsequently induce blood vessel proliferation, resulting in even higher growth rates.

It is thus clear that during progression, several factors may have decisive roles. The predominant factor is doubtless the immune system. Many neoplasia are antigenically different from normal cells. The neoplasm can escape from the immune system by expressing only antigens originating from the host, i.e. by being non-immunogenic. Absence of immunogenicity can also occur in spontaneous neoplasia. The neoplasia can also induce immunodeficiency by producing circulating immunocomplexes or by activating T suppressor cells. The induction of immunodeficiency plays an important part in the case of strongly immunogenic tumors, such as UV-induced neoplasia and viral neoplasia. This immunodeficiency may be specific for that particular neoplasia. However, the host may also be completely deficient. This latter condition plays an important role in the growth of metastases. If the host is treated with immunosuppressives, metastases will develop all the more forcefully. This mechanism has been demonstrated in experimental animals as well as in humans. Virus-induced immunosuppression, in particular, can considerably enhance the progression of cancer.

ASSIGNMENT   12.7

Name and define at least three important steps determining the progression of neoplasia.

*Summary*

Progression is the final phase of the carcinogenesis process, in which a clinically detectable neoplasia develops into a fatal disorder. Tissue invasion and metastasis are the aggressive steps in this process, while immunological control plays a leading role in the defense system of the organism.

2.4   PREDISPOSING FACTORS

In addition to agents which are directly involved, such as initiators, promoters and immunosuppressives, other factors also play an important promoting role.

*2.4.1 Genetic factors*

Cancer is certainly not a genetic disorder; it is an acquired illness. Yet, there are various genetic predispositions which dramatically increase the risk of developing cancer. There are, for instance, rare genetic disorders which are associated with a strongly increased sensitivity to a specific neoplasm. Some of these are autosomal dominant, such as familial polyposis of the colon and retinoblastoma. In polyposis of the colon, multiple polyps appear in the large intestine before the patient has reached the age of 30. They are benign, but may transform into a malignant form later. Retinoblastoma is an inherited bilateral cancer of the eye occurring in children. It is characteristic of such dominant disorders that the tumors develop at an early age and that their occurrence is often multiple and bilateral. Other genetic predispositions are often recessive, such as the aforementioned *xeroderma pigmentosum*.

*2.4.2 Dietary factors*

Limiting caloric intake can be a highly influential factor in the development of cancer. For example, limiting caloric intake in experimental animals can halve the incidence of skin neoplasms caused by dibenzanthracene, or greatly reduce the incidence of spontaneous mammary gland tumors in mice. The caloric value of the diet also plays an important role in humans. This is obvious from the epidemiological finding that people who are 25% overweight or more have a cancer incidence that is 33% higher than that in people whose weight is within the normal range.

Furthermore, the protein content of the diet may play a modifying role in cancer studies with experimental animals, as can certain specific nutrients. A choline-deficient, high-fat diet stimulates the development of liver neoplasia in rats. A high-fat diet increases carcinogenesis in the mammary gland if 7.12-dimethylbenzo[a]anthracene is administered to rats.

Vitamins such as A and E often inhibit the carcinogenesis of epithelial neoplasms in experimental animals. Synthetic vitamin A derivatives, such as 13-cis-retinoic acid, are also active. Trace elements such as selenium can likewise inhibit experimental carcinogenesis and a deficiency of selenium or zinc can enhance specific neoplasms in experimental animals. The mechanisms underlying the effects of these vitamins and trace elements, if known, vary widely. For example, antioxidative vitamins (such as vitamin E) are active during initiation by scavenging reactive metabolites. Vitamin A can do the same, but is also active during promotion and progression, via a less well-known mechanism. Selenium is an essential constituent of glutathione peroxidase. Deficiency of this trace element may result in a diminished protection against lipid peroxidation products such as lipid hydroperoxides.

Finally, a diet may include special natural components which also have an inhibitory effect. Wattenburg showed that cancer-inhibiting derivatives of indole, flavones and structurally related compounds occur in certain plants such as those of the cabbage family (brussels sprouts, cabbages, broccoli, cauliflower). These derivatives are often enzyme inhibitors, so that carcinogenic activation during initiation is inhibited.

*See unit 10 for the action of "radical scavengers"*

### Summary

The process of carcinogenesis can be influenced by predisposing factors such as heredity and diet. Specific genetic predispositions may result in an increased incidence of a particular type of neoplasia. Diet is very important in the epidemiology of neoplasms in humans and animals. A reduction of the total energy content as well as specific dietary components such as vitamin A, C, and E, inhibits the carcinogenic process.

### 3    Molecular genetics of carcinogenesis

The human body exists out of $10^{14}$ cells. For correct functioning of an organism, this huge amount of cells demands a precise fine tuning and task allocation. In cancer the intercellular communication is disturbed and cancer is intrinsic to multicellular existence. For some period, it has been known that cancer is the result of genetic changes in the cell. It is not surprising that the genes involved in cellular communication, regulation of cell growth and differentiation, play an important role in carcinogenesis. Already in 1929 Boveri recognized the role of regulating mechanisms, interpreted to the present knowledge existing of two type of genes. *Oncogenes* are the first type of genes. Oncogenes have growth stimulating capacity, and increased activity of these genes can lead to enhanced cellular growth and/or less well differentiated cells. The second type of genes are *tumor-suppressor genes*. In normal cells these genes inhibit cellular growth; inactivation of these genes leads to enhanced proliferation and loss of contact with neighboring cells.

*Oncogenes*

*Tumor-suppressor genes*

### 3.1 ONCOGENES

Oncos (Gr.) = mass, bulk

If DNA is isolated from cancerous tissue and applied to normal fibroblasts in a culture, after some time the fibroblasts will start to behave quite differently. Instead of growing in an orderly and regular fashion, they form clusters or *foci*. These *foci* consist of fiber cells which have been transformed by the tumorous DNA administered and consequently have lost control of their growth. They have become cancer cells. Not all the DNA of a tumor has such transforming power, only certain genes. These are called oncogenes.

#### 3.1.1 *Identification of viral and cellular oncogenes*

Two types of viruses are associated with the development of cancer in man (see section 2.1.3).

*DNA viruses*
1 kb = 1000 base pairs

*DNA viruses* vary in size from 5 to 200 kb. Some of them are probably responsible for the development of certain human cancers. Examples are the Epstein–Barr virus, herpes simplex virus type 2, papilloma virus and hepatitis B virus.

*RNA viruses*

*Acutely transforming retroviruses*

*Chronically transforming retroviruses*

*RNA viruses* (retroviruses) consist of two units, each of which contains approximately 8500 RNA nucleotides as well as a tRNA, and 50 molecules of DNA polymerase (reverse transcriptase). There are two groups of retroviruses. The first group, the *acutely transforming retroviruses*, is characterized by its specific gene sequences which bear the transforming information; these are the *oncogenes*. A prototype of such retroviruses is the *Rous sarcoma virus* from chicken tumors. Retroviruses of the second group, the *chronically transforming retroviruses*, do not contain oncogenes; they lead to cancer after a long latent period and via an unknown mechanism. The best-known example is the HTLV group.

In the following, the acutely transforming retroviruses will be focused on.

> Study the reproduction of DNA and RNA viruses in the host cell.

A virus attaches itself to the cell via special structures on the cell membrane (receptors). When penetrating the cell, it sheds its protein envelope, so that its nucleic acid is released. This may now reproduce using enzymes already present in the cell or enzymes whose synthesis is controlled by the viral genetic material. After proteins have also been synthesized according to the genetic code of the virus, the nucleic acids and proteins can be combined to form new viruses. Before being incorporated into the host genome, the RNA of RNA viruses is first converted into DNA. Only then does that transcription take place.

In the cell, the genome of the retrovirus is duplicated to form a double DNA strand, which migrates into the nucleus and is then incorporated into the cellular DNA. The viral transcript is called proviral DNA. Not all retroviruses transform the DNA of the host cell in this way, thus converting it into a cancer cell. However, a large number of viruses which do cause tumors are known (see Table 12.8).

A fundamental discovery which led to the development of the oncogene concept was the identification of a gene sequence—known from the Rous sarcoma virus—in the DNA of normal chickens and many other biological species. This so-called *src* sequence was known to have oncogenic properties and to induce transformation of the host cell. So, *src* occurs in healthy DNA of chickens. In other words, the Rous sarcoma virus must have obtained the *src* sequence from the cellular genome, and the virus turns this basically harmless sequence into an oncogenically active one. Another example is the H-*ras*-oncogene. An important finding was that the activation of this gene in tumors was not caused by

TABLE 12.8
Acutely transforming retroviruses and their corresponding oncogenes

| Retrovirus | Origin | Oncogene code |
|---|---|---|
| Abelson leukemia virus | mouse | abl |
| avian erythroblastosis virus | chicken | erb A |
| avian erythroblastosis virus | chicken | erb B |
| avian leukemia virus E26 | chicken | ets |
| Snyder-Thellen feline sarcoma virus (fps) | cat | fes |
| Gardner-Rashmeed feline sarcoma virus | cat | fgr |
| McDough feline sarcoma virus | cat | fms |
| FBJ mouse osteosarcoma virus | mouse | fos |
| Mill-Hill 2 avian carcinoma virus | mouse | mht |
| Moloney mouse sarcoma virus | mouse | mos |
| avian myeloblastosis virus | chicken | myb |
| MC29 avian myeloctomatosis virus | chicken | myc |
| 3611 mouse sarcoma virus | mouse | ras |
| Harvey mouse sarcoma virus | rat | H-ras |
| Kirsten mouse sarcoma virus | rat | K-ras |
| avian reticuloendotheliosis virus | turkey | rel |
| Rochester URII avian sarcoma virus | turkey | ros |
| Simian sarcoma virus | monkey (primate) | sis |
| SKV 770 avian virus | chicken | sid |
| Rous sarcoma virus | chicken | src |
| Yamaguchi avian sarcoma virus | chicken | yes |

viruses. Experiments showed that cultured mouse cells became tumorigenic after transfection of DNA from a human bladder carcinoma cell line. The incorporated DNA appeared to be a mutated version of the human H-*ras*-gene. This mutated cellular gene showed large similarities with the retroviral H-*ras*-gene. The normal version is involved in the regulation of cellular growth. The gene becomes oncogenic by changes, for instance through integration in a virus or by mutations caused by mutagens.

Obviously, retroviruses have been capable of taking up (parts of) human genes during their evolution. The uptake of a growth regulating gene and activation as a result of the integration into the virus-DNA, could have been an advantage for these viruses, and made them survive.

*Three-letter code*

Oncogenes are referred to by a *three-letter code*. This three-letter code (see Table 12.8) is usually an abbreviation of the tumor with which the oncogene is associated. Cellular oncogenes are indicated as c-onc genes; viral oncogenes are indicated as v-onc.

*Proto-oncogenes*

For the reason that cellular oncogenes are in fact normal genes they are called *proto-oncogenes*. Through activation they change into oncogenes.

What mechanism is responsible for the activation of a c-onc in a virus? The oncogenic sequence from the healthy genome is incorporated into the viral genome and thus assumes a different physiological role. The virus may, for example, have a much higher transcriptive activity, resulting in a more frequent transcription. Parts of the oncogene may also be lost as a result of the transfer, which means that there is in fact a mutation. As a result, the product of the gene (protein) may change and become pathogenic.

In a typical experiment, c-onc genes incorporated into the genome of retroviruses after DNA cloning have been found to acquire transforming properties as a result. On renewed "infection", the now carcinogenic viruses then transform the host cell into a cancer cell.

### 3.1.2 Oncogene products

In 1975, Bishop and Varmus demonstrated that *src* is in fact not a viral gene but a copy of a gene present in all cells of chickens. This led to the question of what is the physiological significance of these c-onc genes and their corresponding gene products. Whatever process is responsible for a proto-oncogene becoming an oncogene, the transformation by the oncogene will certainly take place via the gene product (e.g. a protein), the synthesis of which it encodes. This will be similar to the gene product of the original, nontransformed proto-oncogene.

When Erikson and Collett in 1978 isolated the so-called p60 *src* protein from cells infected with the Rous sarcoma virus, they found that this protein had enzymatic activity; p60 *src* catalyzed phosphorylation of cellular proteins.

> ASSIGNMENT   12.8
>
> Why does phosphorylation constitute an important factor in the regulation of cellular enzyme activity?

Proteins encoded by oncogenes or proto-oncogenes appeared to act frequently as protein kinases, particularly in the phosphorylation of tyrosine.

In normal cells, *phosphorylation* of tyrosine-containing protein substrates is uncommon (0.1% of all cellular protein–phosphate binding). A well-known function of tyrosine phosphorylation is related to activation of the membrane receptor for the epidermal growth factor (see Figure 12.7).

Some cellular growth control systems are mediated by extracellular factors and inhibitors circulating in the bloodstream. In recent years, a number of growth

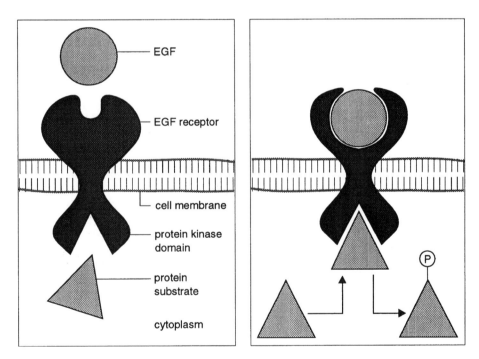

FIGURE   12.7
Receptor for the epidermal growth factor (EGF) with extracellular domains to which EGF binds and an intracellular protein kinase domain which is specific for tyrosine

Binding of an EGF molecule probably alters the conformation of the receptor molecule (right) in such a way that the intracellular domain catalyzes the phosphorylation of a cellular substrate protein. The protein kinase, which is activated by some oncogenes, can mimic the enzymatic activity of the receptor, without prior stimulation by EGF. It thus induces the uncontrolled growth characteristic of tumor cells.

371

factors have been isolated and identified. One of them is the so-called epidermal growth factor (EGF), which transmits its signal by binding to specific receptors in the cell membrane. If growth factors are added to a culture of non-dividing cells, these cells are stimulated to divide once.

If EGF is added to cells bearing the relevant receptors, an increase in the phosphotyrosine content in the cellular proteins can be observed. This implies that the signal to start mitosis is transmitted from the occupied receptor to the interior of the cell through phosphorylation of tyrosine, a target protein or proteins in the cell (Figure 12.7).

*Viruses encoding for protein kinases*

In cells which have been transformed by *viruses encoding for protein kinases*, a tenfold increase in tyrosine phosphorylation has been found. It is conceivable that a protein kinase which is transcribed from a c-onc differs from the normal enzyme involved in activation of the EGF receptor. Perhaps the receptor is already activated even though no EGF is present; such instances are referred to as *pseudo-growth hormone activity*. It may lead to significant disruption of the cell cycle.

*Pseudo-growth hormone activity*

A second type of disruption caused by an oncogene product can result from the action of the so-called c-*ras* genes. These genes encode for a so-called p21 protein. p21 proteins have binding sites with high affinity for GDP (guanosine diphosphate) and GTP (guanosine triphosphate). GDP/GTP binding is characteristic of the activity of the G protein which can activate adenylate cyclase, leading to the synthesis of cAMP. cAMP acts as an intracellular messenger after the cell has been activated by a hormone. The p21 oncogenic product can give a false signal in this process. Thus, various other oncogene products have been identified. During recent years increasing knowledge has become available and oncogenes can be classified in the way their protein products (oncogene proteins) participate in the cellular transformation to malignancy (see Figure 12.8).

Oncogenes can be associated with (1) polypeptide growth factors, (2) growth factor receptors, (3) protein kinase activity, (4) GTP-binding proteins, (5) steroid growth factor receptors, (6) nuclear proteins involved in transcription. (See also Table 12.9).

## 3.2   CELLULAR ONCOGENES AND CANCER

In the previous section it was seen that normal cells contain gene sequences called proto-oncogenes and transfer these to viruses. Under certain conditions, the proto-oncogenes incorporated in these viruses may acquire oncogenic potency, which is expressed when the oncogene-bearing viruses infiltrate other cells. It has been found that oncogenes are present in tumors which have either been induced in experimental animals by means of chemical carcinogens or which have been observed in man without any association with infection by a carcinogenic virus.

*Cellular proto-oncogene*

If in the absence of a viral infection a *cellular proto-oncogene* (some 70 of which are currently known) is transformed into an oncogene, in principal capable of causing tumor formation, this will have its origin in a mutation. The *proto-oncogene turned oncogene* may be transcribed more extensively. As a result of a chromosome break, the proto-oncogene may also be moved to another location on the genome (translocation) where the transcriptive activity is naturally higher. Thirdly, following the induction of a mutation, a sequence of cell divisions may result in an increase of oncogene content of the DNA (oncogene amplification). This may lead to an increased intracellular concentration of the oncogene product. Finally, a point mutation may arise in the proto-oncogene, ultimately giving rise to an oncogene product with modified, now harmful, properties. Some activated oncogenes have been found in human tumors and are specific for a cer-

*Proto-oncogene/oncogene*

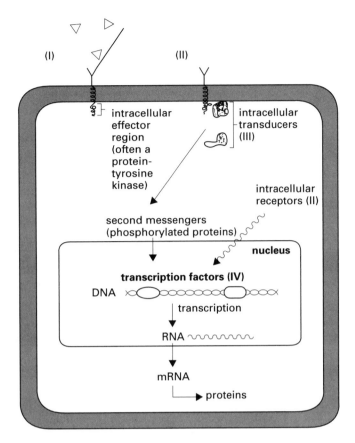

FIGURE   12.8
Growth control involves several types of proteins, the genes for these proteins can give rise to oncogenes. There are growth factors (I), receptors (II), intracellular signal trans-ducers (III), and intranuclear factors (IV).

tain tumor type. In leukemias and lymphomas predominantly chromosomal translocations have been found and in solid tumors deletions and amplifications.

### 3.2.1  MECHANISMS OF ONCOGENE DETECTION

Before any examples are discussed in detail, some of the most relevant methods for the detection of oncogene activation must be dealt with.

*The NIH 3T3 cell transformation test*

The NIH 3T3 cell transformation test is an *in vitro* test. It is used to study the bi-ological effect of DNA transformation by examining whether originally healthy mammalian cells display any properties typical of cancer cells following intro-duction of activated oncogenes. As receiving cells, a fibroblast line is used, orig-inating from NIH 3T3 mouse embryos. These fibroblasts easily take up exogenous DNA and incorporate it into their own genome. Transformation of the 3T3 cells on transfection of activated oncogenes containing DNA can easily be detected if so-called foci are formed in the culture (Figure 12.9).

*The oncogene amplification test*

It is now possible to buy so-called oncogene probes, incorporated in a bacterial plasmid. An oncogene probe contains the genetic code of a certain oncogene or part of it. The plasmid with the oncogene probe is introduced into bacteria, which are subsequently cultured on a large scale. The plasmid is extracted from the

TABLE   12.9

Some oncogenes and their original sources

| Oncogene | Original cancer type | Original source | Activity or product | Cellular location |
|---|---|---|---|---|
| abl | Abelson leukemia | Mouse | Tyr protein kinase | Cytoplasm |
| erb A | Erythroblastosis | Chicken | Thyroid hormone receptor | Nucleus |
| erb B | Erythroblastosis | Chicken | EGF receptor | Plasma membrane |
| ets | Myeloblastosis | Chicken | Regulatory protein | Nucleus |
| fes | Feline sarcoma | Cat | Tyr protein kinase | Cytoplasm |
| fgr | Feline sarcoma | Cat | Tyr protein kinase | Plasma membrane |
| fms | Feline sarcoma | Cat | CSF receptor | Plasma membrane |
| fos | Osteosarcoma | Mouse | Regulatory protein | Nucleus |
| fps | Sarcoma | Chicken | Tyr protein kinase | Cytoplasm |
| jun | Sarcoma | Chicken | Regulatory protein | Nucleus |
| kit | Sarcoma | Cat | Tyr protein kinase; probable GF receptor | Plasma membrane |
| met | Osteosarcoma | Mouse | Tyr protein kinase | Cytoplasm |
| mil | Sarcoma | Chicken | Ser/Thr protein kinase | Cytoplasm |
| mos | Sarcoma | Mouse | Ser/Thr protein kinase | Cytoplasm |
| myb | Myeloblastosis | Chicken | Regulatory protein | Nucleus |
| myc | Myelocystosis | Chicken | Regulatory protein | Nucleus |
| neu | Neuroblastoma | Rat | EGF receptor-like protein | Plasma membrane |
| p53 | Many cancers | | Tumor-suppressor gene | Nucleus |
| raf | Sarcoma | Mouse | Ser/Thr protein kinase | Cytoplasm |
| ras | Sarcoma | Rat | G protein | Plasma membrane |
| rb | Retinoblastoma | Human | Tumor-suppressor gene | Nucleus |
| rel | Reticuloendotheliosis | Turkey | Regulatory protein | Nucleus |
| ros | Sarcoma | Chicken | Tyr protein kinase; probable GF receptor | Plasma membrane |
| sis | Sarcoma | Monkey | PDGF | Secreted |
| sid | Carcinoma | Chicken | Regulatory protein | Nucleus |
| src | Sarcoma | Chicken | Tyr protein kinase | Cytoplasm |
| trk | Carcinoma | Human | Tyr protein kinase | Cytoplasm |
| yes | Sarcoma | Chicken | Tyr protein kinase | Cytoplasm |

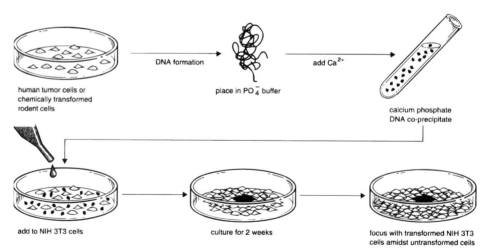

FIGURE   12.9

Diagrammatic summary of the (original) procedure for detection/identification of a cellular oncogene

bacteria and purified. Next, the oncogene probe is isolated from the plasmid with specific restriction enzymes and can be labeled *in vitro* using transcription enzymes and one or more radioactively labeled deoxynucleotides.

The DNA to be studied is isolated from lysed cells, and cut into smaller and larger fragments by restriction enzymes. On a gel, these are separated according to size by electrophoresis, and after denaturation to single-stranded DNA, they are transferred to a nitrocellulose filter (see Figure 12.10). The DNA fragments are then fixed on the filter. This technique is named Southern blotting, after its discoverer Edward Southern. The radioactively labeled oncogene probe is now applied to the filter with the DNA. The filter is then placed on an X-ray film, on which a black band appears where hybridization has taken place.

A similar technique is applied using fragments of mRNA and is humorously referred to as Northern blotting. With this technique it is possible to establish whether oncogene amplification present in the DNA is in fact active, i.e. is actually transcribed.

*Detection of point mutations*

In order to detect point mutations in oncogenes, so-called oligonucleotides can be used. These are produced synthetically and are given a radioactive label. The various oligonucleotide probes differ only in the base sequence of one particular codon. These probes are hybridized with DNA fragments of the cells to be studied. Using advanced techniques, it is possible to establish which specific variation of the oligonucleotide probe hybridizes best.

### 3.3 ONCOGENESIS AS A MULTIPLE-STEP PROCESS

Transfection of DNA originating from human tumors to NIH 3T3 cells transforms these latter embryonic fibroblasts to cells forming foci. DNA originating from the same, but healthy, tissues does not have this property. Up to 20% of the tumors tested contain oncogenes, the transforming potency of which can be de-

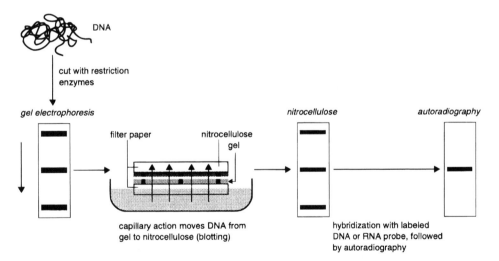

FIGURE   12.10

The Southern blot technique, used for specific analysis of DNA sequences

DNA is cut into fragments using one or more restriction enzymes. The fragments are separated by gel electrophoresis. DNA fragments of known composition are included as markers. The DNA is then denatured and transferred by capillary action from the gel to a nitrocellulose filter. Subsequently, specifically labeled DNA or RNA sequences can then be hybridized with the bound DNA. The hybrid nucleic acids are localized by means of autoradiography. The presence of certain known sequences in the restriction fragments can thus be detected. This technique is so sensitive that even a sequence which occurs only once in, for example, the human genome can be traced in a DNA sample of no more than 10 μg.

375

tected (the question why the remaining 80% apparently do not contain these oncogenes remains unanswered). The tested tumors include carcinomas of the intestine, lung, bladder, pancreas, skin and breast, as well as various sarcomas, including leukemia. In most cases, the oncogene responsible appears to belong to the *ras* family.

*Oncogene activation in human cancer cells*

Various types of oncogene activation have been encountered in the DNA of human cancer cells.

*Point mutations*

*Point mutations* in certain oncogenes have been found in human cells originating from gastric tumors, urinary bladder cancers, colon carcinomas and leukemias, in particular in c-*ras* genes.

*Gene amplification*

*Gene amplification* can also be demonstrated. In approximately 30% of the mammacarcinomas amplification of *erb*B-2 (*neu*)-oncogene has been found. In most cases amplification was observed in patients in an advanced stage of the disease. In neuroblastomas the N-*myc*-gene was shown to be amplified in grade II and grade IV tumors. Therefore, this amplification is thought to be involved in progression of the tumor.

*Translocation*

The classic example of a *translocation* has been described for a type of chronic leukemia involving an abnormality of chromosome 22 (the so-called *Philadelphia chromosome*). In this case, the c-*abl* gene translocates from chromosome 9 to chromosome 22. More complex translocations involving three or more chromosomes have also been described for this disease. Further, in human lymphomas, translocations of c-*myc* have been found. So far, researchers have not been able to determine the exact significance of oncogene translocations in the mechanism of carcinogenesis.

Despite the finding that only 20% of the human tumors studied so far display oncogene activity and that various cellular oncogene families are moreover involved through different activation mechanisms—in other words, despite the lack of consistency in the data available so far—an attempt has been made to develop a theoretical model describing the *role of cellular oncogenes in tumorigenesis*. The American Nobel prize winner Robert A. Weinberg has made his mark in this field.

*The role of cellular oncogenes in the formation of tumors*

When the above theory was developed, *spontaneous or chemically induced carcinogenesis* was already known to be a multistep process. In contrast, the activation of, for example, one H-*ras* gene is a single, individual event. It seems unlikely that activation of a single c-onc gene would be sufficient to lead to tumor formation *in vivo*. It is obvious that here too, a sequence of events plays a role. This is supported by experiments carried out in the NIH 3T3 transfection test. As we have seen from this test, *transfection of a single oncogene* is indeed capable of causing complete cell transformation.

*Transfection of a single oncogene*

If, other cell systems are used, such as a rat fibroblast line or secondary rat fibroblasts, the transforming effects of a single c-onc gene appear to be restricted. The only change initiated by the *ras* oncogene was that the cells could now grow without attachment of the cells being required. Normal cells should be attached in order to grow in a culture.

Cells should be attached to a matrix, for example another layer of cells or the surface of a culture medium.

Unlimited growth was however not possible for these *ras*-transfected cells. As was discussed above, if the *ras* gene is transfected to a more or less immortalized cell system such as the NIH 3T3 line, the transformation is reached in only one step. Apparently, the immortalized cells are able to transform rapidly and completely after addition of a *ras* gene to their genetic information.

*Co-transfection*
co-transfection = simultaneous
transfection

This has been confirmed in studies on the synergism of the *ras* gene and viral oncogenes. In particular, *co-transfection* of a *ras* gene with a v-*myc* gene was shown to induce transformation of the receiving cell.

This finding was supported by the analysis of a *Burkitt's lymphoma* in which an activated c-*myc* gene was found, together with an oncogene capable of transforming NIH 3T3 cells. An attempt was made to achieve controlled transfection of the secondary rat fibroblasts with a *ras* or *myc* gene of cellular origin, either individually or in combination. Here, too, only the *ras-myc* combination appeared to be capable of transforming the fibroblasts and stimulating them to form colonies. If the transformed fibroblasts were then transferred to a host animal, tumors did develop, but they ceased to grow when they had reached a diameter of 2 cm. It was not until a third oncogene was co-transfected (a viral oncogene which very effectively immortalizes cell cultures) that the tumors continued to grow until the host was killed.

*Oncogene interaction*

Thus, *interaction* of at least three oncogenes appears to be necessary for complete tumorigenesis.

## 3.4  TUMOR-SUPPRESSOR GENES

Although activated oncogenes play an important role in carcinogenesis they can be found in only 15% to 30% of human tumors. So, activation of oncogenes is just one part of the story. Recently, a second class of genes has been found which normally block neoplastic growth of cells; in cancer cells these genes are inactivated or lost. These so-called *tumor-suppressor genes* are functionally the opposite of oncogenes and in first instance they were called anti-oncogenes. Whatever the name used, their key feature is that both gene copies (alleles) must be damaged (inactivated) to give rise to malignant behavior, while one damaged copy of an oncogene may contribute to malignant transformation. At the moment, the list of tumor-suppressor genes is short as it is relatively difficult to find them. The first ones were detected by fusing tumor cells with normal cells or with normal microcells (cell fragments with only one or two chromosomes). If malignant behavior is suppressed in these hybrid cells, then one of the added normal chromosomes is thought to contain a tumor-suppressor gene. Since more experiments of this type are being carried out, the list of tumor-suppressor genes will grow steadily.

Important insights how tumor-suppressor genes contribute to malignant growth have been gained from the study of retinoblastoma, a pediatric eye tumor that occurs in both hereditary and sporadic forms. In the hereditary form, the tumors are manifest at an early age and usually bilateral and multifocal; predisposition appears to be transmitted in an autosomal dominant fashion. In contrast, in the sporadic form tumors are usually unilateral and unifocal. It is now known that both forms of retinoblastoma have a common mechanism: inactivation of both copies of a single gene in a single precursor cell. This "two hit" mechanism was already postulated by Knudson in 1971 based on statistical analysis of the retinoblastoma incidence. In hereditary retinoblastoma, one mutant allele would be inherited from a parent and would be present in all of the offspring's cells, including germ cells. In the retina cell already one allele is mutated, a second mutation in the other allele would elicit tumorigenesis. In sporadic retinoblastoma both alleles are intact and two mutations must occur somatically in the same cell to give rise to unifocal, unilateral tumors. It is obvious that this probability is much lower than in the hereditary form. Further studies have shown that the retinoblastoma gene (Rb gene) is a tumor-suppressor gene and that it is inactivated or deleted in a number of human cancers (see Table 12.10).

TABLE 12.10
Genetic changes in human tumors

| Tumor | Benign | Malignant |
|-------|--------|-----------|
|  | adenoma | adenocarcinoma |
|  | papilloma (polyp) | carcinoma |
|  | fibroma | fibrosarcoma |
|  | myxoma | myxosarcoma |
|  | lipoma | liposarcoma |
|  | chondroma | chondrosarcoma |
|  | osteoma | osteosarcoma |
|  | haemangioma | haemangiosarcoma |
|  | lymphangioma | lymphangiosarcoma |
|  | rhabdomyoma | rhabdomyosarcoma |
|  | leiomyoma | leiomyosarcoma |

*Myxomatous = slimy

The loss of chromosomal material is characteristic for many cancers and emphasizes the role of tumor-suppressor genes.

A particular enigmatic member of the tumor-suppressor gene family is the p53 gene (named after the weight of the encoded protein). Mutations in the p53 gene are one of the most common genetic alterations in human cancers. It is not yet clear how the tumor-suppressor gene encoded proteins might regulate cellular processes that prevent rampant proliferation. Any gene that functions in intracellular signal transduction pathways, conducting cell division, differentiation, tissue formation, or aging could potentially be a tumor-suppressor gene. At a more mechanistic level, these genes might be involved in the regulation of DNA replication or gene expression, progression through specific phases of the cell cycle, and the response to extracellular signals. Extracellular growth inhibiting signals will reach the cell by contact-inhibition, via gap junctions or through the action of cytokines (such as TGF-$\beta$). The reaction of the cell can be a pause in cell division (at the end of G1 just before the S phase), post-mitotic differentiation, aging, and apoptosis. In these interrelated pathways products of tumor-suppressor genes may function. Exact mechanisms have to be clarified in future research.

## 4 The colon carcinoma model

It has become clear that an accumulation of genetic events is crucial for the transformation of a normal cell into a cancer cell. As mentioned before a number of oncogenes have to be activated. The same holds true for the inactivation of tumor-suppressor genes. For example, Vogelstein and coworkers reconstructed a sequence of alterations leading to malignancy in the development of colorectal cancer (Figure 12.11). The development of normal colon epithelium into a carcinoma is divided into several adenoma stages; each transition is accompanied by a new genetic alteration. For instance the loss of p53 converts a late adenoma into a malignant carcinoma. So, it is a sequence of genetic alterations leading to more and more malignancy; it seems that each transition has its own genetic change. It includes sequential deletions and mutations of the genes: APC, MCC, K-ras, DCC and p53. After metastasis additional genetic aberations are also found.

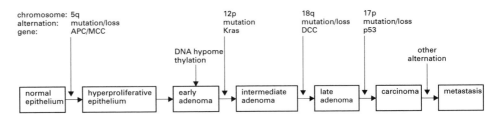

FIGURE 12.11
Multi stage model for colorectal cancer.

## 5 Summary

Since the beginning of the twentieth century, various studies have shown that chemical carcinogens do not supply the cell with any new information, but change the cell's own genetic material. Various researchers have come to the conclusion that there must be one or more genes responsible for the change from a healthy cell to a cancer cell. Such a gene was called an oncogene. In the early 1970s, the first oncogene (*src* oncogene) was isolated from a virus. It soon became obvious, however, that this oncogene was not a true viral gene, but a gene probably derived by the virus from a normal cell. The virus had changed the function of the gene and had somehow caused it to induce cancer.

Such adopted genes are called cellular oncogenes or proto-oncogenes. After infection with an oncogenic DNA virus, the viral genome is incorporated into the DNA of the host cell and is actively transcribed there. In the case of carcinogenic RNA viruses, first, a DNA copy is made after infection, followed by incorporation into the host genome.

Later, in 1976, researchers discovered that normal cells can contain proto-oncogenes. When using an oncogene as a hybridization probe, it also appeared to bind strongly to the DNA of normal cells. A large number of proto-oncogenes have been found in various organisms. It soon became apparent that these proto-oncogenes play an important role in normal cellular metabolism, in particular in the regulation of cellular growth. In the early 1980s, transfection experiments showed that cancer can be induced by non-viral genes.

In a number of spontaneous, probably non-viral tumors in man, and in the DNA of some chemically induced tumors in rats, comparable transforming genes have been detected. These transforming genes appeared to be identical to a cellular proto-oncogene. In transfection experiments, it could be demonstrated that these were activated DNA fragments.

Two ways are currently known in which oncogenes may be activated. Some retroviruses transform proto-oncogenes into oncogenes and some chemicals, hormones and radioactive radiation are also able to do this.

Using recombinant DNA techniques, it has been possible to determine the location where the change takes place in the *ras*-gene of one of the oncogenes. The gene is located at a segment composed of 350 nucleotides in which a single base has been altered. Guanine in the proto-oncogene has been replaced by thymine in the oncogene. This mutation thus involves a single nucleotide of the total of approximately 5000 in a normal human proto-oncogene!

One of the decisive steps in the process of tumor formation by chemical carcinogens could be the activation of proto-oncogenes. However important the function of the oncogene may be, it seems unlikely that activation of an oncogene is in itself sufficient to explain all the changes that occur when a normal cell develops into a tumor cell.

There are several ways in which a proto-oncogene can be activated:

- by a mutation in the oncogene itself; in this case proto-oncogenes and oncogenes differ in only one or a small number of nucleotides;

- by a non-mutagenic change of the oncogene itself, such as amplification. Gene amplification is accompanied by increased gene activity;

- by translocation of the proto-oncogene from one chromosome to another. The proto-oncogene may end up in an area which is actively transcribed.

Besides proto-oncogenes, genes have been discovered in which inactivation leads to uncontrolled cellular proliferation. These so-called tumor-suppressor genes have been found by fusion of tumor cells with normal cells, leading to non-tumorigenic hybrid cells. The loss of this type of growth regulating gene

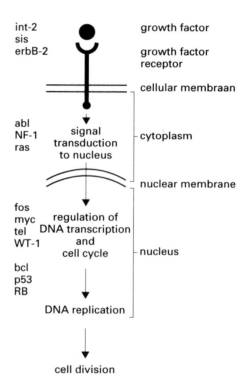

FIGURE 12.12

Functions of oncogenes and tumor-suppression genes (left) in the regulation of cell growth.

Growth factors—The sis-oncogene encoded product is part of platelet-derived growth factor (PDGF), which triggers endothelial cells to proliferate. The gene product of the oncogene int-2 has similarities with epidermal growth factor (EGF). It is obvious that activation of these genes can result in progression of tumor growth.

Growth factor receptors—The erbB-2-oncogene product is the receptor of a still unknown growth factor. Amplification can markedly increase the number of receptors leading to enhanced cell growth, by the action of growth factors.

Messenger molecules—The oncogene abl, the tumor-suppressor gene NF-I, and the ras genes are involved in intracellular signal transduction.

Transcription factors—The proteins of the oncogenes myc, fos, and tcl and of the tumor-suppressor gene WT-1 are functioning in DNA transcription in the nuclei. Amplification of myc and fos can lead to overexpression of these growth stimulating proteins in the absence of any extracellular signal.

Proteins regulating the cell cycle—The Rb-, p53- and bcl-proteins are involved in regulation of the cell cycle. The suppressor gene DCC encoded protein is a cell adhesion molecule; mutation or loss of this gene disrupts the intercellular relationship.

deli-neates the restrictions of normal cell growth. Point mutations and deletions are mechanisms which inactivate tumor-suppressor genes.

Products of oncogenes and tumor-suppressor genes play a role in the interaction between cells. The intercellular communication is crucial for the integrity of a normal functioning tissue. Normal cell behavior is not autonomous but responds to signals from neighboring cells. These extracellular signals regulate cellular differentiation and proliferation. The gene products of oncogenes and tumor-suppressor genes are functioning in this regulation as: growth factors, growth factor receptors, messenger molecules, transcription factors, and cell cycle regulating proteins. Figure 12.12 gives a schematic representation of the position of some products of oncogenes and tumor-suppressor genes in the regulation of cellular growth and differentiation.

SELF ASSESSMENT QUESTIONS

1   Many centuries ago, Galen distinguished between three types of tumors. Name the types and give examples.

2   Name the three hypotheses on cancer which were proposed in the nineteenth century.

3   What is the difference between cellular hypertrophy and hyperplasia?

4   Give three examples of tissues which can develop into sarcomas and into carcinomas.

5   Give the names of the four nucleophilic binding sites in cellular components.

6   What is the problem in patients who are suffering from *xeroderma pigmentosum*?

7   What is a mitogen?

8   How does vitamin E protect against carcinogenesis?

9   In what part of the body does asbestos induce neoplasms many years after chronic exposure?

10  What type of neoplasia can be caused by the AIDS virus and what mechanism is presumed here?

11  Give some examples of processes in which nitrosamines are formed.

FEEDBACK

1   **Answers to the assignments**

12.1 Tissue that is relatively autonomous, with regard to growth. The normal control mechanisms which determine tissue growth lose control over a particular cell population. As a result, these cells start to grow more or less independently and will ultimately overwhelm the organism.

12.2 A genotoxic carcinogen can alter the genetic information of a cell, so that relative autonomy for growth is acquired, or, in other words initiation is elicited. The promotion phase may be most adequately explained by an epigenetic mechanism, because in that phase the altered cells are stimulated to increased cell division, enabling the neoplasm to be visualized.

12.3 When the carcinogen has formed a covalent bond with critical binding sites in DNA, the cell tries to remove and replace the damaged DNA by means of DNA repair mechanisms. If the cell divides soon after the formation of the covalent bond, however, DNA repair may come too late. The mutations may already have become irreversibly fixed in the genetic material of the daughter cells, which may eventually develop into a clinically observable neoplasia.

12.4 Ionizing and non-ionizing radiation are genotoxic. Asbestos, solid-state reactions and chronic irritation are epigenetic.

12.5 I + O; result: no neoplasia
O + P; result: no neoplasia
P + I; result: no neoplasia
I + P; result: neoplasia
(I = administration of an initiator, P = administration of a promoter and O = no treatment)

12.6 A hepatotoxic dose of carbon tetrachloride causes centrilobular necrosis of the liver. The remaining liver cells react by dividing. The initiated cell population reacts more rapidly to this growth stimulus and gradually becomes more visible. If this process is repeated a few times, a neoplasia may form.

12.7 • Invasion into the surrounding tissue.

• Metastasis or dissemination in tissue that is further away via the bloodstream or the lymph vessels.

• Tumor vascularization or ingrowth of blood vessels into the neoplasm.

• Immunological defense or control by the immune system over the antigenically recognizable neoplasia.

12.8 Protein kinases phosphorylate enzymes using ATP. This may result in activation, but also in deactivation of the enzyme involved. In this way, intracellular regulation can be achieved. Protein kinases are of particular importance in the activation of membrane-bound receptors (hormone, etc.). If protein kinase activity is affected by non-physiological factors, this may imply pseudo-stimulation.

2   **Answers to the self assessment questions**

1  • Natural tumors, for example, breast development in female adolescence.

• Tumors which go beyond natural boundaries, for example bone swelling during the healing of a fracture.

• Unnatural tumors, for example, neoplasia.

2
- Irritation hypothesis
- Embryonic hypothesis
- Parasitic hypothesis

3   Hyperplasia is an increase in the number of cells. Cellular hypertrophy is an increase in cell dimensions.

4   Sarcoma: fat, muscle, bone

Carcinoma: intestine, skin, throat

5
- The sulfur atom in methionine
- Water
- The $O^2$ position of guanine
- The $O^2$ position of thymine

6   These patients have a genetic defect in their DNA repair mechanisms, as a result of which they have an increased sensitivity to cancer.

7   A mitogen is a substance which stimulates cell division, resulting in promotion.

8   Vitamin E is an anti-oxidant which scavenges reactive metabolites so that initiation through covalent binding to cellular macromolecules is inhibited.

9   In the mesothelium (pleura or peritoneum) and in the lungs.

10   Kaposi's sarcoma, which is assumed to be induced largely as a result of immunosuppression.

11   Cigarette smoking, drying of beer malt over an open fire, grilling nitrite-treated bacon.

# Contents Study unit 13
## Cancer risk evaluation

0-8493-9232-2/96/$0.00 + $.50
© 1996 by CRC Press, Inc.

# Study unit 13

# Cancer risk evaluation

*H. Van Cauteren, Th. M. C. M. de Kok and F.-J. van Schooten*

## INTRODUCTION

As indicated in the preceding study unit, the causes of cancer in humans and animals can be divided into three large groups. In addition to the physical agents, various types of biological agents or organisms are known to settle in the host and cause cancer. The largest group of carcinogens, however, consists of chemicals. Therefore, this group will be discussed in terms of their potential to induce cancer, and how to determine human cancer risk after exposure to chemicals. This cancer risk evaluation is based on a scientific integration of all available data regarding the potential of a given compound to induce genetic damage and the accompanying consequences for human health. The ultimate goal is to provide tools for health risk management. Based on a risk characterization, public health decisions can be made for risk reduction. In a complete risk evaluation, results of the qualitative analysis of the potential hazard (hazard assessment), exposure assessment and dose-response assessment are integrated (Figure 13.1).

Several aspects of exposure assessment will be addressed in section 1. Both the assessment of dose-response relationships and characterization of the potential human cancer hazard, are based on experimental research using *in vitro* cell systems as well as animal studies. The results from these studies, however, will always have to be extrapolated to the human situation. More direct evidence for identifying and characterizing the human cancer hazard potential is afforded by epidemiological studies in which cancer is attributed to exposure of a specific compound. Therefore, genetic biomarkers are gaining more and more attention. They can provide information on the level of exposure to a given agent, for instance by measurement of urinary excretion of a metabolite, or indicate an early effect on genetic material, such as the formation of DNA-adducts. Possibilities and limitations of both experimental research and (molecular) epidemiology will be discussed in this unit. The main problem in determining the potential carcinogenic hazard, however, is the integration of (frequently) conflicting evidence from epidemiological and experimental research.

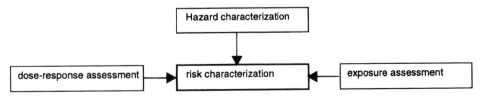

FIGURE 13.1
Major factors in human cancer risk characterization.

LEARNING OBJECTIVES

After studying this unit, you should be able to

— describe the most important research methods for determining carcinogenicity and compare some of these methods
— describe and explain the problems regarding the existence of a no-effect level
— indicate the most important determinants of human exposure to carcinogens
— describe the process of cancer risk evaluation
— describe the conceptual basis of using biomarkers in individual cancer risk assessment
— indicate the most important groups of carcinogenic compounds and describe their (possible) modes of action

*Study hints*

This study unit is a sequel to Study unit 12 and, as such, is closely linked with it. Before starting on the present unit, you should therefore review the principle concepts discussed there. Here several chemical structures will be introduced as an illustration. You do not have to learn these structures by heart, but you should understand the principles of the reaction mechanisms discussed. The study load is about 4 student learning hours.

## STUDY CORE

### 1 Exposure and genetic risk

The risk of developing cancer is strongly associated with the probability of being exposed and the level of exposure to chemical carcinogens. Exposure assessment has two different aspects. The first concerns the evaluation of the type, magnitude, duration and frequency of exposure, which provides information for estimating the concentration of the carcinogen to which a population or individual is exposed. In general, it is of importance for the determination of the total intake, to obtain data on exposure from various sources and intake by all exposure routes, e.g. oral, dermal and/or inhalation. By comparing the determined or estimated exposure level with information on genetic effects derived from epidemiological or experimental research, it is possible to estimate the type and severity of the effect (risk characterization). In order to determine whether a certain situation implies a non-acceptable genetic risk, results of the exposure assessment should be compared with available standards. The process of setting standards is discussed in Study unit 14. The second aspect of exposure assessment concerns the characterization of the exposed population. In addition to the number of exposed individuals in a given population, a profile of individuals at increased risk, for instance as a consequence of hypersensitivity, can be of importance. Usually, these latter aspects are of relevance for risk management, in case public health decisions have to be made concerning one specific population. Several aspects which are of direct influence or relate indirectly to exposure assessment, are discussed below.

### 1.1 OCCUPATIONAL EXPOSURE

In industrial processes, DNA reactive genotoxic carcinogens are very often used. In order to reduce health risks, most of these substances are processed in a closed circuit. Alkylating agents are often used as intermediates in the synthesis of chemical substances precisely because they are reactive and engage in covalent binding. After alkylation, their reactivity usually disappears. The end product which is removed from the circuit no longer reacts with DNA. The most important aspect at this stage is the purity of the end product, since this may still contain a significant residue of the intermediates. One example is the upholstery of a new car, which may contain measurable quantities of nitrosamines as residues of the vulcanization of the synthetic materials used to make the interior. Adequate ventilation is sufficient to solve this problem.

Most cases of exposure to industrial substances are occupational. Employees who are chronically in contact with carcinogens may run an increased risk of developing certain neoplasms. Well-known examples from the past include asbestos fibers in asbestos-mine workers or workers in the building trade, naphthylamines in dye factory workers and aromatic amines in rubber producers. More recent examples include people handling pesticides, working in PVC production, and working with asbestos-containing building materials. Such exposures can be avoided or minimized by the implementation of strict safety regulations at the workplace.

## 1.2  SOCIOCULTURAL FACTORS

*Smoking cigarettes*

Exposure to chemical carcinogens is frequently related to sociocultural habits. The first habit to be mentioned is undoubtedly *cigarette smoking*. Without going into the problem as such, it can be stated that cigarette smoke contains a broad range of carcinogens. The risk of neoplasia increases dose-dependently for the various organs, including in particular the lung, throat, esophagus and urinary bladder. WHO (World Health Organization) estimates show that the total incidence of cancer in the Western world would decrease by about one-third if all cigarette smoking were to stop. These figures are enormous and concern millions of people. An important aspect of the carcinogenicity of cigarette smoke is its activity as a promoter, as has been confirmed by epidemiological studies on former smokers. Cigarette smoking has an important synergistic carcinogenic effect on the development of neoplasms caused by other carcinogens, as for example in asbestosis or in miners exposed to radioactive elements.

*Alcohol*

Another sociocultural custom is the consumption of *alcohol*, which is not carcinogenic as such but can interfere with liver cancer by inducing alcoholic hepatic cirrhosis. There is also an increased risk of esophageal cancer in people who drink calvados (a type of French brandy). The precise mechanism involved is unknown.

*Eating habits*

One of the most important sociocultural habits with regard to exposure to carcinogens is *eating habits*.

The preservation of food with nitrates, or by smoking has largely been replaced by refrigeration and freezing. This has eliminated much of the exposure to carcinogens such as nitrosamines, resulting in a dramatic fall in the incidence of stomach cancer in the western world over the last few decades.

The preparation of food can be accompanied by the formation of significant quantities of carcinogens. The frying of proteins, for example those in meat, can result in the formation of pyrolysis products like polycyclic aromatic hydrocarbons, nitrosamines and tryptophan derivatives. Direct exposure to a flame, as in overgrilled meat on a barbecue, is the main cause of this type of food contamination.

*Composition of the diet*

Finally, the *composition of the diet* is important, as has been discussed in the previous study unit. One example that can be mentioned here is the consumption of mushrooms. Normal, edible mushrooms contain significant amounts of hydrazines, which evaporate during cooking or frying, and are therefore not consumed. In certain countries, for example the USA, mushrooms are very often eaten raw, which means that the hydrazines are also ingested.

ASSIGNMENT 13.1

Give some examples of important sociocultural habits which give rise to an increased risk of cancer. Explain what can be taken to counteract this.

### 1.3 THERAPEUTICAL EXPOSURE

Apart from accidental exposure, humans can also be intentionally exposed to chemicals as part of a certain medical treatment. However, virtually all drugs that are in use nowadays have been tested for their potential mutagenicity and carcinogenicity. Every prospective drug undergoes stringent tests. Apart from the genotoxic cytostatics, which are cytotoxic to cancer cells precisely because of their genotoxic mechanism, the development of a prospective drug is nearly always discontinued when it appears to be potentially genotoxic.

For the older drugs, research to determine genotoxic properties was and still is carried out after they have been developed. Because of this, a few cases are known where a drug proved to be carcinogenic in humans, which was confirmed only later in experimental models.

The International Agency for Research on Cancer (IARC) has played a very important part in the evaluation of the carcinogenicity of drugs. In 1980, for example, an IARC book was issued in which the carcinogenicity of existing suspected drugs was evaluated (cf. IARC monograph, Volume 24, 1980). The principal drugs involved are listed in Table 13.1.

Human drugs which are carcinogenic via a mutagenic mechanism are no longer developed, unless their value outweighs their risk. This is the case for anticancer drugs which kill cancer cells by virtue of their toxic interaction at the DNA level. Such drugs are permitted, although preparations that do not induce point or gene mutations are preferred, particularly in the treatment of comparatively young cancer patients. In that case, after the original cancer has been cured, a second neoplasm may appear many years later, as a result of the treatment with a potent mutagenic drug. This has been observed with direct alkylating agents such as mustard gas derivatives or cyclophosphamide.

For non-mutagenic human drugs that cause carcinogenic effects in studies on rodents, the cancer risk is assessed with the aid of the dose-response curve and supplementary experiments that try to trace the mechanism of the carcinogeni-

TABLE 13.1

Drugs which may be carcinogenic to animals and humans

| group | example | type of neoplasia (species) |
|---|---|---|
| hyperprolactinemic substances | neuroleptic agents | mammary gland neoplasia (mouse) |
| hypolipemic substances | clofibrate | liver cancer (rat) |
| analgesics | phenacetin | urinary bladder cancer (man) |
| sedatives | phenobarbitone | liver cancer (rat, mouse) |
| immunosuppressants | cyclophosphamide | urinary bladder cancer (man) |
| antibacterial substances | arsenic | skin, lung and liver cancer (man) |
| | metronidazole | liver cancer (rat) |
| antifungal agent | griseofulvin | liver cancer (mouse) |

city. Moreover, it can often be checked whether this mechanism is also present in humans. If this is not the case, it is assumed that in humans exposure to a low dose carries a negligible cancer risk. This line of reasoning has been followed for various drugs.

## 1.4 EXPOSURE TO NATURAL CARCINOGENS

The group of natural carcinogens is extremely important in the induction of cancer in humans and may, together with the earlier mentioned sociocultural carcinogens, in fact be the most important of all.

Table 13.2 shows a classification of these agents, illustrated by some examples. Some of these compounds have already been discussed in previous sections, others are new. A few will now be discussed briefly.

*Carcinogenic fungal products*

The best known *carcinogenic fungal products* are the *aflatoxins*. To date, aflatoxin B1 has proven to be the most potent liver carcinogen in the rat. In a cancer study, positive results were found at 1 ppb (one-thousandth of a milligram per kg food). Cereals and ground-nuts, especially, can be infested with *Aspergillus flavus* or *Penicillium puberculum* during growth and after harvesting, particularly in warm and humid climates and under poor storage conditions. In this way, humans and animals can be chronically exposed to aflatoxins. The increased incidence of liver cancer in the populations of certain developing countries is largely attributable to this factor.

*Mushroom*

Like many other fungi, the classical edible fungus, the mushroom, contains hydrazine derivatives which are released after acidic hydrolysis and can subsequently exert their carcinogenic effect. Thus, methylhydrazine can be released from gyromitrin. During cooking, the gyromitrin decomposes and the methylhydrazine evaporates. As a result, these mushrooms constitute a risk only if eaten raw.

*Summary*

The risk of getting cancer is strongly associated with the chance and magnitude of exposure to chemical carcinogens. Both chance and magnitude of exposure may depend on factors like occupational circumstances, medical treatment, environmental and life style factors, such as eating and smoking habits. Knowledge of both source and route of exposure may indicate ways of reduction of the genetic risk.

## 2 Risk evaluation of carcinogens

*Epidemiological research*

*Experimental research*

The aim of applied research on carcinogenicity is to determine the risk of carcinogenicity to humans. To this end, two approaches are possible: *epidemiological research* in humans and *experimental research* using *in vitro* models or laboratory animals (Table 13.3 provides an overview). Furthermore, physico-chemical properties, as well as data on reaction mechanisms, biological availability and biotransformation may be important to the determination of the potential carcinogenic hazard.

Existing suspected agents are evaluated by the IARC, a group sponsored by the World Health Organization (WHO). In the case of new chemical substances, including new drugs, the manufacturer is responsible for the evaluation that is carried out when he applies for registration. Evaluation of such new compounds can, of course, only be based on experimental data, since human epidemiological exposure data are not available yet.

TABLE 13.2
Naturally occurring carcinogens

|  |  | example |
|---|---|---|
| *physical agents* | non-ionizing radiation | ultraviolet light |
|  | ionizing radiation | natural isotopes |
|  | particles | asbestos fibres |
| *chemical agents* |  |  |
| -inorganic | metals | cadmium |
|  | non-metals | hydrazine |
| -organic | macromolecular infectious organisms | cancer viruses |
|  | low-molecular-weight chemicals: |  |
|  | -bacterial products | ethionine |
|  |  | nitrosamines |
|  | -yeast products | ethyl carbamate |
|  | -products of actinomycetes | streptozotocin |
|  |  | actinomycin D |
|  |  | adriamycin |
|  | -fungal products | aflatoxin |
|  |  | griseofulvin |
|  |  | mushroom hydrazines |
|  | -plant products: |  |
|  | pyrrolizidine alkaloids | *Senecio* alkaloids |
|  | glucosides | cycasin |
|  | allyl and propenyl arenes | safrole |
|  |  | estragole |
|  |  | myristicin |
|  | derivatives of 3-furoic acid | ipomeanol |
|  |  | perilla ketone |
|  | hormones | zearalenone |
|  |  | genistein |
|  | -animal products: |  |
|  | natural hormones | estradiol |

TABLE 13.3
Evaluation of carcinogenic agents: overview

| *epidemiological research in humans* |  |
|---|---|
| *experimental research* (*short-term tests*) | mutagenesis: |
|  | -DNA damage and repair |
|  | -point and gene mutation |
|  | -chromosomal aberrations |
|  | *in vitro* cell transformation |
|  | *in vitro* promotion |
|  | *in vivo* carcinogenesis (initiation-promotion models): |
|  | -skin papilloma (mouse) |
|  | -lung adenoma (mouse) |
|  | -liver neoplasia (mouse/rat) |
| *experimental research* (*long-term tests*) | carcinogenicity studies in rodents |

## 2.1 EXPERIMENTAL RESEARCH

The experimental research can be divided into short-term and long-term tests.

### 2.1.1 Short-term tests

Short-term tests include mutagenesis tests, *in vitro* cell transformation tests, *in vivo* promotion tests and short-term *in vivo* carcinogenesis tests.

*Mutagenesis tests*

The three types of mutagenesis test (DNA damage, point mutations, gene mutations and chromosomal damage) provide information on the direct genotoxicity of a chemical, physical or biological agent. Positive results in just one, but even more so in several tests, in this battery, show that the risk of *in vivo* carcinogenicity following prolonged exposure is great, because the agent can act as an initiator, which is an early and irreversible event.

A more detailed discussion of mutagenesis tests can be found in Study unit 11.

*In vitro cell transformation test*

The in *vitro cell* transformation test involves altering the growth characteristics of a cell culture.

*In vitro promotion test*

Substances acting as a promoter of *in vivo* carcinogenesis can be tested for this property *in vitro*, in the so-called V79 metabolic cooperation test. This test is based on the detection of a lack of communication between cells, which is regarded as a characteristic of promoters. Further research, including the mechanism of intercellular communication, is required to validate this test.

*In vivo carcinogenesis*

Short-term studies of *in vivo* carcinogenesis are comparatively recent. Nevertheless, they have already become quite popular, because, linked with long-term cancer studies in rodents, they investigate the mechanism of carcinogenesis as well. These studies can be used to differentiate between initiators and promoters. Besides the *skin papilloma* and *lung adenoma models* in mice, there is also the *initiation–promotion model of liver neoplasia* in mice and rats.

*Skin papilloma model in the mouse*

This test distinguishes between the initiation and promotion phases, so that true promoters can be differentiated from partial carcinogens (initiators) and complete carcinogens. The test is limited to the study of skin carcinogenesis, and it is unclear whether it can be applied for determining carcinogenesis in other organs or tissues.

*Lung adenoma model*

The lung adenoma model in the mouse is based on the fact that a 100% incidence rate of multiple lung adenomas develops in a special strain of mice (strain A) in a lifetime study. In a short-term study, an agent may raise the incidence of lung adenomas and/or cause increased multiplicity by shortening the latency period of the adenomas. Various carcinogens can indeed achieve this effect. However, the main problem with this model is that the end point is always a benign neoplasia, which does not occur in humans.

*(margin labels)* Mutagenesis tests · In vitro cell transformation test · In vitro promotion test · In vivo carcinogenesis · Skin papilloma · Skin papilloma model in the mouse · Lung adenoma model

## Initiation–promotion model for liver neoplasia in mice and rats

The principle of this model is that in order to evaluate a substance as an *initiator*, it is administered in a single dose or over a period of several days or weeks, often after partial hepatectomy to increase the chances of fixation. After several weeks of wash-out, a known promoter (e.g. phenobarbital) is administered in the food, and some months later the number of preneoplastic point lesions, neoplastic benign nodules and hepatocellular carcinomas is assessed (though the latter are often not yet present).

To evaluate whether an agent acts as a *promoter*, the procedure is reversed. Following initiation with a known initiator (e.g. diethylnitrosamine) the substance under investigation is administered orally, at different dosages, over a number of months. This model is valuable in establishing in retrospect the mechanism underlying carcinogenicity, observed in the liver during a long-term study. Liver neoplasia in rodents, and particularly in the mouse, shows an extremely sensitive reaction when the dose of a substance is slightly hepatotoxic. For this reason, liver neoplasia is a frequent problem in long-term studies. For example, the initiation-promotion model has been used to investigate the mechanism of liver neoplasia for certain drugs, pesticides and antioxidants. If it is to provide prospective information on initiator versus promoter properties, however, the model needs to be more standardized than it is at present.

### 2.1.2 Long-term tests

Long-term tests include the so-called lifetime cancer studies in rodents. Such a study can be regarded as a study of a minipopulation of animals that are exposed for the greater part of their lives to different dosages of the substance under investigation. The eventual incidence of neoplasia is then compared with that in an untreated control population.

These studies were first carried out in the 1960s and notorious carcinogens for humans, which had been identified as such by epidemiological studies, produced clearly positive test outcomes (the only exception to date are the arsenic derivatives).

New substances that are clearly positive in these cancer studies are therefore also assumed to be potentially positive in humans, unless epidemiological research shows otherwise. Hence, these studies, using rats and mice (and sometimes also hamsters) are carried out for every existing substance that is suspect, as well as every new substance to which humans will be exposed to any degree. This is the case for new drugs for humans and animals, for new phytochemicals and for new chemicals that are synthesized and traded in large quantities.

## 2.2 MOLECULAR EPIDEMIOLOGY

### 2.2.1 Classical epidemiology

Epidemiology is the study of the occurrence and distribution of diseases in populations, and the identification and quantification of associations between exposures and occurrence of disease. The classical methods of cancer epidemiology have worked well in identifying groups of people who have a high risk of developing cancer. A clear example of this is the association between smoking and lung cancer, which made people aware of the dangers of smoking and to some extent causing them to change their smoking habits. In other words cancer epidemiology has proven its value in cancer prevention. At this point the role of epidemiology in cancer risk assessment will not be discussed in further detail, but the problem of the determination of individual risk will be focused on.

392

### 2.2.2 Molecular epidemiology

When it comes to predicting individual risk, classical epidemiology does not help. Conclusions can only be drawn at the population level and not at the individual level. One of the main problems is that individuals vary dramatically in their responses to carcinogens. For example, only one of ten cigarette smokers actually comes down with lung cancer, which is why classical epidemiology is helpless when asked the question every individual most wants to be answered: "What's my risk of cancer?" A promising development is the new field of molecular epidemiology which potentially can give answers to this question.

*Molecular epidemiology*
*Individual cancer risk*

*Molecular cancer epidemiology* integrates techniques of analytical chemistry, biochemistry, molecular biology and epidemiology to assess *an individual's cancer risk*. This approach may contribute to cancer prevention in a number of areas including the early identification of risk to humans and quantitative risk extrapolation. Central to molecular cancer epidemiology is the study of carcinogen exposure, metabolism, and DNA repair. These factors determine the biologically effective dose of a carcinogen. Equally important, an individual's cancer risk is related to endogenous rates of mutation, genetic instability and non-mutagenic genetic damage.

*Biomarker*

To assess cancer risk far before the onset of clinical symptoms of disease, molecular epidemiology makes use of biological monitoring and so-called *biomarkers*. Biomarkers include measurable biochemical, physiological, cytological, immunological or molecular changes in a biological system related—directly or indirectly—to exposure as well as measurable levels of metabolites in body fluids or compartments. *Biomarkers of exposure, biomarkers of genetic damage* and *markers of susceptibility* can be distinguished.

#### a.    Biomonitoring and biomarkers of exposure

*For monitoring, see Study unit 40*

Classical monitoring strategies to estimate exposure to genotoxic agents are based on measurements of the levels of a compound present in ambient air, for instance personal air sampling of exposed workers. This approach has been called *environmental monitoring*. Estimation of external exposure predicts only the approximate dose received by an organism and gives no information what is really entering a person; a large interindividual variation exists in absorption of a compound. A generally more integrated way of estimating and evaluating an individual's exposure is through biological monitoring. *Biological monitoring* has advantages above environmental monitoring because it measures the internal dose of a compound. Individual differences in absorption, bioavailability, excretion and DNA repair are taken into account. Biological monitoring can be divided into:

(i)    *measuring the internal dose* by chemical analysis of the parent compound—or metabolite—in body fluids or excreta such as blood, urine and expired air.; or

(ii)   *measuring the biological effective dose*, that is the critical dose that actually gets to the site of action or interacts with cellular macromolecules such as DNA and proteins.

Genotoxic carcinogens produce interaction products with macromolecules in the cell such as proteins and DNA. To assess the biological effective dose, molecular epidemiologists have focused on measuring protein- and DNA-adducts. Protein-adducts are considered to be substitutes for DNA-adducts in monitoring carcinogen exposure. Amino acid moieties such as histidine, cysteine and

N-terminal valine in proteins interact with reactive metabolites. Although proteins are thought not to be involved in the carcinogenic process *per se*, it is their abundant accessibility from human blood in the form of hemoglobin and serum albumin that has made them attractive for molecular epidemiology.

Since DNA-adducts may be mechanistically related to carcinogenesis, various sensitive methods to measure DNA-adducts have been developed during the last decade. The most important methods are *$^{32}$P-post labeling assays* and *immunochemical assays*. These methods have been successfully applied, for instance, in molecular epidemiological studies on humans exposed to polycyclic aromatic hydrocarbons (PAHs), e.g. cigarette smokers and occupationally exposed coke oven workers. PAHs are formed during incomplete combustion of organic material and can be found in tar and tar fumes, and tobacco smoke. In lung cancer patients a clear correlation has been found between smoking habits and the levels of PAH-DNA-adducts in lung tissue (which was obtained during surgery). Another observation was that in PAH-exposed experimental animals the levels of PAH-DNA-adducts correspond with the tumorigenic response in the lung. Combining human and animal data, it is tempting to speculate that DNA-adduct measurements in lung tissue are indicative of lung cancer risk in smokers. A problem in this area is the inaccessibility of lung tissue from a healthy smoker. To obtain DNA from an ambulant person, the molecular epidemiologist is restricted towards the relatively easy obtainable white blood cells. Yet it is not known whether DNA from white blood cells can be used as a substitute for lung DNA. Are the levels found in white blood cells a good index for the levels in the lung? This question needs to be answered before DNA-adduct measurements in white blood cells can be used for risk assessment in smokers.

### b. Biomarkers of genetic damage

Because of increasing knowledge of genetic alterations in cancers, the use of genetic markers has become intriguing for molecular epidemiologists. In addition to traditional cytogenetic markers (e.g. chromosomal aberrations, sister chromatide exchanges, micronuclei), genetic markers include other alterations in chromosomal structure such as *restriction fragment length polymorphisms* (RFLPs), loss of heterozygosity, and translocation markers. More recent, specific genetic changes have been identified as critical molecular events in the initiation and development of many cancers. Important among these are *activation of oncogenes*, particularly those of the *ras* family, and *inactivation of tumor-suppressor genes* (e.g., *p53* and *Rb*) by point mutation and/or chromosomal deletions and other structural changes (see also Study unit 12). The relevance of genetic markers is mainly the detection of early biological responses, in efforts to relate exposure to carcinogens to initiating events in the cancer process. This field of research is still in an early stage and future years will show whether genetic markers can be used in individual risk assessment.

### c. Susceptibility markers

In the human population a number of genetic polymorphisms of enzyme activities involved in carcinogen metabolism can be distinguished, both in activating and detoxicating systems.

*Markers of polymorphisms of activating systems* are measurements of the activity of cytochrome P-450 enzymes. The family of cytochrome P-450 enzymes is involved in the conversion of carcinogens into reactive metabolites. A number of P-450 isoenzymes have been identified, and it appears that more than 1000-fold interindividual differences can be found in terms of quantity, substrate specificity and tissue distribution. An example is the cytochrome P-450 isoenzyme (the P-450 IID6 locus) that is involved in the metabolism of blood pressure lowering drugs; the human population can be divided into high, medium and low metabolizers. High metabolizers of debrisoquine have an increased risk for lung cancer.

*Markers of polymorphisms of detoxicating systems* are measurements of the activity of conjugating enzymes such as glutathione-S-transferases, acetyltransferases, sulfotransferases and glucuronyltransferases. For instance, predisposition to cancer has been correlated with genetic polymorphisms of N-acetyltransferases. N-acetyltransferase is an enzyme involved in the deactivation of aromatic amines. After acetylation there is enhanced excretion in urine. Subjects are classified as 'rapid' or 'slow' acetylators, based on their ability to acetylate isoniazid (see also Study unit 4). It has been shown that in a group of arylamine exposed workers the 'slow acetylators' are at increased risk for bladder cancer versus 'rapid acetylators'. Another example is glutathione-S-tranferase μ, an enzyme involved in the detoxication of reactive metabolites. Half of the population has no functional allele for this enzyme and no or low enzyme activity. These persons are at increased risk of lung cancer.

DNA repair enzymes, responsible for the removal of adducts, may also play a role in genetic predisposition to cancer. Depressed rates of DNA repair have been observed in patients with xeroderma pigmentosum, a disorder that increases the susceptibility to UV-induced skin cancer.

Figure 13.2 gives a schematic representation of the position of the developed biomarkers in the sequential cascade of carcinogenic events.

## 3 Classification of chemical carcinogens

### 3.1 INTEGRATION OF EPIDEMIOLOGICAL AND EXPERIMENTAL EVIDENCE

For the classification of chemical carcinogens all relevant data on human potential cancer risk should be combined and integrated. This concerns evidence from both epidemiological and experimental research as was described in the

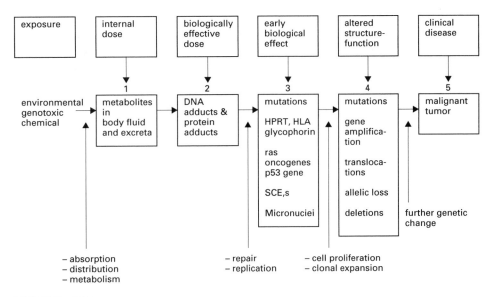

FIGURE 13.2

Conceptual basis for the development of biomarkers for use in molecular epidemiology. SCE, sister chromatide exchange (After Wogan, 1992).

preceding section. Experience shows that type and amount of available information of each carcinogen is different and can vary from a few physico-chemical properties to a wealth of epidemiological data. Frequently, the only direct evidence for potential risk evaluation are results from a long-term animal carcinogenicity test. In that case it is assumed that chemicals inducing tumors in animal studies also pose a carcinogenic hazard to humans. Nevertheless, toxic consequences in humans may be different from those observed in experimental animals due to mechanistic, physiological and biochemical differences or due to a different route of entry. Comparable problems may arise during extrapolation of results from high to low doses, from continuous to intermittent exposures or from one route of exposure to another. Each assumption and extrapolation should be examined for mechanistic and biological plausibility. It will be obvious that such an evaluation is a multidisciplinary and often difficult task.

After critical evaluation, the total body of evidence may be classified into a number of categories. Category 1 contains evidence demonstrating a clear causal relationship between exposure and carcinogenicity, based on relevant and well performed research. On the other hand, evidence from category 4 indicates that repeatedly, no positive relationship is found between exposure and the development of cancer. Figure 13.3 summarizes how by judgment of weight of evidence the carcinogenic hazard can be established.

The judgment of evidence as described above may be summarized in a classification using either an alphnumerical system or brief narrative statements like: 'Known', 'Highly likely', 'Likely', 'Some evidence' or 'Not likely' to be a human carcinogen. However, the entire process of judgment and evaluation of evidence for carcinogenicity as well as the classification of the potential carcinogenic risk is still under development.

It should be stressed that hazard characterization is a qualitative process, and does not address the magnitude or extent of effects under actual exposure conditions. These will be included in the final risk characterization, in which all available data on the potential risk, dose-response relationship as well as exposure assessment are integrated.

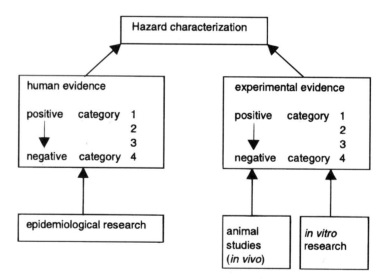

FIGURE    13.3
Hazard characterization by judgment of weight of evidence for epidemiological and experimental research.

## 3.2 CLASSIFICATION OF CHEMICAL CARCINOGENS ON THE BASIS OF THE MODE OF ACTION

Apart form a classification based on the potential carcinogenic risk, carcinogens may also be subdivided into various groups based on other characteristics. Several classes of chemical carcinogens can be distinguished on the basis of their (supposed) modes of action (see Table 13.4).

Additionally, this group of carcinogens can be classified by origin. This approach is important regarding the attempt to avoid exposure to carcinogens. At the same time it emphasizes the fact that naturally occurring carcinogens can be a potential source of carcinogens.

Analogous to section 1, a classification based on origin is presented in Table 13.5. In this section however, only the classification based on mode of action will be elaborated on.

*Genotoxic carcinogens*

*Genotoxic carcinogens* (Table 13.4) as a group encompass substances which alkylate DNA, with or without prior enzymatic activation (the procarcinogens and direct alkylating agents, respectively). A second group consists of chemicals which interfere with DNA in a different way than by direct alkylation. An example is the interaction between DNA polymerase and certain metal compounds.

TABLE 13.4

Classification of chemical carcinogens based on their mode of action

|  | mode of action | example |
|---|---|---|
| *genotoxic carcinogens* (*initiators*) | DNA-alkylating -direct alkylating -procarcinogenic agents | mustard gas nitrosamines, benzo[a]-pyrene |
|  | interfering with DNA (DNA polymerase interaction) | metal compounds |
| *epigenetic carcinogens* (*promoters*) | mitogenic agents -endogenic -exogenic | hormones phenobarbital |
|  | cytotoxic agents -non-specific cytotoxicity -specific toxicity (proliferation of peroxisomes) | $CCl_4$ clofibrate |
|  | immunosuppressive agents | cyclophosphamide |

TABLE 13.5

Classification of chemical carcinogens based on their origin

| 1 synthetic (man-made) carcinogens | 2 natural carcinogens |
|---|---|
| industrial substances sociocultural substances drugs | microbial substances of -fungi -actinomycetes -bacteria substances derived from plants substances derived from animals metals |

*Epigenetic carcinogens* do not interfere directly with the genetic material. The substances in this heterogeneous group are known as *promoters* and their mode of action is mainly based on the induction of increased tissue growth or cell division. This can take place in a direct, more specific manner (*mitogenic agents*) and/or indirectly, through some form of cytotoxicity (*cytotoxic agents*). Moreover, epigenetic carcinogens can stimulate the process of tumor formation by being immunosuppressive.

This section looks at the various classes separately. It concludes with a brief discussion of chemical carcinogens with reference to their origins. However, a few general remarks must be made first. Many genotoxic carcinogens are also epigenetically active (so-called *complete carcinogens*). They are, however, in the first instance classified as genotoxic agents. Some epigenetic carcinogens have been shown to act via various mechanisms, while the mode of actions of others is only partly known. In such cases, the best known mode of action is used as a criterion to classify them.

When looking at the origin of carcinogens a distinction can be made between synthetic and natural carcinogens (Table 13.5).

### 3.2.1  *Genotoxic Carcinogens*

### I      *DNA-alkylating carcinogens*

This group contains the most 'classical' chemical carcinogens. It can be further subdivided into two groups: direct alkylating substances and procarcinogens (Table 13.5)

### I.1     *Directly alkylating agents*

These are chemicals which do not require enzymatic activation to bind covalently to DNA. Their chemical reactivity is an intrinsic property of their chemical structure. Electrophilic groups are present in these molecules and their reaction with nucleophilic groups in the cells occurs spontaneously. The best known classes are the mustard gases and certain active halogen compounds (see Figure 13.4).

In addition to the directly alkylating agents, there are agents which require the presence of water for their alkylating effect. Without water they are stable but addition of water causes their hydrolytic decomposition, following which alkylating or acylating groups are released. A well-documented example is *N*-methyl-*N*-nitrosourea (NMU).

$$CH_3-\underset{\underset{NO}{|}}{N}-\overset{\overset{O}{\|}}{C}-NH_2 \quad \xrightarrow{H_2O} \quad CH_3-\overset{+}{N}\equiv NOH^- + O=C=NH$$

|  | methyldiazonium | isocyanic acid |
| NMU | ion = alkylating | = acylating |

Finally, there are also directly acylating agents, with dimethylcarbamoyl chloride as a well-known representative:

$$(CH_3)_2N-\overset{\overset{O}{\|}}{C}-Cl$$

*mustard gases*

bis(2-chloroethyl)sulfide (mustard gas, Yperite)

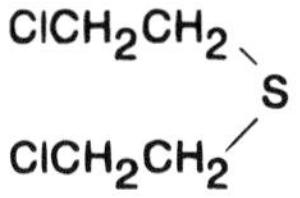

$ClCH_2CH_2$
$S$
$ClCH_2CH_2$

bis(2-chloroethyl)amine (nor-nitrogen mustard gas: R = H, nitrogen mustard gas: R = $CH_3$

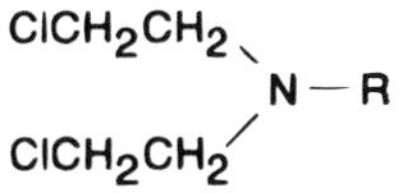

$ClCH_2CH_2$
$N - R$
$ClCH_2CH_2$

cyclophosphamide (cytoxan)

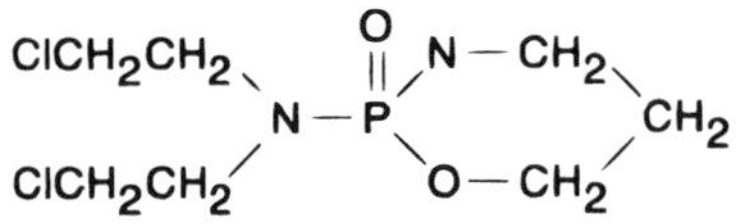

$ClCH_2CH_2$
$N - P$
$ClCH_2CH_2$
O
$N - CH_2$
$CH_2$
$O - CH_2$

2-naphthylamine mustard (chloronaphazine)

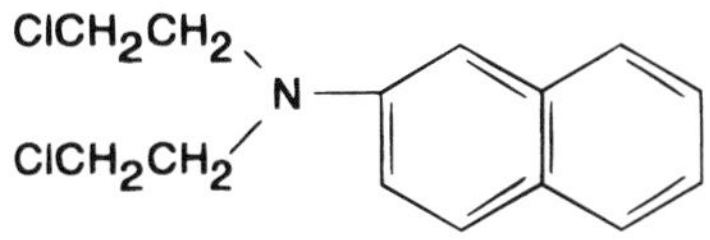

$ClCH_2CH_2$
$N$
$ClCH_2CH_2$

tri-ethylene melamine

$H_2C - CH_2$
$N$
$H_2C$
$N$
$H_2C$
$CH_2$
$N$
$CH_2$

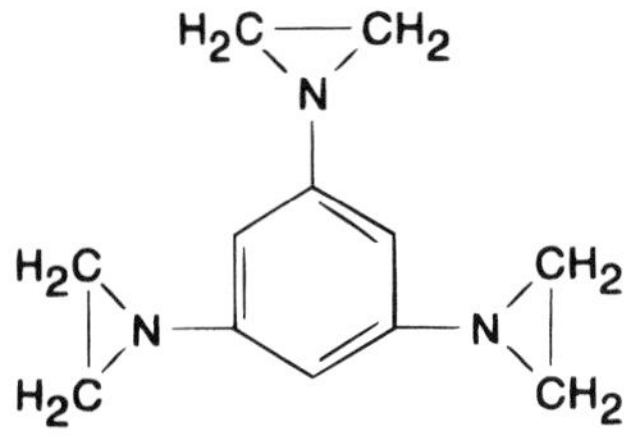

*active halogen compounds*

bis(chloromethyl)ether

$ClCH_2OCH_2Cl$

benzyl chloride

$C_6H_5CH_2Cl$

methyl iodide

$CH_3I$

dimethylcarbamoyl chloride

$(CH_3)_2NCOCl$

FIGURE 13.4
Some examples of direct alkylating carcinogenic chemicals

## I.2 *Procarcinogenic agents*

The majority of genotoxic carcinogens require one or more enzymatic activation steps before they become reactive metabolites. This category is fairly heterogeneous. The various chemical groups will be discussed individually. They are:

a. nitrosamines
b. aromatic amines and nitro derivatives
c. polycyclic aromatic hydrocarbons
d. heterocyclic aromatic hydrocarbons
e. hydrazines
f. halogenated hydrocarbons
g. formaldehyde

For each group one or more examples will be given.

*a.    Nitrosamines*

*Nitrosamines*

This is a very important group of carcinogens. Their basic structure is:

$$R \diagdown \atop R' \diagup N-N=O$$

The prototype, dimethylnitrosamine, used to be applied as a solvent. It was later found to be severely hepatotoxic for humans and animals and, in particular, hepatocarcinogenic in rats and mice. Virtually all nitrosamines are carcinogenic and most of them act on a particular target organ. Dimethylnitrosamine and diethylnitrosamine mainly cause liver cancer in rats, while dibutylnitrosamine induces mainly cancer of the urinary bladder. Others, for example the asymmetric nitrosamines, chiefly induce esophageal cancer. The effect may be different for different animal species. In hamsters, for example, diethylnitrosamine also causes cancer of the respiratory tract, while 2,6-dimethylnitrosomorpholine is responsible for neoplasms of the exocrine pancreas. Nitrosamines are mainly formed by the reaction of a secondary amine with nitrite.

$$2\,HNO_2 \rightleftarrows N_2O_3 + H_2O$$

$$R_2NH + N_2O_3 \longrightarrow R_2N-NO + HNO_2$$

$$R_2NH + HNO_2 \longrightarrow R_2N-NO + H_2O$$

This reaction is known as nitrosation and is stimulated by thiocyanates. These are often derived from cyanogenic glycosides present in normal dietary components. Aldehydes also stimulate nitrosation, by acting as catalysts. Nitrosation can be inhibited by vitamins C and E. The former stimulates the reduction of the nitrite ion, while the latter itself reacts with the nitrite ion, thus preventing nitrosation of secondary amines.

Nitrosamines are the subject of much interest, not only because they occur in large quantities in the macro-environment, but also because they are formed in the organism itself (the micro-environment). In this respect the gastrointestinal tract constitutes the most important micro-environment.

*Sources of nitrosamines*

The *sources of nitrosamines* in the macro-environment are diverse. They can be expected to be present in tanneries, in the upholstery of new automobiles, and also in certain cosmetics. Treatment of meat with nitrites, common practice in the past, also gives rise to the formation of nitrosamines. Heating also leads to nitrosamine formation. This is why frying bacon which has been treated with nitrite results in nitrosamine formation. Beer and whisky may contain traces of nitrosamines if the malt has been dried over an open fire. In cigarette smoke this effect is many times stronger. N-nitrosomorpholine, N-nitrosoanabisine and N-nitrosonicotine are produced in large quantities in cigarette smoke, as nitrates as well as thiocyanates occur in substantial amounts in tobacco.

The problem of nitrosamines in preserved food is directly related to the use of nitrites. Treating meat and fish with nitrates and nitrites is a practice which dates back several centuries. It was done not only to preserve the meat but also to prevent botulism, a frequently fatal food poisoning by bacterial toxins. The development of other preservation techniques, in particular deep-freezing, has largely solved this problem. Other means of food preservation, such as the addition of vitamin E and potassium sorbate, have also reduced the use of nitrites and hence the formation of nitrosamines. Correspondingly, there has been a sharp decline in stomach cancers in the Western countries over the last few decades. This could well be largely attributable to the changes in food-preservation techniques.

*Endogenous formation of nitrosamines*

As far as the micro-environment is concerned, the gastrointestinal tract is one location where large quantities of nitrosamines can be formed. The main source of nitrites here is *endogenous formation*, which means they are not necessarily derived from preserved meat products. Nitrates are formed by the bacterial degradation of proteins in the intestine, or are present as such in substantial quantities in vegetables. After absorption in the gastrointestinal tract they are excreted in the saliva. The bacterial flora of the oral cavity reduce these nitrates to nitrites, which are then transported to the gastrointestinal tract. Nitrites are thus mainly formed endogenously, and nitrosation of secondary amines with the help of catalysts (e.g. aldehydes or thiocyanates) takes place predominantly in the large intestine. This process appears to occur less frequently in the stomach, except in patients whose gastric secretion is inadequate.

Normally, the low pH prevents permanent bacterial colonization of the gastric lumen. However, this is not so in patients who have undergone partial vagotomy as a treatment for gastric ulcers. This surgical procedure strongly increases the pH, so that bacteria can settle in the stomach. This leads to measurable levels of nitrosamines in the stomach. Recent data show that these patients run a higher risk of developing stomach neoplasms. Such neoplasms often do not become apparent until several decades after the operation.

As has already been stated, the main inhibitors of nitrosamine formation in the gastrointestinal tract are certain antagonists, for example the vitamins E and C. However, manipulation of the bacterial flora can also play an important part. A fiber-rich diet, for example, is assumed to inhibit the nitrosating flora.

ASSIGNMENT   13.2

Which stimulating and inhibiting factors influence the formation of nitrosamines in the gastrointestinal tract?

*Aromatic amines and nitro derivatives*

*b.    Aromatic amines and nitro derivatives*

Aromatic amines or arylamines are aromatic molecules with an exocyclic amino group. They do not occur in nature as such but are formed during pyrolysis of natural products, or chemically synthesized. Compounds like *o*-toluidine, *o*-anisidine and phenacetin belong to the *monoarylamines*, a group which has aniline as its prototype (Figure 13.5).

*Monoarylamines*

*Aniline*

*Aniline* itself is not genotoxic, but an increased incidence of splenic sarcoma has been observed in one cancer study. Since this effect was accompanied by an obvious hepatotoxicity, and aniline itself is not genotoxic, it has been assumed that this splenic sarcoma is a secondary effect of the hepatotoxicity.

*Acetaminophen*

*Acetaminophen* [*N-(4-hydroxyphenyl)acetamide* (see Figure 13.6)] is not genotoxic either. Only clearly hepatotoxic doses caused a higher incidence of liver tumors. Here too, it was concluded that the hepatotoxicity was responsible for the increased incidence of tumors in rodents. For the much lower therapeutic doses, no increased risk of liver cancer was observed in humans.

*Phenacetin*

*Phenacetin* is an analgesic previously used very widely as an antipyretic and analgesic (Figure 13.6). An epidemiological study showed that the use of phenacetin is associated with an increased risk of cancer of the urinary tract, with the renal pelvis as a particularly vulnerable site. These neoplasms were al-

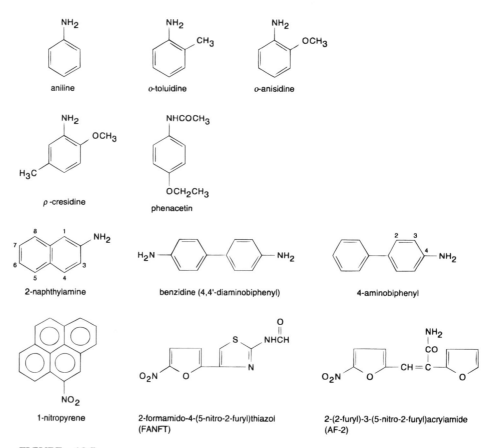

FIGURE 13.5
Some arylamines and nitro derivatives with carcinogenic properties

most always found after long-term, excessive use of phenacetin, which induces a chronic, degenerative kidney disorder. Cacinogenicity was also seen in test animals. It was demonstrated that phenacetin, as well as N-hydroxy phenacetin, is clearly positive in some mutagenesis tests, including the *Salmonella Ames test*. From this it can be concluded that phenacetin is a genotoxic carcinogen, probably due to the formation of N-hydroxy-phenacetin, which occurs as a result of hydroxylation at the nitrogen atom. This would also explain why acetaminophen, the deethylated derivative of phenacetin, is neither a mutagenic nor a genotoxic carcinogen.

*For the Ames test, see Study unit 11*

*Polycyclic aromatic amines 2-Naphthylamine*

The *polycyclic aromatic amines* are undoubtedly more potent carcinogens than the monocyclic aromatic amines. The prototype of this group is *2-naphthylamine* (see Figure 13.7).

*Formation of the nitrenium ion*

2-Naphthylamine is carcinogenic for humans and animals, mainly inducing cancer of the bladder. This property was first observed around the turn of the century, when workers in the dye industry were found to show an increased incidence of this type of cancer. The analog, 1-naphthylamine, is neither mutagenic nor carcinogenic. In the liver, 2-naphthylamine is oxidized at the amino group to N-hydroxynaphthylamine. The hydroxy group is then esterified with glucuronic acid by the glucuronyl transferase, and conjugate is excreted from the circulation into the urine. In the acidic urine, however, the conjugate is very unstable. It splits and, after protonation, it leads to the formation of the *nitrenium ion*, which is considered to be the actual carcinogen (Figure 13.7).

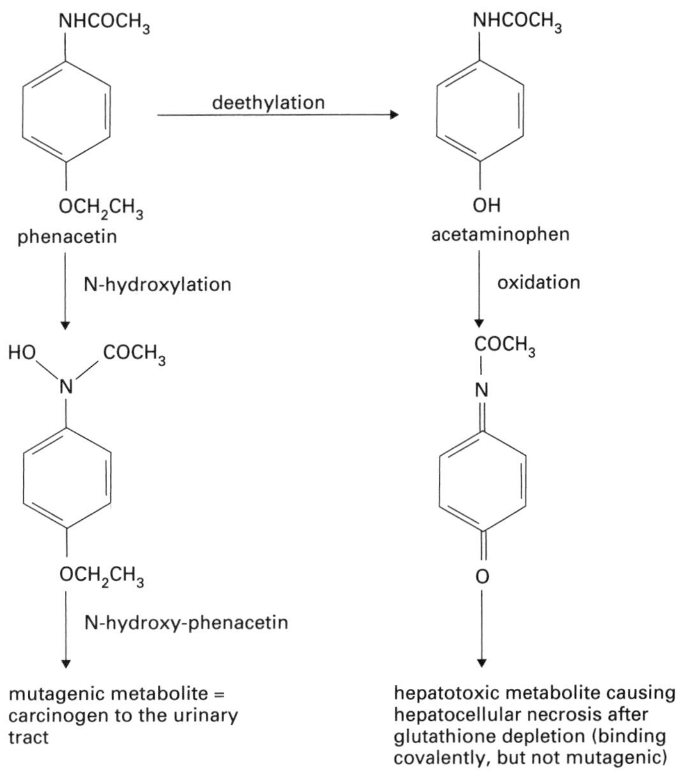

FIGURE 13.6
Metabolic routes of phenacetin
*N*-hydroxylation can lead to mutagenic and genotoxic carcinogenic metabolites. Prior deethylation leads to the formation of acetamidophenol.

*4-aminobiphenyl*
*4,4'-diaminobiphenyl*

The nitrenium binds covalently to the epithelium of the urinary tract, leading to the initiation of carcinogenesis. The binding to the C$^8$-guanine of DNA is particularly important.

*4-aminobiphenyl* and *4,4'-diaminobiphenyl* (*benzidine*, see Figure 13.5) are important carcinogens which are mainly used in industrial chemistry.

*1-Nitropyrene*
*Nitrofurans and nitroimidazoles*

Several nitro precursors of carcinogenic aromatic amines are also carcinogenic. They can be reduced to their respective hydroxylamino compounds and then to amines. An example is *1-nitropyrene* (Figure 13.5), which is also a product of diesel oil combustion. The *nitrofurans* and *nitroimidazoles* are also notorious carcinogens. One of them, *FANFT* or 2-formamido-4-(5-nitro-2-furyl)thiazole (Figure 13.5), is a highly potent agent, inducing bladder cancer in rats. *Furylfuramide* or *AF-2* (Figure 13.5), which was previously used as a food preservative, mainly in Japan, is also mutagenic and causes cancer of the forestomach in rodents. Some drugs also belong to this group, e.g. *metronidazole*.

*Polycyclic aromatic hydrocarbons*

c.   *Polycyclic aromatic hydrocarbons*

The basic structure of these chemicals consists of multiple fused benzene rings (see Figure 13.8). They are very common in the environment, and can be found in coal-tar, soot, crude petroleum, lubricating oils and products of incomplete combustion (cigarette smoke, stoves and incinerators).

*Lung cancer in cigarette smokers*

This group of carcinogens is indisputably involved in the induction of *lung cancer in cigarette smokers* (see also sections 1.2 and 2.2.2).

FIGURE 13.7
2-Naphthylamine: metabolic pathway resulting in the ultimate carcinogen

*Benzo[a]pyrene*

They are good *initiators* but also important *promoters*. Their annual production is enormous - the production of benzo[a]pyrene in the USA alone amounts to 2,000 metric tons per year. Fortunately, direct exposure of humans to polycyclic aromatic hydrocarbons is low. They are photochemically unstable compounds and decompose under the influence of sunlight. Moreover, the human body has a high capacity for metabolic inactivation of this group of molecules.

When these compounds are administered in relatively large quantities to certain parts of the body, they cause neoplasms at that site or elsewhere in the body.

*Structure–activity relationship*

*Structure–activity relationships* for polycyclic hydrocarbons with respect to carcinogenic potency have been extensively studied (Figure 13.8). The basic skeleton consists of anthracene. This is not carcinogenic in itself. Benzo[a]anthracene is a weak carcinogen, but dimethyl substitution at the 7th and 12th positions renders it very potent. The same is true for other substitution products, for example *3-methylcholanthrene*. Further ring addition gives benzo[a]pyrene or dibenzo[a,h]anthracene, which are highly potent carcinogens even without substitution.

The metabolic activation of benzo[a]pyrene is a textbook example of the complexity of this process. The main ultimate carcinogen is benzopyrene-7,8-diol-9,10 epoxide. Studies on covalent binding , *in vitro* and *in vivo* mutagenesis, and *in vivo* initiation have shown that of the four stereoisomers, the anti (+) isomer is by far the most potent ultimate carcinogen.

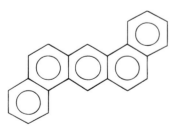

**dibenzo[a,h]anthracene**

*Bay region of the benzo[a]pyrene molecule*

The reason for the potent carcinogenicity of the anti (+) isomer lies in the existence of the so-called *bay region in the benzo[a]pyrene molecule*, between the tenth

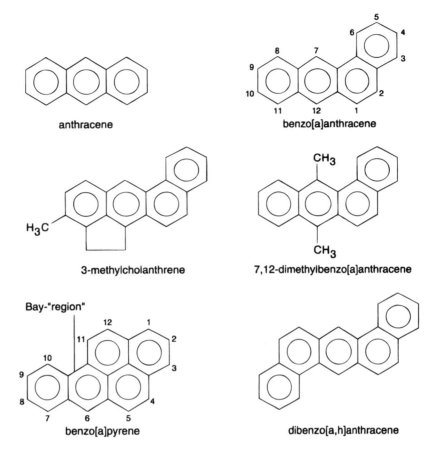

FIGURE 13.8
Some typical carcinogenic, polycyclic aromatic hydrocarbons

and eleventh carbon atoms. It has been demonstrated quantum-mechanically that this region has the strongest electrophilic properties and preferentially enters into covalent bonds. Apparently, the epoxide of the anti (+) isomer provides the most suitable steric configuration for this.

*Heterocyclic aromatic hydrocarbons*

*d.    Heterocyclic aromatic hydrocarbons*

*Quinolines*

This heterogeneous group includes the *quinolines* (quinoline itself, benzoquinoline and an imidazoquinoline) (Figure 13.9). Quinoline is an industrial product, although it is also present in tobacco smoke. These substances are probably active after epoxidation, in analogy with the polycyclic aromatic hydrocarbons. 2-Amino-3-methylimidazol[4,5-*f*]quinoline is a highly potent mutagen and is formed, together with other imidazole quinolines or quinoxalines, during the overheating (frying or boiling) of meat, under normal household conditions.

*Hydrazines*
$H_2N$-$NH_2$ = hydrazine
Hydrazine is an anticorrosive agent that is added to petrol

*e.    Hydrazines*

As an inorganic molecule, at toxic doses *hydrazine* itself is weakly carcinogenic to the lung and liver of rodents. How this effect is established is not known yet. Hydrazine can act as a nucleophile.

*Dimethylhydrazine*

*Dimethylhydrazine* is a potent carcinogen, whether in its symmetric or asymmetric form. After oral ingestion of the symmetric isomer, various types of neoplasms can be induced, including colonic cancer in rats.

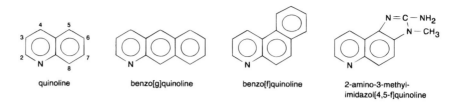

quinoline    benzo[g]quinoline    benzo[f]quinoline    2-amino-3-methyl-
imidazol[4,5-f]quinoline

FIGURE   13.9
Heterocyclic aromatic hydrocarbons (quinolines)

Dimethylhydrazine is metabolically activated by dehydrogenation to azomethane, followed by N- and C-oxidation to methylazoxymethanol and next to methylazoxyformaldehyde (Figure 13.10). The ultimate carcinogen is the methyldiazonium ion, which induces methylation of a nucleophilic group.

*Halogenated hydrocarbons*

### f.    Halogenated hydrocarbons

The group of halogenated hydrocarbons encompasses a large variety of molecules. The best known of these is *carbon tetrachloride (CCl₄)*, which is a relatively weak carcinogen to the liver of rodents, showing the effect only at doses which cause liver necrosis. $CCl_4$ does not appear to be genotoxic in mutagenesis tests. Although its metabolism can give rise to the formation of radicals, these reactive molecules mainly engage in interaction with proteins and fatty acids in the cytoplasm. This leads to cell toxicity but certainly not to initiation of carcinogenesis at the DNA level. For this reason, it is now assumed that $CCl_4$ is mainly an epigenetic carcinogen and exercises its carcinogenic effect through cytotoxic mechanisms.

*Chloroform*

The same applies to *chloroform* ($HCCl_3$), although oxidation of this molecule to trichloromethanol could result in the formation of phosgene, a potent acylating and hence mutagenic molecule.

$$\text{phosgene} \left( O = C \overset{Cl}{\underset{Cl}{\diagdown}} \right), \text{a potent acylating and mutagenic substance}$$

*Carcinogenesis via an epigenetic mechanism*

An *epigenetic mechanism* is also ascribed to other polyhalogenated cyclic substances. These include the pesticides DDT, aldrin and dieldrin, and industrial substances such as *PCBs* (polychlorinated biphenyls) and *TCDD* (tetrachlorodibenzo-*p*-dioxin). These molecules are often used as promoters in experimental carcinogenesis of the liver in rodents.

*Genotoxic*

For vinylchloride and dihalogenated alkanes or alkenes (e.g. 1,2-dichloroethane or 1,2-dibromoethane) the mechanism is quite different. Members of this group too are clearly *genotoxic* in character and cause alkylation of DNA. Vinylchloride (see Table 3.3, Study unit 3) achieves this via epoxide formation, while 1,2-dibromoethane acts via glutathione conjugation. Subsequently, a reactive thiiranium ion is formed. The latter process illustrates once again that the glutathione reaction does not always lead to inactivation, but sometimes to activation.

*Formaldehyde*

### g.    Formaldehyde

Formaldehyde induces nasal neoplasia in rats at cytotoxic dosages. At lower, non-cytotoxic doses, however, it does not show positive carcinogenic activity. It is genotoxic in certain *in vitro* tests, but is not clearly mutagenic *in vivo*. It has

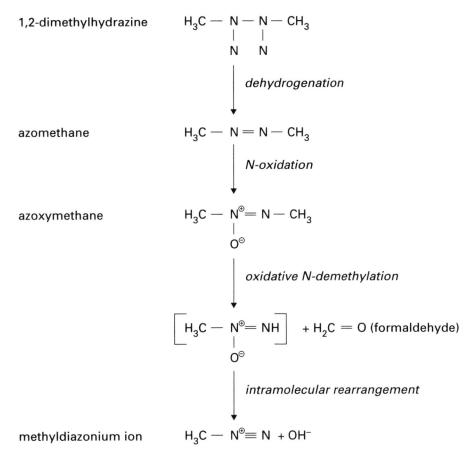

FIGURE 13.10
Activation of dimethylhydrazine

been postulated that *in vivo* the mechanism of cytotoxicity is more important than that of genotoxicity. This would explain why chronic exposure at low dosages is not correlated with an increased risk of neoplasia in humans.

## II Carcinogens interfering with DNA

*Non-radioactive metal compounds*

Several *non-radioactive metal compounds* cause neoplasms in animals and may be carcinogenic in humans. These include nickel, chromium, lead, cobalt and cadmium compounds. Their mode of action in terms of genotoxicity has not yet been elucidated, but several of these metals clearly interfere with DNA repair.

*Interaction with DNA polymerase*

They achieve this by *interacting with DNA polymerase*, thus disturbing the mechanism of DNA synthesis. Some metal compounds (e.g. those of arsenic, cadmium, chromium and nickel) also induce chromosomal aberrations. Organic arsenic compounds are carcinogenic to the human liver through an as yet unelucidated mechanism. Experiments on rodents have not shown them to be carcinogenic, and this is perhaps the only exception to the general rule.

*Intercalation into the DNA chain*

Another form of interference with DNA is the *intercalation* of a molecule into the *DNA chain*, which hampers transcription of the DNA. This happens for example with adriamycin, an actinomycetes product which is, because of this effect, used as a cytostatic.

### 3.2.2 Epigenetic carcinogens

### I Mitogenic agents

The so-called mitogenic agents (Table 13.4) are the prototypes of promoters of carcinogenesis. They stimulate cell division in the tissue in a selective, non-cytotoxic way. The as yet not recognizable, initiated cell population uses this growth stimulus and thereby becomes histologically recognizable.

*Hormones*

Hormones can be considered as natural, endogenous mitogenic agents. One of their specific functions is to keep the cell population, they are controlling, hypertrophic and hyperplastic to the right degree. In the physiological quantities present during most of the organism's life span, hormones do not induce cancer, as is apparent from the epidemiology of humans and animals. Physiologic quantities appear to be below the threshold levels of the dose–response curve for carcinogenesis.

In abnormally large quantities, however, hormones can, after a relatively long period of time, cause an increased incidence of cancer. The hormones themselves are not initiators. It is assumed that they are promoters of cell populations which have been "spontaneously" initiated.

*Endocrine interaction*

The endocrine interaction has been extensively studied (Figure 13.11). The function of an endocrine organ is controlled by a trophic hormone. The organ secretes a certain specific hormone, which influences the secretion of the trophic hormone via a feedback mechanism. Any interruption of this cycle can result in a neoplasia of the organ concerned.

*Interruption of the endogenous feedback*

A classic example is the transplantation of ovarian tissue into the spleen of castrated rodents. The estrogens excreted by the ovarian tissue reach the liver via the splenic circulation, and, for the most part, are metabolized there. This interrupts the feedback cycle to the pituitary (hypophysis). The latter organ therefore produces more gonadotropin, which reaches the spleen, causing the ovarian tissue to grow at such a rate that, after some time, it becomes a neoplasm. The process also takes place if the target organ for a particular hormone, for example the thyroid gland, is removed. This causes the pituitary to produce ever larger quantities of thyroid-stimulating hormones, so that eventually a tumor of the pituitary may develop. Theoretically, this process can occur in all endocrine organs.

*Exogenous administration of hormones*

*Prolactin*

*Exogenous administration of hormones* also shows a dose–response curve. Small, physiological quantities are harmless, but excessive amounts can result in neoplasia. Administering estrogens to rodents results in prolactin-producing neoplasms of the pituitary. Increased prolactin secretion gives rise to neoplasia of the mammary gland in rodents. In mice, these carcinomas are partly due to interaction with an oncogenic virus, the Bitner factor, which is transferred via the mother's milk.

By contrast, prolactin is not considered an important carcinogen in humans, where it is not a progestogenic but a lactogenic hormone, stimulating milk secretion. Lactation in women is regarded as anticarcinogenic for the mammary gland.

*Estrogens*

Administration of normal quantities of *estrogens* to women is considered to be "below threshold value". At higher dosages, however, as used in the treatment of menopause, they can increase the incidence of liver adenomas. These adenomas are benign and regress after treatment is discontinued; however, they can lead to dangerous hemorrhages.

408

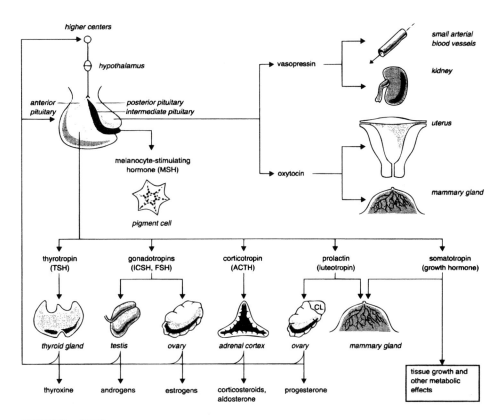

FIGURE 13.11

Schematic representation of the endocrine interaction of the pituitary with its anterior, intermediate and posterior parts and the other endocrine organs and tissues in the body

*Diethylstilbesterol*

The same cannot be said of *diethylstilbesterol* or DES. This synthetic estrogen used to be applied to prevent imminent abortions. It was administered for months in very high doses during pregnancy. The daughters born to DES-treated mothers showed an increased incidence of adenocarcinoma of the vagina.

*Transplacental carcinogenesis*

DES is, therefore, an example of *transplacental carcinogenesis* in humans. It should be regarded as an exception though, since the hormone is genotoxic, unlike the natural hormones or many other synthetic preparations. Although the risk from DES is probably much lower at low doses such as those used in animal husbandry, efforts are now being made to ban this hormone, because of its genotoxicity. Problems concerning the permissibility of other, non-genotoxic hormones should therefore be clearly separated from those related to DES. Exogenous non-hormonal substances can also be mitogenetic agents and promoters at non-cytotoxic doses.

ASSIGNMENT 13.3

How does diethylstilbesterol differ from natural estrogens?

*Tetradecanoylphorbol acetate*

*Tetradecanoylphorbol acetate* (TPA) is a classic promoter of skin carcinogenesis in rodents. Indirect genotoxic effects cannot be ruled out, however, since relatively high doses can induce chromosomal aberrations.

*Phenobarbital*

One of the most extensively studied promoters of liver cancer in rodents is *phenobarbital*. After prolonged administration to mice, it induces liver cancer with-

409

out prior dosage of an initiator. The spontaneous incidence of liver neoplasia in mice is relatively high, however, so that spontaneous or endogenous initiation is supposed to be involved. In rats, promotion following spontaneous initiation is much rarer. An obvious phenobarbital-induced increase in liver neoplasia is only observed after administration of an initiator. To this end a single dose of diethylnitrosamine is often used. The promoter activity of phenobarbital shows a dose–response curve with a threshold value between 20 and 100 mg per kg body weight. This implies that it is not effective as a promoter in the initiation–promotion model in the rat below 20 mg per kg. Phenobarbital is one of the few non-genotoxic promoters for which epidemiological data in humans exist. It has been prescribed as a daily drug for epileptics for several decades. A study carried out in Denmark showed that a daily dose of about 10 mg per kg did not lead to an increased risk of cancer. It may therefore be assumed that here too, there is a threshold value for non-genotoxic carcinogens in humans. Other substances which, like phenobarbital, are promoters include butylated hydroxyanisol (BHA) and butylated hydroxytoluene (BHT). At very low doses, these are generally accepted, safe anti-oxidants, and they are used as food preservatives.

ASSIGNMENT   13.4

Why has the research on phenobarbital as a promoter proved to be so important?

*Non-genotoxic chlorinated hydrocarbons*

*Non-genotoxic chlorinated hydrocarbons*, such as DDT, hexachlorocyclohexane, polychlorinated biphenyls (PCBs) and even the well-known tetrachlorodibenzo-*p*-dioxin (TCDD), can also be regarded as promoters of carcinogenesis. The notorious DDT has not proven to be harmful in genotoxic and carcinogenic terms, even after 40 years of use.

TCDD is perhaps one of the most potent promoters known. It is active as a promoter at dosages of 0.1 $\mu$g/kg bodyweight. A cytoplasmic receptor for this molecule has been identified, which, after binding to TCDD is transferred to the nucleus.

*Saccharin*
See also Study unit 37

*Saccharin*, an artificial sweetener, was first designated as a carcinogen after a long-term cancer study in rats had shown that 50,000 ppm (50,000 mg per kg food!) induced an increased incidence of cancer of the urinary bladder. Saccharin is not genotoxic but it is a promoter. Moreover, at these high dosages, vesical calculi were discovered which, in turn, may influence the carcinogenic process. The fact that lower dosages do not cause an increased incidence of bladder cancer shows that lower doses of saccharin lie below the threshold value and are therefore harmless.

## II   Cytotoxic agents

Any form of cell toxicity that leads to cell death implies a stimulus for cell production to replace the lost cell population. Since many chemicals evoke a certain cytotoxicity at high dosages, promotion of carcinogenesis can be observed in the organ or tissue concerned at these toxic dosages. Below the threshold dose for this response, promotion is no longer present.

*Carbon tetrachloride*

The best example of this group of substances is *carbon tetrachloride* ($CCl_4$), which has virtually no mutagenic properties. At dosages causing liver cell necrosis, which after chronic exposure results in liver cirrhosis, carbon tetrachloride is evidently a promoter of liver cancer in rodents. The same applies to other halo-

410

genated hydrocarbons, for example trichloroethylene and tetrachloroethane, two important industrial solvents.

### III    Immunosuppressive agents

Immunosuppressive agents can also act as epigenetic carcinogens. Neoplasms can be recognized immunologically by the presence of specific antigens on the cells' surface. This might provide the opportunity of arresting the growth of neoplasms by an 'alert' immunological system. Particularly in the progression of tumors by uncontrolled tumor expansion with invasion and metastasis immunosuppression plays a part. Many genotoxic carcinogens have immunosuppression as a side effect. For example in the case of cyclophosphamide, the carcinogenic effect is assumed to be largely attributable to immunosuppression.

## 4    Summary

The carcinogenic risk posed by a certain suspected agent can be determined epidemiologically in humans or by experimental research *in vitro* and *in vivo*. The latter research consists of short-term tests and lifetime cancer studies on rodents. Together, findings from these studies eventually lead to the determination of the cancer risk.

The biological relevance of a positive carcinogenic result in studies on rodents should be evaluated within the context of all the available information. The results of mutagenicity studies, as well as of the study of the mechanism of the carcinogenic effect (initiator versus promoter, hormonal or cytotoxic effects), are extremely important in determining the risk to humans. For the non-genotoxic carcinogens, in particular, the dose and duration of exposure may be more important than the exposure itself.

The way in which the substance concerned is administered obviously plays a very substantial role in the risk evaluation. In this respect a distinction can be made between drugs to which humans are directly exposed, and substances found in the environment and in the food chain. The latter group includes both natural and synthetic carcinogens. Complete avoidance of exposure is often impossible since the substance can also be formed naturally in the environment or in the body, or because contact with it is indirect, for example herbicides via the food chain. Exposure to industrial by-products, such as pyrolysis products after the combustion of fossil fuels (coal, petroleum), also cannot be avoided.

After the dose–response curve in a cancer study has been analyzed, the level of human exposure is assessed. A very important factor here is the time between the administration of the chemicals to the plant or animal and their consumption by humans. Finally, the level of exposure for which the cancer risk is negligible is calculated.

## SELF ASSESSMENT QUESTIONS

1    Name two related aniline derivatives with analgesic properties, one of which was found to be mutagenic and carcinogenic in humans while the other was not. Explain why this is so.

2    Name at least one carcinogen belonging to the class of polycyclic aromatic amines, one belonging to the polycyclic aromatic hydrocarbons, and one belonging to the nitro derivatives.

3    In what way do certain metal compounds interact with DNA to make them genotoxic?

4    How does saccharin cause neoplasia of the urinary bladder?

5    What group of human drugs with genotoxic properties is still permitted today?

## FEEDBACK

### 1    Answers to the assignments

13.1  1    Smoking cigarettes. The best preventive measure is to stop smoking.
2    Overfrying meat. This risk of cancer can be reduced by frying the meat at lower temperatures so that it does not burn.
3    Excessive consumption of alcohol. Chronic use of high-alcohol beverages, e.g. calvados brandy, should be avoided, as well as addiction which leads to cirrhosis of the liver.

13.2  Stimulating factors include an insufficiently low pH in the stomach and the presence of thiocyanates and aldehydes. Inhibiting factors are vitamins E and C.

13.3  Natural estrogens are not genotoxic and have a natural dose-dependent promotional effect on carcinogenesis. DES, however, is genotoxic, and at very high doses it has a transplacental carcinogenic effect.

13.4  Phenobarbital is one of the few well-documented cases where chronic usage in humans does not lead to an increased risk of cancer, although higher doses do cause such a risk in animals. This means that there is a threshold level for non-genotoxic carcinogens.

### 2    Answers to the self assessment questions

1    Phenacetin is mutagenic and carcinogenic, probably because it undergoes N-oxidation to form a genotoxic metabolite. Acetaminophen, by contrast, is not genotoxic in mutagenesis tests and does not lead to an increased risk of liver cancer in humans at therapeutic non-cytotoxic doses.

2    Polycyclic aromatic amines: 2-naphthylamine, 4-aminobiphenyl, benzidine. Polycyclic aromatic hydrocarbons: 7,12-dimethylbenzanthracene, benzo[a]pyrene, 3-methylcholanthrene. Nitro derivatives: 1-nitropyrene, FANFT, furylfuramide (AF-2).

3    Interaction with DNA polymerase during DNA repair interferes with the integrity of DNA synthesis.

4    Probably only very high doses of saccharin stimulate the formation of stones in the bladder. This in turn induces tumors.

5    The anticancer drugs or cytostatics. Some of these kill cancer cells precisely by their interactions with the cell nucleus.

# Contents Study unit 14
# Hazard identification, risk assessment, regulation and legislation

0-8493-9232-2/96/$0.00 + $.50
© 1996 by CRC Press, Inc.

Study unit 14

# Hazard identification, risk assessment, regulation and legislation

*K. N. Woodward*

INTRODUCTION

To a large extent, the science of toxicology has developed in the way that it has because of the demands of regulators, and the public which they serve, that chemicals—whatever their purpose, should be safe for their intended use. Many regulations have arisen in the aftermath of tragedies and disasters—minor and major involving chemicals. Examples of these events are given below:

| chemical | chemical class | event |
|---|---|---|
| asbestos | mineral (thermal insulator) | mesothelioma, lung cancer |
| vinyl chloride | polymer precursor (plastic production) | hemangiosarcoma, "vinyl chloride disease" |
| endrin | pesticide (organochlorine insecticide) | acute toxicity—deaths |
| organophosphorus compounds | insecticides | death, paralysis |
| methylmercury | environmental pollutant | "Minimata" disease |
| thalidomide | drug | birth defects |
| diethylstilbestrol (DES) | drug (hormone) | vaginal cancer in daughters of treated women |

As a result, regulations pertaining to chemicals in a wide range of areas have been developed and regulatory authorities have evolved. In general terms, those chemicals with the greatest propensity to "contaminate" humans, whether directly as in the workplace, or indirectly through food or water intake, form the major areas for regulation. These are:

- industrial chemicals
- pesticides
- food additives
- human pharmaceuticals
- veterinary drugs

The methods for assessing the toxicity of such compounds will form the basis of much of the discussion which foilows and emphasis will be given to the regulatory mechanisms involved.

415

LEARNING OBJECTIVES

After studying this unit, you should be able to:

— describe the elements of toxicity testing
— describe the endpoints behind these tests
— define hazard and risk
— describe risk assessment
— explain the acceptable daily intake and maximum residue limit concepts
— explain the elements of risk management and risk monitoring
— explain the elements of environmental hazard and risk
— briefly describe regulatory philosophies for food additives, industrial chemicals, pesticides, human pharmaceuticals and veterinary drugs
— describe similarities between these, and give some examples of notable differences.

*Study Hints*

Students are assumed to have background knowledge of the elements of pharmacokinetics and pharmacodynamics, as well as a broad knowledge of the major areas of toxicology such as organ effects, teratology, carcinogenicity and genotoxicity. Students are also expected to have some background knowledge of ecology. If your knowledge is lacking in these areas, you should revise it before reading this unit, or consult a reference text if you have difficulties with specific sections.

STUDY CORE

## 1 Toxicity Testing

Over the last twenty years, a recognizable package of toxicity testing requirements has evolved and remarkably, this is similar for the various categories of chemicals. Moreover, there is a remarkable similarity across international boundaries. These requirements will be discussed in more depth later in this unit. At this point, the discussion will concentrate on the types of tests available. These tend to focus on areas of toxicity—acute, short-term, long-term, reproductive, and genotoxicity—and what might best be referred to as specialized studies, covering a range of end points. In addition, there are general requirements for pharmacological data covering both pharmacokinetic and pharmacodynamic effects. The underlying scientific principles underpinning these studies are dealt with in other units. In the present unit, these studies are only considered from the point of view of evaluation for regulatory purposes. The conduct and design of these studies themselves are dealt with in another unit, but overall, they have evolved into a basic set which covers the major areas of toxicology already mentioned. They are listed in Table 14.1.

There are two major aims in conducting these studies. The first is to construct a toxicological profile of the chemical under study; is it a genotoxic carcinogen, a teratogen, a nephrotoxic agent? The second reason is to identify a dose below which the toxic effects of interest do not occur. When doing this, it must be remembered that toxicity itself is not a unique property of the chemical itself. Rather, it is a function of the biological properties of the chemical with its interaction with the organism of interest, and the age, strain, breed, and health status of that organism. The construction of the toxicological profile and the dose without effect are the first stages in hazard identification and risk assessment—

TABLE 14.1
Range of toxicity studies required for general regulatory purposes

| study | comment |
|-------|---------|
| Acute toxicity (rodents) | Emphasis on acute effects and clinical signs, other than on death as with the $LD_{50}$ study (lethality). |
| Subchronic toxicity (usually rodents) | Often used to determine a dose without effect: generally of 28 or 90 days duration. Sometimes referred to as subacute studies. |
| Long-term studies (usually rodents) | Generally of approximately two year duration when rodents are used. May be designed as carcinogenicity studies (to look at ability to induce cancer) or chronic toxicity studies, or may be combined chronic toxicity/carcinogenicity studies. |
| Reproduction studies —multigeneration studies | to investigate effects on reproductive performance, effects on fertility, fecundity, prenatal and perinatal toxicity, lactation, weaning and postnatal developmental and growth. |
| —teratology studies | to investigate the ability to induce defects during pregnancy and feto/embryo toxicity. |
| Genotoxicity studies | Investigation of ability to induce mutations, chromosomal aberrations and other endpoints indicative of heritable genetic damage having predictive relevance for carcinogenicity or the induction of inheritable defects. |
| Specialized studies —skin and eye irritation | to determine the effects of skin and eye contamination e.g. in occupational exposure. |
| —skin sensitization | to investigate the potential to produce allergic sensitization. |
| —immunotoxicity | to investigate the specific effects on the immune system e.g. on the thymus, lymph nodes, bone marrow, and corresponding cellular and humoral effects. |
| —neurotoxicity | to examine specific effects on the peripheral and central nervous systems e.g. with compounds known to be neurotoxic such as organophosphorus compounds. Specific investigations of acute, subchronic, chronic and behavioral toxicity may be required. |
| —other | other specific studies, e.g. to investigate further effects noted in more conventional investigations may be required. Examples might be studies on cardio-vascular, hematological, renal, hepatic and pulmonary effects, and ophthalmic toxicity and ototoxicity. |
| Pharmacology —pharmacokinetics | Studies on absorption, distribution, metabolism and excretion—generally conducted to provide background information which will contribute to an understanding of the mechanism of toxicity and the duration of effects, for example, the generation of toxic metabolites and rates of plasma clearance and excretion. |
| —pharmacodynamics | Essential for understanding the mode of action of human and veterinary pharmaceuticals. Essential for understanding the basis of some types of toxic action e.g. tachycardia leading to myocardial necrosis. |

417

basic concepts in regulatory toxicology, and indeed the basis of many regulations world-wide.

## 1.1 HAZARD IDENTIFICATION AND RISK

*No-observed effect level (NOEL)*

An analysis of the results of a package of toxicology studies allows one to identify the hazards associated with a chemical. Numerous examples can be cited, but for present purposes, a simple candidate may be selected. The substance has been tested in a number of toxicity studies. The only evidence of toxicity was noted in the rat, and the dose at and below which this did not occur is the so-called *no-observed effect level or NOEL*. The NOEL is important because it is the first parameter for use in the process of risk assessment. However, at this point, we need to examine what is meant by these terms, hazard and risk.

*Hazard*

*Hazard*, in the context of toxicology, is the biological property of the chemical in its interaction with the species concerned. To put it simpler, its toxic effects, although this could easily be extended to cover physico-chemical properties such as flammability or explosivity.

*Risk*

*Risk* is more of a statistical term, involving the probabilities of the hazard being expressed. It may be seen as the predicted, or for events which have occurred, as the actual consequences arising from exposure to a hazard.

## 1.2 RISK ASSESSMENT

Risk differs from hazard in that it cannot usually be determined from experimental investigation. It may be inferred from epidemiological investigation of groups of workers exposed to a hazard, or it may be calculated or predicted from mathematical models but rarely can it be "measured" by experimentation. Instead, a more qualitative approach to risk is usually adopted by the regulatory agency.

With the exception of human pharmaceuticals and occupational exposure (where inhalation and skin contact may be the major routes of exposure) most human beings are exposed to chemicals in their food and drinking water. This may be through exposure to food additives deliberately added to food such as colorants, antioxidants and flavor enhancers, or to residues of environmental chemicals or pesticides applied to crops and veterinary medicines administered to food producing animals. To contend with this, the concept of the acceptable daily intake (ADI) was developed by the Joint FAO/WHO Expert Committee on Food Additives (JECFA) several years ago. It is now widely used as the primary method of risk assessment for chemical contaminants in food.

*Acceptable daily intake (ADI)*

The *ADI* is defined as an estimate of the amount of a substance, expressed on a body weight basis, that can be ingested over a lifetime without appreciable health risk. Hence, it is a crude measure of the dose of a chemical which, on a daily basis, will have no adverse effects on health. There is a simple equation for its calculation.

$$ADI = \frac{NOEL}{safety\ factor}$$

As the NOEL is derived from toxicology studies, and has the units of mg (or some other measure of weight) per kg of body weight (bw) per day, then the ADI maintains these units ($mg\ kg\ bw^{-1}\ day^{-1}$). It may be multiplied by a factor, usually 60 kg, to produce a value in mg/person/day; 60 kg being recognized by the WHO as the "standard" human adult weight.

$$\text{So, } ADI = \frac{NOEL}{safety\ factor} mg \times kg\,bw^{-1}.day^{-1}$$

$$\text{or, } ADI = \frac{NOEL}{safety\ factor} 60\,mg \times kg\,person^{-1}.day^{-1}$$

It is important to recognize that the ADI is intended to cover the potential risks arising from life-time exposure as a result of daily intake of the substance. This implies that the NOEL is always derived from long-term studies but this is not the case. It may well be derived from shorter-term studies (e.g. 90 days), or from more specialized studies such as teratology or reproduction studies.

*Safety factor*

Of interest in calculating the ADI is the selection of the *safety factor*. This is a very arbitrary value and a factor of 100 is usually employed based on the contention that there is a 10-fold intraspecies variability in toxicity, and a 10-fold animal-human variability, therefore resulting in the overall factor of 100. However, in practice, this is often replaced by a higher safety factor when there are flaws or omissions in the data package. Such flaws and omissions would not normally be sufficient to completely prevent the calculation of the ADI, but would be great enough to warrant the use of higher safety factors. Again, these are very arbitrary and normally, factors of 200, 500 or 1000 are chosen depending on the problem involved. Conversely, there may either be good human toxicity data available or the chemical in question may be relatively non-toxic but it may possess pharmacodynamic activity. In these cases, a factor of only 10 may be considered sufficient in establishing the ADI.

ASSIGNMENT 14.1

What factors would you take into account for assessing whether or not to use a 100-fold safety factor?

This method of determining the safety factor has recently been challenged, largely as a result of the efforts by Renwick in the UK. The precept is that toxicity is a function of pharmacokinetics and pharmacodynamics (or more correctly, the toxicokinetics and toxicodynamics) in experimental animals. Instead of there now being a 10 × 10 factor of 100, taking in account actual toxicokinetic and pharmacological data, this would introduce a 3.16 × 3.16 factor for interspecies differences in pharmacokinetics and heterogeneity in these parameters. Having selected out these factors of 3.16, it should then be possible to refine them further using actual measurements derived from experimentation.

EXAMPLE

As a relatively simple example, we can take the case of the antioxidant food additive butylated hydroxyanisole (BHA). The data for this compound were analyzed by Wartzen in 1993, and a pivotal study was identified where hyperplasia of the forestomach and body and liver weight changes were identified as the major effects. The NOEL was identified to be in the range of 50–65.5 mg kg bw$^{-1}$ day$^{-1}$ from a long-term study. This, using a safety factor of 100, would give an ADI of around 0.5 mg kg bw$^{-1}$ day$^{-1}$.

However, Renwick, refined the 3.16 factors by examination of a large quantity of toxicological and pharmacological data, and arrived at a new subdivision for each 10-fold factor, as shown below:

| | pharmacodynamics | pharmacokinetics |
|---|---|---|
| interspecies differences | 2.5 | 4.0 |
| interindividual differences | 2.5 | 4.0 |

These values would be the default values, leading to an overall safety factor of 100. However, where there are adequate data, the values can be reduced leading to higher ADI values. The reductions would be based on an analysis of the toxicological and pharmacological data available, with attempts being made to determine the degree of interspecies and interindividual variabilities. Thus returning to BHA, the following analysis is possible .

| pivotal study | forestomach hyperplasia | liver/body weight changes |
|---|---|---|
| **NOEL (mg/kg body weight per day)** | **50** | **65.5** |
| | factors | factors |
| adequacy of data base | 1 | 1 |
| interspecies differences | | |
| —mechanism of action, dynamics | 2.5 | 2.5 |
| —mechanism of action, kinetics | 0.1 | 4 |
| interindividual differences in humans | | |
| —mechanism of action, dynamics | 2.5 | 2.5 |
| —mechanism of action, kinetics | 4 | 4 |
| nature of toxicity | 2 | 1 |
| safety factor (multiplication of individual factors) | 5 | 100 |
| ADI mg/kg body weight per day | 10 | 0.7 |

Although this gives two ADI values, research has shown that forestomach hyperplasia in the rat, and the tumor induction which often accompanies it, are not relevant to human hazard assessment. Hence, the value of 0.7 mg kg bw$^{-1}$ day$^{-1}$ is the preferred value.

This elegant system has much to offer and makes greater use of both toxicology and pharmacology data. However, it must be noted that for many additives and contaminants there are insufficient data to make this kind of analysis and then there is no alternative to the "100" safety factor approach.

Similar concepts can be applied to estimating risk and setting standards for occupational exposure to chemicals and for establishing environmental standards for pollutants. In these cases, exposure is likely to be via inspired air and, in the case of occupational exposure, also through the skin. The same principles apply but these are related to accepted values for inspired air volumes and skin surface area. Such values form the basis for establishing occupational and environmental exposure limits.

*Carcinogens*

A special case exists for carcinogens. *Carcinogens*, as described in other units, fall into two main categories, non-genotoxic carcinogens and genotoxic carcinogens. The two are treated very differently from a risk assessment viewpoint.

*Non-genotoxic carcinogens*

*Non-genotoxic carcinogens*, where there are reasonable data to support an underlying mechanism, are treated in a similar manner to other toxic substances and, where appropriate, NOELs are identified for the underlying toxic or physiological effect responsible for the carcinogenic activity, and an ADI calculated.

A good example is the case of the sulfonamide drugs and their use in veterinary medicine. When used in food producing animals, these leave residues (see later) in certain tissues, particularly in the kidney. Concern was expressed when one of the major drugs in use, sulfadimidine (also known as sulfamethazine), was shown to be a thyroid carcinogen. Further research showed this to be a consequence of a perturbation of the thyroid-hypothalamus-pituitary axis, with concomitant disturbances of thyroid hormone levels. The exact mechanism of action is obscure and research continues on this subject. Nevertheless, there was no indication of a genotoxic mechanism, and it is possible to calculate an ADI on the basis of thyroid follicular cell hyperplasia, a related phenomenon. As the mechanism of action was only partly understood, a safety factor of 500 was employed in the calculation of the ADI. Similar regulatory measures have been taken with other chemical goitrogens which induce thyroid tumors in rodents. There are several groups of non-genetic carcinogens which are regulated in this way. Some examples are given below:

| | |
|---|---|
| phenobarbital<br>chlorinated hydrocarbons<br>ethinyl oestradiol | liver tumors in rodents |
| unleaded gasoline<br>pentachloroethylene<br>1.4-dichlorobenzene | male rats; $\alpha_2\gamma$-globulin<br>nephropathy-related |
| saccharin<br>ascorbate<br>calculi-inducing agents | bladder tumors |
| butylated hydroxyanisole | forestomach tumors in rats |

*Genotoxic carcinogens*

*Genotoxic chemicals* on the other hand, are regulated in a much more stringent way. Genotoxicity can be inferred from a knowledge of chemical structure and reactivity of the chemical and its metabolites, and from activity in a range of short-term tests designed to demonstrate effects on gene mutation, chromosome structure and number, and interaction with DNA. As, in theory at least, a cancer can arise from a single mutated cell, then genotoxic carcinogens have long been regulated on the basis of there being no safe exposure level—again, in theory, one molecule could produce a tumor. Clearly, this is an extreme and very conservative approach as detoxification through metabolism, and elimination through excretion will render many genotoxic chemicals harmless. Even if genotoxic damage does occur, DNA repair mechanisms may mean that tumor development is not inevitable.

421

*Delaney Clause*

However, because it is difficult to identify safe levels for genotoxic carcinogens, many are still regulated in this way throughout the world. In the US, the so-called *Delaney Clause of the Food, Drug and Cosmetic Act* prohibits the use of any additive in food which has been shown to produce cancer in humans or laboratory animals at any dose, regardless of mechanism, unless there is overwhelming evidence that the results of the studies are irrelevant for human hazard and risk evaluation.

ASSIGNMENT 14.2

What factors are of importance in deciding if a substance is a genotoxic or non-genotoxic carcinogen?

In recent years, there has been a move towards the use of mathematical models in predicting risk from a range of toxic chemicals, including genotoxic and non-genotoxic risk. These models are beyond the scope of this textbook but the student should be aware of their existence. Further information can be found in the publications by the *International Agency for Research on Cancer (IARC)*.

*International Agency for Research on Cancer (IARC)*

From a regulatory and common-sense point of view, it is essential to appreciate that there is no activity, object or chemical which is without risk. In deciding what risks might be taken, the regulator and his/her regulatory agency must consider a number of essential points which fall under the broad heading of *risk perception*:

*Risk perception*

*i cost-benefit*

Will the individual or corporate organization be in a position to balance the risks involved with a degree of benefit? It is worthwhile noting that anomalies arise when the parties sharing the risk are different from those enjoying the benefits. A patient with cancer may be content to be treated with a carcinogenic drug if it will cure the disease or prolong his life.

That patient will accept the risk of a drug-induced tumor later in life if there is no alternative but death associated with the current disease. The patient takes the risk and enjoys the benefits. However, this differs significantly from the situation where a farmer applies pesticide by aerial spray to his land. Here, the farmer might be seen as the major beneficiary, with those living nearby being the subject of any risk.

*ii voluntary and involuntary risk*

People may be willing to accept even a relatively high risk, for example smoking or traveling by car, at their own choice, but will refuse to accept a very low risk such as low concentrations of pesticide residues in food, over which they have neither choice nor control.

*iii accepted and acceptable risks*

Driving by a car or traveling by car is a relatively high-risk venture and yet individuals are content to undertake this activity at almost any time, except in illness or extremes of weather. On the other hand, these same people may regard with extreme suspicion, any exposure to chemical agents. Moreover, attempts by regulators to clarify levels of risk by indicating the acceptable levels not only raise questions of "acceptable to who—the regulator or those exposed to these risks?" but also illustrate the concept of "one in a million may be safe, but what if I am that one?".

There are several more examples which might be raised. All illustrate the major problem—conveying to those who are potentially at risk, just what that risk might be. No-one can pretend that this is an easy exercise to perform.

## 1.3 RISK MANAGEMENT

Risk management is the practice of ensuring that the risks associated with the hazard are minimized. They can be minimized in 3 ways.

*i Absolute Risk Management*

This is better termed risk avoidance and in essence, it amounts to measures taken so that the risks associated with a particular hazard are not expressed. Examples would be a complete ban on a chemical or a severe limitation as is the case with the Delaney clause mentioned earlier.

*ii As Low As Reasonably Advisable*

Here, all measures are taken to ensure that the risks are kept as low as possible, by ensuring that, for example, exposure to a chemical is kept as low as possible. This is exemplified by the "zero-tolerance" concept where measures were taken to ensure that residues of pesticides or veterinary drugs in foods were reduced to as low as was achievable, preferably to "zero". The major problem with this approach was that as analytical methods became better, "zero" became lower and lower.

*iii Safety Standards*

Values are adopted by regulators, based upon the hazards involved (toxicity, flammability, explosivity, oxidizing properties) and the risks involved e.g. based on type of product (gas, volatile liquid, dust), the numbers exposed, the types of people involved (trained operators or members of the public) and the possible degree of exposure when precautions are and are not taken. Examples include exposure limits for industrial and environmental contaminants, and maximum residue limits for environmental chemicals, and residues of pesticides and veterinary drugs in food. The broad term safety standards also includes safety labeling, safety precautions and recommendations for protective clothing.

## 1.4 RISK MONITORING

Actions *i–iii* above are the major regulatory options open to regulatory agencies. Having taken these steps, the next responsibility is to ensure compliance—are the recommended steps being observed in practice? Some examples of how this compliance might be achieved are given below:

| | |
|---|---|
| banned drug | pharmaceutical inspection or action by law enforcement officers; |
| banned veterinary drug or pesticide | examination of farm premises for evidence of use of drug e.g. containers; residues surveillance programme for detection of prohibited substances in food of plant and animal origin; |
| occupational exposure limits | factory inspectorate; |
| environmental discharges into air or water | pollution inspectorate; |
| standards set for maximum residues of pesticides and veterinary drugs in food | residues surveillance programme for determination of violations of residue limits. |

ASSIGNMENT   14.3

What do you think a factory inspector would look for during his investigations of chemical exposure?

The important point to note here is that once regulatory decisions have been made, they must be policed. Most countries make use of detailed systems of inspection to ensure that these "decisions", whether for limits for pesticide residues or recommendations for protective clothing, are adhered to.

## 1.5   ENVIRONMENTAL HAZARD AND RISK

Substances may not only be hazardous and pose direct threats to human health and welfare, they may also be indirectly threatening to his well-being or to that of his fellow creatures, animals or plants. This aspect of hazard and risk assessment is almost identical to that for toxicity. Testing is followed by i dentification and evaluation of the environmental hazards involved, and the risks associated with those hazards are then assessed. Decisions are then taken which may require monitoring.

One of the important aspects of environmental hazard is that these are not necessarily restricted to the organism under test. The test animal serves as an indicator species for other similar organisms sharing the same or similar habitats which might also be affected by the chemical. Moreover, the demise of these creatures, if they are important in the food-chain, could very well adversely affect the well-being of other creatures. Hence, they also serve as sentinel organisms for the overall trophic organization of the habitat of interest. The science of investigating the effects of chemicals on the environment is usually referred to as ecotoxicology and is accompanied by ecotoxicity testing. This goes beyond merely examining the effects of the agent on organisms, but also examines the fate of chemicals in the environment, their distribution, and even their effects on the fate of other chemicals.

Ecotoxicity tests fall into broad categories. These are listed below.

| | |
|---|---|
| Single species test | e.g. on *Daphnia* the water flea, and fish. |
| Multispecies ("microcosm") | These act as model ecosystems and serve to test the effects of a chemical on a community of animals, plants bacteria etc. |
| Field ecosystems | To investigate the effects of a chemical on more representative and complex ecosystems. |
| Environmental distribution between<br>—oil, sediments and water<br>—water and air<br>—soil and air<br>—soil/air and plants | To determine where the chemical may concentrate or collect in the environment. Plants are important as food so it is essential to know if uptake in plants occurs. |
| Degradation<br>—physico-chemical<br>—biological<br>—eventual fate | This will provide data on persistence in the environment, rates of degradation and favorable conditions for these. May provide information on whether the breakdown products are more or less toxic than the parent chemical. |
| BOD/COD | Biological oxygen demand (BOD) gives a measure of the ability of micro-organisms to oxidize the substance; chemical oxygen |

demand (COD) gives an indication of the amount of oxygen required to completely oxidize the chemical. BOD also provides an indication of the potential of the chemical to cause oxygen depletion in the water which may lead in itself to death of sensitive organisms or to a build-up in organic matter in water. This in turn may lead to algal blooms, overproduction of oxygen and reduction of sunlight penetration with further adverse effects.

| | |
|---|---|
| Bioaccumulation, bioconcentration and biomagnification | Bioaccumulation in the uptake of chemicals by organisms, bioconcentration in the uptake and retention of chemicals by organisms for the environment, while biomagnification in the uptake and retention of chemicals in the food of organisms. |

*EU stands for European Union, the official name for the European Community (EC) since 1994*

The scope and detail of such tests can be illustrated by reference to the requirements for testing for so-called "dangerous substances", largely industrial chemicals, under European Union (EU) Directive 87/302/EEC and Directive 92/32/EEC, amending Directive 67/588/EEC on the classification, packaging and labeling of dangerous substances. These lay down the testing requirements for toxicity and ecotoxicity testing, and set out "methods for the determination of ecotoxicity". The following are included:

- acute toxicity in fish
- acute toxicity to *Daphnia magna*
- bacterial inhibition
- algal inhibition test
- toxicity for earthworms
- biodegradation
- biodegradation (sewage sludge simulation)
- prolonged toxicity with *Daphnia magna*
- test on higher plant
- prolonged toxicity in fish
- tests for species accumulation (preferably in fish)
- absorption and desorption studies
- toxicity with birds
- additional studies with other organisms

ASSIGNMENT 14.4

What do you think is the major difficulty in studying the results of a package of ecotoxicity tests.

It must be stressed that under this legislation, the testing required depends on annual tonnage of the chemical produced. Consequently, not all the tests are required for every chemical. However, it does illustrate the scope of the possible requirements and precisely where the concerns may lie. Like toxicity testing requirements, and the results of the tests, ecotoxicity testing allows regulatory decisions to be made (e.g. a complete ban, ban on uses near water-courses, restrictions on disposal by burning, suitable labeling requirements and precautions in use and disposal).

## 1.6    OTHER HAZARDS

It is well worth remembering that, in addition to toxic hazards, chemicals present other, more physical hazards. Some have been hinted at already in this unit and they include the following:

- acid/alkaline (corrosive) properties
- flammability
- oxidizing properties
- explosivity
- lubricant ("oil" or "greasy") properties

Such properties need to be borne in mind when an overall evaluation is carried out.

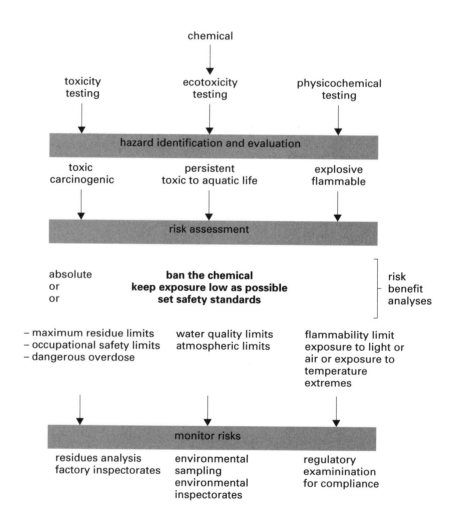

FIGURE    14.1
Testing, hazard evaluation and risk assessment for a chemical.

426

The entire process of testing, hazard evaluation, risk assessment and risk monitoring is represented schematically in Figure 14.1.

## 1.7 GOOD LABORATORY PRACTICE AND QUALITY MANAGEMENT

*Good Laboratory Practice (GLP)*

*Good Laboratory Practice (GLP)* was introduced to combat the fraudulent production of laboratory results. It followed a specific incident in the US. The results of some studies had been fraudulently produced and indeed, some studies, for which there were results and reports, had not even been conducted. As a result GLP was introduced and it is now a requirement of virtually all regulatory authorities.

*Quality management*

*Quality management* is very much related to GLP in terms of its aims and structure. It is not intended to prevent fraud, but it is designed to ensure that studies are valid and are properly conducted, and that the overall structure of the laboratory facilities is established to efficiently serve the needs of testing, that there is adequate personnel who are adequately educated and that there is an adequate quality assurance program. This may be achieved by:

- correct organization and appropriate personnel
- a system of inspections and audits
- maintenance of records and reports
- the establishment of standard operating procedures
- adequate experimental facilities
- development of study plans
- quality control
- archiving facilities for data and samples

## 2 Regulation of Specific Types of Chemical

### 2.1 FOOD ADDITIVES

Unlike pesticides, medicines, veterinary medicines and industrial chemicals (see later), there are no formal guidelines for the testing of food additives such as flavorings, antioxidants, sweeteners etc., in the EU. Safe levels are established by the Scientific Committee for Food using the type of toxicological data set out in Table 14.1. The approach is very much that established by JECFA, and the ADI concept is employed. Indeed, the EU makes use of the JECFA evaluations and Codex Alimentarius standards (see section on veterinary medicines).

In Japan and the US, similar features apply. In the US, additives are divided into two categories, direct and indirect additives. The former are those which are directly added to foods, such as antioxidants and colors, while the latter are those which passively find their way into food such as plasticizers and other chemicals which leak from food contact materials.

*Generally recognized as safe (GRAS)*

Both categories are subdivided into the *generally recognized as safe (GRAS)* and the regulated additive groups. The latter are those which must be subject to toxicological testing.

For the regulated additives, a full package of toxicological tests is required including 2-year studies. New packaging materials and indirect additives require a less stringent package of tests, usually 90-day studies, mutagenicity studies and teratogenicity studies but other tests may be required depending on the results of these initial investigations.

ASSIGNMENT 14.5

Do you think the purpose of an additive should be taken into account in any regulatory decision?

## 2.2 INDUSTRIAL CHEMICALS

Industrial chemicals are closely regulated in the European Union. One of the major instruments of regulation is Council Directive 67/548/EEC which was amended for the sixth time by Directive 79/831/EEC which in turn introduced a notification scheme for industrial chemicals (excluding those covered by other EU legislation such as pesticides, food additives, pharmaceuticals and veterinary medicines). The notification scheme applies to all new chemicals in the EU and to this end, a list of some 100 000 "existing" substances was drawn up so that "new substances" could be identified.

The aim of the scheme is to ensure that any ability of a chemical to cause untoward effects to humans or the environment is known prior to marketing. However, it is not an authorization scheme and no licenses are issued. Rather, it is a scheme which ensures the availability of toxicological and ecotoxicological data, to the governments of Member States, and to companies marketing the substance.

*Toxicological and ecotoxicological testing requirements*

The *toxicological and ecotoxicological testing requirements* are broadly similar to those set out in Table 14.1 but the requirements are established in a step-like manner depending on the annual production tonnage. Substances produced in quantities of more than one ton but less than 10 tons per year, are subject to the so-called base set requirements as set out below:

- acute toxicity
- skin and eye irritancy
- skin sensitization
- 28 day study
- mutagenicity studies

Further testing may be required when annual production of 1000 and 10,000 tons per annum are exceeded. Similar requirements apply to ecotoxicological and physico-chemical tests.

From 1993, Member States will be required to gather information on existing chemicals including data on use, toxicology and ecotoxicology. There will also be a need to identify gaps in these data and to conduct testing accordingly.

In addition to these testing requirements, there is also comprehensive EU legislation on the labeling of substances and preparations. This legislation, where appropriate, requires warning phrases as well as symbolic representations of hazard. Examples include symbolic representations for irritant substances and the skull and crossbones symbol for toxic materials.

*US Toxic Substances Control Act (TSCA)*
*US Environmental Protection Agency (EPA)*

In the US, the *Toxic Substances Control Act (TSCA)* imposes similar toxicity testing requirements on industrial chemicals. This is implemented by the *Environmental Protection Agency (EPA)* and testing may be required where chemicals or groups of chemicals are thought to pose an unreasonable risk, so that gaps in knowledge are filled. Both new and existing chemicals are covered and are subject to the requirements for testing.

*American Conference of Government Industrial Hygienists (ACGIH)*

Many countries establish occupational exposure limits for industrial chemicals and many are based on the Conference values determined by the *American*

*Conference of Government Industrial Hygienists (ACGIH)* although the German government publishes its own list. Many EU exposure limits are based on the ACGIH values. The limits are based largely on toxicology data, especially on data from inhalation studies where this is relevant to the route of human exposure, and from NOELs in such studies, in much the same way that the ADI is calculated.

## 2.3 PESTICIDES

Pesticides are biologically active materials which are used in a variety of applications. They may be used for the control of insect pests, plant pests or fungi, for example. The major groups are shown below:

| used to control | generic type |
| --- | --- |
| insects | insecticides |
| plants | herbicides |
| fungi | fungicides |
| mice, rats etc. | rodenticides |
| mosses, liverworts etc. | biocides |

The major uses are to control insects and weeds which might affect the viability of edible crops and for the control of insects and fungi in timber (wood preservatives) but there are many other applications for this diverse group of chemicals. The three main safety areas of concern are occupational exposure, exposure of consumers to residues of the compounds and their degradation products in edible crops and subsequently in animal tissues, and their effects on the environment. The toxicological requirements for pesticides in general, when looked at from the viewpoints of a number of countries including the EU and the US, reflect these areas of concern and the possible means and routes of exposure. They are given below in Table 14.2.

TABLE 14.2
Toxicity testing and ecotoxicity testing requirements for a number of countries. (After Schmidt-Bleek and Marchal, 1993).

| acute toxicity | (oral*) |
| --- | --- |
| acute toxicity | (inhalation) |
| acute toxicity | (dermal*) |
| skin irritation* | |
| eye irritation* | |
| skin sensitization* | |
| subchronic; chronic* | |
| carcinogenicity* | |
| mutagenicity* | |
| teratogenicity* | |
| reproduction studies | |
| metabolic studies | |
| acute toxicity studies | |
| acute toxicity | fish |
| acute toxicity | *Daphnia magna* |
| acute toxicity | algae |
| toxicity in birds | |
| honey bee toxicity | |
| earth worm toxicity | |
| 28-day | fish |
| 28-day | *Daphnia magna* |

*Required by all 22 regulatory schemes examined; the remainder are required by the majority

429

*Maximum residue limit (MRL)*

Residues of pesticides in human food are generally dealt with by the *maximum residue limit (MRL)* approach. MRLs are largely based on the ADIs (see also the section on veterinary drugs)–the MRL being the quantity of a specific chemical which may be taken in over a life time by humans without adverse effects. Hence, the MRL is a function of what is desirable on toxicological grounds and what is achievable in agricultural practice terms (good agricultural practice). By maintaining specified periods between application of a pesticide to an edible crop (for example), the residues of a pesticide will deplete to below the MRL. This period is usually known as the post-harvest interval.

At the international level, residues of pesticides are examined by the Joint FAO/WHO Meeting on Pesticide Residues (JMPR). This body establishes MRLs for pesticides in the same way that JECFA, a sister-Committee, sets safe levels for food additives and contaminants, and establishes MRLs for veterinary drug residues. These MRLs can be taken up by the Codex Committee on Pesticide Residues, and thus into the Codex Alimentarius standards program.

## 2.4  HUMAN PHARMACEUTICALS

Worldwide, there are 3 major criteria for the evaluation of pharmaceuticals:

- *efficacy*—will the drug do what the manufacturers claim it will do, and how well? In other words, will it work?

- *pharmaceutical quality*—this covers, among many other things, the chemistry of the drug, its synthetic route, its impurity profile, its shelf-life and stability, and methods for its analysis.

- *safety*—its toxicology, safety in clinical trials, epidemiological data (for older drugs, for example).

These three aspects are assessed by regulatory authorities prior to authorization for marketing. Obviously, from the point of view of this unit, it is this latter aspect which is of interest. However, pharmaceutical quality has some bearing on safety issues, particularly from the point of view of impurities as these themselves may be toxic.

*US Food and Drug Administration, FDA*

Although the Food Drug and Insecticide Administration was established in the US in 1927 (it became the *Food and Drug Administration, FDA*, in 1930), largely to control patent medicines, there were no major attempts to control human pharmaceuticals in Europe or indeed elsewhere, for around 30–40 years. Then, following the thalidomide disaster in the 1950s and early 1960s, regulatory agencies were established in the UK, Germany, the Netherlands and in other European countries.

The European Union, introduced its first pharmaceutical legislation as long ago as 1965 when there were only 6 Member States (France, the Federal Republic of Germany, Italy, Belgium, the Netherlands and Luxemburg). This legislation took the form of Directive 65/65/EEC which defined a "medicinal product" and set out the basic regulatory and scientific requirements for the assessment of human and veterinary pharmaceuticals.

Directives 75/318/EEC and 75/319/EEC are extremely important in that the former establishes the requirements for scientific testing, including toxicological studies and clinical trials, while the latter establishes the Committee for Proprietary Medicinal Products (CPMP), the expert body which advises on the scientific aspects of applications.

430

Up until recently, the EU system was only advisory and the CPMP only issued opinions, but in the future its decision will be binding. Applications for human pharmaceuticals in Member States can basically be considered to be of three types.

### i.  National Procedures

The application is made according to national requirements (although this must be in compliance with EU law and requirements) and it is assessed according to national procedures in the Member State(s) concerned.

### ii.  The Multi-State Procedure

This is designed to allow a degree of harmonization across Member States. A marketing authorization (a license) is obtained in one Member State and the holder of that authorization then applies to at least two other Member States using the same dossier. The application is made in accordance with Directives 75/319/EEC and 83/570/EEC and the applicant has access to the CPMP.

### iii.  The Concertation Procedure

This procedure is compulsory for so-called high-technology products. These are products produced by:

- recombinant DNA technology;
- controlled expression of gene coding for biologically active proteins in prokaryotes and eukaryotes;
- hybridoma and monoclonal antibody methods.

However, products which are now active ingredients not previously authorized in a Member State may also be considered by this route. The Concertation procedure operates under Directive 87/22/EEC.

At the present time, the opinions issued under the Multi-State and concertation procedures are not binding on Member States.

*Food and Drug Act*

In the US, the *Food and Drug Act* was enacted in 1986. However, the forerunner of the modern FDA had limited power, until the sulfanilamide tragedy of 1937. Then, a drug supplier produced a sulfanilamide formulation containing diethylene glycol. As a result, 107 people died due to diethylene glycol toxicity, and this led directly to the introduction of the *Food, Drug and Cosmetic Act* of 1938. As in Europe, the thalidomide episode had a profound effect even though the drug was not licensed in the US, and this tragedy was followed by the 1962 Drug Amendments requiring safety and efficacy testing.

*Food, Drug and Cosmetic Act*

For new drugs, the toxicity testing requirements are similar to those required for drugs in the EU. New drugs are any drugs which are not recognized as being safe and efficacious and which are not approved under the 1906 Act. Older drugs are drugs which are not new drugs, or were approved prior to the 1938 Act.

Japanese requirements are also similar. However, although the EU, US and Japanese schemes have these broadly "similar" requirements, there are several major differences. Table 14.3 examines some of these in some detail.

*The requirement for carcinogenicity studies is flexible. There is a general need to test drugs which have a chemical structure closely related to that of known carcinogens or for drugs intended for long-term administration.

431

TABLE   14.3

Differences and similarities in requirements for toxicity testing for human pharmaceuticals in the USA, Japan, Canada and the European Union.* (Adapted from Speid et al, 1990)

| Test | USA | Japan | Canada | EU |
|------|-----|-------|--------|-----|
| Acute toxicity | 3–4 species, at least one non-rodent | at least 2 species 1 rodent, 1 non-rodent | not more than 2 species | at least 2 species |
| | several routes* | oral and parenteral | all parenteral routes to be used clinically | 2 routes at least, one to include clinical route to maximize information obtained |
| | numbers not specified | 5 animals per sex for rodents, at least 2 per sex for non-rodents | numbers not specified | |
| | $LD_{50}$ not required | $LD_{50}$ not required | $LD_{50}$ not required | $LD_{50}$ not required |
| Up to 3 months | usually rat and dog route -as close to route of human exposure as possible | 2 species: rat, 1 other expected clinical route | 2 species, 1 non-rodent routes should include the expected clinical route | 2 species, 1 non-rodent should include expected clinical route |
| | duration: | | | |
| | for use up to 2 weeks in humans, test for 3 months | use for 1 week or less–1 month tests; use 1–4 weeks –3 months test | varies 4–6 weeks and does not exceed 3 months | one or several doses in 1 day–2 weeks; up to 7 days –4 weeks; up to 30 days 3 months |
| | 3 dose levels | at least 3 dose levels | 3 dose levels | 3 dose levels |
| | animal numbers depends on study design | at least 10/sex/group for rodents and 3/sex/group for non-rodents | depends on study design | depends on study design |
| Longer than 3 months | 1 rodent, 1 non-rodent usually rat and dog | 2 species, one for rodents, one non-rodent | species which closely resemble human metabolically | at least 2 species one non-rodent |
| | route: intended clinical route | expected clinical route | expected clinical route | expected clinical route but depends on degree of absorption |
| | dose: from results of 90 day studies | at least 3 | at least 3 | 3 dose levels |
| | duration: 1 month or longer in humans– 12 months | 4 weeks–6 months in humans–6 months test; longer than 6 months 12 months test | beyond 1 month– 12 month | beyond 30 days– 6 months plus |
| | numbers: 10–25 rodents and 2–3 non- rodents/ sex/group | at least 10 of each sex per group for rodents, at least 3 of each sex per group for non-rodents | sufficient for the purpose | sufficient for the purpose |
| | controls as appropriate | vehicle and, if necessary, untreated groups | could include untreated, sham, or vehicle | as appropriate in small groups |

*See note on page 431

As a result of these many discrepancies, companies applying for authorization in several countries often find that they have to carry out different versions of the same study to satisfy different regulatory authorities. Alternatively, they need to conduct composite studies in the hope that these will satisfy all. As a direct consequence, there have been recent moves to harmonize on testing requirements not only for toxicology, but for clinical trials, pharmaceutical quality and efficacy, areas where there are also many discrepancies.

ASSIGNMENT 14.6

A drug has been shown to be teratogenic in rodents and rabbits. Should it be authorized?

## 2.5 VETERINARY MEDICINAL PRODUCTS

Many veterinary medicinal products are intended only for use in so-called companion animals—cats and dogs being the obvious candidates. Here, the safety is judged partly on the results of laboratory animal studies, and partly on the results of clinical trials.

However, the majority of veterinary medicines are used in food-producing animals and this places a different emphasis on the safety testing requirements. Firstly, as is obvious, food-producing animals and their products such as milk, eggs and honey are eaten and there is therefore a requirement for reassurance that these commodities will be free from harmful residues of the administered drugs. These residues are not only the administered parent drug, but also its metabolites, which may themselves be toxic, more toxic even than the parent compound. Secondly, as relatively large quantities of the drug are administered, then potentially, there is a scope for contamination of the environment with the drug and its metabolites. This may be important when slurry (mixtures of urine and fecal material which is often collected in underground sumps or other containers on farms) serves to concentrate these drugs. Thirdly, veterinary drugs are often given by untrained personnel such as farmers and farm workers, and by members of the public. Hence, although subject to the same three criteria of efficacy, quality and safety as applied to human drugs, "safety" tends to examine these other issues in more depth than for human drugs and indeed with veterinary medicines, where the patient may eventually be eaten, consumer safety is usually the issue of paramount importance.

### 2.5.1 Major Classes of Veterinary Drugs

Veterinary medicinal products fall into similar therapeutic categories as human drugs but some groups, especially those used to treat infectious diseases, tend to predominate especially as many of these tend to be given on a herd or flock basis, rather than on an individual animal basis. The major groups can be classified as follows:

*antimicrobial agents*

These may be subdivided into synthetic antimicrobial drugs such as the sulfonamides, and the synthetic, semisynthetic or naturally occurring antibiotics including the β–lactams and drugs such as streptomycin. They are used in the treatment of a wide range of diseases in food producing and companion animals.

*ectoparasiticides*

These are used to treat a variety of external parasites including ticks, fleas and lice on animals. Domestic fleas on cats and dogs are good examples and a variety of products, largely insecticidal in nature including synthetic and natural pyrethroids, carbamates and organophosphorus compounds, are used to combat these.

### anthelmintics

Food-producing animals especially are plagued by a variety of internal parasites which can result in distressing conditions and considerable economic loss. A number of antiparasitic drugs have been developed to treat these diseases, the major ones being the benzimidazole group of drugs typified by thiabendazole and albendazole, ivermectin, a macrolide compound isolated from *Streptomyces avermitilis*, and the drug levamisole.

### antifungal agents

Several drugs are available as topically applied antifungal agents including thiabendazole, ketoconazole and griseofulvin. Nystatin is also active against gastrointestinal infections.

### steroid hormones

These are available for a number of conditions, especially for the treatment of reproductive disorders. They are also widely used as growth promoters in view of their anabolic properties although this particular use is banned in the European Union.

### drugs used in fish farming

Although not a "therapeutic use", this is an example of a new form of intensive farming which has given rise to its own disease problems resulting in the need for specific therapeutic agents. Salmon farming is associated with two major diseases. Furunculosis, a bacterial disease caused by *Aeromonas salmonicida* is prevented and treated with antimicrobial compounds including amoxycillin and oxolinic acid. Infestation by the sea-louse, an arthropod and an external parasite of salmon poses a serious economic problem in terms of fish loss, and is a serious animal welfare problem. It can be treated with organophosphorus compounds and with hydrogen peroxide.

### 2.5.2 Regulatory Control of Veterinary Drugs

As hinted at earlier, veterinary medicines worldwide are regulated according to the three basic principles which also apply to human drugs: safety, quality and efficacy. They offer an interesting area of study in that they reflect the basic requirements for medicines, for fairly obvious reasons, but they share many points in common with pesticides because of their potential to result in residues in food-producing animals, and because they may contaminate the environment.

In the EU, veterinary drugs fall under the same basic regulatory framework as human drugs and are subject therefore to Directive 65/65/EEC. However, the two major veterinary Directives are Directive 81/851/EEC and 81/852/EEC. These two Directives set out the basic rules for the assessment and authorization of veterinary drugs in the European Union. Together, they establish the Committee for Veterinary Medicinal Products (CVMP). This is the expert committee which advises on safety, quality and efficacy. They also establish the basic regulatory framework and the essentials of the legislation controlling veterinary drugs in the EU, and provide the testing guidelines for safety, quality and efficacy.

There is a considerable raft of EU legislation relating to veterinary medicinal products, and for information, these are set out in Table 14.4. However, for present purposes, the major pieces of EU law are those which specify the requirements for toxicological testing. These cover applications made at the national level, by the multi-state procedure and under the concertation procedure as discussed under human pharmaceuticals.

Directive 81/852/EEC, as amended by Directive 92/18/EEC, sets out the major requirements to cover consumer and operator safety. The results of these studies are also useful in appraising safety to the patient–the so-called target species, but these are reinforced by actual safety studies in these species.

TABLE   14.4
Major EU legislation in the veterinary sector

| | |
|---|---|
| 65/65/EEC | —basic regulatory framework on medicines |
| 81/851/EEC | —basic regulatory framework on veterinary drugs, establishes the CVMP |
| 81/852/EEC | —testing and data requirements on veterinary medicines |
| 90/676/EEC | —amends 81/851/EEC; introduces new regulatory requirements |
| 87/20/EEC | —amends 81/852/EEC on testing |
| 92/18/EEC | —further amends 81/852/EEC; completely updates requirements on testing |
| 87/22/EEC | —controls high-technology products |
| 90/677/EEC | —amends 81/851/EEC with additional provisions on immunological products |
| 92/74/EEC | —amends 81/851/EEC, extends provisions for homeopathic products |
| 2377/90/EEC | —requirement for maximum residue limits |
| 92/412/EEC | —principles of Good Manufacturing Practice for veterinary medical products |
| 78/25/EEC | —specific permitted coloring agents for use in medicinal products |
| 90/167/EEC | —provisions for medicated feeding stuffs |
| 90/219/EEC | —contained use of genetically modified organisms |
| 90/220/EEC | —controls release of genetically modified organisms |
| 87/18/EEC | —harmonization of provisions on Good Laboratory Practice |
| 88/320/EEC | —inspection and verification of Good Laboratory Practice |
| 86/609/EEC | —protection of animals used in scientific procedures |
| 93/40/EEC | —amends 81/851/EEC and 81/852/EEC, lays down procedures to be followed under an European Licensing Agency |
| 2309/93/EEC | —establishes an European Agency for the Evaluation of medical products |

(EEC)2309/93 establishes an European Agency for the Evaluation of Medicinal Products. The general requirements for toxicity testing as set out in Directive 92/18/EEC are:

- single dose studies
- repeated dose toxicity
- effects on reproduction
  - reproduction studies
  - fetotoxicity/embryotoxicity including teratology
- mutagenicity studies
- carcinogenicity studies
- immunotoxicity
- observations in humans.

The results of these studies are used to assess consumer and operator hazard and serve as the basis for risk assessment. However, Regulation (EEC) 2377/90 introduces a formal requirement to establish maximum residues limits (MRLs) for veterinary drugs. These MRLs are based upon the ADI concept discussed earlier, but this is matched against drug residue depletion in the target species so that values can be established for tissues and for animal produce.

The MRL requirement under Regulation (EEC) 2377/90 is stringent in that it has two major requirements on the authorization of veterinary drugs by Member States:

1. all existing drugs (i.e.) existing when the Regulation entered into force in January 1992, must have EU MRLs by January 1997. Those that do not achieve this will no longer be permitted in veterinary medicines from this date;
2. from the date of entry into force of the Regulation, Member States may not authorize a veterinary medicine containing a new active ingredient until there is an EU MRL in force.

These MRLs are species-specific because of differences in pharmacokinetics. Hence, although the ADI for a drug is universal, the MRLs must take into account species–specific pharmacokinetics and specific toxic metabolites.

*First phase*

Directive 92/18/EEC also sets of the requirements for ecotoxicity testing. Here, there is a two-phase assessment. The first involves an estimation of the drugs' likelihood of the drug contaminating the environment taking into account:

- the target species and whether the drug is given to individual animals or is for mass-medication of herds or flocks;
- the method of administration and the potential for the drug to enter the environment;
- the excretion of the drug and its metabolites and the persistence of these in excreta;
- disposal of unused or waste drug.

*Second phase*

The second phase involves testing of the drug to determine:

- its fate and behavior in soil;
- fate and behavior in air and water;
- effects on aquatic organisms;
- effects on non-target organisms.

436

Such studies are important for drugs which may contaminate farm wastes including slurry, and for fish medicines which are usually administered by direct entry into the water, and so into the aquatic environment.

Another major and very controversial requirement is the need to assess the effect of antimicrobial drugs on the human gut flora. In theory, antibiotics for example, may alter the make up of the human gut flora either by killing susceptible bacteria so allowing potential resistant pathogens to proliferate, or by creating the conditions for adventitious organisms such as yeasts and fungi to colonize the gastrointestinal tract. Various *in vivo* and *in vitro* tests have been proposed to try to predict the effects of antimicrobial drugs on the gut flora, but these tests remain unvalidated and controversial, and the proposed adverse effects remain unproved. Nevertheless, although this cannot be called "toxicity" testing, these studies are obligatory under Regulation (EEC) 2377/90, and the results are used to establish ADIs on the basis of so-called microbiological end points, in conjunction with the results of toxicity studies.

*US testing requirements*

The *requirements in the US for toxicity testing* are broadly similar but there is no specific requirement for acute studies and the teratology study may be conducted as a component of the reproduction studies. However, should this prove positive or at least give rise to suspicious results, a second formal teratology study may be demanded. The EU requires a structured approach to mutagenicity testing with studies designed to show effects at the level of the gene, and on chromosomes whereas the US guidelines are more vague requiring "a battery of genotoxicity tests" without reference to specific end points. For both the EU and US, the requirements for carcinogenicity testing are flexible depending on comparisons with the structures of known chemical carcinogens, suspect signs in shorter-term studies, and the results of mutagenicity tests. There are no specific requirements for tests on the gut flora in current US regulations.

*Japanese Guidelines*

In the *Japanese Guidelines*, there are many similarities with the EU and US requirements. However, there is still a formal requirement to conduct $LD_{50}$ studies unlike the US and EU, and the repeated dose studies are specified as "21 days or more" again unlike the US and EU which specify 90 days, although there is an additional requirement for chronic studies in the Japanese guidelines which are defined as "3 months or more". The requirements for mutagenicity testing specify particular end points rather like the EU Guidelines, but there are more direct stipulations for particular tests whereas the EU allows discretion so that the investigator has a degree of choice. Oddly, the need to conduct carcinogenicity studies is based on pharmacological effects and chemical structure and the results of shorter-term studies but no direct reference is made to the outcome of genotoxicity studies.

*Residue studies*

In establishing MRLs for veterinary drugs, there is an obvious need to know something of the depletion of the drug in tissues of treated animals. The EU, US and Japanese guidelines share common elements in the need for companies to conduct so-called *residue studies* in the target species. These involve administering the drug to the target animal at the recommended dose and then sequentially slaughtering the animals and analyzing extracts of edible tissues to determine drug/metabolite concentrations. Edible tissues are normally taken to mean muscle, kidney, liver, fat and in some species, skin. Similar studies involving collection of milk, eggs and honey can be used for lactating animals, poultry and bees with these products being collected at suitable time periods after drug administration.

An example of the elaboration of an MRL is given later.

Having established MRLs there is a need to ensure that these are observed in practice. This is done by the imposition of so-called *withdrawal period for veterinary medicines*. These are the minimum times that must elapse after drug administration before animals may be slaughtered for human consumption, or before eggs, milk and honey can be collected. Withdrawal periods are established by again conducting residue depletion studies so that the time the residues decay to below the MRLs in the food commodities concerned can be estimated. These times are then chosen as the withdrawal periods and these form part of the basis for the authorizations.

Risk monitoring in these circumstances may be regarded as the residues surveillance programs which exist in order to determine whether or not withdrawal periods are being observed, and that MRL violations are not occurring. In the EU, there is a complex requirement for residues monitoring in red meat under Directive 86/469/EEC and each year, Member States must present residue monitoring plans to the European Commission for approval. As an example, in the UK, some 40,000 samples of tissue were taken in 1992 and in 1993 for residues analysis from random selected slaughter houses. Compounds analyzed for included various hormones, antimicrobials, anthelmintics, $\beta$ agonists, and nitrofurans. The levels of positives (i.e.) above the MRL were low around 0.5%. The majority of these were accounted for by residues of sulfonamides and tetracyclines in pig kidney samples. Similar problems have been reported in other EU Member States and in the US.

Other non-EU countries also implement residues monitoring plans. In the US for example, residues monitoring responsibilities lie with three government agencies. The US Food and Drug Administration, the Food Safety and Inspection Service (FSIS) of the United States Department of Agriculture, and the US Environmental Protection Agency. The National Residue Program covers monitoring and surveillance, exploratory studies, the development of rapid tests and a residues avoidance program.

At the international level, the Joint FAO/WHO Expert Committee on Food Additives (JECFA) establishes ADIs and MRLs for residues of veterinary drugs, in the same way that the JMPR does for pesticides. These have no regulatory basis as the JECFA has no legal basis–it is an international advisory committee operated by WHO and the FAO. However, the values it elaborates are used by countries which have little or no infrastructure in this area, and so are not able to establish MRLs in their own regulatory authorities. JECFA assesses MRLs in the same manner as do other bodies, as described elsewhere in this unit.

Another FAO/WHO Committee, the Codex Committee on Residues of Veterinary Drugs in Food makes use of these MRLs in setting food standards, as MRLs with different values in different countries may pose barriers to trade. Many countries including the EU Member States and the US, adopt these Codex MRLs to assist the process of international harmonization.

ASSIGNMENT 14.7

What are the major factors in considering a drug for use in food producing animals?

438

## 3    Case Studies

### 3.1    TARTRAZINE

Tartrazine is a coloring agent which has been used in foods and drinks and as a colorant for pharmaceutical products. It is a dye which imparts a deep orange color. Two toxic effects have been attributed to tartrazine. Skin rashes (urticaria) have been ascribed to the agent and the effect has been demonstrated in a range of investigational studies. The other effect is more controversial—the induction of hyperkinetic effects (hyperactivity or purposeless behavior) in children. Some studies have provided evidence for this whereas others have given negative or equivocal results. Tartrazine-free diets in children thought to be affected have resulted in some degrees of improvement.

As a result of the suspicions over tartrazine, its use has been restricted in certain foods in some countries.

### 3.2    IVERMECTIN

Ivermectin is an anthelmintic agent used in veterinary medicine, as described earlier. It is also used in human medicine for some parasitic diseases in tropical countries. Ivermectin is excreted in the feces of treated animals and concerns have been expressed that it may adversely affect insects and other organisms which inhabit cattle dung pats, and so inhibit the rate of decomposition. Some studies using reconstituted dung pats demonstrated that their decomposition rates were indeed much reduced, and so there have been suggestions that the availability of the dung should be restricted on environmental grounds. A recent study has investigated these potential effects in some depth. The study compared the persistence of dung pats from treated and untreated cattle on adjacent pastures. It found no significant differences in the rates of decomposition of dung pats from treated and control animals and there were no effects on pasture quality, the organic matter of soil or the populations of earthworms indicating that ivermectin treatment of the animals had no ecotoxicological impact, at least in the context of the effects on dung decomposition.

### 3.3    RONIDAZOLE

Reactive drugs, or drugs which are converted to reactive metabolites form covalent bonds with cellular macromolecules such as proteins and nucleic acids. In itself, this may have toxic consequences such as cellular toxicity or genotoxic and carcinogenic effects. However, there is concern too that these bound residues may be reactivated in the human gastrointestinal tract to release potentially toxic substances. Normal extraction methods such as those employing solvents, do not reveal the full extent of bound residues, nor do they demonstrate the ease (or otherwise) of their release from macromolecules. Various methodologies have been developed to try to show whether or not bound residues have any toxicological significance.

The drug ronidazole is a nitroimidazole used in the treatment of swine dysentery and a disease called blackhead in turkeys. Its residues rapidly decay *in vivo* but more persistent, bound residues remain for some time after treatment. The drug, like several other members of the class, has shown genotoxic activity, and is carcinogenic in rodents. Concern has been expressed that its bound residues may be released following digestion in humans, and that these residues may possess genotoxic and carcinogenic effects. The questions therefore relate to the bioavailability of bound residues, and the toxicological activity of any bioavailable agent.

An investigation used *in vitro* studies in rat liver, and *in vivo* studies in pigs and rats to try to resolve the problem. The *in vitro* and *in vivo* metabolic studies were first used to show that these were equivalent in their ability to metabolize ronidazole, and hence to validate the *in vitro* systems as models for *in vivo* metabolism. Then, mutagenicity studies were conducted on free and bound metabolites of ronidazole, on synthetic ronidazole cysteine adducts, and on material containing bound residues which had been subject to digestion. All gave negative results suggesting that bound residues were of no genotoxic or carcinogenic significance.

### 3.4 CARBADOX

Carbadox is a quinoxaline-1,4-dioxide drug used in the control of swine dysentery and as a growth promoter in pigs. Extensive testing showed it to be genotoxic and carcinogenic in several studies in rodents, suggesting that its residues might pose a carcinogenic hazard to human consumers of treated pigs.

However, metabolic studies in rodents and residues studies in pigs indicated that the major metabolite was the inactive compound quinoxaline-2-carboxylic acid. On this basis, it can be concluded that residues of carbadox are not a carcinogenic hazard for humans.

### 3.5 CARAZOLOL

Carazolol is an $\beta$-adrenoceptor-blocking agent, which has been used to prevent sudden death in pigs during transport. It was assessed by JECFA in 1991 and this committee reviewed a package of toxicological studies. It was able to identify NOELs in short-term repeated dose studies in rats and dogs, and in teratogenicity studies. The drug was inactive in carcinogenicity and in mutagenicity studies. It is normal practice to adopt the lowest NOEL and this was identified as a pharmacological end point for $\beta$-adrenoceptor activity based on the inhibition of isoproteronol-induced tachycardia in rabbits. The value was 0.02 mg/kg bw.

There was also a range of human pharmacological studies available but it was not possible to identify a clear NOEL (which might have lead to an ADI based on a 10-fold safety factor–see earlier). It was felt in addition that certain populations, for example those with cardiac or respiratory disease, might be particularly at risk, and there were no data available on NOELs in these subjects. Consequently, the ADI was based on the NOEL of 0.02 mg per kg bw in rabbits using a 200-fold safety factor—a safety factor chosen to reflect the degree of uncertainty over the pharmacological effects in humans. This ADI (0.1 mg per kg bw) was given provisional status with more data being required by JECFA to fully define a NOEL in humans.

In the complex process of establishing MRLs, data were considered on metabolism in laboratory animals and in pigs, and residues depletion data, again in pigs. These data indicated that metabolites of carazolol had no significant $\beta$-adrenoceptor-blocking activity, and that the main residues in pigs were located in muscle and fat. Residues in liver and kidney were probably not carazolol. Based on a full analysis of the residues depletion and metabolic studies, the Committee was able to recommend MRLs of 5 mg per kg for muscle and 30 mg per kg for liver and kidney in pigs. These levels, taking into account normal dietary intake of muscle, liver and kidney would result in a daily intake of 6.25 $\mu$g carazolol-derived material, or approximately 0.1 mg per kg. Hence, the ADI would not be exceeded.

## 4. Summary

The regulation of chemicals involves an assessment of the hazards, both biological and physico-chemical, combined with an examination of the possible risks involved following exposure and absorption. Regulatory schemes have often evolved following tragedies where people have suffered illness and death after exposure. Areas of concern include direct effects on human health and indirect effects arising from environmental contamination. The latter may also have profound effects for the well-being of the environment and the constituent ecosystems.

## SELF ASSESSMENT QUESTIONS

1 What are the major groups of chemicals to which humans and the environment are exposed?

2 Which are the main toxicological studies performed to build up a toxicological profile of a chemical?

3 Define hazard and risk.

4 The acceptable daily intake (ADI) is calculated using a safety factor. True or false?

5 What are the prime considerations in regulating non-genotoxic carcinogens?

6 Which of the following are more likely to involve a cost-benefit analysis:

   a. authorizing a new drug
   b. smoking a cigarette
   c. releasing a pesticide into a lake
   d. swimming in a polluted lake
   e. changing from leaded to unleaded fuel in your car
   f. spraying a pesticide on a crop.

7 What are the 3 possible methods of risk management?

8 Ecotoxicity tests fall into several broad categories but what are the two important aspects under investigation?

9 What are the major routes of exposure to industrial chemicals?

10 What parameter is chosen to determine safety for the consumer for residues of pesticides and veterinary drugs?

## FEEDBACK

### 1. Answers to the assignments

14.1 Factors might include:

- were all the usually required studies conducted;
- if not, was there a good reason for the omissions;

- were the studies properly conducted and in particular were the correct numbers, strains, sexes of animals used;

- were the appropriate dose levels employed and were the studies of sufficient duration;

- were the studies conducted in accordance with GLP;

- were there mechanistic explanations of the toxicity seen in the experiments;

- were there any significant effects which might justify a higher safety factor e.g. teratogenic effects.

14.2 Obviously, the compound must have shown carcinogenicity for the question to arise at all. It is then a question of whether there is significant genotoxic behavior in addition to the carcinogenic activity. A battery of tests designed to investigate this will center on effects on the gene, the ability to damage chromosomes, and the potential to bind to DNA. Carcinogens which are active in these studies are genotoxic carcinogens.

14.3 An inspector would look to see if there were any obvious hazards such as open drums of chemicals, leaking containers or vessels or pipes and whether suitable precautions were recommended by management and taken by employees e.g. wearing of protective clothing and respirators. Specifically, he would wish to know which chemicals were in use or were being made, and what the atmospheric levels were in the factory compared with the statutory or advisory limits for these. He would look to see if ventilation and antipollution measures were being taken.

14.4 Many difficulties might be encountered but perhaps the major one is in taking the broader view and asking what it means. If a substance is toxic to *Daphnia magna* is it dangerous? Should a substance be banned if it persists in the environment? The answers depend on the outcome of all the tests, and indeed on the degrees of persistence and toxicity. A substance which is persistent may be acceptable if it is not significantly toxic. A substance which is slightly toxic may be unacceptable if the target organism is a key species in the environment. The results as a whole must be studied.

14.5 The purpose should have some bearing on the regulatory outcome. An additive used to enhance the color of peas has no major importance other than those of consumer choice and financial benefit. However, an antioxidant may preserve the food and prevent breakdown products forming. A regulator may tolerate a low hazard with the latter but not with the former by balancing the benefits against the risks.

14.6 It depends on its intended clinical use. If it is to treat a condition found in men or in elderly women, it would probably be considered acceptable. If it was intended for use in women of child-bearing age, it would almost certainly be unacceptable unless it had a specific use where the benefits outweighed the risks e.g. as an effective drug in the treatment of cervical cancer.

14.7 The major concern is for the consumer and you would wish to be reassured that the drug would be safe. You would therefore wish to establish its toxicological profile, establish a no-effect level (if necessary), calculate an acceptable daily intake and set a maximum residue limit. You would need to be reassured about the safety of the drug *and* its metabolites in all the commodities likely to be eaten e.g. meat, liver, milk, and honey and you would want to know if the absorption of the drug by the target species were such that significant exposure of target organs was likely to occur.

## 2. Answers to the self assessment questions

1 Industrial chemicals, pesticides, food additives, human pharmaceuticals and veterinary drugs.

2 Acute toxicity, short-term toxicity, long-term toxicity and carcinogenicity studies, studies on reproductive function including fertility and terato-genicity and genotoxicity studies.

3 Hazard is the basic property (or properties) of the chemical which might pose a threat to health or the well-being of the environment; risk is the probability of the hazard being experienced.

4 True.

5 Determining the underlying physiological, biochemical or molecular mechanisms, and establishing a suitable no-effect level based on mechanisms or on carcinogenicity

6 All may involve a cost-benefit analysis depending on the individual(s) concerned. However, a, c, e and f are more likely to involve this process.

7 Absolute, as low as reasonably advisable and adoption of safety standards.

8 Determining the toxic potential to organisms in the environment, and then determining the concentration, depletion and persistence of the chemical in the environment.

9 Inhalatory and dermal are the most likely, but oral exposure through contamination of food or cigarette smoking may also occur. Oral exposure can also occur by the deposition of vapor and dusts in the oral cavity and/or coughing up deposited material from the airways, both followed by swallowing.

10 The maximum residue limit or MRL which takes into account the ADI and hence the toxic properties of the chemical.

# Contents Study unit 15
# Cytopathology: general response patterns and morphological aspects

0-8493-9232-2/96/$0.00 + $.50

Study unit 15

# Cytopathology: general response patterns and morphological aspects

### A. Penninks

## INTRODUCTION

*Cytopathological changes lethal or sublethal*

This study unit describes the *cytopathological changes* accompanying *sublethal* and *lethal* cell injury. It introduces Study unit 16, in which important mechanisms of cell death are discussed.

Cytopathology focuses on research into the cause and development of cell injury, studying changes at the morphological, biochemical and molecular level. In toxicology, the morphological assessment of tissues and cells has an important signaling function in the study of harmful effects of foreign substances in the body. Apart from giving an indication of the vulnerability of certain organ systems, the nature and severity of the changes may also provide insight into the toxicity of the compound. This study unit briefly discusses the most common reversible and irreversible changes in cells following injury, as well as the responses to cellular degeneration. Microscopic changes and corresponding pathological concepts are emphasized. These changes, however, provide little information on the subcellular and molecular processes involved. Therefore, further *in vivo* and *in vitro* research is required, in which electron microscopy and biochemical techniques play an important part.

LEARNING OBJECTIVES

After studying this unit, you should be able to

— distinguish between the different phases into which the process of cellular degeneration can be divided
— describe the various ways in which disturbed homeostasis may manifest itself and explain the light-microscopic changes involved
— describe the origins, development and morphological characteristics of the various forms of necrosis
— indicate the processes which may occur following necrosis
— define the following terms: cellular edema, hydropic degeneration, necrosis, karyopyknosis, karyorhexis, karyolysis, eosinophilia, endogenous and exogenous pigments, hyperplasia, hypertrophy, atrophy, coagulative necrosis, liquefactive necrosis, repair by connective tissue, repair by parenchymal regeneration.

*Study hints*

When studying light-microscopic photographs of pathological tissue injury, it is important to be familiar with tissue structures (histology) and possible changes in structure in normal physiological circumstances. Having a histology book within reach may be helpful.

The photographs of microscopic slides discussed in this study unit are in black and white. In order to get a better impression of the microscopic changes involved, you are advised to study the slides in color. You may do so by studying the cytopathology section of the CD-I program "Toxicological Histopathology". The study load for this unit is estimated at 4 hours, but greatly depends on your knowledge of histology and physiology.

STUDY CORE

## 1 Cellular homeostasis

Our fundamental knowledge of the toxic effects of foreign compounds mainly rests on our understanding of the cellular responses to injury, since cellular and subcellular changes constitute the basis of all diseases. Although the primary response takes place at the molecular level, the manifestations of hepatic, renal or neural toxicity reflect changes in physiological processes at cellular and sub-cellular levels. Before discussing the various forms of cellular change following intoxications, it is necessary to introduce a general concept of cell injury. In addition, several relevant concepts will be defined.

In normal physiological circumstances, cells, the integral building blocks of organs and tissues, are in equilibrium (homeostasis) with the surrounding internal environment (Figure 15.1).

*Direct or primary injury*
*Indirect or secondary injury*

Injuries may be *direct (primary)*, or *indirect (secondary)*. Direct liver cell injury, for example, occurs if a toxic substance interacts with one or more cell components. In the case of an indirect liver injury, the damage results from a disturbance in the microenvironment of the cell. This may involve interference with the basic metabolic needs of the cell (decreased supply of oxygen and/or nutrients) or with the regulation of cellular activity (altered hormone levels, for example). The primary effect of the toxic substance, which has led to the disturbance in the microenvironment of the liver cell, occurs elsewhere in the body.

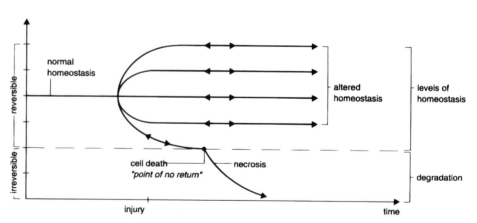

FIGURE 15.1

Schematic representation of a general concept of cell injury.

As a result of sublethal injury, the cell may enter into a phase of altered homeostasis, which is usually reversible. If the injury persists, the cells may remain in such a state of altered homeostasis, in which structural changes such as steatosis, hypertrophy, atrophy, etc. may occur. In the case of direct, lethal injury, or if adaptive responses fall short, the cell reaches the "zero level of homeostasis" (– – –), the so-called moment of cell death, after which repair is no longer possible, even if the cause of injury is removed. Subsequently, a series of degradation reactions takes place in the dead cell, leading to the formation of cell debris.

### Intermezzo

A reduced oxygen supply to cells or a reduced capacity for cells to use the oxygen supplied in their metabolism are good examples of how *indirect* and *direct* cell injuries are brought about.

*Hypoxia Anoxia*
*Ischemia*

Hemolysis is the disintegration of red blood cells, with the release of the pigment hemoglobin, which then appears in the plasma.

If the blood flow is normal, a reduced supply of oxygen may result from a reduced oxygen concentration (*hypoxia*) or a total absence of oxygen in the blood (*anoxia*). If the oxygen level in the blood is normal, a reduced oxygen supply may result from a reduced blood flow (*ischemia*). A decrease in blood oxygen level in the blood may arise from: 1) a decrease in the number of functional erythrocytes as a result of reduced production in bone marrow (e.g. in benzene intoxication), 2) acute hemolysis (e.g. in intoxication with heavy metals such as Pb, Cd) or 3) a decreased capacity of the erythrocytes to transport oxygen (e.g. after carbon monoxide or nitrite poisoning). Ischemia can be caused by impairment of cardiac function, by a marked decrease in blood pressure as a result of the use of vasodilators, or by vasoconstriction.

In hypoxia as well as in anoxia and ischemia, tissues are insufficiently supplied with oxygen, causing an indirect disturbance of energy metabolism which eventually leads to cell injury. Cell injury may also result from direct interaction of toxic substances with cellular metabolism. In potassium cyanide (KCN) intoxication, for example, KCN interacts directly with an enzyme in the electron-transport chain, so that the available oxygen cannot be used. This will eventually lead to a disturbance in energy metabolism. These examples also show that direct and indirect mechanisms of cell injury may lead to the same changes in cellular metabolism.

ASSIGNMENT   15.1

What is the essential difference between a lack of oxygen in tissues as a result of hypoxia or anoxia and one caused by ischemia? Could this difference have any consequences for the extent and rate of degeneration in the tissues concerned?

*Adaptive responses*

When cellular homeostasis is altered, *adaptive responses* play an important role. Their purpose is to adapt the disturbed cellular metabolism in such a way that the effect of the injury is minimized. This is, however, done at a different level of metabolic and functional activity, without loss of viability. These adaptive responses are usually reversible and are often accompanied by morphological changes in the cell. If these adaptive responses fail immediately, or in the long term, for example after chronic exposure, the cell will be irreversibly damaged, leading to cell death. The extent and rate of cell injury may therefore vary considerably. These not only depend on the severity and duration of the damage, but also on the cell type involved and the metabolic state of the cell at the time of injury.

This can be further illustrated by the example discussed in the intermezzo. In the case of a short or slight reduction in $O_2$ supply, damage to the cell can be restricted by adaptation of cellular metabolism. As a measure of adaptation, the cell will try to compensate for the reduction in aerobic ATP formation by increased glycolytic activity (anaerobic ATP formation). However, if there is an acute, serious shortage of $O_2$, this adaptive response may fall short and irreversible cellular degeneration may occur. Similarly, a slight, but chronic reduction in $O_2$ supply may eventually lead to irreversible damage to the cell. The cell type involved is also important, since tissues with high oxygen requirements (i.e. high energy requirements) deteriorate more quickly. In the case of ischemia, for example, irreversible cell damage will occur within a few minutes in neurons, after 15–20 minutes in cardiac muscle cells and after 1–2 hours in the epithelial cells of the proximal tubule of the kidney.

ASSIGNMENT 15.2

Give two possible reasons why, in the case of a serious lack of $O_2$, adaptation by means of increased glycolytic activity may fail.

*Moment of cell death*

It is generally very hard to indicate the exact *"moment of cell death"*. Analysis of the molecular processes involved in cell injury is difficult, as these processes cannot be studied separately. If the adaptive response to the primary injury fails, this will usually affect all sorts of processes of cellular metabolism. If, for example, the increased glycolytic activity from $O_2$ deficiency cannot meet the energy requirement of the cell, all energy-dependent processes, such as protein synthesis, phospholipid metabolism and membrane transport processes (ion balance), will be inhibited. This means that it is very difficult to identify which of the changes is the critical one and the actual cause of cell death. Cell death is followed by a number of changes in the dead cell, the necrotic phase.

Broadly speaking, the process of cellular degeneration following injury can be divided into four phases.

*Initiation phase*

The *initiation phase* is the change in the cellular environment that determines the cell's response to injury (such as decreased ATP levels in $O_2$ deficiency).

*Reversible phase*

The *reversible phase* or phase of altered homeostasis comprises adaptations of the cell's metabolism. These are often reversible and may be accompanied by morphological changes (response to decreased ATP levels → increased glycolytic activity).

*Irreversible phase*

The *irreversible phase* is the phase just before and after the moment of cell death. In this phase, the changes in the cell associated with cell death take place (increased glycolytic activity falls short and inhibition of all energy-dependent processes are inhibited, leading ultimately to cell death).

*Necrotic phase*

The *necrotic phase* comprises the characteristic degenerative changes in the dead cell. Before discussing the structural changes that may occur in tissue injury, we shall first look at some of the techniques and tools that are available for the study of these changes.

## 2  Morphological aspects of cell injury

*Hematoxylin and eosin (HE)*

For routine assessment of changes in tissues, *light microscopy* (LM) is used. Using this technique, one can gain an impression of structural changes in tissues. If necessary, other light microscopic techniques can be used, such as fluorescence and phase-contrast microscopy. For detailed information at the subcellular level, electron microscopy is needed.

Morphological assessment involves staining of tissue sections with dyes. *Hematoxylin and eosin* are used as standard procedure (HE stained sections).

### Intermezzo

*Hematoxylin–eosin stain*

The hematoxylin–eosin stain—better known as the HE stain—is one of the oldest methods for staining histological sections. The stain consists of two dyes: the amphoteric hematoxylin and the anionic eosin. Under normal staining conditions, hematoxylin reacts as a base and binds to the acidic (anionic) cell components. These include the nuclear DNA and RNA and, in active cells, the cytoplasmic RNA. Eosin binds to basic (cationic) cell components. The basic groups of cytoplasmic proteins are eosinophilic. The HE stain thus produces two colors: blue nuclei and pink/red cytoplasm.

*Increased eosinophilia*

Degenerative processes are accompanied by alterations in the binding of these dyes. Usually this leads to increased binding of eosin, shown by more intensely red/pink staining of the cytoplasm. Increased eosinophilia may result from:

- a decrease in the amount of RNA. Less RNA means a decrease in the stainability of the endoplasmic reticulum. As less hematoxylin is bound in the cytoplasm, eosin binding (pink) becomes more dominant.
- denaturation of proteins, providing more binding sites for eosin.

Either or both of these causes may lead to increased eosinophilia.

In addition to the standard HE staining of histological sections, numerous staining techniques are available to study in greater detail the findings obtained from an HE stained section. It is important to be familiar with the normal tissue structure with LM, as well as with physiological variations. Remember that a section only gives a momentary impression of a dynamic process and that histological techniques may give rise to artifacts (e.g. denaturation of proteins and chromatin). Moreover, the rate at which the changes occur cannot always be determined.

In LM examination the following cellular aspects are important:

*Identification of cell type*

*Identification of the cell type that is injured*–Tissues and organs are normally composed of several cell types. A distinction can be made between *parenchyma* and *mesenchyma*. To parenchyma belong the cells responsible for the specific function of the organ concerned, such as the contraction of muscles by muscle cells and the synthesis of blood proteins (e.g. albumin) by hepatocytes.

ASSIGNMENT 15.3
Which tissue components are part of the mesenchyma?

*Severity of cell injury*

*Condition of the injured cell*–Special attention is devoted to cell size, the staining of the cytoplasm, the possible presence of accumulation and the state of the nucleus.

*Changes in arrangement*

*Arrangement of cells within the tissue*—Disruption of the arrangement of cells in a tissue may also be a clear indication of a past or current injury.

Broadly speaking, the changes in tissues that can be observed by light microscopy reflect the phase of altered homeostasis, the necrotic phase or the changes following necrosis. In the following sections a number of common morphological changes will be discussed for each of these phases.

## 3 Morphological aspects of disturbed homeostasis

The reversible, structural changes that can be observed in the phase of altered homeostasis may have several causes:

- a disturbance in the microenvironment of the cell;
- a direct interaction of the toxic substance with general or specific cell functions;
- adaptive responses to disturbances in general or specific cell functions.

ASSIGNMENT   15.4

What is meant by general cell functions and what by specific cell functions?

There are many characteristic manifestations of disturbed homeostasis. Figure 15.2 shows some of the more common ones.

A number of these manifestations of altered homeostasis not only occur following cell injury, but may also be caused by various physiological conditions. In addition, different mechanisms of cell injury may lead to identical morphological changes. These aspects will be discussed in more detail in the specific sections.

### 3.1   CHANGES IN THE CYTOPLASMIC LEVEL OF CELL METABOLITES

*Accumulation or reduction*

Changes (*accumulation* or *reduction*) in the cytoplasmic levels of cell metabolites, such as fat, glycogen or protein, may occur as a result of cell injury by toxic substances. However, this may also happen under normal physiological circumstances, as in the case of increased supply (after a meal) or increased removal (during fasting). An increase in the cellular water content is as a rule only observed in injured cells. Accumulations of cell metabolites and pigments are usually *reversible* and are due to a disturbed balance between supply, metabolism and removal. However, in certain circumstances, excessive accumulation may lead to *irreversible* cell damage.

*Reversible–irreversible*

#### 3.1.1 Water

A disturbed cellular water balance is a common morphological change following cell injury. Control of water content is one of the fundamental characteristics of cells. It is determined by various factors, one of the more important being the difference between the Na$^+$ and K$^+$ levels in the intracellular and extracellular fluids. In mammalian cells, the K$^+$ level inside the cell is higher than that out-

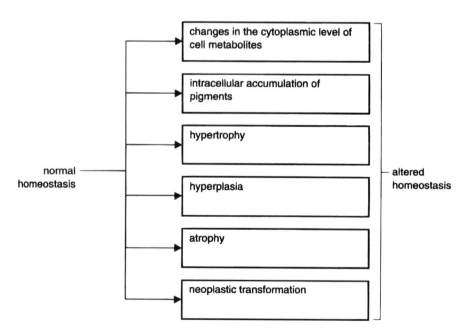

FIGURE   15.2

Schematic representation of some characteristic manifestations of changes in cellular homeostasis.

450

side, while the opposite is true for the Na$^+$ concentration. In order to maintain these differences in ionic levels, the passive inflow of Na$^+$ and the passive outflow of K$^+$ are counteracted by the presence of Na$^+$-K$^+$ carrier systems in the cell membrane. These energy-requiring carriers transport Na$^+$ ions out off the cell and K$^+$ ions into the cell, against the concentration gradient (see Figure 15.3).

*Cellular edema*

Consequently, the maintenance of the ion balance and of the corresponding water content of the cell depends to a large extent on the integrity of the cell membrane and on the membrane-associated Na$^+$-K$^+$ carrier systems. The energy supply of the cell also plays an important role, since the carrier systems are energy-dependent. If the Na$^+$-K$^+$ balance is disturbed, there is an increased influx of Na$^+$, which is accompanied by uptake of water. The increase in cellular water content causes swelling of the cell, or *cellular edema*. Since many intoxications lead, primarily or secondarily, to membrane damage or disturbances in the energy metabolism of cells, an increased uptake of water is frequently observed. The functioning of the Na$^+$-K$^+$ pump may, for instance, be inhibited by direct interaction of a toxic substance, e.g. ouabain, with this carrier system, but also indirectly by a disturbance in the energy metabolism of the cell. Hypoxic conditions and interactions between toxic substances and mitochondrial respiration lead to reduced production of ATP, and hence to decreased activity of the Na$^+$-K$^+$ pump.

In cellular edema, there is an increase in cell size; the cytoplasm stains less intensely and often has a somewhat foamy structure (see Figure 15.4).

The foamy appearance of the cytoplasm is caused by swelling of intracellular structures, such as mitochondria and endoplasmic reticulum, as the increased cellular water content is also distributed over these subcellular structures.

ASSIGNMENT 15.5

Which macroscopic changes in color and weight do you expect to observe in an organ affected by cellular edema?

*Hydropic degeneration*

If the disturbance in the water balance is not counteracted in time, or not well enough, the reversible phase of cellular edema will change into an irreversible phase, known as *hydropic degeneration* or *ballooning*. Histologically, this phase is characterized by increased cellular swelling, while in the cytoplasm numerous small, clearly visible, transparent vacuoles or several large vacuoles can be seen (Figure 15.5).

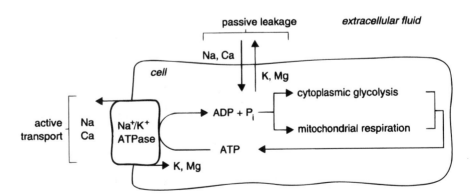

FIGURE 15.3
Schematic representation of the balance between the intracellular and extracellular environments, which depends on the integrity of the cell membrane, on membrane-associated carrier systems and on cellular energy metabolism (see also Study unit 16).

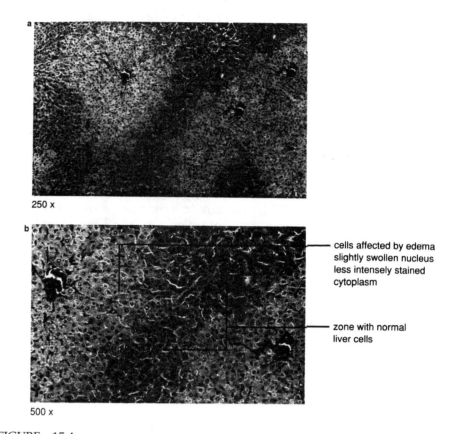

250 x

500 x

cells affected by edema
slightly swollen nucleus
less intensely stained
cytoplasm

zone with normal
liver cells

FIGURE   15.4

Cellular edema in liver cells

Due to their increased water content, some of the liver cells stain less intensely (HE,×250). A higher magnification shows that, in addition to the lighter staining of their cytoplasm, these cells are slightly swollen. This is called cellular edema. The nuclei are also somewhat lighter in color. (HE,×500).

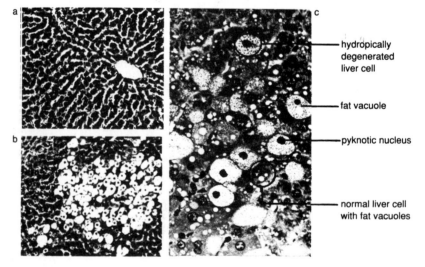

hydropically
degenerated
liver cell

fat vacuole

pyknotic nucleus

normal liver cell
with fat vacuoles

FIGURE   15.5

Hydropic degeneration of liver cells

a. Control section of liver tissue with central vein (HE,×250), b. Liver tissue with enlarged, transparent hepatocytes, hydropic degeneration and condensed nuclei (karyopyknosis) (HE,×250), c. Higher magnification of some hydropically degenerated hepatocytes. The foamy appearance of the cytoplasm is due to the increased cellular water content and the resulting swelling of subcellular structures. Both normal and hydropically degenerated cells in this section also contain small, rounded, transparent fat droplets. Between the hepatocytes, the angular nuclei of macrophages, in particular of Kupffer cells, are visible (HE,×500).

*Karyopyknosis*

In addition, *karyopyknosis* can be seen as a result of the condensation of nuclear DNA. The pyknotic nuclei are smaller than the original nuclei, more compact and strongly basophilic.

### 3.1.2 Fat

*Fat accumulation*

Intracellular accumulation of fat is also a very common change following cell injury. Tissues involved in fat metabolism (liver) or tissues that use fat as a source of energy (skeletal muscle, cardiac muscle and the tubular epithelium of the kidney) are especially prone to fatty changes. However, fat accumulation is not always caused by toxic interactions. Physiological conditions, such as a high-fat diet, may also lead to fat accumulation in, for example, the liver. The various ways in which toxic substances may influence the fat content of the liver will be discussed in more detail in Study units 22 and 23. Morphologically, *fat accumulation* can be easily recognized because of the presence of large, rounded, transparent vacuoles (Figure 15.6).

The round shape of the fat vacuoles is caused by the chemical properties of lipids in an aqueous environment, where they form globular structures. The transparency of these vacuoles is an artifact arising from the treatment of tissue when making histological sections. The fat in the cell is extracted by the solvents used, so that the vacuoles are in fact empty. In extreme cases, the fat droplets may become so large that they press all other subcellular structures, including the nucleus, against the cell membrane.

If the fat vacuoles are small, giving the cytoplasm a foamy appearance, more specific techniques are needed to ensure a clear distinction to be made between fat vacuoles and, for example, cellular edema (the use of snap-frozen tissue in liquid nitrogen is recommended to avoid the extraction of lipids, combined with the use of a fat-specific stain).

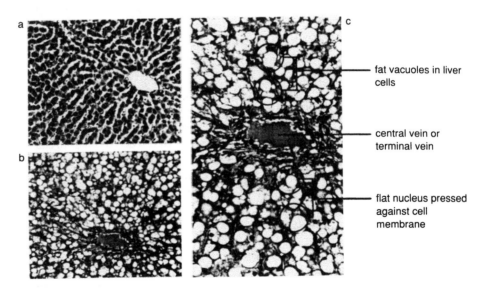

FIGURE 15.6
Fat accumulation (steatosis) in liver cells
a. Control section of liver tissue with central vein (HE,×250), b. Liver tissue severely affected by steatosis, with large, transparent vacuoles in the hepatocytes (HE,×250), c. Small and large fat vacuoles are clearly visible at this magnification. The position of the nuclei is also striking, in that they are no longer located in the center of the hepatocytes. The enlarged fat vacuole presses the nucleus (as well as other subcellular structures) against the cell membrane. Consequently, the nucleus is somewhat condensed, flattened and sometimes even invisible, that is, not hit because of the increased cell volume (HE,×500).

ASSIGNMENT 15.6

Is it possible to distinguish excessive fat accumulation from excessive uptake of water in an HE stained section?

ASSIGNMENT 15.7

Which macroscopic changes in color and weight do you expect to observe in an organ affected by fat accumulation?

### 3.1.3 Glycogen

Changes (increases or decreases) in the glycogen content of tissues play a role particularly in organs in which glycogen is synthesized, stored or used as a source of energy (liver, myocardium and skeletal muscle). Changes in the glycogen content of tissues may also be caused by intoxication or may result from a genetically determined deficiency of an enzyme involved in glycogen degradation. They may, however, also occur under normal physiological circumstances. In that case the 24-hour rhythm must be taken into account.

ASSIGNMENT 15.8

Rats are often used as test animals in toxicological research. What do you expect the glycogen content of the liver to be if dissection is performed at 8 a.m. or at 2 p.m.?

*Glucose-6-phosphatase deficiency* (Von Gierke's disease) is a well-known example of an excessive glycogen accumulation determined by genetic factors. A decrease in the glycogen content of tissues is frequently observed if there is a shortage of oxygen in the tissues (hypoxia, ischemia) or if the oxygen supplied cannot be used, because of mitochondrial damage (KCN intoxication, alcohol intoxication). By way of adaptation, the cells then change to anaerobic respiration, that is, increased glycogen degradation via glycolysis.

*Glycogen accumulation*

As glycogen is colorless in a normal HE section, the cytoplasm of cells with *glycogen accumulation* has a foamy, vacuolated appearance (Figure 15.7).

*PAS stain for carbohydrates*

This vacuolated appearance is caused by the fact that glycogen, which is normally water-soluble, crystallizes into irregular structures during the preparation (e.g. dehydration) of the histological material. Excessive glycogen accumulation in particular leads to large areas with irregular boundaries. To distinguish this foamy cytoplasm caused by glycogen accumulation from, for instance, cellular edema, specific staining methods are needed. The so-called *PAS stain for carbohydrates* stains glycogen red/purple.

### Intermezzo

*PAS stain*

The PAS (Periodic Acid–Schiff) stain is a histochemical reaction with which aldehydes can be demonstrated in cytological and histological preparations. PAS positive material is stained red by the basic fuchsin in Schiff's reagent. PAS positive material includes mucin, mucoproteins, hyaluronic acid, colloids and glycogen. The stain, as well as the staining pattern, can contribute significantly to the diagnosis of the nature of tumors: carcinomas appear to contain more PAS positive material than benign tumors.

### 3.1.4 Protein

*Protein accumulation*

Excessive intracellular protein accumulation is seldom observed. One of the best known examples is the accumulation of protein in the proximal tubular epithelium of the kidney. This form of protein accumulation is nearly always the re-

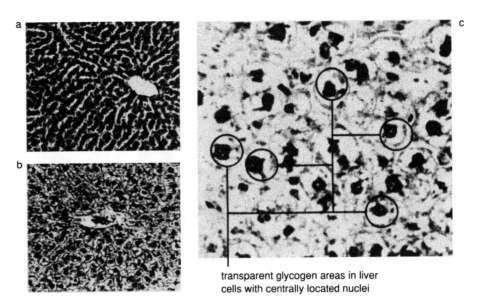

transparent glycogen areas in liver
cells with centrally located nuclei

FIGURE   15.7
Glycogen acculumation in liver cells
a. Cross-section of liver tissue with central vein (HE,x250),
b. Glycogen in hepatocytes visible as transparent areas around centrally located nuclei (HE,x250),
c. The irregular structure of the areas of crystallized glycogen are clearly visible at this magnification (HE,x250)

sult of an increased protein level in the glomerular filtrate. In physiological circumstances, protein is reabsorbed by the proximal tubular epithelium, to restrict protein losses via the urine. If there is an increased protein supply, however, the reabsorption capacity of the epithelial cells becomes saturated, resulting in protein accumulation. Microscopically, this is characterized by the presence of eosinophilic globules (see Figure 15.8).

ASSIGNMENT   15.9

Explain why the protein is present in the shape of globules.

*Hyaline degeneration*

Because of the hyaline appearance of the droplets, this form of protein accumulation is called *hyaline degeneration*. Accumulation of protein globules in proximal tubular epithelium may, for example, occur as a result of acute hemolysis caused by toxic substances (e.g. heavy metals). Since hemoglobin can pass the glomerular membrane, it will be present in the glomerular filtrate in cases of serious hemolysis and can therefore be reabsorbed by the proximal tubular epithelium.

ASSIGNMENT   15.10

Why does protein accumulation only occur in the proximal tubular epithelium and not in other segments of the tubular part of the nephron?

3.2   INTRACELLULAR ACCUMULATION OF PIGMENTS

*Endogenous pigments*

In toxicity studies, cytoplasmic accumulations of dissolved or granular material are frequently observed. Such material is only called a pigment if it clearly has a color of its own. Based on the origin of the accumulated material, a distinction is made between endogenous pigments, originating from the animal itself, and exogenous pigments, originating from the external environment. Most endogenous pigments result from the decomposition of normal cell components

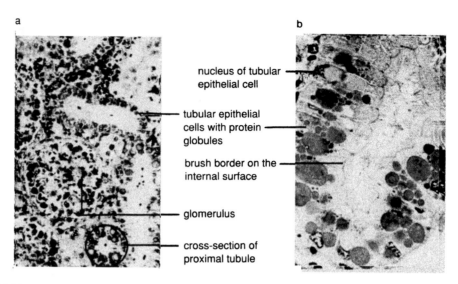

FIGURE   15.8
Protein accumulation in proximal tubular epithelium
a. Cross-section of tubules and glomeruli in the cortical region of the kidney. In the epithelial cells of the proximal tubule globules filled with protein (stained red with HE, i.e. eosinophilic) can be seen. The cross-section of the distal tubules and the collecting ducts (*) show no protein globules (HE,×200). b. Detail of a cross-section of a proximal tubule. At luminal side (*) of the epithelial cells the so-called brush border is clearly visible (enlargement of surface area). In the epithelial cells, small and large globules can be seen. In some, the cell nucleus is visible at the basal side of the cell (HE,×800).

and can be classified, on the basis of their chemical composition, into protein, lipid and hemoglobin pigments.

Melanin is an exception. It is a common, endogenous protein pigment, which determines the color of, for example, the hair and the skin. Increased local production of melanin in the melanocytes may give rise to freckles and birth marks. Diffuse hyperpigmentation may arise following exposure to UV light, arsenic poisoning or hormone administration (ACTH).

*Exogenous pigment*

Uptake of carbon particles by alveolar macrophages (anthracosis) is a well-known example of exogenous pigmentation, which causes the tissues to become black. Tattoo pigments are also exogenous pigments. Accumulation of silica particles (silicosis) or asbestos particles (asbestosis) in alveolar macrophages is also an example of accumulation of material of exogenous origin. However, as these do not change the color of the tissues, they are not classified as pigmentations. Accumulation and formation of pigment usually take place in the lysosomes, so that most pigments are visible as granular deposits in the cytoplasm. Accumulation of pigment as such does not necessarily have to be harmful to the cell. Prolonged, excessive accumulation, however, may give rise to cell degeneration. There are many different types of pigmentation. In this study unit, some common, endogenous pigments will be discussed which are also frequently encountered in toxicological practice (Table 15.1).

### 3.2.1 Lipofuscin

*Lipid peroxidation, see Study unit 10*

The lipid pigment *lipofuscin* is especially present in tissues that are actively involved in lipid peroxidation (a radical-mediated process). Unsaturated fatty acids (in the phospholipids of membranes) are extremely sensitive to free radicals, resulting in peroxidation and further degradation of these fatty acids. The composition of lipofuscin may vary greatly, but it contains mainly degradation products of phospholipids, condensed with proteins and other cellular components, such as carbohydrates.

TABLE 15.1

Some pigmentations, their color and forms of intracellular appearance in a HE stained section

| Pigment | Type | Color in HE section | Form |
|---------|------|---------------------|------|
| lipofuscin | lipid pigment | gold/yellow to brown | granular |
| hemosiderin | hemoglobin derived | yellow/brown | granular |
| hemoglobin | pigments | red/brown | granular |
| bilirubin | | yellow/brown-green/brown | diffuse/granular |
| porphyrin | | fluorescent in UV light | diffuse |
| melanin | protein pigment | brown/red | granular |

Lipofuscin is formed in lysosomes, so that lipofuscin accumulations appear as granular deposits in the cytoplasm. These are stained gold/yellow to brown in an HE section. Changes in the nature and location of the double bonds in its unsaturated fatty acid components give lipofuscin fluorescent properties. This means that the presence of lupofuscin can also be demonstrated by means of fluorescence microscopy (Figure 15.9).

Lipofuscin is also known as the "age pigment", since its appearance increases on aging. This is probably due to the age-dependent decline in defense

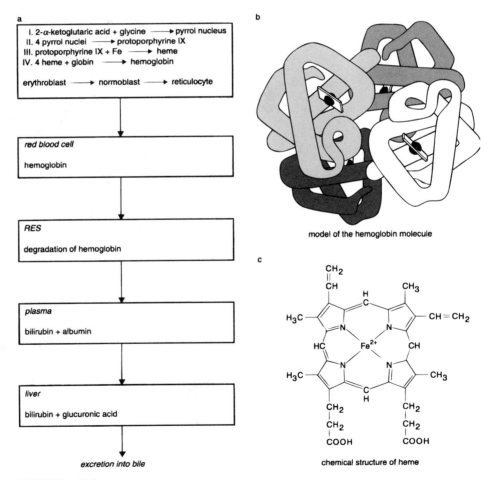

a. Synthesis and degradation of hemoglobin

I. 2-α-ketoglutaric acid + glycine ⟶ pyrrol nucleus
II. 4 pyrrol nuclei ⟶ protoporphyrine IX
III. protoporphyrine IX + Fe ⟶ heme
IV. 4 heme + globin ⟶ hemoglobin

erythroblast ⟶ normoblast ⟶ reticulocyte

red blood cell
hemoglobin

RES
degradation of hemoglobin

plasma
bilirubin + albumin

liver
bilirubin + glucuronic acid

excretion into bile

b. model of the hemoglobin molecule

c. chemical structure of heme

FIGURE 15.9

Synthesis and breakdown of hemoglobin and the production and excretion of bilirubin
a. Synthesis and degradation of hemoglobin, b. Structure of hemoglobin (three-dimensional), c. Molecular structure of heme

mechanisms against continuous exposure to free radicals (antioxidative mechanisms). In elderly people or animals, the pigment is mainly present in organs with high physiological activity, such as cardiac muscle, neurons and thyroid epithelium.

### 3.2.2 Hemoglobin-derived pigments

*Porphyrins*
*Protoporphyrins*

Components of hemoglobin (porphyrins, protoporphyrins), hemoglobin itself or its metabolites (bilirubin, hemosiderin) may show elevated levels in the blood and give rise to discoloration of tissues. *Porphyrins* and *protoporphyrins* are intermediates in the synthesis of the protein hemoglobin. Intoxication with, for example, hexachlorobenzene (HCB), polychlorinated biphenyls (PCBs), lead or alcohol causes disturbances in the synthesis of the heme molecule, so that the blood level of these intermediates increases. In the skin, these compounds may give rise to the formation of free radicals under the influence of sunlight. These reactive compounds cause local cell injuries, followed by inflammation of the skin. Porphyrins are therefore also known as *photosensitive pigments*. Porphyrins are classified as pigments because of their fluorescent properties. On exposure of tissue to UV light, porphyrins show up red.

*Bilirubin*

Under normal circumstances, decomposition of hemoglobin in the RES (reticulo-endothelial system) ultimately leads to the production of the iron-free degradation product of the heme molecule, *bilirubin* (see Figure 15.10).

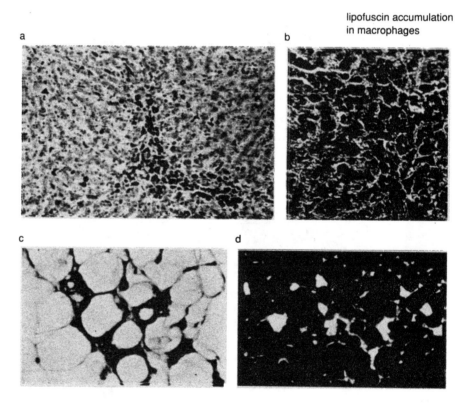

lipofuscin accumulation
in macrophages

FIGURE   15.10

Lipofuscin accumulation

a. As a result of degeneration of liver cells, lipofuscin is formed in the macrophages after phagocytosis of cell debris. In this section, lipofuscin is stained with a specific stain, resulting in a darker color of the cells (PAS,×250), b. See a (PAS,×500), c. Lipofuscin accumulation in macrophages in adipose tissue (frozen section, PAS,×500), d. The fluorescent properties of lipofuscin can be demonstrated by exposing it to light of a certain wavelength. The lipofuscin present in the macrophages of this adipose tissue section shows up yellow (frozen section, PAS,500×).

The bilirubin thus formed is linked with albumin and as such transported via the blood to the liver. There it becomes soluble through conjugation with glucuronic acid, to allow excretion into the bile. Bilirubin can occur in the liver and the circulation at increased levels, either conjugated or not. This may be caused by direct action of toxic compounds on the formation of the conjugate. Liver injury, causing obstruction of the bile flow, has the same effect. This may lead to yellowing of tissues, which is most evident in colorless tissues such as mucous membranes, scleras and the vascular walls. In newborn infants, insufficient maturation of the liver functions may give rise to yellowing. Light microscopically, the bile pigment is visible in the cells as green-brown to yellow-brown granules (Figure 15.11).

*Ferritin*

*Hemosiderin*

*Ferritin* is a colorless, water-soluble, iron-binding protein that functions as an iron depot in the body in normal physiological circumstances (see Figure 15.10). If there is an excessive supply of iron, for example in cases of extreme hemolysis, iron is also stored in the form of *hemosiderin*. This pigment, which probably consists of ferritin aggregates, is insoluble and has a yellow-brown color (see Figure 15.12). It is present in the form of granules in cells of the RES, as well as, under certain extreme conditions, in liver cells and cells of the proximal tubular epithelium of the kidney.

### 3.3 HYPERPLASIA

*Hyperplasia*

*Hyperplasia* can be defined as a controlled increase in the number of cells, which increases the size and the weight of the tissue or organ concerned. It may occur in response to physiological or toxic stimuli in tissues and organs of which the cells still have the capacity to divide. This form of increase in functional tissue cannot take place in, for example, the brain and the striated muscles, as these organs are no longer mitotically active. Examples of tissues that have retained the capacity of cell division are epithelial tissue (tubular epithelium of the kidney, alveolar epithelium of the lung, intestinal epithelium and the epidermis), blood cells (e.g. lymphocytes), thyroid cells and bone tissue.

ASSIGNMENT   15.11

What is an important difference between hyperplasia as defined above and the development of a tumor, which is also characterized by cell proliferation?

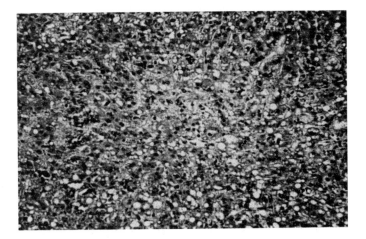

FIGURE   15.11
Cholestasis
Between the liver cells, the yellow/green color of the excess of bile in the bile ductules is visible.

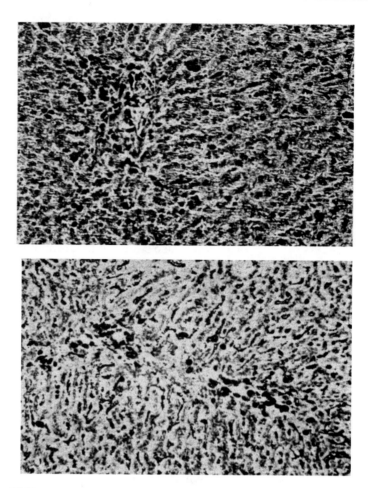

FIGURE   15.12
Hemosiderin accumulation in liver tissue
a. This HE stained section shows a brownish granular pigmentation in the liver cells and a homogeneous cytoplasmic pigmentation in the macrophages (HE,×500), b. Using a specific stain (HH stain = hemoglobin/hemosiderin stain), it has been established that the granular pigmentation in the liver cells, as well as the homogeneous pigmentation in the macrophages, both stained green/blue, is hemosiderin. The erythrocytes in the sinusoids stain red with this particular stain, while the liver tissue itself stains yellow. Since the hemosiderin in the liver cells is present in the lysosomes, which subsequently release their contents into the bile, the pigment granules are mostly located on the side of the liver cell bordering the bile ductule (HH,×500).

A special form of hyperplasia is the local response in the skin following contact with certain xenobiotics such as polychlorinated biphenyls (PCBs), dioxins (e.g. TCDD) and dibenzofurans (e.g. TCDF). This response consists of hyperplasia of the stratified keratinizing epithelium (epidermis), as a result of proliferation of the basal cells. Since the latter differentiate into keratin-producing cells (stratum granulosum) and subsequently die (stratum corneum), there is also an increased production of keratin. This process is known as *hyperkeratosis* (see Figure 15.13).

*Hyperkeratosis*

Hyperplasia of the epidermis is morphologically characterized by thickening of the various cell layers, in particular of the keratin layer. Macroscopically, the skin is locally thickened and scaly. If epidermal proliferation is accompanied by inflammatory reactions, the disorder is known as *chloracne.*

*Chloracne*

460

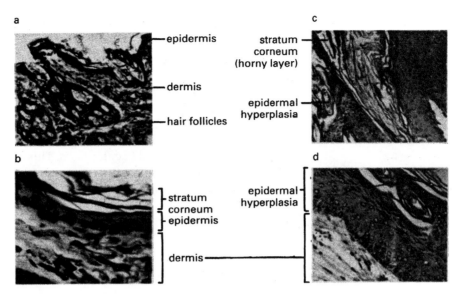

FIGURE 15.13

Hyperplasia of the epidermis

a. Control section of the dorsal skin of a rabbit, showing the epidermis and the dermis with numerous cross-sections of hair follicles (HR,×250), b. This magnification shows the nuclei of the cells of the basal layer, which divide continuously. The newly formed cells differentiate, produce keratin and subsequently die (HE,×500), c. As a result of skin contact with PCB, hyperplasia of the epidermis has developed. The increased mitotic activity of basal cells leads to an increase in the number of cells of all layers and increased keratin production (HE,×250), d. This magnification clearly shows the thickening of the epidermis and the differentiation process of basal cells to flattened cells and subsequently to keratin (HE,×500).

### 3.4 HYPERTROPHY

*Hypertrophy*

*Hypertrophy* is also characterized by an increase in size and weight of the tissue or organ, but, unlike hyperplasia, this is due to the increased size of individual cells (more cytoplasm and cytoplasmic structures). This adaptive response may be initiated under physiological as well as toxic conditions and may have pathological consequences in certain circumstances. Hypertrophy of the myocardium, for example, is a physiological adaptation in top athletes. This phenomenon may also be due to a chronic slight reduction of the oxygen pressure in the blood caused by a toxic agent.

ASSIGNMENT 15.12

Explain why a chronic slight reduction in the $O_2$ level in the blood may give rise to hypertrophy of the myocardium.

ASSIGNMENT 15.13

Suppose you have two HE stained sections, one section of hypertrophic striated muscle and one control section. Would examination by means of light microscopy allow you to tell with certainty which section is that of hypertrophic muscular tissue? Explain your answer.

SER = smooth endoplasmic reticulum

A special form of hypertrophy is frequently seen in the liver as a result of detoxication of foreign compounds by the mixed-function oxidase system (cytochrome P-450 system), located in the smooth endoplasmic reticulum (SER).

*SER proliferation*

Depending on the duration of exposure and the dose of the toxic substance, this enzyme system may be induced, resulting in proliferation of the SER. If the exposure is chronic, *SER proliferation* will lead to hypertrophy of the hepatocytes. Morphologically, the increase in SER gives the cytoplasm a foamy appearance. In the case of chronic induction, the cell membrane becomes more pronounced. Due to the increased SER, other cytoplasmic structures are pressed against the cell membrane, making it appear thicker than normal (see Figure 15.14).

### 3.5   ATROPHY

*Simple atrophy*
*Numerical atrophy*

*Atrophy* is a reduction in the size and weight of an organ or tissue due to a decrease in the total amount of cytoplasm. This decrease may be caused by shrinkage of individual cells, so-called *simple atrophy*, or by a decrease in the cell number, *numerical atrophy*. In the case of simple atrophy, the normal turnover of cytoplasmic structures is often no longer compensated by the formation of new structures. This will lead to a loss of specific functions, while general functions are maintained. Hypoxia, decreased food intake, reduced activity due to immobility (e.g. in the case of bone fractures) and disturbances in hormonal or neuronal stimulation may all lead to muscular atrophy (see Figure 15.15).

*Thymic atrophy*

Numerical atrophy occurs in tissues where the balance between formation and loss of differentiated cells in tissues is disturbed. This may happen in tissues such as the epidermis, intestinal epithelium and lymphoid tissue, where the loss of differentiated cells has to be continuously compensated by formation of new cells from basal cells, crypt cells and lymphoid stem cells, respectively. *Thymic atrophy* is a form of numerical atrophy, which may be caused by physiological factors as well as by toxic substances. The thymus is a primary lymphoid organ, in which stem cells, originating from the bone marrow, proliferate and differentiate into immunologically competent T cells. Depending on age (starting at puberty) a physiological numerical atrophy occurs, caused by a reduction in the

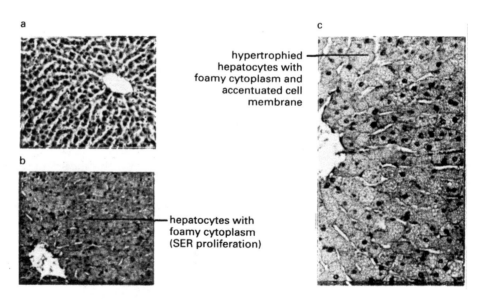

a.

hypertrophied hepatocytes with foamy cytoplasm and accentuated cell membrane

c.

b.

hepatocytes with foamy cytoplasm (SER proliferation)

FIGURE   15.14

Liver cell hypertrophy caused by an increase in smooth endoplasmic reticulum (SER proliferation)

a. Control section of liver tissue with central vein (HE,×250), b. Chronic exposure to foreign compounds that are metabolized via the cytochrome P-450 system leads to an increase in SER (HE,×250). In addition to the increase in cell volume, the thickened appearance of the cell membrane of the hepatocytes can be clearly seen, c. This magnification clearly shows the thickened appearance of the cell membrane and the foamy appearance of the cytoplasm. This foamy appearance is the result of proliferation of the SER with which the cytochrome P-450 system is associated (HE,×500).

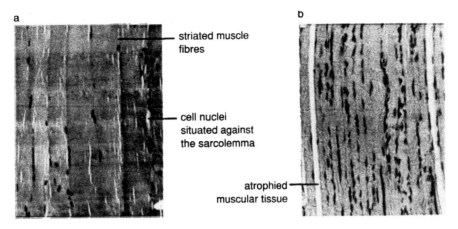

FIGURE   15.15
Muscular atrophy
a. Longitudinal section of striated muscle. The sarcoplasm shows mainly the contractile fibrils (actin and myosin filaments) and the cell nuclei, which are situated against the sarcolemma (HE,×500), b. Atrophied muscular tissue at the same magnification for the control section (HE,×500). Compared with the control section, this section shows the decrease in cell volume by the larger number of cells having been cut and the larger number of visible nuclei.

supply of stem cells. Various toxic substances, such as organotin compounds, disturb the balance between the supply and loss of thymocytes by interfering with the proliferation of stem cells in the microenvironment of the thymus. This results in thymic atrophy.

### 3.6   NEOPLASTIC TRANSFORMATION

*neoplasia = new formation*

Neoplastic transformation of tissues is a special manifestation of disturbed homeostasis. Its main characteristic is the uncontrolled proliferation of cells, resulting in the formation of a neoplasm or tumor. Tumor cells often disobey the rules set for the normal cells of the tissue concerned. In addition to uncontrolled growth, some degree of differentiation of the tumor cells may occur. This may involve morphological changes (formation of abnormal cells and/or tissue structures) as well as functional changes (metabolic or hormonal changes). More information on toxic substances that may cause neoplastic transformation of tissues is given in Study units 12 and 13.

### 4   Morphological Aspects of the Necrotic Phase

The necrotic phase is characterized by the breakdown of cell components after cell death. In this case the chemical processes of *autolysis* and *heterolysis* play an important part. *Autolysis* is the breakdown of macromolecules by the cell's own lysosomal enzymes. After lysis of the lysosomal membranes, these *proteolytic* and *hydrolytic* enzymes occur freely in the cytoplasm, where the local conditions are favorable (low pH) for breaking down the cell components.

*Autolysis*

If necrotic tissue is rapidly infiltrated by inflammatory cells, especially neutrophilic polymorphonuclear leukocytes, the degradation of necrotic tissue will be accelerated by the lysosomal enzymes of these cells. This is called *heterolysis*.

*Heterolysis*

*Denaturation*

*Denaturation* is characterized by rapid flocculation of cellular components due to local conditions. As a consequence, not many macromolecules are broken down to smaller fragments. As the extent of autolytic and denaturating processes may vary between tissues, there are several types of necrosis. The most important types are *coagulative necrosis* and *liquefactive necrosis* (see Figure 15.16).

463

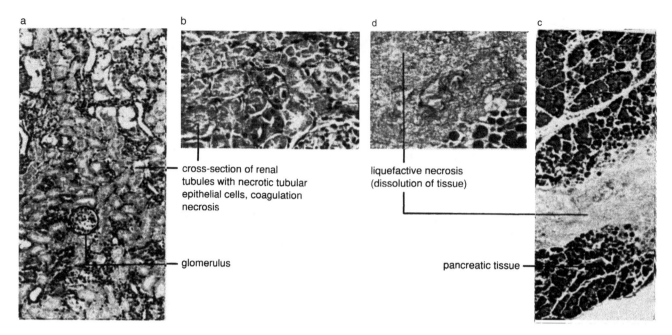

cross-section of renal
tubules with necrotic tubular
epithelial cells, coagulation
necrosis

glomerulus

liquefactive necrosis
(dissolution of tissue)

pancreatic tissue

FIGURE  15.16
Coagulative and liquefactive necrosis
a. Coagulative necrosis of tubular epithelial cells. In nearly all cross-sections of the proximal tubules, epithelial cells are necrotic and stand out because of their different color (eosinophilic) (HE,×250), b. This magnification shows that the outlines of the necrotic epithelial cells are still clearly visible, while the cell nuclei are already fully lysed. This type of necrosis is therefore called coagulative necrosis (HE,×500), c. This section of pancreatic tissue shows intact acinar structures next to areas of fully necrotic tissue (HE,×250). This magnification clearly shows that the tissue has completely 'dissolved' and lost its original structure completely. The various tissue components have reorganized themselves into threadlike (lamellar) structures (HE,×250), d. shows c. at higher magnification (HE,×500)

Circumstances that influence the balance between autolysis and denaturation include the type of tissue (many or few lysosomes), local conditions such as perfusion rate (supply of inflammatory cells) and moisture content of the tissue.

ASSIGNMENT  15.14

Which type of necrosis do you expect to observe in degeneration of muscular tissue, and which type in degeneration of pancreatic tissue? Explain your answer.

*Coagulative necrosis*

As a rule, *coagulative necrosis* is characterized by rapid denaturation, so that cell components are not fully broken down. Morphologically, the cell's outlines and tissue structure are still recognizable and the cytoplasm stains strongly eosinophilic. Probably as a result of the lowering of the cellular pH, DNAases and RNAases (enzymes that break down DNA and RNA, respectively) are activated. The resulting nuclear changes can clearly be seen by light microscopy. The pyknotic nucleus may be fragmented by the enzymes, or may be completely disintegrated and no longer visible. These processes are referred to as *karyorrhexis* and *karyolysis*, respectively (see Figure 15.17).

*Liquefactive necrosis*

In *liquefactive necrosis*, the affected tissue is largely disintegrated due to dominance of the processes of autolysis or heterolysis, if lysosomal enzymes from inflammatory cells were involved in the breakdown process. Morphologically, the tissue has a pale color, while the cell's outlines and tissue structure are no longer recognizable.

464

a          b

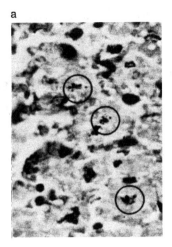
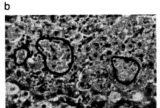

FIGURE 15.17

Karyorrhexis and karyolysis

a. In some of these necrotic hepatocytes, the pyknotic nuclei have broken up into fragments, so-called karyorrhexis (HE,×500), b. In these necrotic cells, the nuclear fragments have been fully broken down and "dissolved" so that they are no longer visible. This is called karyolysis (HE,×500). The nuclear structures that are still visible in the areas indicated belong to macrophages.

## 5  Morphological Aspects of the Responses to Necrosis

*Responses to necrosis*

Processes that may occur in response to necrosis include:

1 changes in necrotic tissue

2 removal of necrotic tissue

3 repair reactions

*Dystrophic calcification*

One of the visible morphological changes that may occur in necrosis of well-perfused tissue is the deposition of Ca salts. This is known as *dystrophic calcification* (see Figure 15.18).

The factors involved in this process are not fully understood, but local conditions such as pH probably play an important part. The increased deposition of Ca salts in necrotic tissue appears in HE stained sections as fine granules of basophilic material. The removal of necrotic material is brought about by the activity of the reticulo-endothelial phagocytic system or by infiltration of granulocytes and/or lymphocytes. Diffusion of cellular breakdown products into the immediate surroundings of the necrotic area plays an important role in attracting cells that are involved in the clearing up process. After the necrotic material has been removed, attempts are made to compensate for the loss of cells by *repair reactions*.

*Repair reactions*

Depending on the type of tissue involved, either a *restitution* or a *repair* reaction may take place.

*Restitution*

In *restitution*, the damaged tissue is completely restored to its original state. This is only possible if the mesenchymal network of the tissue has remained intact and if the parenchymal cells are capable of division (see Table 15.2). The gaps can than be refilled with new parenchymal cells. However, if the mesenchymal network has also been destroyed, restitution is no longer possible. Instead, *repair by fibrosis* will take place. In repair by fibrosis, the original damaged tissue is replaced by connective tissue, and a scar is formed. This type of repair is characteristic of tissues with highly differentiated cells that have lost the capacity to divide (see table 15.2). A special form of repair is *regeneration*. In regeneration,

*Repair by fibrosis*

*Regeneration*

465

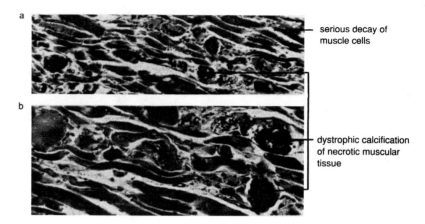

serious decay of
muscle cells

dystrophic calcification
of necrotic muscular
tissue

FIGURE   15.18
Dystrophic calcification
a. At low magnification, the irregular diameter and frequent interruptions (fragmentation) of the muscle fibers
are the most striking features (compare with the control section in Figure 15.15). The irregular, dark colored areas
in some of the muscle cells are calcium deposits (HE,×250), b. Magnification of the calcium deposits in some necrotic
areas (HE,×500).

TABLE   15.2
Examples of the regenerative capacity of various tissues and organs

| Unlimited or moderate capacity | Limited or no capacity |
| --- | --- |
| epithelium of the skin, intestine and uro-genital tract | skeleton, cardiac muscle and smooth muscle |
| bone marrow stem cells such as red and white blood cells, platelets | lung parenchyma |
| tubular epithelium of the kidney | renal glomeruli |
| liver parenchyma | nerve cells of the central nervous system |
| lymphoid tissue | retina and all other sensory organs |
| endothelium | endocrine glands |
| bone tissue | gonad parenchyma |
| peripheral nerve cells | dental structures |
| ductal epithelium of exocrine glands | |

new functional tissue is formed, consisting of both mesenchymal and parenchymal cells. In higher organisms, this type of repair only occurs in the liver, under special conditions.

## 6   Summary

In this study unit, various manifestations of cell injury have been discussed. These may be either reversible (sublethal) or irreversible (lethal) and may be caused by, for example, molecular interaction with toxic substances. In the process of cell decay, four phases can be identified: the initiation phase, the reversible phase or phase of altered homeostasis, the irreversible phase, and the necrotic phase. Based on this general concept, a number of frequently occurring cytopathological changes have been discussed in more detail. The cellular changes in the phase of altered homeostasis often result from adaptive responses of the cell to the altered situation. At this stage, changes in the cytoplasmic levels of cell metabolites and/or accumulation of pigments occur. In addition, hypertrophic, hyperplastic or atrophic reactions may take place. If the cell has been severely damaged or if adaptive responses fall short, irreversible changes may occur, ultimately leading to cell death. The morphological characteristics of the various types of necrosis have been discussed, as well as their development and the repair reactions after necrosis. The study unit has focused on the description of the pathological changes that may occur in the various phases of cell decay and the visual presentation of the light-microscopic changes involved.

SELF ASSESSMENT QUESTIONS

1   What are the phases into which the process of cellular degeneration can be divided? Give a brief characterization of each phase.

2   Pathological conditions are often characterized by increased eosinophilia of the affected tissues. Explain what this means and what causes it.

3   On histopathological examination of liver tissue, foamy cytoplasm and an accentuated cell membrane of the liver cells are observed. How would you describe these observations in pathological terms?

4   Name two types of necrosis and describe how they develop.

5   Resulting from an interaction between a toxic substance and erythrocytes a serious hemolysis occurs. What morphological change do you expect to see in the proximal tubular epithelium?

6   Which type of pigmentation do you expect to see in the macrophages of the liver following degeneration of liver parenchyma?

7   Explain why pigmentations often have a granular appearance.

8   In what ways may repair take place if acute intoxication of the kidney with heavy metals has led to necrosis of the proximal tubular epithelium?

9   Explain why inhibition of mitochondrial respiration may give rise to cellular edema.

10  Describe the changes that can be seen by light microscopy in the case of cellular edema and in hydropic degeneration.

FEEDBACK

1   **Answers to the Assignments**

15.1  As opposed to hypoxia and anoxia, ischemia is characterized by a reduction or complete absence of blood perfusion in the affected tissue. This not only causes a reduction in $O_2$ supply, but also interferes with the supply of nutrients, and the removal of cell metabolites. A reduced supply of nutrients (glucose) combined with accumulation of cell metabolites (especially harmful substances) may have a negative effect on the process of cell decay.

15.2  Possibility 1: Anaerobic degradation of glucose is far less efficient than aerobic degradation and is therefore insufficient (the ATP production is 18 times higher in aerobic degradation of glucose).

Possibility 2: There is a lack of substrate for glycolysis due to:

a    a lack of endogenous glycogen or glucose in the cell

b    an insufficient supply of glucose, or no supply at all.

15.3   Mesenchyma comprises the supporting structures of organs and tissues, including connective tissue, blood vessels, lymph vessels, tissue macrophages, nerve cells, connective tissue cells etc. In liver tissue, for example, only the hepatocytes belong to the parenchyma, while the other structures together make up the mesenchyma.

15.4   *General cell functions*: all basic cell functions that are important for the survival of the cell.

*Specific cell functions*: those cell functions that determine the specificity of the organ or tissue of which the cells are part.

15.5   Macroscopic examination shows that the tissue and/or organ affected by cellular edema has become not only lighter in color but also heavier, due to the increased water content of the cells.

15.6   In an HE-stained section, excessive fat accumulation and excessive uptake of water can be distinguished from each other by the position of the cell nucleus. In extreme fat accumulation, a large fat vacuole is formed which presses the nucleus against the cell membrane. Because of this, the affected cells often have a flat nucleus. In the case of excessive uptake of water, as in hydropic degeneration, the nucleus remains in its place (usually at the center of the cell) and may be pyknotic. The appearance of the cytoplasm is also different. In fat accumulation, the cytoplasm is clear. The large fat vacuole presses the other subcellular structures against the cell membrane. In the case of excessive water uptake, the cytoplasm often has a foamy appearance as a result of swelling of all subcellular structures.

15.7   In the case of fat accumulation, autopsy will show the affected tissue to be lighter in color (often more yellow) and increased in weight.

15.8   Rats are nocturnal animals and therefore eat at night, so that early in the morning, the glycogen content of the liver will be high. In the course of the day, the glycogen content will decrease as glycogen serves as a source of energy for the liver cells themselves and is also transported to other organs. This has to be taken into account in assessing the glycogen content of the liver.

15.9   Proteins that are reabsorbed from the glomerular filtrate are taken up by lysosomes. In these *globular* subcellular structures, the proteins are broken down by enzymes to their building blocks, the amino acids, which are released into the blood at the basal side of the tubular epithelial cells.

15.10 In the kidney, protein accumulation generally occurs only in the proximal tubule (straight part and convoluted part) of the nephron, since this is the only part involved in the reabsorption of proteins from the glomerular filtrate.

15.11 In tumors, cell proliferation is usually uncontrolled. See also Study units 12 and 13.

15.12 In the case of a chronic slight reduction in the $O_2$ level in the blood, the heart will try to compensate for the $O_2$ deficiency by increasing the frequency at which the blood circulates. This implies that the myocardium will have to work harder. Since striated muscle cells are not able to proliferate, this is accomplished by forming new intracellular structures (such as myosin and actin), leading to hypertrophy of the muscle cells.

15.13 In a microscopic image of hypertrophic muscular tissue and a control section (same magnification), the number of muscle fibers can be counted. This is most easily done in a longitudinal section. In the case of hypertrophic muscular tissue there will be fewer muscle fibers because of the increased size of individual fibers. It is also possible to count the number of nuclei in both sections. The control section will contain a larger number of nuclei (see Figure 15.15).

15.14 Muscle cells have relatively low lysosomal activity. Consequently, there is little autolytic activity following cellular degeneration. The result will be that coagulative necrosis occurs. In pancreatic tissue, many digestive enzymes are produced, which may become active after cell death due to the low pH. As a result of this, autolytic processes dominate in the necrotic phase and the tissue material 'dissolves': liquefactive necrosis. This is especially noticeable along the excretory ducts of the pancreas, because pancreatic enzymes already activated in the intestines (due to the low pH) flow back and cause rapid lysis and further breakdown of pancreatic cells.

## 2    Answers to the Self Assessment Questions

1    *Initiation phase*: the changes in the cell that determine the response(s) to injury.
*Reversible phase*: changes in the cell's metabolism, usually reversible adaptive responses which may be accompanied by morphological changes.
*Irreversible phase*: the phase just before and after the moment of cell death, in which changes take place in the cell that are associated with cell death.
*Necrotic phase*: characteristic, degenerative changes in the dead cell.

2    Increased eosinophilia of tissues is an indication of increased binding of eosin (see intermezzo on HE staining). Increased eosin binding may be caused by:

1    detachment of ribosomes (RNA) from the endoplasmic reticulum; this means that less hematoxylin is bound so that apparently binding of eosin dominates.

2    denaturation of proteins, resulting in more binding sites for eosin.

3    a combination of 1 and 2.

3    Foamy cytoplasm and an accentuated cell membrane are highly indicative of SER proliferation, leading to hepatocellular hypertrophy. This morphological finding justifies the conclusion that the animal has possibly suffered chronic exposure to a foreign compound which induces the mixed-function oxidase system.

4    *Coagulative necrosis*: this type of necrosis develops if denaturation is the dominant process in necrotic tissue.

*Liquefactive necrosis*: this type of necrosis develops if autolytic or heterolytic processes dominate in necrotic tissue.

5   In the epithelium of proximal tubules, hyaline degeneration may occur. As a result of lysis of erythrocytes, hemoglobin is released into the blood and part of it is excreted in the glomerular filtrate. In that case, the proximal tubular epithelium will try to reabsorb this hemoglobin, so that protein accumulation may occur.

6   In the case of degeneration of liver parenchyma, macrophages try to remove the damaged cells. The various cell components are processed in the lysosomes of the macrophages, which may ultimately yield the pigment lipofuscin as a residue.

7   Pigmentations often appear in the form of granules because the pigment is stored and processed in lysosomes.

8   Proximal tubular epithelium belongs to the tissues of which the cells are still able to divide. This implies that if the damage is restricted to the epithelium and if the stroma (e.g. the basement membrane) has not been affected, restitution may occur. Tubular epithelial cells that are still intact will start to proliferate and replace the damaged cells and so refill the gaps. If the stroma has been affected as well, there is usually an inflammatory reaction followed by fibrosis. Repair by fibrosis implies that functional tissue is replaced by connective tissue (scar formation).

9   Inhibition of mitochondrial respiration may have consequences for the energy supply of the cell and thus for the maintenance of the ion balance and associated cellular water content. If the energy-dependent $Na^+$-$K^+$ pump does not function properly, the water content of the cell will increase, resulting in cellular edema.

10  *Cellular edema*: in an HE stained section, slightly swollen and less intensely stained cells can be seen. Sometimes the nuclei are also slightly swollen and somewhat lighter in color.
*Hydropic degeneration*: markedly swollen cells, slightly foamy cytoplasm with clear vacuoles and pyknotic nuclei (condensed DNA).

# Contents Study unit 16
# Necrosis and apoptosis: irreversibility of cell damage and cell death

0-8493-9232-2/96/$0.00 + $.50
© 1996 by CRC Press, Inc.

# Study unit 16

# Necrosis and apoptosis: irreversibility of cell damage and cell death

*A. Verheyen*

## INTRODUCTION

In Study unit 15, the general response patterns and morphological aspects of sublethal cell injury have been discussed. It has been emphasized that injurious factors may lead to a disturbance of cellular homeostasis. If the disturbance remains within the limits of homeostatic adaptation (Figure 16.1), the cell can protect itself so that the effect of the injury is minimized or reversed.

If the disturbance in cellular homeostasis exceeds the limits of adaptation, so that the "point of no return" is reached, the cell is doomed to die and irreversible cellular degeneration ensues. The previous study unit dealt with the morphological aspects of necrotic cell death. In this study unit, a second type of cell death is introduced: *apoptosis*. A comparison is made between these two types of cell death. Cell death is often caused by toxic chemicals. Depending on the nature of the chemical substances, various cellular organelles may be affected. The most important mechanisms of cell death are discussed in this unit.

*Ischemia* is caused by inadequate blood flow to an organ or tissue, and this may lead to serious cell injury. Extensive research into the development and

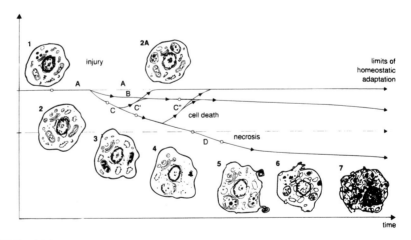

FIGURE 16.1
Homeostatic adaptation after cell injury
1 Cell in its normal, undamaged state (curve A) After acute, sublethal or lethal injury, the cell loses its capacity for homeostatic adaptation according to curve B or C. Certain intracellular changes occur (2,2A,3). Before the point of cell death is reached, repair can take place by removal or neutralization of the injurious factor. This repair may take place according to curve C' or C", and may be either complete or incomplete. Once the point of cell death has been reached (4), however, the cell degenerates completely (5,6,7), as shown by curve D.

473

course of ischemia has contributed to a better understanding of the successive phases of cellular degeneration. One of the aims was to determine the critical moment at which the cell becomes irreversibly damaged as closely as possible by means of ultrastructural and biochemical techniques. From the description of this research, it will become clear that calcium plays an important part in the process of cellular degeneration. The role of calcium in cell death is therefore discussed in more detail in a separate section. The recognition of relatively extensive degenerative changes in organs or organ systems may be important for clinical evaluation. In the final section, certain biochemical parameters of cell death are discussed.

LEARNING OBJECTIVES

After studying this unit about the irreversibility of cell injury and cell death, you should be able to:

— describe the main differences in morphology, occurrence and mechanism between the two types of cell death: necrosis and apoptosis

— indicate in which way toxic substances may cause direct and indirect membrane damage

— describe the primary and secondary consequences of toxic damage to mitochondria, to microtubules and to cellular organelles that are responsible for protein synthesis

— describe the concept of reversible and irreversible damage

— summarize the ultrastructural changes that occur during ischemia and reperfusion of the isolated working heart of a rabbit, with emphasis on the morphological features of the transition from reversible to irreversible damage

— indicate which important changes occur in energy metabolism during ischemia

— describe briefly the calcium homeostasis of a normal cell

— indicate the main consequences of an increased calcium level in the cytosol

— describe the ways in which cell death can be determined biochemically by means of blood plasma analysis.

*Study hints*

This study unit is a continuation of the previous unit. In addition to subcellular changes (at EM level; EM = electron microscopy), various biochemical parameters involved in cellular degeneration are described. You are assumed to be familiar with elementary cell structure and the major concepts of cellular biochemistry. If necessary, read up on these subjects first.

The study load for this unit is estimated at 5 hours, provided that you have sufficient general subject knowledge.

STUDY CORE

1    **Cell death: necrosis or apoptosis**

Nearly all dying cells can be classified into two categories. This classification is mainly based on the existence of two clearly distinct patterns of morphological change, which occur under individually characteristic circumstances. One of these patterns is the classic swelling now known as *necrosis*. Necrosis is caused

*Necrosis*

474

by injurious factors such as toxic substances and ischemia and frequently occurs in groups of cells rather than in individual cells. *In vivo*, necrosis usually leads to exudative *inflammation*. The second pattern is characterized by condensation of the cell and is often regulated by physiological stimuli. This pattern is not associated with inflammation. Originally, this form of cell death was referred to as "shrinkage necrosis", but it is now known as *apoptosis*.

The following sections discuss the morphology, occurrence and mechanisms of necrosis and apoptosis, respectively.

## 1.1   MORPHOLOGY

The changes that characterize the process of cellular degeneration and necrosis are schematically presented below (Figure 16.2). This illustration is based on examination by electron microscopy during ischemic injury to epithelial cells of the renal tubule.

The normal cell displays a certain configuration of cellular organelles (Figure 16.2a), which progressively changes under the influence of injurious factors (Figure 16.2b–d), and eventually degenerates completely (Figure 16.2e).

Figure 16.3 shows a normal (a, b) and a necrotic cell (c and d), visualized by electron microscopy.

Necrotic cells are removed (*phagocytosed* and subsequently digested) mainly by cells of the mononuclear phagocyte system which migrate from the blood to the site of necrosis.

The changes that occur during apoptosis can be divided into two phases, namely *condensation* followed by *fragmentation and phagocytosis*.

The first structural change that can be seen is aggregation of the chromatin to large granular masses lying against the nuclear membrane. Simultaneously, *condensation* of the cytoplasm occurs, as a result of which cells in compact tissues become detached from their neighbors. Following progressive condensation, the affected cells become deformed, often displaying rounded protrusions. Subsequently, the nucleus breaks up into fragments and the cytoplasm also starts to disintegrate into a number of fragments of varying sizes. During this process, the ultrastructure of the subcellular organelles, even those in the fragments, hardly changes. In the second phase, the fragments are phagocytosed by other cells. They end up in phagosomes, where they are degraded to residual bodies by the lysosomal enzymes of the phagocytosing cells. These cells may be *histiocytes* or *tissue macrophages*, but they may also be tissue cells of the same type as the apoptotic cell. The lysosomes of the degenerating cell usually do not take part in the digestion process. During the metamorphosis of certain insects, however, *autolytic* bodies are formed in the initial phase of apoptotic degeneration, that mainly contain mitochondria and ribosomes. Their contents are degraded by lysosomal enzymes of the degenerating cell itself. In Figure 16.5 electron micrographs of a normal and an apoptotic cell can be compared.

## 1.2   OCCURRENCE

Necrosis is always associated with major disturbances in internal as well as external conditions. Changes in physiological conditions may be brought about by physical (mechanical, electrical or thermal damage, ionizing and radioactive radiation), chemical (biological toxins, pesticides, herbicides, pharmaceutical agents, heavy metals) immunological (complement) and biological (viruses, bacteria, fungi, protozoa, metazoa) conditions or by circulatory disturbances (ischemia, hypoxia, anoxia). Hence, the occurrence of necrosis is not

*Marginalia:*

exudate = fluid which has escaped from cells; macroscopically, this often appears as a swelling

*Apoptosis*

*Necrosis*

*Apoptosis*

*Condensation*

*Fragmentation*

histiocyte (tissue macrophage) = phagocyte of the reticulo-endothelial system
*Phagocytosis*
*Histiocyte*

*Autolysis*

*Necrosis*

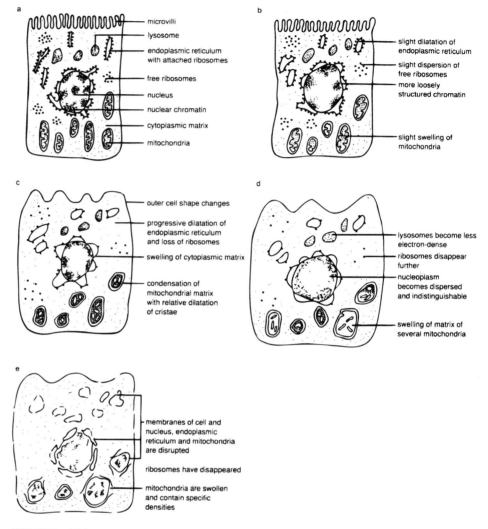

FIGURE 16.2

Schematic representation of cellular degeneration and necrosis

a. Schematic representation of a normal tubular cell of the kidney, showing the major cell organelles that can be seen by electron microscopy

b. Due to the injurious effect of oxygen deficiency, slight changes have occurred in subcellular structures

c. In addition to causing further changes in subcellular structures, prolonged oxygen deficiency also affects the outer shape of the cell

d. The changes due to the oxygen deficiency have progressed to a point where the cell no longer resembles the unaffected cell (a), neither at the subcellular level nor in its outward appearance

e. If exposure lasts long enough, the injury will lead to disintegration of subcellular membranes and ultimately to disintegration of the cell membrane itself

determined by factors that are *intrinsic* to the cell, but by marked *changes in the cellular environment.*

*Apoptosis*

Experimental studies have indicated that apoptotic cell death is associated with withdrawal of stimuli (e.g. of trophic factors) or the occurrence of stimuli (hormones, tumor necrosis factor, growth factors, ionizing radiation, anticancer drugs, toxins) that are not directly lethal. In other situations the presence of any apparent injurious or toxic stimulus could not be defined. There is no evidence of a sudden deficiency of vital substances in the affected cells. This type of cellular degeneration is therefore assumed to be a physiological phenomenon, which explains why it is also known as *physiological cell death.*

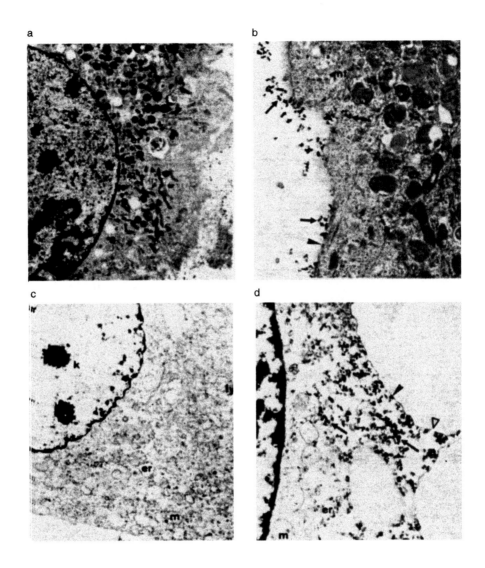

FIGURE   16.3

Normal and necrotic fibroblasts in a cell culture

The cells are derived from a mouse embryo

a.  Overview of a normal cell. (×3,700)

b.  Part of a normal cell at higher magnification. The colloidal carbon present in the incubation medium of the cell culture cannot enter the cell. (×11,500)

c.  Overview of a necrotic cell. The necrosis is caused by the detergent Triton X-100, which causes disintegration of membranes. The changes in the nucleus and other cellular structures are striking. (×3,700)

d.  Part of a necrotic cell at higher magnification. The colloidal carbon has penetrated into the cell. The tracer appears free in the cytosol and is not surrounded by a membrane. (×11,500)

er:  endoplasmic reticulum

n:  nucleus

ly:  lysosome

m:  mitochondrion

mt:  microtubules

r:  free ribosomes

→:  indicates the tracer, colloidal carbon

▶:  indicates the cell membrane

▷:  indicates a gap in the cell membrane

⇀:  the colloidal carbon can only be phagocytosed by a normal cell, not by a necrotic cell. The colloidal carbon is present in cellular organelles, surrounded by membranes

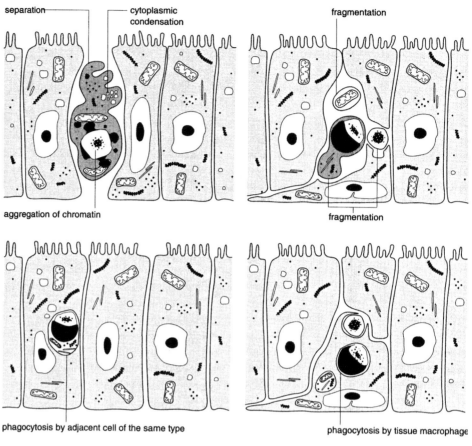

separation — cytoplasmic condensation

fragmentation

aggregation of chromatin

fragmentation

phagocytosis by adjacent cell of the same type

phagocytosis by tissue macrophage

FIGURE   16.4

Ultrastructural changes in apoptotic cellular degeneration

Apoptosis often affects individual, scattered cells. Apoptosis is, for instance, responsible for the physiological turnover of cells in adult tissue. This form of cellular degeneration is regarded as a basic, biological phenomenon which is complementary, albeit counteractive, to mitotic cell division, and hence contributes to the regulation of cell populations in healthy tissues. Apoptosis is also responsible for the removal of cells during normal, embryological development and during metamorphosis. This form of cell death affects relatively large numbers of cells and clearly increases in various types of atrophy, including atrophy of hormone-dependent tissues caused by changes in the plasma levels of trophic hormones. Apoptosis also occurs spontaneously in proliferating neoplasms and during the aging process, and is induced in target cells by the binding of specific T-lymphocytes. The phenomenon is thought to play a role in almost every aspect of immunology, including disease situations like AIDS and autoimmune disease.

## 1.3   MECHANISMS

There is a good deal of evidence for the assumption that the loss of the homeostatic cell volume constitutes a critical step in the development of necrosis. Changed membrane permeability has been demonstrated experimentally by the influx of colloidal material, decreased potassium levels, increased sodium levels and reduced membrane potentials, and the incapacity of cells to exclude specific dyes (visible by light microscopy).

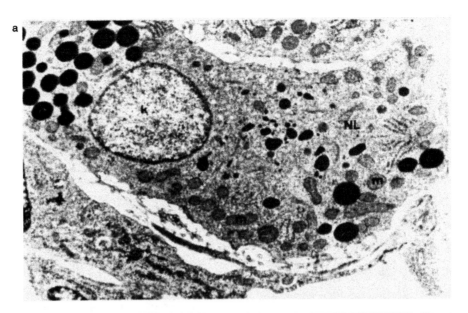

FIGURE 16.5

Apoptosis, electron micrographs

a. Normal lutein cell (NL) in the corpus luteum of a rat ovary. The chromatin is distributed over the nucleus (n). (×6,800)

b. Apoptotic lutein cell (AL). The nucleus (n) has fragmented and shows aggregation of chromatin (arrow) against the nuclear membrane. The cellular organelles are close together, indicating condensation of the cytoplasm. (×6,800)

m: mitochondrion

ASSIGNMENT 16.1

If you know that these specific dyes are negatively charged, can you explain why living, undamaged cells are not stained by them?

**Intermezzo**

*Vital staining*

Staining of living cells or tissues implies that the dye has to pass the intact cell membrane either actively or passively. Cationic dyes (such as Azure A and B and Janus green) are more suitable for this than anionic dyes (such as eosin), since they are soluble in phospholipids. Vital stains are used if a rapid diagnosis is required, and they may be applied to, for instance, aspirates and smears.

479

Various types of injury may increase membrane permeability. Complement and ouabain cause direct changes in membrane function, while certain toxic substances first affect the energy metabolism. Figure 16.6 shows a general schematic representation of the various phenomena occurring in necrosis and their interrelations.

Loss of the homeostatic cell volume, irreversible damage to mitochondria, altered ion concentrations in the cell and a markedly reduced energy supply are of course closely linked to the loss of other vital functions, including the synthesis of macromolecules. A more detailed description of the morphological and biochemical changes related to the processes involved in necrosis is given in section 16.3. The biochemical parameters of necrotic cell death are discussed in section 16.5.

ASSIGNMENT   16.2

Which general conditions does a cell have to meet in order *not* to necrotize?

Some distinct differences between apoptotic cell death and necrotic cell death have been observed.

*Apoptosis*

What are these differences?

*Differences apoptosis–necrosis*

Apoptotic cells do not show increased membrane permeability (at least not before the characteristic morphological changes are already clearly visible): the fluxes of potassium, sodium and calcium ions remain within normal limits and exclusion of vital stains is retained up to an advanced stage. Irreversible morphological changes are not preceded by depletion of intracellular ATP, which means that apoptosis can take place in cells with a normal ATP content.

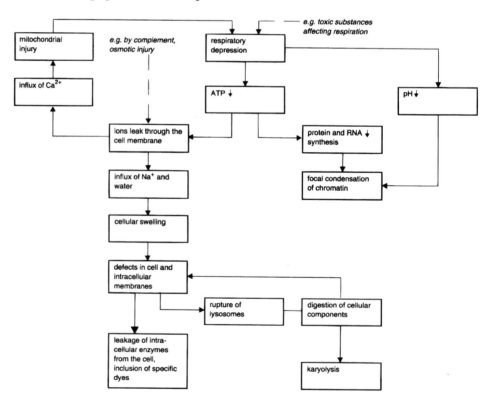

FIGURE   16.6

Schematic representation of the mechanisms involved in necrotic cellular degeneration.
The dotted arrows indicate the primary effect of certain injurious factors. The resultant changes subsequently give rise to a cascade of secondary changes (continuous arrows).

Generally, apoptosis can be defined as an endogenous cellular process whereby an external signal activates a metabolic pathway which results in cell death.

The physiological death of cells which occurs during the development of organisms usually affects a relatively large number of cells and often appears to be regulated by the presence or absence of hormones or by locally diffusing substances. During the metamorphosis of amphibians, the thyroid hormone *thyroxine* is responsible for the degeneration of the muscles of the tail. In mammals, one of the factors influencing the involution of the Müllerian duct is testosterone. The mammary gland tissue and uterine tissue disappear during the menstrual cycle, which is initiated by decreased steroid levels. A substance preventing cell death, the so-called neuronal growth factor, controls degeneration of sympathetic ganglia. So far, a clear relationship has been established between physiological cell death in these developmental processes and the presence or absence of certain humoral substances. Yet, what the primary changes in the cell are that lead to its death is still not clear. Several separate metabolic events are recognized in apoptotic cells which led to the scheme proposed in Figure 16.7. Continuing protein synthesis appears to be a prerequisite for apoptotic cellular degeneration in several cell types. In addition, a set of regulatory genes (oncogenes and oncosuppressor genes) is identified that influence cellular susceptibility to enter the apoptotic process; however, at the moment it is not clear how this occurs.

Cytoplasmic condensation and formation of apoptotic bodies have been associated with the redistribution and disruption of cytoplasmic microfilaments. A biochemical hallmark of apoptosis prior to cell death is a characteristic form of DNA degradation in which the genome is cleaved at internucleosomal sites, generating a "ladder" of DNA fragments when analyzed by agarose gel electrophoresis. How one or more of the described metabolic events fit into a general mechanism underlying this type of cell death is still under investigation. In some situations, apoptosis seems to be the result of coordinated, actively ini-

involution = regressive development

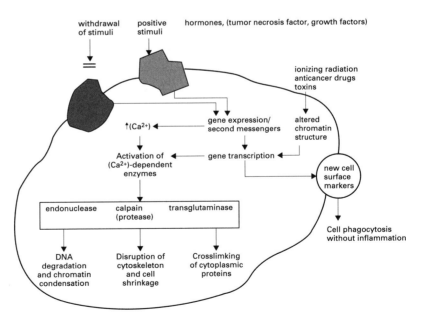

FIGURE   16.7
Common metabolic events in apoptosis.

*Programmed cell death*

tiated processes in the affected cells, as if it were a *programmed cell death*. It is thought that the receptors of certain lethal stimuli and the transduction of these stimuli are genetically controlled.

*Summary*

Nearly all dying cells can be classified into two distinct morphological categories, namely necrosis and apoptosis. The observed differences in occurrence and mechanism of these two types of cell death support the conclusion that these two phenomena are fundamentally different.

## 2    Toxic cell injury

As mentioned previously, chemical substances may give rise to necrotic cellular degeneration. Such substances include the biological toxins (originating from bacteria, fungi, higher plants, arthropods, snakes, amphibians), certain synthetic compounds (e.g. pesticides, herbicides) and certain environmental factors (heavy metals, nitrates). In order to match the cellular defense mechanisms, however, these potentially toxic substances need to be present in sufficiently high concentrations. These concentrations may vary greatly, depending on the nature of the substance. It should also be remembered that many toxic substances are not biologically active as such, but must be converted into reactive metabolites first. This is usually done by the affected cell itself.

What are the major subcellular targets in toxic injury?

The two most important types of substances that may cause acute cell death are those that initially affect the transport system of membranes and those that interfere with mitochondrial oxidative phosphorylation. In addition, degeneration may be initiated by direct damage to the organelle systems involved in protein synthesis (Figure 16.8). Later, it will be seen that damage to less prominent organelles, such as microtubules, may also lead to cellular degeneration.

It is important to realize that, although the subcellular target may vary from one toxic substance to another, sooner or later in irreversibly damaged cells the primary injury will result in damage to the cell membrane.

*Clostridium species are involved in numerous pathological processes, ranging from food poisoning (Clostridium botulinum) to wound poisoning (gas gangrene) (Clostridium perfringens).*

### 2.1   MEMBRANES

Direct injury to the cell membrane is caused by biological toxins such as snake venom and the α toxins produced by certain bacteria (*Clostridium perfringens*). The phospholipase $A_2$ present in snake venom breaks down the phospholipids in the cell membrane. The α toxin produced by *Clostridium perfringens* contains the enzyme phospholipase, which affects some molecules in the cell membrane.

*Direct injury*

The injurious action of these enzymes causes defects in the cell membrane, as affecting its selective permeability.

ASSIGNMENT   16.3

Explain how selective membrane permeability may be demonstrated?

*Indirect injury*

Indirect membrane damage results mainly from two mechanisms: peroxidation of lipids and covalent binding of reactive metabolites to macromolecules.

How does *peroxidation of lipids* give rise to membrane damage?

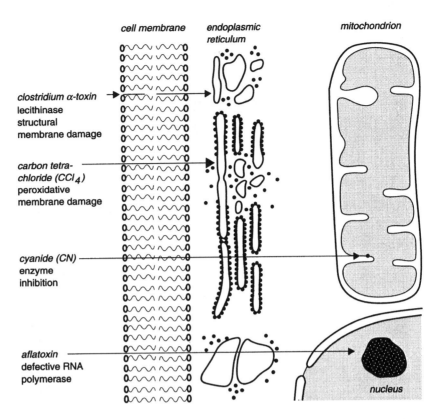

FIGURE 16.8

Several models for the mechanism of toxic cell injury

Several types of toxic substances are indicated together with their mode of action. The arrows indicate which subcellular organelles are primarily affected. This may have direct consequences for other organelle systems. More detailed information is given in the text.

*Injury by lipid peroxidation*

The best-known example of membrane damage by lipid peroxidation is liver cell necrosis induced by $CCl_4$ (Figure 16.9).

Lipid peroxidation is extensively dealt with in Study unit 10. For numbers in text, see Figure 16.9

$CCl_4$ is metabolized by the mixed-function oxidase system in the endoplasmic reticulum of the liver (1). Cleavage of the carbon–chloride bond results in the formation of free trichloromethyl radicals, which are highly unstable and immediately react with membrane components (2). They form covalent bonds with unsaturated fatty acids, or take a hydrogen atom from the unsaturated fatty acids of membrane lipids, resulting in the production of chloroform (3) and lipid radicals (4). The lipid radicals react with molecular oxygen (5), which initiates peroxidative decomposition of phospholipids in the endoplasmic reticulum. The peroxidation process results in the release of soluble products that may affect other membranes, such as the cell membrane (6). Peroxidation of lipids and resulting cell death may occur under various circumstances, but always involves *acute oxidative stress*, to which the cell is very vulnerable.

How may *covalent binding of reactive metabolites* lead to membrane damage?

See also study unit 10
*Injury by covalent binding*

Membrane damage by covalent binding is another mechanism for acute toxicity of various substances. The substances are metabolized by the cytochrome P-450-dependent mixed-function oxidase system in the microsomes, resulting

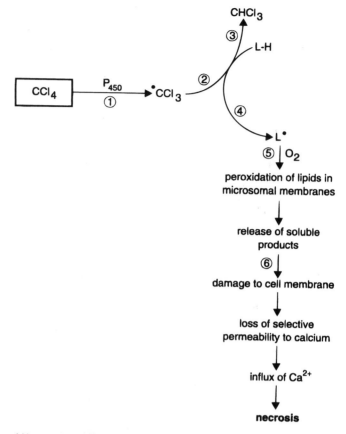

LH = polyunsaturated fatty acid; L• = lipid radical

FIGURE 16.9
Cascade of events in liver cell necrosis induced by $CCl_4$.
An explanation is given in the text.

in the formation of reactive intermediates. The reactive metabolites in turn react with glutathione, leading to a decreased intracellular level of this detoxicating agent. Due to the lack of sufficient free glutathione, the reactive intermediates are no longer detoxicated and bind to the macromolecules that are present. The covalent binding of reactive metabolites to these macromolecules is thought to be responsible for the cell damage. Although biochemical research has demonstrated a clear relationship between the number of covalent bonds and the severity of tissue damage, the exact molecular mechanism of injury by covalent binding still remains to be elucidated.

In addition, a number of substances are known to affect the ionic permeability of cell membranes, and these may thus cause cellular degeneration. To these substances belong the *ionophores*, which form lipid-soluble complexes with cations, and after their incorporation into the membrane these behave like true ion channels. Monensin, for example, is a typical $Na^+$ ionophore and the substance coded A23187 is a typical $Ca^{2+}$ ionophore. Both substances are used in pharmaceutical research. Digitalis and ouabain are cardiotonic glycosides of vegetable origin. They specifically inhibit $Na^+/K^+$-ATPase in the cell membrane, and hence the pumping function. $Na^+$ and water diffuse into the cell, resulting in swelling of the cell and disruption of the cell membrane.

## 2.2   MITOCHONDRIA

*Indirect injury*

Mitochondria contain the enzymes and structures required for the production of ATP. ATP is generated in the citric acid cycle and by oxidative phosphorylation associated with the electron transport system. Mitochondria are highly sensitive to changes in the factors controlling the mitochondrial metabolism, such as $O_2$ tension, water and electrolyte balance, pH, temperature and the levels of glycolytic products required for certain mitochondrial reactions.

*acidosis = accumulation of acids in the body*

Degenerative changes in mitochondria therefore occur as a secondary effect of any systemic cell injury (e.g. as a result of fever, hypoxia, acidosis or intoxication).

*Direct specific injury*

Mitochondria may also suffer *direct* and *specific* injury, as shown in Figure 16.10. This blocks the production of ATP, so that ultimately the energy-requiring processes in the cell can no longer take place. An example is *cyanide intoxication*, which occurs in cattle after consumption of certain plants containing glycosides (with a cyano group). Cyanide inhibits the cytochrome oxidase of the electron transport system, which means that the transfer of electrons from cytochrome *a* to oxygen is interrupted, and the production of ATP is blocked. Other substances, such as the proton ionophores (*dinitrophenols*), block the driving force of ATP production. The lack of energy ultimately results in secondary changes that may lead to cell death. Lethally injured mitochondria display a characteristic *sequence of ultrastructural changes*.

*Sequence of ultrastructural changes*

*The mitochondria are first denser than usual. They then begin to swell, so that at a certain shape they seem to have regained their normal structure, but then they continue to swell abnormally.*

These comprise changes in the volume and distribution of certain cellular components and in the emergence of substances in the matrix:

- rapid condensation, accompanied by a loss of ions and water due to inhibition of the pumping systems (ATPases);
- slight swelling with temporary resemblance to the normal structure;
- distinct swelling;

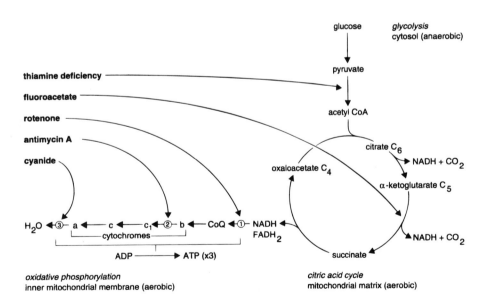

FIGURE   16.10
Pathology of mitochondrial metabolism
The arrows indicate where the presence or absence of certain substances affects (mitochondrial) metabolism. As a consequence, the production of high-energy phosphates is inhibited.

- disorganization of the cristae;
- appearance of flocculent densities;
- possible deposition of $Ca^{2+}$ salts.

## 2.3   CELLULAR ORGANELLES INVOLVED IN PROTEIN SYNTHESIS

Disruptions in protein synthesis are the result of structural damage to the nucleoli (disturbed transcription of DNA), to the ribosomes (disturbed translation and abnormal peptide formation), or to the Golgi apparatus (disturbed conjugation and packaging of proteins). Substances that affect the DNA or the polymerases responsible for transcription of the genetic code cause the most rapid and extensive changes in protein synthesis. Aflatoxin, for example, which is produced by certain strains of the fungus *Aspergillus flavus*, has a direct toxic effect on the DNA-dependent RNA polymerase in the nucleolus. This effect is immediately followed by degenerative changes in the ribosomes, which then separate from the membranes of the rough endoplasmic reticulum. As the enzymes and structural proteins necessary for normal functioning of the cell are no longer produced, the degenerative process may expand to involve the cell membrane, the mitochondria and other cellular organelles, ultimately leading to cell death.

## 2.4   MICROTUBULES

Microtubules are organelles consisting of tubulin molecules which join to form tubular structures with an average outer diameter of 25 nm. The length of these organelles can be altered by polymerization or depolymerization of the tubulin units. Microtubules are sensitive to cold, to high hydrostatic pressure and to a number of specific chemicals. They may occur unattached in the cytoplasm or form complex structures such as mitotic spindles, centrioles, cilia and flagella. They play a part in movements of the cell as a whole or parts of it, in mitotic cell division, in the cytoplasmic transport of certain subcellular organelles and in the cell structure.

Colchicine and vinca alkaloids are applied as cytostatics

The formation of microtubules is prevented by chemical substances such as colchicine, vinca alkaloids and benzimidazole derivatives.

---

EXAMPLE

Some benzimidazoles are used to exterminate parasitic worms. These substances cause the microtubules in certain digestive cells of the host parasite to disappear. As a result, the transport of specific secretory granules is no longer possible in the affected cells. However, the production of secretory material, including proteolytic and hydrolytic enzymes for the extracellular digestion of dietary components, continues unabated. As external excretion no longer takes place, adequate nutrition for the worms is not possible. The progressive intracellular accumulation and release of lytic enzymes result in autolysis. This eventually leads to the death of the affected cells and ultimately to that of the parasite.

---

*Summary*

Toxic substances may attack various sites in the cell. The main subcellular targets are the cell membrane, the mitochondria, the endoplasmic reticulum and the nucleus. Certain organelle systems may be injured directly or indirectly, which, in the case of irreversible damage, will ultimately lead to injury to the cell membrane.

### 3    Ischemic cell injury: determination of the point of no return

As indicated previously, *ischemic cell injury* is due to a circulatory disturbance. More accurately, *ischemia* may be defined as a condition in which, due to reduced perfusion with arterial blood, the oxygen supply of certain organs or parts of organs does not meet the normal oxygen requirements. The degree of ischemia depends on the severity and duration of the perfusion disturbance. In man, perfusion disturbances are often caused by atherosclerotic narrowing of blood vessels or by thrombosis. The effects of ischemia are most pronounced in well-differentiated tissues, such as those of the heart, skeletal muscle, kidney and the brain. These tissues need large amounts of oxygen to generate the energy required for their specialized functions. Serious perfusion disturbances often lead to extensive tissue damage, resulting in, for example, cardiac or cerebral infarction. Ischemic diseases still constitute the major cause of mortality and morbidity in our industrialized world. Extensive studies are therefore still being carried out to improve our understanding of the various phenomena that ultimately result in ischemic cell death. The aim is to achieve more rational prevention and treatment of these diseases. A focal point of these studies is determining the transition from reversible to irreversible damage. Since a considerable amount of knowledge has been gathered on ischemia of the myocardium, the changes in this tissue will be discussed here as an example of the irreversibility of cell damage.

#### 3.1    CONCEPT OF REVERSIBLE AND IRREVERSIBLE DAMAGE

The concept of reversible and irreversible damage will be clarified with the help of the following experiment. Under general anesthesia, the heart of a dog is dissected free, in such a way that the blood vessels supplying the heart are clearly visible. Subsequently, one of the large coronary arteries is completely clamped off. After a certain period of time the occlusion is lifted, restoring the blood supply to the myocardium (*reperfusion*). During the periods of occlusion and reperfusion certain measurements are taken and tissue specimens are obtained for morphological and biochemical research.

> What pathophysiological processes will occur after acute occlusion of such an important coronary artery?

First, there is a marked decrease in the arterial blood supply, so that the oxygen demand rapidly starts to exceed the supply (within 8–10 seconds). The myocardial tissue becomes *hypoxic*, causing the energy metabolism to change over from aerobic to anaerobic metabolism (glycolysis). However, the amount of high-energy phosphates produced via the anaerobic route is insufficient, so that the ischemic cell loses its contractile force and ultimately stops functioning.

Although the affected cell is no longer able to contract, it does not die. If the arterial flow is restored within, for example, 15 minutes (= reperfusion), the ischemic cell can resume its electrical and mechanical activities. This period is called the *reversible phase* of ischemic injury. If, however, the occlusion lasts for more than 40–60 minutes, the affected cell will die.

*Reversible phase*

If the arterial flow to the affected cells is restored after this period, the cells show explosive swelling, resulting in necrosis. In other words, the damage is irreversible. At some point between the period of the reversible and the irreversible phase, there must be a critical moment beyond which the damage is irreparable, the so-called *point of no return*. Scientists have tried to determine this point

*Point of no return*

487

with the aid of ultrastructural and biochemical methods. These not only involved *in vivo* experiments as described above, but also experiments with isolated hearts and cultures of myocardial cells.

### 3.2    ULTRASTRUCTURAL RESEARCH

*Degenerative changes due to ischemia*

The descriptions of the ultrastructural changes in myocardial cells after ischemia and reperfusion are manifold. There has been some confusion with regard to experiments concerned with determining the transition point between the reversible and irreversible stage of ischemic cell degeneration. The confusion is due to variation in species of test animals, topographic difference in sampling between epicardium and myocardium, uneven reperfusion of the myocardium and differences in experimental conditions and tissue repair. What the studies have demonstrated, however, is that rupture of the sarcolemma, pyknosis of the nucleus, the occurrence of flocculent densities in the mitochondria (*Jenning granules*, see inset of Figure 16.11c) and the death of muscle cells are structural signs of irreversible damage.

*Jenning granules*

These degenerative changes are, however, so pronounced that they are more likely to be late than early signs.

Further ultrastructural and cytochemical research carried out on isolated working rabbit heart, has led to the establishment of additional criteria, which probably are much closer to the *point of no return* (see Table 16.1 and Figure 16.11).

**Intermezzo**

The cytochemical research has used the so-called phosphate pyroantimonate technique. This technique is based on:

a  stabilization of $Ca^{2+}$ by potassium phosphate present in the fixative;

b  subsequent removal of all nonstabilized cations such as $Na^+$ and $Mg^{2+}$ with the aid of potassium phosphate in distilled water;

c  conversion of the stabilized $Ca^{2+}$ to an electron-dense deposit of the calciumpyroantimonate salt

d  removal of excess pyroantimonate

In normal, undamaged myocardial cells, the electron-dense deposit is mainly bound to the inner surface of the sarcolemma and on the T tubules connected to it (Figure 16.11a). The only other sites with slight deposit are the mitochondria.

These experiments have demonstrated that after a certain period of ischemia, the sarcolemma loses its capacity to bind $Ca^{2+}$ ions (Figure 16.11b). If after this well-defined period the heart is reperfused, an increase is observed in the amount of $Ca^{2+}$ in the mitochondria (Figure 16.11c). The moment at which these two phenomena, the sarcolemma no longer being able to bind $Ca^{2+}$ after ischemia and the increased uptake of $Ca^{2+}$ by the mitochondria during post-ischemic reperfusion, concur is thought to be the limit of reversibility. Although the sarcolemma still appears to be morphologically intact, it might have undergone some important changes, which could be responsible for the loss of $Ca^{2+}$ homeostasis and possibly also of that of other ions. Reperfusion at this point therefore causes marked cytoplasmic swelling, rupture of all subcellular organelles, a distinct degree of contraction resulting in rupture of the sarcolemma (contraction band necrosis), karyopyknosis, disintegration of the sarcolemma and an increase in number and size of Jenning granules in most mitochondria. If reperfusion is performed at a later stage in ischemia, the mitochondria will no longer take up $Ca^{2+}$ and will already contain Jenning granules at the end of the ischemic period, before reperfusion. At this stage, reperfusion no longer causes additional damage to the myocardial cell.

a
normal myocardial
tissue (control)

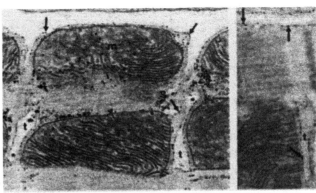

b
ischemic tissue
(45 minutes)

c
ischemic tissue
(45 minutes), followed
by 30 minutes
reperfusion: inset =
Jenning granules

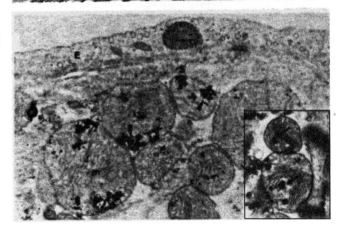

FIGURE 16.11

Normal and ischemic myocardial tissue. Morphological aspects and cytochemical localization of Ca²⁺.

a. The normal myocardial tissue shows electron-dense deposits (arrows) on the sarcolemma and the T tubules (t). These deposits visualize membrane-bound $Ca^{2+}$. The right-hand panel shows an unstained preparation: the membrane-bound $Ca^{2+}$ deposits are clearly visible. (×21,000)

b. After 45 minutes of ischemia, all of the $Ca^{2+}$ deposit on the sarcolemma have disappeared. The structure of the myocardial tissue itself is still largely normal. (×21,000)

c. After 45 minutes of ischemia followed by 30 minutes of reperfusion, the cell is severely damaged (ruptured sarcolemma, swollen mitochondria) and the mitochondria contain large amounts of $Ca^{2+}$ deposit (arrowhead). (×21,000)

Inset: flocculent densities (arrows), so-called Jenning granules, can be seen in the mitochondria of a necrotic myocardial cell (×10,300)

s: sarcolemma
m: mitochondria

TABLE 16.1

Time-dependent structural and cytochemical changes during ischemia and after reperfusion. The number of cells that show changes and the severity of the changes increase with the duration of ischemia.

| | 15-30 minutes ischemia (reversible) | 30-45 minutes ischemia (partly reversible) | 60-75 minutes ischemia (irreversible) |
|---|---|---|---|
| reversible | • loss of normal mitochondrial matrix granules<br>• decrease in the amount of $Ca^{2+}$ deposit bound to the sarcolemma<br>• swelling of mitochondrial matrix<br>• intracellular edema<br>• depletion of intracellular glycogen<br><br>during reperfussion:<br>• repair of structure and normal pattern of $Ca^{2+}$ deposit on the sarcolemma<br>• slightly increase in $Ca^{2+}$ deposit in mitochondria<br>• reappearance of mitochondrial matrix granules | | |
| irreversible | | • swelling of mitochondrial matrix with damage to cristae<br>• loss of $Ca^{2+}$ deposit at sarcolemma without intracellular $Ca^{2+}$ accumulation<br>• focal degeneration of some cells (damaged sarcolemma and mitochondria with Jenning granules)<br><br>during reperfusion:<br>• pronounced damage to all cellular organelles<br>• no restoration of $Ca^{2+}$ deposit on the sarcolemma<br>• accumulation of large amounts of $Ca^{2+}$ deposit in mitochondria except in those with Jenning granules<br>• contractile ring necrosis<br>• karyopyknosis<br>• disintegration of the sarcolemma | |
| irreversible | | | during reperfusion:<br>• absence of $Ca^{2+}$ deposit on the sarcolemma and in mitochondria<br>• Jenning granules<br>• cellular degeneration with contractile ring necrosis and/or cytolysis<br>• no concomitant changes |

It is not known why the sarcolemma loses its capacity to bind $Ca^{2+}$ during ischemia. Explanations which have been suggested include changes in affinity, and change in the amount or the conformation of phospholipids in the membrane, possibly combined with changes in the pH of the cytosol.

The increased uptake of $Ca^{2+}$ by the mitochondria to keep the cytosol free of $Ca^{2+}$ probably results from an increased influx through the sarcolemma, which has become highly permeable to this ion during the ischemic period. The fact that mitochondria only take up Ca²⁺ during reperfusion and not during the ischemic period suggests that the sequestration of Ca²⁺ is an oxygen (energy)-dependent process.

ASSIGNMENT 16.4

Can you explain why mitochondria containing Jenning granules no longer display Ca²⁺ accumulation after reperfusion?

## 3.3 BIOCHEMICAL RESEARCH

Most of the biochemical research on ischemic necrosis, *in vivo* as well as *in vitro*, has concerned energy metabolism. Table 16.1 mentions the decrease in glycogen content of myocardial cells as an early sign of ischemia.

How could this be determined biochemically?

The answer can be found in Figure 16.12.

Because aerobic energy metabolism is no longer possible, the cells very rapidly switch over to (anaerobic) glycolysis. In the course of ischemia or anoxia this is manifested by a decrease in the glycogen content of the tissue on the one hand, and the accumulation of lactate on the other. The amount of high-energy phosphates produced by the anaerobic sequence to glycolysis cannot, however, prevent the progressive depletion of these phosphates. The result is rapid depletion of phosphocreatine, which in turn leads to depletion of ATP and a gradual increase in the levels of ATP degradation products (Figure 16.13).

Since resynthesis of adenine nucleotides is impossible without aerobic metabolism, and since the rate of glycolysis decreases considerably, most of the ATP (more than 90%) will have disappeared after approximately 90 minutes in *in vitro* experiments (Figure 16.14)

*In vivo*, this low energy state is already reached after 40 minutes. At that point, the affected cells also show the structural signs of irreversible damage. Various interrelated hypotheses have been put forward to explain the transition to irre-

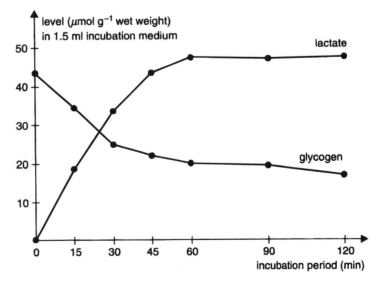

FIGURE 16.12

Levels of lactate and glycogen (glucose equivalents) in anoxic cultures of myocardial cells.
Average values of five different experiments.

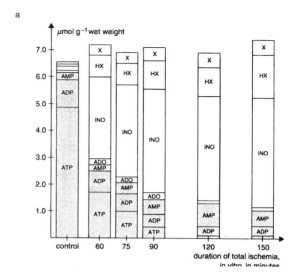

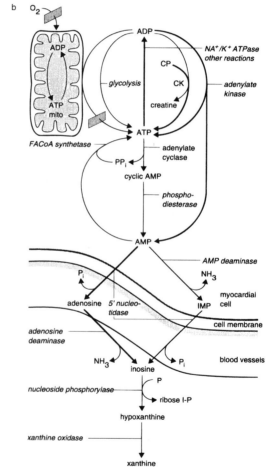

## FIGURE 16.13

### Degradation of adenine nucleotides

a. The adenine nucleotides (ATP: adenosine triphosphate; ADP: adenosine diphosphate; AMP: adenosine monophosphate) gradually disappear as total ischemia continues. This is accompanied by a proportional increase in adenosine (ADO), inosine (INO), hypoxanthine (HX) and xanthine (X). This diagram represents total ischemia. Total ischemia is imitated in *in vitro* experiments by subjecting samples of myocardial tissue to autolysis in the absence of oxygen.

b. The main metabolic pathways for the degradation of adenine nucleotides during myocardial ischemia are shown. The bold arrows indicate the pathways that are quantitatively most important.

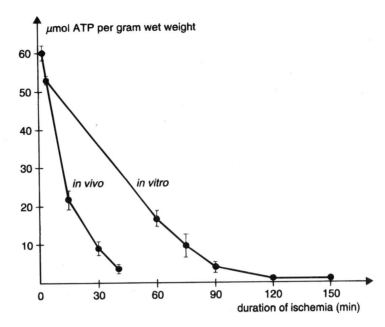

FIGURE 16.14
ATP depletion in total ischemia
The rate of ATP depletion in total ischemia is higher *in vivo* than *in vitro*.

versible damage in ischemia. All of these hypotheses center around the altered energy metabolism. As was mentioned above, the most generally accepted hypothesis focuses on changes in the membrane structure that results in membrane damage. $Ca^{2+}$ appears to play an important role in this process.

*Summary*

Deficient arterial blood supply leads to well-defined structural and biochemical changes in the affected cells. If these changes remain limited, and hence reversible, repair can take place on reperfusion. If the changes resulting from ischemia become too large, the cells are irreversibly damaged, so that reperfusion will also result in necrosis. Two ultrastructural changes, viz., the loss of the capacity of the cell membrane to bind calcium ions (before reperfusion) and the increased uptake of $Ca^{2+}$ into the mitochondria during post-ischemic reperfusion, are thought to occur just beyond the point of no return. Changes in the energy state of ischemic cells provide important information on their chances of survival.

## 4    The role of calcium in cell death

Calcium plays an important role in the regulation of many metabolic and functional processes, such as the coupling of excitation and contraction in muscle cells, enzyme activation and hormone secretion. Calcium is also considered to be one of the key factors maintaining the integrity of the cell membrane.

Free calcium is present in large quantities in the extracellular environment ($10^{-3}$ mole $l^{-1}$), while the intracellular calcium concentration in most cells at rest is much lower ($10^{-6}$ to $10^{-7}$ mole $l^{-1}$).

> What are the consequences of this difference in calcium concentration between the intracellular and the extracellular environments?

Together with the negative membrane potential, this concentration difference provides a very high electrochemical gradient for $Ca^{2+}$ across the cell membrane, so that $Ca^{2+}$ can easily flow into the cell in certain activation processes. In an activated muscle cell, for example, the $Ca^{2+}$ concentration increases by a factor of 100. Subsequently, the excess calcium has to be removed again from the cytosol to allow relaxation. To this end, the cell has, among other things, membrane-bound calcium pumps, a mitochondrial exchange mechanism, a $Na^+/Ca^{2+}$ exchange system and a number of $Ca^{2+}$-binding proteins at its disposal (Figure 16.15).

These mechanisms, which are largely energy-dependent, are also responsible for maintaining cellular $Ca^{2+}$ homeostasis. The lining of the membrane surface plays a particularly important role here. Needless to say, changes in the integrity of the cell membrane may have important consequences for calcium homeostasis, as was already briefly discussed in the previous section.

Necrotic cells have been known for a long time to contain abnormal quantities of calcium. Morphologically evident liver cell necrosis induced by ischemia or by galactosamine intoxication is accompanied by a significant increase in the calcium content of the liver. This association between morphological degeneration and calcium content does not of course necessarily imply that there is a causal relationship between the two phenomena. The increased $Ca^{2+}$ level could also be attributed to the passive establishment of equilibrium caused by the steep electrochemical gradient. A causal relationship has, however, been clearly

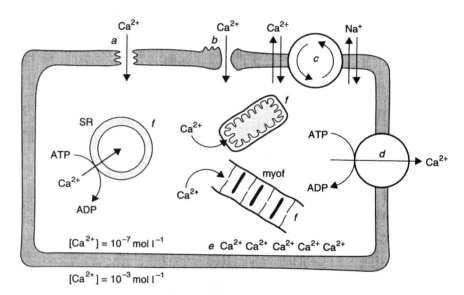

FIGURE 16.15

Mechanisms that allow $Ca^{2+}$ to pass cellular membranes. These transport mechanisms are involved in maintaining calcium homeostasis.

a. membrane-potential dependent calcium (influx) channels

b. receptor-bound calcium (influx) channels

c. $Na^+/Ca^{2+}$ exchange. Increased calcium concentrations may also result from release of calcium from endogenous reserves. Decreases in cytoplasmic calcium concentrations can be brought about through $Na^+/Ca^{2+}$ exchange.

d. ATP-dependent calcium pumps

e. binding to specific calcium-binding proteins such as calmodulin

f. storage in intracellular structures

MT = mitochondria

S = sarcoplasmic reticulum

myof = myofilaments

demonstrated in *in vitro* experiments. For example, toxic substances affecting the integrity of the cell membrane appear not to cause necrosis if the extracellular environment is devoid of $Ca^{2+}$. Furthermore, substances preventing the influx of $Ca^{2+}$, the so-called $Ca^{2+}$ entry blockers, have a protective influence. If the injurious factor is removed at this point, that is after administration of $Ca^{2+}$ entry blockers, the cells can recover.

In the absence of the protecting $Ca^{2+}$ entry blockers, however, or if $Ca^{2+}$ is added, the potentially reversible damage changes into irreversible damage, followed by necrosis.

> At what calcium concentration and in what way can the excess of intracellular $Ca^{2+}$ give rise to cell necrosis?

Recent measurements of the intracellular $Ca^{2+}$ level have demonstrated that an increase in the concentration of $Ca^{2+}$ ions to levels exceeding $10^{-5}$ mole $l^{-1}$ may have a pathological effect. Such an increase activates not only physiological $Ca^{2+}$-dependent mechanisms, but also cellular processes that are not affected by $Ca^{2+}$ under normal physiological conditions. The latter include:

- changes in the shape of the cell;
- so-called bleb formation (see Figure 16.16 and Study unit 10);
- changes in ionic conduction;
- excessive contraction or release of transmitters;
- dramatically decreased ATP levels due to activation of the $Ca^{2+}$ pump;
- rupture of mitochondria due to excessive ATP-dependent uptake of $Ca^{2+}$, ultimately leading to reduced functioning of the $Ca^{2+}$ pump as a result of ATP depletion;

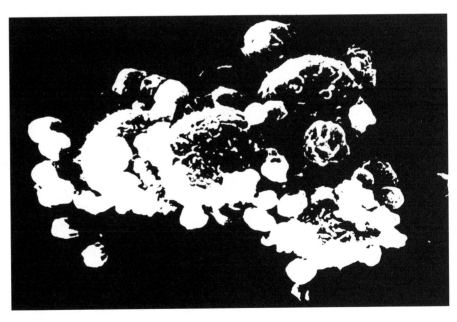

FIGURE   16.16
Bleb formation in rat hepatocytes as a result of intoxication with isothiocyanates
Scanning electron micrograph (×2,500) By: J.H.M. Temmink (Wageningen)

- enzyme activation (proteases, nucleases, phopholipases, transglutaminases) or inhibition (adenylate cyclase).

The effects of ischemic and toxic cell injury on the distribution of ions and the resultant cellular changes are set out in the diagrams in Figures 16.17 and 16.18.

*Difference in degeneration due to ischemia/toxic substances*

Cellular degeneration resulting from toxic injury to the cell membrane usually progresses much faster than that caused by ischemic cell injury. This can be explained by the acute effect on the cell membrane without the mitochondria being affected first. As a consequence, the mitochondria very rapidly take up the excessive $Ca^{2+}$ at the expense of their energy-producing function. Finally, it is important to note that, although $Ca^{2+}$ clearly plays a role in cell necrosis, the increased $Ca^{2+}$ level is not always the primary cause of the phenomena observed.

ASSIGNMENT 16.5

What are the consequences of cellular energy depletion for the $Ca^{2+}$ homeostasis in the cell?

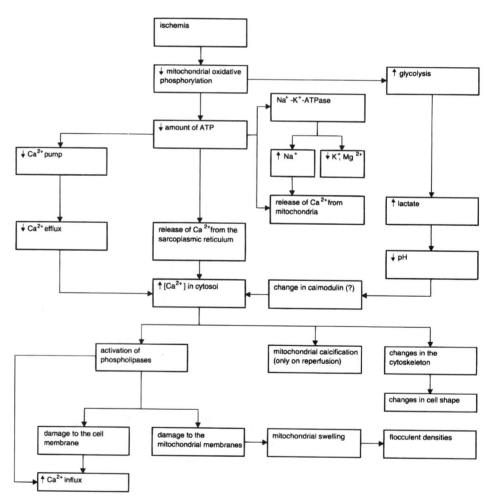

FIGURE 16.17

Representation of the effects of ischemia on ion distribution and resultant cellular changes.
↑ increase
↓ decrease

496

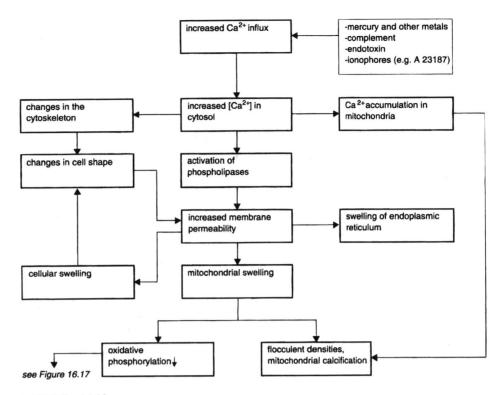

FIGURE   16.18
Representation of the effects of increased Ca²⁺ influx into the cell, as a result of exposure to certain toxic substances

## 5    Biochemical parameters of cell death

### 5.1    SOME BASIC PRINCIPLES

The release of certain soluble components from a cell is usually assumed to be indicative of damage to the cell membrane, which is often irreversible. These soluble components enter the bloodstream and can be determined biochemically by means of serum or plasma analyses. In that way, clear correlations have been demonstrated between increased serum activity of individual cytosol enzymes on the one hand, and the dosages of certain toxic substances, the concentration and virulence of an injected virus or the size of an ischemic area on the other. Clinical studies have also demonstrated a correlation between the severity of certain pathological conditions and the serum levels of certain enzymes.

This is in contrast to the discordance between morphological changes and results from serum analysis. In acute viral hepatitis and acute liver hypoxia, for example, high enzyme activity in the serum appeared to be accompanied by only slight liver cell necrosis. These findings may be comparable to those described for anoxia of cultured myocardial cells. Very soon after anoxia is initiated, significant amounts of free cytosolic enzymes (lactate and malate dehydrogenases) are released into the extracellular environment. As the anoxia continues, this release increases still further, and a clear correlation with the decrease in the cellular ATP content then becomes apparent. During this period, however, the cell membrane remains intact and cell damage is reversible. This shows that a release of cytosolic enzymes does not necessarily indicate irreversible cell damage. Release of cytosolic enzymes in the reversible phase is thought to result from a disturbed balance between energy production and energy expenditure in the cell.

Finally, systemic degradation of cells by, for instance, various types of atrophy, appears not to be accompanied by a release of soluble components into the blood at all. In contrast to necrotic cell death, apoptotic cell death is hardly reflected in demonstrable changes in the biochemical composition of the serum. The various results show that, on the one hand, irreversible degeneration does not always result in biochemically demonstrable changes in the serum, and that, on the other hand, changes in the serum levels of certain soluble cell components are not always attributable to irreversible cellular degeneration. Although certain results have to be interpreted with caution, clinical serum analyses often play an important part in the diagnosis of organ pathology. Enzyme analyses are quite frequently used for determining metabolite concentrations and enzyme activity.

## 5.2 ORGAN-SPECIFIC ENZYMES, ISOZYMES AND ENZYME PATTERNS

*Determination of organ-specific enzymes*

Because of differences in their functions, organs and tissues usually differ in their enzymatic composition. These differences are mostly of a quantitative nature. Certain enzymes, however, may occur in such extreme levels in certain organs, so that they may indeed be regarded as organ-specific.

Examples are *creatine phosphokinase* in striated muscle and the *sorbitol dehydrogenase* and *ornithine carbamyl transferase* in the liver.

*Determination of heterogeneity of the protein pattern of enzymes*

Another way of differentiating between organs is to make use of differences in enzyme distribution. Enzymes with the same catalytic function present in different organs or even in different compartments of the same organ, may be discriminated as structurally different proteins, with identical specificity: the so-called isozymes. Such heterogeneity has been demonstrated for many enzymes, but from a practical point of view the analysis of the *isozymes of acid phosphatase* is of most importance.

*Determination of the enzyme pattern*

A third tool for determining the origin of an increase in the serum or plasma levels of cellular enzymes is to determine *enzyme patterns*.

The characteristic pattern, or more accurately, the relative concentrations of the various enzymes allows a diagnosis to be made of the involvement of a specific organ, especially in cases of acute, pronounced damage.

Finally, measuring tissue-specific enzymes, isozymes or enzyme patterns in the serum enables us to trace the origin of a pathological increase in enzyme activity. This is possible in the case of acute and extensive damage to organs that are rich in enzymes or that contain specific enzymes. In the case of chronic or slight damage, or if the tissues involved contain only few enzymes, such measurements are often very difficult.

## 6    Summary

In this study unit a number of changes associated with the "point of no return" in necrotic cell injury have been introduced. In continuation of the previous study unit, the ultrastructural and biochemical parameters have been discussed. In addition to necrotic cell death as a result of intoxication, a more natural type of cell death, apoptosis, has been described and compared with necrosis.

Experimentally induced ischemia in myocardial cells has been used as a model of (irreversible) necrosis. *In vitro* as well as *in vivo* experiments have been described. In view of the importance of an exact determination of the "point of no return", various ultrastructural and biochemical characteristics have been dealt with. The role of calcium in particular has been discussed in detail.

Finally, in the last section the possibilities of using clinical-chemical parameters in the determination of organ-specific necrosis have been highlighted.

## SELF ASSESSMENT QUESTIONS

1   What are the main morphological differences between necrosis and apoptosis?

2   What characterizes the occurrence of necrosis and apoptosis?

3   Hormone-controlled cyclic growth and atrophy of the corpus luteum in the ovaries is observed in non-pregnant mammals. Which specific type of cell death is shown by the degenerating cells, and why?

4   Explain briefly how a $Ca^{2+}$ ionophore may cause cell death.

5   What is the underlying mechanism of lipid peroxidation as a cause of cell death?

6   Describe briefly the primary and secondary effects of fluoroacetate intoxication that ultimately lead to cell death. Make use of Figure 16.10.

7   One of the amatoxins, the toxic substances produced by the poisonous mushroom *Amanita phalloides*, binds to nuclear RNA polymerase, resulting in inhibition of the enzyme. What are the consequences of this?

8   What cytological phenomena mark the transition from reversible to irreversible damage in the necrosis of myocardial cells caused by ischemia?

9   For treating of ischemic cellular damage, pharmaceutical agents with a particular property are prescribed. What property would this be? Explain your answer.

10  Three possible methods of localizing cell death in specific organs by means of biochemical analysis of plasma or serum have been described. What are these methods?

## FEEDBACK

### 1   Answers to the assignments

16.1   The outer membrane of normal, undamaged cells is negatively charged, so that the dye is rejected. In severe membrane damage with gap formation (see morphology of necrosis) the negatively charged layer has locally disappeared, allowing the specific dye to enter the cell.

16.2   There should be no loss of ATP or intracellular potassium; membrane permeability should not increase; synthesis of macromolecules should be maintained.

16.3   By measuring the loss of potassium, the increase in intracellular sodium, and the reduction in the membrane potential; by staining the cytoplasm with vital dyes and by demonstrating the influx of tracer material.

16.4   The mitochondria concerned have lost their energy and their energy-generating capacity in the course of the preceding ischemic period. As $Ca^{2+}$ sequestration is a highly energy dependent process, it can no longer take place.

16.5 Since the membrane-associated calcium pumps are energy-dependent, they cannot fulfill their normal function if not enough energy is available in the cell. Consequently, the influx of $Ca^{2+}$ into the cell as a result of the steep electrochemical gradient cannot be adequately counteracted. This may ultimately lead to pathological intracellular accumulation of $Ca^{2+}$.

## 2 Answers to the self assessment questions

1 

| Necrosis | Apoptosis |
|---|---|
| • usually affects several adjacent individual cells | • usually affects scattered cells in an organ or tissue |
| • inflammation | • no inflammation |
| • nuclear chromatin becomes less dense | • condensation of nuclear chromatin |
| • cytoplasmic swelling with degeneration of cellular organelles | • cytoplasmic condensation with the structure of the cellular organelles hardly affected |
| • degeneration of cell | • fragmentation of the cell as a whole |

2 Necrosis is caused by distinct external injurious factors. Apoptosis occurs under the influence of an external stimulus, which by itself does not induce cell death. The affected cell produces intrinsic metabolic events which lead to the typically apoptotic degeneration.

3 Apoptosis. The death of the cells is not caused by a distinct, external injurious factor, but occurs under the influence of hormones.

4 The $Ca^{2+}$ ionophore causes an increased $Ca^{2+}$ concentration in the cytosol of the affected cell. This triggers certain cellular processes that would not take place under normal conditions, such as the activation of certain enzymes (e.g. phospholipases) and the uptake of abnormal amounts of $Ca^{2+}$ into the mitochondria. These processes cause, respectively, membrane damage and a reduction in energy production, resulting in cell death.

5 Peroxidation of lipids may occur under various circumstances. There is, however, always a common mechanism: acute oxidative stress. Lipid radicals react with molecular oxygen, causing peroxidative degradation of phospholipids. This leads to membrane damage and cell death.

6 Fluoroacetate blocks the citric acid cycle (primary effect) so that oxidative phosphorylation can no longer take place (secondary effect). Consequently, ATP can no longer be generated via the oxidative pathway. Due to ATP depletion, numerous energy-dependent processes can no longer take place, which ultimately results in cell death.

7 The result is that the transcription of the genetic code of DNA, which is regulated by this enzyme, cannot continue. As the production of certain structural proteins required for the normal functioning of the cell is cut off, other cellular organelles are affected, ultimately resulting in cell death.

8   The moment at which the sarcolemma loses its capacity to bind $Ca^{2+}$ ions during the ischemia (i.e., before reperfusion), in combination with the increased uptake of $Ca^{2+}$ by the mitochondria during post-ischemic reperfusion.

9   Pharmaceutical agents that prevent the increased $Ca^{2+}$ influx: so-called $Ca^{2+}$ entry blockers, since this $Ca^{2+}$ influx plays an important part in the pathology of ischemic cell necrosis.

10  Determining organ-specific enzymes, isozymes and enzyme patterns in the serum.

# Contents Study unit 17
# Dermatotoxicology: toxicological pathology and methodological aspects

0-8493-9232-2/96/$0.00 + $.50
© 1996 by CRC Press, Inc.

# Study unit 17

# Dermatotoxicology: toxicological pathology and methodological aspects

*R. J. M. Niesink*

## INTRODUCTION

### Use of skin-bleaching soap endangers lives

The European Parliament has been asked to force closure of a factory in Dublin, Ireland, which manufactures poisonous soap. The factory, the Soap Company of Ireland, has caused countless victims in West Africa with its massive export of "mercury soap". The mercury enters the circulation through the skin, leading to kidney poisoning, brain damage and even to death.

The manufacturer recommends its products to colored people, especially women, as a skin bleach. In Nigeria and Cameroon, mercury-containing soap is freely available, even though its sale has been prohibited by the Government. Through illegal import the soap also reaches black communities in Western Europe. In these communities it is also popular to use other remedies, such as cream and ointments, which contain hydroquinone in unacceptably high percentages. Hydroquinone causes the skin pigment to disappear, causing white patches. The substance is used in photography, and regular skin contact can cause severe damage.

The skin is one of the main organs involved in the uptake of toxic substances. This study unit will briefly describe some aspects of the structure and function of the skin which are important with regard to dermatotoxic phenomena. In addition to this concise overview of skin anatomy and physiology and a discussion of factors which determine the absorption of xenobiotics by the skin, some pathophysiological and pathological phenomena will be discussed, and a few important dermatotoxic chemicals will be reviewed. To conclude the study unit,

503

two dermatotoxicity tests will be discussed to illustrate the specific problems arising in the development of new dermatotoxicity tests.

LEARNING OBJECTIVES

After studying this unit you should be able to:

— describe the anatomy/physiology of the skin and indicate which anatomical and physiological factors are important in dermatotoxicological processes

— describe the most important disorders which may result from exposure of the skin to chemicals

— give examples of some dermatotoxic chemicals and their effects

— indicate the similarities and differences between allergic disorders and primary irritant disorders

— give a description of the similarities and differences between various forms of phototoxic injury to the skin and provide examples of chemicals which can cause these processes

— classify the various types of skin tumors and indicate to what extent these are toxicologically relevant

— give a description of current research into the dermatotoxicity of chemicals and the specific problems which can arise in the development of new models.

*Study hints*

In studying dermatotoxic phenomena, it is important that you are familiar with the structure and function of the skin. Should you feel that your knowledge is insufficient, you should read up on the anatomy and physiology of the skin in an anatomy/physiology book before you commence this unit. The study units on exposure (2) and on uptake and excretion (5) also discuss various aspects of the toxicology of the skin. You are advised to re-read these. The study load for this unit is estimated at no more than 3 hours.

The CD-I program Toxicological Histopathology gives examples of the following dermatotoxic disorders: chloracne, hyperkeratosis, acanthosis, blistering, contact urticaria and carcinomas.

## STUDY CORE

### 1 Structure and function of the skin

The skin protects the body against invading foreign organisms and substances. The skin, however, is certainly not one homogeneous organ which can merely be seen as a membrane with certain physical properties.

> Consider the properties of the skin which differentiate it from a "simple" membrane.

The skin differs from a membrane in, for instance, the following respects:

- it is a dynamic, living organ;

- it is capable of metabolic activity, although these metabolic processes generally proceed more slowly than in the rest of the organism;

- the skin does not have one uniform structure: its thickness and composition, for example, differ with the location on the body;

- although the basic anatomical structure is largely uniform, different species never have exactly the same skin.

504

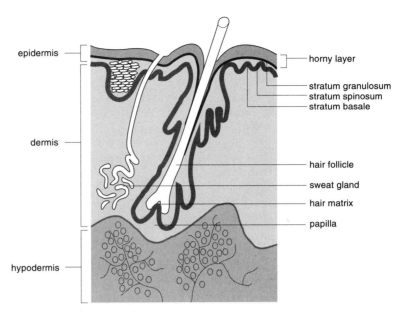

FIGURE 17.1
Schematic cross-section of the skin of a mammal

All surface-forming structures are essentially built according to one basic pattern. There is an upper layer of epithelial cells, covering a subepithelial connective tissue layer, with afferent and efferent blood vessels embedded in it. Most surface layers also possess specialized structures in connection with the specific function of the surface layer. Figure 17.1 shows a schematic cross-section of a mammalian skin. Non-mammalian skin structure differs from this in certain respects.

*Epidermis*

Normally, three layers can be distinguished in a cross-section of the skin: the *epidermis*, a keratinized squamous epithelium; the *dermis*, a thick underlying layer of dense, fibro-elastic connective tissue which supports and nourishes the epidermis; the *hypodermis*, or subcutaneous layer, a layer of loose, connective tissue containing variable amounts of adipose tissue. Hair follicles, sweat glands, sebaceous glands and nails are epithelial structures, termed epidermal appendages, since they originate during embryological development from downgrowths of epidermal epithelium into the dermis and hypodermis.

The epidermis is the only layer that is important in penetration of xenobiotics. It comprises five layers.

*Stratum basale*

- The bottom layer, the *stratum basale or stratum germinativum*, is the germinal layer of the epidermis. Apart from the differentiating epidermal cells mentioned above, this layer also contains the *melanocytes* and so-called *Langerhans cells*, although the latter are mainly found in the stratum spinosum.

*Stratum spinosum*

- The *stratum spinosum* contains cells which are in the process of keratinization.

*Stratum granulosum*

- The *stratum granulosum or granular layer* is characterized by the presence within the cells of granules which contribute to the process of keratinization.

- The *stratum lucidum*, which is only present in extremely thick skin, appears as a homogenous layer between the stratum granulosum and the keratinized layer.

*Stratum corneum*
*Horny layer*
Keratin = horny substance

- The *stratum corneum* or horny layer consists of flattened, fused cell remnants composed mainly of the fibrous protein *keratin*.

The basal cells proliferate and differentiate as they migrate outward. The columnar cells become rounded and then flattened as they move through the loosely defined layers and finally to the stratum corneum, the primary barrier to penetration. In man, the process of maturation of a basal cell through to desquamation takes approximately 27 days.

ASSIGNMENT 17.1

What are the functions of the melanocytes and Langerhans cells?

The upper layer of the epidermis, the stratum corneum, constitutes the most important protective layer of the skin. The thickness of the epidermis varies considerably, depending on the part of the body. For instance, the epidermis is thin on the back, eye and scrotum, but thick on the palms of the hands and the soles of the feet.

*Dermis (= corium)*

Below the epidermis lies the *dermis*, a dense network of connective tissue cells. These cells produce collagen. The dermis also contains the finest branches of the blood vessels and the endings of various nerve fibers. In addition to the connective tissue cells, there are also other types of cells in the dermis, such as the histamine-containing mast cells, which play an important role in various injuries caused by toxic substances.

*Hypodermis*

Under the dermis is the *hypodermis*, which consists mainly of fat cells. Blood vessels and nerve fibers are also present in this layer. The blood vessels which supply the skin with nutrients and oxygen play an important part in dermatotoxic processes.

Important *structures in the skin* are hairs, sweat glands and sebaceous glands. There is considerable variation between species, both in number and makeup of these structures. Human beings, for example, have little body hair, in contrast with most animal species.

The epidermis is the main protective layer. The outer layer, the stratum corneum, is basically impermeable to water and hence also to water-soluble polar chemicals. The stratum corneum also prevents evaporation of water from the underlying cell layers. Since in normal conditions the stratum corneum is highly hydrated, the skin can still take up polar substances, albeit slowly, through passive diffusion. Lipophilic substances can be absorbed by the skin through passive diffusion by dissolving in the lipid matrix of cellular membrane components. Depending on their lipophilicity, substances are taken up more or less rapidly, up to a certain limit of lipophilicity and molecular size. Once they have penetrated the dermis, the chemicals can reach the blood or lymph vessels via the interstitial fluid transport and thus be further transported.

Xenobiotics can also invade the skin via the hair follicles and sebaceous glands. It is, however, largely unknown whether these routes are actually relevant to dermatotoxicology.

*Specific barrier*

Every so often, the existence of a *specific barrier* to xenobiotics, which is thought to be present in the skin, is announced in the scientific literature. Many researchers question the existence of such a barrier. An American research group established the involvement of a particular hydroxylated linoleic acid deriva-

506

tive in the barrier function of the epidermis. This substance might perhaps be formed in the bottom layer of the stratum corneum.

### 1.1 FACTORS INFLUENCING PERCUTANEOUS ABSORPTION

Factors which can influence the uptake of substances through the skin can be divided into two groups. On the one hand, there are the substance-specific factors, which depend on the nature of the substance. On the other hand, there are factors which relate to the properties of the skin itself.

> Can you think of any factors belonging to the first group and factors belonging to the second group?

The most important properties which determine whether a toxic substance can penetrate the skin are shown in Table 17.1.

Once a substance has penetrated the epidermis, the subsequent uptake of that substance by the vessels is an important factor in its distribution. This uptake can be influenced by properties of the xenobiotic itself or by those of its solvent. For instance, certain xenobiotics (or their solvents) cause constriction or dilation of the blood vessels in the skin, and this may have consequences for the uptake of the substance in question, or other substances.

## 2    Pathology of the skin

The reaction pattern of the skin in various disorders is often non-specific. Primary lesions may be obscured by secondary infections and by trauma as a result of scratching itchy spots. The basic changes which arise in various skin disorders can be divided into primary and secondary lesions. Table 17.2 provides an overview of these primary and secondary lesions.

TABLE   17.1
Properties determining the penetration of the skin by a xenobiotic
a properties of the substance
b properties of the skin

*a.*

| Property | Details |
| --- | --- |
| ionic state | non-ionized molecules penetrate easily |
| molecular size | small molecules penetrate more easily than large molecules |
| lipophilicity | lipophilicity facilitates penetration |
| viscosity | the greater the viscosity, the more difficult the penetration |
| concentration | penetration depends on the concentration of the toxic substance |
| facilitation | penetrability may be facilitated/hindered by the properties of the solvent  of the xenobiotic |

*b.*

| Properties | Details |
| --- | --- |
| species | possibility of penetration of the skin is strongly species dependent |
| localization | penetrability varies from site to site (compare, for example, the sole of the foot with the skin on the back) |
| hydration and pH | amount of water in the stratum corneum influences penetrability |
| ambient temperature | penetrability may be increased/decreased by changes in the ambient temperature |
| state of health | damage to the horny layer (mechanical, solvents) as well as edema increases the permeability to xenobiotics |

TABLE   17.2
Classification of skin disorders into primary and secondary lesions

| *Primary lesions* | |
|---|---|
| *macula* | flat, well-defined area of change in skin color |
| | - red (hyperemia/hemorrhages) |
| | - brown/black (local pigment accumulation) |
| | - white (local depigmentation) |
| *papule\** | area elevated to a few millimeters (pimple) |
| | - epidermis (hyperplasia/intercellular or intracellular edema) |
| | - corium (thickening of the corium caused by an increase in the number of cells, e.g. inflammation/tumor) |
| *nodule* | larger than a papule: inflammation/neoplasia |
| *weals\** | well-defined swelling of the skin as a result of edema in the dermis |
| *vesicle\** | well-defined swelling as a result of accumulation of fluid (blister); edema, blood |
| *pustule* | well-defined inflammatory swelling of the skin as a result of accumulation of pus in or under the epidermis |
| *Secondary lesions* | (arising from dried-up exudate, tissue degeneration or proliferation) |
| *aquamae* | horny scales |
| *crustae* | scrabs of dried-up exudate |
| *erosions* | superficial injuries exposing the corium |
| *ulcers* | injuries reaching down into the dermis |
| *lichenification* | thickened, inflexible areas of skin; normal relief becomes sharply pronounced |

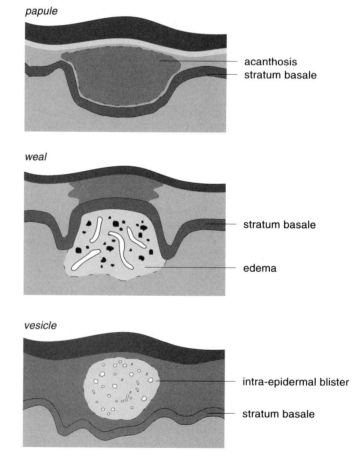

FIGURE   17.2
Examples of some basic skin changes; papule (= nodule), weal and vesicle (blister)

The skin disorders relevant in toxicology belong mainly to one of the following groups:

- circulatory effects
- degenerative changes
- hypertrophic changes
- inflammation
- blister formation
- tumors

## 2.1   TOXICOLOGICAL PATHOLOGY OF THE SKIN

Dermal exposure to injurious substances can result in a multitude of disorders. The majority of these involve the skin itself, but in a small number of cases the target of the toxic substance may be the hairs or the sweat and sebaceous glands.

*Contact between a xenobiotic and the skin*

If a *xenobiotic comes into contact with the skin*, the following situations may arise:

- The skin constitutes an impenetrable barrier to the substance. The substance does not cause any (toxic) effect.
- The substance reacts with the skin cells. This can lead to skin irritation, followed by dermatitis (inflammation).
- The substance invades the skin and reacts with the local proteins. This may result in so-called contact sensitization.
- The substance penetrates the skin and is further distributed. This may lead to systemic effects.

The two most important toxic effects on the skin are direct injury or *irritation* and immunological reaction (*allergy*). The response of the skin to these disorders is mainly limited to *degeneration, proliferation* and *inflammation* or some combination of these basic processes. Inflammation often dominates. For many toxic skin disorders the term *contact dermatitis* is used. This term encompasses a whole range of diverse skin disorders caused by harmful substances.

Urticaria or hives = skin rash with severe itching and formation of superficial swellings (so-called weals). This disorder, which usually heals quickly, is a type of anaphylactic allergy

The following disorders will be discussed in order: primary irritations or irritant dermatitis, allergic reactions, phototoxic and photo-allergic disorders, acne, contact urticaria, pigment disorders and various forms of skin cancer.

## 2.2   PRIMARY IRRITATION

Primary irritation or irritant dermatitis is probably the most common toxic skin reaction. As in many cases the molecular mechanism of this toxic effect is unknown, its classification has to be based on the extent of the damage, whether mild or severe. Dermatitis is an inflammation of the skin frequently accompanied by an inflammatory reaction and pain.

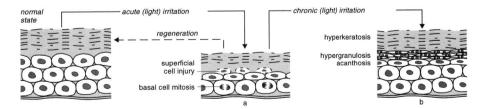

FIGURE   17.3
Epidermal response to acute (a) and chronic mild irritation (b)

*Mild contact dermatitis*

In its mildest form, damage is limited to the epidermis. If there is only one (acute) injury, the basal cells usually react swiftly to the damage in the more superficial layers by increased cell division, so that the epidermis is quickly repaired. If the injury persists, the cell proliferation also continues, resulting in thickening of the skin. The response of the skin to a continuous mild irritation is thus dominated by hyperplasia. The terms used for the various forms of hyperplasia in the skin are shown in Figure 17.3.

Proliferation of the stratum corneum is known as *hyperkeratosis*; of the stratum granulosum, *hypergranulosis*; and of the stratum spinosum, *acanthosis*. The thickened skin on the palms of a craftsman's hand is also an example of hyperplasia as a result of slight irritant injury. As long as the basement membrane is not affected, a mild irritant dermatitis does not cause effects in the dermis, except for a reversible vasodilatation.

*Severe contact dermatitis*

The histological reaction in *severe irritant dermatitis*, also known as *corrosion*, is characterized by degeneration. The severity of this condition depends on how deep the substance has penetrated the skin, but the epidermis, the basement membrane and part of the upper dermis have died off. The result is an inflammatory reaction at the transition of necrotic and living tissue. This inflammatory reaction is immediately followed by proliferation of epithelial and connective tissue cells, by which the organism attempts to repair the damage. The precursor cells of this epithelial regeneration mainly derive from undamaged tissue, such as the cells of the hair follicles, which lie much deeper in the dermis and are often therefore still undamaged. The dead cell layer on the surface is usually shed after the damage has been repaired. The site of the damage is often marked by a scar. Concentrated acids and bases are classic examples of substances causing corrosive lesions, but many other organic chemicals have the same effect. Since the lesions form quickly and are easily observed, it is usually simple to determine which substance has caused the damage.

*Moderate form of contact dermatitis*

Most forms of contact dermatitis are intermediate between the mild and severe forms; mild and very mild forms are usually not seen or not treated. Continuous exposure to the substance causing the effect results in combinations of effects, such as degeneration, proliferation and inflammation. Clinically, these symptoms are described as *eczema*.

Eczema is an extensive disorder of the upper skin layers. Five stages may be distinguished:

1   appearance of small red patches on swollen skin, with itching
2   the red patches become vesicles
3   the vesicles become pustules
4   the pustules burst and secrete fluid
5   the pustules dry out and a scaly layer forms at the site.

The different stages are often seen at the same time

*Histological picture*

At first, the *histological picture* is dominated by the *inflammatory reaction*. Vasodilatation (erythema), edema, exudation and migration of leukocytes are prominent. Locally, fluid may accumulate and vesicles or blisters may form. The accumulation of polymorphonuclear leukocytes can cause small abscesses in the epidermis, while larger accumulations can cause pustules. On continuous exposure to a substance, epidermal proliferation increases, and the skin becomes thicker and may split (chap formation). The proliferation of keratinocytes may also become abnormal and cell nuclei may be present up to the horny layer.

Detergents, soaps and many organic compounds are among the causes of mild or moderate contact dermatitis. In the early stages of exposure there is often no obvious reaction. This is also the reason why the cause of this type of contact dermatitis is often more difficult to trace than those caused by highly corrosive substances.

## 2.3  ALLERGIC DERMATITIS

It sometimes happens that the first contact of the skin with a substance does not produce any reaction, but that *repeated exposure* suddenly leads to an intense reaction. The latency period of this delayed reaction can vary from a few days to several years. This delayed type allergic reaction (type IV in Gell and Coombs classification) is based on a complex immunological mechanism. The first contact with the substance leads to sensitization. The substance involved is usually not a complete allergen, but rather a hapten. In many cases the substance first has to penetrate the horny layer and bind to a certain protein in order to become a complete allergen. In the hypodermis, this allergen is bound to T-lymphocytes and transported to a local lymph gland. This process, which can last 1–2 weeks, is known as *sensitization*. If the skin is exposed to the substance again, the sensitized T lymphocytes are induced to produce lymphokines. These lymphokines cause an inflammatory process at the site of contact. Once sensitization has taken place, a reaction may occur anywhere on the skin. Once an allergy has been established, it may persist for years, even if there are no symptoms. Figure 17.4 illustrates the process of sensitization.

*Sensitizing capacity*

Some substances have a greater *sensitizing capacity* than others. This means that they induce allergic effects in a larger number of people.

As was mentioned above, contact dermatitis takes some time to develop. The effects seldom appear after the first exposure to a new substance. It usually takes some 15–20 days before a reaction is observed. In some cases, the condition of the skin enables contact dermatitis to develop more quickly. This happens, for instance, in simultaneous exposure to substances which cause skin irritation and substances with an injurious effect. The combination of dermatotoxic agents can

*Synergism*

sometimes lead to *synergism*, one example being so-called cement eczema.

---

EXAMPLE 17-1

Cement eczema is the most common skin disorder associated with a profession and arises from a combination of factors which can lead to an allergy. Firstly, there is the toxicity caused by the alkaline nature of cement (pH = 12); wet mortar can cause skin irritations. Secondly, the sharp silicate particles can cause mechanical damage. Finally, cement contains various allergens, such as chromium and cobalt. These substances may be present in the raw materials or be added during the production process, as a result of wear and tear in the machines.

---

*Cross-hypersensitivity*

Apart from synergism, there is also *cross-hypersensitivity*. This occurs when a person is sensitized to a certain substance and also appears to have become allergic to a substance to which he/she has never been exposed before. In most cases the substances are chemically closely related.

*Patch test*

To see whether a particular substance is responsible for contact dermatitis, a dermatologist performs a so-called *patch test*. The test plaster is removed after 48 hours and the skin examined; 24 hours later, it is examined a second time. If there is a positive reaction, a small eczema reaction can be seen.

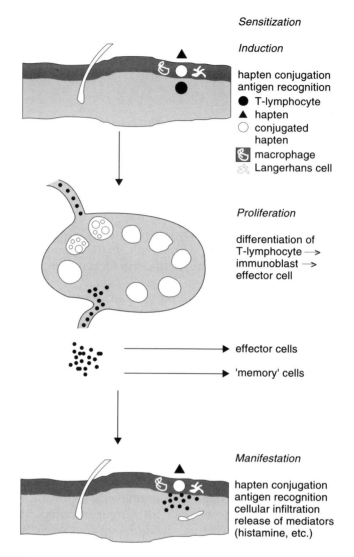

Sensitization

Induction

hapten conjugation
antigen recognition
● T-lymphocyte
▲ hapten
○ conjugated hapten
🖐 macrophage
🐾 Langerhans cell

Proliferation

differentiation of
T-lymphocyte —>
immunoblast —>
effector cell

→ effector cells

→ 'memory' cells

Manifestation

hapten conjugation
antigen recognition
cellular infiltration
release of mediators
(histamine, etc.)

FIGURE 17.4
Schematic representation of the process of sensitization by a hapten, resulting in allergic dermatitis

Histologically, the first reaction is vasodilatation, followed by perivascular accumulation of mononuclear leukocytes. The next phase shows migration of leukocytes into the epidermis, resulting in hyperplasia. It should be noted, however, that these tests are not entirely without risk, since there is a danger of the patient becoming sensitized to one or more of the test substances used.

Allergic dermatitis is quite common following local exposure to drugs, such as antibiotics, local anesthetics, antiseptics and stabilizers like ethylene diamine. Other examples are plants ('poison ivy'), metal and metal components (chromium, cobalt, nickel), dyes and industrial agents.

Table 17.3 lists a number of substances that can cause allergic dermatitis.

## 2.4 PHOTOTOXIC REACTIONS

*Sunlight*

By phototoxic reactions are meant disorders which can be caused by the combined effect of *sunlight* and toxic compounds. The pathological phenomena are basically not much different from the disorders discussed in sections 2.1 and 2.2.

512

TABLE 17.3
Substances which can cause allergic skin reactions.
The second column indicates the professions which involve frequent exposure to the relevant substance

| Substance | Profession |
| --- | --- |
| dichromate salts | metal industry (welding) |
| | paint industry (in pigments) |
| epoxy resins | plastics industry |
| accelerators | rubber industry |
| hexachlorophene | antiseptic |
| formaldehyde | building industry |
| nickel/cobalt | plastics industry, garages |
| aromatic amines | |
| p-phenylene diamine | antioxidant in rubber industry |
| substituted aromatic amine derivatives | |
| (incl. local anesthetics) | pharmaceutical industry |
| cement | building industry |
| chromium | building industry, metal industry |
| cosmetics | beauticians |

The molecular mechanism is still unknown, but since some reactions require oxygen, it is suspected that free radicals are formed under the influence of sunlight and that a lipid-peroxidation process is initiated. Consequently, certain cells die and this leads to local inflammatory reactions. These reactions are mostly seen immediately after the first exposure. The symptoms closely resemble those of sunburn. Depending on the site of the toxic effect, local phototoxicity and systemic phototoxicity are distinguished.

### 2.4.1 Local phototoxicity

Local reactions arise at the site where the skin is in *direct contact with the toxic substance*. Examples of such substances are soot and tar products (anthracene), furocoumarins (substances of vegetable origin) and certain dyes such as eosin and methylene blue. In the past, the dye Disperse Blue, an anthraquinone, was used in swimwear. This is a classic example of a substance which causes local photodermatotoxic effects.

### 2.4.2 Systemic phototoxicity

In the case of systemic phototoxicity, the substance usually enters the body by a route other than through the skin, after which it reaches the skin *via the circulation*. On subsequent exposure to light skin reactions may follow. Examples include certain drugs, such as tetracyclines, phenothiazine and sulfonamides, and porphyrins (heme derivatives). If the heme synthesis is disturbed, for instance by hexachlorobenzene (HCB), too many abnormal porphyrins enter the circulatory system. Under the influence of sunlight, skin reactions may then occur. Substances occurring in food (such as certain components of buckwheat and Saint John's wort) can also cause phototoxicity in cattle. In some animal species, hepatogenic phototoxicity may occur due to phylloerythrin, a pigment derived from chlorophyll. Normally, this substance is only partially absorbed, and excreted again via the bile. In the case of impaired liver function, the amount of phylloerythrin in the circulation may be increased.

### 2.4.3 Photoallergic reactions or photosensitization

In this type of skin reaction, antigens are formed in the skin *under the influence of (sun)light*. The conjugation of a hapten with a skin protein, which results in an antigen, is "catalyzed" by a photochemical reaction. Following the formation of antibodies, any further contact of the affected person or animal with the substance will produce a reaction at the site on the skin which is exposed to sunlight. Examples of photoallergic agents are: phenothiazine derivatives (drugs), sulfonamides (also drugs), quinine, thiocarbamine (a fixative in photography, which is also present in substances used for vulcanizing rubber), cyclamates (sweeteners) and halogenated phenols such as hexachlorophenes (formerly used as an antiseptic). Photoallergic disorders are much less common in practice than immediate phototoxic disorders. Many substances are phototoxic as well as photoallergic.

*Clinically*, the photoallergic reaction manifests itself by delayed papules and eczema, but it can also appear directly in the form of urticaria. *Histologically*, the disorder is characterized by a dense, perivascular accumulation of inflammatory cells in the dermis.

The direct reaction probably arises as a result of antibody-mediated processes, while the delayed reaction type involves a cell-mediated immune response. The best known photoallergens are formed by the group of halogenated salicyl anilides. These substances used to be added to soaps as bacteriostatics.

### 2.4.4 Radiation involved in phototoxic and photoallergic reactions

The previous sections, phototoxic effects are caused by radiation. Most biological effects appearing as erythemas and pigmentations are caused by radiation with a wavelength below 320 nm. The wavelength range of sunlight begins at about 290 nm. UV radiation emitted by artificial light sources may have somewhat shorter wavelengths.

Although UV radiation of somewhat longer wavelengths less readily causes erythemas, it is precisely this type of radiation which is responsible for the majority of phototoxic and photoallergic reactions.

## 2.5  HYPERPIGMENTATION AND HYPOPIGMENTATION

*Melanin*

The color of the skin is determined largely by the pigment *melanin*, produced by the melanocytes in the epidermis. Some chemicals are known to be capable of causing local depigmentation of the skin. A number of these substances have proved to be *selectively melanotoxic*. They often show a structural similarity to tyrosine, the most important structural component of melanin. Figure 17.5 shows the structural formulae of some of them.

**Intermezzo**

*Hypopigmentation*

Depigmentation under the influence of phenols with a tertiary alkyl group and polyhydric phenols, such as hydroquinone and derivatives thereof, can be imagined to take place as follows.

The parent compound for the biosynthesis of the skin pigment melanin is tyrosine (see Figure 17.6). Two reactions catalyzed by phenol oxidase (tyrosinase) then result in the formation of dopa and dopaquinone, respectively. The formation of dopaquinone via two non-enzymatic routes, in which (other) quinoid structures act as intermediates, may ultimately lead to polymerization reactions which produce melanin:

- addition of the thiol groups of amino acids and amino acid residues in proteins (e.g. cysteine) to dopaquine, followed by oxidation;
- formation of indole quinones.

Cosmetic disfigurement caused by hypopigmenting chemicals may be quite considerable. This is of course particularly true for highly pigmented people. Apart from substances which cause selective hypopigmentation, there are also substances producing a combination of effects. One example is arsenic, which causes general hyperpigmentation, in combination with well-circumscribed depigmentated areas.

514

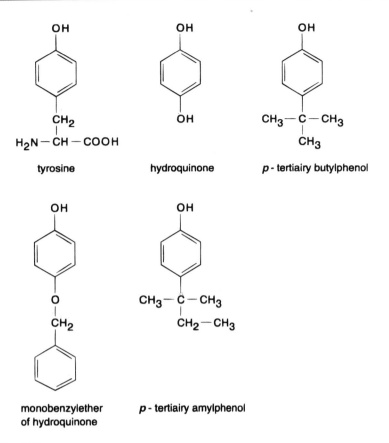

FIGURE   17.5
Chemical structure of tyrosine (structural component of the pigment melanin) and some hypopigmentating chemicals structurally related to tyrosine

*Hyperpigmentation*

There are also chemicals which are known to cause local or more diffuse *hyperpigmentation*. Some examples of these are given in Table 17.4.

These reactions often involve a sequel to phototoxic reactions. This is specifically the case for coal tar products, pitch and psoralene. Some substances, like barbiturates and phenolphthalein, cause local, recurring erythemas or dermatitis. A localized depigmented area remains at the affected sites. The mechanism is not known. Histological examination reveals an accumulation of melanin-containing macrophages in these areas.

Changes in the color of the skin do not necessarily occur because of an accumulation of, or a decrease in, melanin. Accumulation of exogenous or endogenous pigments can also influence the skin color. One well-known example is the orange color that can be caused by an excess of carotenoids.

## 2.6   ACNE

Acne is a lesion of the hair follicle. It arises from the hyperproliferation of keratinized cells in the follicle. This results in the formation of keratin plugs, retention of fat from the sebaceous glands and distension of the follicle lumen (blackheads or comedones). When the follicle eventually bursts, its contents cause an inflammatory reaction in the underlying dermis. *Acne vulgaris* is the term used for pimples in adolescents, while chemically induced acne is referred to as *acne venenata*, or *acne induced by environmental contaminants*. Many variants have been described, but the best known are oil acne and chloracne. Oil acne used to be a frequent occupational skin disease, which arose from repeated ex-

*Acne venenata or acne induced by environmental contaminants*

515

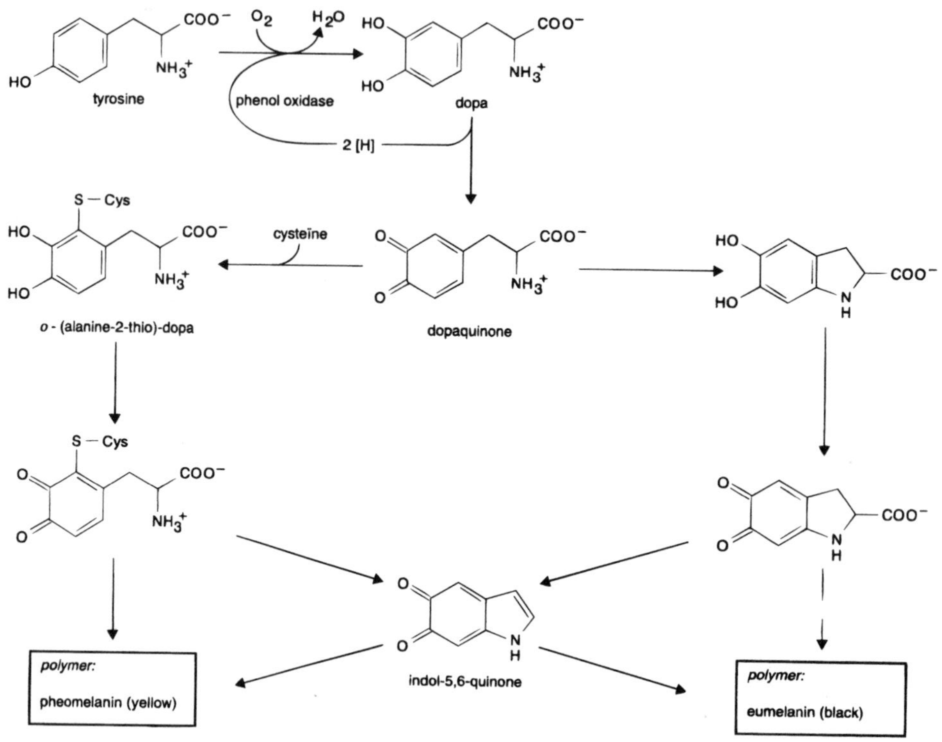

**FIGURE 17.6**

Biosynthesis of melanin

The quinoid monomeric units probably determine the color of melanin.

The phenolic compounds mentioned are highly effective reducing agents.

Hence two mechanisms can be proposed for depigmentation:

—inhibition of the oxidative steps in the biosynthesis of melanin

—reduction of the quinoid monomeric units to (colorless) hydroquinoid structures

**TABLE 17.4**

Substances known to be capable of causing hyperpigmentation of the skin

| | |
|---|---|
| heavy metals | silver (argyria) |
| | bismuth |
| | arsenic |
| | mercury |
| drugs | various acridines (antimalaria drugs) |
| | 4-aminoquinoline (antimalaria drug) |
| | phenothiazines |
| | tetracyclines (antibiotics) |
| alkylating agents | busulphan |

posure to cutting oil (oil used for the sharpening of knives) and petroleum. Thanks to stricter hygiene, oil acne is now much less common than before.

*Chloracne*

There is no doubt that there is a connection between *chloracne* and exposure to chlorinated hydrocarbons. This type of acne is much more serious and lasts much longer than that caused by oils. The first lesions consist of pale and yellow cysts on the face. *Histologically*, the first symptoms comprise a thickening of the follicular epithelium, followed by formation of comedones. At a later stage, the sebaceous glands are radically changed and turn into keratin-filled cysts. Important acne-inducing substances are the polyhalogenated biphenyls (PCB, PBB), and 2,3,7,8-tetrachlorodibenzo-*p*-dioxin. The chloracnegenic action of PCB and PBB is probably caused by contamination with polychlorinated dioxins and dibenzofurans. Substances are tested for potential acnegenicity by the *rabbit's ear test*. In this test, the substance is applied almost daily over a period of at least 2 weeks. At the end of this time, it is determined histologically whether hyperkeratosis has occurred in the follicles.

## 2.7 CONTACT URTICARIA

Lichenification is a coarsening of the skin surface with decreased pliability and the appearance of polygonal skin segments separated by deep narrow grooves

*Classification*

This disorder is accompanied by itching (which leads to scratching), erosions, lichenification and eczema. It is a special type of reaction involving in particular that part of the skin that is in direct contact with the substance in question, although systemic effects are sometimes also observed. The systemic effects are accompanied by a more general urticaria and even anaphylactic reactions. Contact urticarias are classified according to severity:

- localized urticaria, limited to the site of contact (grade 1)
- more extensive skin reaction with extensive angiedema (grade 2)
- urticaria in combination with bronchial asthma (grade 3)
- anaphylactic reactions (grade 4)

Grade 1 (for example, stinging nettle, *Urtica dioica*) and grade 2 reactions are limited to the skin and are the most common. Pathogenetically, two forms may be distinguished: contact urticaria caused by immunological and non-immunological mechanisms. The most severe forms (grades 3 and 4) are caused exclusively by immunological mechanisms.

In contact urticaria based on *non-immunological mechanisms*, the urticaria appears rapidly. The xenobiotic, which is quickly absorbed by the skin, has either a direct influence on the dermal blood vessel walls, or causes an indirect vascular reaction, probably through degranulation of mast cells. This results in the release of histamine, bradykinin, eicosanoids and other vasoactive substances. The consequences are pain, itching and edema. This type of reaction is observed after local exposure to substances such as trafuryl (the tetrahydrofuryl ester of nicotinic acid) and cobalt chloride solutions.

*Immunological mechanisms* may underlie local as well as more generalized forms of urticaria and naturally also anaphylactic reactions. Substances suspected of causing contact urticaria via immunological mechanisms include 1-chloro-2,4-dinitrobenzene, diethyltoluamide, tetanus antitoxin, penicillin and streptomycin. In some people who are sensitive to these agents, potatoes and tulips are also able to induce contact urticaria via immunological mechanisms.

## 2.8 SKIN TUMORS

It has been suspected for more than 2 centuries that soot can cause skin cancer. Some studies have indeed shown that soot and related substances such as tar, creosote oil, shale oil and cutting oil can cause skin and other tumors. Exposure to arsenic and arsenic compounds is also thought to be linked to skin tumors. Local application of polycyclic aromatic hydrocarbons, such as benzo[*a*]pyrene and heterocyclic compounds like benzo[*c*]acridine, for example, cause skin cancer in experimental animals.

Skin cancer is the most common form of cancer

*Skin cancer* is the *most common form of cancer* (an estimated 20–75 cases per 100,000 persons per year). There are several forms of skin cancer known and their progress and prognoses all vary considerably.

Skin tumors can originate in the epidermis, hair follicles, sweat and sebaceous glands, as well as in the dermis and hypodermis. Besides benign skin tumors, there are also malignant skin tumors.

ASSIGNMENT 17.2

Skin tumors can be divided into epithelial and mesenchymal tumors. Indicate whether tumors originating in the epidermis, hair follicles, dermis and hypodermis should be assigned to the epithelial or mesenchymal category.

*Epithelial tumors*

The most common *epithelial tumors* are:

- papilloma
- squamous-cell carcinoma
- basal-cell carcinoma (basiloma)
- epithelioma

*Mesenchymal tumors*

*Mesenchymal tumors* include:

- fibroma
- fibrosarcoma
- sarcoid
- histiocytoma
- lipoma
- hemangioma
- mastocytoma
- neurofibroma
- leucosis

A few skin tumors that are important in toxicology are briefly discussed in the following section.

*Papillomas*

*Papillomas* are benign epithelial tumors in which the epithelial cells cover finger-like protrusions of the stroma. They are found especially in places which are covered by stratified squamous epithelium (skin and cutaneous mucosa). They are often cauliflower-like formations, protruding from the skin surface. These tumors do not infiltrate or metastasize, and ulceration only occurs as a result of trauma. Microscopically, they consist of a narrow connective-tissue nucleus that splits off into a multitude of primary, secondary and tertiary papillae, all of which are covered by the proliferating epithelium. Sometimes the stroma component makes up a large part of the tumor. This form of tumor is called a fibropapilloma.

*Squamous-cell carcinomas*

*Squamous-cell carcinomas* are malignant tumors stemming from the stratified squamous epithelium. Sunlight is thought to play an important role in the onset of this tumor. As it grows, the tumor infiltrates, but metastasizes only relatively slowly (moderately malignant). The surface is irregular, with deep grooves, giving these tumors their cauliflower-like appearance. Hemorrhages and necrosis may result from external damage. Microscopically, the tumorous tissue is made up of strands and groups of squamous epithelial cells, accompanied or surrounded by stroma. The proliferating cells of the stratum basale can differentiate to a greater or lesser degree, so that the number of cells in the stratum spinosum and horny layers can vary greatly. The nuclei of the tumor cells can be distinguished from those of the normal epithelial cells by their variable size and abundance of chromatin.

*Basilomas or basal-cell carcinomas*

Tumors arising from proliferations of the stratum basale are called *basilomas* or *basal-cell carcinomas*. The overlying skin may have a normal appearance, but is often ulcerated. The tumor is well defined, while the cross-section is characterized by its lobular structure and white color. Histologically, various forms can be distinguished, of which the most typical form is characterized by the presence of strands and small groups of epithelial cells, separated by strands of collagenous connective tissue. In the strands and at the periphery of the groups the epithelial cells are arranged in parallel longitudinal axes. Although the histological picture often displays malignant characteristics, the biological behavior appears to be benign.

ASSIGNMENT 17.3

What does it mean if basilomas display histologically malignant characteristics, and yet are biologically benign?

The basal-cell carcinoma has a fairly favorable prognosis (95% chance of recovery) because it hardly ever disseminates and can easily be removed. It is recognizable as an ulcer which does not heal quickly.

*Epithelioma*

*Epitheliomas* are benign proliferations of the epidermis and may be subdivided into keratinizing epitheliomas (intracutaneous), necrotic and calcifying epitheliomas and tricho-epitheliomas. In *keratinizing epitheliomas*, there is a lumen under the skin whose wall is lined with proliferating, well-differentiated squamous epithelium. The lumen is usually open to the air. *Necrotic* or *calcifying epitheliomas* consist of one or several intradermal and subcutaneous lumina. The walls of these lumina consist of a more or less thick layer of basal cells which keratinize abruptly. The lumen contains keratinized cells in which an empty patch is visible where the nucleus ought to be; the so-called shadow cells. Considerable amounts of calcium deposition may occur in these tumors. *Trichoepitheliomas* consist of agglomerations of cysts which look like hair follicles.

*Fibromas*

*Fibromas* are benign tumors deriving from the connective tissue cells. They are roundish, sometimes lobed tumors of varying size. They are well defined and solid, and may be solitary or multiple. Their cross-sections display a fibrous structure and grayish white to pink color. The tumor tissue is surrounded by a connective tissue capsule and consists of tangled bundles of collagenous fibers and connective tissue cells. A distinction can be made between *fibroma durum* and *fibroma molle*. Unlike the latter, the former is rich in collagen and has few cells, with the nuclei showing similarities with those of normal, resting connective tissue cells. In addition, there are often spindle shaped cells with large, more rounded nuclei that are poor in chromatin.

durus (Lat.) = hard
mollis (Lat.) = soft

*Fibrosarcoma*

A *fibrosarcoma* is a malignant tumor derived from connective-tissue cells. Unlike a fibroma, this tumor is not completely encapsulated. This tumor is also poorly demarcated, because it usually infiltrates the surrounding tissue.

*Melanomas*

*Melanomas* are tumors originating from melanocytes, the melanin-forming cells in the skin. Embryologically, these cells arise from the neural crest. In addition to clearly black or brown melanomas, there are also those lacking pigment. Since the pigment cells lie dispersed among the bundles of connective tissue, the tumor tissue have a fibrous structure. The tumor cells may be spindle shaped, have protrusions, or may be epithelioid in shape. The nuclei are round or oval and they often lie hidden under the pigment. Apart from tumor cells, the melanoma commonly contains macrophages which have accumulated melanin. Melanoma is the *most malignant form of skin cancer*. It displays an unpredictable, aggressive behavior. The patient's chances of survival depend greatly on the size and the site of the tumor: the more deeply situated in the skin, the more dangerous. The mean chance of survival is low, only 63%, compared with 95% for basal-cell carcinoma.

Melanomas are considerably less common in people with brown or black skin. Discussions on the onset of melanoma always focus on the role of sunlight (ultraviolet radiation) in the etiology of the tumor. Recently, however, there is increasing doubt about the causal relation between sunlight and melanoma. Some recent epidemiological studies have reported a greater risk of melanoma for workers in, for instance, the (petro)chemical and nuclear industries. There is also evidence that the rise in incidence is primarily seen in industrialized countries. The incidence is higher in urbanized areas than in rural areas.

> ASSIGNMENT 17.4
>
> The higher incidence of melanoma in coastal regions compared with inland areas, for example, in Australia, is often cited as support for the sunlight theory. How could this higher incidence be explained in terms of the theory that environmental factors (xenobiotics in particular) play a role in the development of melanomas?

The distribution of different types of skin cancer is uneven. A study performed in four dermatological practices and a group of residents of the Haarlem area (the Netherlands) revealed the following distribution if skin cancers were divided into four classes (see Table 17.5).

*Age distribution*

As expected, the distribution of skin tumors over age categories is not consistent either. It appears that two-thirds of patients are aged over 60, while 15% are younger than 50. Squamous-cell carcinomas are common in older patients, basal-cell carcinomas in the middle age bracket and melanomas primarily in younger people. Figure 17.7 shows the distribution of these three tumors over the age groups.

To summarize, skin cancer may be caused by UV light and ionizing radiation, but also by polycyclic aromatic hydrocarbons (PAHs), arsenic and combinations of furocoumarins (psoralenes) with UV light. Moreover, it has become increasingly clear that a large number of chemicals can influence the carcinogenic effect of UV light.

## 3 Dermatotoxicity tests

In previous sections, some substances responsible for dermatotoxic disorders were mentioned. Quite often, the effect is exerted by the original substance, but like other organs, the skin is an active biotransformation organ. The epidermis is particularly active in this respect.

TABLE 17.5

Distribution of tumor types in 1188 patients with skin cancer

| Tumor type | Patients | |
|---|---|---|
| | *number* | *%* |
| basal-cell carcinoma | 936 | 79 |
| squamous-cell carcinoma | 123 | 10 |
| melanoma | 94 | 8 |
| other skin tumors | 35 | 3 |

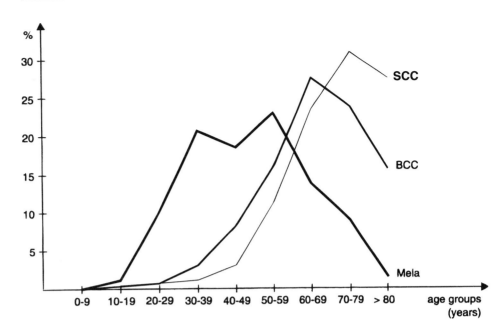

FIGURE 17.7
Age distribution of 978 patients with basal-cell carcir na (BCC), 307 patients with squa-mous-cell carcinoma (SCC) and 1331 patients with a melanoma (Mela)

It has been demonstrated that metabolites of benzo[a]pyrene, including epox-ides, can be formed in the skin. It is also well-known that some drugs applied locally to the skin are biotransformed. In addition to metabolic transformation, chemicals in the skin are sometimes exposed to photochemical reactions under the influence of UV light. Not only local biotransformation processes, but also those in other organs can play a part in toxic pher mena in the skin. In such cases of systemic toxicity, the reactive intermediates which cause the skin injury are in fact formed elsewhere and then transported to the skin.

An example of a substance which causes such a systemic effect is hexa-chlorobenzene. This substance produces an accumulation of uroporphyrins and coproporphyrins through its interaction with the synthesis of porphyrin in the liver. These porphyrin metabolites accumulate in the skin and sensitize it to phototoxic activity, since they actively absorb light with a wavelength of 400 nm. The result is photoactivation and injury to the cell membrane and cell components.

*Macroscopic observations*

The identification of primary irritations is largely limited to *macroscopic obser-vations*, in which reactions such as *erythema* and *edema* are quantified. Time has shown that of the many laboratory animals used in dermatotoxic research the rabbit is the most sensitive to irritative changes. Since the human skin is also very sensitive to irritant changes, the rabbit is widely used for this type of re-search. Unlike guinea-pigs, rabbits have a thin skin, so that subepidermal and subcutaneous inflammation can easily be recognized. On the other hand, the skin of the guinea-pig is more sensitive to lipoid substances.

*Draize test*

The *Draize test* forms the basis for testing primary irritant changes. This method consists of a single application of the test substance, over a period of 24 hours, to the shaved skin of a rabbit. The site of administration is usually isolated or covered with a plaster.

Why is this site often covered up?

The covering prevents the experimental animal from scratching or licking the site of administration. The erythema and edema reactions are inspected after 24 and 72 hours.

Inflammatory phenomena in the skin of a mouse can be provoked by local administration of a multitude of substances. Well-known examples are phenols, croton oil, benzalkonium chloride, ethylphenyl propionic acid and methyl salicylic acid. Histologically, all these substances cause edema, cellular inflammatory infiltrate and vascular dilatation, but the time it takes for the effects to develop varies from substance to substance.

A large number of chemicals are capable of causing epidermal hyperplasia. As discussed above, a distinction is made between hyperplasias with and without degenerative changes. TPA (12-O-tetradecanoyl-phorbol-13-acetic acid), the active ingredient in croton oil, is an example of a substance that causes hyperplasia without degenerative phenomena. After application of this substance, the epidermis hypertrophies. This is accompanied by reduced basophilia, widening of the intercellular spaces and protrusion of the stratum granulosum.

In contrast, treatment of the skin of a mouse with 3-methylcholanthrene or benzo[a]pyrene first causes degeneration of the epidermis, followed by regenerative hyperplasia.

ASSIGNMENT 17.5

A single local administration of a substance (A23187) to the skin of mice causes epidermal hyperplasia. Ten minutes after the administration, an increased prostaglandin $E_2$ level is measured. It appears that the development of epidermal hyperplasia in the mice can be inhibited by preliminary administration of a prostaglandin synthetase inhibitor, such as indomethacin. What conclusion should be drawn from this regarding the development of hyperplasia?

It has been shown that a large number of cosmetic products cause epidermal hyperplasia in the skin of rabbits. Examples include sodium lauryl sulfate, suntan lotions and various antiperspirants.

*Animal models for detection of chloracne*

One of the most specific skin disorders resulting from interaction with chemicals is *chloracne*. Most of the data on substances which can cause this disorder actually come from research on humans. There are three animal models for the detection of chloracne: the inner surface of the auricle of the rabbit, the facial skin of the rhesus monkey and the skin of the nude mouse. Of these models, the rabbit ear is considered to be the most sensitive. However, chloracne in the rabbit can only be provoked on the inside of the auricle and not on other parts of the skin. Similar preference of chloracne for specific parts of the skin is also observed in humans. Epidermal necrosis can be provoked in the skin of the rabbit by sodium lauryl sulfate and hexachlorophene.

*Challenge*

A variant of the Draize test constitutes also the basis of hypersensitivity tests. This is an extremely important aspect of research into the toxicity of cosmetics (perfumes and others). White guinea-pigs are mainly used for this and they are treated in various ways. The reliability of the test is limited, however, which is why supplementary research is carried out on volunteers. This nearly always involves a *challenge* technique, which means that the first administration of the test substance is followed by a second one, once the immune system has been activated by the first. Hypersensitivity tests may be improved by adding substances to the first test substance exposure which activate the immune system, but which have a different target in the immune system than the test substance itself. A promising technique is an *in vitro* test system using human hair follicles.

## 3.1   DEVELOPMENT OF NEW MODELS IN SKIN TOXICITY TESTING

The following section contains the description of the development of two new models for dermatotoxicology.

> ASSIGNMENT   17.6
>
> Compare the two methods described in the following section. Indicate the similarities and differences between them, mentioning the advantages and disadvantages of each.

### Two new models for skin toxicology

The uptake of toxic substances by the skin and the ensuing damaging effects are nearly always investigated in laboratory animals. In evaluating the results of animal skin experiments, one should be aware that the anatomy and physiology of the skin of experimental animals differs from that of human skin in important ways. Due to its lack of fur, the temperature of the human body is regulated by the skin. For this purpose, the dermis contains large numbers of sweat glands and blood vessels.

The human epidermis is also considerably thicker than that of most laboratory animals, owing to the absence of "protective" body hair. This may cause differences in the rate of penetration of substances and in the sensitivity of the skin to the toxic effect of substances. This restricts the predictive value for humans of the results of skin toxicology tests on animals. It is reasonable to assume that the predictive value for humans is greatest for methods which are based on human skin.

## 3.2   ALTERNATIVE MODELS FOR SKIN TOXICITY TESTS

Two models for skin toxicity testing that have been developed recently are described here. In these models the human skin itself can be examined. The first model uses cultured human epidermis cells (Figure 17.8). These cultures show many similarities to the living part of the *in vivo* epidermis, where the irritants, after passing through the horny layer, have their initial effects. Using cell cultures, the processes taking place there can be investigated. An added advantage of this model is that it reduces the numbers of experimental animals used.

In the second model, human skin is grafted onto an immunodeficient, nude mouse (Figure 17.9). It has been shown by immunological methods that the epidermis of the graft remains identifiable as human for at least 6 months. In the course of time, however, mouse blood vessels grow into the dermis, gradually changing the nature of the human dermis to that of a mouse. This model therefore has its limitations for research into the penetration of the skin by substances and the irritant properties of these substances for the skin.

Both models are currently being evaluated for skin toxicity testing. By way of illustration, the results from some of the experiments will be described below.

### 3.2.1   *Cultured human epidermis*

In the first series of experiments, the general cytotoxic response of epidermis cell cultures was investigated. For this purpose, the effects of a number of model substances on the membrane and the metabolic activity of cells were measured.

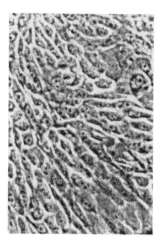

FIGURE 17.8
Phase contrast micrograph of cultured human skin cells

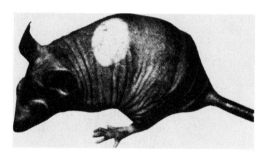

FIGURE 17.9
Human skin graft transplanted onto a nude mouse

The cell membrane is the site of the first encounter between the cell and the toxic agent. If the membrane is damaged by this encounter, this can lead to leakage of components from the cell. Leakage of various enzymes proved to be insufficiently sensitive as a measure of membrane damage. In contrast, the decrease in potassium concentration proved to be a very good indicator.

When the toxic substance passes through the membrane, possibly without even damaging it, this may affect processes inside the cell. In many cases, this will lead to a change in energy metabolism. This is expressed as the extent to which glucose is taken up from the medium in the hours following exposure. This uptake can be used as a measure of the vitality of the cell cultures and the rate at which the toxic substance exerts its effect. As an example, Figures 17.10 and 17.11 show the effects of three substances, sodium dodecyl sulfate (SDS), anthralin and tributyltin (TBT).

In all experiments, the concentration of these substances was $2.10^{-4}$ M. Groups of six cultures were exposed to the substances for 30, 60 or 120 minutes. Loss of potassium from the cells was measured immediately after exposure. Glucose uptake was monitored up to 48 hours after the start of exposure. The potassium loss shows that anthralin has a slight effect, SDS an intermediate effect and TBT a large effect on the membrane (Figure 17.10). The highly irritant effect of TBT was confirmed by the termination of glucose uptake, even after an exposure of 30 minutes (Figure 17.11). SDS only had an effect after a 2-hour exposure. Anthralin causes a delayed effect. Between 24 and 48 hours after exposure, hardly any glucose is taken up. This signifies that during this period cell death occurs.

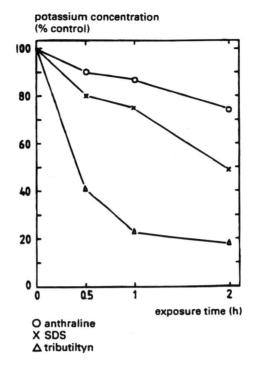

potassium concentration
(% control)

exposure time (h)

O anthraline
X SDS
△ tributiltyn

FIGURE   17.10
Potassium loss from cultured epidermal cells, measured immediately after exposure for 30, 60 and 120 minutes to various toxic compounds, at a concentration of $2.10^{-4}$ M. The potassium concentration is expressed as a percentage of the concentration in untreated cultures

These examples illustrate how with relatively simple measurements on cultures of human epidermis cells data can be obtained on the irritant effect, the target sites and the rate of action of chemical agents. As far as extrapolation of the results to intact human skin is concerned, the results obtained so far are in good agreement with what is known about the effects of these substances on the skin of living humans.

### 3.2.2 *Human skin grafted onto mice*

As an example of a penetration test on human skin grafted onto a mouse, results of a study of cholinesterase-inhibiting organophosphates are presented. The uptake of these substances by the skin was determined by measuring the amount of (irreversible) inhibition of the enzyme cholinesterase (ChE) in a few drops of mouse blood.

Figure 17.12 shows that intravenous administration of various doses of the cholinesterase-inhibiting organophosphate soman leads to a dose-dependent inhibition of blood ChE. This inhibition was determined 60 minutes after the administration of soman; each point in the graph shows the maximum inhibition for a particular dose. Figure 17.13 shows how much soman is present in the blood at each point in time up to 150 minutes after application to the skin. It also shows how the inhibition of the blood ChE eventually levels off as a certain dosage of soman is applied to the mouse skin or the grafted human skin.

Comparing the results of Figures 17.12 and 17.13, it appears that a considerable amount of soman is degraded or bound in the skin. Figure 17.13 shows that 150 minutes after administration of soman to the skin of non-grafted mice or to that of a mouse with autotransplanted skin, the maximum inhibition of blood

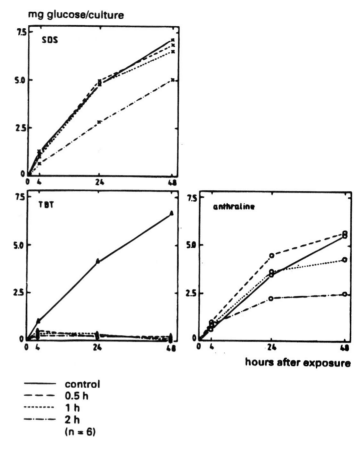

FIGURE 17.11

Uptake of glucose by cultured epidermis cells, measured 0–48 hours after exposure to $2.10^4$ M SDS, TBT and anthralin for various durations

ChE was 75%. A comparable inhibition can be achieved by intravenous injection of 9 µg soman/kg (Figure 17.12). It can thus be concluded that about 85% of the soman is inactivated in the mouse skin. Figure 17.13 also shows that the grafting in itself has no influence on the rate of uptake by the skin, since this rate is virtually the same for the grafted and the non-grafted mouse skin. It is also clear from the same figure that at the dose of soman used here, 60 µg kg$^{-1}$ cm$^{-2}$, the uptake in human skin is slower than that in mouse skin.

### 3.3 FURTHER RESEARCH

The anticipated suitability of cultured human epidermis cells for skin toxicity is being tested in a series of experiments. The study on general cytotoxic response as described above is the first. Other aspects that will be included in this evaluation are the mode of action of the specific skin irritant, mustard gas, the effects of toxic agents on the epidermal differentiation process and the role of the epidermis in the production of inflammation mediators.

Evaluation of the model of grafted human skin on a nude mouse is at an advanced stage. It does not look as if the model is a genuine improvement on existing animal models for research into subcutaneous absorption of substances. It has, however, proved to be suitable for research that focuses on the epidermis of the human skin, of which the human characteristics are contained in the graft. Excellent results have been obtained in an experiment in which thera-

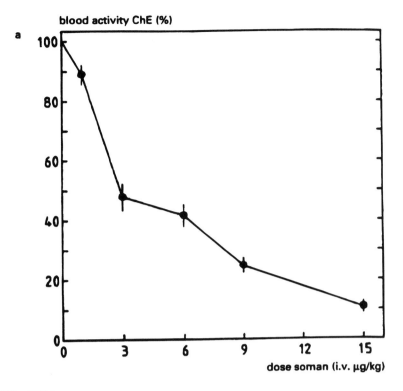

FIGURE 17.12
Inhibition of blood cholinesterase in a mouse after intravenous injection of varying doses of soman

peutic agents were tested on grafts which were infected with the *herpes simplex* virus. Such experiments performed on animal skins yield unreliable data owing to the differences in thymidine content between the skins of humans and animals.

Although the evaluation of these two new skin models will require some additional time, the available data already allow the conclusion that both models can make a valuable contribution to experimental skin research.

## 4    Summary

The skin is one of the largest organs in the human body, based upon surface area, and its location makes it an important target organ for the toxic effects of a multitude of substances. Although there are some substances with a systemic action, the majority of toxic effects in the skin are caused by local exposure.

Toxicological disorders of the skin consist of only a limited number of reactions, or combinations of these. There are three basic processes: inflammation, degeneration and proliferation. Local exposure of the skin can lead to various types of lesions, including inflammation, hyperkeratosis, erosions, ulcerations and necrosis. In addition to these lesions, which have a more acute nature, chemicals can also cause more chronic disorders, or disorders which do not appear until much later. Examples are the various types of skin tumors and skin disorders involving the immune system, such as hypersensitivity reactions and contact allergy. The conventional model of skin toxicology research is the shaved skin of the rabbit, since it is generally agreed that rabbit skin is as sensitive as, if not more sensitive than, human skin. Guinea-pigs are widely used to test new cosmetics for contact allergy.

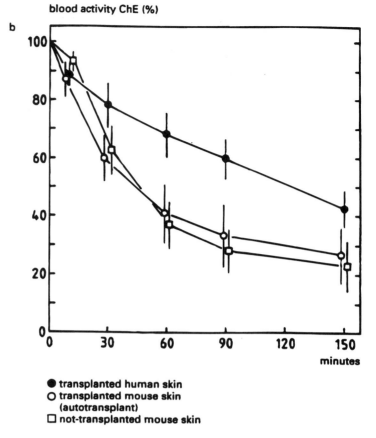

**blood activity ChE (%)**

● transplanted human skin
○ transplanted mouse skin
   (autotransplant)
□ not-transplanted mouse skin

FIGURE   17.13
Inhibition of blood cholinesterase in the mouse after application of 60 $\mu$g soman kg$^{-1}$ cm$^{-2}$ skin

## SELF ASSESSMENT QUESTIONS

1   Why are melanomas not regarded as mesenchymal tumors?

2   How do you explain the fact that, despite the greatly increased incidence of melanomas (more frequent diagnosis), mortality as a consequence of melanomas has not risen, even though no definitive treatment has yet been developed?

3   It is expected that the number of patients with skin tumors will rise in the future. On what assumption is this based?

4   In research on (dermato)toxic substances, two types of control group are sometimes used along with the actual test groups. What are these two control groups and why are they used?

## FEEDBACK

### 1   Answers to the assignments

17.1 The melanocytes produce the pigment melanin and thereby determine, for instance, the color of the skin; melanin also acts as a filter against radiation. The Langerhans cells have a function in immunological defense.

17.2 Skin tumors deriving from epithelial tissue are classified as epithelial tumors, those deriving from mesenchymal tissue as mesenchymal tumors. Of the examples given, the tumors stemming from the epidermis and hair follicles (as well as from sweat and sebaceous glands) are epidermal, while those stemming from the dermis and hypodermis are mesenchymal.

17.3 Histologically malignant characteristics include: abundant mitosis in the cells, large numbers of cells and infiltrative growth. Biologically benign characteristics include: no metastasis, no unlimited growth, rare recurrence.

17.4 The higher incidence of melanoma in coastal areas as compared with inland areas could point to a greater exposure to xenobiotics due to the higher degree of urbanization in coastal regions.

17.5 The data show that an increase in prostaglandin $E_2$ is necessary for hyperplasia and possibly also causes it.

17.6 The answer to this assignment can be found in section 3.2.

## 2 Answers to the self assessment questions

1 Mesenchymal tumors are tumors deriving from tissues which develop embryologically from the mesodermal germ layer. Melanocytes derive from a different germ layer (neural crest).

2 The earlier diagnosis not only of melanomas but also of their precursors ensures that the anticipated increase in mortality is largely annulled.

3 The following are mentioned as causes of the increase in the number of cases of skin cancer: the aging population, increased exposure to sunlight (ozone layer depletion), changes in fashion and forms of recreation, and other external factors such as air and soil pollution. Since these factors can be expected to become more important in the future, the number of patients with skin cancer will increase further.

4 What is meant here is a positive and a negative control group. The negative control group consists of animals that only receive the solvent (vehicle) and should thus not show any (negative) response. The positive control group consists of animals that receive a substance other than the substance to be tested, but which is known to cause toxic effects at the dosage used. This substance is administered to determine whether the experimental animals are sufficiently susceptible to detect a possible toxic effect of the test substance.

# Contents Study unit 18
## Respiratory toxicology: pathophysiology, toxicological pathology and mechanisms of toxicity

0-8493-9232-2/96/$6.00 + $.50
© 1996 by CRC Press, Inc.

# Study unit 18

# Respiratory toxicology: pathophysiology, toxicological pathology and mechanisms of toxicity

*V. J. Feron, R. B. Beems, P. G. J. Reuzel and A. Zwart*

INTRODUCTION

In mammals, the respiratory organs form a complex system, with the uptake of oxygen and the excretion of carbon dioxide as the main functions. Due to their large surface area and the thin barrier between air and blood, the lungs are particularly suitable for the uptake of volatile substances, but also of non-volatile substances which penetrate into the lungs. Gases and vapors are also readily absorbed in other parts of the respiratory tract, in particular in the nose. Inhaled particles are efficiently cleared from the air passages by the mucociliary system and by macrophages.

The lungs also play an important part as excretory organs. Volatile substances, such as the solvents benzene and carbon tetrachloride, which have entered the body via a different route, are excreted by the lungs in the expired air. The lungs and the mucous membranes of the nose and bronchi also contain very active biotransformation enzymes, such as cytochrome P-450, which can convert xenobiotics into toxic, reactive intermediates. The respiratory tract may therefore be damaged by substances that are inhaled or have entered the body via a different route. Smoking tobacco is a dramatic example of inhalational exposure to a mixture of gases and particles which may lead to a wide range of detrimental effects in the respiratory tract.

The present study unit provides a brief description of the structure and function of the respiratory tract. It then goes on to discuss interactions of toxic substances with the pulmonary tissue and the kinetics of inhaled substances. A good deal of attention is given to disturbances of the pulmonary function and to the general and toxicological pathology of the respiratory tract, including tumors and hypersensitivity reactions. A number of examples serve to highlight the toxicological problems resulting from pollution of the indoor and outside environment.

LEARNING OBJECTIVES

After studying this unit, you should:

— have strengthened your knowledge of the structure and function of the various elements of the respiratory tract

— be able to describe the processes of inhalation, exhalation and gaseous exchange, and highlight the changes they may undergo due to exposure to toxic substances

— be able to indicate how disturbances of pulmonary function can be detected

531

— be able to describe the factors that play a role in the absorption, accumulation, biotransformation and excretion of gases and aerosols

— have gained an impression of the general pathological anatomy of the respiratory tract, and more specifically of the disturbances that may result from contact with toxic substances

— know a number of toxic substances relevant to the respiratory tract and their effects and underlying mechanisms

— be able to indicate what factors are of importance in the development of lung cancer

— be able to indicate which hypersensitivity reactions can be distinguished in the respiratory tract and how these are brought about

— on the basis of examples, give a summary of the problems arising from indoor and outside air pollution from a toxicological point of view.

*Study hints*

To be able to study the respiratory organs, it is important that you know their anatomy and physiology. Should you doubt whether your knowledge of these subjects is satisfactory, you are advised to review the relevant topics of the anatomy and physiology of the respiratory tract in a textbook on anatomy/physiology before studying this unit. In the study units on exposure (Study unit 2) and on absorption and excretion (Study unit 5), various aspects of the toxicology of the respiratory tract have already been discussed. It is recommended that you read these units again.

The study load for this unit is approximately 6 hours, assuming that your knowledge of the anatomy and physiology is sufficient.

The optional available CD-I program includes the following examples of the pathology of the respiratory tract: carcinomas, emphysema, pulmonary edema, fibrosis, oxygen-, nitrogen- and ozone-induced pulmonary disorders, and disorders induced by particles from welding fumes.

## STUDY CORE

### 1 Structure and function of the respiratory tract

The respiratory tract consists of an air-conducting portion, through which air is transported, and a respiratory portion, in which the gaseous exchange takes place. The former consists of the nose, pharynx, larynx, trachea and bronchi/bronchioles, and the latter of the alveoli (see Figure 18.1).

### 1.1 NOSE AND NASAL CAVITY

During inhalation, the air generally enters the body via the nose. Exceptions are, for example, humans and dogs, who may also inhale through the mouth. The structure of the nose is such that the incoming air is filtered. Larger dust particles are trapped by the hairs in the first part of the nose, while further on in the nose, particles settle due to sedimentation or collision as a result of mass inertia. Although particles smaller than 100 μm readily penetrate into it, the nose is very efficient in trapping particles. Of those larger than 10 μm, practically 100% are caught. The efficiency rapidly diminishes with the size of the particles. Trapped particles may dissolve and subsequently be absorbed into the blood. Insoluble particles are transported to the pharynx by the ciliated epithelium, together with the mucus. Since there is no ciliated epithelium in the most

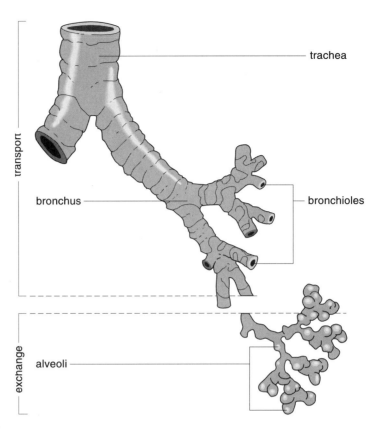

FIGURE   18.1
Diagram of the anatomy of a portion of the respiratory tract

proximate part of the nose, particles may remain there for a long time. They are removed by sneezing, rubbing or other extrinsic methods.

*Nose*

In man, the structure of the *nose* is relatively simple. Its complexity increases in various animal species depending upon the importance of the sense of smell. The nose consists of the following elements:

1 a paired opening through which the air is aspirated and which opens out into a slight dilatation, the vestibule;

2 the actual nasal cavity, a paired space both halves of which are divided by a partition (septum);

3 the connection of the nasal cavity with the pharynx (pharyngeal duct; nasopharynx).

The actual nasal cavity contains a number of partitions, the nasal conchae, that project into the lumen and may be branched. These structures increase the surface area of the nasal mucosa and divide the nasal cavity into separate air passages. The number and anatomical complexity of the nasal conchae depend on the species. The nasal cavity has tubular connections with the paranasal sinuses.

*Epithelial lining*

The *nasal cavity* is lined with three types of *epithelium*: squamous (pavement), respiratory and olfactory. The vestibule is lined with *keratinizing squamous epithelium*, which is continued for a short stretch in the ventral parts of the nasal cavity. Inside the nasal cavity, starting with the more dorsal parts, the squamous epithelium gives way to *respiratory epithelium*. This type of epithelium consists of cuboidal to columnar ciliated cells and many mucus-producing goblet cells. The histology of respiratory epithelium is determined largely by its location. In the dorsal parts, for example, there are relatively few ciliated cells and the epithelium seems to be pseudostratified. This latter type of epithelium is now recognized as a fourth type of nasal epithelium and is called nasal non-ciliated cuboidal epithelium (NNCE).

The *olfactory epithelium* is a complex, pseudostratified neuro-epithelium consisting of supporting cells, neurons and basal cells. It has a characteristic structure: above the basement membrane there is a single row of basal cells, followed by about eight layers of densely packed neurons and finally, on the luminal side, the supporting cells, rich in cytoplasm with dark nuclei and microvilli. On the one side, the neurons are connected with the olfactory nerve fibers in the submucosa via their axons; on the other side, they are in contact with the lumen via the dendrites passing between the supporting cells. Underneath the epithelium of the nasal cavity, there are many serous and mucous glands. Partly because of the activity of the goblet cells, the epithelium is covered by a thin layer of mucus. The pharyngeal duct is lined with squamous epithelium, as is the pharynx (the posterior part of the oral cavity, into which both the pharyngeal duct and the larynx open).

## 1.2 LARYNX

The larynx consists of several parts. On the side of the oral cavity is the epiglottis, which is covered by keratinizing squamous epithelium and which serves to close off the lower respiratory tract during swallowing. The vocal cords (of rats) are covered with relatively thin stratified epithelium composed of polygonal cells. In rats, there is a small area of ciliated epithelium between the epiglottis and the vocal cords. These cells are particularly sensitive to toxic substances which may cause degenerative or hyperplastic/metaplastic changes in this area. Several cartilage structures give the larynx its firmness.

## 1.3 TRACHEA, BRONCHI AND BRONCHIOLES

On the caudal side of the vocal cords, the stratified epithelium of the larynx abruptly changes into the respiratory epithelium which lines the trachea and bronchi. This non-stratified and columnar epithelium consists of the following types of cell:

- *basal cells,* i.e. stem cells of other cells in the respiratory epithelium;
- *ciliated cells,* which are responsible for the clearance of moisture, mucus and foreign particles;
- *mucous cells or goblet cells* producing mucus;
- *small mucous granule cells,* that may differentiate into either mucous or ciliated cells.

The lungs consist of several lobes, the exact number of which varies per species, but is often five. Within the lungs, the conducting airways are the bronchi and bronchioles. In addition to *ciliated cells,* the bronchioles also have the rather large *Clara cells,* which protrude into the lumen and produce phospholipids. They are the stem cells of the bronchiolar epithelium and are capable of metabolizing organic substances due to the relatively high activity of biotransformation enzymes, such as those of the mixed-function oxidase type. The epithelium of the lower conducting airways contains small numbers of APUD (*a*mine *p*recursor *u*ptake (and) *d*ecarboxylation) cells (Kulchitsky cells) which have neuroendocrine properties. These cells produce various biologically active polypeptides.

## 1.4    LUNGS

Via the terminal bronchioles and respiratory bronchioles, the bronchioles transition into the alveoli.

The alveoli are lined with type I and type II pneumocytes. *Type I pneumocytes* are flattened cells which are in close contact with the underlying endothelial cells of the capillaries in the alveolar wall. They contain few organelles. Gaseous exchange takes place via these cells. *Type II pneumocytes* produce pulmonary surfactant and act as stem cells from which type I pneumocytes develop. This type of cell is more round in shape and contains the characteristic lamellar inclusion bodies which play a role in the production of surfactant. In contrast to type I pneumocytes, type II pneumocytes contain a considerable amount of biotransformation enzymes. In case of damage to the alveolar epithelium, regeneration takes place by proliferation of type II pneumocytes. These then differentiate to form the flattened type I cells.

ASSIGNMENT    18.1

What is the purpose of surfactant?

The walls of the alveoli contain not only capillaries but also fibroblasts. The joint surface area of the alveoli is enormous (values in man vary from 35 to 100 m$^2$). The walls of the alveoli which separate air and blood are extremely thin (0.35–2.5 $\mu$m in man), a property which contributes to the rapid and efficient exchange of gases. This of course implies that any gaseous pollutants in the inhaled air are also absorbed quickly and efficiently.

How, i.e. in what form, is $CO_2$ transported from the tissues?

Proteins can bind $CO_2$ to their free $NH_2$ groups; such a $CO_2$-protein complex is called a carbamate. Both plasma proteins and hemoglobin can transport $CO_2$ in this way.

The blood transports $CO_2$ from the tissues to the lungs in dissolved form (5%), as carbamate (30%) and as bicarbonate (65%). The bicarbonate form plays an important role in maintaining the body's pH. This is achieved by removing more or less $CO_2$. The lungs not only absorb oxygen and excrete carbon dioxide, but also serve as excretory organs for volatile substances dissolved in the blood. Examples of this are the pulmonary excretion of acetone in inadequately regulated diabetes patients and of alcohol after drinking.

a

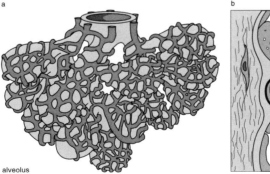

alveolus

b

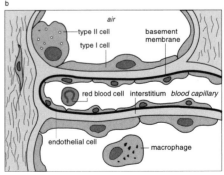

FIGURE    18.2

Smallest functional unit in the respiratory system, the alveolus

On the right a diagram of the electron micrograph of a cross-section through an alveolar membrane, with the various types of cells.

## 2 Pulmonary physiology

### 2.1 MECHANICS OF BREATHING

The respiratory system (see Figure 18.3) consists of a number of rather rigid components.

In small mammals, exhalation is usually active, while in humans, it is passive if a person is at rest. A number of characteristic levels of pulmonary volume have been defined (see Figure 18.4), the size of which changes with pathological conditions.

1   The Tidal Volume ($V_T$) is the change in pulmonary volume which takes place during calm and regular breathing.
2   The Functional Residual Capacity (FRC) is the pulmonary volume at the end of a normal exhalation.
3   The Residual Volume (RV) is the pulmonary volume after a forced maximum exhalation.
4   The Total Lung Capacity (TLC) is the pulmonary volume at the end of a maximum inhalation.
5   The Vital Capacity (VC) is the maximum inhaled volume after a maximum exhalation.

In pulmonary physiology, volume is indicated by V (l). The change in volume per unit of time is indicated by placing a dot above the variable: [$\dot{V}$] (1 min$^{-1}$).

The difference in pressure between the pleural cavity (intrapleural pressure) and the outside air during inhalation and exhalation can be subdivided into the pressure difference between the intrapleural space and the alveoli and that between the alveoli and the outside air. The difference in pressure between the alveoli and the outside air gives rise to a flow of air. The magnitude of the flow ([$\dot{V}$], in 1 min$^{-1}$) is determined by the mass (inertia, I) that needs to be set in motion and by the

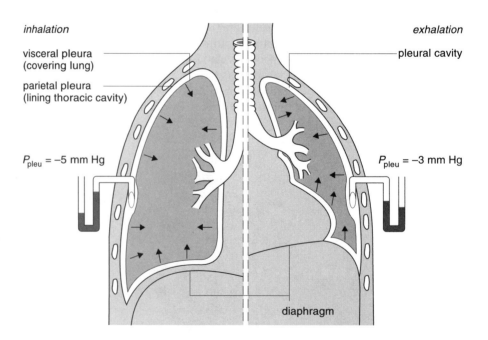

FIGURE   18.3
Elastic forces in the lungs during inhalation (left) and exhalation (right)
The arrows indicate the direction in which the forces are acting. The forces give rise to a "negative" pressure ($P_{pleu}$ = intrapleural pressure) in the pleural cavity in relation to the pressure outside the body.

536

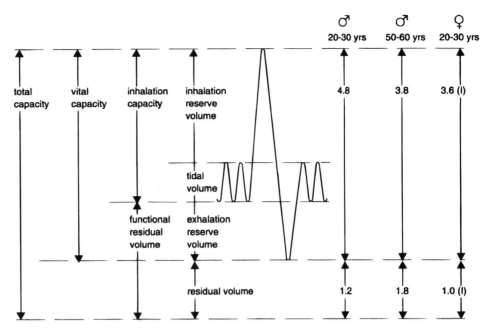

FIGURE 18.4
Diagram of the pulmonary volumes and capacities in man
The values for the vital capacity and the residual volume (right) show that these parameters vary with age and sex.

*Compliance*

airway resistance (R) which, at constant air velocity, indicates the ratio of air flow and pressure. The difference in pressure between the alveoli and the pleural cavity is determined by the force of retraction of the alveoli and is expressed as the *compliance* (C), which is defined as the ratio of the change in pulmonary volume and the change in pressure difference required to produce it.

If the air passages become narrower due to bronchoconstriction or formation of mucus, airway resistance is increased. The compliance changes when the properties of the surfactant change (edema) or when histological changes take place (emphysema, fibrosis).

> ASSIGNMENT 18.2
>
> In an asthma attack, there is increased airway resistance due to bronchoconstriction. In order to relieve the tightness of the chest, patients are trained to breathe out calmly and if necessary to press the exhaled air against partly closed lips. What is the purpose of this advice on breathing out and why is inhalation less problematic?

## 2.2 EXCHANGE OF GASES

The respiratory system consists of repeatedly branching air passages (generations) which continually diminish both in length and in diameter. In contrast, the total surface area is increased with each generation of air passages, so that, passing from the larger into the smaller air passages, the airflow rate decreases continually. In the large airways, this rate is so great that it completely determines the gas transport (convective transport). At the walls of the large air passages, evaporation of water does take place, but these walls are virtually inert to the physiological gases oxygen and carbon dioxide. This is because there is no hemoglobin or myoglobin to bind $O_2$, and no carbonic anhydrase to allow rapid establishment of an equilibrium between $CO_2$ and carbonate.

Because the airflow rate decreases ever further, as deeper levels of the lungs are reached, gas transport at the molecular level (diffusion) will at a certain point become equally important as gas transport by convection. At that point, a strong concentration gradient is established during inhalation (diffusion front, critical zone). Beyond the diffusion front, the contribution of diffusion to gas transport is predominant. For gaseous substances and during normal breathing, this diffusion front is situated near the transition point between bronchioles to alveoli. Exchange of gases between blood and air in the alveoli takes place by diffusion across the extremely thin cell membrane. In normal lungs, the exchange is so effective that the blood leaving the lungs is in balance with the gas in the alveoli. For $CO_2$, this is possible because of the rapid establishment of the equilibrium between $CO_2$ and carbonate catalyzed by the carbonic anhydrase present there.

*Physiological dead-space volume, $V_D$*

*Anatomical dead-space volume, $V_{D, anat}$*

The last-inhaled portion of the tidal volume, which is on the oral side of the diffusion front at the start of exhalation, does not contribute to the exchange of gas with blood or air in the alveoli (*alveolar air*) and is called the *physiological dead-space volume ($V_D$)*. When a subject is at rest, this volume is virtually equal to that contained by the rigid airways, which is called the *anatomical dead-space volume ($V_{D, anat.}$)*. If breathing is rapid and shallow, the physiological dead space is considerably smaller than $V_{D, anat.}$, while in the case of physical effort it is often the other way round. The total ventilation (minute ventilation, $\overset{o}{V}_T$ in l min$^{-1}$) is the product of tidal volume $V_T$ and breathing frequency $f$ ($\overset{o}{V}_T = V_T \times f$). Because of the dead-space volume, only part of this (the alveolar fraction) can effectively participate in the gas exchange. The alveolar ventilation ($\overset{o}{V}_A$, in l min$^{-1}$) is calculated as follows:

$$\overset{o}{V}_A = \overset{o}{V}_T \times \frac{V_T - V_D}{V_T}$$

where $(V_T - V_D)/V_T$ is the *alveolar fraction* ($V_D/V_T$ = dead-space fraction). The level at which the equilibrium between the concentration in the alveoli and that in the blood is established, depends on the transport capacity of the ventilation ($\overset{o}{V}_A$), the transport capacity of the bloodstream ($\overset{o}{Q}$) and the partition coefficient ($\lambda$). At equilibrium, $\lambda$ represents the ratio of the concentrations in the two phases. The bloodstream has a low transport capacity for gases with a small $\lambda$: relatively little of the gas is extracted from the air and much of it is taken up from the blood. Of gases with a large $\lambda$, relatively more is extracted from the air and little released from the blood.

Inhomogeneities in the distribution of the flow of air to various areas of the lungs, which may occur as a result of regional changes in airway resistance or compliance, are largely compensated for by adaptation of the distribution of the bloodstream to these areas of the lungs (*autoregulation*). Because of this the ratio of the regional transport capacities of air and blood remains homogeneous. This is essential for good overall gas exchange. Pathological disturbances in the respiratory tract (e.g. increase in regional airway resistance due to tumors) or in perfusion (embolism) often cause insufficient $CO_2$ excretion or $O_2$ absorption due to failure of the compensatory mechanism.

### Intermezzo

The regulation of the pH mentioned at the beginning of this section is achieved by variation in $\overset{o}{V}_A$. Such variation can be brought about by changes in the tidal volume (primarily) and also in the breathing frequency.

Heat regulation is established by altering $\overset{o}{V}_T$. However, the increased heat dissipation should not interfere with the pH. This is achieved by keeping $\overset{o}{V}_A$ constant. In heat regulation, an increase in $\overset{o}{V}_T$ is reached by increasing breathing frequency (primarily) and also by reducing the tidal volume. This "panting" is characterized by a large dead-space fraction combined with a tidal volume which is sometimes smaller than the anatomical dead space.

ASSIGNMENT 18.3

Emphysema is accompanied by enlarged air spaces at the alveolar level resulting from the disappearance of gas exchange epithelium and increased compliance. The functional residual capacity (FRC) is greatly increased. Give two explanations for the latter phenomenon.

## 3 Absorption, accumulation and excretion of substances

### 3.1 GASES AND VAPORS

Section 2 showed that gas exchange of $CO_2$ and $O_2$ takes place mainly in the alveoli, and that interaction with the walls of the conducting air passages is negligible. Respiratory temperature regulation, however, is based on the fact that evaporation of water in nose and trachea leads to an equilibrium in the main bronchi. Gases and vapors which are used in inhalation-toxicological research can generally be absorbed over the entire respiratory system. The site of deposition is closely related to the solubility and/or reactivity of the gas. The absorption of gases into mucus, tissue and blood is via *diffusion*. The driving force in this process is the *partial pressure* or *tension* (unit of pressure Pa), which is related with, but not equal to, the *concentration* (g cm$^{-3}$). An equilibrium on two sides of a boundary is reached when the partial pressure at both sides is the same.

$\lambda$ = coefficient representing the ratio of the concentrations of a substance on both sides of a biological boundary

The ratio of the concentrations on both sides of the boundary layer is the *partition or solubility coefficient* $\lambda$. In a state of equilibrium, the concentrations on either side are the same only if $\lambda = 1$. $\lambda$ has been defined for a wide variety of transitions, such as air–liquid, liquid–solid, liquid–liquid, etc. In practice, however, $\lambda$ is virtually always given as an air–liquid or air–solid partition coefficient.

### 3.2 ABSORPTION

The site at which gases and vapors are absorbed is to a large extent determined by the lipid solubility of the substance concerned.

*3.2.1 Absorption of gases and vapors with high water solubility ($\lambda > 10$)*

If a mixture of air which contains a gas with a large $\lambda$ passes along the walls of the respiratory system, a considerable portion of the gas will be absorbed into the mucus and tissue. When the air is inhaled, the partial pressure in it will therefore decrease rapidly as deeper levels of the respiratory tract are reached. If breathing takes place through the nose, the large surface area in the nose has already caused the concentration in the air to have dropped considerably when the larynx is reached, so that virtually none of the mixture is transported to the alveoli. If breathing is through the mouth, such gases will penetrate more deeply into the respiratory tract. On exhalation, the air leaving the alveoli contains virtually none of these gases. This air passes along the walls which had absorbed the gases on inhalation. Part of the absorbed gas is released again into the exhaled air. Only if the gas has low *chemical reactivity* will a portion of the absorbed substance be able to enter the bloodstream (via the tissue) and spread through the body. If it is highly chemically reactive, the gas will already be converted in

*Chemical reactivity*

the mucus or epithelial layer and, depending on the volatility of the reaction products, be removed by the flow of mucus or exhaled air. If this type of substance is administered via the inhalational route, the toxic effects will be exerted in the superficial layers of the upper respiratory tract. Due to differences in the structure of the nose and mouth or nasal breathing, the sites of toxic action will be different between species.

### 3.2.2 Absorption of gases and vapors with low solubility ($\lambda < 0.1$)

Absorption of gases with low solubility in the upper airways is limited and highly dependent on their chemical reactivity. Absorption in the blood is also of minor importance. If such a gas has low chemical reactivity, it will readily pass across the alveolar epithelium, and equilibrium with the blood and other tissues in the body will soon be reached. Toxic effects may then be exerted both in the walls of the respiratory tract and systemically. If the gas has high chemical reactivity, its toxic effect will be restricted to the respiratory system. The concentration of this type of substance in the tissue will always be low.

### 3.2.3 Absorption of gases and vapors with intermediate solubility ($0.1 < \lambda < 10$)

Absorption of these gases in the upper airways is limited, but the gases display a marked exchange with the blood if their chemical reactivity is low. For gases with a rather high $\lambda$, the partial pressure in the alveoli will drop sharply due to exchange with the blood, so that soon after the gas has entered the body, the partial pressure in the blood is only a fraction of that in the inhaled air. The absorption capacity of the body for these gases is usually high. The systemic concentration of such gases builds up only slowly (minutes to hours). All anesthetics administered via the inhalational route belong to this category of gases with intermediate solubility.

The action of these anesthetics is typically systemic. Depending on their partition coefficient $\lambda$, anesthesia is rapidly (e.g. cyclopropane, $\lambda = 0.5$) or slowly induced (e.g. diethyl ether, $\lambda = 10$). To speed up slow induction, a high partial pressure is often given at the beginning of anesthesia, but this may irritate the air passages and lead to too deep a level of anesthesia if maintained for too long.

It is apparent from the above that gases and vapors with low chemical reactivity do not accumulate and that at most an equilibrium is established. This is not the case for gases which are chemically reactive and whose metabolites are toxic. If these substances are non-volatile, they remain in the body and may accumulate either in specific tissues due to high solubility, or regionally by local binding.

Removal of gases is determined by the same diffusion processes as absorption, and takes place mainly via the respiratory system. A small proportion of the gases and their non-volatile metabolites is excreted via the kidneys.

### 3.3 AEROSOLS

The size of particles is defined in section 2.6.1 of Study unit 19.

Aerosols are reasonably stable mixtures of air and solid dust particles or droplets of fluid. Transport of aerosol particles in the respiratory system takes place largely by convection. The particles are swept along by the airflow. Deposition of aerosol particles in the respiratory system depends greatly on the strength of the flow of air and the size of the particles.

*Impaction*

*Deposition mechanisms* include *impaction, sedimentation, diffusion* and *interception*. *Impaction* is based on the mechanical law of conservation of momentum. When the flow of air in the air passages changes direction, the aerosol particle will attempt to continue its course in the original direction of flow. In the case of large particles (effective diameter 5–30 $\mu m$), the transfer of momentum by collision with surrounding gas molecules is highly ineffective. These large particles therefore do not follow the change in direction of the carrier gas well and collide against the wall. The greatest changes in the direction of flow occur in the nose and the larynx and this is why deposition through impaction is very important here.

*Sedimentation*

*Sedimentation* is based on the fact that, under the influence of gravitation, particles of a certain size drop out of a homogeneous mixture. This process concerns particles measuring 1–5 $\mu m$, for which deposition by impaction is negligible. They are, however, too large to maintain a homogeneous concentration in the airflow by means of diffusion. Since the airflow rate decreases with decreasing airway diameter, sedimentation takes place mainly in the trachea, bronchi and bronchioles. In this part of the respiratory tract changes in direction are also far more gradual than in the nose and larynx, so that impaction become less important.

*Diffusion*

Particles with an effective diameter < 1 $\mu m$ display a Brownian movement extensive enough for *diffusion* to make an important contribution to their transport. In the alveoli, diffusion transport will cause the aerosol particles to collide with the walls, resulting in their deposition.

The shape of an aerosol particle may be important for its contact with the walls of the respiratory tract. Acicular (needle-shaped) crystals come into contact with the wall sooner than particles with the same mass but a more compact shape.

*Interception*

In the case of such *interception*, many parts high up in the respiratory tract show signs of deposition, without this being attributable to impaction.

Whether the substance constituting an aerosol particle is absorbed after deposition in the respiratory tract is closely related to the solubility and the hydrophilic or lipophilic properties of the molecules being dissolved.

Absorption of *hydrophilic* substances by tissue and bloodstream is a matter of transport determined by diffusion and is closely related to molecular size and diameter of the transport channels present. The most important barrier for hydrophilic substances is the alveolar membrane with its transport channels measuring 10 Å.

Absorption of *lipophilic* compounds is also determined to a large extent by diffusion, but the routes of transport are different from those for hydrophilic substances. For some substances there are specific transport systems, such as carrier-mediated systems. Other substances accumulate in the lungs, even when they have been ingested orally (e.g. paraquat in type II pneumocytes).

The removal mechanism is, to a large extent, determined by the site of deposition. In those parts of the respiratory system where the walls are covered by ciliated epithelium, removal with the mucus is the most important means of transport. The speed at which the mucus flow moves depends greatly on the site in the respiratory system. In the nose and the trachea, particles trapped in the mucus move at about 7 mm min$^{-1}$, in the main bronchi at about 1 mm min$^{-1}$, and in the bronchioles at 0.5 mm min$^{-1}$.

Figure 18.5 pictures the transport of radioactively labeled aluminum silicate particles.

A striking feature is that 200 minutes after exposure, nearly all the radioactive material in the nose and pharynx has been removed to the gastrointestinal tract. The action of this removal system can be strongly influenced by the properties of the aerosol particles. Physical properties of the mucus may be altered, or the ciliated epithelium may be immobilized or destroyed. In the alveoli, where ciliated epithelium is lacking, the main removal route is that via phagocytosis by macrophages. The macrophages carrying the particles can probably move by amoe-

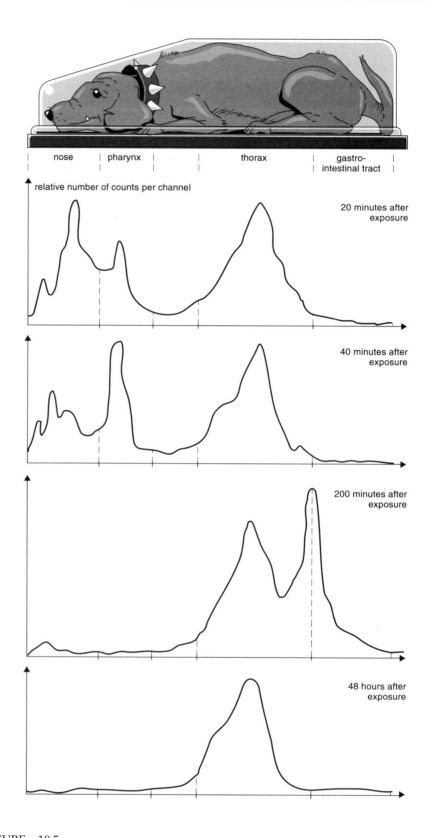

FIGURE    18.5
Clearance of radioactively labeled aluminum silicate in the dog
The immobilized dog is exposed to the labeled aluminum silicate by inhalation. The place where the labeled material is present is measured at 20, 40 and 200 minutes and at 48 hours after exposure.

boid movement to the interstitium, the ciliated epithelium or the lymphatic system. This transport system is very slow and it may take months before most of the material has been removed. Such a long period during which a substance remains in the body gives it ample opportunity to dissolve, even if it is poorly soluble.

ASSIGNMENT 18.4

Ozone and formaldehyde are both highly reactive gases. Inhalation experiments have revealed histopathological changes in the nose for both substances. Ozone has also been found to lead to histopathological changes in the pulmonary epithelium at the alveolar level. What does this show with respect to the water–gas partition coefficient of formaldehyde in comparison to that of ozone?

ASSIGNMENT 18.5

Alveolar ventilation and pulmonary perfusion are both approximately 5 l min$^{-1}$. A gas which has an anesthetic effect is administered in a concentration which is twice as high as that causing anesthesia? Compare the effect after 1 minute of an anesthetic gas with $\lambda = 0.5$ and one with $\lambda = 10$. What is the difference in the resulting levels of anesthesia?

## 4    Pulmonary function tests

Pulmonary function tests are aimed at detecting and quantifying pathological changes in the respiratory system. These are changes in the mechanical properties of the respiratory system and in the effectiveness of gas exchange. Table 18.1 lists a number of parameters together with the pulmonary functions which are tested by measuring them.

A large number of tests have been developed in human medicine to test pulmonary function. Most of them are based on cooperation on the part of the pa-

TABLE 18.1
Parameters measuring pulmonary function

| Parameter | Definition |
| --- | --- |
| breathing rate | number of breaths per minute (frequency) |
| tidal volume | volume of air exchanged per normal respiratory movement |
| minute volume | volume of air exchanged per minute |
| total lung capacity (TLC) | total volume of air in the lungs |
| vital capacity (VC) | volume of air exhaled in a maximum exhalation following a maximum inhalation |
| residual volume (RV) | volume of air remaining in the lungs after a maximum exhalation |
| functional residual volume (FRV) | volume of air remaining in the lungs after a normal exhalation |
| compliance | index of the 'stiffness' of the respiratory system; reduced compliance means increased stiffness |
| forced exhaled volume per unit of time | maximum exhaled volume per unit of time on forced exhalation ($FEV_1$ = forced exhaled volume in 1 second) = $MEV_1$ |
| lung perfusion | |
| diffusing capacity | gas exchange across the blood-gas barrier in the alveolus |
| blood gas analysis | analysis to determine the concentration of gases in the blood |

tient, who receives extensive instructions concerning the respiratory movements to be carried out. This means that these tests cannot readily be applied in experimental animals. For this reason, the respiratory movements required are usually forced, which means that the animal has to be intubated (introduction of a tube via the mouth into the trachea) while anaesthetized. In animal research, there is a great need for test methods which can be applied in animals breathing spontaneously. The development of the necessary techniques runs parallel to developments in human medicine, where there is also a need for pulmonary function tests which are independent of patient cooperation. The purpose of tests which do not require any special effort is to avoid putting too much strain on the patient, something which is of particular importance in the newborn and in children. To this end methods have been developed which make it possible to measure the relevant parameters under circumstances in which the experimental animal (or human subject) can continue to breathe spontaneously. Complicating factors are the species differences in breathing rate (man: 20 $min^{-1}$; mouse: 360 $min^{-1}$) and in breathing volume (man: 600–3000 ml; mouse: 0.3–1 ml).

## 4.1    MEASURING TECHNIQUES

Adequate measurement of the airflow rate and/or changes in thoracic volume is essential in order to be able to determine airway resistance, compliance and time-dependent relationships between pressure, lung volume and volume flow. Some of the techniques employed are discussed below.

### 4.1.1 Airflow rate

The airflow rate $\mathring{V}$ is determined by measuring the pressure difference over a resistance ($P_1$)

The *airflow rate* is sometimes measured by directing the flow of air to and from via a flow resistance, and measuring the *pressure drop* over that resistance. The latter is constructed in such a way that the relationship between the drop in pressure and the airflow rate is *linear* (laminar flow) and that, at maximum airflow rate, the pressure drop is in an order of magnitude that does not put too much of a strain on the respiratory system. A laminar flow is obtained by placing a large number of *tubes parallel* to each other (Fleisch pneumotachograph) or by using one or more layers of *fine-meshed gauze* (Lily pneumotachograph).

The small respiratory volumes of experimental animals may easily lead to unacceptable rebreathing (inhalation of air just exhaled). This can be avoided by applying a bias flow (see Figure 18.6), in which case the experimental animal breathes air from a continuous flow of air which is maintained with the help of a critical orifice (constant source of airflow). A critical orifice is constructed in such a way that, if the pressure difference over the orifice is more than 0.5 atm (50 kPa), a constant air flow is maintained because the flow rate in the orifice then reaches the speed of sound. The flow rate can never exceed the speed of sound ($P = 1/2mv^2$; Bernouilli's law). Because the sum of the airflow caused by the animal's breathing and the airflow over the resistance is constant, the airflow over the resistance and hence the pressure difference varies with the flow of breath. The airflow rate (due to breathing) can also be calculated by differentiation of a change in volume.

### 4.1.2 Volume measurement

Volume measurement ($V$) = measuring changes in volume resulting from changes in pressure, the latter being proportional to the change in volume of the thorax ($P_2$)
*Pressure-constant system*

Volume measurement can be carried out in two ways: by using a system in which either the pressure or the volume is kept constant.

In *pressure-constant systems*, the respiratory system is connected to a *spirometer* in which the pressure remains constant. The changes in the content of the bell of the spirometer resulting from the respiratory movements are measured by mea-

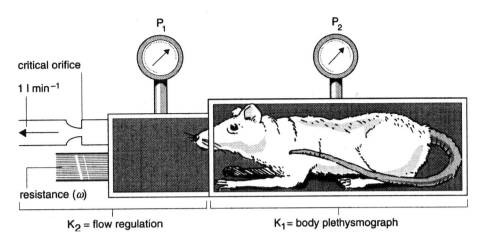

FIGURE 18.6
Plethysmograph set-up for pulmonary function tests in experimental animals (in this case a rat).
The anterior and posterior compartments are separated from each other by a membrane around the nose.

suring the height of the bell. Due to the large mass which is to be displaced, the system has a poor *frequency response*, causing a distorted view of rapid changes.

*Measurement of mouth flow*

When the *mouth flow* of an experimental animal in a whole-body plethysmograph is measured, a continuous flow of 1 l min$^{-1}$ is maintained in the anterior compartment from which the animal breathes (see Figure 18.6), to prevent rebreathing. The airflow over the resistance and thus the pressure over the resistance R, measured with pressure gauge $P_1$, varies with the airflow rate.

*Volume-constant system*

In a *volume-constant system*, mass varies with respiratory movement and causes a change in pressure in the measuring system. The course of this change in pressure is linear together with the change in volume in the respiratory system. If a process proceeds slowly and if there is efficient heat exchange with the surroundings (isothermal process), then:

$$\Delta P = -(\Delta V \cdot P)/V$$

where:

$\Delta P$ = measured change in pressure (on meter)

$\Delta V$ = change in volume (thorax displacement)

$P$ = prevailing total pressure

$V$ = air volume within plethysmograph

If a process takes place rapidly and without heat exchange (adiabatic process), then:

$$\Delta P = -1.4(\Delta V \cdot P)/V$$

### 4.1.3 Plethysmography

In body plethysmography, the test subject or experimental animal is placed entirely inside the measuring box. The human test subjects and the test animals breathe air from a separate adjacent measuring box, the former through a mouthpiece, the latter through a close-fitting opening in a partition round the neck (see Figure 18.6). Changes in pressure in the box correspond with the thorax movements of the test subject or experimental animal. The flow of breath can be measured independently at the mouth. In this *barometric* method, the person or animal breathes from the measuring box. The observed fluctuations in pressure are the result of differences in thorax displacement and displacement of air. The difference in displacement is caused by the addition of water vapor during inhalation and the rise in temperature of the inhaled air. The amplitude of the fluctuations in pressure are proportional to the total release of energy to the inhaled air, and they are therefore an *indication of the respiratory volume*. The barometric method is a useful method to measure breathing frequency and breathing pattern.

### 4.1.4 Lung volumes and forced exhalation (spirometry)

Figure 18.7 shows the course of the various lung volumes in man and the influence of various pathological conditions on them. Forced exhalation is often shown in a separate flow rate–volume curve.

*MEV₁ (maximum exhaled volume in 1 s)*

An important variable in human medicine is the $MEV_1$ (maximum exhaled volume in 1 s). This value is greatly reduced by obstruction of the airways. The respiratory movements of humans are simulated in experimental animals by anaesthetizing and tracheally intubating them and placing them in a plethysmograph. Instead of using the plethysmograph to measure thorax displacement, a negative pressure is applied around the thorax to simulate maximum inhalation. The change in lung volume can be calculated by integration of the breath flow. The negative pressure around the thorax is then quickly changed into a positive pressure, so that a forced exhalation follows. The results of this test strongly depend on the negative and positive pressures applied.

Determining the size of the residual volume requires an additional measurement. If the airways of an experimental animal are closed off with a pressure gauge, the pressure in the lung can be measured and the plethysmograph can determine the change in thoracic volume resulting from the spontaneous respiratory movements of the animal. By applying *Boyle's and Gay-Lussac's law* (combined in the equation $PV = RT$) the lung volume can then be calculated. Gas dilution methods can also be applied to measure lung volume.

### 4.1.5 Compliance and airway resistance

*Definition of compliance*

*Hysteresis (Gr.) = the phenomenon of an effect failing or lagging behind another effect to which it is causally related due to exceptional circumstances.*
*Compliance has been defined for static situations.*

*Dynamic compliance*

Compliance was originally defined as the ratio of the change in lung volume and the necessary change in pressure over the lung to produce it. Since hysteresis is quite common in this connection, compliance is defined for static situations (long-term apnea). To measure the pressure, a catheter is introduced into the pleural cavity. A rather less invasive method is to pass a pressure gauge (a small latex balloon connected to a manometer) into the esophagus. The pressure in the esophagus is considered representative for the pressure in the thoracic cavity since the esophagus runs through it. The measurement of *dynamic compliance* uses the plethysmograph, by changing the pressure at the mouth during spontaneous breathing. The resulting change in pulmonary volume is determined by the pressure change in the plethysmograph, onto which the changes in pressure due to spontaneous breathing are superimposed. However, it should be noted that the total pressure difference between mouth and plethysmograph is used here, instead of the intrapleural pressure.

Airway resistance can be determined with an intrapleural catheter (see Figure 18.3).

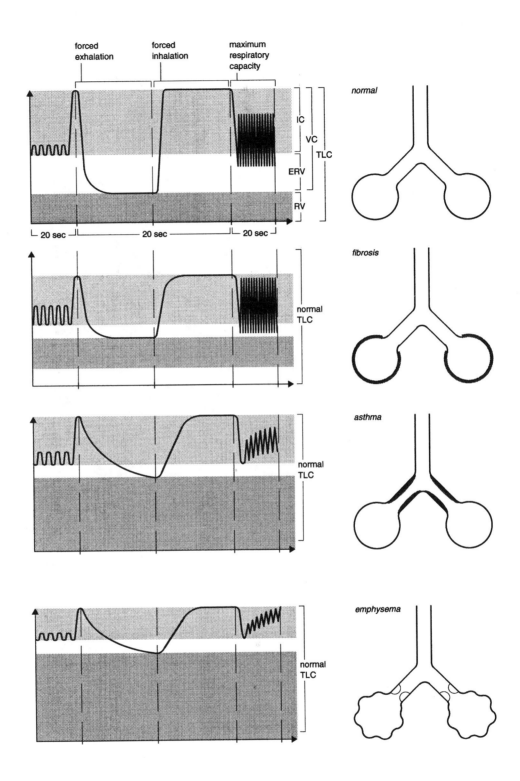

FIGURE 18.7
Spirogram of a healthy test subject (normal) and of patients with pulmonary fibrosis, asthma and emphysema
TLC = total lung capacity
VC = vital capacity
IC = inhalation capacity
ERV = exhalation residual volume
RV = residual volume

547

Figure 18.8 shows the principle of combined compliance and airway resistance in an experimental animal breathing spontaneously. Compliance is measured by dividing the difference in lung volume at moments of breathing pause (transition between inhalation and exhalation) by the corresponding pressure difference. *Airway resistance* is determined by dividing the measured pressure

*Measurement of airway resistance*

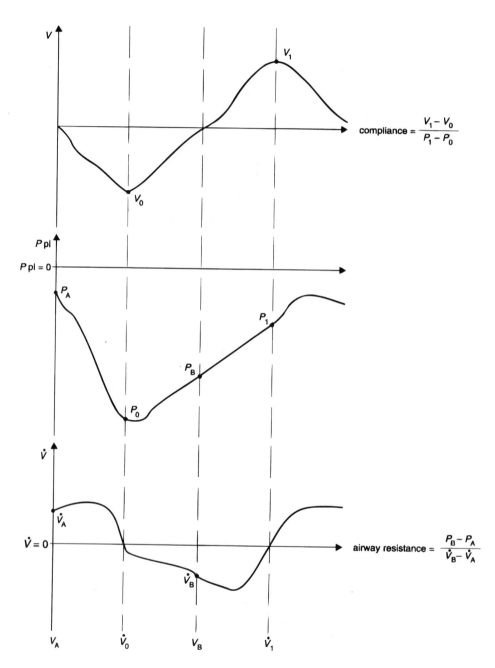

$$\text{compliance} = \frac{V_1 - V_0}{P_1 - P_0}$$

$$\text{airway resistance} = \frac{P_B - P_A}{\dot{V}_B - \dot{V}_A}$$

FIGURE 18.8

Examples of measurement of compliance and airway resistance in an experimental animal breathing spontaneously

$V$ = tidal volume
$P_{pl}$ = intrapleural pressure
$\dot{V}$ = airflow rate

The vertical lines $\dot{V}_0$ and $\dot{V}_1$ indicate the points at which the airflow rate is zero. $V_A$ and $V_B$ indicate the points at which the lung volumes are the same during inhalation and exhalation.

difference by the difference in airflow, at constant lung volume during inhalation and exhalation. It should be borne in mind that the direction of the breath flow during breathing in and out is in opposite directions (i.e. one is positive, the other negative), and that any hysteretic phenomena are not taken into account. A relatively new technique still under development and which does not require cooperation on the part of the test subject or experimental animal is the *forced oscillation technique*.

*Forced oscillation technique*

In this technique, rapid pressure oscillations are applied at the mouth or around the thorax, with a frequency several times higher than the spontaneous breathing frequency (3–40 Hz in man; 20–200 Hz in rats). These oscillations cause changes in the breath flow. The connection between the pressure applied and the resulting breath flow depends on the mechanical properties of the respiratory system. In human subjects, the pressure oscillations are usually applied at the mouth, and the flow measurement is also at the mouth, thus determining the so-called *input impedance*. If small experimental animals are used, it is usually more practical to apply the pressure oscillations around the thorax (in a plethysmograph) and to measure the breath flow at the mouth, to determine the *transfer impedance*. If measurements are carried out over a wide range of frequencies (20–200 Hz), (computer) parameter estimation systems can be used to determine the values of airway resistance, pulmonary compliance, inertia and lung volume. The advantage of this method is its reproducibility and the absence of surgical intervention.

*Input impedance*

*Transfer impedance*

*Respiratory patterns* may provide important indications of pathological changes in the respiratory system. Properties which are easily measured are the ratio between inhalation time and exhalation time which changes dramatically in the presence of irritation or edema, the occurrence of interruptions in the breath flow during exhalation as a result of collapse of the airways in the case of emphysema, the flow–volume curve whose shape changes greatly under the influence of airway resistance, and the sensitivity to provocation with $CO_2$, in which the adaptation of the respiratory minute volume strongly depends on the effectiveness of the gas exchange.

*Respiratory patterns*

**Intermezzo**

*$CO_2$ sensitivity test*

In the $CO_2$ sensitivity test a subject is exposed to $CO_2$ via the respired air, in order to stimulate the respiratory system by pH regulation. In the case of pathological changes, this stimulation will only lead to a small increase in the respiratory minute volume. In healthy test subjects and experimental animals, breathing at rest can be increased by a factor of up to 20!

So far, gas exchange techniques that can measure the concentrations of $O_2$, $CO_2$ and inert gases in the exhaled air have proven to be almost useless in pulmonary function studies in small experimental animals. This is due to the technical problems associated with small breathing volumes and high breathing frequencies. These techniques will therefore not be discussed any further.

ASSIGNMENT 18.6

Study Figure 18.9 and the legend accompanying it.

a Give the names of the lung volumes a, b and c.

b a is the normal lung. Which syndromes are characterized by b, c and d?

c The respiratory loop formed is the result of hysteresis (change in volume lags behind change in pressure). What is the consequence of this for the measurement of compliance in situation a?

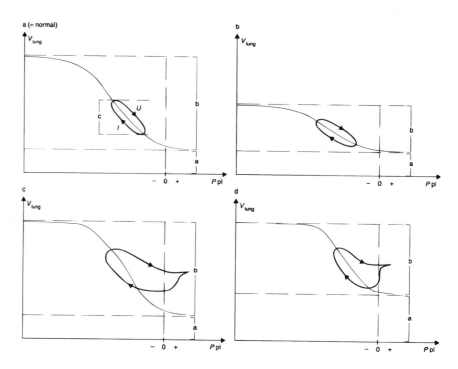

FIGURE   18.9

Pressure–volume curves for breathing at rest

The data were obtained by measurement of the intrapleural pressure ($P_{pl}$) and by integration of the flow of breath at the mouth, which yielded the volume ($V_{lung}$). Figures b, c and d represent various pulmonary abnormalities. The figures also show the pressure-volume relationship as it is obtained for static measurement (thin line), i.e. measurement at the moment that no airflow is present.

## 5    Pathology of the respiratory tract

### 5.1    GENERAL REACTIONS OF THE RESPIRATORY TRACT AND LOCATION OF THE REACTION

Reactions of the respiratory tract to inhaled particles and gases include:

*Toxic reaction*

1.  *toxic* or pharmacological *reactions* to the direct effect of a substance (e.g. irritating substances);

*Immune reactions*

2.  *immune reactions*, acting indirectly, via the immune system (often by substances of animal or vegetable origin).

*Degeneration, proliferation and inflammation*

Both types of reaction encompass *degeneration, proliferation and inflammation*. Since the epithelial lining of the respiratory tract is very thin, the underlying connective tissue, including capillaries, easily come into contact, in the case of intoxication, with the xenobiotic and with the external environment. Hence, intoxication of the respiratory tract is often accompanied by inflammation.

The nature and location of the reactions to the substance depend on its chemical properties, solubility in water, particle size and the relative sensitivity of the epithelium at the site of deposition.

> Where in the respiratory tract are the effects of gases with high water solubility to be expected?

The site of deposition of inhaled particles depends on their size and shape. Particles measuring 5–30 $\mu$m, for example, are trapped in the nasopharynx, particles of 1–5 μm in the trachea and bronchi and particles smaller than 1 μm can reach the lungs (see Section 3.2). Fibriform particles (e.g. asbestos) can easily reach the lungs and remain there because there is no adequate clearance mechanism for them. Effects of gases with high water solubility are of course to be expected early on in the conducting airways (nose, pharynx), because they can dissolve in the mucosa there.

The severity of an effect is determined by the concentration and the duration of exposure.

*Bleomycin is an antibiotic used as a antitumor agent.*

In addition to inhaled substances, some *systemically* administered substances may also damage the respiratory system. Examples are bleomycin, paraquat and nitrosamines.

*Biotransformation*

The sensitivity of the lungs to damage is partly influenced by their great metabolic capacity, mediated by the large quantities of detoxifying enzyme systems which are present, in particular in the Clara cells and type II pneumocytes. Because of their significance as ports of entry to the body, the lungs are also significant detoxicating organs. Other important properties are their enormous surface area and the fact that, in the case of systemic intoxication, the entire cardiac output perfuses them.

### 5.1.1 Species differences in reactions of the respiratory tract

As regards the effects of inhaled gases or particles, there may be differences between humans and experimental animals which result from morphological and physiological species differences described below.

- *Method of breathing*: nasal (animals) or oronasal (man). Many rodent species are obligate nose breathers, while humans tend to breathe more through the mouth.
- *Anatomy* of the nose and in particular of the conchae. The human nose is poorly developed in comparison to that of rodents.
- *Orientation* (horizontal/vertical) and total *surface area* of the lungs. Both factors influence the site of deposition of particles and the local concentration of a toxic substance.
- *Number of branches* of the respiratory tract (23 in man). Some substances exert their most pronounced effect on the epithelium at those points where the conducting airways branch off.
- *Breathing frequency.*
- *Clearance* (see also Section 5.1.3).
- *Respiratory pattern.*
- Differences in metabolizing *enzyme systems* in the respiratory tract.

These differences between man and experimental animals indicate that the results obtained from animal experiments cannot as such be taken to apply to the human situation (see Study unit 19, Section 5). The nature of the substance and of its effect should be considered in relation to any differences in the morphology and physiology of the respiratory tract between man and experimental animals.

ASSIGNMENT 18.7

Where may effects be expected to take place in man, if in rodents they are found in the nose?

*5.1.2 Clinical symptoms in the case of intoxication of the respiratory tract*

Damage to the respiratory tract manifests itself first in the form of clinical symptoms. These include:

- changes in the respiratory movements;
- production of a noise during respiration caused by constriction of the conducting airways or partial obstruction by inflammatory exudate;
- cyanosis, a blue discoloration of the skin and mucous membranes, caused by the difference in color between oxygenated and deoxygenated blood;
- sense of tightness in the chest.

The nature of the clinical phenomena depends on the site and nature of the injury. Knowledge of the histomorphological changes may explain the clinical observations, since the latter are linked to the former.

*5.1.3 Clearance*

Two mechanisms can remove inhaled particles (mechanically) from the respiratory tract. These are mucociliary clearance and alveolar clearance.

*Mucociliary clearance*

*Mucociliary clearance* takes place in the conducting airways through the production of mucus by mucous cells, and the removal of the mucus together with the particles and debris trapped in it, to the oral cavity by ciliated cells. Mucociliary clearance is influenced by:

1 the site where the particles are deposited;
2 pollution (e.g. smoking);
3 therapeutic drugs and abusive drugs;
4 conditions like chronic bronchitis;
5 viscosity of the mucus.

*Alveolar clearance*

*Alveolar clearance* is effected by alveolar macrophages, which phagocytize the particles and transport them to the capillaries and lymphatic vessels. Part of the material can be removed to the mediastinal or other local lymph nodes. Alveolar clearance is influenced by:

1 size, shape and solubility of the particles;
2 conditions such as emphysema and certain viral infections.

Malfunctioning of clearance may cause accumulation of particles in the lungs leading to reduced respiratory capacity, toxic effects due to accumulation of toxic substances, or infections because micro-organisms are not removed.

ASSIGNMENT 18.8

What other defense mechanisms are important in connection with respiration?

6 **Toxicological pathology**

6.1 PATHOLOGY OF THE CONDUCTING AIRWAYS

*6.1.1 The nose*

Although rats, mice and hamsters have been widely used in inhalation studies, until recently little attention has been paid to the nose as a target organ. Depending on water solubility and the specific sensitivity of the various types of epithelium in the nose, toxic effects may be manifested locally. As for many organs, reactions in the nose can be classified as adaptation, degeneration, proliferation or inflammation. If a substance is too noxious to be dealt with by adaptation processes, such as increased mucus production, the nasal epithelium will degenerate. As in the other parts of the respiratory tract, this virtually always leads to inflammation, followed by regeneration. Continued or repeated exposure may lead to chronic inflammation, or to proliferation. *Proliferative reactions* such as *squamous metaplasia* and *goblet cell hyperplasia* are sometimes interpreted as adaptation processes. Squamous epithelium is less sensitive to toxic effects than the highly specialized respiratory epithelium. Mucus hampers contact between the harmful substance and the underlying epithelium. In certain circumstances, however, excessive proliferation may also lead to neoplasia. In the case of intoxication of the nasal mucosa, several of the reactions mentioned here are often seen simultaneously, often in different locations. The most important reactions of the various types of epithelium in the nose are discussed in the following.

*Proliferative reactions*

The *squamous epithelium* lining the vestibule is relatively insensitive to intoxication. Only on contact with highly irritant gases (e.g. $Cl_2$, HCOH) will erosion or ulceration develop here. The major part of the nasal cavity is lined with *respiratory epithelium*. Relatively mild forms of intoxication cause loss of cilia. In more severe cases, there is degeneration and exfoliation (desquamation of the epithelium). Repeated exposure may lead to squamous metaplasia, in which the ciliated epithelium is replaced by squamous epithelium. Squamous epithelium is relatively insensitive to irritant gases, and squamous metaplasia is a common form of adaptation of the nasal mucous membrane. From a toxicological point of view, however, this form of "adaptation" should be considered as an undesired effect. If the irritant gas dissolves well in water, the free edges of the conchae and the adjacent lateral wall of the nasal cavity are often damaged. Examples of substances causing squamous metaplasia are acetaldehyde, formaldehyde, hexaethyl phosphoramide and butenolide. If the metaplastic epithelium shows a high degree of keratinization, a keratin plug may block off the airway completely, which after some time causes death in rodents.

*Squamous epithelium*

*Respiratory epithelium*

*Goblet-cell hyperplasia*, which may occur after exposure to formaldehyde gas, for example, is also a form of adaptation. The resulting increased production of mucus leads to dilution and accelerated removal of the dissolved gas and protects the underlying epithelium.

*Goblet-cell hyperplasia*

The *olfactory epithelium* is also very sensitive to the influence of toxic gases (See Table 18.2). The damage sometimes occurs locally, while adjacent areas do not show any abnormalities. Various types of reactions are possible. In the case of mild intoxication, the cilia of the olfactory cells may be lost. Olfactory cells may perish selectively while the supporting cells, or sustentacular cells with their microvillus borders, are preserved, though the latter may undergo change. The olfactory epithelium may also be lost as a whole, possibly followed by regeneration. Depending on the properties of the irritant gas and the site and extent of the damage, new olfactory epithelium may be formed, squamous metaplasia may take place (possibly accompanied by keratinization) or the olfactory epithelium may be replaced by respiratory epithelium. In addition, the subepithelial connective tissue may become thicker and start to display an abnormal appearance, or the mucous glands (Bowman's glands) may be reduced in number.

*Olfactory epithelium*

In most cases, the dorsomedial part of the nose appears to be the most sensitive. Virtually no information is available on the effects of the substances mentioned above on man.

553

TABLE 18.2
Examples of compounds which affect the olfactory epithelium

| Substance | Effect |
|---|---|
| acrolein* | metaplasia, inflammation, thickening of the submucosa |
| furtural* | loss of olfactory cells, accumulation of olfactory cells in the submucosa |
| formaldehyde and acetaldehyde | atrophy of the olfactory epithelium, loss of bundles of nerve fibers, proliferation of basal cells, squamous metaplasia |

*Component of cigarette smoke

*Nasal cancer*

*Cancer* of the nose is rare in man, but does occur as an occupational disease in wood and leather processing industries and in companies producing nickel. In experimental animals also, spontaneous nasal cancer hardly ever occurs. However, a number of substances have been found to induce nasal cancer in rats or hamsters after long-term exposure. Examples are formaldehyde, bis(chloromethyl) ether, hexamethyl phosphoramide, epichlorohydrin and vinyl chloride. It is remarkable that, although workers are often exposed to some of these compounds for long periods of time, there are no epidemiological indications that they have an increased risk of nasal cancer. This may be explained by the fact that, unlike humans, rodents are obligate nose breathers. It may be that, in man, harmful effects do occur in the lower airways, where they are less noticeable due to the complicating effects of smoking.

*Development of tumors from hyperplasias*

Animal experiments have suggested that tumors may develop in areas with hyperplastic and metaplastic epithelium. If treatment is continued, foci with atypical cells appear in the metaplastic areas. In addition, papillary and nodular hyperplasias may develop. Both occur after treatment with carcinogens. This does not necessarily mean that this type of change always leads to cancer. Whether a change is *preneoplastic* (and thus irreversible) or *metaplastic* (basically reversible) depends on a number of factors. In the case of acetaldehyde, one of these factors is concentration.

---

EXAMPLE

The metaplastic changes resulting from long-term exposure of hamsters to acetaldehyde were reversible at 1500 ppm, but irreversible at 2500 ppm. At 2500 ppm, tumors of the nasal mucosa also developed. Similar effects have been observed in rats and mice exposed to various dosages of formaldehyde.

---

*Tumors in the respiratory epithelium*

The most important *tumors* that can develop *in the respiratory epithelium* are squamous-cell carcinomas and adenocarcinomas. Squamous-cell carcinomas are induced in rats by long-term administration of 15 ppm formaldehyde or 3000 ppm acetaldehyde. Tumors of the olfactory epithelium include *aesthesioneuro-epitheliomas* (aesthesio = sensation), which are characterized by the formation of pseudo-rosettes and the ultramicroscopic presence of neurosecretory granules and neurotubules; and *adenocarcinomas* deriving from the olfactory epithelium and Bowman's glands, which are composed of secretory cells. Abnormalities in the nasal mucosa induced by gases often occur locally. For this reason, it is important that microscopic examination of the nose in toxicological experiments is carried out in a standardized manner, to ensure that the same cross-sections are examined in all animals.

### 6.1.2 The lower conducting airways

*Degeneration*

Of the lower airways, the ciliated cells are most sensitive to the effects of toxic compounds. The first reaction is inhibition of movement of the cilia, followed by their degeneration. This process obviously affects mucociliary clearance.

In addition, there may be changes such as abnormal flattening of the epithelium, abnormal variation in the shape and size of the cells and nuclei (pleomorphism) and syncytium formation (tissue composed of a multinucleated mass of protoplasm). In severe acute intoxication, necrosis of the epithelium sets in, followed by desquamation (rejection of epithelial cells). The damage may even extend into the subepithelial tissue. These reactions involving necrosis are virtually always accompanied by inflammation.

*Proliferation*

After acute injury, regeneration is brought about by mitotic activity of basal cells, followed by differentiation of the proliferating cells until the epithelium has resumed its normal aspect. In the bronchioles, regeneration occurs by division of the Clara cells. If exposure is continued, there may be *hyperplasia*, in which the number of cells of a particular type, usually basal or mucous cells, is increased and the epithelium loses its normal appearance.

ASSIGNMENT  18.9

When does the term metaplasia apply?

In the trachea and the bronchi *squamous metaplasia* may be found, in which the highly specialized pseudo-stratified epithelium of ciliated, mucous and basal cells is replaced by stratified squamous epithelium. This process may also include keratinization to a greater or lesser extent.

Severe damage, where subepithelial tissues are also affected, is accompanied by *fibrosis* (formation of connective tissue). Damage followed by hyperplasia and metaplasia can be caused by exposure to irritant substances such as ozone, $NO_2$, $SO_2$ and tobacco smoke.

It will be evident that mucociliary clearance is inefficient if the conducting airways or parts of them are lined with metaplastic, non-ciliated epithelium (see Figure 18.10).

ASSIGNMENT  18.10

What will be the result of inefficient mucociliary clearance?

*Bronchospasmic reactions*

Bronchoconstriction is a common reaction to the inhalation of harmful substances. Bronchoconstriction (asthma) is the contraction of smooth muscles in the bronchial wall, which leads to a reduction in the diameter of the lumen and insufficiency of the airconducting capacity. The walls of the bronchioles also contain smooth muscles which may cause constriction. The *etiology of bronchoconstriction* can be diverse.

*Etiology of bronchoconstriction*

### 1.    Action of irritant compounds

Bronchoconstriction caused by irritant gases or aerosols often occurs soon after exposure and is not necessarily accompanied by degeneration or necrosis. The reaction probably develops because the irritant substance reaches receptors situated in the bronchial epithelium. This is followed by a reflex via the vagus nerve, which leads to the release of acetylcholine, and constriction of the smooth muscles in the bronchial wall. Examples of irritant substances causing bronchoconstriction are $SO_2$, formaldehyde, and various household chemicals and cosmetics used in the form of sprays.

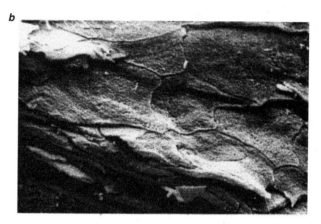

FIGURE    18.10

Scanning electron micrographs of the bronchial lining

a normal epithelium with clearly visible cilia

b the result of squamous metaplasia: the ciliated cells have all been replaced by flattened pavement cells

*2.    Immune reactions (allergy)*

A classification of immune reactions is provided in the intermezzo in Section 6.4.

In particular, type I and III immune reactions can lead to bronchoconstriction.

*3.    Reactions caused by pharmacological agents*

Examples are $\beta$-blockers and cholinergic substances.

*4.    Idiosyncratic reactions*

This term refers to the extreme sensitivity of individuals to certain substances. The cause of such pronounced sensitivity is still unknown. In inhalation toxicology, a remarkable interindividual variation is sometimes seen in sensitivity to inhaled substances. Examples of substances for which idiosyncratic reactions have been reported are non-steroid anti-inflammatory agents, anesthetics, and tartrazine. Another example is the constriction of the small bronchioles in hairdressers on exposure to certain types of hair spray. Although the majority of hair spray users do not experience any effects, some people are extremely sensitive. Reactions include granuloma formation with monocytes and multinucleated giant cells.

## 6.2 ALVEOLI

### 6.2.1 General reactions of the alveoli

*Alveolitis*

The first defense against intoxication is performed by macrophages in the form of detoxication and removal. If their action is insufficient or disturbed, *alveolitis* may develop. This may be characterized by desquamation (rejection of cells) of type I pneumocytes, proliferation of type II pneumocytes, metaplasia and the formation of hyaline membranes. In general, type I pneumocytes are considerably more sensitive to intoxication than type II pneumocytes. This may be due to the relatively large surface area and small number of organelles of the former.

Hyaline membranes are protein-like structures covering the alveolar cells.

*Regeneration*
*Fibrosis*

*Regeneration* takes place by means of the mitotic activity of type II pneumocytes. In the case of a chronic reaction, *fibrosis* may eventually develop with, among others, increased rigidity of the tissue.

*Alveolar bronchiolization*

A general reaction of the alveolar epithelium to a large number of toxic substances is *alveolar bronchiolization*. This disorder is characterized by replacement of the flattened epithelium of the alveoli by cuboidal, basophilic epithelium resembling that of the bronchioles. In most cases this concerns type II pneumocytes. The change is usually limited to the peribronchiolar areas, and is generally accompanied by a limited infiltrate of inflammatory cells. In some cases, alveolar bronchiolization precedes the formation of pulmonary tumors, in particular of bronchoalveolar adenomas or carcinomas in mice and rats.

Orally ingested substances that may damage the lungs include paraquat (see Section 7.2.7) and bleomycin.

### 6.2.2 Emphysema

Emphysema is a condition in which the respiratory part of the lungs (distal from the terminal bronchioles) contains cavities due to the loss of alveolar structure, caused by damage to the alveolar walls and fusing of alveoli.

> ASSIGNMENT 18.11
> What will be the physiological consequence of emphysema?

Macroscopically, the emphysematous part of the lung is voluminous, spongy and pale in color. Emphysema may occur after long-term exposure to relatively low concentrations of irritants, such as cigarette smoke.

It has been suggested that emphysema is the result of degradation of the alveolar wall due to lysis of the connective tissue, and the mechanical pressure of breathing. Another theory on its development is the ever-increasing accumulation of air in the alveoli, due to obstruction of the more proximal airways which may be caused by inflammation, the presence of exudate in the lumen or collapse of the bronchioles during exhalation (see Figure 18.7).

In contrast to humans, most experimental animals are relatively unlikely to develop emphysema.

### 6.2.3 Edema

Edema develops as a result of damage to the capillary endothelium in the alveolar wall, which leads to leakage of a protein-rich *fluid into the alveolar spaces*. Edema may occur as an acute reaction to the inhalation of irritant substances, such as phosgene. This is then called primary edema. Secondary edema may result from other disorders or abnormal physiological or external conditions, such as high blood pressure, hypoproteinemia, nephrotoxicity due to water retention, reduction of air pressure, or oxygen deficiency.

ASSIGNMENT 18.12

How does edema affect respiration physiologically?

### 6.2.4 Lipidosis

In experimental animals, lipidosis develops after administration of substances with an amphophilic structure (mixed polar and apolar) and is characterized by the presence of foamy cells in the alveolar spaces. It is possibly caused by an induced increase in surfactant, which is then taken up by the alveolar macrophages, giving them their foamy appearance. However, disturbance of macrophage catabolism of lipids appears to play a more likely role. Electron microscopically, the macrophages also show lamellar bodies derived from type II pneumocytes. Different strains of rats display distinct differences.

### 6.2.5 Vascular disorders

Other possible disorders of the lungs include thickening of the tunica media of the arteries due to hypertension. The vessels in the lungs may also play a role in other ways, since vasodilatation or vasoconstriction by toxic or pharmacologically active substances may affect intrapulmonary blood pressure.

### 6.2.6 Pneumoconiosis

Pneumoconiosis is the condition in which *inhaled inorganic particles* are present in the lungs, resulting in a tissue reaction. Most dust particles are trapped by the mucus in the conducting airways and removed by mucociliary clearance. If particles still reach the alveoli, the severity of a subsequent reaction is initially determined by their toxicity to the alveolar macrophages. To be removed, the particles must first be phagocytized by the macrophages, and then transported to the upper conducting airways or, via the lymphatic vessels, to the bronchial and mediastinal lymph nodes. Several different forms of pneumoconiosis will be described in the following.

*Carbon damage*

*Carbon* causes relatively little damage. However, if there is a large burden of carbon particles, as may be the case for miners, the capacity of alveolar clearance is insufficient and particles will accumulate in the macrophages and draining lymph vessels. This condition, known as *anthracosis*, does not usually lead to severe damage. It may, however, persist for a long time, even after the exposure to carbon particles has ceased.

*Silicosis*

*Silicosis* is an occupational disease encountered in the quartz-processing industry. In contrast to anthracosis, silicosis involves severe tissue reactions to the presence of silica dust. The *histopathological picture* is characterized by *granulomas* consisting of concentric layers of collagen-containing connective tissue, and in the center a mixture of macrophages, cellular debris and silica particles. These granulomas are located in the lymphatic vessels of the lungs, so that further removal of the material is hampered. The granulomas gradually increase in size and may eventually fuse, thus creating *massive fibrosis*. In this stage, the lung shows a nodular surface. The dust particles and the reaction to them are often distributed unevenly over the lungs. In addition, emphysema may develop around the fibrotic areas.

*Asbestosis*

*Asbestosis* is caused by inhaling asbestos fibers. It is an occupational illness found among workers in the shipbuilding and other industries. The histopathological picture is completely different from that of silicosis, and is characterized by a thickened pleura, fibrotic areas and needle shaped particles surrounded by cells.

Asbestosis, in particular if combined with smoking, is a highly predisposing factor for the development of bronchial carcinoma. The development of mesothelioma is also very typical of this occupational disease.

*Particles from welding fumes*

In the lungs of experimental animals, *particles from welding fumes* cause extensive inflammatory reactions with fibrosis, hyperplasia of epithelium and accumulation of the particles in macrophages. Similar conditions have been observed in the lungs of welders.

Another specific example of pneumoconiosis is the occupational form found in dental technicians who polish dentures.

## 6.3 TUMORS OF THE LOWER AIRWAYS

### 6.3.1 *Lung cancer in man*

*Chemically induced tumors*

Lung cancer is one of the most illustrative examples of *chemically induced tumors* in man. The relationship between lung cancer and inhalation of cigarette smoke is beyond all doubt and the extent of the lung cancer epidemic surpasses the effects of exposure to any other carcinogenic compound. Bronchial carcinoma is the main cause of death from cancer in males. For women, the risk of dying from lung cancer is only 1/10 of that for men, but the incidence is on the increase, probably due to the fact that in the past 35 years women have been smoking more and more.

*Occupational factors*

In addition to smoking cigarettes, there are a number of *occupational factors* which are known to influence or suspected of contributing to the development of lung cancer. They include exposure to:

- asbestos
- arsenic
- bis(chloromethyl) ether
- chromium
- mustard gas
- nickel
- polycyclic aromatic hydrocarbons
- uranium
- vinyl chloride
- radon

The type of tumor induced is sometimes different from that induced by cigarette smoke. Asbestos, for example, induces mesothelioma, a tumor derived from the mesothelium which lines the thoracic cavity. This type of tumor rarely occurs spontaneously, but it is regularly found in workers in the asbestos-processing industry. The latency period is very long; sometimes more than 30 years.

*Bronchial carcinoma*

*Histological classification of lung tumors*

A number of different types of lung cancer occur in man. Most of them originate in the bronchi and bronchioles. *Bronchial carcinoma* is defined as a malignant epithelial tumor derived from one of the types of cell which line the bronchi and bronchioles. The *histological classification of lung tumors* most commonly applied in human medicine is based on the microscopic growth pattern and the type of cell and, to a lesser degree on the histogenesis of the tumor cells. The most important types are listed below:

*Squamous-cell carcinoma*

1   *Squamous-cell carcinoma*, consists of keratinizing or non-keratinizing squamous (or pavement) cells. Since the lining of the airways does not normally consist of pavement cells, it is assumed that the tumor develops in areas in the conducting airways where there is squamous metaplasia and dysplasia.

*Small-cell bronchial carcinoma*

2   *Small-cell bronchial carcinoma* consists of small uniform cells which may show great variation in growth pattern. There are strong indications that

*Adenocarcinoma*

this is a tumor of neuro-endocrine origin, derived from the APUD cells (Kulchitsky cells) in the conducting airways.

3  *Adenocarcinoma* is a tumor in which glandular structures can be recognized, for example in the form of acini around which the cells are arranged, or in which mucus production can be demonstrated. Adenocarcinomas can develop from a variety of cell types found in the respiratory or conducting part of the airways. Adenocarcinomas in the peripheral lung are associated to a lesser extent with inhalation of cigarette smoke.

*Large-cell bronchial carcinoma*
pleomorphic = having more than one form

4  *Large-cell bronchial carcinoma* consists of large, often pleomorphic cells without clear signs of differentiation. This probably involves poorly differentiated varieties of other types of lung cancer.

*Combined types*

In addition to the types of lung cancer mentioned above, *combined types* may be encountered, in which the properties of two or more types of tumor are combined. One hypothesis is therefore that lung cancer develops from pluripotent cells, which may display a range of phenotypic expression, sometimes within one and the same tumor. Lung tumors are invasive and metastasize rapidly. The results of lung cancer therapy have so far been disappointing, and only few patients are still alive 5 years later.

### 6.3.2 Lung cancer in experimental animals

*High spontaneous incidence of broncho-alveolar tumors in mice*

Lung cancer rarely occurs spontaneously in experimental animals. An exception is the mouse; in certain strains so-called broncho-alveolar tumors may reach a high spontaneous incidence. This may lead to problems in toxicological experiments, since it is often unclear how to interpret the increased incidence of a type of tumor which also frequently occurs spontaneously. Many researchers assume that such an increase does not necessarily in all cases mean that the substance tested is carcinogenic. In such cases more extensive research in different species, or research into the mode of action is virtually always necessary.

*Induction*

A large number of carcinogens can induce tumors of the airways in rats, hamsters and mice. Induction may take place by *inhalational exposure*, by *intratracheal intubation* of a suspension of the carcinogen, or by *systemic administration*. An example is the induction of tumors of the trachea and bronchi in hamsters by intratracheal intubation with benzo[*a*]pyrene and *iron oxide*. This treatment is followed by the development of squamous-cell and other carcinomas which are very similar to those seen in man. Other examples of substances causing lung tumors in experimental animals are methylcholanthrene and various nitrosamines after intratracheal intubation or subcutaneous injection.

ASSIGNMENT  18.13

Explain how substances administered subcutaneously can induce tumors specifically in the lung.

### 6.3.3 Pathogenesis of lung cancer

Only cells capable of dividing can give rise to hyperplastic, metaplastic or neoplastic change. The pathogenesis of lung cancer can be studied in experimental models. The model mentioned above, in which benzo[*a*]pyrene mixed with iron oxide is intubated in the trachea of Syrian golden hamsters, can serve as an example. Within a few weeks after the first exposure, areas displaying squamous metaplasia can be observed in the trachea and bronchi. In these areas, the normal pseudostratified epithelium consisting of basal, ciliated and mucous cells has been replaced by squamous epithelium. The cells situated closer to the lumen are flattened to an increasing extent and the epithelium is often covered in a keratinous layer. If treatment with the carcinogen is continued, atypical changes develop in the metaplastic areas, characterized by abnormal variation in the size, shape and orientation of the cells, abnormal keratinization (i.e. keratinization in the deeper layers of cells) and abnormal mitoses. The basement membrane, however, remains intact. In such cases, the term *dysplasia* is often used. The dysplastic areas increase in size, and groups of cells penetrate through the basement membrane and infiltrate the underlying tissue. Such *invasion* is considered a criterion for the malignancy of a tumor. If this criterion is met, the tumor is called a carcinoma.

*Dysplasia*

*Invasion*

ASSIGNMENT   18.14

What are the harmful effects of a malignant tumor?

Once a tumor has become invasive, it can invade large parts of the organ concerned and even adjacent organs, and thus make it impossible for these organs to function properly or to function at all. In addition, a malignant tumor may disseminate by *metastasis* to other organs.

*Metastasis*

Most hyperplastic and metaplastic changes of the larynx and the tracheo-bronchial epithelium are non-specific and occur in reaction to both carcinogens and non-carcinogenic toxic substances. They may moreover form part of 'normal' inflammatory reactions such as those to the presence of microorganisms and in some nutritional conditions, such as vitamin A deficiency. Alveolar bronchiolization is also a general response to a large number of inhaled substances, including many non-carcinogenic substances. In general, however, the metaplastic changes induced by carcinogens are considered to be potential precursors of cancer, in particular if there is *atypia* and *dysplasia* (so-called preneoplastic changes). Not all these metaplastic changes, however, develop into tumors. Experiments have shown that most metaplasias disappear after a while and that only a few proceed to form tumors. Nevertheless, an inhalational toxicology experiment must also take into account metaplastic reactions when evaluating the carcinogenic potential of a substance, more particularly so if tumors have also been found in the same tissue.

*Atypia and dysplasia are preneoplastic changes*

The bronchi of heavy smokers display metaplastic and dysplastic changes which are similar to those found in the hamster after intratracheal intubation of benzo[*a*]pyrene. Intubation of a condensate of cigarette smoke also causes this type of change in hamsters. In smokers too, the metaplasia is reduced in severity and extent after smoking is given up.

## 6.4   ALLERGIC REACTIONS

The continuous need for breathing means that it is practically impossible to avoid being exposed to particulate or volatile substances in the air. These particulate or volatile substances may originate from plants or animals, or they may be microorganisms or man-made products. In the course of evolution, both man and animals have succeeded in adapting to the presence of foreign substances in the air by equipping the body with various defense mechanisms. One of these is the *immune system*, which tries to make the substance or organism which has entered the body harmless. The action of the immune system, however, is not always adequate, so that reactions may arise that are highly undesirable. Such unwanted reactions, which are usually excessive and accompanied by tissue damage, are called allergic or *hypersensitivity reactions*.

*Immune system*

*Hypersensitivity reactions*

Hypersensitivity to a substance develops after single or repeated exposure to that substance, i.e. after *sensitization*. Sensitization to substances in the air mainly

*Sensitization*

561

occurs by inhalation, but may also take place following regular skin contact with the substance. In the latter case, a hypersensitivity reaction may also occur if the substance is inhaled. Knowledge of the sensitizing properties of substances for the respiratory tract is usually derived from experience of people suffering from hypersensitivity. There are as yet no generally accepted animal models with sufficient predictive value to establish the sensitizing properties for man of inhalable substances.

### Intermezzo

*Type I hypersensitivity*

Hypersensitivity reactions can be classified into four different types. *Type I hypersensitivity*—immediate type or anaphylactic type. This type of hypersensitivity is characterized by the rapid appearance of the effects after contact with the substance (within a few minutes). Being in contact with the substance only once may suffice for sensitization. Sensitization is initiated by the production of *immunoglobulin E(IgE)* by B-lymphocytes against the substance (antigen). These IgE antibodies bind to basophils or mast cells at specific receptor sites. On renewed contact, the substance (antigen) interacts with the substance-specific IgE immunoglobulin molecules bound to the mast cells. As a result of this reaction, the mast cells release *vasoactive substances*, of which histamine is the most important. Vasoactive substances have a cholinergic-like action, which means that they cause contraction of the smooth musculature in the bronchial walls, and cause vasodilatation and greater permeability of the venules and capillaries. This allows fluid to pass into the extravascular spaces more easily. Related to the lungs this means a swelling of the mucous membrane in addition to the constriction of the airways by muscular contraction. Histamine, moreover, stimulates the exocrine secretion of mucus.

*Local allergy*

Type I hypersensitivity is a *local allergy*, which means that the signs occur at the site the antigen is touching the tissue.

*Hay fever*, an allergy to pollen, is one of the best-known examples. If the pollen only comes into contact with the mucosa of the upper part of the airways, the effects will be restricted to this area (runny nose, sneezing, watering eyes). If it also reaches the lungs, asthma-like symptoms will determine the overall picture. Many asthma attacks are the result of type I hypersensitivity.

Type I hypersensitivity may be caused by a large number of substances (see Table 18.3).

*Type II hypersensitivity*

*Type II hypersensitivity*—This reaction is caused by antibodies directed against *antigens incorporated into cellular membranes*. By this interaction, the cells are destroyed (e.g. reaction on combination of different blood groups or rhesus factors). This type of hypersensitivity probably does not play a role as far as inhalation toxicology is concerned.

*Type III hypersensitivity*

*Type III hypersensitivity*—These reactions are mediated by *immunoglobulins IgM and IgG*. Under normal circumstances, these immunoglobulins interact with antigens to form a complex, which is subsequently cleared by cells of the reticulo-endothelial system. In the case of frequent exposure to antigens, for example in cases of chronic infection, exposure to dust particles, such as those originating from plants or animals, or in autoimmune disease, complexes may be formed which are not readily cleared. As a result, *depositions of complexes* will develop. Such depositions are found mainly in the kidneys, arteries, joints, skin and lungs. The complexes give rise to an inflammatory reaction, which starts with the release of vasoactive amines from mast cells and basophilic leukocytes. This renders the blood vessel walls more permeable, so that fluid leaves the vessels and polymorphonuclear leukocytes are attracted. The latter try to clear the complexes by means of lysosomal enzymes, but these attempts are not always successful. However, if a polymorphonuclear leukocyte is adjacent to intact pulmonary tissue, for example, the enzymes will destroy this tissue locally, giving rise in turn to a more severe inflammatory reaction followed by fibrosis. In the long run, large

TABLE 18.3

## Compounds which may cause a type I hypersensitivity reaction

| | |
|---|---|
| drugs | dust mites |
| TDI (toluene diisocyanate) | flour, spices |
| down, feathers | ethereal oils from |
| artificial fertilizer | flowers/plants |
| flakes of skin from animals | cleaning products |
| dust from some types of wood | formalin |

parts of the lung may be destroyed in this way. Examples of type III reactions are farmer's lung, caused by frequent inhalation of spores from a fungus growing on damp hay, and bird fancier's lung, caused by dust particles from pigeon or budgerigar droppings.

On exposure by inhalation, the reaction does not occur until *several hours after inhalation*. It is manifested in severe tightness of the chest (asthma).

ASSIGNMENT 18.15

What differences in the effects on pulmonary function do you expect type I and type III hypersensitivity reactions to have?

*Type IV hypersensitivity*

*Type IV hypersensitivity*—delayed-type hypersensitivity. The clinical signs do not reach their maximum until *1–3 days after contact with the antigen*. This type of hypersensitivity is observed in chronic infectious diseases caused by bacteria (tuberculosis), protozoa, endoparasites and fungi. Type IV hypersensitivity too is probably not important as far as inhalation toxicology is concerned. The characteristic property of this reaction is that it does *not* involve any *antibodies*. The antigen sensitizes T-lymphocytes. On renewed interaction with the antigen, the sensitized T-lymphocytes release lymphokines. The latter stimulate the action of macrophages, and it is possible that these macrophages are responsible for the hypersensitivity reaction. Examples of this type of hypersensitivity are: contact hypersensitivity to nickel or acrylates, granuloma formation in the lungs in tuberculosis, and the tuberculin reaction in tuberculosis.

## 7 Effects of air pollution in the internal and external environment

### 7.1 AIR QUALITY

This section describes the nature, occurrence, harmful effects and established limit values of six common, important air-polluting substances. These substances will be used to elucidate the problem of air pollution. The great importance attached to the reduction of air pollution is apparent from the fact that the World Health Organization (WHO) has laid down so-called "Air Quality Guidelines for Europe" for 28 substances. In addition, two examples will be given of substances that can cause severe pulmonary injury (paraquat and oxygen).

### 7.2 EXAMPLES OF POLLUTANTS

#### 7.2.1 Ozone

Ozone ($O_3$) is one of the most powerful oxidizing substances. It is formed in the troposphere by the action of sunlight on nitrogen dioxide. Direct emission of ozone into the atmosphere as a result of industrial activity is only very limited. Ozone is an important component of photochemical smog, and its formation in the atmosphere depends to a large extent on the absolute and relative concentrations of volatile organic substances on the one hand and nitrogen oxides ($NO_x$) on the other. The maximum *natural background concentration*, expressed as the average over a period of 24 hours, is 120 µg m$^{-3}$ (0.06 ppm), the 50% values lying between 40 and 60 µg m$^{-3}$.

In rodents, approximately 50% of the ozone present is removed from the inhaled air in the nose. The highest tissue concentration, in both man and experimental animals, is found in the transitional area between the bronchioles and the alveoli. Exposure to ozone causes damage to all parts of the respiratory tract. The effects exerted are determined largely by the *concentration*. At relatively low concentrations (400 µg m$^{-3}$), effects are observed mainly in the lungs, while at higher concentrations (800–1600 µg m$^{-3}$) the nasal mucosa is also affected. The *effects* range from reversible interference with pulmonary function, increased enzymatic activity, reduced resistance to pulmonary infections, proliferation of type II pneumocytes, and hyperplasia and metaplasia of the respiratory epithelium in

*Concentration-dependent effects*

*Mechanism of action*

the nose, to permanent pulmonary fibrosis. The *toxic mode of action* is based on the oxidation of amino acids and polyunsaturated fatty acids in cell membranes. The most sensitive cells are those with a large surface area in relation to their volume.

*Extrapulmonary effects* have also been observed after exposure to ozone, in particular biochemical and morphological changes in erythrocytes. Whether these effects are caused by ozone itself or by reactive intermediates, or are perhaps results of pulmonary effects, is as yet unclear. Clinical and epidemiological studies in man have suggested that exposure to concentrations between 160 and 340 µg m$^{-3}$ may be followed by respiratory complaints such as coughing, dry throat, chest pain and tightness of the chest.

*WHO limit values*

The World Health Organization has recently recommended the following *limit values*: a 1-hour average of 150–200 µg m$^{-3}$ (0.08–0.1 ppm) and an 8-hour average of 100–120 µg m$^{-3}$ (0.05–0.06 ppm).

### 7.2.2 Nitrogen dioxide

Nitrogen dioxide ($NO_2$) is a powerful oxidant. *Natural background concentrations* are low and vary from 0.4 to 9.4 µg m$^{-3}$. The main human activity causing pollution of the air by $NO_2$ is the combustion of fossil fuels (heating, coal/oil-fired power stations, petrol/diesel engines). Welding and the manufacture of nitric acid also contribute to this type of pollution. Indoors, cigarette smoke, gas cookers and oil stoves are important sources of $NO_2$.

Maximum 1/2-hour and 24-hour averages in the open air are 850 µg m$^{-3}$ (0.45 ppm) and 400 µg m$^{-3}$ (0.21 ppm), respectively. In urban areas, the *open air concentration* varies greatly with the time of day, season and weather. There is usually a low background concentration with two "peaks" per day, which coincide with traffic peak hours. The exposure per person is mainly determined by indoor exposure; important sources are cigarette smoke and stoves lacking a flue. Concentrations of 500–2000 µg m$^{-3}$ (0.25–1.0 ppm) have been found in kitchens while a meal was being cooked.

*Inhalation*

On *inhalation*, 80–90% is absorbed. Up to 40% is absorbed in the nose. However, during strenuous physical effort combined with oral breathing, most of the $NO_2$ reaches the lungs.

*Effects*

It has been established in experimental animals that low concentrations (0.2 ppm) can influence prostaglandin metabolism even within 30 minutes. At much higher concentrations (2 ppm), pulmonary edema develops, as well as changes in pulmonary lipids and pulmonary enzyme activity indicating injury to pulmonary cells. Type I pneumocytes and ciliated cells are particularly sensitive to $NO_2$; type II pneumocytes and Clara cells proliferate. Long-term exposure to 0.1 ppm with occasional peaks up to 1.0 ppm causes lung emphysema in experimental animals. In mice, long-term exposure to $NO_2$ has proved to be a potential cause of death from pneumonia. There are many indications that $NO_2$ also weakens human resistance (e.g. the alveolar macrophages) and thus increases the risk of pulmonary infection.

In healthy persons, exposure to 2.5 ppm $NO_2$ leads to reduced pulmonary function. Whether people suffering from bronchitis or asthma are more sensitive is not known. The results of clinical studies are highly contradictory, and so far, epidemiological research findings have not proven to be conclusive.

*WHO limit values*

The World Health Organization has recently recommended the following limit values: a 1-hour average of 400 µg m$^{-3}$ (0.21 ppm) and a 24-hour average of 150 µg m$^{-3}$ (0.08 ppm).

### 7.2.3 Radon

Bq = becquerel, IS unit of radioactivity

Radon is a radioactive noble gas. It is formed by the disintegration of radium in the soil and is found in the form of so-called *radon daughters*. The concentration of radon in the air just above the ground ranges from 0.1 to 10 Bq m$^{-3}$, the average being 3 Bq m$^{-3}$. In many buildings, the concentration is much higher than in the open air. In poorly ventilated buildings, it may be very high indeed (2000 Bq m$^{-3}$). Radon in the indoor air originates from the ground on which a house is built and from building materials (plaster, concrete, bricks). In Finland and the United States, the indoor radon concentration is higher than 100 Bq m$^{-3}$ in no fewer than 10% and 5% of houses respectively.

*Deposition*

Radon itself is an inert gas, but radon daughters penetrate deeply into the bronchi and lungs, where the larger proportion is *deposited*, producing a high local dose of radiation. The half-life of the radon daughters is approximately 30 minutes.

In the past, uranium miners have been exposed to high concentrations of radon and radon daughters, resulting in an increased incidence of lung cancer. Smoking is inadvisable for people exposed to high concentrations of radon because the combination of radon and cigarette smoke increases the risk of lung cancer more than would be expected on the basis of mere addition of the effects. People living in houses with high radon concentrations (e.g. more than 400 Bq m$^{-3}$) also run a relatively high risk of developing lung cancer. The average radon concentration in the *indoor air* is estimated at 15 Bq m$^{-3}$. This is an average value for temperate areas as far as the radium content of the soil is concerned. On the basis of recent calculations, exposure to indoor radon daughters is thought to be responsible for 10–40 cases of lung cancer per year per 1 million people. This means that 5–15% of all cases of lung cancer are attributable to exposure to radon daughters.

*WHO recommendations*

The risk of developing lung cancer is of course even greater for persons living in houses with radon concentrations of 100 Bq m$^{-3}$ or higher. The World Health Organization recommended in 1988 that alterations should be made to dwellings with an indoor air concentration higher than 100 Bq m$^{-3}$ to reduce the radon concentration; for houses with radon concentrations above 400 Bq m$^{-3}$, such alterations should be of short-term priority, according to the WHO.

### 7.2.4 Sulfur dioxide

The complex mixture of sulfur dioxide, sulfuric acid and inorganic and organic dust particles forms an important component of the air pollution in densely populated areas. This mixture is found mainly after the combustion of fossil fuels.

*Exposure to sulfur dioxide*

*Exposure to sulfur dioxide* (SO$_2$) causes bronchoconstriction and acute or chronic bronchitis. Asthma patients are particularly sensitive. Research in humans has shown that setting recommended values should aim mainly at avoiding peak exposure levels. The lowest peak concentration (duration of exposure 10 minutes) which has harmful effects on the human lung is 1000 $\mu$g m$^{-3}$ (0.35 ppm). Exposure to 500 $\mu$g m$^{-3}$ for 10 minutes is not considered to constitute a health risk. Exposure to sulfuric acid aerosols is mainly harmful to the mucociliary defense mechanism. The critical concentration is 10 $\mu$g m$^{-3}$.

*Effects on health*

*Effects on health* due to exposure to dust particles are observed mainly if there is simultaneous exposure to sulfur dioxide and sulfuric acid. Even at concentrations of only 180 $\mu$g m$^{-3}$ as 24-hour average, reduced pulmonary function can be diagnosed. At peak concentrations of the mixture, severe acute respiratory problems may occur.

*WHO recommendations*

The World Health Organization recommends a 1-hour average of 350 $\mu$g m$^{-3}$ for sulfur dioxide and indicates that at a sulfuric acid concentration of 10 $\mu$g m$^{-3}$ the sulfuric acid concentration in the atmosphere should be measured frequently. For combinations of sulfur dioxide and dust particles, it recommends 24-hour averages of 125 $\mu$g m$^{-3}$ SO$_2$ and 120 $\mu$g m$^{-3}$ particles.

### 7.2.5 Formaldehyde

Formaldehyde (H$_2$CO) is the simplest and most common aldehyde. At room temperature it is a colorless gas with a pungent odor. As the gas contained in chipboard, it created a considerable stir when in the early 1980s, the first reports of formaldehyde causing nasal cancer in rats started to come through in the United States.

*Use*

Formaldehyde is commonly used as a disinfectant and preservative, is released from certain insulating materials, is present in car exhaust gases and is found in high concentrations in cigarette smoke.

*Effects*

*Genotoxic substances*

Irritation of the eyes, nose and throat can be clearly observed at concentrations above 1 ppm (1.2 mg m$^{-3}$). Repeated skin contact with aqueous solutions may lead to allergic contact dermatitis. Formaldehyde is mutagenic and can react with DNA and proteins, causing formation of irreversible crosslinks. It should therefore be regarded as a *genotoxic substance*. In rats, it induces nasal cancer after long-term exposure to high concentrations (around 15 ppm). Such a high concentration is highly cytotoxic and causes severe damage to the nasal mucosa, followed by regenerative hyperplasia and metaplasia of the nasal epithelium. This *tissue damage* has appeared to play such an important role in the development of nasal cancer in rats that it may be safely stated that exposure to concentrations of formaldehyde which are not cytotoxic (1 ppm and less) carry only a negligible risk of developing cancer. Considerable support for this statement comes from the results of a study on formaldehyde in rats, in which the nasal mucosa of some of the animals had been severely damaged by electrocoagulation. This study showed that nasal cancer developed only in animals with damaged nasal epithelium which were exposed to a high concentration of formaldehyde (10 ppm). Exposure to 1 or 0.1 ppm formaldehyde did not induce nasal cancer. Apparently, two conditions must be met for nasal cancer to be induced: both mucosal damage and a high concentration of formaldehyde. It is for this reason that formaldehyde is one of the few genotoxic carcinogens whose carcinogenic activity was of secondary importance in comparison to its cytotoxic activity when a MAC value (1 ppm) and an air standard for the population (0.1 ppm) were established. Such an approach is also justified by the fact that, despite extensive epidemiological research, formaldehyde has not yet been convincingly shown to induce cancer in man.

*Relationship cytotoxicity-carcinogenicity*

> ASSIGNMENT 18.16
>
> Research in rats has shown that exposure to formaldehyde in a concentration that damages the nasal mucosa but not the lungs reduces the pulmonary effects of simultaneous exposure to ozone. What might explain this finding?

### 7.2.6 Wood dust

Furniture makers and woodworkers run a greatly increased risk of developing nasal cancer as a result of exposure to wood dust, in which toxic substances, for example fungus toxins, may occur naturally or which may contain chemical additives, such as preservatives, artificial resins and glues. A distinction is made between dust from hardwoods (trees shedding their leaves in winter), which mainly causes adenocarcinomas, and dust from softwoods (trees remaining green in winter), which mainly induces squamous-cell carcinomas and anaplastic carcinomas. Clinical studies have shown the incidence of metaplasia of the nasal epithelium to be significantly higher in furniture makers than in other persons. Metaplasia of the nasal epithelium is considered to be a precursor stage of cancer. Up to now, it is unclear how far mechanical or chemical irritation plays a role in the induction of nasal cancer by wood-dust particles. However, studies using hamsters have shown that exposure to wood dust does cause metaplasia and dysplasia of the nasal epithelium. A few animals developed a nasal carcinoma. It therefore seems reasonable to assume that it is specifically the combination of mechanical/chemical irritation (leading to tissue damage followed by regenerative hyperplasia) and the presence in wood dust of genotoxic substances that is decisive in the development of nasal cancer. It would seem worth establishing the highest concentration of wood dust that does not damage the nasal mucosa in hamsters. It may safely be assumed that even long-term exposure to such a concentration of wood dust will not or not significantly increase the risk of nasal cancer. One should then of course attempt, where necessary, to reduce the concentration of wood dust at the work place to the "no-observed-adverse-effect level" found in the animal experiments. In conclusion, it should be noted that exposure to wood dust may also lead to acute dyspnea, chronic rhinitis and bronchitis, pulmonary fibrosis and certain forms of asthma and allergic rhinitis.

### 7.2.7 Paraquat

Many cases of paraquat intoxication are known, mainly caused by improper use. In the lungs, paraquat is absorbed specifically by the type I and type II pneumocytes, and is then *reduced to an active metabolite* which in its turn produces superoxide radicals. In case of intoxication, the depletion of co-factors (e.g. NADPH) for the metabolism of free radicals also plays a role. At relatively low dosages, damage is restricted to the lungs and (to a lesser extent) the kidneys. At higher dosages other organs may also be affected. The uptake of paraquat into the pneumocytes requires energy. Toxic effects are only observed above a certain dosage. If the level of exposure remains below that minimum dosage, the substance is entirely metabolized to harmless products.

*Acute phase*

*Regenerative phase*

Intoxication comprises an acute and a regenerative phase. The *acute phase* starts with damage to type I and type II pneumocytes, followed by desquamation. The result is edema, alveolitis and exudation of granulocytes. The *regenerative phase* is characterized by a marked proliferation of fibroblasts, which causes fibrosis of the lungs and in many cases death. Paraquat intoxication shows close similarities to intoxication with oxygen.

### 7.2.8 Oxygen

*Free radicals*

Exposure to an excessive amount of oxygen leads to the intracellular formation of *free radicals* such as $OH^\bullet$ and other reactive oxygen species such as $H_2O_2$. These may damage cells and cause cell death, followed by infiltration of granulocytes and macrophages. As a result, even more radicals are formed, so that the process reinforces itself. Oxygen intoxication is reinforced by:

- radiation;
- certain drugs;

- inhibition of superoxide dismutase and other protective enzymes, such as catalase and glutathione peroxidase;
- depletion of scavengers of free radicals, such as vitamins C and E;
- depletion of co-factors for enzymes metabolizing free radicals, such as glutathione and NADPH.

Oxygen intoxication can be reduced by the induction of protective enzymes.

## 8 Summary

This study unit has discussed the structure, function, physiology and pathology of the respiratory system.

The nature and location of a toxic effect in the respiratory system are closely related to its anatomy. This is reflected, for example, in species differences, which need to be taken into account when designing experiments and interpreting their results. The functioning of respiration in living organisms can be measured by means of pulmonary function tests. Pathological changes can be detected and quantified on the basis of the results of such experiments, in particular those changes which are connected with mechanical properties and the shape of the respiratory system, and with gas exchange. In addition to toxic effects following the direct action of harmful substances, immune reactions also play an important part in the respiratory system. These reactions are brought about indirectly by activation of the immune system.

As is the case for many organ systems, the reactions of the respiratory system can be divided into adaptation, degeneration, proliferation and inflammation. In addition, the lungs also have at their disposal the mechanisms of alveolar and mucociliary clearance, by means of which foreign particles can be removed.

The nature and location of the effects depend on the chemical properties of the inhaled gas. In addition to the reactivity of a gas, its solubility in water is very important in this context. Gases which readily dissolve in water have their effect in the upper areas of the respiratory system. In the case of aerosols, the size and shape of the particles determine where deposition in the respiratory tract is likely to take place. Smaller particles will penetrate more deeply and affect the lower airways.

Pneumoconiosis is a term used to refer to a group of occupational diseases caused by inhaled inorganic particles of various origin and the tissue reactions they cause. The pathology of lung cancer has been discussed in detail, as an example of a chemically induced type of tumor in man. Lung cancer may be related both to lifestyle and to occupational exposure to carcinogenic compounds.

Finally, there is a discussion of the toxicology of several substances known to cause air pollution and of substances causing severe pulmonary injury in other ways.

## SELF ASSESSMENT QUESTIONS

1   The compliance of a lung affected by fibrosis is decreased. During normal respiration, this does not really hinder breathing. What, however, are the consequences for the vital capacity, and why is this so?

2   If a subject is in the lateral position, the top and bottom halves of the lungs are unevenly ventilated (inhomogeneous ventilation). In healthy people, this does not have any observable consequences for the blood-gas values

and pH, but in patients with respiratory problems, such a position may lead to fatal desaturation of arterial blood. Explain why this is so.

3   Can you think of a technical intervention which enables the study of the effect of formaldehyde at the bronchiolar level (which is where it is active in man)?

4   An aerosol of a solid substance which is soluble in a highly acidic environment is given during a short-term inhalation exposure experiment. After approximately 3 hours, the toxic response is at its maximum. How can this be explained and what was the size of the particles in the aerosol?

5   Study Figure 18.9 and read the legend.
    a.   In Figure c, there is a significant change in $P_{pl}$ at the beginning of exhalation, while the lung volume does not change much. What does this indicate?
    b.   Figures c and d show a large increase in pressure during exhalation, at virtually constant volume. What does this indicate?
    c.   Why is there a rapid change in volume at the beginning of the exhalation in Figure d, unlike that in Figure c?

6   Explain why the effects of inhaled gases or particles in humans may be different from those in experimental animals.

7   State differences and similarities of the concepts of hyperplasia, metaplasia and neoplasia.

8   Why is attention devoted to the occurrence of metaplastic changes in carcinogenicity studies?

9   Explain the tightness of the chest which patients experience in a type I hypersensitivity reaction in the lungs.

10   Why is it to be expected that formaldehyde and radon will not influence each other's effects in the respiratory tract, while formaldehyde and wood dust almost certainly will?

FEEDBACK

1   **Answers to the assignments**

18.1   The purpose of the surfactant is to moisten the surface of the alveolar epithelium and to maintain the correct surface tension. The former is necessary to ensure effective gas exchange, the second to prevent collapse of the alveoli.

18.2   The increased airway resistance hampers the air flow. To overcome this resistance, patients tend to exhale actively, which may cause the intrapleural pressure to become positive and the bronchi to become more constricted or entirely closed. This additional constriction can be prevented by breathing out calmly. By pressing against half-closed lips, the patient ensures that the greatest drop in pressure does not take place within the thoracic cavity, so that the pressure difference between the airways in the thoracic cavity and intrapleurally remains negative even when exhalation is active, and additional constriction of the bronchi is thus prevented. On inhalation, bronchoconstriction will lead to an extra negative intrapleural pressure, which will in part counterbalance the bronchoconstriction.

18.3 1  Enlargement of the residual volume leads to an increased surface area available for gas exchange, which in part compensates for the loss of gas exchange epithelium.

2  The great compliance present in emphysema causes the negative pleural pressure to be low, so that the airways may easily collapse during exhalation. Increasing the residual volume means that the negative pleural pressure is increased, so that a collapse is prevented. In fibrosis, in which gas exchange is also disturbed because diffusion has to take place across a thickened membrane, an increase in FRC leads to unacceptably high negative pleural pressures.

18.4  Formaldehyde is almost entirely removed from the inhaled air in the nose of the rat and is therefore not able to exert any cytotoxic effects at the alveolar level. The reason for this is that formaldehyde dissolves very well in the nasal mucus. Ozone is removed only to a limited extent because it dissolves far less readily in the nasal mucus. A large proportion of the inhaled ozone can therefore reach the alveolar level.

18.5  After 1 minute, the blood concentration of the gas with $\lambda = 0.5$ has significantly exceeded the level required for anesthetic action and narcosis will have set in. For the gas with $\lambda = 10$, the concentration in the alveolar air is reduced to about $1/10$ of the exposure concentration. After 1 minute, the blood concentration is by no means high enough to induce anesthesia.

18.6 a.  a = residual volume, b = vital capacity, c = tidal volume.

b.  Figure b: a large change in pressure gives only a small change in volume, hence a so-called "stiff lung" is involved (= fibrosis). Figure c: hardly any change in compliance, normal residual volume, i.e. no alveolar changes, inhalation is hardly a problem, great increase in pressure on exhalation (may even become positive), i.e. asthma. Figure d: large FRC, no problems during inhalation or exhalation, no flow at positive pleural pressure, i.e. emphysema.

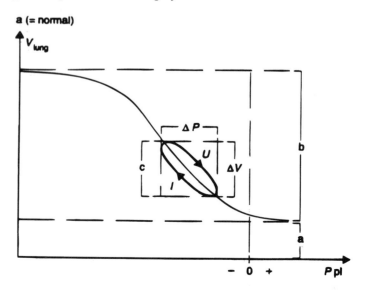

c.  The intrapleural pressure difference ($\Delta P$) between end inhalation ($V_{max}$) and end exhalation ($V_{min}$) is greater during respiration than in the static condition.

18.7  In the upper airways one may expect effects of gases which dissolve readily in water, while in the lower airways it is the gases which dissolve poorly in water which cause damage.

18.8  In addition to mucociliary and alveolar clearance, the respiratory tract also has defense mechanisms such as biochemical reactions (biotransformation), immune reactions and adaptation of the lining epithelium, e.g. hyperplasia of certain cell types and increased production of mucus or surfactant.

18.9  The term metaplasia is used for mature epithelium if a type not normally found at the site concerned is formed.

18.10  The poor functioning of mucociliary clearance leads to the accumulation of particles in the lungs.

18.11  An important adverse result of emphysema is the decrease in surface area of the respiratory part of the airways. This reduces the capacity for gas exchange.

18.12  Pulmonary edema may lead to hypoxia, as gas exchange is inhibited by the fluid. This effect is greater for the transport of oxygen than for that of carbon dioxide.

18.13  Substances administered systemically can be metabolized in a variety of tissues in the body, not only in the liver. In some cases, reactive metabolites may be formed which may act as initiators. If the substance concerned is metabolized in the lungs, lung tumors may develop.

18.14  The harmful effects of a malignant tumor include:
— dysfunctioning of the organ of origin due to compression, closing off of vessels and ducts and other structures, destruction of the original tissue, necrosis, hemorrhage, perforation;
— dysfunctioning of adjacent organs due to invasion or of remoter organs due to metastasis;
— harmful effects of substances produced by the tumor, such as mucus or hormones.

18.15  Type I hypersensitivity is acute and may be accompanied by severe dyspnea. If contact with the substance stops, there is a clear recovery of pulmonary function. A type III reaction is less acute and lasts longer. Pulmonary function eventually becomes disturbed permanently as a result of great pathological changes in the lung.

18.16  An obvious explanation is that formaldehyde changes the respiratory pattern in such a way that less ozone reaches the lungs.

## 2.  Answers to the self assessment questions

1  In fibrosis, the vital capacity is greatly reduced because very large negative pleural pressures are required (exertion of breathing muscles) to increase the lung volume during inhalation.

2    In healthy people, the inhomogenity of regional ventilation is fully compensated for by adaptation of regional perfusion. The regional ventilation/perfusion ratio is not changed. In patients with respiratory problems, this compensation fails. Induction of additional ventilation inhomogeneity then results in additional ventilation/perfusion inhomogeneity. Patients with respiratory problems therefore tend to lie on their back or half erect, or use the accessory muscles of respiration.

3    In order to study the effect of formaldehyde at the bronchiolar level, the gas would have to be administered without being led along the nasal epithelium. This can be achieved by performing a tracheotomy. This means that an opening in the trachea is made surgically and a tube providing direct access is installed.

4    The moment of maximum toxic response strongly indicates that the material has been deposited in the upper airways, has left the respiratory tract via the mucociliary transport system, has been taken up orally and has dissolved in the stomach. The most important deposition, considering the time aspect, must have taken place by sedimentation and the size of the particles must have been mainly 1–5 $\mu m^3$.

5    a.   The great change in pleural pressure at the beginning of the exhalation and the large surface area of the hysteretic loop are indications of great airway resistance.
     b.   The behavior of the pressure–volume curve during exhalation at $P_{pl} =$ zero or greater indicates total closing off of the airways. In c (asthma), this is the result of bronchoconstriction. In d (emphysema), it is the result of the collapse which occurs in flaccid passages in which high speeds occur.
     c.   At the beginning of the exhalation, the emphysema patient has a low airway resistance, in contrast to the asthma patient.

6    Many rodent species are obligate nose breathers, while man has a greater tendency to breathe through the mouth (during physical effort, speaking, smoking). Because of this, it is to be expected that effects observed in the nose in rodents will occur in the lower airways in humans.

7    A common property of hyperplasia, metaplasia and neoplasia is that they involve proliferation of cells.
     *Hyperplasia* is an increase in the number of cells of a certain type in a tissue.
     *Metaplasia* is defined as the alteration of a particular type of differentiated epithelium into a different type of differentiated epithelium which is not normally found at that location, such as the change from pseudo-stratified columnar bronchial epithelium into flattened stratified squamous epithelium. Both hyperplasia and metaplasia are reversible processes.
     *Neoplasia* is an autonomous and irreversible proliferation of a certain cell type; it is the process of tumor formation.

8    In carcinogenicity studies, metaplastic changes are also taken into consideration because tumors are often (but not always) preceded by metaplasia. This is the case, for example, in the respiratory tract. An increase in the number of metaplasias means a higher chance that a number of them will progress to form tumors.

9    The bronchoconstriction, the swelling of the mucosa and the increase in the amount of mucus in the bronchi mean that the lumina of the airways are very much constricted, so that airway resistance is greatly increased. Breathing is very difficult and requires considerable muscle action. The transport of air to the alveolar area is reduced, so that not enough oxygen is supplied and not enough carbon dioxide is removed.

10   Formaldehyde primarily acts on the nose and radon on the lungs, while wood dust and formaldehyde both affect the nasal mucosa. Moreover, the two latter substances have a similar effect on the nasal epithelium. (NB: Assignment 18.16 has shown that secondary influences are also possible, so that drawing up hypotheses of this kind calls for great care.)

# Contents Study unit 19
## Inhalatory exposure: extrapolation and methodological aspects

# Study unit 19

# Inhalatory exposure: extrapolation and methodological aspects

*V. J. Feron, R. B. Beems, P. G. J. Reuzel and A. Zwart*

## INTRODUCTION

Inhalation toxicology is concerned with the toxicology of substances entering the body during breathing. Since breathing is essential to stay alive and exposure to substances in the air we breathe is unavoidable, inhalation toxicology is of great importance. One of the consequences of the great expansion of industry, including the chemical industry, over the past few decades has been that ever larger groups of people came into contact with all kinds of chemical products constituting an inhalational hazard. Examples are products containing volatile components, such as paints, cleaning agents, adhesives, and products applied in the form of aerosols, such as cosmetics, insecticides, disinfectants and air fresheners. In the United States this development led to the introduction of a number of government measures in the 1960s, and later also in Europe. The initial purpose of these measures was to protect the workers in the industry. In the United States, lists of so-called Threshold Limit Values (TLVs) were established and still are. As far as the upper limits of concentration of contaminants allowed in the air of the workplace are concerned, the so-called MAC list is used, in which MAC stands
*Maximum Allowable Concentration*
for *Maximum Allowable Concentration*. For a large number of substances, the MAC list states the average concentration which, on the basis of an 8-hour working day, is considered the highest concentration allowable in the ambient air. It is easy to see why attention was at first focused on workplace conditions. In the occupational setting, inhalation is by far the most important way of exposure. During an 8-hour working day, a person who is physically reasonably active inhales approximately 8 m$^3$ air, which comes into contact with the sensitive and active internal surface of the respiratory tract. Moreover, a series of disorders have long been known to be associated with the inhalation of substances at the workplace.

Can you give examples of such disorders?

Standards for ambient air are not only used with reference to the workplace. There is a growing awareness that such standards are also required to protect the population as a whole, as regards both the internal and the external environment.
*Air Quality Guidelines*
The *World Health Organization* has published so-called *"Air Quality Guidelines"* for 28 substances. These guidelines do not have the force of law, but are recommended values that can be applied by the various countries when determining their own policy when setting standards for substances in the atmosphere.

Recommended values and standards for the concentrations of airborne substances should be based on health considerations. These are of course in their turn based on the qualitative and quantitative toxicity data of the substances concerned. If any information is available on the toxicity of a substance in man (e.g. from epidemiological studies, or from studying cases of poisoning, or from experiments in volunteers), this should be used where possible. However, information derived from cases of acute poisoning and from studies in volunteers does not provide information on the chronic effects.

ASSIGNMENT   19.1

What would be the disadvantages of epidemiological research in comparison to inhalation toxicity research?

If insufficient or no information on the harmful effects of a substance in man is available, as is the case for every newly developed substance, toxicity data have to be obtained from experiments in animals or *in vitro* systems. The value of such toxicity data depends largely on the quality of the data and the relevance of the experimental model used. The present study unit describes the design and execution of various types of inhalation toxicity research. The technical and biotechnical aspects of inhalation tests are also dealt with. A further point for discussion is that of the concentration–time and concentration–response relationships and how these should be applied in the interpretation of acute inhalation toxicity data. To conclude, inhalation-specific aspects of extrapolation of toxicity data from experimental animals to humans are briefly discussed.

LEARNING OBJECTIVES

After studying this unit, you should:

— be able to describe the purpose, design, and execution of the various types of inhalation toxicity experiments
— be able to list the various tests aimed at detecting specific effects in the respiratory tract
— have some notion of the set-up of and the equipment used in a modern laboratory for inhalation toxicology
— be able to outline the specific problems connected with concentration–time and concentration–response relationships in inhalation toxicology
— be able to describe how data from inhalation toxicity research in experimental animals can be extrapolated to man.

*Study hints*

Some parts of the present study unit are rather descriptive, while others also deal with quantitative aspects. In the latter case, it goes back to the knowledge you have gained while studying Study unit 7.

If you have sufficient ready knowledge of dose–response relationships, the study load of this unit should not be more than 4 hours.

## STUDY CORE

### 1   Pulmonary and inhalation toxicity research

#### 1.1   TYPES OF RESEARCH

The design of inhalation toxicity experiments should meet the same conditions as those that apply to toxicity experiments in which the substance is administered via a different route, the difference being that special attention is paid to the respiratory tract.

These conditions are as follows:

- selection of species: commonly used species include the rat, mouse, hamster, guinea pig and dog;
- selection of sex: both sexes are usually used;
- size of groups: e.g. 10 animals per sex per group in a 90-day study and 50 animals per sex per group in a chronic study;
- number of groups: usually 4, of which 3 are test groups and 1 is a control group;

*Parameters studied*
- the *parameters studied* may be: body weight, food consumption, clinical observations, hematology, biochemistry, urine tests, function tests, organ weights and pathology.

Research for registration purposes is usually carried out according to standardized OECD (Organization for Economic Cooperation and Development) procedures. The various experiments can be classified as follows:

*Classification*

a   acute (less than 24 hours of exposure);

b   subacute (usually 2 or 4 weeks of exposure);

c   subchronic (usually 13 weeks of exposure);

d   chronic (usually 78–130 weeks of exposure).

### 1.1.1 Acute inhalation toxicity research

Acute inhalation toxicity is the total of harmful effects caused by a substance as a result of a single uninterrupted period of inhalational exposure of less than 24 hours. The purpose of acute toxicity studies is to establish the acute toxicity of a substance in relation to that of other substances and to obtain information on the mechanism by which the substance exerts its effect. The acute toxicity data of a substance serve as the basis on which the relative risk to health for man is assessed.

The most common tests carried out are:

1   limit test;

2   $LC_{50}$ test (concentration at which mortality is 50%);

3   inhalation hazard test;

4   test to determine the concentration–time and concentration–response relationships.

### Ad 1 and 2

The limit test and the $LC_{50}$ test are most frequently used. Both are characterized by concentration ($C$) and exposure time ($T$). Exposure time is usually 4 hours, though 1 hour is also frequently applied. After exposure, the animals are held for observation for 14 days.

*Limit test*
An $LC_{50}$ test usually starts with a limit test. An experiment is a *limit test* if, at the technically highest possible concentration (OECD guideline), less than 50% mortality is found in a group of experimental animals, or if, at the indicated maximum concentration of 5 mg substance per liter air, there is no mortality as a result of the exposure. If mortality is 50% or more, at least two more groups are exposed once to different concentrations. Using a certain method of calculation, the $LC_{50}$ is then determined with confidence intervals.

$LC_{50}$ values are used not only to classify substances into different classes of inhalation toxicity, but also as basis for further inhalation research.

*Ad 3*

In an *inhalation hazard test*, the exposure lasts 7 hours. To generate the test atmosphere, a standardized evaporating vessel is used which always contains the same volume for each substance to be tested. The evaporating vessel is kept at a temperature of 20°C. If a fixed air volume per unit of time is supplied to the vessel, the volatile components evaporate. In the case of a solid substance, the smaller particles are also carried along with the airflow. All substances are thus treated identically. The concentration of the substance is determined by its volatility, and in the case of solid substances also by physical properties related to aerosol formation. The results of this test only indicate whether the substance concerned constitutes an inhalation hazard or not.

*Ad 4*

Although an $LC_{50}$ value gives information on acute inhalation toxicity, test methods are being developed that can provide more relevant information. Recent experiments have shown that, if both exposure time and concentration are varied, and only two instead of ten animals are exposed in each group, considerably more information can be obtained from the same number of animals. Concentration–time and concentration–response relationships will be discussed in Section 3.

### 1.1.2 Subacute, subchronic and chronic inhalation toxicity tests

*Duration of exposure*

Subacute, subchronic and chronic inhalation toxicity comprise the harmful effects caused by a substance as a result of repeated daily inhalational exposure. *Subacute toxicity* studies involve exposure during a period of more than a day up to 1 month. For *subchronic toxicity* studies, the period is longer than a month but preferably not longer than 10% of the life expectancy of the experimental animal concerned (OECD). *Chronic toxicity* research takes more than 10% of the life expectancy of the animal. The periods of exposure are usually 14 or 28 days in a subacute experiment, 90 days in a subchronic experiment and 78–130 weeks in a chronic experiment. During the period of exposure, the animals are usually exposed 5 days per week and 6 hours per day.

Chronic inhalation tests can be subdivided into:

1. chronic toxicity tests;
2. carcinogenicity tests;
3. combined chronic toxicity/carcinogenicity tests.

The purpose of these toxicity tests is:

a. establishing the nature of the harmfulness of a substance after repeated inhalational exposure for the periods indicated above;

b. determining the target organs of a substance, with specific attention to the respiratory tract;

c. establishing the highest concentration at which no harmful effect is observed (no-observed-adverse-effect level), and if possible a dose–response curve.

As an example, Table 19.1 lists the various elements of a standard subacute inhalation experiment.

### 1.2 SPECIFIC INHALATION RESEARCH

In addition to the more or less standardized inhalation toxicity research briefly described above, a substance can also be studied for more specific detrimental effects. Examples are the following:

TABLE 19.1
Design of a fictitious subacute inhalation toxicity experiment in rats

| Route of exposure | Inhalation ("total-body exposure"; head-only or nose-only exposure) |
| --- | --- |
| species | rat |
| duration | 4 weeks (6 hours per day; 5 days per week) |
| set-up | 4 groups of rats of 10 males and 10 females each |
| | group A: control |
| | group B: low-concentration group |
| | group C: moderate concentration group |
| | group D: high-concentration group |
| criteria | appearance and behavior, body weight, hematology, clinical chemistry, organ weight, pulmonary function, macroscopic and microscopic pathology |

1  teratogenicity—fertility research; research into the harmful effect on the developing embryo/fetus or on fertility;

2  specific carcinogenicity research; all other non-standardized methods of carcinogenicity research;

3  *in vivo* mutagenicity research, for example dominant lethal tests, sister chromatid exchange tests and chromosome aberration tests;

4  research into the sensitizing properties of substances with respect to the respiratory tract; good experimental animal models have not yet been found;

5  research into the detrimental effects of a substance on alveolar macrophages;

6  biochemical examination of bronchoalveolar lavage fluid;

7  biochemical examination of lung homogenate;

8  determination of connective tissue in the lungs;

9  tissue transplantation techniques;

10  tissue isolation techniques.

The experiments mentioned under points 1 to 4 have already been dealt with, or will be dealt with elsewhere. Here, only methods 5–10 will be described.

5.  *Research into the harmful effects of a substance on pulmonary macrophages*

The detrimental effects which substances can have on the functioning of alveolar macrophages can be studied both *in vivo* and *in vitro*.

*In vitro macrophage test*

In the *in vitro BAM test (Bovine Alveolar Macrophage test)*, fresh lungs of slaughtered cattle are used to obtain alveolar macrophages by means of pulmonary lavage. The lungs are rinsed with a phosphate-buffered saline solution. The bronchoalveolar rinsing fluid is centrifuged and the supernatant (including macrophages) is suspended in a tissue culture medium. By diluting, the number of cells in the cell suspension is reduced to $2 \times 10^5$ per ml. In this dilution, the macrophages are allowed to adhere to cover slips. The latter are then placed in a medium in which the substance to be studied is dissolved or suspended.

The toxicity of the substance to the cells is established by determining the following parameters:

- the *survival rate* of the macrophages after 18 hours of exposure;
- the *phagocytic activity* of the macrophages, which is determined by placing the macrophages (after 18 hours of exposure) in a medium containing latex globules (diameter of 1–4 μm) for a duration of 45 minutes, after which the percentage of the macrophages containing one or more globules is determined by microscopy.

*In vivo macrophage test*

In the *in vivo alveolar macrophage test*, experimental animals are exposed by inhalation for a certain length of time, after which they are anesthetized and bled. The lungs are rinsed *in situ* with a sterile saline solution administered via the trachea. The lavage fluid from the lungs is centrifuged to separate cells and fluid. The supernatant is poured off and the resulting pellet of centrifuged cells is suspended in a tissue culture medium. In the suspension thus formed, the following parameters can be determined:

- *Concentration of macrophages* (number per ml).
- *Percentage of living macrophages*, determined by means of a vital staining method, which stains only the living macrophages clearly.
- *Survival rate after an incubation period*; the macrophage suspension is incubated for 20 hours, at 5% $CO_2$ in the air and at a temperature of 37°C, after which the number of macrophages still alive is once more determined.
- *Phagocytic activity* (see *in vitro* macrophage test).

ASSIGNMENT 19.2

Would there be any point in incorporating a test of alveolar macrophages into a study on the toxicity of a gas or vapor?

6. *Biochemical examination of lung lavage fluid*

In the case of damage to the pulmonary epithelium, the damaged cells release endogenous substances into the alveolar lumen. If the permeability of the blood capillaries is altered, albumin may pass through, and, in the case of epithelial injury, may also enter the alveolar spaces. In addition, surfactant may be affected. By analyzing lung lavage fluid, an impression of the effect of a substance on the lungs can be acquired after a relatively short period of exposure. The lung lavage fluid is obtained as described under 5. The determinations are carried out on the supernatant that is left after centrifugation of the fluid.

The following measurements can be carried out:

- *enzymes* such as lactate dehydrogenase (LDH), peroxidases, elastase. Increased LDH and peroxidase activities are both indicative of rather non-specific cell damage. An increase in the amount of elastase indicates degradation of the loose connective tissue in the lungs, but it is not a very sensitive parameter;
- *proteins*: total protein, albumin, globulins. Increases are found in the case of inflammation in the lungs and of pulmonary injury;
- *phospholipids*: the surfactant of the lungs consists of phospholipids. Increases or decreases in certain phospholipid concentrations may indicate some effect on surfactant.

7. *Biochemical examination of lung homogenate*

*Enzymes* can also be determined in a lung homogenate. An increase or decrease in enzymatic activity as compared to that of homogenates of control lungs indicate the damage that is caused. Sometimes, also, the type of cells involved in the damage can be determined.

Enzymes that are determined include glutathione peroxidase, glutathione transferase, glucose-6-phosphate dehydrogenase and cytochrome P-450.

### 8. Determination of connective tissue in the lungs

Many substances are known to cause an increase in the amount of dense connective tissue in the lungs. As a result, the elasticity of the lungs diminishes, which can considerably impede gas exchange in the lungs. Extensive connective tissue formation in the lungs is clearly recognizable light microscopically, but slight increases in connective tissue are not. The connective tissue content of the lungs can also be determined quite satisfactorily chemically. This is done by measuring the hydroxyproline content (protein forming the connective tissue) of hydrolyzed pulmonary tissue. Even minor increases in the amount of connective tissue can be demonstrated in this way.

> ASSIGNMENT   19.3
>
> Exposure to amorphous $SiO_2$ for a longer period of time causes a slight to severe increase in connective tissue in the lungs. Why, in this case, is the chemical method more suitable to determine the connective tissue content than light microscopy?

### 9. Tissue transplantation technique

This technique is used in order to answer questions on details. An example is the subcutaneous implantation of the trachea of one rat into another rat. To avoid graft rejection, the rats must of course be syngenetic.

The trachea is usually implanted near the shoulder blade. Both ends of the implanted trachea are sutured to the incised skin, thus creating an open connection with the ambient air containing the substance to be studied. This arrangement bypasses the nose and therefore allows comparison with oral breathing.

A variety of manipulations can moreover be carried out on the trachea without posing any threat to the life of the carrier animal.

### 10. Tissue isolation techniques

Tissues of treated or untreated animals can be removed from the body and used in in vitro experiments. An example of this are organ perfusion techniques (see Study unit 25).

## 2   Inhalation chambers

Definition

The inhalation chamber enables exposure of animals or human subjects to a test atmosphere in predetermined conditions. An inhalation chamber can thus be defined as a virtually air-tight room in which animals or humans can be exposed under previously established circumstances. The test atmosphere may contain an aerosol of either a liquid or a solid substance; a gas or vapor; or a combination of gases and/or vapors and/or aerosols. The type of test atmosphere must be taken into account in the design of the inhalation chamber. In general, there is little uniformity as to the design and actual construction of inhalation chambers. Publications on this subject are few and far between, so that many researchers have developed their own. Over the past few years, however, a number of companies have ventured to produce a range of chambers. Inhalation chambers require substantial space, are expensive to purchase or construct, and require much infrastructural and peripheral equipment.

*Manner of exposure*

Based on the *manner of exposure*, exposure systems can be divided into three different types:

1 *total-body* system, in which the entire body of a human subject or experimental animal is exposed;

2 *head/nose-only* system, in which only the head or the nose is exposed;

3 systems in which only the lungs or part of the lungs are exposed by means of a *tracheal tube*. Since this is a highly invasive procedure which only can be performed under general anesthesia, it is only rarely applied.

## 2.1 TOTAL-BODY EXPOSURE VERSUS HEAD/NOSE-ONLY EXPOSURE

Some advantages and disadvantages of total-body exposure and of head/nose-only exposure are listed in Table 19.2.

In a total-body system, exposure to aerosols causes the fur of animals to become contaminated. By the grooming behavior of the animals (licking the fur) oral uptake may be considerable. Particularly in the case of substances acting systemically, the question then arises whether the effects are caused by oral or inhalation intake. This is one of the main reasons why head/nose-only systems tend to be used when studying the effect of aerosols.

Newly developed chemicals as test materials are mostly available in short supply. Also, the chemicals are often quite costly. As considerably less of the test substance is needed in the head/nose-only system than in a whole body system, this system is preferred to test such substances.

TABLE 19.2
Advantages and disadvantages of total-body and head/nose-only experiments on inhalation exposure

|  | Head/nose-only exposure | "Total-body" exposure |
|---|---|---|
| advantages | —rest of body not contaminated with substances<br>—takes up relatively little space<br>—requires small amount of test material<br>—rapid increase and decrease in concentrations | —large numbers of animals exposed simultaneously<br>—animals can move freely, no stress due to restriction of movement<br>—behavior and clinical symptoms of animals readily observable<br>—suitable for both short-term and long-term studies<br>—least labor-intensive<br>—dosing usually easier due to relatively large volume |
| disadvantages | —stress and discomfort caused by fixation<br><br>—behavior and clinical symptoms not or not readily observable<br>—labor-intensive<br>—exposure of large numbers of animals not very practical | —total body surface exposure<br>—requires large amount of test material<br>—chamber takes up relatively much space<br>—concentration of test substance may vary widely at different levels<br>—slow increase and decrease in concentrations<br>—pollution of test atmosphere due to presence of excrement and urine under cages<br>—high purchasing price |

### 2.1.1 Total-body inhalation chambers

From an aerodynamic point of view, a cylindrical chamber must be considered the ideal inhalation chamber. Since such a chamber does not have any dead corners, the airflow is very even throughout, and the concentration of the substance tested is equal in the various parts of the chamber. All animals are thus exposed to the same concentration. Especially in the case of aerosols, which are subject to sedimentation and deposition, a good aerodynamic shape of the chamber is very important.

In practice, however, cylindrical chambers only find limited application, since they are very difficult to construct and therefore very expensive, especially the larger sizes. As they are easier to construct (cheaper), most inhalation chambers are 4- and occasionally 6-sided. The roof and bottom may be flat, but are usually pyramidal or conical in shape. An example of a chamber that used to be applied extensively is the hexagonal inhalation chamber designed by the University of Rochester.

This chamber has a conical roof and a tangential upper inlet to ensure the best possible distribution of the test air over the chamber. This chamber was later simplified by Laskin, who made it rectangular rather than hexagonal in cross-section, with a pyramidal roof and bottom. It is now the most frequently used chamber, as its construction is cheaper.

*All the animals should inhale the same concentration*

In inhalation experiments, it is very important that all the animals exposed should inhale the same concentration of the substance under investigation. An equal distribution of the test substance over the chamber is therefore essential. The air is usually let in at the top of the chamber and exhausted at the center of the bottom plate. Every object placed inside such a chamber may disturb the airflow pattern and as a result of that the distribution of the test substance in the chamber. This is of particular importance if aerosols are tested, as great differences then arise in the concentrations of the substance in the various locations of the chamber. In the case of gases, these differences are usually limited.

The major objects in the test chamber are the test animals and the cages in which they are kept. Large chambers are generally multitiered. If, in addition, pans are mounted under the cages to collect feces and urine, then there is of course by no means an even distribution of the airflow throughout the chamber.

For this reason, alternative inhalation chambers have been developed, including one type in which the flow is horizontal, and one that has cages that are moved around by means of a rotating suspension mechanism. Neither type of chamber has found general acceptance.

A chamber which is currently much used in various laboratories is a multi-tiered chamber in which cages are placed at different heights, in a kind of zigzag pattern (see Figure 19.1). If sufficient space is left between the cages, a flow pattern results which ensures that all cages receive approximately the same amount of fresh air. The chamber also has a reasonable distribution pattern for aerosols.

There is a wide variety of different chambers, in addition to those described above, ranging from a "jam jar" to chambers measuring 15 m³.

ASSIGNMENT 19.4

Why is a good and even airflow particularly important in the case of aerosols?

### 2.2 EQUIPMENT FOR HEAD/NOSE-ONLY EXPOSURE

The equipment consists of a closed single- or double-walled cylinder (Figure 19.2). There are openings in the cylinder wall in which animal holders can be placed that can hold only one animal. The holders consist of glass or plastic

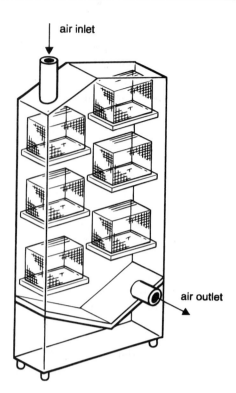

FIGURE 19.1
Diagram of an inhalation chamber for total-body exposure
The cages are placed in a zigzag pattern to ensure good airflow.

tubes, which taper at one end to a more or less conical shape. The conus is shaped such that head and neck of the animal fit into it well enough to seal off the holder air-tight, without injuring the animal. At the other end of the animal holder is a stopper plate which pushes the animal into the conus and prevents it from retracting its head from the conus or turning around. The nose of the animal should protrude somewhat from the holder into the lumen of the cylinder. In a double-walled system, the nose of the animal protrudes into the space between the two walls.

An advantage of the double-walled system (see Figure 19.2b) is that the animals always inhale fresh test atmosphere, while in the single-walled system (Figure 19.2a) the exhaled air of the other animals is added to the test air.

Chambers for head/nose-only exposure are generally kept in a hood with an exhaused system, since there is a slight overpressure in the system, and leakage past the animals is difficult to prevent.

## 2.3    SELECTION OF MATERIALS

The materials from which chambers may be built and their various advantages and disadvantages are listed in Table 19.3.

## 2.4    ANIMAL HOUSING IN INHALATION CHAMBERS

*Lighting*

In total-body inhalation chambers, animals are housed in stainless steel wire cages. If the substance to be tested is an aerosol, the animals should preferably be single housed, since group housed animals will huddle together and hide their nose in the fur of their cage mates. This causes filtration of the test air. In the case of exposure to a gas or vapor, these behavioral factors do not play a role.

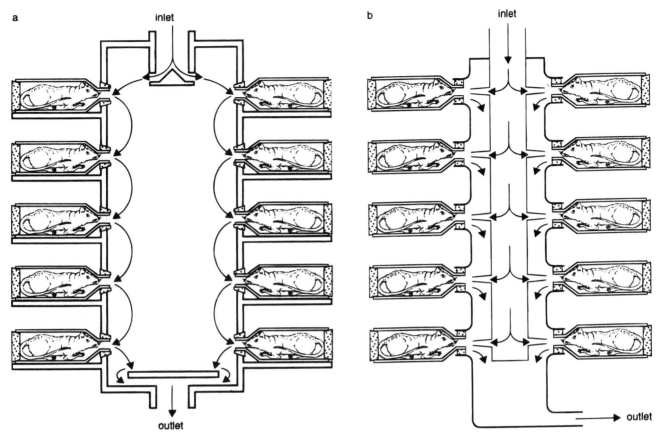

FIGURE 19.2
Diagram of an inhalation chamber for head/nose-only exposure
a. Single-wall system
b. Double-wall system

TABLE 19.3
Some advantages and disadvantages of materials used for the construction of inhalation chambers

| Material | Advantages | Disadvantages |
|---|---|---|
| stainless steel | chemically inert<br>strong<br>durable | expensive |
| aluminium | inexpensive<br>durable<br>fairly strong | not chemically inert<br>difficult to process |
| plastics | light in weight<br>transparent<br>easy to work | vulnerable<br>builds up static electricity<br>permeable to vapors<br>susceptible to damage by chemicals |
| glass | inexpensive<br>durable<br>chemically inert<br>transparent | fragile<br>difficult to process |

If the inhalation chamber contains too many animals, it is very difficult to maintain the temperature and relative humidity within reasonable limits. Moreover, the concentrations of the gases exhaled by the animals and of the degradation products from the feces and urine ($NH_3$) may become unacceptably high. This has led to the general rule that the volume of the total number of animals should not exceed 5% of the volume of the chamber. Inhalation chambers are usually illuminated indirectly (via windows and/or transparent doors) from the room in which they are placed. The inhalation chamber itself does not usually contain any sources of light, on account of lack of space, electrical safety during cleaning with water, danger of explosion if explosive gases are tested, but also because the light intensity is often too high for the animals close to the light source. Albino animals in particular (and most experimental animals are albino rodents) can eventually develop damage to the eyes (retinal injury) if the light intensity is too high.

### 2.4.1 Ventilation

The air required to generate test atmospheres should be cleared of contaminating components. This can be achieved by using dust filters, washers or activated carbon filters. The temperature in the inhalation chamber should be approximately 20–24°C, and the relative humidity about 40–70%. In the case of total-body chambers, the heat and moisture production of the animals themselves should be taken into account, so that the air supplied should usually be dryer and cooler. The air in the inhalation chambers is refreshed at least 10 times per hour, although 15 times is more common. More frequent ventilation is also possible, provided the velocity of the air flow in the chambers does not become too high (not higher than about 0.20 m s⁻¹), to avoid draft.

Temperature, relative humidity, air flow and underpressure have to be monitored continuously.

Exhausted test atmosphere can be cleared of the test substance by means of filters, washers or afterburners, after which it can be discharged.

The chambers are continuously kept under a slight underpressure, to avoid the test substance leaking into the laboratory. A set-up of an inhalation chamber with peripheral equipment is shown in Figure 19.3.

### 2.5 GENERATION OF GASES AND VAPORS

### 2.5.1 General

The generation of a test atmosphere consists of the introduction of a certain amount of a gas or vapor into a certain amount of air. Although a gas and a vapor are the same aggregation state of a substance, they are distinguished for inhalation technical reasons. A vapor then is the gaseous state of aggregation of a substance which at the current barometric pressure has a boiling point higher than the current temperature (room temperature).

The methods for generating a gas or vapor test atmosphere should be such that a homogeneous, stable and well-controllable test atmosphere is obtained. The gases and vapors can be obtained as follows:

1 from gas cylinders;
2 by generating gases by means of a chemical or physical process;
3 by evaporation of a liquid or sublimation of a solid substance.

The preferred method depends on the exposure system to be used.

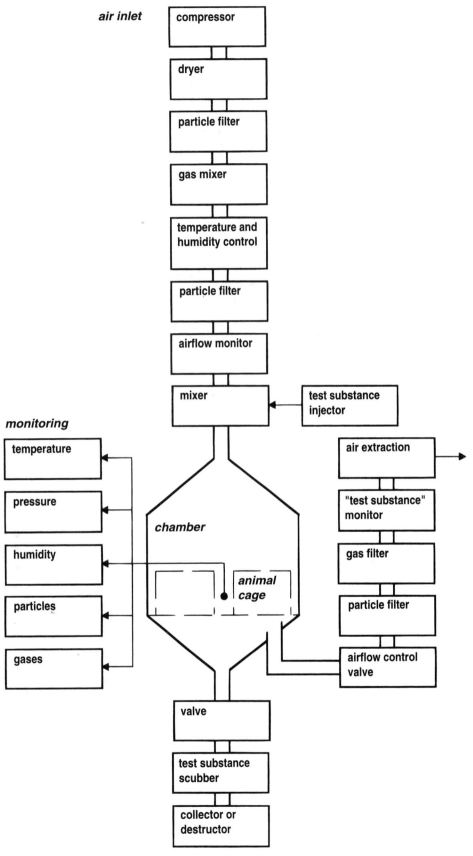

FIGURE 19.3
Inhalation chamber and peripheral equipment

### 2.5.2 Static and dynamic exposure systems

When generating a test atmosphere of gases or vapors, a distinction can be made between static and dynamic systems.

*Dynamic system*

- A *dynamic* system is characterized by a constant supply of newly generated test atmosphere, which is exhausted after it has passed through the inhalation chamber.

*Static system*

- A *static system* is a closed system to which no fresh test atmosphere is supplied.

In by far the most experiments, exposure takes place in a dynamic system. If the description of an inhalation experiment does not specify the system, a dynamic system is usually inferred.

Because a static system is a closed system, the respiration of the animals present will cause the *oxygen content* of the atmosphere to decrease, while the *carbon dioxide content* and the relative *humidity* will rise to unacceptably high values. Technical measures must therefore be taken to supplement the oxygen consumed and to remove the carbon dioxide and water vapor from the atmosphere. In principle, the reduction in oxygen content and the increase in carbon dioxide content are more or less equal. This principle is made use of to keep the composition of the air constant. The static system is used mainly for short experiments with small numbers of animals. It is, for example, applied in research into the metabolism of volatile substances.

ASSIGNMENT  19.5

Explain why only static systems are used in studies into the metabolism of volatile substances.

### 2.5.3 Generating test atmospheres in a static system

A test atmosphere of a gas or volatile liquid in a closed system can be generated by introducing a known volume of the gas or liquid into the known volume of the system. Before the gas or liquid is introduced, a small underpressure is applied to the system to prevent overpressure. After the liquid has been introduced and has evaporated, the pressure is again made equal to the barometric pressure.

The concentration of the gas in the test atmosphere, expressed in ppm (parts per million) then is:

$$C\,(\text{ppm}) = (V_g / V_{st}) \times 10^3 \qquad (19.1)$$

where:

$V_g$ = volume of the gas in ml
$V_{st}$ = volume of the system in l

The concentration can also be expressed in mg $1^{-1}$ or mg m$^{-3}$. To this end, Avogadro's law should be applied, which states that the number of molecules present in equal volumes of gas, at equal pressure and temperature, is the same for all gaseous compounds. At $T = 20°C$ and at a pressure of 1 atm, 1 mole of any gas takes up a volume of 24.2 l. When the concentration is expressed in mg m$^{-3}$, Equation 19.1 reads as follows ($T = 20°C$):

$$C\,(\text{mg m}^{-3}) = (V_g / V_{st}) \times 10^3 \times M / 24.2 \qquad (19.2)$$

where

$V_g$ = volume of the gas in ml

$V_{st}$ = volume of the system in l

$M$ = molecular mass

ASSIGNMENT   19.6

If the concentration of a substance is expressed in mg m$^{-3}$, what is a quick way to calculate the concentration in ppm?

### 2.5.4 Generating gases and vapors in a dynamic system

In a dynamic system, a quantity of test substance is constantly added to a continuous airflow. This is most easily carried out by using compressed gases from air cylinders. Sometimes a gas or vapor needs to be obtained from a continuous chemical or physico-chemical process.

In the case of chemical reactions, a large number of variables may influence the production of the substance concerned, such as the concentrations of the various substances involved, solubility, temperature and the concentrations of the reaction products formed. Such influences can make it very difficult to generate a stable test atmosphere.

Examples of physical methods of generating a test atmosphere are the following:

1   electrolysis;

2   thermic decomposition;

3   photochemical reactions;

4   ionization and other electrical phenomena.

Very different methods are used to generate a test atmosphere from a vapor, a liquid or a solid substance, respectively. The most common systems are the following:

1   direct injection of a highly volatile liquid into the air supplied;

2   atomization of liquids in the air supplied, after which the aerosol rapidly evaporates;

3   evaporation of the substance on a heating element;

4   leading a controlled air or nitrogen flow through or across a supply of liquid or solid substance at a controlled temperature;

5   diffusion using a permeation tube.

### 2.5.5 Control of the test atmosphere

The concentration of a substance in the air can be expressed in two ways, namely as nominal concentration or as actual concentration.

*Nominal concentration*

*Actual concentration*

The *nominal concentration* is the concentration which is theoretically present that can be calculated from the quantity of test material and the volume of air or gas into which it is distributed. The *actual concentration* is the concentration that is actually measured. In principle, these two values should be the same, but in practice the actual concentration is usually somewhat lower than the nominal concentration. The difference is strongly substance-linked, but also system-linked. It is caused by loss of the test substance resulting from instability, adsorption at the walls, absorption and metabolism by the animals, and possibly leakage from the inhalation chamber.

The most common methods of measuring the concentrations of gases or vapors during inhalation experiments are the following:

1   gas chromatography/total carbon analysis;
2   infrared analysis;
3   colorimetry;
4   HPLC;
5   compound-specific sensor;
6   (classical) chemical analytical methods.

## 2.6   ADMINISTRATION OF AEROSOLS

### 2.6.1  Particle size

*Monodisperse aerosol*
*Polydisperse aerosol*

If all the particles in an aerosol are the same size, the aerosol is referred to as a *monodisperse aerosol*. If the particles vary in size, the aerosol is called a *polydisperse aerosol*. Monodisperse aerosols are used, for example, to calibrate instruments and to study deposition in the respiratory tract of animals. Most aerosols to which man is exposed, however, are polydisperse. This is why the great majority of inhalation toxicity studies use polydisperse aerosols.

In inhalation studies with aerosols, it is important to generate particles which can enter the airways. Whether a particle can enter or not depends on its size. It is therefore important to get to know the particle size distribution of the aerosol. Particle size is expressed in terms of the geometric diameter or the aerodynamic diameter.

*Geometric diameter*

The *geometric diameter* is the measured diameter. For a globular particle, it is easy to determine. For irregularly shaped particles, this becomes much more difficult.

*Aerodynamic diameter*

The diameter most frequently used in inhalation toxicology is the *aerodynamic diameter* which is defined as the diameter of a globe with a density of 1, and which has the same sedimentation rate as the particle concerned.

This means that a particle with an aerodynamic diameter of 5 $\mu$m has the same sedimentation rate in air as a globe with a diameter of 5 $\mu$m and a density of 1. It is therefore the aerodynamic diameter that determines whether a particle can follow an air flow bending away, or will precipitate. A fluff particle has a relatively large surface area and a low density. As a result, it will easily be carried with the air flow. The aerodynamic diameter is very small, while the geometric diameter is relatively large. A small piece of lead, in contrast, has a high density and a relatively small surface area. Air therefore has relatively little grip on a lead particle. The aerodynamic diameter is large in relation to the geometric diameter.

For the effect on the lungs, it is the total mass of a substance entering a particular compartment of the respiratory tract which is important. After all, 1000 droplets of 1 $\mu$m diameter will fit into one drop of 10 $\mu$m in diameter. For this reason, the particle size distribution of an aerosol is usually not expressed in terms of number of particles per diameter class, but of the mass distribution of particles which are in the same range of aerodynamic diameter.

### 2.6.2  Aerosol generators

Generating aerosols is much more difficult than generating gas or vapor test atmospheres. In the case of liquids, the viscosity and surface tension of the substance play an important role. In the case of solid substances, the particle size,

*Hygroscopic substances*

the degree of agglomerate formation, static electricity and particle size distribution of the primary particles play an important role. Aerosols may consist of *hygroscopic substances*. If these particles are present in a humid environment, they can absorb water and consequently become larger. This can influence the deposition pattern.

A large number of aerosol generators have been described in the literature. Most generators fall into one of the following two categories:

a    equipment for dispersing dry, powdered substances;

b    atomizers for atomizing liquids.

### 2.6.3  Electrostatic charge

The friction of the particles against the internal surface of the generators may give rise to a strong electric charge on the particles. The presence of that charge will have a great influence on the behavior of the particles in the airways, the degree of agglomeration, and the precipitation in the tubing and on the walls of the inhalation chamber and on the cages. This effect can be so pronounced that less than 1% of the substance introduced is eventually found in the air as a respirable aerosol. By ionizing the air of the aerosol, the electrostatic charge is partly neutralized. Ionization of the air can be achieved by leading the aerosol through a tube containing a krypton-85 radioactive source.

### 2.6.4  Measurement of concentration and characterization of aerosols

Measurement is usually carried out outside the exposure chamber. This means that an amount of test atmosphere must be extracted from the test chamber. To obtain a faithful reflection of the real concentration and the particle size distribution of an aerosol, samples should in principle be taken under isokinetic circumstances. Since inhalation experiments are usually carried out with particles of a diameter less than 10 $\mu$m, which are barely sensitive to non-isokinetic sampling, a sampling speed of 1.25 m s$^{-1}$ is used in practice, which is approximately the speed at which the air travels through the nose.

*Measurement of concentration*

A number of methods used to measure the *concentration* of the aerosol in a test atmosphere are listed in Table 19.4.

*Particle size distribution*

*Particle size distribution* is usually determined with specially developed equipment (see Table 19.5).

### 2.6.5  Other techniques for the administration of aerosols

It is not always possible to administer aerosols via inhalational exposure. Inhalation experiments are very labor-intensive and consequently expensive. Moreover, they sometimes use up large amounts of the substance to be studied. The latter is determined largely by the amount of test atmosphere to be generated, but also by the efficiency during generation of the substance. As a result

TABLE   19.4
Examples of methods to determine aerosol concentrations in inhalation chambers

gravimetric (by weighing filters before and after sampling)
chemical (HPLC, colorimetry, gas chromatography after sampling on filter or in a liquid)
using specially developed instruments (impactors, substance meters, spray meters, etc.)

TABLE 19.5

Examples of instruments and techniques to measure particle size distribution of aerosols in inhalation chambers

| Technique/instrument | Principle |
|---|---|
| cascade impaction (aerodynamic) | Per unit of time, an equal quantity of air is led through ever narrower openings so that the velocity of the airflow is increased in steps. Under each opening, there is a small plate which deflects the airflow. Depending on the velocity, particles are able or unable to follow this change in course; in the latter case they precipitate onto the plate. At high velocities, the large particles precipitate first, followed later by ever smaller particles as the velocity becomes even higher. The amount of aerosol per plate can be measured. |
| aerodynamic particle size meter (APS) | Air is led through a narrow opening and is accelerated. Large particles move less rapidly than smaller ones; the difference in time of passage between two points is measured. |
| condensation nucleus counter (CNC) | Particles are separated by difference in mobility in an artificial electrical field. They are led with a gas through a condenser, so that the gas condenses around the particles. These 'enlarged' particles are counted by optical means. |
| optical detectors | Analyzers measure the light which is dispersed by a particle as it passes through a beam of light. The intensity of the dispersed light is a measure of the size of the particle. |
| light and electron microscopy | — |
| spray meters (geometric) | Particles passing through a beam of light obstruct the light. This can be measured. |

of deposition in the pipes, on the walls of the inhalation chamber, on the cages and on the fur of the animals, a large amount of the substance under investigation is lost. In extreme cases, this may mean that the efficiency is less than 1%.

Administration of the substance to the experimental animals by a route other than inhalation may be for the following reasons:

- the substance is very costly and/or scarce;
- the substance is a great health hazard to man and animals (e.g. strong carcinogens); the risk of human contact with the substance should be restricted to a minimum;
- it is technically not possible to make an aerosol of the substance;
- there are no facilities for inhalation experiments;
- to avoid the complicated "barrier" of the nose in experimental animals and thus approach the human situation of oral breathing and the very simple nasal structure.

Two alternative techniques will now be discussed, namely intratracheal intubation and intrapulmonary implantation.

*Intratracheal intubation*

Instead of exposing animals to a test atmosphere, it is also possible to introduce the substance into the trachea in the form of a suspension. The respiratory movements of the animals distribute the suspension over both lungs, and the particles penetrate into the alveolar spaces. The technique of intratracheal intubation works as follows. The suspension is prepared by suspending the test substance in a physiological saline solution. One should take care that most particles are smaller than 10 $\mu$m. If the material cannot be suspended, a small amount of a non-toxic emulsifier may be added.

The animals to be treated are anesthetized and a certain amount of suspension is injected via a blunted cannula which is inserted through the mouth into the trachea (*intratracheal intubation*). The amount injected depends on the size of the animal. For rats and hamsters this is approximately 0.2–0.5 ml.

This treatment can be repeated on a regular basis, e.g. once a week, for a long period of time and is fairly well tolerated by the animals.

> ASSIGNMENT 19.7
>
> Workers are constantly exposed to a low concentration of a readily soluble aerosol. Is there any point in studying the effects of this substance by means of an intratracheal intubation experiment?

*Intrapulmonary implantation*

In another method, the test substance is mixed with a carrier, for example bees wax. This mixture is made into a pellet which is introduced with a hollow needle into the lungs via the thoracic wall (*intrapulmonary implantation*). From the pellet the test material is then slowly released into the lungs.

This technique is most frequently used to study the carcinogenicity of compounds. An important disadvantage of the above techniques is that they are clearly less comparable to the way in which people are exposed. The following reasons are relevant:

- the upper parts of the respiratory tract are not exposed;
- exposure is unevenly distributed; peak exposure (especially in intubation);
- intratracheal intubation requires repeated anesthesia;
- in the case of implantation, it is not possible to check whether the observed effect was caused only by the test substance, or by the irritation of tissue caused by the presence of the pellet in combination with the test substance.

## 3  Concentration–time and concentration–response relationships

### 3.1  INTRODUCTION

The relationships involved have already been discussed in Study unit 7. The present section will look in greater detail at a number of aspects that are specifically connected with inhalation toxicology. Concentration–time and concentration–response relationships in acute inhalation toxicology can be described by probit relationships, in which a probit is a linear transformation of the sigmoid probability curve of the normal distribution. Experimentally, such a probit relationship can often be described as follows:

$$P = pr = b_0 + b_1 \ln C + b_2 \ln T + b_3 V \qquad (19.3)$$

where:

$P = pr$ = probit (related to % scored response of a well-definable effect);

$b_0, b_1, b_2, b_3$ = coefficients;

$C$ = concentration administered;

$T$ = duration of exposure;

$V$ = any other variables (sex, weight, temperature, etc.);

A. What do the coefficients ($b_0$ to $b_3$) stand for?

B. What influences the value of the coefficients?

C. What can be learned from experimentally determining these factors?

## 3.2   COEFFICIENTS

Consider the simple situation in which an $LC_{50}$ is determined. The concentration is an independent, the response a dependent variable.

$$P = pr = b_0 + b_1 \ln C \tag{19.4}$$

*Width of the distribution curve*

$b_1$ is a measure for the *width of the distribution curve* which has been determined experimentally. If $b_1$ is *large*, then the variation in concentration between a response of 10% and 90% is small (small relative activity range $LC_{90}/LC_{10}$). If $b_1$ is *small*, the variation in concentration between 10% and 90% response is large (large relative activity range $LC_{90}/LC_{10}$).

$b_0$ does not play a role in the assessment of toxicity and can be influenced by many factors, such as the units in which $C$ is expressed (ppm, kg m$^{-3}$, etc.) and $b_1$.

Figure 19.4 shows the concentration–response relationship, in which Equation 19.4 is represented for two substances with equal $LC_{50}$ but different $b_0$ and $b_1$.

If, in addition to the concentration, the exposure time is also varied, the concentration–time response relationship is as follows:

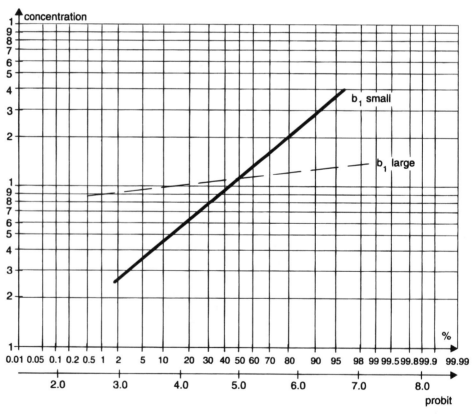

FIGURE   19.4

Effect of coefficients $b_0$ and $b_1$ on the course of the concentration–response relationship of two substances with the same $LC_{50}$ (see also text)

y-axis: concentration (logarithmic presentation) x-axis: effect in probits and corresponding cumulative response in %

$$P = pr = b_0 + b_1 \ln C + b_2 \ln T \qquad (19.5)$$

In this way, the response in relationship to the independent variable $C$ and the response in relationship to the independent variable $T$ are both described as a normal distribution curve. In practice, Equation 19.5 is often written as:

$$P = pr = b_0 + b_2 \ln C^{b_1/b_2} \cdot T = b_0 + b_2 \ln C^n \cdot T \qquad (19.6)$$

Equations 19.5 and 19.6 indicate that the same response may occur at different combinations of $C$ and $T$. If this same response occurs at a constant value for $C \times T$ (total dose administered) then Haber's rule applies. If the same response occurs for a constant value of $C^2 \times T$ ($n = 2$), then halving the concentration means that there is no response until after 4 times the original exposure time. Concentration–time relationships are therefore determined by measuring the response at various combinations of $C$ and $T$, for example by determining the dependence on $C$ for five different periods of exposure. Equation 19.5 is then solved using computer programs for statistical applications, such as Genstat.

*$n = b_1/b_2$*
*Haber's rule*

If $n = 1$, the same response is observed for a constant dose ($C \times T$). In this case, the concentration–time response relationship agrees with *Haber's rule*. Haber found a similar relationship while experimenting with the war gas phosgene.

If $C$ is the concentration, and $T$ the time, then the product of the two (K = the toxic effect) is constant:

$$C \times T = K$$

This is Haber's rule, which can be applied to poisonous gases and in many (although not all) other cases.

For most gases for which the concentration–time and concentration–response relationship has been measured, $n$ is found to be greater than 1. It has also been found that $n$ can vary with the duration of exposure.

Figure 19.5 shows how time dependence in $n$ is expressed in $LC_{50}$ observations. The value of $\ln C$ at $LC_{50}$ is plotted against $\ln T$ for three different substances. The line at 45° corresponds to $n = 1$ (Haber's rule). For $n > 1$, the slope of the line is less steep. The concave line shows that $n$ increases with time $T$.

If factors for sex and/or weight are incorporated into Equation 19.3 as indicated, the factors $b_1$ and $b_2$ are assumed not to be affected, and that men and women, for example, may differ in absolute sensitivity, but that the relative activity range will remain constant ($LC_{90}/LC_{10}$). In other words the slope remains the same. Exposure to ammonia is a good example of this. However, such a simplification is certainly not always allowable.

### 3.3 FACTORS DETERMINING COEFFICIENTS

*Individual differences*

Individual sensitivity is only one of the factors determining the relative activity range. Together with the mode of action of the substance concerned, also *individual differences* in absorption rate (respiratory minute volume, cardiac output), distribution (individual differences in perfusion of the various compartments of the body) and metabolism kinetics (first-order, zero-order) are important determinants of the activity range. These factors also determine the ratio $b_1/b_2 = n$. This can be illustrated by the following (fictitious) examples.

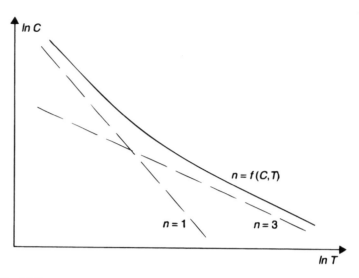

FIGURE 19.5
Effect of factor $n$ on the shape of the concentration–time and concentration–response relationship curve
The figure shows the lines for $n = 1$, $n = 3$ and the line indicating the slope for the various curves (see also text).

*The substance as irritant*

1 The *substance* acts exclusively and reversibly as an *irritant* in the respiratory tract and there is a direct relationship between its concentration in the surface tissue of the airways and breathing frequency.

After only a few inhalations, the concentration in the surface tissue of the airways has reached a fixed fraction of the concentration supplied. This means that the relative activity range with respect to the concentration ($b_1$) depends only on the individual sensitivity. There is no dependence on the exposure time ($b_2 = 0$); $n = b_1/b_2 = \infty$ (infinite).

*The irritant is a metabolite*

2 The *irritation* is not caused by the substance itself but by a *metabolite* which is formed in the tissue and accumulates there. First-order or zero-order kinetics may apply in this situation.

*First-order kinetics*

—*First-order kinetics*
The concentration of the metabolite, $C_m^{(t)}$, depends on the concentration of the substance ($C$), the exposure time ($T$) and the metabolic rate constant ($k$).

$$C_m^{(t)} = \int_0^T k \cdot C \, dt = k \cdot C \cdot T \tag{19.7}$$

$C_m^{(0)}$ shows the characteristic of the dose relationship $C \times T$ (Haber's rule), with $n = 1$.

*Zero-order kinetics*

—*Zero-order kinetics*
$C_m$ is independent of the concentration supplied ($b_1 = 0$) and increases linearly with time. $b_2$ is finite and depends on the individual metabolic capacity. For this situation, $b_1/b_2 = n = 0$.

*Systemic effect*

3 The action of the substance is *systemic* only, and its effect depends on the concentration in the arterial blood ($C_B$).

*Linear increase*

—Shortly after the start of exposure, $C_B$ increases linearly with time;
$C_B = k \times C \times T$. Again, $n = 1$ for the dose–response relationship. The rate at

which $C_B$ increases depends, among other things, on the respiratory minute volume and cardiac output which may vary individually and influence $b_1$.

*Equilibrium*

—After a long period of exposure, an *equilibrium* sets in between $C_B$ and $C$. At that moment, $C_B$ is no longer dependent on $T$ ($b_2 = 0$) and $n = b_1/b_2 = \infty$. $b_1$ no longer depends on the respiratory minute volume and cardiac output. As a result, the relative activity range will be reduced, in other words, $b_1$ becomes larger.

Figure 19.6 shows how the course of the concentrations in the blood and in the liver change after step-wise alterations in the concentration in the atmosphere supplied with a test substance with a small blood-gas partition coefficient ($\lambda$).

*Systemic action; metabolism in the liver*

4 *Systemic action* of a *metabolite* of the substance administered. *Metabolism* takes place *in the liver*. Metabolites formed are released directly into the blood. Again, kinetics may be first-order or zero-order.

*First-order kinetics after exposure*

—*First-order kinetics* (immediately *after exposure*). Shortly after exposure, the concentration in the blood is:

$$C_B = k \times C \times T$$

The quantity of metabolite formed, distributed over the body, will now be:

$$C_m = k \int_0^T C \cdot t \, dt = \frac{1}{2} k \cdot C \cdot T^2 \tag{19.8}$$

From Equation 19.8 it follows that $n = 1/2$.

The activity range depends on respiratory minute volume, cardiac output and liver perfusion.

*First-order kinetics (saturation)*

—*First-order kinetics* (saturation). The blood concentration becomes saturated, e.g. $C_B$ approaches $C$.

$$C_m = k \int_0^T C \, dt = k \cdot C \cdot T \tag{19.9}$$

This means that when saturation is reached, $n = 1$.

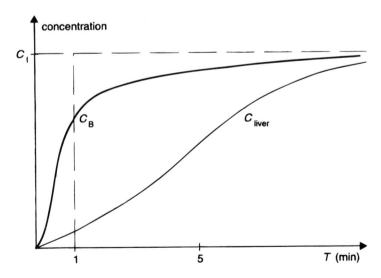

FIGURE 19.6
Relationship between exposure time ($T$) and the concentrations of substances in the inhaled air ($C_I$), in the blood ($C_B$) and in the liver ($C_{liver}$)

The activity range no longer depends on the respiratory minute volume and the cardiac output. The activity range will decrease ($b_1$ increases).

*Zero-order kinetics (saturated metabolism)*

—*Zero-order kinetics (saturated metabolism)*. After a very short initial period (see under first-order kinetics, immediately after exposure), $C_m$ becomes independent of $C_B$ or $C$. This means that $n = 0$. The activity range as a function of time ($b_2$) becomes highly dependent on, for example, individual differences in metabolic capacity, which does not play a role in the case of first-order kinetics.

## 3.4 RELEVANCE OF DETERMINING CONCENTRATION–RESPONSE RELATIONSHIPS

*Conclusion*

As is apparent from the above examples, $b_1/b_2 = n$ may vary from 0 to $\infty$, both for irritants and for substances acting systemically. For the processes discussed, substances acting directly ($1 \leq n < \infty$) and substances exerting their effect via a metabolite ($0 < n < 1$) can be distinguished. The examples also showed that time-dependent changes in the relative activity range are related to the substance's mode of action. Experimental determination of the concentration–time and concentration–response relationships therefore provides useful information for the study of the mode of action of a substance, which is of major importance both as regards risk analysis and when extrapolating to other species or to human beings.

# 4 Extrapolation of animal data to human beings

## 4.1 INTRODUCTION

In addition to the results of epidemiological and toxicological research in man and the results of in vitro studies, information obtained from toxicological research in animals makes it possible to predict the harmful effects of substances in man. The more adequate the toxicity study is carried out and the closer the study approaches the human situations the greater it's predictive value for man. Except for the occasional general remark, this section concentrates exclusively on those aspects of extrapolation that are relevant to inhalation studies only.

*Qualitative aspect*

Extrapolation has a qualitative and a quantitive element. The *qualitative aspect* concerns the *nature of the harmful effect*. For example: does the substance cause hepatic degeneration, or degeneration of the tubular epithelium in the kidney, or damage to brain cells, or pulmonary edema? If there are no indications to the contrary, it is assumed that the same type of injury is induced in man as was observed in experimental animals.

*Quantitative aspect*

The *quantitative aspect* concerns the question *at what dose* the harmful effect occurs, or, from a more practical point of view, what is the lowest dose that causes a harmful effect that can only just be observed (minimum adverse effect level). Of even greater practical importance for extrapolation is the highest dose at which the harmful effect is no longer observed (no-observed-adverse-effect level; NOAEL).

One component of the qualitative element that can greatly increase the predictive value of toxicity data obtained in experimental animals is knowledge of the way in which a harmful effect is brought about (the substance's mode of action). This is partly so because studies on the mode of action are now not only carried out in (cells and tissues of) experimental animals, but to an increasing extent also in cells and tissues of human orgin. The closer the metabolism of human beings corresponds to that of the animal species, the higher the predictive value of the animal data for the human situation.

*Phases of extrepolation*

Quantitative extrapolation comprises two phases. The first phase consists of the bridging of the *difference in body size* between the experimental animal and human beings. The second phase is the application of *safety factors* intended to compensate for uncertainties such as observational errors and species differences in the mode of action of the substance and sensitivity. The following section will briefly discuss a number of aspects specific to extrapolation of inhalation toxicity data.

## 4.2 BRIDGING T1HE DIFFERENCE IN BODY SIZE

*Extrapolation on the basis of energy requirement*

It is generally accepted that in the case of inhalation experiments, there is no need to correct for difference in body size. The NOAEL found in the experimental animal is also the no-observed-adverse-effect level for man. This approach is based on the fact that for both man and animals one of the reasons for breathing is to cover their oxygen need (= energy need). They are therefore automatically exposed to substances present in the inhaled air in proportion to their energy needs. Correction should, however, be made for differences in exposure time between the animal experiment and the human situation. For the workplace, a standard is used of 8 hours per day, 5 days per week, for a duration of 40 years. For the population at large, calculations are based on exposure for 24 hours per day, 7 days per week, for a period of 70 years. Common patterns of exposure in animal experiments are 6 hours per day, 5 days per week for 4, 13, 52 or 104 weeks.

---

EXAMPLE

In a 13-week inhalation experiment in rats with a certain gas (exposure 6 hours per day, 5 days per week), a NOAEL of 100 mg m$^{-3}$ of air was found. Furthermore, the lowest concentration at which a harmful effect (necrosis of the renal tubules) was observed was 300 mg m$^{-3}$. On the basis of the usual 5-day working week of 8 hours per day, the NOAEL for workers becomes $6/8 \times 100 = 75$ mg m$^{-3}$. This calculation does not, however, take into account uncertainties such as potential species differences between rats and humans. These uncertainties should be accounted for in the safety factor, which could in this case (arbitrarily) be established at 10. Application of that safety factor then leads to a recommended value (for a MAC value) of 7.5 mg m$^{-3}$. The recommended value of this gas for an air quality guideline for the population as a whole can be determined from the above animal data as follows. For man, the NOAEL established for the rat (100 mg m$^{-3}$) becomes $6/24 \times 5/7 \times 100 = 17.9$ mg m$^{-3}$. Application of a safety factor of 20 (see section 4.3, on safety factors) gives a recommended value of 0.9 mg m$^{-3}$.

---

In the calculations carried out above, it was assumed that the product of concentration and exposure time is constant ($C \times T =$ constant). This is by no means always the case. If the true concentration–time response relationship is known (which is hardly ever the case), then this should of course be accounted for in the calculation.

Nor did the above example include a correction for the (maximum) exposure time of 40 years for workers and 70 years for the general population. As it happens, in practice this is usually not corrected for when non-carcinogenic effects are concerned. Extrapolation of inhalation toxicity data on the basis of body weight is applied less and less, as this method is scientifically not quite correct and involves more uncertainties than extrapolation on the basis of energy requirement. However, just to illustrate, extrapolation on the basis of body weight is applied to the experiment in rats described above.

---

EXAMPLE

Calculation is as follows:

On the basis of a respiratory minute volume of 125 ml for a rat weighing 200 g, it can be calculated that rats inhale 225 l of air per kg body weight in 6 hours. The NOAEL expressed in mg per kg body weight per day thus becomes $100 \times 0.225 = 22.5$. If a worker weighing 70 kg inhales 8 m$^3$ of air during an 8-hour working day, the NOAEL at the workplace is 197 mg m$^{-3}$ (70 $\times$ 22.5 divided by 8). For this method of extrapolation, a safety factor of 15 seems suitable. Application of that safety factor then results in a recommended value of 13.1 mg m$^{-3}$.

A recommended value for the general population can be derived as follows: if a person weighing 70 kg inhales 15 m$^3$ of air during 24 hours, the NOAEL is 105 mg m$^{-3}$ (70 $\times$ 22.5 divided by 15). Application of a safety factor of 30 (see section 4.3) gives a recommended value of 3.5 mg m$^{-3}$ for the population.

---

4.3   SAFETY FACTORS

Safety factors are applied to reduce the chance that the recommended exposure level leads to detrimental effects on health in man. Examples of variations and uncertainties that safety factors should cover, are: inter- and intraspecies variations in sensitivity, observation errors, uncertainties in bridging the difference in body size between experimental animals and humans, and the possibility of interaction in the case of simultaneous exposure to various substances.

The magnitude of the safety factor is arbitrary and may vary greatly, for example from 2 to 100 or more. A safety factor of 100 is very common and is always used in establishing the Acceptable Daily Intake (ADI) based on oral toxicity experiments and extrapolation on the basis of body weight. Practice has proved the usefulness of this factor in nutritional toxicology (see Study unit 36). Since extrapolation in inhalation toxicity experiments usually is mostly based on energy need, a smaller safety factor of 30, for example, is usually sufficient. Even so, establishing the magnitude of the safety factor is still an arbitrary matter. It should be carried out by toxicologists experienced in this field, after they have studied all available toxicity data and have carefully considered the abovementioned aspects to be accounted for.

> ASSIGNMENT   19.8
>
> Why is it that the safety factor for extrapolation to the work situation can be smaller than that for extrapolation to the general population?

The more relevant, high quality information is available, the smaller the safety factor can be and the more realistic and reliable the recommended value for an acceptable level of exposure for man can be. Determining a safety factor is a matter of much deliberation, and independent experts operating as private persons have their own social background. Therefore, it is absolutely necessary that the way in which a recommended value has been reached and the considerations which have played a role in establishing the safety factor, should be made public in sufficient detail.

## 5    Summary

The present study unit discussed the various forms of inhalation toxicity research, such as acute, subacute, subchronic and chronic studies. Experimental animals can be exposed to test atmospheres in various ways, e.g. via total-body or head/nose-only systems. The preferred method has consequences for the housing of the animals and for the generation and measurement of the actual concentrations in the test atmosphere. The differences between test materials in the form of a gas or vapor, and those in the form of an aerosol should also be taken into account. For acute toxicity experiments, this study unit has shown how the concentration–time response relationships which are so important for risk analysis can be calculated by means of probit analysis. The connection between these relationships and the toxicokinetic and metabolic properties of the tested compound were also highlighted. Finally, the problems of extrapolation to a different exposure time and concentration on the one hand and to a different species on the other conclude this study unit.

## SELF ASSESSMENT QUESTIONS

1    For the assessment of an acute risk due to a substance for man, an inhalation risk test is of greater value than an $LC_{50}$ experiment. Explain why this is so.

2    Why is an overpressure maintained in a head/nose-only system?

3    Does a droplet with a density of 2 and a geometric diameter of 1 μm have a smaller or a larger aerodynamic diameter than a droplet of 1 μm and a density of 1?

4    In an experiment with mice intended to determine the concentration–time relationship for $H_2S$, both the 50% mortality value and the 50% righting reflex (failure of an animal turned on its back to get back on its legs within one second) were determined. The concentration–time curves of both variables are shown in Figure 19.7.

The course of the $LC_{50}$ is best described by a straight line.
a.   What does this show for the value of $n$?

The response for the righting reflex (RR 50%) appears to be better represented by a convex curve.
b.   What does this show for the value of $n$?

In case b, the following values can be calculated if the concentration is varied and the exposure time is kept constant:
1 min = 10.3
2.5 min = 10.6
5 min = 8.4
7.5 min = 7.5

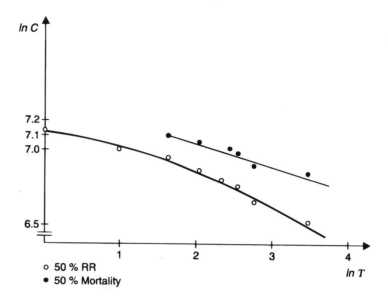

FIGURE 19.7

Concentration–time curves for $H_2S$ in mice; 50% mortality values and 50% righting reflexes (RR)

10 min = 9.07
12.5 min = 6.8
15 min = 7.2
30 min = 5.7.

c. Does this entirely explain the change in $n$?

5  During their work in an office building, a typist and a cleaner are exposed daily to a hepatotoxic gas. Which of the two runs the highest risk of hepatic injury if the MAC value for this gas is exceeded?

6  A gas is itself cytotoxic to the nasal mucosa, while another gas induces renal injury (mechanism unknown). On the basis of what consideration might in the first case a smaller safety factor be acceptable than in the second?

## FEEDBACK

1  **Answers to the assignments**

19.1 Compared to inhalation toxicity research, epidemiological research is very insensitive due to the generally relatively low exposure levels, the simultaneous exposure to other substances and the heterogeneous group of individuals. Moreover, reliable exposure data are rarely available.

19.2 In general, no pulmonary macrophage test will be carried out in the context of research into gases or vapors. Phagocytic function may, however, very well be impaired by the gas or vapor, so that the defense system of the lungs against, for example, microorganisms may be reduced.

19.3 The light-microscopic picture is a two-dimensional projection of a three-dimensional form. If the amount of connective tissue is increased by, for example, 50%, which is in fact rather much, the increase can easily be determined chemically. In the two-dimensional light-microscopic picture, however, it shows up as no more than a 31% increase, which is impossible or very difficult to discern. A smaller increase in the amount of connective tissue will be even more difficult, if not impossible, to observe by light microscopy.

19.4 The loss of aerosol particles as a result of sedimentation and deposition on cages is quite considerable in comparison to the loss of gas or vapor as a result of absorption. A constant supply of fresh aerosol is therefore necessary. Moreover, in an area where the flow is reduced, the loss of gas can be compensated for by diffusion from well-ventilated areas.

19.5 The decrease in the concentration of a substance as a result of the animal's metabolism cannot be measured in a dynamic system due to the surplus of the substance to be studied. In a static system, the test substance is not replenished so that absorption and metabolism by the animal will lead to a reduction in its concentration. Moreover, the formation of any volatile metabolites will be measurable in a closed system.

19.6 $C \text{ (mg m}^{-3}) = V_g/V_s \times 10^3 \times M/24.2 = C \text{ (ppm)} \times M/24.2$
in other words, ppms are obtained by multiplying the number of mg by $M/24.2$.

19.7 No. A readily soluble substance already dissolves while the suspension is being made. This solution will enter the lungs. For a brief period of time, the pulmonary tissue will be exposed to a high concentration, after which the substance is taken up into the blood and transported elsewhere. The occupational situation is completely different. It is therefore necessary to select an inhalation experiment in which animals are, for example, constantly exposed to a relatively low concentration for 6 hours per day.

19.8 In a group of workers, the intraspecies variation is smaller than in the general population, since workers form a more homogeneous group (no children, elderly people or sick people). Moreover, workers who are highly sensitive to a particular substance can find work elsewhere, at least in principle. Another consideration is that the concentration of substances in the ambient air at the workplace can be measured relatively easily, so that intervention is possible if the MAC value is (almost) exceeded.

## 2 Answers to the self assessment questions

1 An $LC_{50}$ value only gives an indication of the acute toxicity of a substance, but does not give any information on whether the substance is easily inhaled. An inhalation risk test gives the resultant of the volatility of a substance or its capacity to be atomized, combined with its toxicity. A highly volatile, only mildly toxic substance can thus, in practice, be much more dangerous than a highly toxic, but not very volatile substance.

2 As has been stated, there is always a chance that air will leak past the animal. In the case of underpressure, air leaks in past the head of the animal. This air mixes with the test atmosphere and thus dilutes it. This cannot happen when there is overpressure.

3    The aerodynamic diameter of the first droplet is larger. Since the density is greater and the diameter remains the same, the sedimentation rate of the first particle is higher.

4    a.    $n$ for the mortality data is 6.3 (check in Figure 19.7).

    b.    $n$ decreases at longer exposure times.

    c.    $n$ calculated from the tangent line to the curve from point $\ln T = 0$ and $\ln T = 3$ is reduced from $n = 10$ to $n = 4$. The change in $b_1$ therefore almost fully explains the change in $n$; $b_2$ will be virtually constant.

5    The cleaner's job is physically harder than that of the typist. This means that the cleaner's oxygen demand is greater. She inhales more air, and is thus exposed to a larger amount of the hepatotoxic substance than the typist. It is therefore the cleaner who runs a higher risk of liver injury if the MAC value is exceeded.

6    For the substance that appeared to have a direct cytotoxic effect, the chance of a metabolite being formed in man which is more toxic than the parent substance is smaller than for the nephrotoxic, systemically acting substance, of which the metabolism is not known.

# Contents Study unit 20
# Gastrointestinal toxicology: structure, function and enterohepatic circulation

0-8493-9232-2/96/$0.00 + $.50
© 1996 by CRC Press, Inc.

# Gastrointestinal toxicology: structure, function and enterohepatic circulation

*W. Coussement*

INTRODUCTION

It is a well-known fact that the use of aspirin (acetylsalicylic acid) may cause hemorrhaging in the gastrointestinal tract. The mechanism underlying gastroduodenal ulceration caused by the use of aspirin has, however, still not been completely explained. Alcohol aggravates aspirin-induced lesions.

> ### "Poisoned soil causes illness in children"
>
> Dieren (The Netherlands)—"Some of the inhabitants of a new housing estate in the city of Dieren fear that the symptoms of illness recently shown by their children are due to soil pollution. Four years ago, evidence of serious pollution was found under the buildings, which are less than 10 years old. Some of the 49 houses were built on a former rubbish dump. The soil was shown to contain carbide, slack, household refuse, paint residues, solvents, industrial waste and rubble. The groundwater is polluted with phenols, ammonia and the solvents, perchloroethylene and trichloroethylene. The polluted ground is covered by only a thin layer of clean soil.
>
> The parents have called for an investigation because of the symptoms shown by their children. Several children have *gastrointestinal complaints*. The authorities have promised to give a definite answer on the action that will be taken to decontaminate the polluted soil before 1 July of this year."

This article, from a Dutch regional newspaper, suggests that exposure to environmental contaminants may cause toxic effects in the gastrointestinal tract. In the course of the following two study units, it will become clear that environmental contaminants can indeed cause toxic effects in the gastrointestinal tract. The gastrointestinal system is one of the larger organ systems of the human body. It is also one of the major routes for entry and thus the first site of contact for many xenobiotics in the body. Acute lesions in the gastrointestinal tract may lead to life-threatening disorders and may sometimes be fatal.

These two study units give an overview of the methods used to trace chemically induced gastrointestinal toxicity, illustrated by some examples. The function of the gastrointestinal wall is, on the one hand, to form a barrier to ingested substances and on the other to act as a 'modifier' of specific substances. Knowledge of the basic principles governing the normal gastrointestinal system is essential in understanding the mechanisms of absorption and metabolism. Therefore a brief description of the normal morphology of the gastrointestinal tract will be given. In addition, the toxic effects of xenobiotics on the gastrointestinal tract will be covered in detail.

LEARNING OBJECTIVES

After studying this unit you are expected to be able to

— describe the structure and function of the gastrointestinal tract as relevant to toxicology

— indicate how and by what mechanisms xenobiotics can be absorbed into the gastrointestinal tract

— describe the factors influencing the absorption of xenobiotics

— indicate how the enterohepatic circulation may influence the availability of xenobiotics

— describe the role of the gastrointestinal tract in the elimination and excretion of xenobiotics

— explain the factors that influence fecal excretion of xenobiotics and their mode of action

— name the main biotransformation processes in the enterocyte

— describe the role of the intestinal flora in modifying the absorption, elimination and toxic effects of xenobiotics in the gastrointestinal tract.

*Study hints*

In studying gastrointestinal toxicology, it is essential to have sufficient knowledge of the structure and function of the gastrointestinal tract. Should you have any doubts as to the adequacy of your knowledge in this field, it is recommended that you review gastrointestinal anatomy and physiology from a general textbook of anatomy and physiology before studying this unit. The study units on exposure (Study unit 2) and on absorption and excretion (Study unit 5) also cover various topics related to gastrointestinal toxicology. You may find it useful to read these units again. The study load of this unit should be no more than 4 hours.

The optional available CD-I program *"Toxicological Histopathology"* provides various examples of histopathological phenomena resulting from toxic lesions of the gastrointestinal tract.

STUDY CORE

## 1 Morphology of the gastrointestinal tract

Knowledge of the morphology of the gastrointestinal tract is necessary to understand the effects of various xenobiotics. Besides knowing the classic disposition and biotransformation, it is also important to know how the various organ systems grow, differentiate, proliferate, adapt and recover after exposure to toxic agents.

*Gastrointestinal tract*

The digestive systems of common laboratory animals (rat, mouse, rabbit, dog) and that of man are very similar anatomically and morphologically. Based on

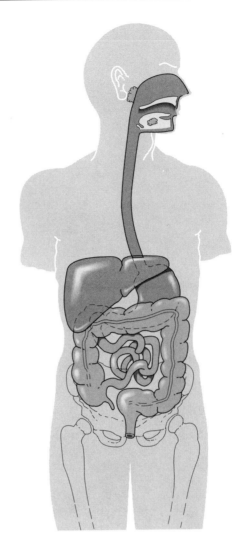

FIGURE   20.1
*In situ* position of the various elements of the gastrointestinal tract in man.

function and morphology, the digestive tract can be subdivided into the oral cavity, esophagus, stomach, small intestine and large intestine. The digestive tract starts at the oral cavity and ends at the anus (Figure 20.1).

*Oral cavity*

The oral cavity is lined by stratified squamous epithelium, which may be more or less keratinized. The degree of keratinization depends on the location. The tongue and palate are highly keratinized (as they are subject to great mechanical friction). The muscular tissue is composed of striated voluntary muscle.

*Pharynx*

The pharynx is morphologically very similar to the oral cavity, except for the muscles. They are also striated, but in this case, involuntary.

*Esophagus*

The morphology of the esophagus reflects its mechanical function. The lining is keratinized stratified squamous epithelium, supported by the lamina propria of wide-mesh collagenous connective tissue. The muscular coat has two layers, a firm inner circular muscle and an outer longitudinal muscle. The propulsion of the food bolus is effected by the opposing muscle layers.

*Stomach*

The *stomach* is a bag-like widening of the digestive tube (Figure 20.2a). In it, food is mixed and enzymes are secreted. The morphology of the stomach varies with

609

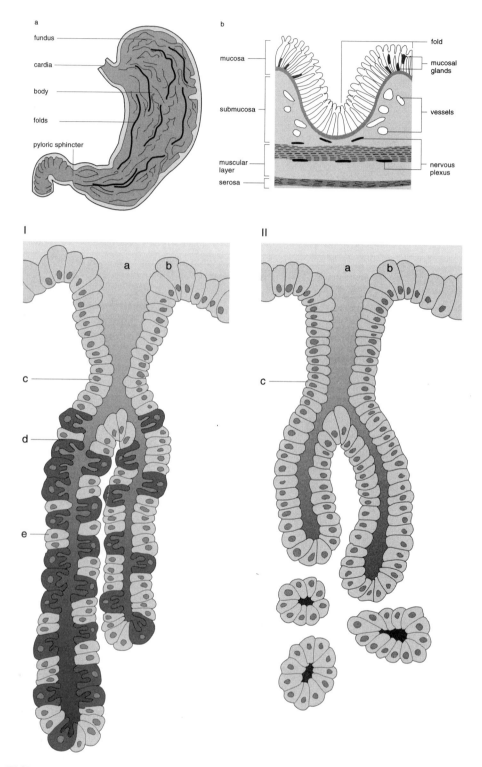

FIGURE 20.2

The stomach

a. longitudinal section of the stomach

b. cross-section of the stomach wall

c. longitudinal section through a gastric gland in the fundus (I) and through a cardial or pyloric gland (II)

a = stomach groove; b = mucous surface epithelial cell; c = mucous neck cell; d = parietal cell; e = chief cell.

the species. In man, the stomach can be subdivided into the cardia, fundus, body and pylorus.

The stomach of the rat has its own specific anatomy. A fold separates the forestomach from the true glandular stomach. This fold is the reason that rats cannot vomit.

The stomach wall (Figure 20.2b) contains cardial, fundal, body and pyloric glands. The cardial glands contain differentiated and undifferentiated mucosal cells. Cell types include *columnar cells* of the mucosa as well as *endocrine cells*. The glands of the fundus and body (Figure 20.2c) are made up of various types of specialized cells. At the surface there are *goblet cells,* producing mucus. The *neck cells* are stem cells responsible for the production of new adult cells. The *chief cells* produce pepsinogen. Oxyntic cells also release acid into the lumen. The muscular layer of the stomach consists of an inner longitudinal, a middle circular and an outer longitudinal layer.

> How does the stomach mucosa offer protection against (some) xenobiotics?

The stomach mucosa provides protection against xenobiotics by means of its mucous layer and its low pH.

*Intestines*

The intestines include the duodenum, jejunum and ileum. The histological structure of each of these parts is virtually identical, with only a few local differences (Figure 20.3). Digestion and absorption are the main functions of this portion of the gastrointestinal tract. The mucosal coat forms the villi and contains the crypts of Lieberkühn. The villi are difficult to discern macroscopically. They are packed close together, as seen under the microscope. The glands of Lieberkühn are short, tubular structures that open between the villi.

*Enterocytes*

*Enterocytes* or *absorptive cells* (Figure 20.4) are columnar epithelial cells with a striated border. They are the most common cells on the villi. Electron microscopy shows the striated border to consist of parallel cylindrical microvilli. On the cell membrane of these microvilli there are microfilaments consisting of mucopolysaccharides.

> What is the role of these microfilaments?

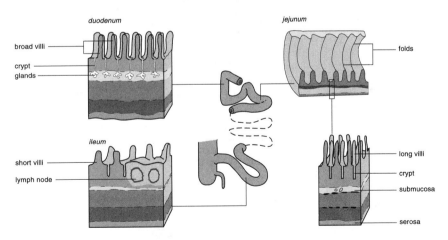

FIGURE   20.3
Local differences within the small intestine.
The height of the villi and the number of villi per unit of surface area decrease towards the ileum. Lymph nodes typically occur in the ileum.

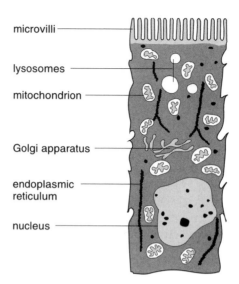

FIGURE 20.4
Typical structure of a cell of the (small) intestine (= enterocyte)

These microfilaments protect the microvilli against proteolytic enzymes, and thus prevent autodigestion of the intestinal wall. The microvilli provide various enzymes that play a role in the final steps of the digestion of nutrients. The villi and microvilli provide the small intestine with a very large surface area, eminently suitable for the absorption of nutrients.

*Goblet cell*

Mucus-secreting *goblet cells* are scattered among the more numerous enterocytes. The mucous mass is always secreted as a whole and protects the epithelium against mechanical damage.

*Paneth's cell*

*Paneth's cells* are rare and occur mainly in the crypts of Lieberkühn. They contain typical eosinophilic granules. These cells are thought to produce a bacteriolytic enzyme called *lysozyme*.

The *lamina propria* contains many blood and lymph vessels. The *submucosa* of the duodenum is characterized by the presence of Brünner's glands.

The intestine has two muscular layers: the inner layer is circular and the outer longitudinal.

The large intestine consists of the cecum, appendix, colon, rectum and anal canal. The mucosa of the large intestine does not have villi and the intestinal crypts are considerably longer. The various epithelial cell types are analogous to those of the small intestine. The crypts contain more goblet cells than the small intestine. As a result, less absorption takes place here.

The *anus* is a short canal that forms the transition between intestinal mucosa and normal skin. Its mucosa is characterized by a stratified, moderately keratinized squamous epithelium. The lamina propria contains a venous plexus. The muscular layer includes a circular layer that fuses to form the anal sphincter.

*High mitotic activity*

Of all the organs, the gastrointestinal tract displays the highest mitotic activity. This is very important for its toxicology. Rapid division and replacement of cells is an important adaptive mechanism of the gastrointestinal tract. Disturbance of mitotic kinetics leads to various pathological conditions. Mitotic activity is highest in the small intestine (see also Figure 20.5). The proliferative activity of the cells has a certain rhythm. The stomach reaches its peak activity at approx-

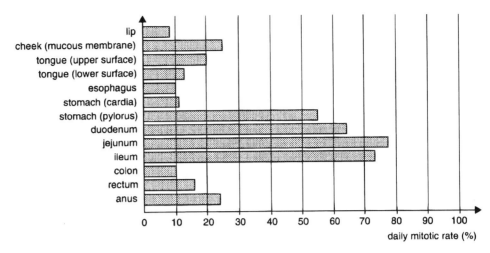

FIGURE 20.5
Percentages of cells renewed by mitosis each day in the epithelium of various parts of the gastrointestinal tract (rat).
The figure shows that mitotic activity is relatively low at the beginning and end of the gastrointestinal tract and reaches a peak in the area of the stomach and small intestine.

imately 4 p.m. and 5 a.m. Mitotic activity in the small intestine is regulated by hormones, including corticosteroids and prolactin.

Certain xenobiotics, in particular drugs such as salicylates, steroids, non-steroidal anti-inflammatory drugs and prostaglandins, interfere with proliferative activity, leading to an increased loss of cells. The gastrointestinal mucosa has the most rapid turnover of the entire body. The migration of enterocytes is accompanied by continuous proliferation and differentiation.

> What are the consequences of increased and decreased cell production?

Increased cell production and increased age of cells may result in hyperplasia. Increased loss of cells or reduced cell proliferation may lead to atrophy or ulceration.

As was mentioned above, the gastrointestinal epithelium retains the same basic structure and migration cycle along the entire tract. It is only the daily mitotic rate that differs.

Figure 20.5 shows the daily mitotic rate in the epithelium of the various parts of the gastrointestinal tract of an adult rat.

## 2 Gastrointestinal physiology

The most important functions of the gastrointestinal tract are the digestion of ingested substances and the absorption of these products, together with water and electrolytes. In order to function properly, the various parts of the gastrointestinal system must operate as a unit, both anatomically and functionally.

*Absorption*

Although the basic structure of the digestive tract is the same from mouth to anus, considerable local differences may be found. In the stomach, for example, very little *absorption* takes place, except for a few lipid-soluble substances, in particular alcohol. The small intestine is the site of greatest absorption of food. It is also where a large proportion of the absorption of vitamins, minerals, monosaccharides, amino acids and water occurs. The bile salts are absorbed primarily in the ileum. The function of the colon, finally, is to absorb large quantities of liquid and electrolytes.

*Barrier*

The mucosa of the small intestine is an important *barrier* to the absorption of liquid and other materials from the intestinal lumen into the circulation. This barrier is reinforced by the presence of a so-called "tight junction" complex. The junctions are impermeable to large molecules, but they allow passage of smaller molecules and water. Calcium plays an important role in maintaining these tight junctions. For a long time, the mechanism by which water is taken up from the intestinal lumen remained a mystery. Water is absorbed together with the food. The transport of liquid takes place via the lateral intercellular spaces and is driven by the osmotic pressure gradients between the cellular and the intercellular compartments.

*Smooth muscle cell*

The *smooth muscle cells* of the intestine ensure that the contents of the intestine are mixed. They produce a longitudinal movement of the intestinal contents so that the digestive enzymes have the greatest opportunity to exert their effects.

The smooth muscle cells are present in the gastrointestinal tract from the middle of the esophagus to the anus. In certain parts, such as the sphincters, they have undergone specific changes. The smooth muscle cells are arranged both longitudinally and circularly. An important structural feature of smooth muscle cells is the presence of 'cell-to-cell junctions'. These allow a direct mechanical contact between the cells.

*Transit mechanism*

The mechanism which moves a food bolus from the mouth to the stomach is a strictly ordered sequence of events. The swallowed bolus is moved to the pharynx by lifting and retracting the tongue against the palate. In this phase, breathing stops and the bolus is transported to the esophagus through contraction of the pharyngeal muscles and relaxation of the esophageal sphincter. The initiation of swallowing is a voluntary act but once started it is entirely involuntary.

*Vomiting*

*Vomiting* is the result of a sudden expulsion of the contents of the stomach and intestines. The positive effect of vomiting is the elimination of certain substances. Not all mammals are capable of vomiting (the horse and the rat, for example, are not). The vomiting reflex is controlled from the brain stem. The reflex may be stimulated by distension of the stomach and intestine, by certain agents that act on the vomiting center or by an effect on the chemoreceptor trigger zone in the brain.

The efferent action controlled from the vomiting center is primarily a coordination of respiratory muscles, pectoral muscles and abdominal muscles. Vomiting is preceded by a forced inspiration with closed glottis and nose. Vomiting can be observed in muscarine and carbachol intoxication (acetylcholine agonists).

*Defecation*

When the residual matter enters the rectum, the latter is distended, resulting in a reflex which relaxes the internal anal sphincter and leads to the urge to *defecate*. Defecation takes place through voluntary and involuntary reflexes, resulting in relaxation of the external anal sphincter.

*Absorption of water and food in the small intestine*

Various studies have shown that the absorption of sodium is essential for the absorption of various other substances (sugars, amino acids and ions).

The apical side of the enterocyte is adjacent to the intestinal lumen, while the basal side adjoins the basement membrane.
basolateral = on the side of the basement membrane and adjacent epithelial cells

The energy required for the entry of sodium through the apical cell membrane is provided by both electrical and biochemical processes. It is obvious that the outflow of sodium through the basolateral membrane takes place against an electrochemical gradient, and will therefore require energy. That energy is obtained from hydrolysis of ATP. The enzyme responsible for this process is the $Na^+/K^+$ dependent ATPase, which is located in the basolateral cell membrane (Figure 20.6).

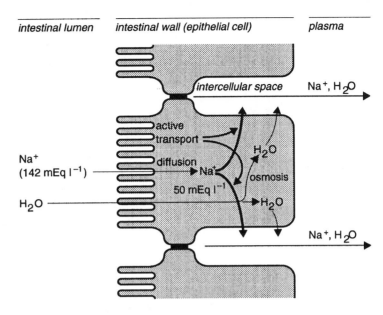

FIGURE 20.6

Schematic representation of passive absorption of $Na^+$ from the lumen and its subsequent active secretion into the plasma. Water follows passively.

Water-soluble compounds, including sugars, amino acids, vitamins and bile salts, are absorbed through the apical cell membrane. The transport of substances from the cell through the basolateral membrane does not require energy because this process is driven by the concentration gradient. This movement may also involve a carrier-mediated mechanism.

*Electrolyte transport in the colon*

*In vivo* studies have shown that sodium and chloride are absorbed, whereas potassium and bicarbonate are secreted. The driving force for the entry of sodium through the apical cell membrane is the combined chemical and electrical gradient. The removal of sodium through the basolateral membrane takes place via the $Na^+/K^+$ dependent ATPase. The result is a negative potential in the lumen. The mechanism of transcellular chloride absorption has not yet been completely explained. A schematic representation of this is provided in Figure 20.7.

*Regulation of absorption and secretion*

Electrolyte transport by the intestine can be influenced by various endogenous substances. The gastrointestinal wall has peptides and neurotransmitters available that are present in both intrinsic and extrinsic neurons and in the endocrine cells.

Various substances, such as 5-hydroxytryptamine (serotonin), substance P, catecholamines, ATP and acetylcholine, play a role in the regulation of intestinal absorption and secretion.

Catecholamines, for example, increase the absorption of sodium and chloride. Glucocorticoids and mineralocorticoids cause increased absorption of salt and water in the colon. This effect is partly due to the increase in $Na^+/K^+$ dependent ATPase activity. Changes in ion transport can also be observed before changes in $Na^+/K^+$ dependent ATPase activity are discerned. The acute increase in ion transport in the colon caused by aldosterone is the result of an increase in sodium absorption through the apical cell membrane.

## 3 Gastrointestinal absorption of xenobiotics

From a toxicological point of view, the gastrointestinal tract is the main penetration route for toxic agents ingested with or absorbed from food. Digestion is second only to respiration in exposing the body to harmful substances.

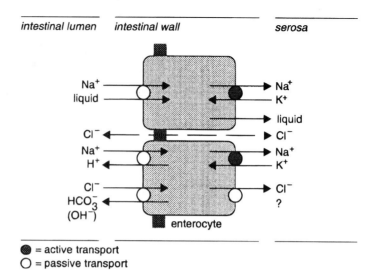

intestinal lumen     intestinal wall                    serosa

● = active transport
○ = passive transport

FIGURE 20.7
Schematic representation of the mechanism of liquid and electrolyte transport by enterocytes in the small intestine.

ASSIGNMENT 20.1

Explain how substances that have been inhaled can later be found in the gastrointestinal tract.

Gastrointestinal absorption also plays a role in the systemic disposition of xenobiotics, which are excreted in the bile and reabsorbed in the intestines (see enterohepatic circulation; section 4).

Extensive excretion followed by repeated reabsorption is known to be the retention mechanism for a variety of toxic substances. This explains why both the degree and extent of gastrointestinal absorption are important parameters in determining the intensity and duration of the biological effects of xenobiotics.

*Absorption*

The following pages will deal with the gastrointestinal absorption of xenobiotics. The term *"absorption"* will be used to refer to the entire process. This includes the breakdown of the ingested compounds to their absorption and transport from the mucosa through the intestinal epithelium to the blood or lymphatic vessels.

### 3.1 MECHANISMS OF GASTROINTESTINAL ABSORPTION

The mucosal layer that separates the intestinal contents from the blood and lymphatic vessels has a very complex multi-layered structure. Many researchers have studied the permeability and transport functions of the gastrointestinal barrier with respect to xenobiotics. Three major routes by which xenobiotics are absorbed have been described: passive diffusion, diffusion through pores and carrier-mediated absorption. Each of these routes will be described separately, although a particular xenobiotic may be absorbed via more than one transport mechanism.

Absorption is also dependent on other factors. Thus, the degree of absorption is partly determined by the dose of the ingested xenobiotic and by the site of absorption.

*Passive diffusion*

The most common mechanism of gastrointestinal absorption of xenobiotics is *passive diffusion*. Passive diffusion is influenced by various factors.

616

ASSIGNMENT 20.2

Which factors influence passive diffusion through the intestinal wall?

The barriers to absorption by diffusion may consist of one or more epithelial structures of the enterocyte, depending on the physicochemical properties of the compound.

An aqueous layer present on the surface of the enterocytes constitutes an initial barrier to absorption of xenobiotics into the blood. The aqueous layer may be a limiting factor for hydrophobic structures and for substances that bind to mucin.

The apical membrane, the cytoplasmic structures, the basement membrane and the capillary walls of blood and lymph vessels, all of which are lipoidal in structure, are more permeable to lipophilic than to hydrophilic substances. The cellular membranes have also been shown not to be very permeable to ionized elements.

The limiting factor in gastrointestinal absorption is the xenobiotic's removal from the site of absorption by blood capillaries or by lymphatic drainage. The rate of intestinal absorption of xenobiotics, which easily pass through membranes, may be limited by the blood vessels in the villi. The relatively high perfusion of the small intestine does, however, mean that the velocity of the blood flow is not usually a limiting factor in the absorption of xenobiotics. Examples of substances that are absorbed by passive diffusion are: ethanol, amidopyrine and aniline.

*Absorption through pores*

Aqueous pores, localized where the apical sides of several enterocytes meet, allow passive penetration (paracellular transport). The diameter of these pores may range from 0.3 to 0.8 nm. *Paracellular transport* is the main mechanism of water and electrolyte absorption. Substances in aqueous solution can also be absorbed in this manner. Uptake of certain low molecular weight xenobiotics (122–188 daltons), such as acetylsalicylic acid (aspirin) and antipyrine, takes place in this way. Absorption through pores depends on the osmotic gradient across the mucosal membrane. Mucosa-to-serosa transfer of various compartments is reduced in the presence of certain osmotic agents, probably because swelling of cells reduces the diameter of the pores.

*Carrier-mediated absorption*

There are specialized transport systems that are entirely or partly responsible for the gastrointestinal absorption of many nutrients and endogenous substances such as water-soluble vitamins and sugars.

ASSIGNMENT 20.3

What characterizes carrier-mediated absorption?

The absorption of some xenobiotics also proceeds via a carrier-mediated process. Analogs of pyrimidines and penicillamine are taken up by specialized transport systems. The carbamate pesticides are metabolized in the enterocyte and their metabolites are taken to the serosal side of the intestine by a carrier-mediated transport mechanism.

Intestinal absorption of quaternary ammonium compounds is also carrier-mediated. In their inorganic form, some non-essential metals, such as lead and aluminum, are absorbed via specialized transport systems.

*Absorption via lipids*

Gastrointestinal absorption of lipophilic xenobiotics and similar substances takes place via the same mechanism as that by which dietary lipids are absorbed. Intestinal lipid absorption proceeds via the following steps:

- formation of micelles by bile salts
- diffusion of micelles through the aqueous layer on the enterocyte
- dissociation of micelles and uptake of lipids
- intracellular formation of chylomicrons, release of chylomicrons, penetration of the basement membrane and release into the lymphatic drainage system

Not all lipids are absorbed in this manner. Some fatty acids are taken up by the cells as chylomicrons. Many lipid-soluble substances, such as DDT and polychlorinated biphenyls, are transported via the lymph vessels. The solvent in which the xenobiotic is dissolved also plays an important role. This explains how the systemic availability of non-water soluble components can be altered by the use of oil or solvents for fats.

*First-pass metabolism*

Substances that are absorbed via intestinal blood capillaries will first have to pass the liver before they reach the systemic circulation. Many xenobiotics are extensively metabolized during their first passage through the liver. This effect is generally called *"first-pass"* metabolism or presystemic *metabolism.*

> Name an important consequence of absorption via the lymphatic vessels.

Absorption via the lymph vessels allows xenobiotics to avoid metabolism in the liver and may result in greater systemic availability.

*Absorption of macromolecules*

Intestinal absorption of macromolecules such as heparin and insulin has long been known to take place in man. The significance of this type of absorption is usually minimal. However, toxicological practice shows that even extremely small quantities of, for example, botulinum toxin may be fatal. The exact mechanism has not yet been clarified, but it probably involves pinocytosis and phagocytosis. This type of absorption mechanism is very important for intestinal absorption of immunoglobulins by the newborn.

*Pinocytosis*
*Phagocytosis*

Solid particles are thought to be absorbed by phagocytosis. For example, small percentages of quantities of asbestos fibers ingested by rats have been recovered from the lymph.

*Persorption*

A second mechanism that plays a role in the absorption of large molecules is called *persorption*. This term refers to the mechanism by which material can penetrate into the lumen of a villus when an enterocyte at the tip of that villus dies, leaving a gap.

*Damage to epithelial membrane*

A third mechanism by which large molecules can be absorbed involves damage to the epithelial membrane.

Cephalosporins are antibiotics first isolated from the fungus *Cephalosporium acremonium*

Absorption of macromolecules can be promoted by previous exposure to certain substances. Various cationic surfactants, for example, may have a disruptive effect on the mucosal membrane and thus facilitate the absorption in the stomach and small intestine of cephalosporins that are not easily absorbed.

Whatever the mechanism by which macromolecules are absorbed, they will eventually be transported via the lymphatic vessels to the systemic blood circulation.

> ASSIGNMENT 20.4
>
> What is the main difference between phagocytosis and persorption?

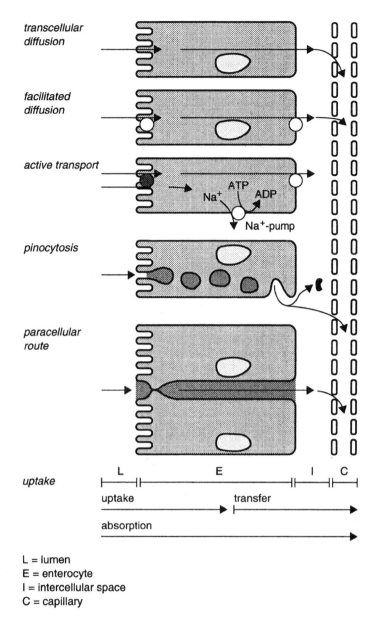

L = lumen
E = enterocyte
I = intercellular space
C = capillary

FIGURE   20.8
Absorption of xenobiotics through the intestinal mucosa.
This figure does not show the basement membrane.
ADP = adenosine diphosphate
dark crcles = active transport; light circles = facilitated diffusion

## 3.2   FACTORS INFLUENCING ABSORPTION

The previous sections have considered the importance of permeability and of transport systems through the intestinal epithelium. Gastrointestinal absorption of a substrate *in vivo* also depends on a number of other factors.

List some of these factors!

*Site-dependent*

As has been mentioned, there are considerable morphological differences between various regions of the gastrointestinal system. It is not surprising therefore that the absorption of xenobiotics is *site-dependent*. There are various reasons for this.

*Acidity*

The extent to which an ionized structure is absorbed via passive diffusion is known to depend primarily on the fraction of that structure that is present in non-ionized form at the site of absorption. This fraction is determined by the ionization constant ($pK_a$) of the structure and by the pH of the gastrointestinal fluids. Based on these data it is obvious that optimum absorption of acid substances ($pK_a < 4$) takes place in the stomach and that optimum absorption of alkaline substances takes place in the intestine (pH of the stomach is 1–2; pH of the large intestine is 6–7).

*Mucosal surface*

The rate of diffusion is proportional to the surface area of the absorptive membrane. Hence the small intestine has the greatest capacity for absorption via diffusion, since its villi and microvilli greatly enlarge its surface area. Pathological conditions in the intestine involving villus atrophy result in a great reduction of the intestinal surface area and thus reduce the absorption of substrates.

*Gastric emptying*

The amount of gastrointestinal absorption is also determined by the degree of gastric emptying. Stomach emptying ensures that xenobiotics pass to the primary site of absorption, the small intestine.

*Gastrointestinal motility*

Gastrointestinal motility may also affect the absorption of xenobiotics. Materials which are absorbed only slowly, such as cholesterol, will be absorbed to a lesser extent if gastrointestinal motility is high.

Intake of food causes changes in gastrointestinal physiology. The presence of food influences the gastrointestinal absorption of xenobiotics by:

- retarded gastric emptying
- release of gastric secretions
- increased intestinal motility
- increased intestinal perfusion
- food sometimes being an absorbent of xenobiotics.

*Food*

Intake of food also stimulates the release of bile into the intestine, thus allowing increased absorption later.

## 4 Enterohepatic circulation of xenobiotics

Bile is excreted into the intestine and returns from the intestinal tract to the liver via the venous blood. The result is that xenobiotics, which are excreted in the bile, may again be transported to the liver. This process, called *enterohepatic circulation (EHC)*, means that endogenous or foreign compounds, which are excreted in the bile, have not yet really left the body.

A brief overview of the enterohepatic circulation will be provided below, with special attention being paid to toxicologically significant xenobiotics.

### 4.1 THE PROCESS OF ENTEROHEPATIC CIRCULATION

Transport of xenobiotics in the enterohepatic circulation can be subdivided into four stages.

ASSIGNMENT 20.5

Describe the four stages of the enterohepatic circulation.

A schematic representation of these stages is provided in Figure 20.9.

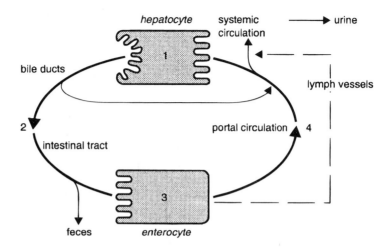

FIGURE   20.9
The various stages to which a compound is subjected in the enterophatic circulation.

*Transport from blood to bile*

Xenobiotics whose molecular mass exceeds 350 and which have a polar character are excreted directly in the bile. Other substances are transported in the bile via specific transport mechanisms (such as binding to bilirubin). Transport of components from the blood to the bile requires their absorption by the liver cells through the sinusoidal membrane, followed by intracellular transport, biotransformation and finally transportation to the bile ducts.

ASSIGNMENT   20.6
Explain why conjugation with glutathione is important for the excretion of xenobiotics.

*Passage from bile to intestine*

Substances which are transported through the canalicular membrane enter the bile canaliculi. These are extracellular spaces between adjacent hepatocytes. The surface of these canaliculi is covered with microvilli, allowing both excretion and reabsorption to take place. The larger bile ducts are lined with cuboidal epithelium. In most species, half of the total volume of bile is released directly into the duodenum, while the other half is collected in the gall bladder. This means that xenobiotics can reach high concentrations in the gall bladder. Thus large quantities of them can be suddenly released into the intestine. Intestinal motility moves them towards the anus. Whilst passing through the intestine, xenobiotics may interact with components of the intestinal contents. They may be bound by non-absorbable food components. Indigestible fibers, for example, can bind bile salts.

The interaction of substances with the *intestinal microflora* is essential for the enterohepatic circulation of various chemical substances.

*Phenolphthalein = drug that stimulates defecation; laxative. Also known as a pH indicator.*

The laxative effect of the substance phenolphthalein (Figure 20.10) is not only increased and prolonged, but even made possible by the enterohepatic circulation. When administered orally, phenolphthalein is first absorbed from the small intestine and then excreted in the bile as a glucuronide.

The polar character of this compound enables transfer to the colon, where the microflora are responsible for its decomposition. Diphenol (the active product) is released in the process.

Biotransformation by the intestinal flora may influence the absorption and excretion of substances. Anaerobic bacteria produce $\beta$-glucuronidase, an enzyme that splits glucuronides into their components, thereby considerably enhancing

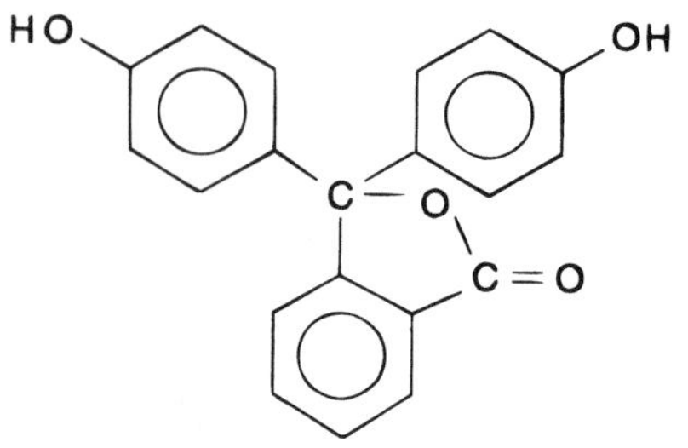

FIGURE 20.10
Structural formula of phenolphthalein.

absorption. It is generally assumed that hydrolysis of the lipophilic component leads to more rapid absorption. This is the case with chloramphenicol, DES and LSD.

*goitrogenic = causing goiter*

Biotransformation by the intestinal flora (see section 7.2) also affects the toxicity of substances in the enterohepatic circulation. Arylamines are formed from the biliary metabolites of the antibiotic chloramphenicol by bacterial nitro reduction and subsequent reabsorption. They are suspected of causing the goitrogenic effect, which this antibiotic displays in rats.

*Reabsorption through the intestinal wall*

Biliary metabolites can be reabsorbed in various parts of the intestinal tract. Components which do not require prior microbial transformation are usually reabsorbed in the small intestine. Absorption of components conjugated with glucuronic acid is facilitated by microbial hydrolysis, which implies that the primary site of reabsorption for such components is the large intestine. For example, morphine, when administered orally, is absorbed in the small intestine but reabsorbed in the large intestine, after prior cleavage of the glucuronide.

*Transfer by blood*

When substances, which have been reabsorbed are returned to the liver, they may either undergo further biotransformation or enter the systemic circulation. The metabolites formed after reabsorption are excreted in the bile or passed on to the bloodstream. Another possibility is that certain substances do not return to the enterohepatic circulation, but enter the systemic circulation directly, especially when absorption takes place via the lymphatic vessels of the gastrointestinal tract.

ASSIGNMENT 20.7

Explain the fact that some of the xenobiotics in an enterohepatic circulation appear directly in the systemic circulation, without having undergone biotransformation?

*Persistence in the enterohepatic circulation*

The *persistence* of a substance *in the enterohepatic circulation* is determined by the rate at which it is eliminated from the enterohepatic circulation.

Describe the various ways in which a xenobiotic can be removed from the enterohepatic circulation.

There are two ways for a xenobiotic to leave the enterohepatic circulation by excretion either in the feces or in the urine. *Fecal elimination* can be observed for DES and LSD in rats and for indomethacin in dogs. In man, estrogens are excreted primarily in the *urine*. The rate of fecal excretion is determined by the degree of reabsorption. This in turn is influenced by the lipophilic character of the substance and by the metabolic transformations that may increase or decrease the lipophilicity. The loss of substances from the enterohepatic circulation to the urine is dependent upon the extraction capacity of the liver.

## 4.2 EXAMPLES OF SUBSTANCES UNDERGOING ENTEROHEPATIC CIRCULATION

*Endogenous substances*

Of the endogenous substances undergoing enterohepatic circulation, the bile salts have been studied most extensively. In addition, substances such as bilirubin and steroid hormones (aldosterone, estradiol, progesterone and testosterone) are also known to display an enterohepatic circulation.

*Drugs and food additives*

Many drugs with diverse pharmacological activity undergo enterohepatic circulation. Generally, the molecular mass of these substances exceeds 200. Many drugs are excreted in the bile as glucuronides, which means that their reabsorption and enterohepatic circulation are determined primarily by the extent of glucuronide hydrolysis in the large intestine. Examples of such substances include diazepam, testosterone and spironolactone.

*Pesticides*

The enterohepatic circulation also plays an important role with insecticides belonging to the carbamate esters. In rats, DDT and chlorinated organic insecticides are eliminated after enterohepatic circulation, primarily in the feces.

Pentachlorophenol (PCP), a fungicide used all over the world as a wood preservative, undergoes enterohepatic circulation, as has been shown in experiments with rhesus monkeys. During the first week after oral administration, approximately 90% is excreted in the bile, whilst 3% is eliminated in the feces.

HCBD (hexachloro-1,3-butadiene), which is used in vineyards and is a by-product of halogenated hydrocarbons, is excreted primarily in the bile.

## 4.3 CONSEQUENCES OF THE ENTEROHEPATIC CIRCULATION

*Disposition*

The enterohepatic circulation can have an influence on the elimination, distribution, biotransformation and bioavailability of xenobiotics. It prolongs the presence of a substance in the body by reduced fecal excretion. Whilst a substance undergoes enterohepatic circulation, it can also enter the systemic circulation and thus have a longer plasma half-life.

The 'entry' of an orally administered substance into the enterohepatic circulation results in presystemic elimination, leading to reduced availability of the substance. Because of this the enterohepatic circulation plays a major role in reducing the effective concentrations of drugs or toxic substances that enter the body via the oral route.

*Effect*

The enterohepatic circulation may significantly influence the toxicity of substances. This is mainly determined by the site at which the xenobiotic exerts its effect, either inside or outside the enterohepatic circuit. The effect of the enterohepatic circulation on a toxic substance, whose target site lies within the enterohepatic circuit, is an increased biological effectivity, during the transport of the toxic molecule to its site of action.

Penicillins are excreted in the bile, so that the enterohepatic circulation enables them to be more effective in the treatment of biliary tract infections. Theoretically, the enterohepatic circulation increases the risk of toxic effects in the liver and intestines since it provides higher concentrations of the substance.

If the enterohepatic circulation takes the toxic substance into the systemic circulation, the effect will be prolonged. It is thought that the enterohepatic circulation plays a major role in maintaining the effects of contraceptive steroids. Contraceptive failure may occur when antibiotics are used concurrently due to the resulting reduction in the enterohepatic circulation of the contraceptive steroids. This theory is supported by studies on rhesus monkeys. It was shown that administration of rifampicin increased the fecal excretion of ethynodiol diacetate and reduced the plasma half-life from 44 to 24 hours.

## 5 Role of the gastrointestinal tract in the elimination of toxic substances

### 5.1 FECAL EXCRETION OF XENOBIOTICS

The fecal excretion of a substance is a very complex process that is not yet completely understood. This route of xenobiotic elimination has so far received little attention.

*Meconium = the green or brown-black sticky feces present in the intestines of the unborn fetus and excreted after birth.*

Feces are considered as a residue of those parts of the food that have not been absorbed. Recently, this opinion has been subject to considerable change, largely as a result of improved methods of analysis. Examination of meconium and of feces excreted during periods of hunger provides clear indications of the various endogenous sources influencing the formation of feces.

*Passage*

Various nutrients and xenobiotics, present in food, are not absorbed and only pass through the gastrointestinal tract. Most chemicals display a certain degree of lipophilicity, which implies that they are able to penetrate biological membranes. The exceptions to this rule are macromolecules and, in particular circumstances, some salts and weak organic acids and bases. Small molecules and highly lipophilic substances, however, are readily absorbed, so that very little unabsorbed material remains in the feces.

*Excretion in the bile*

In fecal excretion the most marked contribution is from the unabsorbed portion of substances excreted in the bile. Most xenobiotics excreted in the bile have undergone a phase I and/or phase II biotransformation reaction in the liver. Both processes result in less lipophilic structures or substances of higher molecular mass.

*Intestinal excretion*

The intestine is the main route of elimination of many lipophilic substances, more so than the urinary route. The excretion of xenobiotics in the feces has so far been assumed to take place via the bile. New data have shown that other sources are also involved (Figure 20.11). Tetrachlorobiphenyl and hexachlorobenzene, for example, are excreted in the feces, even when the bile ducts are ligated. Similar effects have been reported with dieldrin. It is not unusual for lipid-soluble substances to reach the intestinal lumen together with other endogenous lipids. Two mechanisms are thought to be responsible for this:

- exfoliation of the intestinal cells,
- excretion of lipids via the intestinal mucosa.

*Intestinal wall and flora*

The role of the intestinal wall and flora in the biotransformation of substances is discussed in detail in the following sections. In the fecal excretion of xenobiotics, only those biotransformations are of importance that influence the elimination.

Rather more information is available concerning the influence of the intestinal flora on the fecal excretion of substances. Feces contain fecal bacteria, which account for 30–40% of dry matter. Most of these bacteria originate from the large intestine.

624

Substances present in the non-absorbed portion of an oral dose, excreted in the bile or excreted through the intestinal wall, can be taken up by these bacteria. A large part of xenobiotics excreted via the fecal route will therefore be present in the voided bacteria. On the other hand, substances can also be retained by fecal bacteria, rather than excreted with them. This occurs primarily in the large intestine, where the intestinal flora and contents remain for up to 24 hours.

## 5.2    FACTORS INFLUENCING THE FECAL EXCRETION OF XENOBIOTICS

Table 20.1 summarizes the intrinsic and extrinsic factors that may influence the fecal excretion of xenobiotics.

### 5.2.1  Intrinsic factors

The excretion of substances, both by active and passive processes, involves fluids, moving in a direction opposite to that of absorption and reabsorption. Both absorption and excretion require passage through one or more barriers, usually membranes. The nature and role of these barriers in relation to absorption have been studied in detail. Whether it is absorption or excretion that predominates is determined by the concentration gradient, the particular site in the intestine

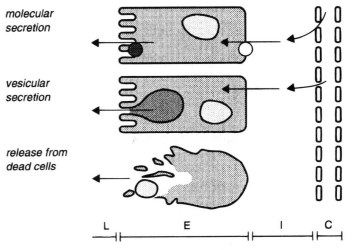

FIGURE   20.11
Schematic representation of the manner in which xenobiotics can be excreted into the intestine.
L = lumen, E = enterocyte, I = intercellular space, C = capillary.
light circle = facilitated diffusion
dark circle = active transport

TABLE   20.1
Factors which may influence the fecal excretion of toxic substances.

| Intrinsic | Extrinsic |
|---|---|
| route of transport | route of administration |
| concentration gradient | dose and formulation |
| intestinal transit | lipid/water solubility |
| site of excretion | molecular weight |
| quantity and composition of feces | $pK_a$ |
| intestinal flora | therapy (drugs) |
| species | diet |
| age | |
| disease | |

and many other intrinsic factors. It is the combination of these factors, which determines the net flux in a particular direction.

*Type of transport*

Most substances are transported through membranes or other barriers by means of active transport. This is the most important mechanism in the elimination of substances that are not excreted in the bile. Passive diffusion is of even greater importance than active intestinal secretion if the transport capacity is saturated. Carrier-mediated transport plays a role mainly in the fecal excretion of those xenobiotics that reach the gastrointestinal system via the bile. Active secretion of many substances takes place in the intestinal tract and for some xenobiotics this is their main route of excretion.

*Concentration gradient*

*Concentration gradients* are important determinants in the absorption/excretion ratio of substances. For example, immediately after intravenous administration of a substance, the concentration gradient induces excretion, whereas after oral administration it induces absorption. The volume of distribution at the serosal side is, however, much greater than at the mucosal side. As a result, the excretory pressure after intravenous administration is much smaller than that promoting absorption after oral administration.

*Transit of the intestinal contents*

The excretion/absorption ratio is dependent on the transport properties. Active transport is generally faster than passive diffusion. Other factors also play a role. *Transit of the intestinal contents* is faster in the small intestine than in the large intestine, while the surface area in the small intestine is larger than that in the large intestine.

*Quantity and composition of the feces*

Another determining factor in the fecal excretion of toxic substances is the quantity of feces excreted per unit of time. Apart from this quantitative aspect, the qualitative composition of the feces of course determines the lipophilicity of the intestinal contents.

*Intestinal flora*

Intestinal microorganisms reduce or slow the fecal excretion of xenobiotics by neutralizing the effects of phase I biotransformation reactions. In other cases, a phase II biotransformation product may be hydrolyzed in the intestine, after which it may be absorbed and enter the enterohepatic circulation. As a result, fecal excretion is retarded.

*Age*

Changes in the excretion of bile, in the quantity of intestinal enzymes, in the transport processes and in gastrointestinal flora, due to age, may influence the excretion of xenobiotics. Newborn mammals have a low capacity for biliary excretion of xenobiotics. In rats, biliary excretion of foreign substances is known to decrease with advanced age.

### 5.2.2 Extrinsic factors

Extensive research has been carried out into the role of extrinsic factors in the excretion of xenobiotics in the bile, whereas other factors have hardly received attention.

*Route of administration*

For xenobiotics with low bioavailability and for those excreted via the kidneys, the route of administration, either oral or parenteral, is most important. Absorption of many metals in the intestine is limited. As a result there is a considerable difference in their fecal excretion after oral administration or after injection. On the other hand, fecal excretion is not primarily determined by the route of administration with substances of high bioavailability and those that are excreted mainly in the feces.

*Lipid/water solubility*

Good lipid solubility usually leads to absorption and thus reduces the fecal excretion of unbound material. At the same time, good lipid solubility makes a substance less suitable for biliary excretion. Only highly polar compounds are excreted in the bile, after which they are transformed into less polar, more lipophilic substances in the intestinal lumen.

Xenobiotics which are excreted into the intestinal lumen may have either a low or a high lipid/water solubility coefficient. Large quantities of water in the intestinal lumen lead to extensive fecal excretion of water-soluble substances, whereas a high fat content in the intestine provides a vehicle for lipid-soluble substances to be more readily excreted.

*Molecular mass*

The absorption of substances is reduced with increasing molecular mass. Excretion of the non-absorbed portion of an orally administered substance via the fecal route is therefore more important for xenobiotics of high molecular mass. A high molecular mass stimulates their excretion in the bile and thus in the feces. The role of molecular mass in the fecal excretion of substances that are excreted into the intestine is less well-known. Molecular mass may also determine the intestinal excretion of substances that are excreted by passive diffusion. Increased molecular mass may lead to reduced intestinal excretion and therefore reduced fecal excretion.

*(Drug) therapy*

Administration of non-absorbable lipids reduces the absorption of lipophilic xenobiotics and thus increases their excretion. Interruption of the enterohepatic circulation of toxic substances, by oral administration of binding substances such as cholestyramine, can cause the route of excretion to change from urinary to fecal. The fecal excretion of substances may also be altered after induction of hepatic enzymes, if the metabolites produced are excreted primarily in the feces. Moreover, treatment, for example, with antibiotics may change fecal excretion by interference with the intestinal microflora.

*Diet*

Generally, a diet rich in lipid-soluble substances will promote the absorption of lipophilic substances, whereas a high content of non-absorbable lipids will lead to reduced absorption and increased intestinal excretion of xenobiotics.

## 6 Biotransformation in the intestinal mucosa

Since the intestine is frequently exposed to xenobiotics, it is not surprising that the intestinal mucosa is so resistant to functional and morphological damage caused by substances. The small intestine has greatest contact with toxic and carcinogenic substances. The microsomal enzymes make up the biochemical system responsible for this resistance. Although the body is protected against xenobiotics primarily by biotransformation in the liver, the intestine also has its own mechanism of biotransformation.

Figure 20.12 gives an overview of the manner in which xenobiotics can enter the systemic blood circulation from the gastrointestinal tract. Biotransformation may take place in the enterocyte (intestinal first pass) or in the hepatocyte (hepatic first pass).

Many xenobiotics are lipophilic, which means that they can easily pass through the biological membranes. Partly as a result of their high lipophilicity, they are also difficult to remove from the body. This is why the organism has at its disposal a biotransformation system that makes lipophilic substances more water-soluble and thus facilitates their removal from the body. Such biotransformation takes place largely in the liver. Extrahepatic tissues may, however, also make an important contribution to biotransformation. Due to its major role in biotransformation, the liver is also an important source of undesirable reactive metabo-

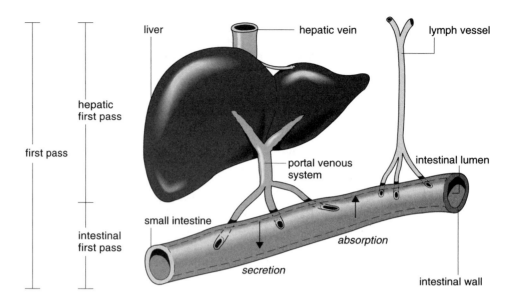

FIGURE   20.12
Presystemic circulation: possible fate of xenobiotics after oral administration.

lites. These may cause considerable damage to the organism, both in the liver itself and elsewhere in the body. However, the organ-selective toxicity of certain xenobiotics may also be caused by *in situ* activation and/or disturbed detoxication in the extrahepatic tissues themselves. Compared with that of the liver, the cellular composition of extrahepatic tissues is very heterogeneous. The localization and relative quantities of biotransformation enzyme systems, in certain cell populations of the gastrointestinal tract, may thus result in very selective toxic lesions. In many species, the presence of a variety of biotransformation enzymes has been demonstrated in the small intestine. More particularly, substances that are conjugated with glucuronic acid or sulfate, have been shown to undergo a first-pass metabolism in the intestinal epithelium. Typical examples of such substances are morphine, isoproterenol and ethinylestradiol. The activity of oxidative enzyme systems in the intestinal epithelium seems to be considerably less. Nevertheless, there are indications that various dietary components are able to induce oxidative enzyme systems.

6.1   LOCALIZATION AND DISTRIBUTION

The epithelial cells of the intestinal mucosa contain a variety of biotransformation enzymes. Most biotransformation enzymes are located in the endoplasmic reticulum of the epithelial cells. The distribution of the enzymes in the small intestine has been shown to have the highest activity in the proximal part of the small intestine and this activity gradually decreases in the more distal parts of the intestine. An exception to this is cytochrome P-450, the distribution of which is diffuse along the entire length of the small intestine. Distribution in the villi is such that the cells at the tips display P-450 activity 6–10 times greater than that displayed by crypt cells.

Structurally connected with the smooth endoplasmic reticulum are the UDP glucuronyltransferases, the monooxygenases (including cytochrome P-450) and epoxide hydrolase. The mitochondria and the cytoplasm of the enterocytes also contain biotransformation enzymes. The most important mitochondrial enzyme of the cells in the gastrointestinal tract is monoamine oxidase (MAO); two-thirds of the cytochrome P-450 enzymes in the gastrointestinal tract are mitochondrial cytochrome P-450. As mentioned before, alcohol dehydrogenase, various esterases, $\beta$-glucuronidases and sulfatases are capable of splitting various compounds into components. Furthermore, the cytoplasm of the enterocytes contains a variety of enzymes including sulfotransferases, acetyltransferases, S- and O-methyltransferases, glutathione S-transferases and enzymes that catalyze glycine conjugations. It must be noted that there are considerable species differences in the activity of various enzymes. Table 20.2 gives some examples.

Compounds usually undergo more than one biotransformation reaction, sometimes simultaneously. Hence, a substance may undergo a phase I reaction, followed by a phase II reaction, although in the intestine the reverse sequence is also common. The mixed-function oxidase reactions in the intestine are thought to be physiologically less important than the glucuronidation reactions. From a toxicological point of view, mixed-function oxidase reactions are certainly important, because it is precisely these reactions, which may produce the most reactive substances or intermediates.

## 7    Interaction between xenobiotics and the gastrointestinal flora

The gastrointestinal tract contains many bacteria with a high metabolic activity, which make an important contribution to the metabolism of ingested material. Biotransformation by the intestinal flora plays a major part in the effect and kinetics of xenobiotics in the body. Bacteria may also affect the release of endogenous substances into the intestinal lumen. The microflora can produce substances that penetrate into the host through the mucosal membrane and then produce a systemic effect (see Figure 20.13).

It is not surprising, then, that the microflora contribute to both the morphology and function of the gastrointestinal tract. Anaerobic bacteria are difficult to study, but from a toxicological point of view, their biotransformation of xenobiotics merits greater attention.

There is an obvious difference between the metabolism of xenobiotics in the liver and that in the intestinal flora. Cytochrome P-450-mediated oxidative reactions require oxygen, whereas most intestinal bacteria are strictly anaerobic.

### 7.1    GASTROINTESTINAL MICROFLORA

No part of the gastrointestinal tract is sterile. Approximately $10^{10}$ bacteria are estimated to live in the mouth of a healthy individual. They are continually washed down to the stomach. Food and liquids, usually, also contain large numbers of bacteria. The esophagus and the stomach, normally, have virtually no bacteria,

TABLE   20.2
Species differences in metabolic activity of microsomal enzymes in the intestinal tract and the presence of cytochrome P-450.

| Species | Enzymatic activity in the small intestine as a percentage of that in the liver | | | | |
| --- | --- | --- | --- | --- | --- |
| | Ethylmorphine N-demethylase | Biphenyl Hydroxylase | Aniline Hydroxylase | Cytochrome c Reductase | Cytochrome P-450 |
| rabbit | 18.6 | 14.1 | 20.4 | 75.7 | 34.6 |
| guinea pig | 23.3 | 16.4 | 19.8 | 78.7 | 12.4 |
| rat | ND | 9.3 | ND | 42.0 | ND |
| mouse | ND | 9.0 | ND | 79.6 | 4.0 |
| hamster | ND | 6.8 | ND | 60.7 | 13.0 |

ND = not detectable

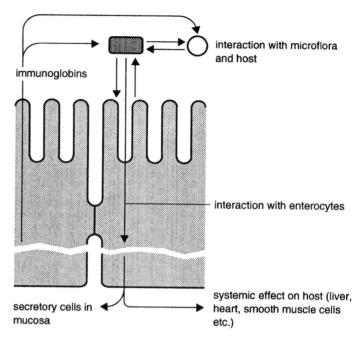

immunoglobins

interaction with microflora and host

interaction with enterocytes

secretory cells in mucosa

systemic effect on host (liver, heart, smooth muscle cells etc.)

FIGURE 20.13

Schematic representation of the manner in which the interaction between xenobiotics and intestinal microflora can lead to certain effects in the host

Immunoglobulins released from the enterocyte can influence the bacteria; the bacteria can produce substances which are absorbed by the enterocyte, etc.

due to the presence of hydrochloric acid in the gastric juice. The small and large intestines, on the other hand, contain large numbers of bacteria.

The only strictly aerobic bacteria found in the human intestinal tract belong to the *Pseudomonas* species. Facultatively anaerobic bacteria, such as *E. coli*, *Klebsiella* and *Proteus mirabilis* are more common. The anaerobic *Bacteroides fragilis* is the most common intestinal bacterium in man. The mouth, the intestines and the feces also contain large numbers of *Peptococci* and *Peptostreptococci*. Saliva is a main source for bacteria entering the intestinal tract, whilst food is another important source. In the duodenum, the jejunum and the proximal ileum, the flora increase and various anaerobic species are found. The ileum contains both aerobic and anaerobic bacteria, while the large intestine has mainly anaerobic bacteria.

Some intestinal bacteria live in close relation with the host's mucosal cells. Germ-free animals have a thinner intestinal wall and a reduced total mucosal surface, with thinner villi, in comparison with animals who have a normal intestinal flora.

A disturbance of the bacterial balance may cause serious side effects. Excessive bacterial growth in the small intestine may lead to reduced availability of vitamin $B_{12}$. Bacteria use this vitamin or convert it into an inactive form that competes with the active form.

7.2 BIOTRANSFORMATION OF XENOBIOTICS BY THE INTESTINAL FLORA

The main glycosidases produced by intestinal bacteria are $\beta$-glucuronidase, $\beta$-galactosidase and $\beta$-glucosidase. The presence of $\beta$-glucuronidase in the intestinal tract has certain consequences for chemotherapy. Some therapeutic substances, such as chloramphenicol, are administered in their glucuronidated form. They pass down the gastrointestinal tract unchanged until they reach the

*Hydrolysis*

large intestine, where they are hydrolyzed by intestinal bacteria to the active antibiotic. In some cases, bacterial $\beta$-glucuronidase can have a major influence on the enterohepatic cycle. Changes in intestinal microbial ecology as a result of antimicrobial therapy can also lead to alterations in the metabolism of other xenobiotic components in the body.

ASSIGNMENT 20.8

Explain how the use of antibiotics can cause failure of contraceptives.

The administration of ampicillin increases the fecal excretion of conjugated estrogens. This increase is the result of reduced bacterial metabolism. Administration of antibiotics has the same effect on the metabolism of progesterone.

*Reduction*

Reduction of nitro groups in the intestine is largely due to microbial activity. The reduction of heterocyclic nitrocompounds such as metronidazole is carried out by intestinal bacteria. Intestinal bacteria are also able to reduce N-containing dyes to aromatic amines, which may be highly mutagenic.

### 7.3 FACTORS AFFECTING THE INTESTINAL FLORA

The effect produced by various toxic agents taken up from food or the environment depends on their interaction with the intestinal bacteria. Dietary habits determine to a large extent the composition of the gastrointestinal flora. In addition, the influence of antibiotics on the flora should not be underestimated.

### 7.3.1 Diet, flora and carcinogenesis

An association is suspected to exist between bacterial mediators and cancer of the colon. The microflora present in the colon are able to convert inactive procarcinogens into mutagenic substances. The risk of developing cancer of the colon is higher in populations with a western dietary pattern. Such a dietary pattern, with a high meat content, seems to increase the $\beta$-glucuronidase activity in fecal bacteria. In rats, research has shown that glucuronidase inhibition reduces the carcinogenic potential.

Diets rich in fats are thought to be able to change the intestinal flora so that carcinogenic substances are activated more rapidly. High fat content in the diet increases the secretion of bile into the intestine as well as bile synthesis. Conversion of certain bile acids (for example deoxycholic acid) could produce potentially carcinogenic substances.

Fecapentaenes are polyunsaturated hydrocarbons produced by various intestinal bacteria. They have mutagenic properties. Nitrates also occur in high concentrations in the western diet. Under certain circumstances, they can be converted into carcinogenic nitrosamines. The reduction of azo derivatives, which are used as food additives, may result in potential carcinogens.

ASSIGNMENT 20.9

What factors promote the development of cancer of the colon?

### 7.3.2 Reduction of toxic risk by bacterial activity

Not all bacteria stimulate the formation of tumors in mammals. *Lactobacilli,* for example, reduce the risk of colonic cancer.

Research has shown that the acute effect of dimethylnitrosamine and dimethylamine was less serious in normal rats than in germ-free rats. This suggests that the absence of a microflora can make the animals more susceptible to the toxic effects of certain xenobiotics.

## 8    Summary

The gastrointestinal tract consists of a tubular canal, starting at the mouth and ending at the anus. The stomach has a low pH, which constitutes a protective factor against some xenobiotics. The absorptive surface of the small intestine is enlarged by villi. These contain various types of cells, of which the absorptive cells are the most numerous.

The physiology of the absorption of water and food in the small and large intestines is a complex process that usually requires energy. The mechanism is also regulated by hormones.

Gastrointestinal absorption can take place via passive diffusion, absorption via pores, or by carriers. The absorption of macromolecules is of secondary importance. The physiological properties (acidity and site) play an important role.

The enterohepatic circulation (EHC) can be subdivided into four stages: transport from blood to bile, passage to the intestines, transport through the intestinal wall and passage to the blood. The fecal and urinary routes allow substances to leave the enterohepatic circulation.

The enterohepatic circulation can influence the length of time during which a substance is present in the body, its disposition and its effect.

Xenobiotics can be excreted via the bile, the intestine or the intestinal bacteria. Both intrinsic (method of transport, concentration gradient, intestinal flora, feces and age) and extrinsic factors (route of administration, solubility, molecular mass, diet or drug therapy) ultimately determine the contribution of the fecal route to excretion.

The gastrointestinal flora can convert xenobiotics by various enzymes. The microflora also has an influence on the induction of intestinal cancer, which may be either positive or negative.

## SELF ASSESSMENT QUESTIONS

1   How is the absorptive surface of the small intestine enlarged?

2   What are the advantages and disadvantages of vomiting with respect to the toxicity of xenobiotics?

3   What substances are excreted directly into the bile?

4   What are the consequences of phase I and phase II reactions?

5   Why are the contents of the stomach virtually germ-free?

6   How can the effect of antibiotics on the biotransformation of foreign substances be explained?

7   Describe the role of the dissociation constant ($pK_a$) of a particular xenobiotic and the acidity of the environment in the passive diffusion of that xenobiotic.

8    Explain the role of the enterohepatic circulation in the laxative effect of phenolphthalein.

9    How can one verify that xenobiotics undergo enterohepatic circulation?

10   What is the main difference between biotransformation reactions in mammalian cells and those in microorganisms?

FEEDBACK

1    **Answers to the assignments**

20.1  Small particles that have been inhaled and are deposited in the pharynx are removed from the tracheo-bronchial tract by cilia. When they are subsequently swallowed, they enter the gastrointestinal tract.

20.2  The factors that play a role in passive diffusion are the following:

- concentration gradient
- aqueous diffusion
- lipid solubility
- effective surface area available for diffusion
- intrinsic permeability of the mucosal barrier
- acidity.

20.3  Carrier-mediated absorption is characterized by:

- transport against a concentration gradient
- saturation factor
- dependence on metabolic energy supply
- substrate specificity
- localization at specific sites in the intestine.

20.4  Phagocytosis presupposes a well-functioning intestinal mucosa, whereas persorption is possible only after a cell at the tip of a villus has died.

20.5  The enterohepatic circulation can be subdivided into the following four stages:

- transport from blood to bile
- passage from bile to intestine
- transport through the intestinal wall
- passage to the blood.

20.6  Glucuronidation and conjugation with glutathione are very important in making the excretion of xenobiotics into the bile possible. These processes increase the molecular mass and make the substances more polar. In addition, their toxic effect is reduced.

20.7  The liver's extraction capacity can become saturated. If that happens, some of the xenobiotics enter the circulation directly.

20.8 Antibiotics can kill intestinal bacteria, which means that cleavage of conjugated estrogens is inhibited, resulting in increased fecal estrogen excretion.

20.9 • Diets rich in fats change the intestinal flora so that carcinogenic substances can be activated more quickly.

• A high dietary fat content leads to increased secretion and synthesis of bile, and to conversion of certain bile acids into potentially carcinogenic substances.

## 2  Answers to the self assessment questions

1  The absorptive surface of the small intestine is enlarged by:

• the villi
• the microvilli.

2  The advantage of vomiting is that toxic substances are eliminated from the body. The disadvantage is that the irritation of the stomach caused by corrosive xenobiotics also leads to irritation of the esophagus. Besides, frequent vomiting may cause the esophagus to be damaged by the acid of the gastric juice.

3  Xenobiotics with a molecular mass exceeding 350 and a polar character are excreted directly in the bile.

4  Phase I and phase II biotransformation of substances results in greater water-solubility and higher molecular mass. These changes allow fecal excretion to be increased.

5  The low pH causes the contents of the stomach to be almost sterile.

6  The intestinal bacteria are partly responsible for biotransformation of xenobiotics. Since antibiotics may affect these bacteria, they can interfere with biotransformation indirectly.

7  When $pK_a$ (= ionization constant) equals pH, the molecule is by definition 50% ionized. Where a xenobiotic is best absorbed will depend on whether it is a weak acid or a weak base.

8  Phenolphthalein is administered orally, absorbed in the small intestine and excreted in the bile as a glucuronide. The glucuronide is then transported to the colon, where microbial $\beta$-glucuronidase activity splits it. Its hydrolysis is accompanied by the release of the laxative diphenol.

9  It is possible to verify whether substances undergo enterohepatic circulation by experiments in which their concentrations in the various compartments of the body and excretory products are measured. It is very important to compare the biliary concentrations with those in the feces.

10  The greatest difference between biotransformation reactions mediated by mammalian cells and microbial biotransformations is that the former are mainly oxidative reactions and conjugation reactions, whereas the latter are predominantly reductions and hydrolyses of substances and/or their conjugates.

# Contents Study unit 21
# Gastrointestinal toxicology: toxicological pathology and sources of intestinal toxicity

0-8493-9232-2/96/$0.00 + $.50
© 1996 by CRC Press, Inc.

# Study unit 21

# Gastrointestinal toxicology: toxicological pathology and sources of intestinal toxicity

*W. Coussement*

## INTRODUCTION

There are various reasons why the gastrointestinal tract is a target organ for toxic substances.

- Like the skin and lungs, the gastrointestinal tract is in direct contact with substances from the environment. Moreover, in food toxicity studies it is the first organ that substances meet.
- It is inevitable that the gastrointestinal tract is exposed to high concentrations of substances administered orally. Exposure to substances excreted into the bile can often be repetitive so that the effects show a corresponding increase.
- The critical balance between cell division and cell loss is very delicate. This can easily lead to erosion or hyperplasia of the tissue. Except for gastric ulceration caused by non-steroidal anti-inflammatory agents, non-proliferative lesions of the gastrointestinal tract, as a result of exposure to xenobiotics, are rare.

The previous study unit dealt extensively with the mechanisms of absorption and metabolism in the gastrointestinal tract, as well as with the role of the microflora in gastrointestinal toxicology. This study unit focuses on the pathology resulting from exposure to xenobiotics. It also discusses some specific groups of substances, including drugs, heavy metals and food additives.

Besides the toxicology of the gastrointestinal tract, this unit also deals with the toxicology of the pancreas as an exocrine organ. Information on the pancreas as an endocrine organ can be found in Study unit 30.

### LEARNING OBJECTIVES

After studying this unit, you should be able to:

— describe the origin and pathogenesis of the most common pathological changes in the gastrointestinal tract

— describe the toxic effects of substances on the gastrointestinal tract and, if possible, the mechanisms by which these effects are induced

— name the sites of action of toxic substances in the gastrointestinal tract and describe and explain the specific effects of interaction of xenobiotics with these sites of action.

637

*Study hints*

This study unit is a sequel to unit 20. Before you start on this unit, you should have studied unit 20. The present study unit uses some terms and concepts from oncology and cytopathology, which have been dealt with in Study units 12, 13 and 15. Make sure you are able to use these terms and concepts correctly. You are not expected to memorize the tables listing the numerous substances. Instead, try to understand why the author included a particular table. This unit accounts for approximately 4 student learning hours.

STUDY CORE

## 1 Pathology of the gastrointestinal tract

Toxification, degeneration and detoxication are all effects of metabolic processes that also may take place in the gastrointestinal tract. They may be connected with the intrinsic physiological activity of the gastrointestinal tract, or they may be mediated by the intestinal microflora. Considerable species differences have been observed. Some of these differences can be traced back to the different means by which HCl is released into the gastric juice in the various species. One example is the acute toxicity of zinc phosphide. The acute toxicity of zinc phosphide is related to the formation and absorption of phosphine:

$$Zn_3P_2 + 6HCl \rightarrow 3ZnCl_2 + 2PH_3$$

Many substances can cause acute injury to the gastrointestinal tract. This injury can influence absorption directly. It can sometimes also influence toxicity indirectly by inducing vomiting. The various mechanisms that may cause symptoms of intoxication can be classified as follows:

- direct injury to the mucosal cells
- interaction of toxic substances with receptors of the gastrointestinal tract
- reduction of peristalsis by xenobiotics
- carcinogenesis.

Highly oxidative substances or marked changes in pH can damage the cellular membrane of the mucosal cells and elicit a necrotizing effect.

In acute oral poisoning with substances such as muscarine or carbachol, entry of these substances into the stomach produces massive stimulation of cholinergic receptors. This stimulation leads to a sudden excessive contraction of the gastric muscle and explosive vomiting.

Other receptor interactions may involve substances which increase or decrease neurotransmitter concentrations (organophosphate esters → acetylcholine).

Acute intoxication by psychotropic drugs often leads to complicated situations because gastrointestinal peristalsis is affected. Figure 21.1 gives an example of such a situation after intoxication with a neuroleptic drug.

It is essential in these situations to restrict absorption from the gastrointestinal tract to a minimum, for example by gastric lavage.

The induction of tumors, the last item on the above list, is discussed in section 1.2.

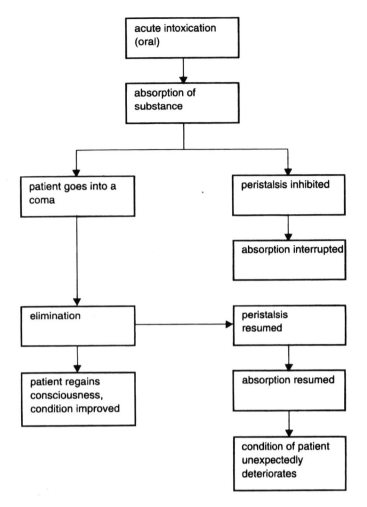

FIGURE 21.1

Effects of acute intoxication by a neuroleptic drug on gastrointestinal peristalsis
The absorption of the substance is indirectly affected.

## 1.1 NON-NEOPLASTIC CHANGES

Most cases of epithelial injury in the gastrointestinal tract involve mild lesions (irritation). These are manifested in the same way as in other organs, namely by degeneration, inflammation or proliferation, or a combination of these, depending on the nature and extent of the exposure and the site of injury. Especially important is the site at which the damage occurs, since the structure of the intestinal mucosa is not the same throughout the gastrointestinal tract.

> ASSIGNMENT 21.1
>
> How do you reconcile the above statement, that the structure of the gastrointestinal mucosa is not the same throughout, with that made in unit 20, that the basic structure throughout is the same?

Depending on the site in the gastrointestinal tract and its function at that precise site, the mucosa can display considerable differences. A schematic representation of its various structures is provided in Figure 21.2.

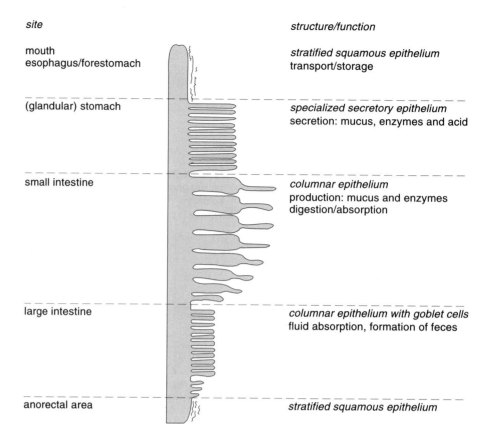

| site | structure/function |
|---|---|
| mouth esophagus/forestomach | *stratified squamous epithelium* transport/storage |
| (glandular) stomach | *specialized secretory epithelium* secretion: mucus, enzymes and acid |
| small intestine | *columnar epithelium* production: mucus and enzymes digestion/absorption |
| large intestine | *columnar epithelium with goblet cells* fluid absorption, formation of feces |
| anorectal area | *stratified squamous epithelium* |

FIGURE 21.2
Schematic representation of the local structure of the mucosa in the gastrointestinal tract

The following subsections will deal with the pathological changes caused by xenobiotics in the various parts of the gastrointestinal tract.

### 1.1.1 Esophagus and forestomach

This region of the gastrointestinal tract is subject to many irritant changes. Numerous examples are known, from the rat in particular, since this is the species most frequently used in toxicological research.

The pathological response is identical to that in the skin (see Study unit 17). Mild injuries cause mild, proliferative changes that may result in hyperkeratosis or acanthosis. Highly irritant substances cause necrosis of the epithelium and induce a pronounced inflammatory reaction in the underlying stroma. If the substance continues to exert its degenerative effect, degenerative proliferation may occur, resulting in thickening of the epithelium with wart-like structures that are easily recognizable at post-mortem examination. With certain chemicals, this papillomatous hyperplasia may easily develop into neoplasia.

Figure 21.3 gives a schematic representation of the difference between acute inflammatory reaction and papillomatous hyperplasia in the forestomach of a rat.

### 1.1.2 Glandular stomach

One would expect the highly specialized epithelium of the glandular stomach to be very sensitive to irritant substances. The epithelial layer of the stomach is, however, protected quite effectively by a layer of mucus. Hence, irritant lesions occur less frequently than expected. There are some substances that are important exceptions. These cause erosive and ulcerative changes of the stomach wall.

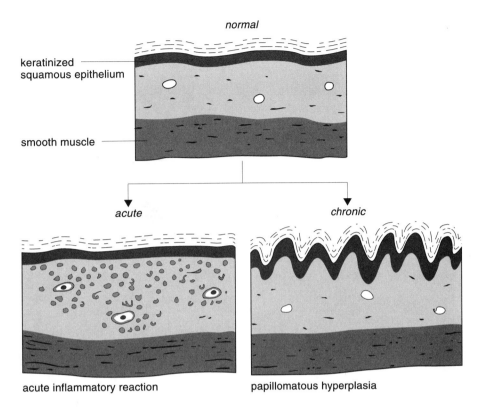

FIGURE 21.3
Pathological reactions of the rat forestomach to acute and chronic exposure to irritant substances

Among this group of xenobiotics are the non-steroidal anti-inflammatory drugs, such as aspirin. The probable mechanism by which these substances cause gastric erosions and ulcers, or both, is discussed in section 3. The pathological changes that may be found in the glandular stomach include erosions, ulcers and diffuse gastritis.

*Erosion*

An *erosion* is a superficial ulcer of the mucosa. It is formed by focal necrosis of the epithelium and associated stroma (see Figure 21.4) and is restricted to the superficial layer of the (glandular) mucosa. Usually, several erosions occur simultaneously and are often situated in the folds of the stomach wall. Initially there is hemorrhage from the damaged area. This may show up at necropsy as brown threads or clots radiating from the area of injury. Inflammation and repair follow. In the absence of repeated insult, the tissue will further recover. Sometimes repair may be observed although the exposure is continued. This phenomenon is called adaptive cytoprotection. The protective action is associated with the synthesis of prostaglandins in the mucosa.

ASSIGNMENT 21.2

What are the consequences of adaptive cytoprotection in determining gastrointestinal toxicity in studies using laboratory animals?

*Ulcer*

*Ulcers* are deeper lesions of the stomach wall and they are often solitary or few in number. They extend beyond the mucosa and penetrate into the adjacent layers (see Figure 21.4). In extreme cases they may even penetrate the muscular lay-

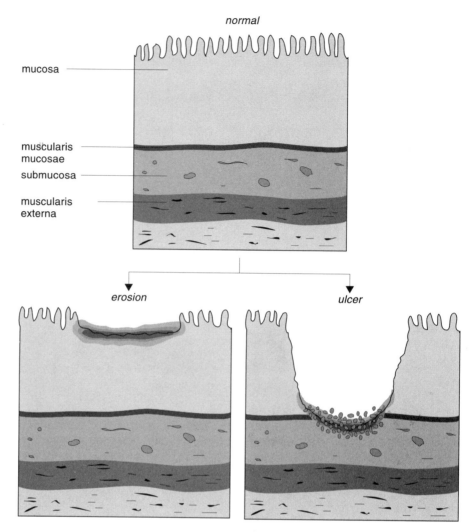

normal

mucosa

muscularis mucosae

submucosa

muscularis externa

erosion

ulcer

FIGURE 21.4
Focal injury to the wall of the (glandular) stomach: erosion and ulcer

ers of the stomach and provide an open connection with the abdominal cavity. These ulcers are termed perforating ulcers. Ulcerations produce a more pronounced inflammatory reaction than erosions. Repair takes place by regeneration and fibrosis. The regenerated epithelium may appear different from the original epithelium. It is often similar to intestinal epithelium or to the mucus-producing epithelium found in the pyloric region.

ASSIGNMENT 21.3

What are these changes in cell type called?

Fibrous scars in the pyloric region may inhibit pyloric sphincter functioning and thus interfere with gastric emptying.

*Diffuse gastritis*

Some chemicals cause more diffuse lesions to the gastric mucosa. These may vary from mild, superficial injury, as seen after administration of aspirin or consumption of hot (spicy) food, to a serious, necrotizing gastritis, as caused by ingestion of caustic liquids. The more chronic forms of mild irritation may result in hyperplasia of the mucosa.

### 1.1.3 Small intestine

The most common pathological changes of the small intestine develop when its complex physiological balance is disturbed. This disturbance results mainly in functional changes including excessive loss of fluid or electrolytes or both, malabsorption, vomiting and diarrhea. Again, non-neoplastic morphological changes are rarely observed.

*Erosions and ulcers*

The mucosa of the small intestine is lined with a layer of columnar epithelium and is theoretically as sensitive to erosions and ulcerations as the stomach. In practice, however, ulcerative injury is far less common here than in the stomach.

> ASSIGNMENT 21.4
>
> What factors may contribute to the protection of the small intestine from this type of injury?

It must be noted, however, that enterohepatic recirculation can cause the intestinal mucosa to be exposed to a substance so often, that ulcerations and erosive injuries or both, do develop. A well-known example is the injury to the small intestine of dogs as a result of recirculation of non-steroidal anti-inflammatory agents. Here too, injury may occur with various degrees of severity.

*Enteritis*

A more diffuse irritation, accompanied by inflammatory reactions, is called *enteritis*. It may develop after exposure of the intestine to caustic substances or metals such as arsenic or mercury.

*Villous stunting*

Chemicals that inhibit the mitotic activity of the precursor cells in the crypts at the base of the intestinal villi retard the growth of the villi.

Stunting of the villi may also be caused by an increased cell death rate of the cells at the tips of the villi, without the same rate of replacement by new cells. Increased cell division rates cause the crypts to elongate. The villus to crypt ratio will thus shift in favor of the crypt.

There is also a third form of villous atrophy; the mechanism by which this develops involves a defect in the immune system.

---

EXAMPLES

Methotrexate reduces DNA synthesis by inhibition of the enzyme dihydrofolate reductase. This causes acute injury to the intestinal epithelium, characterized by reduced mitotic activity in the crypts and shortening of the villi. The second type of villous stunting, where there is an increase in the number of cells dying at the tips of the villi, can be induced by alcohol and iodoacetamide.

The best known example of immunologically induced villous atrophy is hypersensitivity to gluten. Gluten is a protein found in wheat. The mucosa of people suffering from this immunological abnormality recovers when gluten is removed from the diet.

*Lipid accumulation*

Occasionally, chemicals cause very different effects, as in the accumulation of lipids caused by tetracycline. Some substances, for example, erythromycin esters and detergents, permeate the absorptive cells and are phagocytosed by the underlying macrophages. They interfere with the liposomal enzyme system and accumulate in the macrophage forming "foam cells" in the lamina propria of the

643

villus. If the ingestion of these substances is continued, "foam cells" can also be found elsewhere, for example in the mesenteric lymph glands or the liver. Figure 21.5 gives an overview of some morphological changes that may occur in the small intestine as a result of contact with toxic chemicals.

*Diarrhea* is a common response of the small intestine to the ingestion of toxic substances. It may be accompanied by obvious injury to the mucosa (gastritis) but not necessarily. Diarrhea may result from several causes: sensory irritation, a direct effect on the muscle cells, hyperosmolarity of the agent in the lumen, an effect on the membrane of the enterocytes. Essentially the control, of the liquid and electrolyte balance or both, is disturbed.

Detergents in the diet may destroy the brush border membrane of the villi and thus interfere with the uptake of nutrients, which may result in diarrhea.

### 1.1.4 Large intestine

The mechanism and pathology of injury to the large intestine are essentially identical to those relating to the stomach and small intestine. NSAIDs and some other chemicals may cause erosions or ulcers. Occasionally they may also give rise to more diffuse inflammation as in colitis. Chronic ingestion of some substances can lead to hyperplasia, squamous metaplasia or sometimes to neoplasia. Some substances may also accumulate in the tissue. As was discussed in the previous study unit, chemicals may exert indirect effects on the large intestine by affecting the microflora.

Intoxication with chemicals by the rectal route is most unusual, except for a small number of drugs. An example of a substance that has lead to poisoning and eventually death via this route of administration is tribromoethanol.

*Diarrhea*

NSAIDs = non-steroidal anti-inflammatory drugs

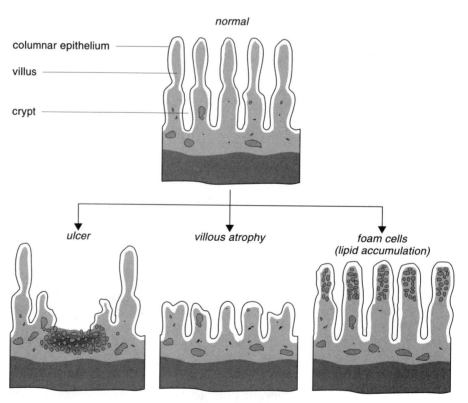

FIGURE 21.5
Examples of structural changes induced by chemicals

Individuals suffering from hepatic insufficiency are particularly sensitive to this anesthetic, which is administered rectally.

## 1.2 PROLIFERATIVE LESIONS

If the gastrointestinal system is exposed to toxic substances that damage its surface, the mucosa of every intestinal segment is capable of repair and regeneration. Every segment has its own cell turnover. The turnover of cells in the small intestine has been studied thoroughly concerning the maintenance of the normal length of villi and depths of crypts.

reflux = flowing back
esophagitis = inflammation of the esophagus

Increased cellular proliferation in the esophagus occurs in patients suffering from reflux esophagitis. This regenerative process is essential for the tissue to survive. From a toxicological point of view, interest is focused more on the processes of hyperplasia, metaplasia and dysplasia that develop on exposure to substances or drugs administered orally, rather than daily repair. It should be remembered that these changes are often related to carcinogenesis. See also the study units on carcinogenesis! Each segment of the gastrointestinal tract has its own mucosal layer. As a result, each displays a specific pattern of hyperplasia–dysplasia–neoplasia. In some cases this may be a pattern of atrophy–metaplasia–neoplasia, or of adenoma–carcinoma.

The following sections will outline the development of proliferation in the various segments of the gastrointestinal tract, using some well-researched examples as illustrations.

### 1.2.1 Esophagus

The esophagus is lined with keratinized stratified epithelium.

Achalasia is a disturbance of motility, associated with stagnation of the contents.
*Chemical esophagitis*

Lesions which may occur in the esophagus are similar to those found in the oral cavity. Epidemiological studies have shown that this keratinized epithelium displays tumorous changes in individuals exposed to dyes for many years. Carcinomas of the esophagus are often seen in patients with achalasia, bacterial growth or *chemical esophagitis*. Chemically induced esophageal inflammation is characterized by infiltration of lymphocytes and plasma cells into the submucosa, dilatation of the blood vessels and a papillomatous surface.

*Atrophy-hyperkeratosis-carcinoma sequence*

This form of esophagitis seems to be a precursor of cancer. Heat lesions caused by ingestion of very hot food, the daily intake of carcinogens in food and vitamin deficiencies may also play an important part in the development of cancer. In monkeys receiving 1-methyl-1-nitrosourea in the diet, an *atrophy–hyperkeratosis–carcinoma sequence* was observed. After about a year, carcinomas were found in 71% of the treated monkeys. This result gives an impression of the progression in the pathogenesis of carcinomas in the esophagus.

### 1.2.2 Stomach

resection = partial removal

The incidence of stomach cancer in individuals with pernicious anemia, gastric polyps, chronic gastric ulcers or who have undergone gastric resection, is higher than that in a normal population. High-risk populations are furthermore to be found in Chile, Japan, Costa Rica, Iceland and Finland. Several ingredients in the diet, including salt, have been associated with carcinogenic processes. Extensive research has been carried out into the induction of tumors as a result of dietary intake of nitrates.

ASSIGNMENT 21.5

How are nitrates ingested with the food?

*Gastritis–atrophy–metaplasia–carcinoma sequence*

Studies of patients with pernicious anemia, as well as research on carcinogenesis with laboratory animals, have shown that gastric carcinomas can develop following a *gastritis–atrophy–metaplasia–carcinoma sequence*. It is assumed that the gastric atrophy phase shows bacterial overgrowth on the mucosa. This results in colonization of the epithelium by micro-organisms that convert nitrates into nitrites. This reaction, which takes place at low pH and in the presence of amines, may lead to the formation of carcinogenic nitrosamines.

*Classification of gastric carcinomas*

From a histological viewpoint, stomach carcinomas can be subdivided into two types. Gastric carcinomas may adopt the cellular structure of the intestinal epithelium or resemble the gastric mucosa cell. Some cell types form adenocarcinomas and others form carcinomas. In Study unit 12, adenocarcinomas are defined as malignant tumors in which the glandular structure is still easily recognizable. In contrast, the glandular structure of carcinomas is no longer discernible.

The quantity of mucus present in the gastric adenocarcinomas varies greatly, the greatest quantity being found in adenocarcinomas containing signet cells. These cells are so named because the nucleus is displaced to one side, resembling a signet ring.

*Dysplasia versus carcinoma*

*Dysplasia* of the gastric mucosa is characterized by cellular atypia, abnormal differentiation and poorly organized gastric architecture when compared with normal tissue. Cellular atypia also means hyperchromatism and irregular arrangement of the nuclei. A gastric carcinoma is distinguished from a serious dysplasia by the following characteristics: loss of cell differentiation, disoriented structure of the glands, invasive and infiltrative growth into the surrounding tissue, abrupt deformation in comparison with the surrounding tissue and displacement of the normal tissue.

### 1.2.3 Small intestine

The small intestine displays relatively few adenocarcinomas.

Give a number of reasons why adenocarcinomas will be relatively uncommon in the small intestine.

*Adenocarcinomas*

Several factors contribute to this: the rapid transit of the intestinal contents, the relatively sparse intestinal flora and the rapid turnover of the enterocytes. Consistent with other segments of the intestinal tract, chronic inflammation processes may be found in the small intestine, as in Crohn's disease with partial obstruction, changes in the intestinal flora and stimulation of repair hyperplasia. These processes are preneoplastic. Crohn's disease is suspected of increasing the risk of development of *adenocarcinomas*.

*Lymphosarcoma*
See also section 1.1.3

An increased incidence of *lymphosarcoma* of the small intestine is observed in long-term suffers of coeliac disease, non-tropical sprue. In this disease, there is incoordination due to sensitivity to gluten in the diet. This results in premature death of the enterocytes, hyperplasia of the crypts of Lieberkühn. There is pronounced diffuse proliferation of lymphocytes and plasma cells are present in the intestinal submucosa.

### 1.2.4 Large intestine

Two procarcinogenic lesions of the large intestine have been described: ulcerative colitis and colorectal adenoma.

*Ulcerative colitis*

*Ulcerative colitis* is characterized by chronic inflammation of the colonic epithelium. The crypts of the colon display cellular degeneration and cell death. The crypts and the *lamina propria* also contain granulocytes. The acute inflammatory reaction in the crypts produces ulceration. Lymphocytes and plasma cells participate in the inflammatory process. Regenerative hyperplasia is frequently observed, while dysplasia and carcinomas are less common. Dysplasia sometimes manifests itself macroscopically as a flat mucosa, a villous mucosa or a polypoid mucosa.

*Colorectal adenoma*

*Colorectal adenomas* consist of masses of neoplastic epithelium protruding above the normal mucosal surface of colon and rectum. Various histological types have been described. Tubular adenomas are seen as dysplastic tubules of the colonic or rectal epithelium, with little lamina propria in between. Villous adenomas consist of finger-like projections of dysplastic epithelium. The frequency with which adenomas occur in the colon and rectum increases with age.

Figure 21.6 shows some examples of tumors of the colon.

### 1.3 AGENTS

The following sections give an overview of chemicals known to be involved in the induction of neoplasms in the gastrointestinal tract.

*Nitrosamines*

*Nitrosamines* are the products of the reaction between amines and nitrites in an acidic environment. Amines ingested in the food or amine-containing drugs can

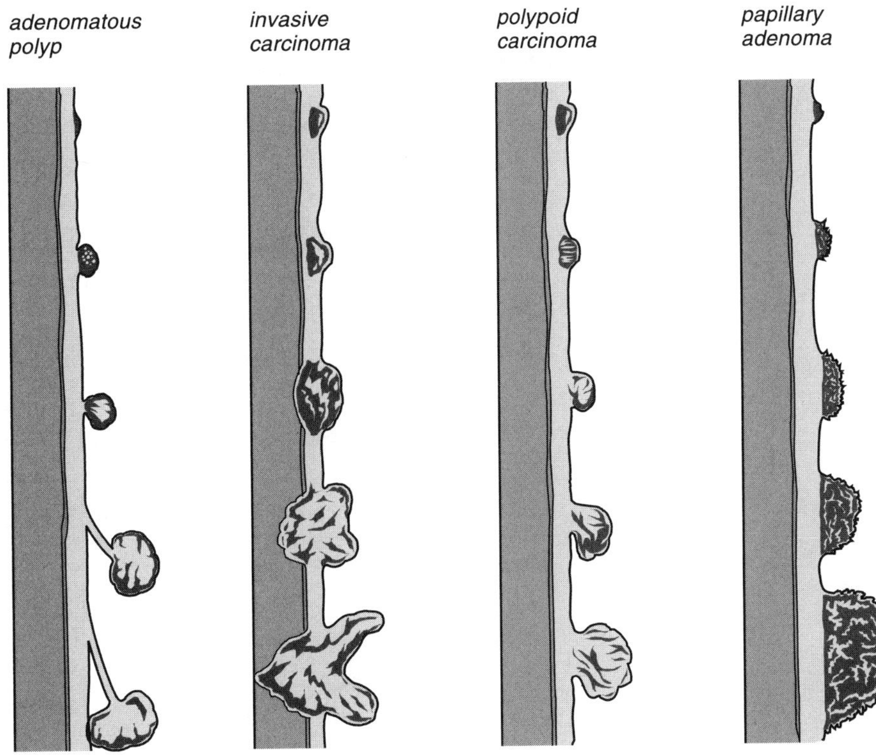

FIGURE 21.6
Some examples of malignant tumors of the colon (polypoid = resembling a polyp)

$$\begin{array}{c} R_1 \\ \diagdown \\ \diagup \\ R_2 \end{array} NH + NO_2^- + H^+ \longrightarrow \begin{array}{c} R_1 \\ \diagdown \\ \diagup \\ R_2 \end{array} N - N = O + H_2O$$

FIGURE 21.7
In an acidic environment, secondary amines and nitrite are converted into (carcinogenic) nitrosamines

*Nitrates*

be converted in the presence of nitrite into nitrosamines, e.g. in the stomach (see Figure 21.7).

Various nitrosamines are carcinogenic, primarily to the gastrointestinal tract. They can be formed either exogenously or endogenously (in the stomach).

Vegetables grown on nitrate-rich soil contain nitrates, which microorganisms can convert into nitrites. Nitrites and nitrates are also frequently used in meat preservatives. Cooking allows nitrosamines to be formed.

*Nitrates* are sometimes present in drinking water. Endogenous nitrates can be converted into nitrites by bacteria in the mouth or by the flora in the more distal segments of the intestinal tract. Nitrites form a normal component of saliva and can also be formed endogenously by interactions with ammonium from the intestine.

Various pharmaceuticals contain amino groups which can, at least in principle, be converted by a reaction with nitrites in the stomach to N-nitroso compounds. These substances are carcinogenic to various organ systems such as the esophagus and stomach. Organ selectivity is determined by species, chemical structure, site and route of administration and daily dose (see Table 21.1)

---

EXAMPLE

*N-methyl-N'-nitro-N-nitrosoguanidine*

N-methyl-N'-nitro-N-nitrosoguanidine is the nitroso compound most commonly used in experimental research. It can induce chemical ulcers, intestinal metaplasia or atrophy of the gastric mucosa in various species. Each of these processes is considered to precede development of adenocarcinomas.

The following mucosal changes were demonstrated in the stomachs of rats given methyl-nitro-nitrosoguanidine in their drinking water:

• edema and inflammation of the epithelium
• cystic changes of the glands
• loss of glandular epithelium.

In addition, atypical glandular hyperplasia and carcinomas of various degrees of differentiation can sometimes be found.

---

2-Acetylaminofluorene is known to induce neoplasia of the glandular portion of the rat stomach. This substance was tested as a candidate insecticide.

2-acetylaminofluorene
20-methylcholanthrene

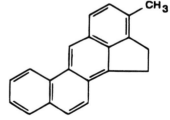

2-acetylaminofluorene          20-methylcholanthrene

TABLE 21.1
Some nitrosamines and their gastrointestinal effects in laboratory animals.
The species in which the effect was demonstrated is given in brackets.

| Substance | Species | Lesion |
|---|---|---|
| N-propyl-N'-nitro-N-nitrosoguanidine | rat (Wistar) | intestinal metaplasia, adenomas and adenocarcinomas of the stomach |
| N-nitrosopiperidine | guinea pig | esophageal and gastric carcinomas |
| 1-propyl-1-nitrosourea | rat (F344) | duodenal adenomas; adenocarcinomas; hemangiomas |
| N-alkyl-N'-nitro-nitrosoguanidine | rat (Wistar) | intestinal metaplasia; adenocarcinomas of the stomach |
| N-propyl-N-nitrosourethane | rat (ACI) | papillomas and squamous cell carcinomas in pharynx and esophagus |
| ethylnitrosourea 2-hydroxyethyinitrosourea carboxymethyinitrosourea 1-nitroso-5,6-dihydrouracil 1-nitrosohydantoin N-methyl-N-nitrosobenzamide ethyinitrosocyanamide | rat (MRC Wistar) | papillomas and carcinomas of forestomach, pharynx and tongue |
| N-nitrosomethyl-N-propylamine N-nitrosomethyl-N-butylamine N-nitrosomethyl (2-hydroxypropyl)-amine N-nitrosomethyl (2,3-dihydroxypropyl)-amine | rat (F344) | esophageal carcinomas |
| N-nitrosomethyl (2-oxopropyl)-amine N-nitroso-3,5-dimethylpiperidine | rat (F344) | esophageal carcinomas |
| N-nitrososarcosine ethyl ester | rat (Sprague-Dawley) | carconomas of esophagus and forestomach |

A structural analogue of this compound, N,N-2,7-fluorenyldiacetamide, can be used to demonstrate a clear sequential development of atrophy, hyperplasia and neoplasia of the rat stomach. Adenocarcinomas of the entire intestinal tract have also been found.

*Polycyclic aromatic hydrocarbons* occur as contaminants in commercial food products. The carcinogenic effects of 1,2,5,6-dibenzanthracene and 20-methyl-cholanthrene have been shown in mice.

*Polycyclic aromatic hydrocarbons*

The first morphological changes can be observed in the crypts of Lieberkühn. The epithelium becomes hyperplastic, sometimes pseudo-stratified, with many mitoses. In the formation of a carcinoma, the process extends to the serosa and there are metastases to the regional lymph glands.

In rats, cancer has been shown to develop in the glandular portion of the stomach and in the forestomach, which is comparable to the esophagus in man, treated with methylcholanthrene. The treatment used slow release ampoules with 8–12

649

months delivery times. After 16 months 17 of the 27 animals displayed a squamous carcinoma of the forestomach. Methylcholanthrene is considered to be the most active of the polycyclic aromatic hydrocarbons that induce tumors in the forestomach. Benzo[a]pyrene is also carcinogenic to the forestomach of the mouse.

*Dimethylhydrazine*

*Dimethylhydrazine* and derived structures such as azoxymethane are often used in experimental colonic tumor models.
Hydrazines are found in tobacco and mushrooms.
Dimethylhydrazine is oxidized in the liver to form azomethane and is further converted into azoxymethane (see Figure 21.8).

It should be noted that this substance retains its selectivity for the colon and small intestine even after intravenous administration. Histologically, the first perceptible change is a mucosal hyperplasia in the folds of the mucosal layer. In more advanced cases, expansion of the adenomatous zones with formation of a polyp can be observed. Large polyps are malignant in character.

*Sequence*

Dimethylhydrazine induces a hyperplasia–adenoma–carcinoma sequence and sometimes a hyperplasia–carcinoma sequence.
Rats and mice treated with azoxymethane react in the same way as they do to dimethylhydrazine. After 10 weeks of exposure the mice had colon tumors and the rats had duodenal tumors. In the colon, adenomatous polyps, adenocarcinomas and mucinous adenocarcinomas were seen. Polyps and adenocarcinomas were found in the small intestine. Mucinous carcinomas of the colon display the greatest malignancy. They develop in the mucosa located above the lymphoid nodes of the intestine.

*Polychlorinated biphenyls*

*Polychlorinated biphenyls (PCBs)* have been used in industry for some 40 years. They are resistant to high temperatures, do not conduct electricity and are non-flammable. They are used in heat exchangers, in the plastics industry and in paints and glues. PCBs have been found in many animal species.

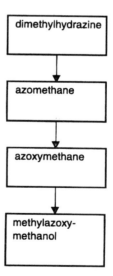

FIGURE   21.8
Metabolic conversion of dimethylhydrazine into azoxymethane via hepatic oxidation into azomethane

Ingestion of PCBs may have various effects. Hypertrophic gastritis is the most important. It has been observed in primates and pigs but not in rabbits, dogs or sheep. In monkeys, this lesion has been simulated experimentally. The first histological observation is a drastic change in the cellular population at the level of the gastric mucosa. As the lesion becomes aggravated, there is a total transformation into mucous cells, with hypertrophy of mucus-rich epithelium.

*T-2 Fusarium toxin*

*T-2 Fusarium toxin* (Figure 21.9) is the main component in alcoholic extractions of *Fusarium poae* and *Fusarium sporotrichioides* cultures. These fungi are responsible for the toxicity of bread made from inadequately stored cereals. T–2 *Fusarium* toxin is one of the most toxic and irritant of the mycotoxins.

In rats, T–2 *Fusarium* toxin produces hyperplasia and sometimes tumors of the gastrointestinal tract.

*Carrageenan and dextran sulfate*

*Carrageenan and dextran sulfate* are sulfate compounds of galactose polysaccharides, found in various species of seaweed. They are frequently used in food products, cosmetics and pharmaceuticals, mainly as stabilizers and emulsifiers. Carrageenan is extracted from red seaweed. It was used in France to treat peptic ulcers. This therapy led to inflammation, metaplasia and neoplastic changes.

In experiments on rats, it caused colitis with crypt abscesses, infiltration by neutrophils, small ulcers and atrophy of the colonic epithelium. In high doses tumors develop. Rabbits develop ulcers in the colon and polyps but no signs of malignancy.

*$H_2$ histamine antagonists*
Two different receptors have been shown to be important for the main actions of histamine. They are called $H_1$ and $H_2$ receptors.

Following the success of the *$H_2$ antagonist* cimetidine in the treatment of peptic ulcers, the pharmaceutical industry has been eager to develop competitive products. Attention has recently been drawn to the dangers of long-term use of $H_2$ histamine antagonists, which may result in neoplasia. Several researchers have pointed out that patients, treated with these products on a long-term basis, may either develop neoplasms or develop malignant from benign tumors. It is possible that the combination with a nitro group produces nitrosocimetidine, a nitrosoguanidine with a structure similar to that of N-methyl-N'-nitro-N-nitrosoguanidine. However, it has been reported that long-term administration of cimetidine, 53 months, to dogs did not induce metaplasia, dysplasia or neoplasia. Nor was an increase of tumor incidence observed after long-term administration to rats.

## 2    Food, food additives and contaminants

Potential toxins, present in food, enter the body via the oral route and are thus present in higher concentrations in the gastrointestinal tract than they are in other tissues. These high concentrations may cause specific lesions, such as ir-

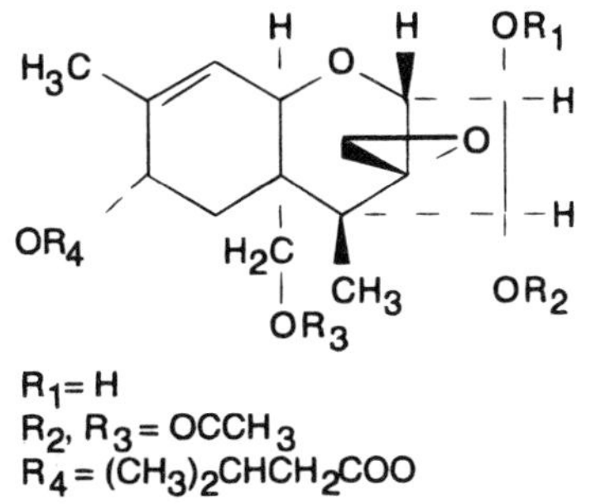

$R_1 = H$
$R_2, R_3 = OCCH_3$
$R_4 = (CH_3)_2CHCH_2COO$

FIGURE   21.9
Chemical structure of T-2 *Fusarium* toxin, a carcinogenic mycotoxin

ritation. In addition, biotransformation may be carried out by microorganisms or by the cells of the gastrointestinal mucosa. Toxic substances in the food may originate from microbial metabolites or degradation products, formed during decomposition or storage.

An overview is provided in Table 21.2.

The highly varied composition of food makes it difficult to make a quantitative or qualitative assessment of the exposure to toxic or carcinogenic substances. Exposure to a single component leaves unresolved the problem of possible synergistic effects with other food components.

## 2.1 FOOD-INDUCED CHANGES

In animal experiments, some substances cause enlargement or distension of the cecum, as with sorbitol, lactose and pectins. This is not in itself fatal but it is considered to be either a toxic or an adaptive process. These substances may be absorbed by the intestine very slowly or not at all. They may also exhibit osmotic activity. Other additives, as is the case with carrageenan, may cause ulcerative lesions in the intestine.

## 2.2 TOXIC FOOD COMPONENTS

Most nitroso derivatives, which are formed from nitrates ingested with the food, are carcinogenic in laboratory animals. They are also likely to be carcinogenic in man. Some tumors, including stomach cancer, are associated with the presence of nitrosamines.

*Nitrates*

Nitrates are natural components of certain plants, as spinach, celery and rhubarb. Nitrates are also used as additives for their antibacterial effect. They may be present in the drinking water. Large quantities of nitrates have been shown to be formed by bacterial nitrate reductase in the human liver.

*Nitrosamides/nitrosamines*

More than 100 nitrosamines and nitrosamides have been tested in rats. The majority are carcinogenic. The lower gastrointestinal organs are affected mainly by the action of nitrosamides, whereas the nitrosamines primarily affects the esophagus and pharynx.

*Phytotoxins*

Various toxins of vegetable origin have been shown to be carcinogenic in laboratory animals but the relevance of these findings for man has not yet been proved. Many hydrazines are carcinogenic and mutagenic. Large amounts of them are found in edible mushrooms. Quercetin and kaempferol are the most common flavonoids in plants. Both substances have mutagenic and genotoxic

TABLE 21.2

Examples of toxic substances in food

| Toxic substance | Active agent | Origin | Effect/target organ |
|---|---|---|---|
| naturally occurring in | | | |
| -plants | glucosinolates | cabbage | goiter |
| | nitrites-nitrates | spinach | methemoglobinemia |
| -animals | lipoproteines | fish | vomiting, headache |
| | nitrosamines | nitrites and secondary amines | carcinogenic |
| preparation of food | heated products | proteins | carcinogenic |
| contaminants | pesticide residues | organophosphates | central nervous system |
| food additives | saccharin | diet | carcinogenic |
| | butylated hydroxyanisole | fats and oils | |

652

properties and can be a risk for man. Quercetin is found mainly in coffee and tea. Its carcinogenic potential is controversial.

*Cereal or flour toxins*

Cereals and flour may contain toxins including mycotoxins, that can be mutagenic and carcinogenic. Aflatoxin is the most familiar example of these substances.

### 2.3   FOOD ADDITIVES

Food additives can be defined as substances added to food deliberately to retain its quality or improve its color and smell. In general, food additives are physiologically inert. Nevertheless, they may cause toxic effects on the gastrointestinal tract. Most important is the possibility of the metabolic degradation of the additive by the intestinal microflora. This may result in a higher toxicity than that of the parent molecule. Cyclamates, for example, are converted by the intestinal bacteria into cyclohexylamine, which is suspected to be carcinogenic. The additive may also be absorbed and excreted in the urine unchanged, as is the case with saccharin. Some examples of what may happen to food additives are provided in Table 21.3.

Some examples of food additives and their toxic effects are presented in Table 21.4.

*Dietary lipids*

Epidemiological studies have shown that there is an association between *dietary lipids* and the incidence of tumors, primarily at the level of the colon. Rancid fats may constitute the causal factor. Unsaturated fatty acids and cholesterol are easily oxidized by various methods of preparation and may form mutagens, initiators and promoters. Moreover, hydroperoxides produce oxygen radicals, which in turn may form mutagens and carcinogens.

Lipids are assumed to influence the development of colon cancer in various ways:

*   increase in concentrations of secondary bile acids (not in man)
*   change in intestinal flora
*   effect on drugs and metabolites.

Some contradictory data concerning the relationship between dietary intake of lipids and colon cancer might be explained by the protective effect of dietary fiber.

TABLE   21.3
Fate of some food additives in the gastrointestinal tract

| Food additive | Changes in the gastrointestinal tract |
| --- | --- |
| sodium saccharin | unchanged absorption and excretion via urine; may cause changes in intestinal flora |
| hexamethylenetetramine | dissociates in duodenum, forming formaldehyde and ammonia; formaldehyde binds to proteins |
| carrageenan | partly decomposed in small intestine; degradation products cause ulcerative lesions |
| nitrate | enters stomach-saliva circulation, followed by bacterial reduction to nitrite |
| polyglycerol esters | are hydrolyzed in the intestine; resulting fatty acids are absorbed |
| sorbitol | absorbed slowly in duodenum by passive diffusion; remaining sorbitol is acted on by microflora, which produce osmotically active substances and gases, resulting in cecal distention in rats |

TABLE 21.4
Examples of food additives and their suspected effects, based on animal experiments

| Class | Food additive | Presumed effect |
|---|---|---|
| antioxidants | butylated hydroxytoluene | carcinogenic to liver (mouse) |
| | butylated hydroxyanisole | carcinogenic to stomach (rat) |
| | alkyl gallates | carcinogenic |
| antibacterial agents | benzoic acid | allergy |
| | nitrosamines | carcinogenic |
| | sodium chloride | hypertension |
| coloring agents | erythrosin | thyroid carcinogen |
| | caramel colorants | cecal distension |
| | azo dyes | allergy |
| sweeteners | saccharin | carcinogenic to bladder (?) |
| | cyclamates | carcinogenic to bladder |
| fungicides | o-phenylphenol | carcinogenic to bladder |
| flavor enhancer | monosodium glutamate | Chinese restaurant syndrome |

*Pyrolysis products*

Most foods for human consumption are cooked. Heat reaction products, *pyrolysis products*, are highly complex. So far, not much is known of the toxic properties of these reaction products.

> What is the danger of eating well grilled or roasted meat? Explain!

Various methods of preparation seem to have an effect on mutagenicity. Large amounts of polycyclic aromatic hydrocarbons are formed when food is fried, roasted or grilled.

*Pyrolysis of tryptophan*

Smoked food and roasted coffee are the main sources of polycyclic aromatic hydrocarbons. The mutagenicity of well-cooked products is due to pyrolysis of amino acids and proteins. Tryptophan is supposed to have the greatest mutagenic effect of all the amino acids, after pyrolysis.

In addition, the degradation products of amino acids and sugars, including caramelization of sugars, may contain large amounts of DNA-damaging factors.

Pyrolysis of lipids provides various components, whose structures have not yet been elucidated. These include many carcinogenic substances.

## 3 Drugs and gastrointestinal toxicology

*See Study unit 38 for a definition of "side effect"*

Most drugs that are taken orally may cause an adverse reaction or side effect. The term 'side effect' will be used in this study unit as a synonym of the toxic effect of a drug. Although many drugs exert a toxic effect on the gastrointestinal tract, the intensity may range from very mild, for example nausea, to very severe, as in pseudomembranous colitis.

In hospitalized patients, 20–40% of the side effects of drugs take place in the gastrointestinal tract. The list of possible side effects is long. Note that there are many contradicting opinions concerning the cause and effect relationships of pharmaceuticals and their side effects. Often, the description of side effects is not supported by sufficient evidence, while in other cases, the side effect is hypothetical or based only on animal experiments.

For many pharmaceuticals, detailed knowledge of the side effects is available. Acetylsalicylic acid, for example, causes dyspepsia in approximately 6% of patients. It has also been shown to cause bleeding in the gastrointestinal tract at a dose of 50 mg per day. The population may be subdivided into "bleeders" and "non-bleeders". Normal therapeutic doses can lead to blood loss of 3 to 15 ml per day into the intestinal lumen. In chronic use, there is good correlation between the use of aspirin and increased hemorrhage in the gastrointestinal tract and gastroduodenal ulcerations.

*Ulcer*
See also section 1.1.2

*Erosions*

An *ulcer* is a well-defined loss of tissue from the surface of an organ. This loss results in necrosis of tissue due to cell destruction by substances. Ulcers are the most common and most important inflammatory lesions. Ulcers which do not permeate the muscularis mucosae are called *erosions*. Most ulcers are found in the stomach. In man, gastric ulcers usually develop near the pyloric sphincter.

Ulcers in the duodenum are also usually located close to the pyloric sphincter. Macroscopically, ulcers are crater-shaped with sharply delineated edges. Chronic ulcers should not be confused with incipient neoplasms.

*Peptic ulcer*

The main complications of a *peptic ulcer*, which develops due to excessive production of gastric juice, are hemorrhage, perforation and obstruction.

*Drug-induced ulcers*

The pathogenesis of *drug-induced* gastrointestinal *ulcers* usually involves direct irritation and inflammation of the mucosa or direct or indirect hypoxia i.e., lack of oxygen. Chemically induced ulcers caused by non-steroidal anti-inflammatory drugs (NSAIDs) are characterized histologically by the absence of inflammatory cells.

An important feature of ulcerogenic salicylates is the presence of a non-esterified carboxyl group.

Chronic rheumatoid patients, taking aspirin, show a 50% incidence of gastric erosion and a 20% incidence of gastric ulcer. The occurrence of gastric ulcers is also determined by the product formulation of the aspirin. Enteric-coated formulations cause fewer ulcers. The mechanism of ulcer induction by aspirin has not yet been completely clarified. A topical effect causes rupture of the mucosa, influx of protons into the cells takes place and submucosal hemorrhage follows.

*Aspirin and other NSAIDs*

*Aspirin and other NSAIDs* inhibit prostaglandin synthesis. The development of gastric ulcers is clearly associated with this process. The inhibition of prostaglandin synthesis leads to vasoconstriction and increased gastric secretion. Other presumed effects of aspirin are increased capillary fragility, increased fibrinolysis and prolonged bleeding time. The ulcerogenic action of aspirin may be associated with the inhibition of the synthesis of mucosal glycoproteins.

*New generation of anti-inflammatory agents*

Alcohol aggravates the lesions induced by aspirin both in man and in rats. The *new generation of anti-inflammatory agents* of which ibuprofen is the best-known example, appear to have fewer adverse effects on the gastrointestinal tract.

At present, it is impossible to give a definitive overview of the gastric toxicity of these drugs. Naproxen has frequently been associated with hemorrhage and ulcerations or both. Ketoprofen is suspected of having toxic effects on the stomach in 20–42% of patients. With ibuprofen these effects are seen in 10–33% of patients and with diclofenac in 13–20% of patients.

Ibuprofen is an example of a drug whose dosage has had to be increased to achieve adequate effectiveness. As a result, some gastric toxicity occurs.

Benoxaprofen was withdrawn from the market in 1982 because it was found to have serious side effects on the liver, the gastrointestinal tract, the skin and the nails. Its gastric toxicity was estimated to be lower than that of similar substances, because it does not inhibit prostaglandin synthesis to the same extent. Nevertheless, ulceration was occasionally found; other side effects including vomiting, nausea and epigastric pain were observed mainly in elderly people.

*Acetaminophen*

A common painkiller is *acetaminophen* (paracetamol). This drug has antipyretic as well as analgesic properties. Side effects are rare, although gastrointestinal hemorrhage may sometimes occur. Acetaminophen is a mild inhibitor of prostaglandin synthesis. In rats, acetaminophen reduces the incidence of gastric ulcers induced by aspirin. In dogs, the combination of aspirin and acetaminophen has been shown to have no greater adverse effects than those of either component used separately.

Table 21.5 gives an overview of substances that may cause lesions to the gastrointestinal tract and the mechanism by which they are suspected to work.

ASSIGNMENT 21.6

Describe the pathogenesis of drug-induced ulcers.

## 4 Toxic substances from environment and industry

This section gives an overview of the substances in the environment with effects on the gastrointestinal system. The classification is based on structure, symptoms or mechanism of action.

### 4.1 INORGANIC SUBSTANCES

*Fluorides*

*Fluorides* can produce widely varying symptoms of toxicity, dependent upon whether the intoxication is acute or chronic. In acute fluoride intoxication, symptoms can include vomiting, diarrhea, anorexia and abdominal pain.

Histopathologically, inflammation, swelling, hemorrhage and necrosis of gastrointestinal tissues may be observed. The stomach is very sensitive to fluorides. If the intoxication is chronic, osteoporosis and hypoplasia of the teeth can occur. Fluoride toxicity in the intestines causes the inhibition of sodium absorption and hence of the transport of fluids through the intestinal wall.

Fluorides also inhibit numerous enzymes, such as adenyl cyclase and acetylcholinesterase. This explains the diarrhea observed in fluoride intoxication.

*Corrosives*

*Corrosives* are agents with a typically local effect. Ingestion is followed by vomiting, abdominal pain and blood-stained diarrhea. Histologically, necrosis of the gastrointestinal tissue is found mainly in the stomach and proximal part of the small intestine. Hemoglobin is broken down, which explains the dark color of the stools. Alkaline materials damage an organ primarily by hydrolysis, which results in tissue with a somewhat gelatinous appearance.

*Other inorganic substances*

Detergents are known to induce vomiting. Typical examples are the commercial detergents, like the polyphosphates in washing powder. Ingestion of borates causes nausea, vomiting, abdominal pain and diarrhea.

### 4.2 ORGANIC SUBSTANCES

*Halogenated aliphatic hydrocarbons*

Gastrointestinal symptoms of intoxication with *halogenated aliphatic hydrocarbons* are nausea, anorexia, vomiting, abdominal pain, diarrhea and hemorrhage. All halogenated substances produce the same signs of intoxication. The toxicity of halogenated aliphatic substances increases in the sequence: F < Cl < Br < I. Local effects do not seem to play an important role in the induction of intestinal toxicity. This is shown in that the symptoms are identical after oral and parenteral administration. Intestinal toxicity caused by halogenated aliphatic hydrocarbons is

TABLE 21.5
Some drugs and their adverse effects and possible cause

| Exposure | | Lesion | Cause |
|---|---|---|---|
| Location | Drug | | |
| oral mucosa | phenylbutazone<br>antibiotics<br>-tetracycline<br>-bleomycin<br>-penicillin<br>-chloroamphenicol<br>-metronidazole | inflammation and ulcers<br>inflammation of tongue | hypersensitivity reaction,<br>bone marrow suppression |
| | phenytoin | gingival hyperplasia | hypersensitivity |
| esophagus | antibiotics<br>-doxycycline<br>-tetracycline | ulcers | |
| | beta blockers<br>-alprenolol<br>-propranolol | erosions | |
| | anti-inflammatory drugs<br>-acetylsalicylic acid<br>-phenylbutazone<br>-indomethacin | erosions | |
| stomach | digitalis glycosides<br>oplates | vomiting | effect on vomiting center |
| | tetracyline | vomiting | irritation of gastric mucosa |
| | anti-inflammatory drugs<br>-acetylsalicylic acid<br>-Indomethacin<br>-phenylbutazone | gastric hemorrhage,<br>ulceration | inhibition prostaglandin<br>synthesis<br>affects gastric mucosa |
| | analgesics-antipyretics | hemorrhage | inhibition prostaglandin<br>synthesis |
| | corticosteroids | ulceration | affects gastric mucosa |
| | alcohol | hemorrhage, ulceration | |
| small and large intestines | potassium chloride | ulceration | |
| | anti-inflammatory drugs | ulceration | |
| | antibiotics<br>-penicillin<br>-ampicillin<br>-tetracycline | inflammation | irritation<br>affects intestinal flora |
| | tripazonol | inflammation | blocks cholesterol<br>synthesis |

virtually always accompanied by hepatic injury. Metabolic activation as a possible mechanism is associated with the induction of gastrointestinal neoplasia.

The supposed mechanism underlying the intestinal toxicity and carcinogenicity of dichloroethane is the formation of sulfur mustard, a type of alkylating molecule. Chlorinated dicyclic pesticides, as with chlordane or aldrin, exhibit an intestinal toxicity similar to that of chlorinated aliphatic hydrocarbons. An overview of the intestinal and hepatic toxicity of some halogenated hydrocarbons is provided in Table 21.6.

TABLE 21.6
Intestinal and hepatic toxicity of halogenated aliphatic hydrocarbons

| Substance | Hepatic lesion | Vomiting | Diarrhea | Abdominal pain | Intestinal hemorrhage | Congestion | Anorexia | Species |
|---|---|---|---|---|---|---|---|---|
| $CH_3Cl$ | x | x | | | x | x | | animal |
| | x | x | x | x | x | | x | man |
| $CH_2Cl_2$ | x | | | | | | | animal |
| | | | | | | | | man |
| $CHCl_3$ | x | x | | | | | | animal |
| | x | | | | | | | man |
| $CCl_4$ | x | | | | x | | | animal |
| | x | x | x | x | x | | x | man |
| $ClCH_2CH_3$ | x | | | | x | x | | animal |
| | | | | | | | | man |
| $ClCH_2CH_2Cl$ | x | | | | x | | | animal |
| | x | x | x | x | x | | x | man |
| $Cl_2CHCHCl_2$ | x | | | | | | x | animal |
| | x | x | x | x | | x | | man |
| $Cl_2CCHCl$ | x | x | | | | | x | animal |
| | (x) | x | | x | | | | man |

**Halogenated aromatic hydrocarbons**

*Halogenated aromatic hydrocarbons* cause hepatic and intestinal toxicity. Little is known about the mechanism of action.

Poorly chlorinated hydrocarbons usually cause a necrotic type of degeneration, whereas highly chlorinated hydrocarbons cause hyperplastic growth. This hyperplasia of the intestinal mucosa is species dependent. Cows usually show gastric hyperplasia. Monkeys have injury to both the stomach and intestine. Dogs only show hyperplastic changes of the intestinal mucosa.

**Aldehydes**

*Aldehydes* are typically potent, locally irritant substances. As a result, their toxic effect is on surface epithelia and is determined by the route of administration. Oral administration is followed by hyperemia. After a high dose, necrosis can be seen.

**Formaldehyde**

*Formaldehyde* is the most toxic member of this group. In diluted aqueous solution, formaldehyde is present as a monomer. Polymerization occurs at higher concentrations. Only the monomer is highly reactive. Its action involves a sequence of steps, including addition to the carbonyl group and a condensation step. This leads to the formation of methylene bridges between functional protein groups.

**Epoxides**

The oxirane ring in *epoxides* is highly reactive. Epoxides are electrophilic and have alkylating properties. Two other important reactions of epoxides are the addition of HCl and water, resulting in the formation of epichlorohydrins and glycols, respectively. Many epoxides undergo this reaction in the acidic environment of the stomach. These reactions should be considered as detoxication processes.

There is little difference between the acute and chronic toxicity of epoxides. Nausea, vomiting, diarrhea and weight loss are the most common symptoms. They are related to the cytostatic and cytotoxic actions of epoxides. Loss of cells and flattening of the mucosa can be observed. Partial loss of intestinal function reduces the ratio of water absorption to reabsorption. This results in diarrhea.

**Other alkylating agents**

Similar biological effects are brought about by *other alkylating agents*, as with dimethyl sulfate, diethyl sulfide and others. Because of their alkylating properties epoxides are classified as carcinogens. For example, after oral administration, they can cause stomach cancer.

*Aromatic amines*
For methemoglobinemia, see
Study unit 27

*Aromatic amines* are usually responsible for two toxicological changes: methemoglobinemia and carcinogenicity. Monocyclic aromatic amines are generally inactive or only slightly carcinogenic. The most active aromatic amines are those with two or more aromatic rings. Aromatic amines display specific organ selectivity. Cancer of the urinary bladder is the most well-known example of their effect but selectivity for liver, auditory meatus or breast may also occur.

Attempts have been made to determine how cancer of the colon is induced. There are indications that N-hydroxylation is followed by glucuronidation in the liver. After the substance has been excreted in the bile, it reaches the colon, where it is deconjugated by intestinal bacteria.

*N-nitroso compounds*

*N-nitrosamines* require metabolic activation for their carcinogenicity. Many researchers claim that enzymatic hydroxylation, requiring oxygen and NADH dependent hydroxylation, is responsible for this activation. In contrast with nitrosamines, nitrosamides and N-methyl-nitrosourea do not require previous activation, since their action is primarily alkylating. Nitrosamines display great organ selectivity. This tissue-specific pattern is thought to be determined by the site of biotransformation.

The carcinogenicity of nitrosamides and nitrosourea is determined by their plasma kinetics and route of administration, since these substances act as direct alkylators.

*Dimethylhydrazine*

*Dimethylhydrazine* is used in experimental models for the induction of colon cancer. The substance requires a complex metabolic activation to induce cancer.

Two mechanisms have been proposed. Either dimethylhydrazine is activated exclusively in the intestine or in the liver. In the latter case, the metabolic products are excreted in the bile to reach the intestine. The organ selectivity of the substance is dose-dependent. Low doses cause liver and lung cancer; higher doses induce tumors of the colon.

ASSIGNMENT 21.7

How do aromatic amines induce colon cancer?

*Cholinesterase inhibitors*

Various carbamates and organophosphorus compounds are *cholinesterase inhibitors*. The best known cholinesterase inhibitors, like paraoxon, are believed to bind irreversibly to acetylcholinesterase by phosphorylation of serine in the active center of the complex. Inhibition of the enzyme leads to a build up of acetylcholine which then exerts its toxic effect. Carbamates bind reversibly. Acetylcholinesterase inhibitors by this build up of acetylcholine cause toxic symptoms in the gastrointestinal tract. Nausea, belching, vomiting, intestinal cramps and defecation with diarrhea occur. There is an increase in tone, amplitude of contractions and peristaltic activity of both the stomach and intestines, together with increased secretions. These phenomena manifests themselves as bouts of abdominal pain. A central mechanism is assumed to be the cause of nausea and vomiting.

## 5 Metals

*Acute intoxication*

Some metals are essential in that they are necessary for the proper functioning of tissues or organs. They can cause toxic reactions if they are ingested in large quantities. Gastrointestinal metal intoxication is usually acute in character. The symptoms usually disappear after a short time and the toxic dose is often much higher than the quantity normally ingested. The symptomatology is mainly non-specific and is rarely associated with a precise biochemical modification of the intestine.

*Chronic intoxication*

*Chronic* metal *intoxication* may also have latent characteristics, which means that the symptoms do not appear until after a long latency period. A typical example is chronic lead poisoning, in which disturbances of the central nervous system take years to become manifest.

## 5.1 SOURCES OF METALS CAUSING GASTROINTESTINAL SIDE EFFECTS

The adverse effects of metals depend on the site of exposure. Ingestion, inhalation and skin contact constitute the main penetration routes. Toxic effects of metals on the gastrointestinal tract usually occur in abnormal circumstances, as in administration of metal-containing drugs or after accidental overdosage with mineral supplements for prophylaxis.

Another source of exposure to metals is the pollution of the environment by industrial emissions, emissions by cars or combustion of fossil fuels. Metals are also important ingredients in a range of therapeutic substances. Antacids, which are used in the treatment of gastrointestinal disturbances, contain aluminum hydroxide or bismuth salts.

Salts, such as copper sulfate and zinc sulfate have been used to induce vomiting. It should be noted that copper, while being an essential metal with very low toxicity, can produce severe poisoning in the salt form.

The therapeutic use of lithium carbonate by many manic-depressive patients is sometimes accompanied by mild gastrointestinal disturbances.

A well-known source of metals is the use of mineral supplements in nutritional prophylaxis. Iron sulfate pills are often prescribed to prevent anemia. Zinc salts are used therapeutically in the treatment of wounds and superficial anorectal disorders. Normal use of these substances does not lead to side effects, but accidentally taking an overdose may do so. Industrial pollution is a common source of intoxication by heavy metals such as lead, cadmium and mercury. Lead poisoning leads to nausea, vomiting, diarrhea or constipation. Exposure to cadmium is thought to play an important role in Japan in the etiology of serious bone diseases.

Mercury originating from a plant was the cause of dramatic poisoning in Japan. In another case, dozens of persons were seriously intoxicated by eating fish containing extremely high levels of mercuric chloride.

## 5.2 EFFECTS AND MORPHOLOGICAL CHANGES

The symptoms of poisoning caused by ingestion of large quantities of metals are non-specific, since the same effects can often be found after long-term exposure to many substances and drugs. The symptoms may vary from loss of appetite, nausea and abdominal pain to more localized lesions, including ulceration and necrosis of the gastrointestinal tract. Symptoms, such as anorexia, nausea and vomiting develop, shortly after ingestion of the toxic substance. The specific mode of action is not clear. The composition and color of feces or vomit may provide indications of the metal involved.

*Black stools*

*Black stools* or blood-stained diarrhea often suggest corrosive metals which cause ulcerations in the gastrointestinal tract.

*Blue-green vomit*

A *blue-green* color of the *vomit* is an indication of possible copper intoxication.

TABLE 21.7
Symptoms of gastrointestinal metal intoxication

| Symptoms | Metals |
| --- | --- |
| loss of appetite, nausea, vomiting, abdominal pain | most metals |
| diarrhea | Au, Ba, Cd, F, Hg, Li, Na, Sb, Sn, Th, Zn |
| constipation | Ca, P, Pb |
| malabsorption | Al, Au, Be, Ca, Cd, Fe, Mg, Pb, Zn |
| gastrointestinal ulceration, necrosis | Ba, Bi, Cr, Fe, Hg, Na, Sb, Zn |
| gastrointestinal infections | Au, Bi, Fe, Th |

*Histological picture*

Histologically, the lesions may vary from non-reversible ulcerations and necrosis to, for example, intranuclear lead inclusion bodies. Metal-induced ulcerations of the gastrointestinal tract, necrosis and perforation of the intestinal wall occur in the same area as after exposure to strong acids but the lesions are far more superficial. Villous atrophy is a common response of the intestinal mucosa to toxic substances.

*Iron*

The use of *iron* preparations in the treatment of iron deficiency in anemia in mothers appears to increase the risk of iron poisoning in children. Overdosage with mother's pills taken in mistake for sweets is a recurrent cause. Iron poisoning causes irritation of the gastric mucosa, vomiting and blood-stained diarrhea.

Another complication of iron overdosing is stimulation of gastrointestinal infection. The cause of this effect has not yet been explained but iron is essential for the growth of most microorganisms. Thus the ingestion of excessive quantities may stimulate the growth of pathogenic bacteria.

It should be noted that a worse response in excessive overdose is the deposition of iron in the peripheral blood vessels.

*Calcium*

*Calcium* is thought to play a role in the pathogenesis of intestinal obstruction in newborn children. It used to be administered as a mineral supplement to prevent neonatal rickets. Calcium-containing antacids are associated with gastrointestinal disturbances such as steatorrhea in patients with pancreatic insufficiency.

steatorrhea = excess fat in the stools; in this case due to insufficient lipase activity.

*Lead*
colic = severe spasmodic griping pain

Ingestion of large quantities of *lead* may cause anorexia, diarrhea or constipation. The most serious symptoms are lead colic and anemia.

*Cadmium*

*Cadmium* causes only mild symptoms but animal experiments have shown that small quantities of cadmium inhibit certain enzymes. In man, cadmium has been shown to inhibit the absorption of calcium.

*Aluminum*

Frequent use of aluminum-containing antacids produces metabolic changes, such as hypophosphatemia. Aluminum precipitates phosphate in the intestine and prevents the absorption of phosphorus.

## 6 Xenobiotics and the pancreas

### 6.1 MORPHOLOGY OF ENDOCRINE AND EXOCRINE PANCREAS

The pancreas is a secretory organ. In adults, most of its cells are concerned with exocrine secretion. The acinar cells secrete digestive enzymes or inactive precursors of enzymes.

*Endocrine cells*

The *endocrine cells*, which produce the hormones insulin and glucagon are set in clusters, the so-called islets of Langerhans; these are distributed randomly in the exocrine pancreas. The cells of the exocrine pancreas are pyramidal in shape, with their nucleus located at the base. The lower part of the cell rests on a basement membrane. The cytoplasm around the nucleus contains a well-developed rough endoplasmic reticulum and numerous mitochondria. The apical zone of the cell contains eosinophilic, membrane-bound zymogen granules.

*Exocrine cells*

The *exocrine cells* produce various enzymes, including amylase, lipase and trypsin, which play a role in the digestive process in the small intestine. Exocrine secretion is subject to hormonal and neural regulation.

Microscopically, the islets of Langerhans consist of strands of cells, embedded in a small amount of connective tissue, with a rich capillary network. Various cell types are present but they can only be distinguished ultrastructurally. The *β cells* are the most common. They tend to be located towards the centers of the islets. These are the cells which produce insulin. The *α cells* are less numerous and are usually encountered at the periphery of an islet. They produce glucagon.

*β cells*
*α cells*

### 6.2    TOXICOLOGICAL PATHOLOGY

Pathological conditions of the pancreas caused by the action of xenobiotics are rarely observed. Table 21.8 gives an overview of some of the possible toxicological lesions of the exocrine pancreas.

The following sections discuss several examples of the effects of xenobiotics on the pancreas.

### 6.3    SUBSTANCES WITH A TOXIC EFFECT ON THE EXOCRINE PANCREAS

#### 6.3.1 Soybeans and pancreatic hypertrophy

Soybeans contain a range of proteins, of which trypsin inhibitors are the best known. The proteins are present in their active form in the raw beans but are inactivated by heat.

> ASSIGNMENT   21.8
>
> What function does trypsin have in the digestive process and how can it contribute to self-destruction of the pancreas?

TABLE   21.8
Possible toxicological lesions of the exocrine pancreas

| Pathology | Caused by |
|---|---|
| degranulation (= loss of zymogen granules) | furosemide |
| acinar atrophy | ethionine, copper deficiency |
| acinar degeneration | zinc deficiency |
| necrosis | puromycin, 4-hydroxyaminoquinoline-1-oxide |
| pancreatitis | manganese |
| acinar hyperplasia/hypertrophy | pentagastrin, soybeans |
| fatty change | ethanol |
| interstitial cell vacuolization | antibiotic |
| formation of hepatocyte-like cells | N-nitroso-methyl(2-oxopropyl)amine |

The raw soybeans increase the protein synthesis in the pancreas and stimulate the secretion of enzymes.

The trypsin inhibitors in soybeans increase the secretion of pancreatic enzymes by the formation of inactive trypsin–trypsin inhibitor complexes. In so doing, they reduce the suppression of the release of pancreatic enzymes that free trypsin exerts. The presence of trypsin inhibitors in the duodenum results in the release of cholecystokinin. Cholecystokinin also acts as a trypsin inhibitor and can cause hypertrophy of the pancreas.

### 6.3.2 Acute pancreatitis induced by xenobiotics

The exact mechanism by which xenobiotics may cause acute pancreatitis has not yet been elucidated. The initiation of pancreatitis is autodigestion. Pancreatic proteases are activated in the pancreas itself by disorders including ischemia, anoxia and trauma. These activated enzymes, primarily trypsin, activate other enzymes, which eventually results in steatosis of the pancreas and surrounding tissue.

*Alcohol*

The two main causes of acute pancreatitis are *alcohol* and disorders of the bile ducts. In the US and Australia, alcohol is responsible for approximately 50% of the cases of acute pancreatitis.

*Drugs*

*Drugs* which lead to pancreatitis can be subdivided into three categories.

- Drugs clearly associated with pancreatitis if they cause inflammation while being used, if the symptoms disappear when administration is discontinued and if the symptoms recur when administration is resumed.
- Drugs are potentially associated with pancreatitis if they are suspected of displaying the above characteristics.
- Drugs have doubtful association with pancreatitis, if the available data are inadequate or contradictory.

Drugs with a clear association are azathioprine, sulfonamides, thiazide diuretics, estrogens (oral contraceptives), tetracycline and valproic acid.

A possible association with pancreatitis is displayed by chlorthalidone, procainamide, L-asparaginase and methyldopa.

There is a doubtful association between pancreatitis and corticosteroids. Common complaints include nausea, vomiting and abdominal distension as a result of hypomotility and chemical peritonitis.

### 6.3.3 Chronic pancreatitis

Alcohol is by far the most common cause of chronic pancreatitis. Its mode of action has not yet been completely explained but animal experiments have shown that protein precipitates in the secretory ducts, which is followed by stenosis, obstruction, atrophy of the acinar cells and fibrosis of the pancreas (Figure 21.10). Protein plugs consist of precipitated pancreatic enzymes and partially degraded trypsinogen and trypsin.

Infiltration of leukocytes and plasma cells can be shown histologically. A reduction in the number and size of the pancreatic acini may also be observed. The secretory ducts show segmental dilatations and stenoses.

## 7 Summary

Toxic substances can damage the gastrointestinal epithelium. The mucosa is capable of repair and regeneration. Various patterns of proliferative change may develop in the stomach and intestine.

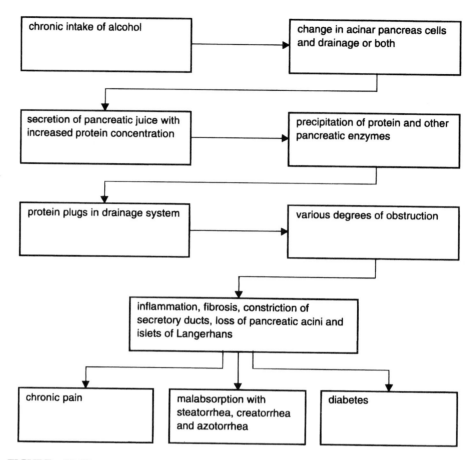

FIGURE 21.10

Schematic representation of the process of alcohol-induced pancreatitis

Steatorrhea is the presence of fat in the stools, creatorrhea is the presence of undigested muscle fibers in the stools and azotorrhea is excess protein in the stools.

Many food components give rise to gastrointestinal pathology. Nitrosamines in particular have been studied in detail. Dietary lipids are thought to play a role in the induction of colon cancer. Pyrolysis products, formed in over-cooked meat, are known to be carcinogenic.

Many drugs have gastrointestinal side effects, gastric ulcers being the most frequent lesions. Anti-inflammatory agents, of which acetylsalicylic acid is the best-known example, are associated with gastric ulceration.

Both inorganic substances (fluorides, corrosives, detergents) and organic substances (e.g. halogenated aliphatic or aromatic hydrocarbons) may lead to irritant lesions and cancer in the gastrointestinal tract.

Metals usually cause non-specific gastrointestinal injury. Frequent sources are industrial pollution and mineral supplements used in prophylaxis. Acute and chronic pancreatitis may be induced by ethanol or pharmaceuticals.

SELF ASSESSMENT QUESTIONS

1 Why is the consumption of overdone grilled meat inadvisable?

2 Name some drugs with a toxic effect on the gastrointestinal tract.

# Hepatotoxicology: structure, function and toxicological pathology

*J. Vandenberghe*

## INTRODUCTION

Alcohol is the most common hepatotoxin which is ingested voluntarily. Everybody is familiar with alcohol and will associate its use with liver complaints.

In western countries there is a direct relationship between the level of alcohol consumption and prevalence of cirrhosis (See Figure 22.1), as may be shown by the following examples. In France, the years 1941 to 1947 saw a very noticeable reduction (80%) in the mortality from cirrhosis. During that same period, wine rations were reduced from 5 liters to 1 liter per week. In the US, cirrhosis is the fourth cause of death among white males. Cirrhosis is more common in lower socio-economic groups in countries where alcoholic beverages are cheaper.

**Intermezzo**

Cirrhosis of the liver (hepatic cirrhosis) is a chronic liver disease which manifests itself by the presence of dense perilobular connective tissue, degenerative changes of parenchymal cells, fatty infiltration and single-cell necrosis. The blood flow through the tissue is altered; there is increased resistance and decreased flow. The proliferation of connective tissue first causes the liver to be enlarged, but at a later stage it shrinks in size, becoming small and hard. In man the disease is most common in alcoholics, in particular in men over forty. Cirrhosis of the liver may also be caused by other factors (such as carbon tetrachloride, aflatoxins or viral infections).

Certain occupations are more commonly associated with alcoholism than others. Those employed in the catering industry in particular form an important high-risk group. A daily intake of 160 g of alcohol is sometimes considered to be an acceptable limit. The real safe margin, however, is 60 g per day for men and 20 g for women. Many alcoholics suffering from cirrhosis have been consuming some 160 g per day or more for a period of 10 years. Considerable interindividual differences should, however, be taken into account. In addition to alcohol, there are numerous other hepatotoxins, which may affect the organism by highly diverse mechanisms. For a good understanding of the mechanisms underlying the effects of hepatotoxins, insight into the anatomy and function of the liver is required.

LEARNING OBJECTIVES

After studying this unit you will be able to:

— describe the anatomical structure and physiology of the liver
— describe the various anatomical concepts of liver structure and explain their significance for toxicology

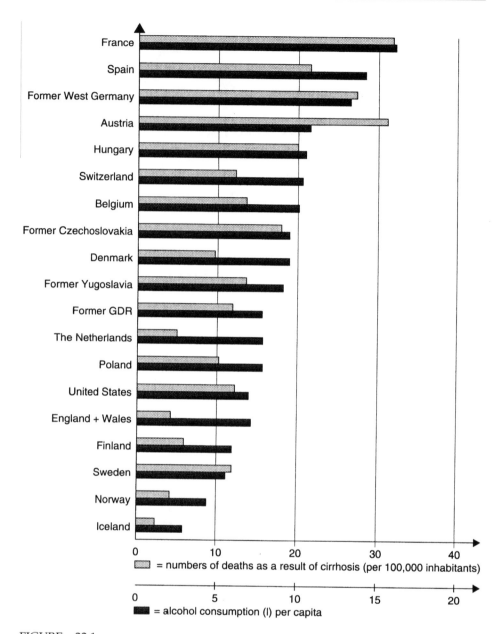

FIGURE 22.1
Numbers of deaths from cirrhosis of the liver and per capita consumption of alcohol in a number of European countries in the middle of the 1970s.

— describe the function of the liver as an organ for the elimination of toxic substances and the role of the formation and excretion of bile in this function

— explain the effects of toxic substances on the liver on the basis of its anatomy and physiology

— give an overview of the most important anatomical–pathological changes in the liver resulting from the effects of xenobiotics

— describe toxic hepatic damage and the role of steatosis, adaptive changes and the enterohepatic circulation in causing the damage

— name and interpret the macroscopic, microscopic and biochemical criteria for the evaluation of hepatotoxicity

*Study hint*

As in the case of other organs, you are assumed to be familiar with the anatomy and physiology of the liver, in particular with its anatomical structure, blood supply and metabolic function. Read up on these subjects in a textbook on anatomy and physiology if necessary. Depending on your previous knowledge, you will need approximately 4 hours to complete this unit. The optionally available CD-I program enables you to study a large number of microscopic sections demonstrating hepatotoxic effects.

STUDY CORE

1    **Anatomy and function of the liver**

1.1    ANATOMY

The liver of an adult human being weighs approximately 1200–1500 g. It is subdivided into lobes by grooves. The organ is enveloped in a capsule of connective tissue (Glisson's capsule) invested with peritoneum. The hilum or porta hepatis is well defined. This is where the main blood vessels and bile ducts are found. Cords of connective tissue enter the liver, in particular in the hilar region, but also from the capsule. They ramify irregularly and eventually form the matrix for the surrounding stroma of the regular pyramidal liver lobules. The hepatic artery, the portal vein, the lymph vessels and the bile ductules follow the course of these branches.

*The liver lobule*

*1.1.1 Microscopic and functional aspects of liver cells*

The liver lobules are visible in histological sections as regular hexagonal structures, surrounded by the septa and spaces of Kiernan with connective tissue stroma. There is clear radiation from the central vein, located centrilobularly, via the cords of liver cells and the liver sinusoids, to the surrounding stroma. *Kiernan's space* is a triangular connective tissue space containing the portal triad, where a branch of the portal vein, a branch of the hepatic artery and a bile ductule meet. Such spaces of Kiernan also contain lymph vessels. Several lobules are arranged around Kiernan's space, while adjacent lobules are separated by the septa. These contain the smaller branches of the artery and vein from the space of Kiernan, the smallest bile ductules and small lymph capillaries, which commence at blind ends in the septa.

The cords of parenchymal cells are strings of polygonal hepatocytes fitted closely together, which have a life span of approximately 150 days in laboratory animals. The hepatocyte has three important contacts via its lateral surfaces: one with the sinusoids, one with the bile canaliculi, which are responsible for biliary transport, and one with the surrounding hepatocytes. The nucleus of the hepatocyte is large and round and contains one or two prominent nucleoli. Polyploidy develops with increasing age.

The mitochondria are localized in the cytoplasm. Mitochondrial enzymes are involved in the respiratory chain, oxidative phosphorylation, oxidation of fatty acids, protein synthesis and important parts of the citric acid cycle. They also play a role in the control of ion balance and water metabolism.

Ribosomes may be unattached or associated with the endoplasmic reticulum (ER), which has a lamellar profile. They are involved in protein synthesis, especially that of albumin. In addition, they synthesize enzymes such as glucose-6-phosphatase and combine triglycerides (TG) and proteins to lipoproteins,

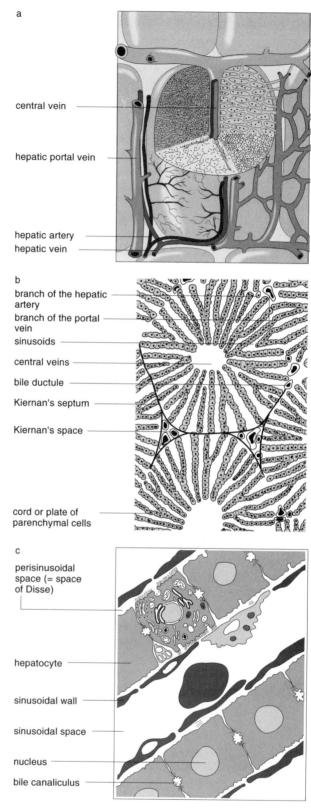

a

central vein

hepatic portal vein

hepatic artery
hepatic vein

b
branch of the hepatic
artery
branch of the portal
vein
sinusoids

central veins

bile ductule

Kiernan's septum

Kiernan's space

cord or plate of
parenchymal cells

c
perisinusoidal
space (= space
of Disse)

hepatocyte

sinusoidal wall

sinusoidal space

nucleus

bile canaliculus

FIGURE 22.2

Schematic representation of the anatomy of the liver
a. three-dimensional representation of the portal lobule with blood vessels
b. two-dimensional representation, showing two central veins
c. cross-section through cords of parenchymal cells.

which are subsequently secreted through exocytosis. The rough endoplasmic reticulum (RER) plays a role in glycogenesis. The smooth endoplasmic reticulum (SER), which has no ribosomes attached to it, forms tubular and vesicular structures. The endoplasmic reticulum is involved in the metabolism of proteins, sugars and lipids and in the biotransformation of foreign substances through oxidation, reduction, hydrolysis or conjugation. Through these reactions, lipophilic substances are converted into hydrophilic. The main functions are the degradation of steroids, the metabolism of cholesterol, bilirubin, lipid-soluble vitamins and fatty acids and the storage of glycogen.

**Intermezzo**

*Endoplasmic reticulum*

There are two types of endoplasmic reticulum, namely rough endoplasmic reticulum (RER) and smooth endoplasmic reticulum (SER). Rough endoplasmic reticulum is studded with ribosomes, which give it a rough appearance. The ribosomes are involved in protein synthesis, which explains why rough endoplasmic reticulum is found primarily in cells where protein synthesis plays an important role. Membrane-bound enzymes involved in the metabolism of hormones, drugs and lipophilic xenobiotics are found on smooth as well as on rough ER. Smooth endoplasmic reticulum, however, contains more enzymes of the cytochrome P-450-dependent monooxygenase system and of the FAD-containing monooxygenase than rough endoplasmic reticulum. Some enzyme-inducing xenobiotics give rise to proliferation of the smooth endoplasmic reticulum. This process is often reversible. After the enzyme inducer has been removed, the amount of SER returns to its normal level.

Closely associated with the SER are the *peroxisomes*, which contain peroxidases. They play a role in fat metabolism.

*Lysosomes* and the *Golgi apparatus* are located primarily between the nucleus and the bile canaliculi. Lysosomes may be regarded as the "cleaners" in the hepatocyte and contain numerous hydrolytic enzymes. They play a role in the processing of macromolecules and organelles, endogenous metabolites and exogenous compounds and in the accumulation of indigestible substances. Lysosomes may contain digestive residues such as ferritin, lipofuscin, bile pigment and copper. The Golgi complex envelops certain lipoproteins, the so-called VLDL or Very Low Density Lipoproteins, in secretory vesicles, which are secreted into the sinusoids. The complex is also involved in the synthesis of glycoproteins.

Lipoproteins are particles surrounded by phospholipids and proteins (apoproteins), which make it possible for cholesterol and triglycerides to be transported in the blood.

Table 22.1 gives an overview of the various lipoprotein fractions in the body.
*Microtubules* and *microfilaments* may be considered to form the skeleton and muscles of the cell. In hepatocytes they are of particular importance for the structural integrity of the bile canaliculi.

ASSIGNMENT 22.1
Draw up a table of the cellular organelles encountered in the hepatocyte, including their function.

*Liver sinusoids*

*Space of Disse*

The *liver sinusoids* are irregular, anastomosing, blood-filled spaces, located between the hepatocytes. They connect the portal vein with the centrilobular vein. The perisinusoidal space between the sinusoidal wall and the hepatocytes is called the *space of Disse*. The sinusoidal wall is made up of endothelial cells and Kupffer cells. The highly fenestrated endothelial cells form a wall with numerous micro-openings, which allow effective metabolic exchange between the blood and the hepatocytes. This porous condition of the sinusoidal wall allows the blood plasma to enter the perisinusoidal space. The microvilli of the hepatocytes are responsible for the uptake of the products to be processed and the release of processed products such as blood proteins, glucose, etc.

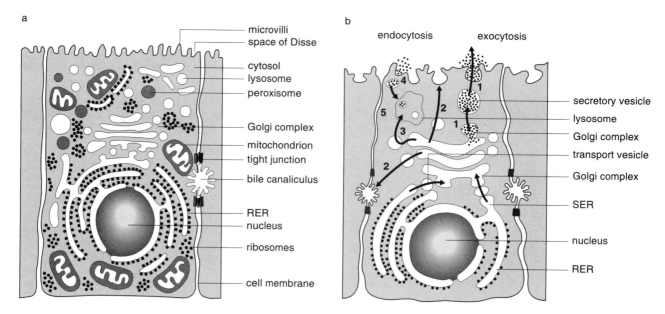

FIGURE 22.3

Schematic representation of the organelles in the hepatocyte

a. important cellular organelles

b. the processes of exocytosis, endocytosis and vesicular transport of macromolecules:
  (1) budding off of vesicles from Golgi apparatus,
  (2) incorporation of endogenous macromolecules in transport vesicles, e.g., in lysosomes,
  (3) invagination of cell membrane,
  (4) formation of vesicles,
  (5) fusing of vesicles with a lysosome.

TABLE 22.1

Lipoprotein fractions in the body, their composition and function.

| Lipoprotein fraction | Function |
| --- | --- |
| chylomicrons | transport of dietary fat from intestine to tissue and liver |
| high density lipoproteins (HDL) | transport of cholesterol from tissue to liver |
| low density lipoproteins (LDL) | transport of cholesterol |
| very low density lipoproteins (VLDL) | transport of triglycerides from liver to other tissues |

*Kupffer cells*

*Kupffer cells* are elongated, irregular cells displaying marked phagocytic activity. The perisinusoidal space contains fat-storing cells. These are involved in the synthesis and accumulation of fat, in the metabolism and storage of vitamin A and in intralobular fibrogenesis as well as supporting the sinusoidal structure. The space of Disse also contains some reticulin fibers, which have a supportive function. They fuse centrally with the basement membrane of the centrilobular vein and peripherally with the basement membranes of the canals in the septa of Kiernan. There is no direct central or peripheral connection between the perisinusoidal space and other canals.

*The canalicular system*

The *canalicular system* consists of small tubular canals (± 1 μm) located in the intercellular space between two hepatocytes. Irregular microvilli project into these canals, supported by microfilaments. Centrally, the canals commence at blind ends and peripherally, they lead into the interlobular bile ductules via the canals of Hering, which form the transition between the hepatocellular canaliculi and the cells of the bile ductules.

674

The *bile ductules* are located in the portal triad, although they are sometimes also found in the lobular periphery. They consist of two to six cuboidal epithelial cells with short microvilli, arranged round a lumen. The transition from bile ductule to intrahepatic bile duct is gradual. As the diameter of the ductule increases, the epithelial cells change from cuboidal to columnar. The cytoplasm of these cells often contains pinocytotic vacuoles, which indicate active resorption and secretion. For example, the composition of the canalicular bile is altered in the bile ductules by secretion of bicarbonate and chloride or by resorption or secretion of water. In addition, electrolytes and macromolecules are transferred to the lumen of the bile ductule. The innervation of the liver is both parasympathetic and sympathetic. The vagus nerve, for example, stimulates the secretion of bile.

### 1.1.2 Overview of hepatic circulation

Figure 22.4 gives an overview of the blood supply to the hepatocytes.

The portal vein and the hepatic artery ramify lobularly and interlobularly in the portal zone. The portal vein carries the largest volume of blood directly to the sinusoids. The hepatic artery supplies oxygenated blood. These blood vessels follow the lobular division and the interlobular connective tissue stroma. At the level of the liver lobule, they form the terminal portal venule and arteriole. Branches of the terminal arteriole form a plexus around the bile ductules. The arterial blood passes directly or indirectly into the sinusoids. Indirect pathways are through the periductular plexus or through the terminal portal venule. The blood thus supplied contains oxygen, nutrients and substances to be

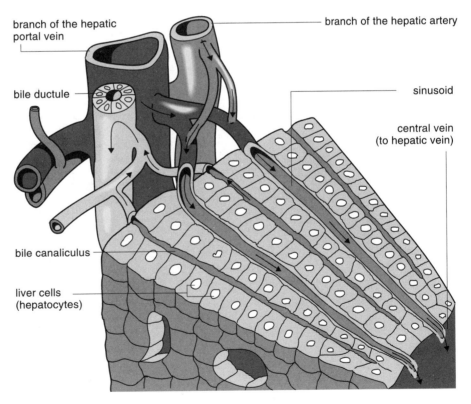

FIGURE 22.4

Schematic representation of two adjacent sinusoids and their blood supply by the hepatic portal vein and the hepatic artery, and drainage by the hepatic vein.
The direction of the bile transport has also been indicated.

processed and reaches the lobule at the periphery. As a result, the peripheral cells are most generously provided with nutrients and oxygen. This results in an activity gradient going from peripheral to central. Morphologically, this is expressed in greater basophilia and more fat accumulation at the periphery than in the center of the unit.

The space of Kiernan thus holds a key position in the circulation, and structural disturbance will have its effect on the portal lobule. The blood leaves the lobule through the terminal central venule. These centrilobular veins, which have a very thin lining of endothelial cells, are in direct contact with the sinusoids. They join to form sublobular veins and eventually connect via the hepatic vein into the inferior vena cava.

*Lymph*

*Lymph* capillaries are found in the capsule of the liver and in the portal zone, but not among the parenchymal cells. They do not have an open connection with the perisinusoidal spaces. Protein-rich fluid diffuses from these spaces via the perilobular stroma into the lymph capillaries in the portal triad. The lymph flows through an extensive lymphatic network around the arteries and veins in the liver to ever larger lymphatic vessels and eventually to the capsule. The large lymph vessels combine in the hepatic portal vein.

ASSIGNMENT  22.2

Draw up a schematic overview of the blood supply to and drainage from the liver.

### 1.1.3 Bile ducts

The intrahepatic bile drainage includes the bile canaliculi, the bile ductules and the bile ducts. Extrahepatic bile drainage is via the larger biliary ducts (see Figure 22.5).

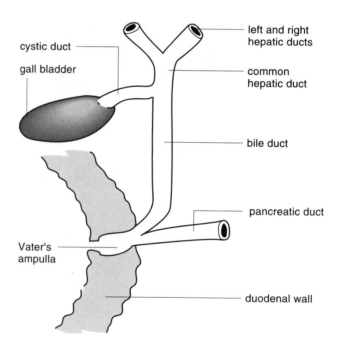

FIGURE  22.5
Schematic representation of the bile drainage and gall bladder
Not all mammals have a gall bladder.

lism, the glucuronidation of xenobiotics, the pinocytosis of nutrients, the metabolism of proteins and the formation of plasma proteins. In addition, they are probably also active in the secretion of bile salts, and are exposed to higher concentrations of bile salts in the plasma. In comparison to zone 3, this zone has wider bile canaliculi, and contains more mitochondria and less SER.

Important functions of *zone 3* are the storage of glycogen and the formation of fat and pigments. Chemical substances are metabolized in the liver via oxidation or reduction. The oxidative enzymes need oxygen and NADPH or NADH. The NADPH and NADH reductase reactions take place primarily in the cells of zone 3. Zone 3 cells contain an ample amount of SER with mixed-function oxidases (the cytochrome P-450 system). Phenobarbital, for example, will cause marked SER proliferation in combination with induction of cytochrome P-450. The morphological changes, accompanied by swelling of the liver and an increase in hepatocellular volume, first take place in zone 3 and may spread to zone 2 from there.

Substances which induce the cytochrome P-450 system may intensify the metabolism of chemicals. Substances which inhibit NADPH regeneration will consequently also inhibit biotransformation. The hydroxylation of steroid structures and of long-chain fatty acids, such as oleate, palmitate and stearate, are also mediated by NADPH-dependent enzymes. The degradation of fatty acids normally takes place by β-oxidation, mediated by the mitochondria. Histochemical and enzymatic analyses have allowed the predominant localization of various enzymes to be determined. The results are presented in Table 22.2.

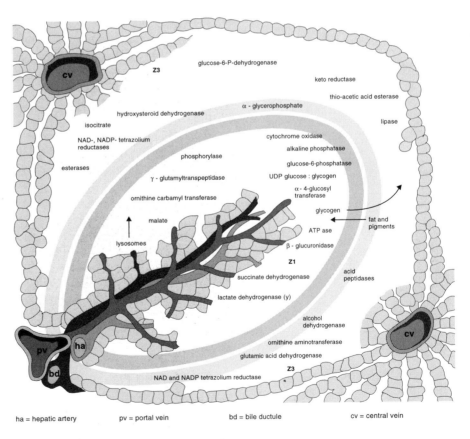

FIGURE    22.8
Enzyme distribution in the various zones of the liver acinus according to Rappaport.

679

TABLE 22.2
Localization of various enzymes in the liver lobule.

| Enzyme | Major zone of activity |
|---|---|
| alkaline phosphatase | periportal |
| alcohol dehydrogenase | periportal |
| cytochrome oxidase | periportal |
| glucose-6-phosphatase | periportal |
| glucose-6-phosphate dehydrogenase | centritobular |
| glutamate dehydrogenase | centritobular |
| lactate dehydrogenase | periportal |
| malate dehydrogenase | periportal |
| succinate dehydrogenase | periportal |

**Biochemical differences zones 1 and 3**

*Biochemically*, zones 1 and 3 display the following differences:

- zone 1: high activity of enzymes involved in the citric acid cycle and the respiratory chain. Lysosomal enzyme activity, in connection with the uptake of nutrients;
- *zone 3*: glycogen storage, glycolytic activity, drug metabolizing enzymes, storage of fats and pigments.

**Electron-microscopic differences zones 1 and 3**

*Electron microscopy* reveals the following differences between the cells of zones 1 and 3:

- *zone 1*: diffusely distributed RER among many and large mitochondria, zone not much glycogen;
- *zone 3*: large amount of SER, RER accumulated in clusters, much glycogen, small mitochondria.

The differences in metabolic capacity between the zones constitute the basis for their specific susceptibility for toxic substances, nutritional deficiencies, avitaminoses or circulatory disorders. A common type of degeneration of the liver parenchyma, for example, is one which starts at the central vein and spreads from there to all of zone 3, sometimes leading to a reticulate pattern, as the zones 3 of adjacent acini touch each other.

The classic pathological terminology is based entirely on a two-dimensional, purely morphological concept for the classification of lesions, starting from the central vein, the portal periphery and the intermediate area. The acinar concept, by contrast, is based on a three-dimensional physiological image.

Subdividing the acinus into microcirculatory zones with different oxygen concentrations means that the localization of hepatic lesions will vary with the mechanism underlying the adverse effects of substances. Under the microscope, lesions which occur primarily in zone 1 are observed mainly periportally; those occurring in zone 3 are visible perivenously.

If zone 3 of one acinus is affected more than that of another acinus, eccentric (perivenous) lesions develop. Zone 3 lesions which are fairly symmetrical first give rise to triangular patterns, which on further development form starfish-shaped patterns and eventually turn into a periacinal pattern, enclosing the entire acinus. Damaged tissue then completely cuts off the terminal hepatic venule from the portal supply (see Figure 22.9).

1.3  THE ELIMINATION FUNCTION OF THE LIVER

**Biotransformation**
**See Study units 3 and 4**

*Biotransformation* has been discussed extensively elsewhere. It is important to remember that the microsomal fraction in the SER of the liver is the main site of this biotransformation. The system is dependent on NADPH and oxygen. Drug metabolism takes place via phase I and phase II reactions.

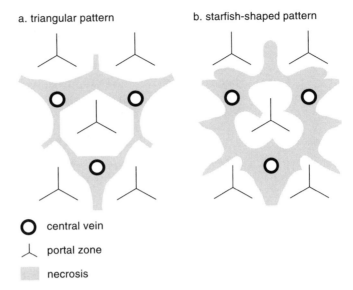

a. triangular pattern     b. starfish-shaped pattern

○  central vein

⊥  portal zone

▪  necrosis

FIGURE   22.9
Tangential section showing incipient liver necrosis in zone 3 (a) to extensive necrosis (b).

### 1.3.1 The liver and fat metabolism

*Non-esterified fatty acids = NEFA*

*Non-esterified fatty acids* (NEFA) are transported in the blood in the form of non-polar electrostatic complexes with albumin. Some of these fatty acids are caught by the hepatocytes and are bound within the cells to two different protein fractions, protein Y and protein Z. Protein Y is not very specific and its level increases after phenobarbital administration.

A hypolipidemic substance lowers the plasma lipid levels.

Protein Z, which is somewhat more specific, is found in high concentrations after treatment with clofibrate. Clofibrate is a hypolipidemic substance. It reduces the VLDL secretion from the liver and thus lowers plasma concentrations of cholesterol and triglycerides.

*Acetyl CoA-bound*

Some of the fatty acids, the *acetyl CoA-bound* fractions, are oxidized in the mitochondria of the hepatocytes. Most of the NEFA are transformed into complex lipids such as phospholipids, cholesterol esters, triglycerides and glycolipids. These products are partly used for the cell's own maintenance and growth, but the major part is incorporated in lipoproteins and excreted into the circulation via the perisinusoidal spaces.

*Cholesterol*

*Cholesterol* is a steroid alcohol with lipophilic properties. It is a precursor of bile acids and steroid hormones. It is, in particular, the liver and the intestines which synthesize cholesterol; in the microsomal fraction and the cytosol cholesterol is synthesized mainly from acetate. Synthesis in the liver is inhibited by massive cholesterol administration or by fasting. In the membranes and the bile, cholesterol is found almost exclusively in the form of free sterol. In the plasma, the liver, the adrenal glands and the skin, it is also found in an esterified form. Enzymatic esterification is continued in the plasma by lecithincholesterol acyltransferase, an enzyme synthesized in the liver. The liver produces cholesterol, esterifies it with long-chain fatty acids, converts part of it into bile acids and secretes it into the bile.

**HO**        **cholesterol**

*Phospholipids*

*Phospholipids* are a fairly heterogeneous group of compounds. They are phosphate esters containing a polar part, including heterogeneous bases such as choline or ethanolamine, and a large non-polar part, consisting of, for instance, long-chain fatty acid residues. They are found primarily in the membrane. Lecithin is the most common example.

*Triglycerides*

Triglycerides (TG) are made up of glycerol molecules whose -OH groups have been esterified by the enzyme triglyceride synthetase with a wide range of fatty acids. Within the cell the triglycerides are hydrolyzed by lipases, resulting in the release of the fatty acids. Further, the triglycerides constitute a source of energy by forming acetyl CoA.

*Transport proteins*

Cholesterol, phospholipids and TG are not water-soluble and, as a result, they cannot occur in the plasma in their free form. Their transport is achieved by means of lipoproteins (see also Table 22.1). The physicochemical properties of the lipoproteins are partly determined by their fat composition and by changes in their protein content. One group of lipoproteins, the High Density Lipoproteins (HDL), migrate with the $\alpha$-1-globulins in an electrical field, whereas another group, the Low Density Lipoproteins (LDL), migrate with the $\beta$-globulins. A third group consists of the VLDL and the chylomicrons make up a fourth.

### 1.3.2 Bile formation

*Bile*

*Bile* is a complex aqueous solution of organic and inorganic components. The primary bile components include bile pigments (mainly conjugated bilirubin), bile acids and their salts, cholesterol, phospholipids (especially lecithins) and alkaline phosphatase. Bile facilitates the emulsification and resorption of dietary lipids.

*Bilirubin*

*Bilirubin* is formed from hemoglobin (released from red blood cells) and from other hemoproteins, such as liver cytochromes and myoglobin. In adults, approximately 6 grams of hemoglobin undergo oxidative degradation and 30 milligrams of bilirubin is formed per day. The production of bilirubin takes place in the cells of the reticulo-endothelial system, especially in the spleen and the liver.

Bilirubin is found in the plasma, lightly bound to albumin and $\alpha$-1-globulin. Bilirubin is separated from its blood proteins near the sinusoidal hepatocellular membrane and transported by proteins, such as ligandin, from the cell membrane to the ER.

Unconjugated bilirubin is non-polar and lipid-soluble. It is conjugated with glucuronic acid by the enzyme glucuronyl transferase, as a result of which it becomes polar and water-soluble, so that it can be excreted in the bile. Bilirubin conjugation increases following phenobarbital administration and is deficient in the newborn.

*Bilirubin conjugates*

In man, the most important conjugated form of bilirubin is the diglucuronic conjugate, which is formed near the cell membrane. Conjugations with sulfate, xylose and glucose also take place. Conjugated bilirubin is excreted via the bile canaliculi and the larger bile ducts into the small intestine. In the colon, bacteria hydrolyze bilirubin to urobilinogen.

*Bile acids*

*Bile acids* are formed in the liver from cholesterol. Their formation is controlled by the amount of bile acids resorbed by the liver via the enterohepatic circulation. Bacteria in the colon convert these primary bile acids to secondary bile acids by dehydration. In the liver, bile acids are conjugated with the amino acids glycine and taurine to form bile salts. Glycine conjugation in particular is quantitatively important. Bacteria are able to hydrolyze the bile salts back to bile acids

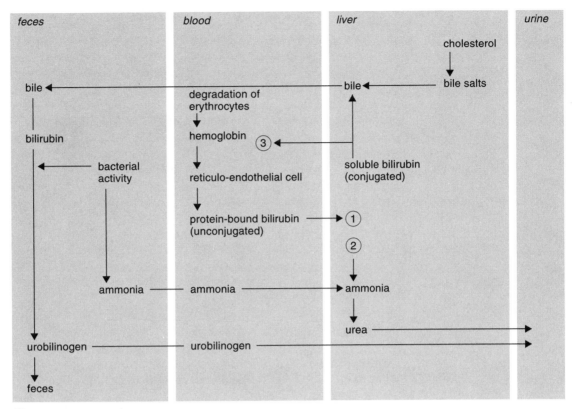

① removal of proteins and renewed conjugation

② deamination of amino acids

③ small percentage returned to blood

FIGURE   22.10
Schematic representation of the formation of bilirubin and its excretion in the bile.

and amino acids. Bile salts are excreted into the canaliculi via an active transport process. The bile salts are incorporated into micelles, together with cholesterol and phospholipids (Figure 22.11).

Changes in the size of the micelles influence the osmotic activity of the active excreted product, allowing the supply of water to the bile to be controlled. In addition, the bile salts, which are steroidal in nature, might influence the bile flow via functional changes in the canalicular membrane. The bile salts are resorbed by the liver from the portal venous blood at a later stage. The synthesis of bile salts is controlled via negative feedback. Bile salts influence the activity of pancreatic lipase and stimulate the secretion of pancreatic enzymes.

After synthesis in the hepatocellular microsomal membranes, the biliary fats, cholesterol and phospholipids are excreted via the microtubular transport system into the bile canaliculi. In the bile ducts, water and electrolytes, especially sodium carbonate and sodium chloride, are added to the canalicular bile flow. Small amounts of water and sodium chloride are resorbed. Here bile drainage is controlled by secretin.

Table 22.3 summarizes the various activities with respect to bile formation in the canaliculi and the ductules.

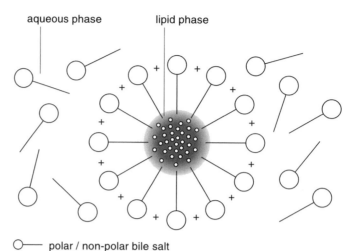

aqueous phase            lipid phase

O— polar / non-polar bile salt

cholesterol

+        phospholipid

FIGURE   22.11
Structure of a biliary micelle.

TABLE   22.3
Formation of bile in the canaliculi and ductules of the liver.

| Localization | Activity | Mechanism |
|---|---|---|
| canaliculi | active secretion of:<br>- bile pigments<br>- organic anions<br>- bile salts | bile salt-dependent |
| | active secretion of:<br>- water<br>- electrolytes | bile salt-independent<br>$(NA^+/K^+\text{-ATPase})$ |
| ductules | resorption of electrolytes<br>secretion of water | secretin-mediated |

## 1.4   ENTEROHEPATIC CIRCULATION—(NORMAL SITUATION)

*Bile salts*

In the small intestine, *bile salts* from the bile are brought into contact with cholesterol and phospholipids in the form of micelles. In the ileum and the proximal colon, they undergo degradation by bacteria and absorbed via the portal blood. The hepatocytes absorb the bile acids formed and conjugate them to form salts again. They are once again secreted in micellar form via the bile.

Bile salts undergo this enterohepatic circulation two to five times a day. Lithocholic acid, which is resorbed only marginally in the intestine, does not participate in this circulation under normal conditions. Few bile acids appear in the general circulation.

*Conjugated bilirubin*

*Conjugated bilirubin* passes into the intestinal tract and is there converted by bacteria to urobilinogen. Most of this urobilinogen is broken down further by bacteria and is excreted in the feces, giving the latter their normal color. Ten to fifteen percent of intestinal urobilinogen is resorbed from the ileum and the colon into the portal circulation. Most of this is taken up by liver cells and is once again secreted into the bile as bilirubin. This completes the enterohepatic circulation of bilirubin (see Figure 22.13). Approximately 20% of the urobilinogen resorbed appears in the normal circulation and is excreted via the urine.

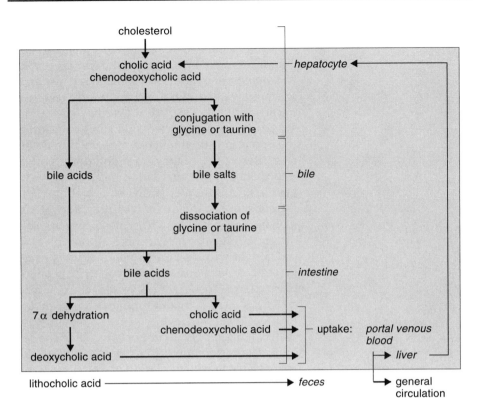

FIGURE 22.12
Schematic representation of the enterohepatic circulation of bile acids.

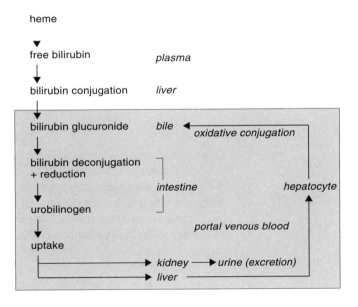

FIGURE 22.13
Representation of the enterohepatic circulation of bilirubin.

*Xenobiotics*
See also Study unit 20 for the
enterohepatic circulation of
xenobiotics

The hepatocytes can excrete foreign compounds into the bile. Lipophilic substances enter the bile via passive diffusion, while polar compounds are transported mainly via carrier-mediated processes. The latter type of transport requires energy. Lipid-soluble molecules, which are found in the aqueous phase of the plasma are excreted primarily via the kidney and to a much smaller extent in the bile. Polar compounds: drugs, endogenous substances, metabolites with a molecular mass of between 300 and 1000 are usually excreted in large quantities in the bile. Some compounds are excreted following *conjugation with glucuronic acid* by the microsomal enzyme glucuronyltransferase. Glucuronides are more water-soluble and are poorly resorbed from the intestines. After having been hydrolyzed by the bacterial $\beta$-glucuronidase, the active, more lipophilic substance can be released again and be resorbed via passive diffusion through the lipoid intestinal mucosa into the portal venous blood or be excreted in the feces. Resorption of the compound rounds off the enterohepatic circulation. The importance of this circulation depends on the quantity of a substance excreted via the bile. If there is sufficient excretion via the bile and effective resorption, the effect of one dose of a drug may be prolonged, as is the case with digitoxin in man. Such a situation may also result in a second increase in the plasma level of a certain substance. For compounds with a molecular mass below 300, species differences with respect to bile-mediated excretion may be observed. The resorption of substances with cholephilic properties may, to a certain extent, take place even in the larger biliary ducts. Such resorption may be considerably increased if the gall bladder mucosa has been damaged.

*Bile acids*

*Bile acids* often play an important role in the hepatobiliary transport of xenobiotics. Their excretion is bile acid-dependent. If insufficient bile acids are available as a result of cannulation of the common bile duct the excretion of bile, and hence of substances for which excretion is bile acid-dependent (including digitoxin), may be considerably inhibited.

## 2    Effects of chemicals on the liver

The liver with its metabolic, detoxicating, secretory and excretory functions is extremely vulnerable to harmful substances. This is particularly true for the highly differentiated parenchyma which allows the organ to perform its specific functions.

The action of a harmful substance on hepatocytes may result in atrophy, degeneration or necrosis.

ASSIGNMENT   22.4

Give a description of these three cytopathological processes.

Liver function is disturbed if there is interference with the hepatocellular metabolic processes or bile secretion. Such interference may take place after acute or chronic exposure to hepatotoxins and results either in lesions with a more acute character, such as cytotoxic and cholestatic changes, or in lesions displaying a more chronic pattern, such as chronic active hepatitis, subacute liver necrosis, steatosis, phospholipidosis, cirrhosis, hepatovascular lesions, tumors and granulomatous lesions.

### 2.1    ACUTE CYTOTOXIC LESIONS

*Fatty changes*

The liver holds a key position in fat metabolism. Changes in fat metabolism may lead to an increased fat content of the parenchymal cells of the liver.

A normal liver contains 5% fat. A seriously fatty liver may contain up to 50% fat, primarily in the form of triglycerides.

ASSIGNMENT   22.5

What are the causes of excessively increased amounts of fat in the liver?

The term fatty changes of liver parenchymal cells is used if the increase in the amount of fat has become visible by light microscopy. The parenchymal cells are then characterized by the presence of rounded, optically empty vacuoles in the cytoplasm. The size of the vacuoles may vary from barely visible, via small vacuoles (microvesicular steatosis) to large vacuoles formed by fusion of such smaller vacuoles, where the cell is swollen and the nucleus has been pushed aside (macrovesicular steatosis).

Steatosis may affect the entire acinus or only particular zones (zone 1—periportal; zone 3—centrilobular). Macroscopically, the liver is enlarged and has a pale yellow color which shows up diffusely or in a pattern of islets, depending on the localization in the acinus. The edges of the liver are too rounded and its texture is softened.

Such fatty infiltration may be the result of hepatocellular degeneration, but it may also develop independently of any degeneration. Table 22.4 gives a number of examples of substances and factors which may induce steatosis.

Steatosis as an expression of hepatotoxicity is fairly non-specific. The changes (microvesicular or macrovesicular) should be regarded as symptomatic of direct toxic effects.

*Parenchymatous degeneration*  *Parenchymatous degeneration* is the mildest form of liver degeneration. The hepatocytes are swollen and the cytoplasm displays a fine eosinophilic granulation as a result of swollen mitochondria. If the hepatocellular damage becomes

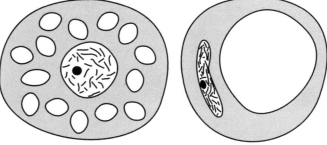

FIGURE 22.14
Examples of microvesicular and macrovesicular steatosis in a hepatocyte.

TABLE 22.4
Overview of some groups of xenobiotics and factors which may induce steatosis.

| Group | Examples |
| --- | --- |
| nutritional and metabolic factors | fasting |
| | diet* |
| | diabetes mellitus |
| | hyperlipidemia |
| toxic agents: | |
| - infectious toxic | baterial toxins |
| | phytotoxins |
| - chemically toxic | phosphorus |
| | arsenic |
| | copper |
| | carbon tetrachloride |
| hypoxia | insufficient perfusion |
| | oxygen tension too low (=anemia) |

*low protein/high fat and carbohydrate content, lack of lipotropic substances (choline, methionine)

*Hydropic degeneration*

more severe, *uptake of water* (sometimes even of plasma proteins) may cause the liver cell to swell very considerably, to several times its original volume, with smaller or larger optically empty cytoplasmic areas developing (*hydropic degeneration*). The nucleus, usually located centrally, is enlarged and has a loose chromatin structure; there may also be multinuclear cells. Transitional stages between ballooning degeneration and liquefactive necrosis may also be encountered. Nuclear changes such as karyopyknosis and karyorrhexis and degeneration of the cell membrane are indications of necrosis. Ballooning of liver cells may be mild to severe and may be of varying distribution; zone 3 is frequently affected, but diffuse acinar changes may also be observed. Macroscopically, the liver is swollen, with rounded edges, and is too pale, with a softened texture; depending on the distribution of the degeneration in the acinus, an islet pattern may be visible. Hydropic changes may be caused by increased glycogen accumulation or by marked swelling of the cisternae of the endoplasmic reticulum. The latter in particular may cause hepatocellular death. An example of a substance which may give rise to such degeneration is halothane.

Necrosis of the liver parenchyma may be caused by a large number of xenobiotics and other harmful factors. It is often encountered simultaneously with degeneration (ballooning) and steatosis. There is usually a secondary phagocytizing reaction by reticulo-endothelial cells (Kupffer cells and other macrophages) and polymorphonuclear leukocytes. These cells take up the hepatocellular debris. Granulocytes frequently infiltrate. Necrosis may occur in individual cells distributed across the parenchyma or in foci of cells.

Focal necrosis usually develops in the centrilobular zone, caused by substances such as carbon tetrachloride and acetaminophen, but sometimes also periportally, caused by e.g. alkyl alcohol, cocaine.

Necrosis may be followed by regenerative mitotic activity, if the liver is still capable of such activity. Fibrotic reactions are also observed, with inflammatory reactions at the level of the surrounding stroma. The differential diagnosis to distinguish this condition from viral hepatitis is difficult.

*Apoptosis*

Small acidophilic bodies may sometimes be found in the liver. Such acidophilic bodies represent a form of necrosis referred to as *apoptosis*.

ASSIGNMENT 22.6

What is meant by apoptosis?

The direct cytotoxic lesions mentioned above develop following administration of carbon tetrachloride, cytostatics, salicylates, acetaminophen, tetracyclines, tuberculostatics, anti-inflammatory agents (including phenylbutazone), halothane and other substances. The tuberculostatics, anti-inflammatory agents and halothane are dose-independent in causing their toxic effects, unlike the other substances mentioned.

## 2.2   CHOLESTATIC LESIONS

*Cholestasis*

*Cholestasis* develops as a result of disturbed transport and conjugation of bilirubin, as a result of bile stasis or damage to the biliary passages. Rifampicin, an antibiotic, interferes with bilirubin transport and conjugation. This results in an increase in the amount of bilirubin present, without any hepatic lesions. Depending on the site of interference with the bile secretion, cholestasis is referred to as extrahepatic (obstruction of the larger biliary passages outside the liver) or intrahepatic (inside the liver). Morphological changes include an increase in the amount of bile in the liver cells and the biliary tract. The bile canaliculi are dilated and sometimes filled with secreted bile. Cells of the mononuclear phagocyte system infiltrate. A reactive inflammation with bile duct proliferation may occur in the portal triad. Portal fibrosis may also occur, and may develop into biliary cirrhosis after prolonged cholestasis.

*Clinical picture*

The *clinical picture* shows increased blood levels of all components which are normally excreted via the bile: conjugated bilirubin, bile acids and bile salts. The low concentrations of bile acids and salts in the intestine reduce the resorption of fats, lipid-soluble vitamins and calcium from the intestine and cause the feces to be pale and grayish in color. In serious cases, the kidneys are swollen and pale as a result of bilirubin deposition in the renal tubules. After a certain period of time jaundice develops. There is pruritus (itching) and xanthomas (deposits of cholesterol crystals with inflammation) may form in the skin.

*Types of cholestasis*

Chemically induced cholestasis may be classified according to whether it is caused by *hepatocellular* or *canalicular* disturbances. The first group includes cholestasis caused after administration of chlorpromazine. Oral contraceptives and anabolic steroids cause canalicular disturbances.

---

EXAMPLE

Well known substances causing cholestasis are the estrogens. Estrogens have always been widely used in oral contraceptives. They inhibit or reduce the bile acid-dependent flow of bile in the liver by inhibiting $Na^+/K^+$-ATPase, by increasing the permeability of the tight junctions and by changing the fluidity of the membrane. As a result, the bile acid-dependent bile flow decreases and the concentrations of carrier protein for bile acids in the membrane of the bile canaliculi drop.

---

ASSIGNMENT   22.7

In Figure 22.15 the symbols A–D indicate how cholestasis may be induced. Discuss the various possibilities.

### 2.3   CHRONIC LIVER DISORDERS

*Chronic active hepatitis*

*Chronic active hepatitis* is characterized by extensive portal and periportal inflammation with lymphocyte and plasma cell infiltration, usually in combination with single-cell necrosis (Figure 22.16). Small groups of liver cells become isolated by fibrotic bands, resulting in 'rosette' formation. Eventually, cirrhosis becomes prominent. Causes of chronic active hepatitis include viruses (e.g. hepatitis A and B, rubella), autoimmune mechanisms (*lupus erythematosus*), alcohol and drugs such as isoniazid, sulfonamides, propylthiouracil and acetaminophen. The syndrome only develops if treatment with these drugs is continued after liver injury. Discontinuance of treatment will lead to complete or partial repair.

*Subacute liver necrosis*

The liver sometimes displays lesions of acute or *subacute necrosis* and cirrhosis, which may be accompanied by regeneration. Depending on the duration of the effect, cirrhosis becomes more prominent. The necrotic lesions can be caused by a variety of xenobiotics, such as tetrachloroethane, trinitrotoluene, dinitrobenzene and mixtures of chlorinated biphenyls and chlorinated naphthalenes.

In patients with subacute liver necrosis, infection with hepatitis B has been

689

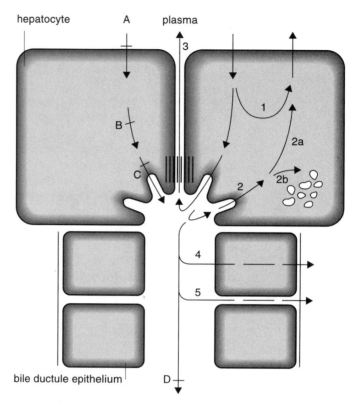

FIGURE   22.15
Schematic representation of the processes which may cause cholestasis (A–D; see the answer to assignment 22.7) and the hepatocellular uptake and release of substances (1–5)
1. uptake of substances from and release of substances into the plasma, following biotransformation or otherwise
2. release and uptake of substances into/from the bile, followed by release into the plasma (2a) or incorporation into vesicles by the Golgi complex (2b)
3. diffusion of bile to the plasma via the tight junctions, uptake of substances from bile through epithelial cells (4) or via spaces between epithelial cells (5).

demonstrated as well as methyldopa-induced toxicity. This suggests that it may represent a transition to chronic active hepatitis or cirrhosis.

*Steatosis*

Fatty degeneration of the liver (steatosis) often occurs as a precursor to a more serious disorder, as in the case of ethanol or methotrexate. Histologically, a distinction is made between microvesicular and macrovesicular deposits.

*Microvesicular changes* comprise the more acute forms of fatty degeneration. Fatty changes of the liver can result from glucocorticoid-induced metabolism of fat from the fat depots. Methotrexate can also cause fatty changes, although eventually cirrhosis will become the most serious effect. Asparaginase, an antimetabolite of bacterial origin, causes steatosis in 50–90% of patients. The resulting liver lesions are usually reversible. Treatment with puromycin, another anticancer drug, may also be accompanied by fat accumulation.

*Phospholipidosis*

*Phospholipidosis* is characterized by the presence of swollen, foamy hepatocytes. This foamy appearance can also be observed in the Kupffer cells and in extrahepatic cells. The lesion has been reported after administration of 4,4'-diethyl-aminoethoxyhexesterol, a cardiovascular drug. The lesions only occur after prolonged administration and may eventually progress to cirrhosis. Phospholipidosis frequently occurs

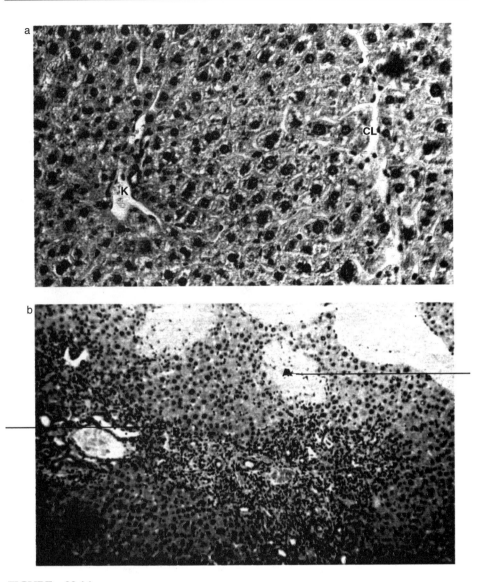

FIGURE 22.16
Microscopic representation of chronic hepatitis in a mouse. Control section above, chronic hepatitis below
CL = centrilobular vein
K = Kiernan's space with bile duct
A. zonal necrosis
B. inflammatory reaction from the space of Kiernan (bile duct proliferation and inflammatory cells).

in laboratory animals after administration of amphophilic cationic substances and results from reactions of these substances with phospholipids in the cells.

*Fibrosis*

*Fibrosis* is defined as the presence of an increased amount of newly formed reticulin and collagen fibers. New formation of connective tissue is the result of fibroblast activity but other cells, in particular the fat-storing cells or lipocytes, are likely to play a role in the process as well. Although these cells may be directly activated, new formation of connective tissue will virtually always be preceded by more or less extensive parenchymal necrosis.

*Cirrhosis*

*Cirrhosis* is defined as a diffuse process characterized by fibrosis and transformation of the normal liver architecture into hyperplastic nodules of abnormal structure.

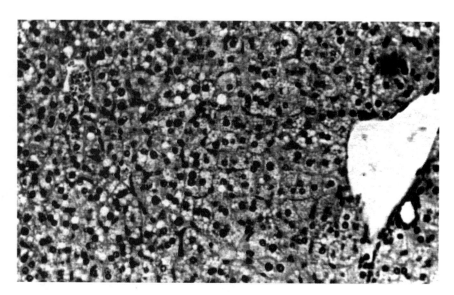

FIGURE   22.17
Micrograph of steatosis  with hepatocellular (micro)vacuolization in mouse liver.

Cirrhosis of the liver usually consists of diffuse, progressive fibrosis and nodular, regenerative hepatocellular transformation. It follows hepatocellular necrosis and affects the lobular organization of the liver. The microcirculation is disturbed and portal hypertension develops. There is often vascular insufficiency, in particular at the level of zone 3. Basement membranes are formed in the spaces of Disse, leading to disturbances in liver cell metabolism. Fibroblasts infiltrate into the necrotic liver tissue and into the portal zones. This renders the fibrosis irreversible.

On the basis of macroscopic and microscopic criteria, a distinction is made between micronodular and macronodular cirrhosis.

*Micronodular cirrhosis*

In *micronodular cirrhosis*, the liver acquires a finely nodular appearance, with the nodules displaying marked uniformity. The liver may be either normal or enlarged in size. Persistent micronodular cirrhosis shows a tendency to progress to macronodular cirrhosis.

*Macronodular cirrhosis*

In *macronodular cirrhosis*, the liver acquires a coarsely nodular appearance, with the nodules being highly variable in size but always larger than 3 mm. The liver may be normal in size, but has often shrunk. This type of cirrhosis will develop especially if large areas of liver parenchyma displaying hyperplastic changes remain beside areas of extensive degeneration and fibrosis. Histologically, the nodules may comprise several portal areas and central veins.

In addition, cirrhosis may be accompanied by inflammatory reactions of varying extent, involving lymphocytes, plasma cells, histiocytes, (pigment-containing) macrophages and a varying number of polymorphonuclear leucocytes. The fibrotic areas often display bile duct proliferation. Moreover, parenchymal necrosis may occur, either as a primary reaction to the cause of the cirrhosis or as a secondary effect resulting from insufficient circulation in the hyperplastic nodules. Cholestasis is also frequently encountered.

*Postnecrotic cirrhosis* may develop following acute necrosis (caused by e.g., isoniazid), or subacute necrosis (caused by e.g., methyldopa), or it may evolve from chronic active hepatitis.

In man, exposure to methotrexate is associated with steatosis and cirrhosis, in

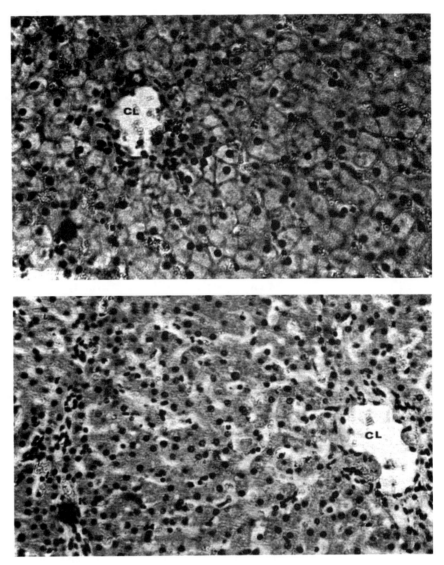

FIGURE 22.18
Phospholipidosis in a dog (above), accompanied by a centrilobular inflammatory reaction (CL) and swollen hepatocytes. Below: control section.
CL = centrilobular vein
K = Kiernan's septum.

particular after prolonged administration, after administration of high doses and in combination with predisposing factors (obesity, diabetes, alcoholism). Methotrexate is a predictable hepatotoxin.

*Chronic intrahepatic cholestasis* is very similar to primary biliary cirrhosis and is characterized by destruction of the bile ducts. It is accompanied by a high serum cholesterol level and skin disorders. Primary biliary cirrhosis may occur after administration of phenothiazines, in particular chlorpromazine. The chronic disorder often starts with acute cholestasis followed by incomplete repair. Cholestasis leads to degeneration and necrosis of periportal hepatocytes, destruction of the interlobular bile ducts and moderate periductular inflammation. Chronic cholestasis will eventually lead to cirrhosis.

FIGURE 22.19
Macroscopic picture of hepatic cirrhosis.

## 2.4 HEPATOVASCULAR LESIONS

Administration of oral contraceptives, estrogens or androgens may produce vascular lesions in man and rodents. The process starts with sinusoidal dilatation. The sinusoidal wall shows further focal dilatation and finally ruptures, giving rise to a blood-filled lacuna (peliosis hepatis) in which thrombosis may occur.

The lesions are often accompanied by hepatocellular tumoral changes. Sudden abdominal hemorrhages may lead to increased intrasinusoidal pressure, resulting in increased resistance of the efferent venous system. The intrasinusoidal pressure may also rise as a result of hepatocellular necrosis, as a result of insufficient structural support of the sinusoidal cells (e.g. by reticulin fibers), or as a result of circulatory disorders in tumors.

Dimethylnitrosamine and pyrrolizidine alkaloids have toxic effects on hepatocytes and sinusoidal cells. They cause the reticulin network surrounding the central vein to collapse and produce hemorrhages.

The mechanism by which hepatovascular disorders cause liver necrosis is identical to that observed in right-sided heart failure. The elevated pressure in the right ventricle and the hepatic veins causes sinusoidal dilatation and congestion close to the central vein. The output of the right side of the heart decreases, which in turn leads to a reduced supply of blood and oxygen to the liver, causing centrilobular necrosis. Chronic congestion of hepatic tissue will lead to increased degeneration of hemoglobin, and thus to increased bilirubin formation. The centrilobular congestion and necrosis cause collapse of the liver, which in turn leads to collagen formation. Liver necrosis and bilirubin formation give rise to jaundice. The fibrosis originates centrilobularly, so that the portal triad becomes enclosed in the surviving lobular parenchyma.

## 2.5 TUMORS

The liver is very susceptible to induction of cancer by a large number of carcinogens. These may be of synthetic as well as of natural origin. Table 22.5 lists a number of synthetic and naturally occurring hepatocarcinogens.

*Adenomas*

*Adenomas* are associated with the use of oral contraceptives. The risk is minimal but increases with the duration of use (> five years) and the dosage. Adenomas

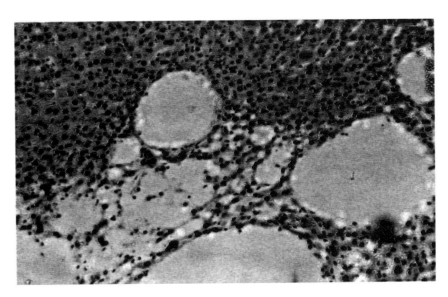

FIGURE 22.20
Micrograph of a hepatovascular lesion (peliosis hepatis) in a mouse.

consist almost entirely of hepatocytes and no longer display a lobular or portal structure. Sometimes fibrotic bands can be found. Compression of bile ducts may give rise to jaundice. Painful hemorrhages may occur in the tumor. Neoplastic hepatocellular changes have been frequently reported in laboratory animals, not only as age-associated lesions but also as a result of induction or promotion. Criteria for the evaluation of focal hepatocellular hyperplasias have yet to be agreed upon.

*Focal hepatocellular changes*

*Focal hepatocellular changes* either may be associated with old age or may result from administration of xenobiotics. If the focal changes cover an area larger than a liver lobule and cause compression of the surrounding liver parenchyma, they are referred to in laboratory animals as hyperplastic nodules. These are similar to adenomas in man. They may vary in diameter from less than 1 mm to several centimeters.

*Carcinomas*

True hepatocellular tumors or *carcinomas* seldom occur spontaneously. These are characterized by marked mitotic activity and/or invasion and/or metastasis. Administration of initiators and promoters leads to more frequent and more prominent occurrence of these hepatocellular neoplasms. In man, some rare cases of hepatocellular carcinoma have been associated with the use of anabolic steroids, contraceptives and estrogens.

TABLE 22.5
Some synthetic and naturally occurring hepatocarcinogens.

| Synthetic | Natural |
|---|---|
| dimethylnitrosamine | aflatoxin $B_1$ |
| diethylnitrosamine | pyrrolizidine alkaloids |
| DDT | cycasin |
| PCBs | safrole |
| $CCl_4$ | |
| chloroform | |
| vinyl chloride | |
| acetylaminofluorene | |

695

*Hemangiomas*
*hemangiosarcomas*

*Hemangiomas* and *hemangiosarcomas* (benign and malignant tumors of the blood vessels, respectively) have occasionally been reported in rats and mice. They may become more frequent after administration of carcinogens. In man, exposure to vinyl chloride may give rise to peliosis hepatis and hemangiosarcomas.

## 2.6 GRANULOMATOUS LESIONS

Granulomatous infiltration of the liver may occur in combination with hepatocellular or cholestatic lesions following exposure to xenobiotics, such as long-acting sulfonamides, methotrexate, halothane, phenylbutazone. Granulomas may be found both in the lobular and in the portal areas and are indicative of an immunological process. They consist of small masses of cells of the mononuclear phagocyte system.

## 3 Summary

Anatomically, the liver is subdivided into liver lobules embedded in a matrix of surrounding stroma. Blood provided by the portal vein and the general circulation enters the liver sinusoids and drains into the central veins. The liver is responsible for certain processes of degradation and synthesis, mediated by hepatic enzyme systems. Through these enzymatic processes, it participates in protein, fat and sugar metabolism and is responsible for the biotransformation of foreign compounds. The liver plays an important role in the digestive process through the formation of bile and its key position in the enterohepatic circulation. Some chemicals may interfere with the metabolic processes in the liver or with the formation or secretion of bile, resulting in acute or chronic liver disorders.

## SELF ASSESSMENT QUESTIONS

1   In the following figure, indicate the hepatic lobule, the portal lobule and the microcirculatory liver acinus.

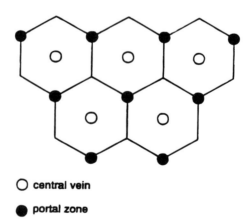

○ central vein

● portal zone

2   Where will the hepatotoxicity of carbon tetrachloride or allyl alcohol be primarily localized? $CCl_4$ is activated by the microsomal enzymatic system, while allyl alcohol undergoes toxic metabolic activation to acrolein by alcohol dehydrogenase.

3   What is the physiological distinction between protein-bound and unbound bilirubin?

4    Give a schematic representation of the conversion of cholesterol into bile acids.

5    Where in the lobulo-acinar hepatic structure is cytochrome P-450 located? What light microscopic and electron microscopic phenomena can be observed after administration of phenobarbital?

6    Which types of liver damage are distinguished cytopathologically?

7    How does necrosis of the liver develop as a result of toxic effects on the sinusoidal wall?

## FEEDBACK

1    **Answers to the assignments**

22.1  The table below lists the main cellular organelles and their functions.

| Cellular organelle | Function |
| --- | --- |
| mitochondria | oxidative processes, oxygen-dependent (amino acid, carbohydrate and lipid oxidation) |
| | citric acid cycle<br>respiratory chain<br>ATP formation |
| endoplasmic reticulum:<br>- rough endoplasmic<br>  reticulum (RER) | transport of proteins formed in ribosomes, metabolism by attached enzymes, biotransformation of xenobiotics |
| - smooth endoplasmic<br>  reticulum (SER) | as RER, but with emphasis on biotransformation of xenobiotics |
| ribosomes | protein synthesis |
| Golgi complex | formation of secretory granules; secretion of polysaccharides, proteins |
| lysosomes | protein transport and degradation of endogenous and foreign compounds |

22.2  The figure below gives a schematic representation of the blood supply to the liver.

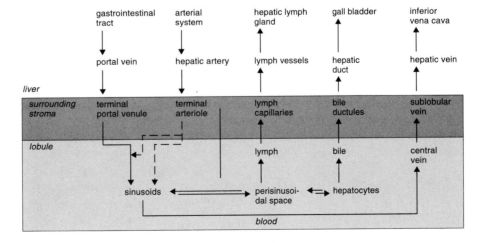

22.3 The area around the central vein is of course the most vulnerable to obstructions as a result of circulatory disorders, since it is here that accumulations and pressure differences will first, and most noticeably, become apparent.

22.4 Atrophy is characterized by a reduction in the quantity of cytoplasm, with deterioration of, initially, the specific cellular functions (general functions at first remain intact). It is a slow process, which may be reversible.

Degeneration implies a quantitative and/or qualitative decline in both specific and general cellular functions, which may be either reversible or irreversible ("point of no return"). Degeneration is often, although not always (biochemical lesion), accompanied by morphological changes in cellular structures and by accumulation of substances (including water and fat) in the cytoplasm.

Necrosis is the visible expression of cell death, and can be either coagulative or liquefactive.

22.5 The most important causes of such excessive increase in the amount of fat are increased supply of fatty acids to the liver, increased production of triglycerides by the liver parenchyma and decreased formation or excretion of lipoproteins.

22.6 Apoptosis is a phenomenon of active self-destruction by the cell, which also takes place under normal, physiological conditions, as a mechanism for regulating the amount of parenchyma in an organ. The cell displays progressive condensation of chromatin and cytoplasm, followed by karyorrhexis and the budding off of cell fragments, which are soon resorbed by Kupffer cells and liver parenchymal cells. See also Study unit 16.

22.7 Non-obstructive cholestasis may be the result of (a) a disturbance in the uptake of substances by the hepatocyte; (b) an intracellular metabolic disturbance; (c) a disturbance in bile formation. Obstructive cholestasis (d) may be localized both intrahepatically and extrahepatically.

2    **Answers to the self assessment questions**

1    The figure below shows the various conceptions of the liver lobule and acinus.

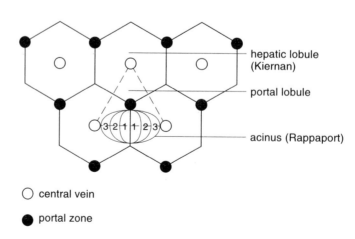

central vein

portal zone

2    Carbon tetrachloride is activated to the trichloromethyl radical ($CCl_3^-$)by the mixed-function oxidase system, which is localized in zone 3. Carbon tetrachloride intoxication will therefore manifest itself first in zone 3. The same can be said for acrolein which is formed by alcohol dehydrogenase in zone 3 (periportally).

3    Bilirubin bound to protein is unconjugated, which means it is lipophilic and not easily soluble in water (and therefore in bile). Unbound bilirubin is capable of being conjugated, as a result of which it will become water-soluble, and thus soluble in bile (see also Figure 22.10).

4    The diagram below shows how cholesterol is converted into bile acids.

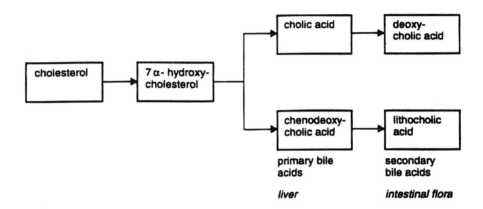

5    The cytochrome P-450 system is localized primarily in zone 3 of the microcirculatory liver acinus (theory of Rappaport) or in the centrilobular area of the classic hepatic lobule.

Administration of phenobarbital leads to induction of cytochrome P-450. Marked proliferation of the smooth endoplasmic reticulum ensues and the hepatocellular volume in zone 3 increases. This effect may extend to zone 2. Macroscopically, the liver is swollen and increased in weight.

6    A more acute course can be observed in cytotoxic and cholestatic changes. Chronic active hepatitis, subacute liver necrosis, steatosis, phospholipidosis, cirrhosis, hepatovascular lesions, tumors and granulomatous lesions are found mainly in chronic liver disorders.

| Type | Course |
| --- | --- |
| cytotoxic | mainly acute |
| cholestatic | mainly acute |
| chronic active hepatitis | mainly chronic |
| subacute liver necrosis | mainly chronic |
| steatosis | mainly chronic |
| phospholipidosis | mainly chronic |
| cirrhosis | mainly chronic |
| hepatovascular lesions | mainly chronic |
| tumors | mainly chronic |
| granulomatous lesions | mainly chronic |

7    Damage to the sinusoidal wall undermines the supporting structures of the sinusoidal cells. This results in a collapse of the reticulin network, in

particular around the central vein. The sinusoids dilate and the wall will display irregular distensions, which may even be enlarged to form blood-filled lacunae. The pressure in the liver sinusoids drops, the circulation in the liver stagnates to a certain extent and the centrilobular $O_2$ supply decreases. The eventual result is liver necrosis.

# Contents Study unit 23
# Hepatotoxicology: mechanisms of liver toxicity and methodological aspects

0-8493-9232-2/96/$0.00 + $.50
© 1996 by CRC Press, Inc.

# Hepatotoxicology: mechanisms of liver toxicity and methodological aspects

*J. Vandenberghe*

## INTRODUCTION

The liver has an important place in toxicology by virtue of its functions, both qualitatively and quantitatively. The reasons for this include its metabolic capacity and its position in the circulation. Virtually all substances absorbed from the gastrointestinal tract pass through the liver before entering the central circulation. This is true for food, food additives, contaminants and drugs. In the previous study unit, it was seen that xenobiotics are able to bring about adaptive phenomena and a variety of toxic processes. The eventual effects may vary. The way in which hepatotoxic agents produce these effects may also differ. Some xenobiotics cause direct injury to the liver cell through their specific affinity for the hepatocellular membrane, or for the cell components. Others first undergo metabolic conversion, resulting in the formation of toxic substances. Substances which have similar hepatotoxic effects in several species are called *intrinsic hepatotoxins*. Many toxicological liver disorders can be induced experimentally by drugs, usually in high dosages. Table 23.1 shows a number of hepatotoxic effects, and the drugs that cause these conditions.

In addition to intrinsic hepatotoxins, there are also substances whose hepatotoxic effect is not predictable. Exposure to these may result in a hepatotoxic effect in only a percentage of the population.

> ASSIGNMENT   23.1
>
> What type of substances will these be?

The previous study unit discussed in detail the various symptoms of hepatotoxicity. Acute and chronic cytopathological changes were covered. The present study unit describes the mechanisms by which chemicals cause these cytopathological changes.

In addition to describing the mechanisms of hepatotoxicity, this unit also discusses some clinico-chemical parameters which are used to diagnose hepatotoxic lesions.

> LEARNING OBJECTIVES
>
> Having studied this unit you should be able to:
>
> — describe the ways in which the hepatotoxicity of chemicals can manifest itself morphologically

— describe the way in which the effects of chemicals can cause fatty degeneration
— explain the location and severity of the liver changes caused by some substances on the basis of the subdivision of the liver parenchyma into functional units and the metabolic activity displayed by hepatocytes in the various zones of those units
— indicate why certain clinico-chemical parameters can be used in diagnosing hepatotoxic lesions
— describe the hepatotoxic mechanism underlying the toxicity of acetaminophen, halothane, isoniazid and ethanol
— explain the use of certain clinico-chemical parameters in hepatotoxicology
— describe and explain the regenerative capacity of the liver.

*Study hints*

The present study unit is a continuation of unit 22. It is only possible to study this unit after you have completed the previous one. For some of the cytotoxic mechanisms, you are referred to Study unit 10. It is not necessary to learn the various structural formulae and diagrams by heart. Instead, make sure you understand the various steps in the reactions. The study load of this unit is approximately 4 hours.

STUDY CORE

1    **Mechanisms of liver injury**

It is very difficult to classify hepatotoxic xenobiotics exclusively on the basis of the mechanisms underlying their toxic effects. There is often not enough information on the exact mechanism, so that such a classification is based partly on

TABLE   23.1
Examples of drug-induced hepatotoxic disorders

| hepatotoxic disorder | drug |
| --- | --- |
| acute hepatitis | isoniazid |
| | rifampicin |
| | methyldopa |
| | methotrexate |
| | cyclosporine A |
| severe hepatitis | acetaminophen |
| | halothane |
| steatosis | tetracycline |
| | methotrexate |
| cholestasis | sex hormones (estrogen, androgens, progesterone) |
| | chloropromazine |
| | tolbutamide |
| chronic hepatitis, liver cirrhosis | oxyphenisatin |
| | methotrexate |
| | methyldopa |
| peliosis hepatis | anabolic steroids |
| | ovulation inhibitors |
| | pyrrolizidine alkaloids |

assumptions. For this reason, a large number of researchers have based classification of hepatotoxic substances on morphological aspects. However, a classification based on a combination of mechanism and morphological aspects is preferable to this.

See also Study units 10, 15 and 16

Chemically induced cell injury can be seen as a sequence of events that take place within the organ or elsewhere in the organism:

a.   absorption and bioactivation of the initiating parent compound

b.   detoxication of the toxic agent, or early cellular injury

c.   repair or irreversible changes

d.   cellular changes, sometimes followed by cell death.

ASSIGNMENT   23.2

Various mechanisms may form the basis of cellular damage. Give some examples of intracellular targets for toxic substances.

See Study unit 10

In the course of the past decade, attention has focused primarily on the role of toxic metabolic activation in the induction of cell injury. Many xenobiotics, including drugs, may cause cell damage via biotransformation to reactive intermediates, such as carbene and nitrenium ions.

The reactive intermediates thus formed can bind covalently with cellular macromolecules such as nucleic acids, proteins, co-factors, lipids and polysaccharides. By doing so, they may interfere with the functions of the cell. Many bioactivation reactions are catalyzed by the cytochrome P-450 monooxygenase system. The bioactivation can be induced by pretreatment with phenobarbital or 3-methylcholanthrene. Preliminary treatment with enzyme inhibitors such as piperonyl butoxide or SKF-525A can inhibit bioactivation. On the other hand, conjugation with, for example, glutathione may ensure rapid elimination of the toxic metabolites, and prevent cell damage. Whether or not xenobiotics will in fact produce cell damage often depends on the balance between activation and detoxication. In this respect, the location of the activating and detoxicating enzymes in the liver is of significance.

## 1.1   DIRECT VERSUS INDIRECT EFFECTS

The intrinsic hepatotoxins mentioned in the Introduction can be classified into direct and indirect intrinsic hepatotoxins by the manner in which they exert their effects. *Direct hepatotoxins* cause primary lesions that result in disturbances of the cell's metabolism. Examples of such substances are phosphorus and tannic acid. *Indirect hepatotoxins*, however, exert their effects by interference with the cell's metabolism, so that eventually the integrity of the cell is lost. Examples of indirect hepatotoxins are some anabolic steroids and ethionine. Cholestatic indirect hepatotoxins such as contraceptive steroids and lithocholic acid also belong to this group.

In addition to the intrinsic hepatotoxins, there are also substances that exert their hepatotoxic effects via an immunological mechanism. The substance itself or one of its metabolites reacts with a hepatocellular component. On renewed exposure the immune system then recognizes the combination as an antigen. Figure 23.1 gives a schematic explanation of the difference in mechanism between a direct hepatotoxin and a hepatotoxin whose effects result from interactions with the immune system.

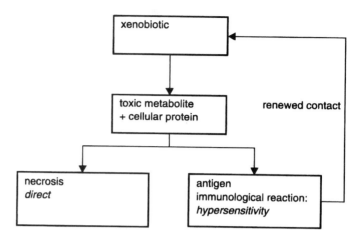

FIGURE   23.1

Direct and immune-mediated hepatotoxicity

Examples of substances with direct hepatotoxic action are the free radicals formed from carbon tetrachloride by bioactivation. An example of immune-mediated action can be found in the metabolite of halothane.

### 1.1.1 Biochemical mechanisms

Stable compounds are converted by microsomal enzymes into alkylating, arylating or acetylating substances, which bind to essential macromolecules and thus cause necrosis. Usually, conjugation of the toxic metabolite takes place with, for example, glutathione, as in the case of acetaminophen. Therefore insufficient glutathione for detoxifying toxic metabolites may also lead to liver toxicity. The risk of necrosis is increased by pretreatment with enzyme inducers, such as phenobarbital, and is reduced by enzyme inhibition (resulting from, for example, fasting).

The response is usually dose dependent and predictable. However, responses may also be totally unpredictable, as in the case of isoniazid, when administered in combination with rifampicin.

The differences in liver injury caused by xenobiotics are partly based on differences in metabolism. In laboratory animals, liver necrosis can be induced by administration of a low dose of isoniazid, after pretreatment with phenobarbital. Phenobarbital activates cytochrome P-450, thereby increasing the formation of the hepatotoxic reactive metabolite.

### 1.1.2 Immunological mechanisms

A xenobiotic or one of its metabolites can bind to hepatocellular membrane components and thus introduce antigenic properties. The presence of the antigen may sensitize lymphocytes. Renewed exposure to the substance may then cause a delayed immunological reaction that may result in hepatocellular necrosis. Here too, differences in biotransformation play an important role. The oxidative conversion of *halothane*, which may lead to hypersensitization, is an example.

### 1.1.3 Cholestatic mechanisms

The toxicity of *chlorpromazine* is accompanied by cholestasis, cellular reactions and direct hepatotoxic phenomena. Its activity is concentrated mainly on the intracellular membranes. There is a decrease in the bile acid-dependent bile flow resulting from loss of bile acids via defective bile canaliculi. In addition, the $Na^+/K^+$ pump and hydroxylation of cholesterol to bile acids are inhibited. The chlorpromazine group includes antirheumatic drugs, chemotherapeutics, cytostatics, antithyroid agents, anti-arrhythmic drugs, laxatives and antimetabolites.

Oral contraceptives and synthetic anabolic *steroids* with a $C_{17}$-substituted 19-norsteroid structure inhibit bile flow and excretion of organic anions, such as bilirubin and bile salts. The permeability of the canalicular membranes is increased, the formation of micelles blocked and the pericanalicular microfilament structures are affected. In this way, ethinylestradiol inhibits the active transport of bile acids in the liver. It also increases the permeability of the cells in the bile ductules, so that the reabsorption of bile components is increased.

Steroid compounds cause a purely cholestatic disturbance; chlorpromazine causes cholestasis combined with inflammatory reactions.

## 2    Examples of hepatotoxic substances

It is often difficult to distinguish between the various types of liver disorders, because exposure to xenobiotics is often followed by combinations of pathological phenomena.

*Acetaminophen*

*Acetaminophen* (N-(4-hydroxyphenyl)acetamide; see Figure 23.2), an analgesic and antipyretic, is frequently abused as a means to commit suicide. It is used not only as a drug, but also in the production of azo dyes and in the photographic industry. The oral $LD_{50}$ in mice is 338 mg kg$^{-1}$ and the intraperitoneal $LD_{50}$ is 500 mg kg$^{-1}$. Under normal circumstances, acetaminophen is inactivated by sulfation and glucuronidation. A limited amount of acetaminophen is converted via the microsomal enzyme system to a toxic metabolite, which in turn is detoxicated by conjugation with reduced glutathione. If glutathione is depleted, the metabolite binds to hepatocellular macromolecules (arylation) and causes centrilobular necrosis with slight steatosis and inflammation. Long-term administration may lead to chronic hepatitis. Treatment consists of administration of glutathione substitutes, or of substances that protect glutathione, such as cysteamine and N-acetylcysteine. The protective effects of cysteamine, methionine and N-acetylcysteine are thought to be based on stimulation of glutathione synthesis.

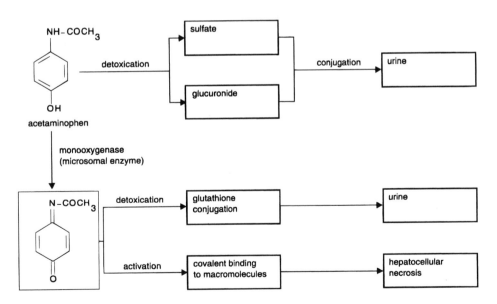

FIGURE   23.2
The metabolism of acetaminophen and its hepatotoxicity

cachexia = extreme general ill-health combined with severe weight loss

Acetaminophen induced hepatotoxicity is observed mainly in alcoholics and cachectic persons.

Acetaminophen is generally believed to be metabolically activated by cytochrome P-450 dependent monooxygenase into N-acetylimidoquinone. There are indications that an oxidative stress resulting from interactions of the imidoquinone with free thiol groups leads to disturbance of calcium metabolism and ultimately to the hepatotoxic effect of acetaminophen.

*Phenylbutazone*

*Phenylbutazone* and other anti-inflammatory agents may cause acute hepatitis, sometimes in combination with cholestasis and usually with a general hypersensitivity reaction.

*Halothane*

*Halothane* is a commonly used anesthetic. As a hepatotoxin it is interesting because its hepatotoxicity is rather different from that of other hepatotoxins. The effect of halothane is manifested by centrilobular necrosis, although a pure centrilobular necrosis is hardly ever found in patients. Much more frequently, there is a mild form of necrosis accompanied by an increase in serum enzyme activities.

As stated above, liver disorders may also be induced by immunological mechanisms. In that case serious liver necrosis may arise. Halothane is converted primarily via an *oxidative route* into the relatively harmless compound trifluoroacetic acid (see Figure 23.3). Some of the halothane, however, is metabolized via an *anaerobic, reductive route*. The reactive intermediates formed via the latter route are thought to be responsible for the liver lesions which can be induced in laboratory animals. The reductive routes by which chlorodifluoroethylene and chlorotrifluoroethane are formed have also been demonstrated in man.

Studies on metabolism in rabbits suggest that the formation of antigens from halothane takes place via the reductive route. However, because the oxidative route is much more important in terms of quantity, there must be other factors involved to cause such severe forms of immune-dependent hepatotoxicity. Figure 23.4 provides a possible explanation of the interaction between the oxidative and the reductive route in the development of immune-dependent hepatotoxicity. It is likely that a combination of direct cytotoxicity caused by reactive intermediates formed via the reductive route and immunotoxicological processes is responsible for the variety of clinical effects.

While intermediates of halothane are thought to cause a direct cytotoxic effect, binding of a reactive intermediate to hepatocellular proteins is thought to result in the formation of antigens, which in turn stimulates the production of antibodies. These might bind to the changed surface of the hepatocyte, which makes the cell an easy target for cytotoxic lymphocytes. According to this hypothesis, the liver becomes a target organ for an immunological response after the hepatocytes have been changed by the reactive intermediates of the toxicant.

*Carbon tetrachloride*

*Carbon tetrachloride* is perhaps the best studied hepatotoxic compound. Because of its carcinogenic properties (demonstrated in animal experiments) it is now hardly used. It used to find general application as a solvent for oils, fats and waxes, as well as for dry cleaning. Carbon tetrachloride is very suitable for use as a model compound in hepatotoxicity and cytotoxicity research because its effect is brought about via the formation of a free radical. This free radical is formed in a cytochrome P-450-mediated reductive process.

Carbon tetrachloride is converted into the *trichloromethyl radical* ($CCl_3^{\bullet}$) and the *trichloromethylperoxy radical* ($CCl_3O_2^{\bullet}$). These radicals are extremely reactive, and their duration of action is often short. Carbon tetrachloride-induced necrosis is most severe in the centrilobular hepatocytes (zone 3), as here the concentration of cytochrome P-450 is highest. As seen above, the free radicals initiate

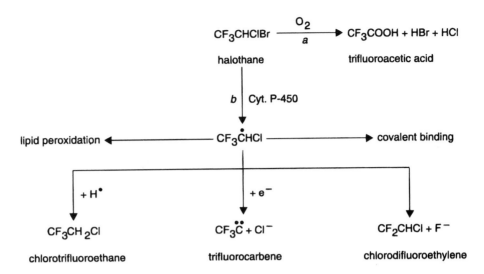

FIGURE   23.3
Metabolism of halothane via the oxidative route (a) and via the reductive route (b)

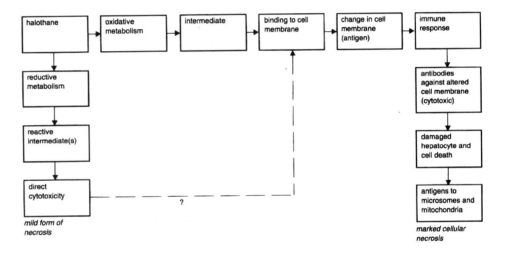

FIGURE   23.4
Toxic effects caused by (reactive) intermediates of halothane
The direct toxicity of reactive intermediates formed by the reductive metabolic route is considerably less severe than the necrosis mediated by immune mechanisms.

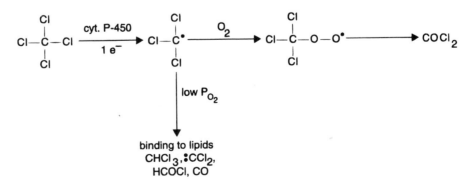

FIGURE   23.5
Formation of free radicals from carbon tetrachloride

lipid peroxidation of biological membranes and bind covalently to lipids, proteins and nucleic acids. It is now assumed that the trichloromethyl radical forms covalent bonds and that the trichloromethylperoxy radical is the initiator of lipid peroxidation. The reason for this is that the conversion of the trichloromethyl radical to the trichloromethylperoxy radical takes place much more rapidly than binding to cellular components. Lipid peroxidation leads to a cascade of events. Figure 23.6 shows the possible consequences of peroxidation of biological membranes in the hepatocyte.

Damage to the cellular membrane structures leads to cellular necrosis. The toxic effect is enhanced as a result of enzyme activation by alcohol or barbiturates and decreased by a low protein diet. The centrilobular hepatocytes initially display a hydropic to fatty degeneration.

*Isoniazid*

The major route of metabolism for *isoniazid* is acetylation, followed by hydrolysis to yield isonicotinic acid and acetylhydrazine (see Figure 23.7). Acetylhydrazine is subsequently converted by the microsomal enzyme system to a reactive metabolite, which can cause liver necrosis. Fast acetylators therefore run a higher risk, because they convert isoniazid more extensively into its reactive metabolite. Combination with rifampicin, an enzyme activator, also increases the risk of liver necrosis induced by isoniazid.

*Alcohol*

A healthy individual is capable of metabolizing 160–180 g of alcohol per day. *Alcohol* induces enzymes so that an alcoholic can metabolize large amounts of alcohol per day, provided his liver has not been damaged. One gram of alcohol provides 7 calories. Alcohol only has energetic value, no nutritional value. This is why alcoholics tend to neglect their diet, as a result of which the toxic effects of alcohol abuse become even more prominent. Ethanol (see Figure 23.8) can be metabolized to acetaldehyde via various routes. Conversion by alcohol dehydrogenase is by far the most important one. Under normal conditions, the hydrogen peroxide-dependent reaction accounts for only 10% of metabolic alcohol conversion. Acetaldehyde is toxic to the mitochondria and the cytosol, and can induce cellular necrosis. Acetaldehyde is converted to acetyl CoA with acetaldehyde dehydrogenase acting as a coenzyme. The next step is conversion into acetate, followed by oxidation to $CO_2$ and $H_2O$. Acetyl CoA can also be converted into fatty acids and other compounds via the citric acid cycle.

The high $NADH/NAD^+$ ratio resulting from the conversion of alcohol causes the synthesis of triglycerides (TG). The citric acid cycle takes place more slowly, so that the oxidation of fatty acids is reduced. The synthesis of lipoproteins is increased, while at the same time the synthesis of proteins is reduced. The result is steatosis (fatty degeneration of the liver).

Alcohol is also metabolized by the microsomal ethanol-oxidizing system. Alcohol itself is an inducer of this system. This explains the exceptional tolerance of regular alcohol users to substances (including sedatives) that are metabolized by the microsomal enzymes. Men may even display feminization as a result of increased degradation of testosterone.

ASSIGNMENT 23.3

What may be the result of administration of clofibrate on the metabolism of alcohol? Clofibrate is known to stimulate peroxisomal fatty acid oxidation.

Alcohol stimulates fibrogenesis and collagen synthesis. The high lactic acid levels in the blood also play a role in collagen formation in the liver. The development of cirrhosis is probably based on these two processes.

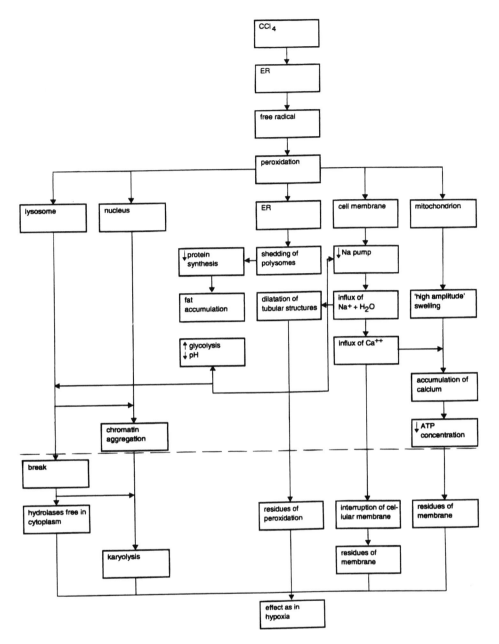

FIGURE   23.6
Sequence of hepatotoxic effects following lipid peroxidation induced by free radicals formed in carbon tetrachloride metabolism

Alcohol abuse is without doubt the main cause of cirrhosis of the liver. Because, for a long time, it was impossible to induce liver cirrhosis in experimental animals by exposing them to alcohol without concurrent *nutritional deficiency* (choline, proteins, methionine, vitamin $B_{12}$), nutritional deficiency used to be regarded as the primary cause of liver cirrhosis. However, a small group of researchers eventually did succeed in inducing cirrhosis in monkeys without a simultaneous nutritional deficiency. This led to the conclusion that alcohol itself is a hepatotoxic agent.

Immunological mechanisms also play an important role in the hepatotoxicity of alcohol. This also explains the progressive development of chronic lesions

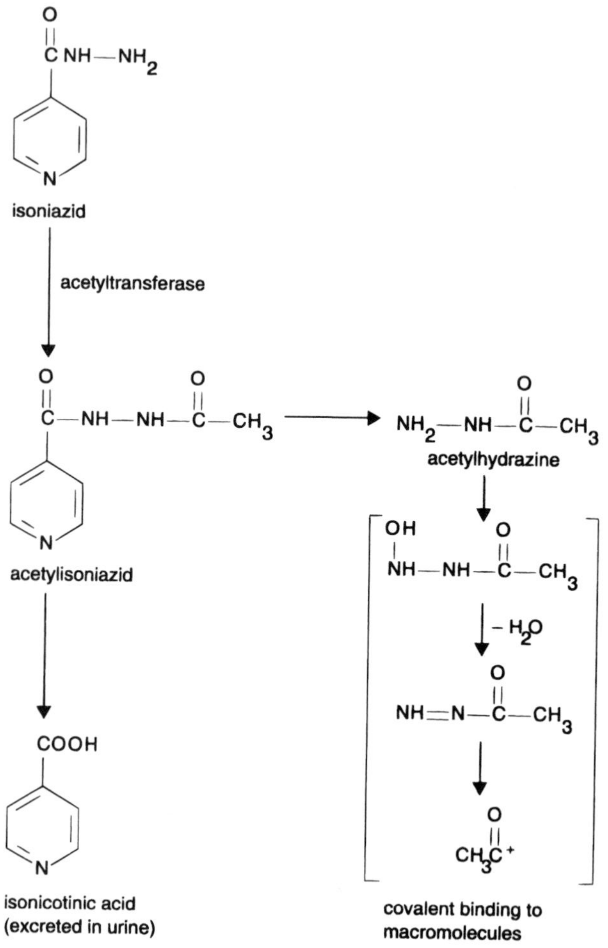

isoniazid

acetyltransferase

acetylisoniazid

acetylhydrazine

isonicotinic acid
(excreted in urine)

covalent binding to
macromolecules

FIGURE 23.7
The metabolism of isoniazid

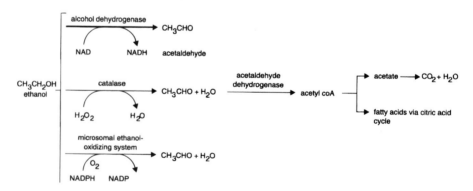

FIGURE 23.8
The metabolism of ethanol

despite a healthy diet and abstention from alcohol. Alcohol causes metabolic activation, so that more oxygen is used. This results in a reduction in $pO_2$ around the central vein. Therefore, hypoxia, necrosis and collagen formation occur primarily in the centrilobular area.

Acute hepatitis is characterized by enlargement of the liver (hepatomegaly) and lipid accumulation. Polymorphonuclear lymphocytes surround the necrotic liver cells and the Kupffer cells proliferate. The centrilobular zones in particular are affected. There is cholestasis, and the portal zone displays fibrosis and cellular infiltration. In serious cases there is centrilobular fibrosis. The lesions slowly develop into micronodular cirrhosis. The cirrhosis does not seem to be related to the lipid accumulation, but to the hepatocellular necrosis.

### 3 Mechanisms of hepatic steatosis

*Imbalance between synthesis and secretion*

Liver steatosis develops as a result of an *imbalance between synthesis and secretion* of triglycerides (TG). Such an imbalance may be caused by an increased supply of non-esterified fatty acids (NEFA), or by changes in the TG or lipoprotein fractions. There may be an increased synthesis of TG or other lipid fractions, or the synthesis of the protein components of the molecules may be inhibited. The result may be that the lipid and protein components are not assembled. Another possibility is that secretion of the lipoproteins formed is impeded. The main metabolic routes of proteins, sugars and lipids are shown in Figure 23.9.

#### 3.1 INCREASED SUPPLY OF NON-ESTERIFIED FATTY ACIDS

*adipocyte = fat cell*

When the liver cell functions normally, steatosis may develop as a result of an increased supply of non-esterified fatty acids (NEFA). These NEFA can be transported bound to albumin. They originate from the adipocytes and are released into the blood as a result of increased local lipase activity, which is controlled by the cAMP level. The level of cAMP in adipocytes rises if adenylate cyclase is stimulated or cAMP phosphodiesterase is inhibited.

*Food*

*Food* frequently provides too much fat. After hydrolysis of the TG, the surplus of NEFA is taken up by the hepatocytes. Hyperlipidemic dietary patterns result in fatty degeneration of the liver. This effect is reinforced by the fact that intake

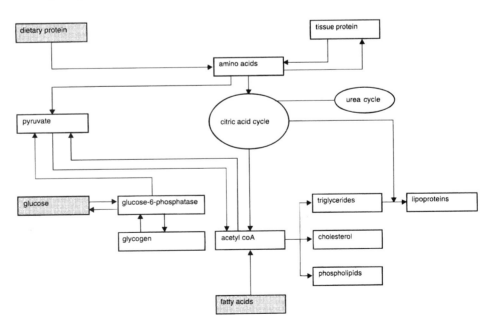

FIGURE 23.9
Major metabolic routes for proteins, sugars and lipids in the liver

of food with a high fat content is often accompanied by unbalanced intake of other components, such as a relatively low protein intake.

*Phenobarbital* causes a rapid increase in the absorption and transport of NEFA. This leads to steatosis of the liver. Chronic administration of phenobarbital causes liver steatosis through increased TG synthesis resulting from an increased production of NEFA from acetyl CoA. After all, phenobarbital activates the SER.

## 3.2   DISTURBED HEPATIC FUNCTION

There are various causes of disturbed liver function. One is the increase in transport protein concentration by phenobarbital, leading to hepatic steatosis. The present section summarizes the main causes.

*Increased synthesis of free fatty acids*

Liver steatosis may result from *increased synthesis of free fatty acids* from acetyl CoA. Such an increase may be caused by a lack of essential fatty acids, acute alcohol intoxication, threonine deficiency or administration of phenobarbital.

*Reduced oxidation of fatty acids*

White phosphorus and ethionine cause steatosis by a *decrease in the oxidation of fatty acids*. Choline deficiency has a similar effect. Certain vitamins (niacin, riboflavine, pantothenic acid) are involved in the formation of co-factors for fatty acid oxidation; deficiency of these vitamins also results in fatty degeneration.

*Decreased production of lipoproteins*

Steatosis may also arise as a result of *reduced lipoprotein production*. The synthesis of lipoproteins may, for example, be suppressed because certain essential components are lacking or because certain structures (SER, Golgi apparatus) normally involved in lipoprotein synthesis are disturbed. Certain phospholipids play an important role in combining the hydrophilic and hydrophobic parts of lipoprotein macromolecules. The lower the availability of phospholipids, the fewer lipoproteins are formed. The decreased synthesis of lecithin, for example, is the main cause of liver steatosis in the case of choline deficiency.

*Interference with mitochondrial oxidation of fatty acids*

Chlortetracycline and oxytetracycline *interfere with the mitochondrial oxidation of fatty acids* and with the synthesis of lipoproteins. This disturbs the elimination of triglycerides. The changes observed are very similar to those found in pregnancy-induced steatosis. Microvesicular fat droplets are found in the cytoplasm and there is centrilobular and midzonal necrosis.

*Inhibition of protein synthesis*

Certain substances cause liver steatosis via *inhibition of protein synthesis*. The toxins produced by *Amanita phalloides* block the synthesis of messenger RNA. Ethionine inhibits the formation of aminoacetyl-tRNA, and puromycin and tetracyclines inhibit the binding of transfer RNA to the ribosomal fractions. The synthesis of apoproteins is inhibited and a shortage of VLDL arises, causing fatty changes.

*Interference with methionine and choline*

The steatogenous effect of methotrexate is the result of its *interference with methionine and choline*, and inhibition of the synthesis of purine and pyrimidine bases.

*Combination of factors*

Carbon tetrachloride-induced hepatic steatosis is caused by a *combination of factors*. In fasting experimental animals, carbon tetrachloride is able to reduce the plasma concentration of TG to half its original value within 30 minutes. Two hours after administration of $CCl_4$, accumulation of TG in the liver cells can be observed. Such carbon tetrachloride-induced accumulation has been studied by examining incorporation of labeled fatty acids, through morphometric determinations of well-stained liver sections and with the aid of liver perfusion techniques (See Study unit 25). First, TG accumulation develops due to reduced lipoprotein secretion via interaction with the tubulin system. The tubulin system is responsible for the transport of lipoproteins. Oxidative stress plays an important role in this process; it causes increased supply of NEFA. Later, inhibition of protein synthesis becomes more prominent as a cause of decreased lipoprotein synthesis. At the same time, the oxidation of fatty acids decreases. There are also indications that carbon tetrachloride blocks the release of triglycerides from the liver.

*Interference with protein synthesis*    Asparaginase *disturbs protein synthesis* via deamination of the amino acid asparagine. This takes place particularly in neoplastic cells. Steatosis of the liver is observed in 50–90% of patients.

> ASSIGNMENT   23.4
>
> Without consulting the previous section, draw up a table of the main mechanisms by which fatty degeneration can develop and give examples of relevant toxic agents.

## 4    Adaptive phenomena (hepatomegaly)

Experimental animals react to a number of xenobiotics (including drugs, insecticides, antioxidants, food additives) by hepatomegaly (enlargement of the liver). This increase in liver weight may occur after administration of substances that increase the functional demands on the liver. The organ reacts to this by increasing or decreasing the production of specific enzymes, by increasing the number of specific organelles and by hepatomegaly. Ultrastructurally, three prominent changes can be observed:

1    proliferation of the SER;

2    proliferation of peroxisomes;

3    proliferation of mitochondria.

The observed hepatomegaly is accompanied by hyperplasia, characterized by increases in DNA synthesis, mitogenic activity and hypertrophy. Hepatomegaly is an adaptive phenomenon and is not accompanied by clearly degenerative hepatocellular changes, unless absolutely unphysiological quantities of a substance are administered, with additional non-specific toxic effects. As a result of continuous, prolonged administration, rats and mice may also develop hepatocellular tumors.

### 4.1    CHANGES IN ENZYMATIC ACTIVITY

Figure 23.10 shows how enzyme induction in the hepatocyte manifests itself when viewed by light microscopy.

Phenobarbital and some other xenobiotics activate the mixed-function oxidase system. The hepatocellular SER is increased as a result of *de novo* synthesis. The proliferation first occurs in zone 3 and spreads from there to zones 2 and 1. As a result of chronic administration of DDT, chlorinated biphenyls or other substances that cause proliferation of the SER, concentric membrane figures may develop. Two important groups of xenobiotics can be distinguished.

The first group of enzyme inducers (the most important example of which is *phenobarbital*) induces cytochrome P-450 and stimulate a large number of enzymatic processes, such as mediated by epoxide hydrolase and glucuronyltransferase.

The second group (the most important member of which is 3-methylcholanthrene) induces cytochrome P-448 and stimulates the hydroxylation of benzo[*a*]pyrene.

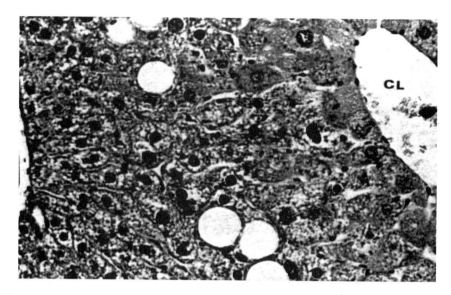

FIGURE 23.10
Centrilobular (CL) swelling of hepatocytes following administration of high doses of phenobarbital to mice.

Increased enzymatic activity due to specific induction or growth of the liver caused by xenobiotics leads to an increase in the enzymatic degradation of sex hormones, glucocorticoids and thyroid hormones. Hormonal homeostasis prevents these processes resulting in adverse effects. If homeostasis mechanisms are ineffective, a hormonal imbalance will arise. Furthermore, phenobarbital, for example, stimulates biliary secretion via an increase in bile acid-independent components. It is difficult to draw any general conclusions because of large interindividual differences and interactions between the xenobiotics.

## Intermezzo

*Effects of hypolipidemic agents on the liver*

The intended purpose of administration of hypolipidemic agents is to reduce cardiovascular morbidity and mortality by lowering increased plasma lipid fractions. After administration to experimental animals, there is a reduction in cholesterol and fatty acid synthesis and in the secretion of VLDL. Hypolipidemic agents, such as clofibrate and its analogues, and industrial plasticizers, such as phthalate esters, induce proliferation of hepatocellular peroxisomes in rats, mice and hamsters. Macroscopically, reversible swelling of the liver can be observed within 2 weeks after administration, combined with an increase in liver weight. This hepatomegaly is caused by hepatocellular hyperplasia and hypertrophy. This does not involve a hyperplastic reaction to hepatocellular necrosis. The increase in peroxisomes in the cytoplasm of liver cells can be demonstrated by light microscopy as well as by electron microscopy (the latter in ultrathin sections). Peroxisomes possess, among other things, important catalase activity and contain the enzymes for $\beta$-oxidation of long-chain fatty acids. The catalase activity is approximately doubled. In addition, the activity of carnitine acetyltransferase, which is also found outside the peroxisomes in the microsomes and mitochondria, is increased by a factor of about 10. The latter effect has not been demonstrated for substances that activate the microsomal enzymes, such as phenobarbital. The peroxisomal $\beta$-oxidation of fatty acids also differs from mitochondrial oxidation in that the first step in dehydrogenation is reduction of $O_2$ to $H_2O_2$. The resulting increased production of $H_2O_2$ is accompanied by a 15- to 30-fold increase in peroxisomal fatty acid oxidation, and this may be responsible for the increased catalase activity. The peroxisomal enzymatic effects, including overproduction and detoxication of $H_2O_2$, are thought to lead to promotion of liver tumors in rats and mice exposed to hypolipidemic substances. Hypolipidemic agents activate the microsomal enzyme system, but to a far lesser extent than phenobarbital.

The administration of xenobiotics that induce the microsomal enzyme system leads to adaptive phenomena. At a certain dose, the maximum effect on enzyme activity, size of the liver and DNA synthesis is obtained after a few days. Subsequently, a new equilibrium is reached (steady state).

The increase in liver weight, the quantity of DNA and the enzyme activity are dose dependent.

The adaptive changes are reversible (de-adaptation). The rate of de-adaptation is related to the elimination rate and therefore also to the half-life. In the case of de-adaptation, *de novo* synthesis of cellular components is temporarily suppressed. There is also a temporary increase in the number and size of autophagocytic vacuoles, in combination with increased lysosomal enzyme activity for the digestion of parts of the ER. The microsomal enzyme activities then return to normal. The increase in DNA may persist for several weeks, probably because DNA is metabolically more stable and the hepatocytes have a low turnover. Eventually, the DNA returns to normal.

## 5    Effects of chemicals on the enterohepatic circulation (EHC)

*Effects of xenobiotics on the EHC*

Administration of xenobiotics can affect the EHC *through hepatobiliary transport* or *intestinal reabsorption*. Substances which induce the hepatocellular microsomal enzymes can either accelerate or decelerate biliary excretion of substances soluble in bile. For example, phenobarbital, benzo[*a*]pyrene, spironolactone and other substances can increase the excretion rate. They are able to do so via increased biotransformation, as in the case of bilirubin, diethylstilbestrol, digitoxin and indomethacin.

After pretreatment with phenobarbital, sulfobromophthalein is excreted more rapidly because of increased conjugation with glutathione. The excretory capacity can also be increased via accelerated hepatobiliary transport. This has been demonstrated for various bile-soluble substances (including eosin and dibromosulfthalein) which are not metabolized.

Other inducers, such as the halogenated hydrocarbons, including the chlorinated biphenyls, suppress biliary excretion of substances by interfering with the energy supply of the liver cells. The suppression may *also* be caused by inhibition of biotransformation or by administration of anesthetics such as diethyl ether.

*Consequences of the EHC*
*See also Study unit 20*

The EHC influences the distribution, biotransformation, elimination and availability of chemicals. If a substance undergoes enterohepatic circulation and then enters the systemic circulation, it has a longer half-life (e.g., digitoxin, methylmercury). The EHC may also eliminate a substance presystemically, so that it does not become systemically available at all. At high plasma concentrations, a substance may also find its way to other organs, bypassing the EHC. This is how substances ingested by pregnant animals may also reach the fetal liver and in particular the fetal intestine.

> ASSIGNMENT   23.5
>
> What may be the effect of administration of antibiotics on the enterohepatic circulation of steroid contraceptives?

The EHC can strongly enhance the effective biological activity of circulating biologically active compounds. Penicillins, for example, are excreted in the bile in an active form, which increases their effectiveness in treating cholangitis. High concentrations of a xenobiotic in the EHC may, however, also increase the risk of toxic effects. For example, polycyclic aromatic hydrocarbons may lead to liver tumors, bromobenzene to liver necrosis, lithocholic acid to cirrhosis and estrogens to cholestasis.

717

The pharmacological and toxic effects of substances, whose effects are outside the EHC, are weakened by uptake from the general circulation into the entero-hepatic circulation (e.g. diethylstilbestrol, DES). The effectiveness is reinforced if the opposite takes place: return from the enterohepatic circulation to the general circulation. In this way, the EHC is important for the effectiveness of contra-ceptives and digitoxin. Via the EHC, glycosides are returned to the general circulation, where they may give rise to cardiotoxic effects if present at high plasma concentrations.

## 6 Evaluation of hepatotoxicity

The hepatotoxicity of xenobiotics can be classified as predictable and non-pre-dictable liver lesions.

*Predictable reactions*

The *predictable reactions* are dose-dependent. Sufficient ingestion, depending on the individual, results in hepatotoxic damage in experimental animals and humans.

Well-known examples are the following:

- methotrexate-induced toxic hepatitis;
- necrosis induced by carbon tetrachloride and acetaminophen;
- jaundice resulting from interference of xenobiotics with the metabolism of bilirubin, via binding of sulfonamides and salicylates to serum pro-teins, and through interference by novobiocin with UDP glucuronyl-transferase;
- liver steatosis induced by tetracyclines via inhibition of protein synthesis.

*Non-predictable reactions*

If potential toxic effects in an individual or experimental animal cannot be fore-seen, this is referred to as *non-predictable reactions*. Such reactions are rare (<1%). There are of course no adequate animal models for them. In these cases, the liver toxicity is not dose-dependent.

Examples of this group are:

- cholestasis induced by anabolic steroids;
- chlorpromazine-induced cholestatic hepatitis;
- acute hepatitis induced by halothane;
- granulomatous hepatitis induced by methotrexate.

### 6.1 CLINICAL CRITERIA

If dealing with liver patients, one should first obtain information regarding lifestyle, nutritional habits, use of drugs on prescription or without, and pos-sible exposure to pollutants. One should also enquire into the use of alcohol, smoking, contact with persons suffering from jaundice and possible previous history of liver or biliary disorders. A complete physical examination is usu-ally carried out.

### 6.2 LIVER FUNCTION TESTS

*Serum enzymes*

Several clinical tests for determining liver injury are based on the activities of serum enzymes. The transaminases, alanine aminotransferase (ALT) (= serum glutamic pyruvic transaminase (= SGPT)) and aspartate aminotransferase (AST) (= serum glutamic oxaleacetic (= SGOT)) and the phosphatases SAP (serum al-kaline phosphatase) and $\gamma$-GT ($\gamma$-glutamyltranspeptidase) are the most specific for determining liver disease.

AST

*AST* is a mitochondrial enzyme that is found in the heart, liver, skeletal muscles and kidneys. It catalyzes the following reaction:

$$\alpha\text{–ketoglutaric acid + aspartic acid} \rightarrow \text{oxaloacetic acid + glutamic acid}$$

If one of the abovementioned organs is damaged, the serum level of AST rises. Hepatocellular necrosis and myocardial infarction are the most important areas indicated by the AST assay.

ALT

*ALT* is a cytosolic enzyme, which is more specific for the liver than AST. The reaction it catalyzes is the following:

$$\alpha\text{–ketoglutaric acid + alanine} \rightarrow \text{pyruvic acid + glutamic acid}$$

Raised transaminase levels results from hepatocellular necrosis, or leakage of the enzymes into the blood, not because of cellular necrosis, but through changes in membrane permeability. Hepatocellular necrosis may be induced by hepatotoxins, specific disorders (such as infections and diabetes mellitus), liver tumors, passive congestion and drugs (including corticosteroids, estrogens, androgens, chloramphenicol, erythromycin and salicylates).

SAP

*Serum alkaline phosphatase* (SAP) is present in many tissues. It is not a very organ-specific enzyme. In the liver, it is closely connected with lipid membranes in the canalicular zone, so that any interference with the bile flow, whether intra- or extrahepatic, leads to an increase in SAP. The detergent effect of the accumulated bile acids on the lipid membranes is probably the cause of this. Cholestatic changes are accompanied by a marked rise in SAP, while a normal to mild increase is caused by leakage or hepatocellular necrosis.

$\gamma$-GT

*$\gamma$-GT* acts in a similar way to SAP. It is particularly important because its levels are often increased in the case of microsomal enzyme induction, by e.g. alcohol in man.

*Liver function tests*
*BSP (Bromosulfthalein*
*ICG (Indocyanine green)*

The functional criteria for diagnosing hepatotoxic injury are based on determination of either endogenous or exogenous components. Liver function can be tested by intravenous administration of *BSP (bromosulfthalein, sulfobromophthalein)* or *ICG (indocyanine green)*. BSP binds to blood albumin and is subsequently released in the liver. In the hepatocytes, most of it is conjugated with glutathione and eliminated in the bile. A dose-elimination-time curve can be plotted, which gives an impression of liver function. ICG is more specific for the liver. It is not conjugated or metabolized, does not enter the EHC and is not eliminated via extrahepatic routes. It behaves like an organic anion, is bound intraheptically to Y and Z proteins and is excreted in the bile. Measurement of bile salts in the serum is fairly complex. Numerous other tests are often not specific enough to assess liver function.

*Bilirubin and cholesterol*
*determinations*

Serum bilirubin levels can be measured using a specific procedure termed the Van den Bergh reaction. The so-called Direct Van den Bergh reaction shows the quantity of conjugated bilirubin after 15 minutes. The total amount of bilirubin is determined in the presence of methanol or caffeine benzoate, in order to accelerate the reaction. The quantity of unconjugated (indirect) bilirubin is calculated from the difference between the two previous values. In complete obstructive jaundice, the bilirubin level is highest compared with hepatocellular lesions. An increase in hemolysis leads to an increase in conjugated bilirubin in particular, while hepatocellular injury leads to an increase in both conjugated and unconjugated bilirubin. Because the entire portal drainage system is involved, injury to the bile ducts or extrahepatic cholestasis will lead to an increase in the level of conjugated bilirubin in particular.

Measurement of cholesterol is not a very specific indicator of hepatotoxicity, although an increase may be indicative of intrahepatic or posthepatic cholestasis, in which little or no cholesterol is excreted into the bile. A high fat diet is accompanied by high plasma cholesterol levels. Low cholesterol levels are found with malnutrition or decompensation. In chronic disorders marked increases in cholesterol levels may occur, while in cirrhosis of the liver plasma cholesterol levels are usually normal.

*Serum albumin and prothrombin half-life*

Amino acids enter the plasma via food intake and degradation of tissues. From the plasma, they are transported to the liver, where they are metabolized. Some amino acids are converted by transamination and deamination into keto acids, which subsequently enter the citric acid cycle. Others are transformed in the urea cycle to ammonia and urea. In chronic liver disorders, the synthesis of urea is inhibited. The human liver synthesizes albumin, fibrinogen, prothrombin, haptoglobin, glycoproteins, transferrin and ceruloplasmin. The immunoglobulins are synthesized by immunocytes. Disorders of the liver, including cirrhosis, are accompanied by *hypoalbuminemia* due to reduced synthesis and turnover, which results in a prolonged half-life. The albumin level changes only slowly in liver disorders. In chronic liver disease, serum albumin levels fall and the serum globulin level rises. *Hyperglobulinemia* is found in acute and chronic hepatocellular disorders and arises as an inflammatory reaction of the reticulo-endothelial system.

The serum levels of proteins with a short half-life, e.g. prothrombin, rapidly decrease in acute liver injury. Vitamin K is essential for prothrombin synthesis, which plays a role in coagulation. In the case of disturbed liver function, conversion into prothrombin may be impaired, as a result of which coagulation disturbances may occur. Vitamin K deficiency may also arise from insufficient uptake of the lipophilic vitamin K due to insufficient secretion of bile (e.g. as a result of biliary obstruction). Serum proteins are not specific for the liver. Hypoalbuminemia, for example, may also occur as a result of disorders of the kidney, insufficient protein intake and marked loss of proteins.

---

EXAMPLE

A 31-year-old woman was treated for pulmonary tuberculosis with isoniazid and rifampicin. The values for serum transaminase activity increased quite considerably. After cessation of the therapy, the transaminase levels normalized. On resuming therapy with isoniazid alone, no renewal of the increase was observed, but as soon as isoniazid was administered in combination with rifampicin, the transaminase levels rose again.

---

ASSIGNMENT   23.6

What conclusion can you draw from this case?

6.3   MORPHOLOGICAL CRITERIA

*Weight*
*Light microscopy*

In experimental animals, it is possible to compare clinical and functional biochemical parameters with morphological changes. The anatomical and pathological data include the *weight* and macroscopic and microscopic examination of the most important organs. In toxicity studies, *light-microscopic examination* of hepatocellular structures is essential. Light-microscopic changes may be examined in detail using electron-microscopic, autoradiographic, immunocytochemical and histochemical techniques. In the case of induction of the microsomal enzyme system, for example, the weight of the liver and the hepatocellular volume will increase. Proliferation of the SER can be demonstrated by electron microscopy. These changes are signs of physiological adaptation, rather than a pathological process.

Human liver biopsy specimens are frequently taken and examined for diagnostic purposes. Contra-indications for liver biopsy include coagulation disturbances, vascular tumors, abdominal dropsy (ascites) and poor general health (cachexia).

*In vitro tests*

The effects of xenobiotics on the liver can be verified in an isolated and perfused liver. It is also possible to use isolated hepatocytes in suspension or culture. In suspension, freshly isolated hepatocytes cannot be kept for more than a few hours, but in a culture medium they can survive for days. By using isolated hepatocytes, it is possible to establish whether any membrane disturbances occur, whether changes occur in the cellular macromolecules (such as inhibition of protein or RNA synthesis or increased synthesis of DNA) and whether intermediary metabolism or activity and growth of hepatocytes are altered.

### 6.4 REVERSIBILITY AND REPRODUCIBILITY

Adaptive changes in the liver are accompanied by functional changes (such as increases in serum microsomal enzyme levels) and morphological changes. Such changes are reversible in humans and animals if administration of the causative substance is stopped. If there are clear signs of hepatotoxicity, exposure to a suspicious compound must be stopped or prevented. Sometimes, administration of a mildly hepatotoxic drug will be continued (e.g. cytostatic agents). Another possibility is that on prolonged administration liver function returns to normal. A good clinical follow-up is certainly necessary if therapy is discontinued because of hepatotoxicity, and if the therapy is continued. If the administration is stopped, repair may take place after days or months, depending on the severity of the changes. Nevertheless, even when the therapy is stopped, acute hepatitis may often give rise to complete insufficiency or chronic active hepatitis and cirrhosis (e.g., isoniazid). If cessation of administration is not followed by recovery, other causes must be considered.

The reversibility of changes can be verified in experimental animals by discontinuing administration after signs of liver intoxication have been observed. After a period of recovery the animals are examined for functional and morphological repair. In animals, liver toxicity can be determined by repeated experiments or, after a recovery period, by exposing the same animal to certain dosages over a longer period of time. Only in rare cases are humans also subjected to repeated administration of substances to which they display hepatotoxic symptoms. In such cases, administration takes place under strict medical control, at low dosages and once only or for a short period of time. Particular criteria have to be met to justify this procedure: the substance must be essential for the patient's therapy, the patient must run a high risk of being re-exposed to the substance in his environment, the patient must be in good health and must not have an allergic predisposition.

### 7 Summary

Hepatotoxic effects can be caused by biochemical or immunological mechanisms. They result in cytotoxic or cholestatic changes or in combinations of both. Research into hepatotoxicity using hepatotoxic substances such as acetaminophen, bromobenzene and carbon tetrachloride in experimental animals has elucidated some of the processes involved in the formation of necrosis of the liver.

1    Liver injury may develop after the formation of only a small amount of a metabolite, as that metabolite may be highly reactive.

2    A certain threshold "dose" of the metabolite in the tissue must be exceeded before tissue damage results.

3    Endogenous substances such as glutathione play an important role in protecting the cell against reactive metabolites, by removing the metabolite and by keeping the thiol groups of biologically important cellular proteins in a reduced state.

4    Other biochemical processes such as epoxide hydrolase-mediated conjugation with water also play a role in protecting the cell.

5    Substances which induce or inhibit oxidative enzymes influence the toxicity of hepatotoxins.

The above also applies to the toxicity of xenobiotics in other organs, such as the kidney and lung.

Liver steatosis occurs frequently and results from increased availability of fatty acids or disturbed hepatocellular function. On administration of xenobiotics, the liver undergoes adaptive changes, such as hepatomegaly in the case of phenobarbital or clofibrate. The evaluation of hepatotoxicity is based on clinical, functional and morphological criteria.

## SELF ASSESSMENT QUESTIONS

1    Why is liver necrosis after ingestion of acetaminophen mainly observed in alcoholics and cachectic persons?

2    Epinephrine, norepinephrine, cortisol, adrenocorticotropic hormone and some prostaglandins, as well as some stress situations, increase adenylate cyclase activity. Methylxanthines, caffeine and theophylline inhibit cAMP phosphodiesterase. By what mechanism might these substances cause liver steatosis?

3    What changes of the cellular organelles can be observed in adaptive hepatomegaly?

4    What are the limitations of ALT and AST as parameters of hepatotoxicity?

5    Name the two best known mechanisms that cause hepatomegaly via changes in enzyme activity. Give an example of a relevant substance for each of these mechanisms.

## FEEDBACK

1    **Answers to the assignments**

23.1  These will primarily be substances that exert their effects via an immunological mechanism, via biotransformation mechanisms only found in a small proportion of the population, and, for example, via disturbances in the biotransformation system, by which the effect can only occur in individuals with defective metabolism.

23.2 Cell damage may result from, e.g. enzyme inhibition, depletion of co-factors or metabolites, interaction with receptors and changes in the membrane.

23.3 Clofibrate stimulates peroxisomal fatty acid oxidation and increases the level of $H_2O_2$ in the hepatocyte. As a result, the conversion of alcohol through the catalase system is increased.

23.4 See section 3.2.

23.5 If steroid contraceptives are taken orally in combination with antibiotics, the EHC of these steroid compounds may be diminished in its function as a depot for the active agent, because of reduced bacterial hydrolytic activity.

23.6 An increase in aspartate aminotransferase level (AST) may indicate cytotoxicity of soft tissue cells, particularly of hepatocellular necrosis or a myocardial infarction. Increased activity of skeletal muscle may also cause increased AST concentrations. Because in this case the effect appears to be directly related to exposure to drugs, the second factor can be excluded here. It is most likely that a hepatotoxic effect of rifampicin is manifested. On the basis of this information alone, the possibility of a combined hepatotoxic action of isoniazid and rifampicin cannot be excluded. Necrosis of myocardial cells cannot be excluded either.

## 2 Answers to the self assessment questions

1 The livers of alcoholics and cachectic persons have a reduced supply of glutathione. Therefore, reactive intermediates formed from acetaminophen are less easily eliminated than by persons with a healthy liver.

2 Cyclic AMP modulates the local lipase activity of adipocytes. The cAMP level in the adipocytes rises because of stimulation of adenylate cyclase or inhibition of cAMP phosphodiesterase. Thus, the compounds mentioned raise the cAMP level so that the local lipase activity increases. The result is that more NEFA are released into the blood. These NEFA can be transported to the liver while bound to albumin. The increased availability of NEFA leads to steatosis of the liver.

3 Proliferation of SER, peroxisomes and mitochondria.

4 Serum aspartate aminotransferase (AST) is not very specific for hepatotoxicity. Cytotoxic damage to the heart, skeletal muscles and kidney also increases its plasma levels. Alanine aminotransferase (ALT) is somewhat more specific for the liver, although its plasma concentration is also raised in the case of increased membrane permeability.

5 Hepatomegaly may result from induction of the microsomal enzyme system. Phenobarbital and other xenobiotics activate the mixed-function oxidase system. At the same time, proliferation of the smooth endoplasmic reticulum occurs. Phenobarbital, for example, mainly induces cytochrome P-450, and 3-methylcholanthrene induces cytochrome P-448. Hepatomegaly may also develop following administration of substances that induce proliferation of hepatocellular peroxisomes. Hypolipidemic substances, such as clofibrate, are examples.

# Contents Study unit 24
# Nephrotoxicology: toxicological pathology and biochemical toxicology

0-8493-9232-2/96/$0.00 + $.50

Study unit 24

# Nephrotoxicology: toxicological pathology and biochemical toxicology

*J. F. Nagelkerke*

INTRODUCTION

The kidney is often a target for the toxic substances to which man is exposed. An impression of the frequency with which renal insufficiency is caused by toxic substances can be obtained from the data given below, derived from a letter to the editor of *The Lancet* in 1986, from the director of a center for hemodialysis in West Berlin. An average of 13% of all West German patients who registered for hemodialysis in 1983 suffered from renal insufficiency caused by excessive use of non-narcotic analgesics such as acetylsalicylic acid, phenacetin and acetaminophen. In the various towns and cities of West Germany, the percentages of these patients varied greatly, from 0% to 50%. In the Berlin hemodialysis center, the percentage was 33. Approximately 10% of Berlin out-patients take painkillers of various types more than once a day. Three billion analgesic tablets were sold in West Germany in 1983, a quantity that corresponds to a consumption of 1.3 grams per capita. This is much lower than the consumption of analgesics in Australia (40 g) and Switzerland (22 g), but higher than that in Scandinavia (1 g). In 1983, West Germany had seventeen thousand patients suffering from terminal renal disease, which means that the 13% mentioned above corresponds to 2200 cases caused by abuse of analgesics.

If there are as many potential patients not registered in the hemodialysis centers, this approximately equals 5000 cases of renal disease caused by analgesics. There are an estimated 600,000 people using an excess of pain killers. The risk of developing a renal disorder is therefore approximately 1%. This percentage does not seem very high, but this is likely to be an underestimate because:

- renal injury caused by abuse of analgesics is difficult to detect clinically, and
- patients do not like to admit abuse.

One should also take into account that people who qualify for hemodialysis have a terminal renal disease. Other, less serious cases are therefore not in this percentage. Besides the analgesics mentioned, there are many other compounds to which man is exposed that have primarily a nephrotoxic action.

The purpose of this study unit is to create a framework based on the anatomy and physiology of the kidney within which it will be possible to understand why nephrotoxic substances exert their effects and where they do so. Following the delineation of this framework, the potential consequences of renal damage and the ways in which it can be detected are described. A number of nephrotoxic substances and their specific mechanisms of action are discussed. In conclusion, a brief outline is given of the manner in which cell death can eventually be brought about by nephrotoxic substances.

LEARNING OBJECTIVES

After having studied this unit you should be able to:

— describe the anatomical, cellular and functional aspects of the kidney
— define the following concepts:
  glomerulus
  proximal convoluted tubule
  loop of Henle
  distal convoluted tubule
  collecting tubule
  juxtaglomerular apparatus
— distinguish glomerulonephritis from tubulonephritis and give examples of the ways in which they can arise
— explain why nephrotoxicity caused by foreign compounds occurs at specific sites
— describe a number of morphological phenomena encountered in nephrotoxicity
— name some causes of protein accumulation in the tubular epithelium (hyaline droplet formation)
— describe the process of degeneration and repair in acute tubular degeneration, such as that caused by Hg intoxication
— describe some clinical/chemical factors which are of importance in nephrotoxicity.

*Study hints*

You are expected to have a thorough knowledge of the anatomy and physiology of the kidney. If necessary, read up these subjects in a textbook on anatomy/physiology before you start.

A number of matters discussed in this unit have been dealt with previously (e.g., in section 5 of Study unit 15, and in Study unit 10). The study load for this unit is approximately 3 to 4 hours. You will have the opportunity to study the histopathological changes dealt with here in more detail in the optionally available CD-I program.

STUDY CORE

## 1 Anatomy and physiology of the kidney

### 1.1 STRUCTURE

You are expected to have a thorough knowledge of the anatomy and physiology of the kidney. To create a framework for the subject matter of the present study unit, however, a brief outline of the structure of the organ is given.

The kidney can be roughly divided into two zones: the outer zone or cortex and the inner zone or medulla, with the papilla. The smallest functional unit is the *nephron*; it consists of the glomerulus, the proximal convoluted tubule, the loop of Henle and the distal convoluted tubule (see Figure 24.1).

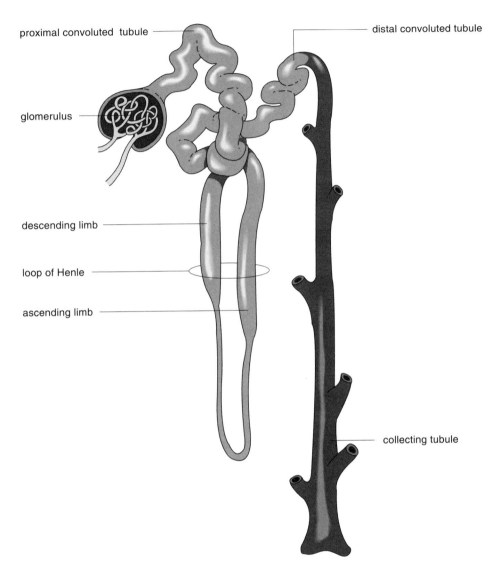

proximal convoluted tubule

glomerulus

descending limb

loop of Henle

ascending limb

distal convoluted tubule

collecting tubule

FIGURE   24.1
Structure of the smallest functional unit of the kidney, the nephron, with the collecting tubule

*Glomerulus*

The *glomerulus* consists of a tuft of blood capillaries enclosed in Bowman's capsule. The epithelial cells of Bowman's capsule (podocytes) form processes that together form a fine network. The openings between the podocytes allow filtration to take place. The capillaries are made up of three layers, which ensure that the glomerular filtrate is formed (see Figure 24.2b). The first filter to be passed consists of a layer of endothelial cells that have openings (fenestrae) small enough to prevent all blood cells from passing. The filtrate must then pass the basement membrane, which holds back all large molecules.

ASSIGNMENT 24.1

Does the basement membrane select exclusively on the basis of molecular size?

Behind the basement membrane, there is another layer of epithelial cells, whose role in the filtration process has not yet been fully elucidated. The filtrate formed in the glomerulus subsequently flows into the proximal convoluted tubule, through the loop of Henle to the distal convoluted tubule and finally arrives in the collecting tubule that eventually leads into the ureter.

*Blood supply*

The blood reaches the nephron via the afferent arteriole. Some of the blood is filtered and enters the tubule, while the remaining blood flows on via the efferent arteriole and, after a large number of turns around the tubules, which allow extensive contact between the blood and the tubular cells, is collected in the interlobular veins (see Figure 24.3).

An electron micrograph of a section of the kidney (see Figure 24.4) shows the glomerulus, and next to it cross-sections of proximal convoluted tubules.

*Brush border*

That part of the membrane of the proximal tubular cell, which borders on the actual tubular lumen (the luminal membrane), is densely covered with microvilli and is therefore called the *brush border*. It can be discerned in Figure 24.5.
   The part of the membrane that faces the blood vessels, the basolateral membrane, displays a great number of invaginations and protrusions. These create a large surface area and allow easy interchange with the blood (see Figure 24.6).

At the base of the microvilli, the luminal membrane invaginates to form canaliculi, where small vesicles are formed, which contain small amounts of the filtrate. After these vesicles have budded off, they are transported into the cell. The cells contain many mitochondria, which are present mainly at the side of the basolateral membrane. The electron-microscopic image in Figure 24.6 also shows lysosomes, indicating that biomolecules can undergo degradation in these cells.

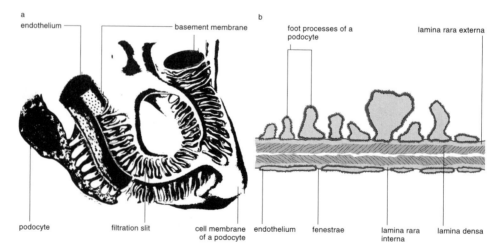

FIGURE 24.2
Schematic representation of a glomerular capillary and Bowman's capsule
a. the blood flows through the capillary and passes through the capillary wall due to the filtration pressure. Blood cells are held back by the endothelial layer and high-molecular-weight components by the basement membrane
b. cross-section through the filtration membrane in the glomerulus.
The laminae rarae interna and externa and the lamina densa together form the glomerular basement membrane.

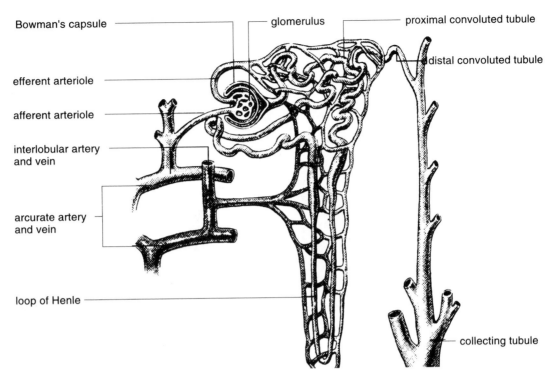

FIGURE   24.3
Blood supply to the nephron
The figure shows the cortical blood supply

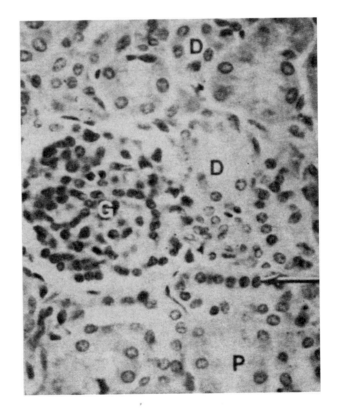

FIGURE   24.4
Light-microscopic image of a piece of cortex
The letters in the figure indicate the macula densa of the glomerulus (G), a cross-section of a proximal convoluted tubule (P) and a distal convoluted tubule (D).

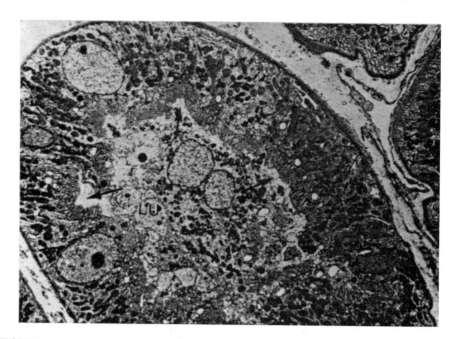

FIGURE 24.5

Electron-microscopic image of a normal human kidney

The renal tissue shown was obtained from biopsy, which is why the lumen (LU) is filled with components of cells damaged during biopsy. The cells look otherwise normal. The arrows indicate the brush border.

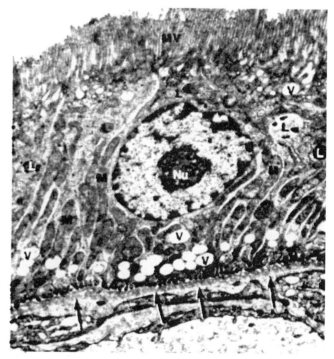

FIGURE 24.6

Image of a proximal tubular cell

MV = microvilli, L = lysosomes, M = mitochondria, Nu = nucleus.

The arrows indicate the invaginations of the basement membrane on the basolateral side.

Proximal tubule

The cells of the *proximal tubule* can be divided into three distinct types: those of the early part, or proximal convoluted tubule $PCT_1$, those of the middle and late parts, or proximal convoluted tubule $PCT_2$, and those of the straight part or pars recta (PR). Table 24.1 shows a number of functions that are carried out by these specific cell types.

## 1.2 PHYSIOLOGY AND FUNCTIONS

### 1.2.1 Filtration

The kidneys of an adult are perfused by approximately 1.2–1.3 liters of blood per minute. This means that the total circulating volume of blood (about 6 liters) passes through the kidneys once in 4 to 5 minutes. This high perfusion rate serves two goals. The blood is filtered at a very high rate, which allows constant control of its composition. The large supply of blood also ensures an adequate supply of *oxygen*; this is necessary because the renal tubular cell has the highest oxygen consumption of all cells of the body. From the 1.25 liters of blood passing through the two kidneys per minute, approximately 125 ml of filtrate is formed by glomerular filtration, 124 ml of which is reabsorbed. Glomerular filtration can take place because the net hydrostatic pressure in the arterial capillaries is higher than that in the tubule. This net filtration pressure amounts to approximately 25 mm Hg. The filtrate has the same composition as the blood; only large molecules, with a molecular mass of more than 70,000, are unable to pass the basement membrane filter of the glomerular capillaries, and do not enter the glomerular filtrate. Selective filtration not only takes place on the basis of molecular size, but also on the basis of electric charge. On the glomerular endothelium there are negatively charged groups that also play a role in the selection process.

### 1.2.2 Reabsorption and secretion

Active transport

After the filtrate has entered the tubule, the reabsorption of certain substances begins. In the proximal part, all the glucose, 85 % of the sodium chloride and the water are reabsorbed. The reabsorption of glucose and sodium and chloride ions takes place by *active transport* and requires expenditure of ATP, while water passively follows the osmotic gradient. The reabsorption capacity for glucose is limited, and an excess of glucose present in the glomerular filtrate allows glu-

TABLE 24.1
Classification of proximal tubular cells and their specific functions

| Name | Abbr. | Reabsorption | Secretion | Other functions |
|---|---|---|---|---|
| early proximal convoluted tubule | $PCT_1$ | $Na^+$, $Cl^-$, $K^+$, $Ca^{2+}$, $PO_4^{3-}$, urea, amino acids, uric acid, glucose, acetate | secretion of uric acid, organic acids and bases increases from $PCT_1$ to PR | phagocytosis and pinocytosis; uptake and degradation of protein; formation of ammonia |
| middle and late proximal convoluted tubule | $PCT_2$ | small amount of $Na^+$, $Cl^-$, $K^+$, $Ca^{2+}$, $PO_4^{3-}$, urea, amino acids, uric acid, glucose, acetate | | |
| straight part or pars recta | PR | $HCO_3^-$, and very smal amounts of $Na^+$, $Cl^-$, $K^+$, $Ca^{2+}$, $PO_4^{3-}$, urea, amino acids, uric acid, glucose, acetate | urea (?) | degradation of protein |

cose to be excreted in the urine (e.g., in diabetes mellitus). Besides the molecules and ions mentioned above, many essential substances are also reabsorbed, such as amino acids and vitamin C.

*Pinocytosis*

A special form of uptake is *pinocytosis*: filtrate present in the canaliculi is enclosed by vesicles, which bud off and are transported into the cell. Inside the cell, the vesicles fuse with lysosomes, and material present in the filtrate (mainly proteins) is degraded.

*Endocytosis*

*Endocytosis* proceeds in the same manner, but this process involves receptors that bind certain components in the filtrate, after which endocytic vesicles are formed.

*Transport lumen/tubular cell*

Via the tubular cell, direct transport from the blood to the tubular lumen also takes place. It is mediated by the organic and inorganic *anion and cation transport systems* (see Figure 24.7 and Table 24.2).

These transport systems play an important role in eliminating positively and negatively charged xenobiotics from the blood. It has recently been shown that transport from the lumen to the cell is also mediated by organic ion transport systems.

*Glutathione and cysteine conjugates*

The transport systems for *glutathione and cysteine conjugates* are also important for renal toxicology. Some potentially nephrotoxic substances have been shown to reach the kidney by this route.

Figure 24.8 shows the various reactions involved in this form of transport. Glutathione conjugates are either taken up by the cell directly or are first degraded in the filtrate to the cysteine conjugate and are then taken up. In the cell, a reaction involving the enzyme $\beta$-lyase may then form a molecule with a reactive thiol group (see Figure 24.9).

ASSIGNMENT 24.2

Apart from in the kidney, where are many of the glutathione conjugates formed? What is the function of glutathione conjugation?

TABLE 24.2
Some endogenous compounds (a) which are recognized by organic transport systems, as well as some foreign compounds (b) which are transported by active transport systems

| | | |
|---|---|---|
| a | acetylcholine | histamine |
| | choline | 5-hydroxytryptamine |
| | creatinine | methylguanidine |
| | dopamine | methylnicotinamide |
| | epinephrine | norepinephrine |
| | guanidine | thiamine |
| b | amiloride | morphine |
| | amprolium | neostigmine |
| | atropine | procaine |
| | isoproterenol | quinine |
| | mecamylamine (inversine) | tetraethylammonium |
| | meperidine (demerol) | tolazoline (priscoline) |
| | mepiperphenidol (darstine) | |

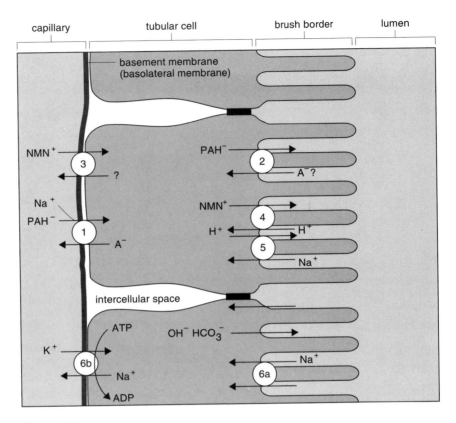

FIGURE 24.7

Diagram of a proximal tubular cell with a number of transport systems

1. Carrier for anions (with para-aminohippuric acid, PAH-, as an example) from the blood into the tubule cell
2. Carrier which transports anions to the tubular lumen
3. System by which cations (e.g. N-methylnicotinamide, NMN+) enter the cell from the blood
4. Pumping out of cations by exchange for H+ ion
5. System which exchanges H+ ions for Na+ ions, which maintains the H+ gradient
6. Maintenance of Na+ gradient by Na+/K+-ATPase
a. active reabsorption of Na+ ions from the tubular lumen to the capillary (Na+ followed by negatively charged ions and water)
b. active transport from the tubular cell to the blood.

*Passive uptake*

Besides active transport, *passive uptake* from the tubule also takes place. Compounds excreted at the start of the tubule may diffuse back into the cell lower down the tubule. Because the pH is different there, they are better able to pass the cell membrane. Reabsorption of substances in the kidney prevents loss of low molecular weight blood components, such as glucose and amino acids. There is excretion of substances that are water soluble and that are not easily reabsorbed. These include endogenous waste products such as urea and xenobiotics (possibly metabolized or conjugated) such as drugs. Moreover, the kidneys are also involved in the synthesis of prostaglandins (which tend to work locally) and of hormones (such as renin).

### 1.2.3 Formation of urine

The excretion of hypertonic urine by the collecting tubules is made possible because chloride ions are pumped into the surrounding interstitial spaces during passage of the filtrate through the ascending limb of the loop of Henle. This segment of the loop of Henle is impermeable to water, which means that the water cannot follow the osmotic gradient that is built up. The net result is that the interstitial tissue is kept highly hypertonic. The filtrate leaving the loop of Henle is itself hypotonic (see Figure 24.10).

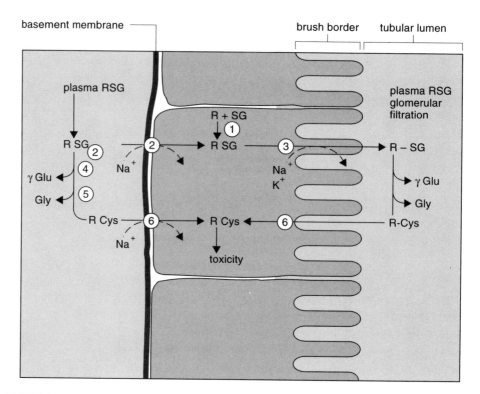

FIGURE   24.8

Diagram of uptake of glutathione conjugates (RSG) and cysteine conjugates (R-cys) by the kidney cell

RSG can be produced in the cell itself (1) or enter the cell from the blood via the organic ion transport system (2), after which it is transported to the tubular lumen (3). In the lumen, and probably also in the capillary on the basolateral side of the cell, glutamine and glycine are separated (4,5), leaving the cysteine conjugate, which is subsequently transported into the cell (6).

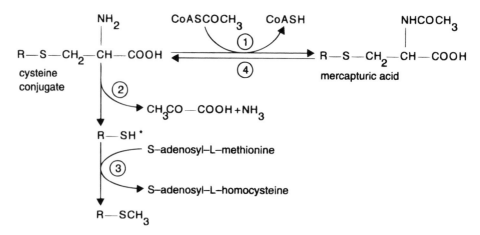

FIGURE   24.9

Metabolism of the cysteine conjugate

The cysteine conjugate can be converted into a mercapturic acid, after which it is excreted in the urine (1), but it may also be converted into a reactive thiol compound* by the enzyme β-lyase (2). This reactive thiol compound can in its turn be detoxicated by methylation. In addition, mercapturic acids formed in the liver can enter the cell via the organic ion transport system and be converted via deacetylase into a cysteine conjugate (4).

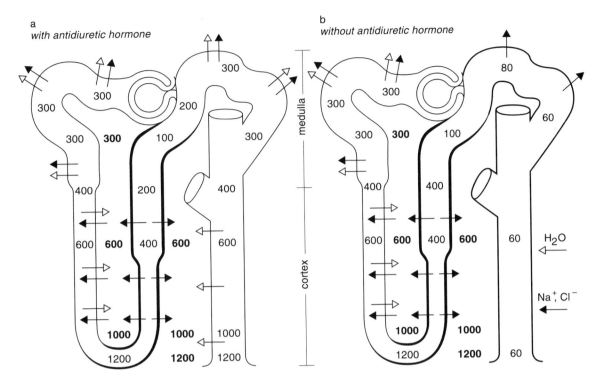

FIGURE   24.10
Schematic representation of the formation of urine
The numbers indicate the relative osmolarity.
On the right the effect of the countercurrent system; on the left that of the antidiuretic hormone.
The dark tubular walls are impermeable to water.

ASSIGNMENT   24.3

Explain how hypotonic urine can be formed.

Compare Figures 24.10a and 24.10b.

When the filtrate again flows through the medulla via the collecting tubule, re-absorption of water by the interstitial tissue will take place, as a result of which the urine will become hypertonic. This is where the antidiuretic hormone (ADH) exerts its effect: reabsorption of water is possible only in the presence of ADH, since without the effect of this hormone, the wall of the collecting tubule is impermeable to water.

### 1.2.4 Regulation of ion balance and the volume of extracellular water

Renin-angiotensin system

The cells of the juxtaglomerular apparatus, which is located immediately next to the glomerulus, at the start of the afferent arteriole, produce *renin*. This hormone interacts with the plasma protein angiotensinogen, converting it into *angiotensin I*. This in turn is converted into *angiotensin II*, which stimulates the secretion of aldosterone by the adrenal cortex. *Aldosterone* regulates the reabsorption of sodium by the cells of the distal tubule. When the concentration of sodium in the blood threatens to become too low, the secretion of renin is stimulated, thus leading to a reduction in sodium excretion.

Aldosterone

To understand what follows in this study unit, it is important to know the nature of the flows of liquids and particles encountered in the kidney. Therefore a brief summary is provided below.

a.   Glomerular filtration leads to the formation of a liquid containing all the components of the blood, except those with a molecular mass higher than

70,000 and those of low molecular weight that form a complex with high molecular weight components.

b.  Immediately at the start of the tubule, all the glucose and many sodium and chloride ions are reabsorbed, which implies that transport takes place through the proximal tubular cell.

c.  Endogenous products and xenobiotics can be transported into the proximal tubular cell via the organic anion and cation transport system (and be excreted again in the urine).

d.  Further "downstream" in the tubule, reabsorption and/or secretion of sodium and chloride takes place.

e.  Once the distal tubule has been reached, reabsorption of a variety of substances can again take place, in particular of substances that are reasonably lipid-soluble.

f.  Dependent on the concentration of the antidiuretic hormone, reabsorption of water into the interstitium takes place in the collecting tubules.

How these flows of liquids can affect the concentrations of substances in the tubule and thus their toxicity is shown in Figure 24.11.

In Figure 24.11, the plasma concentration for all the substances has arbitrarily been set at 1. Figure (a) shows how neither secretion nor reabsorption of inulin takes place after glomerular filtration: its concentration in the tubule rises as more water is reabsorbed. Figure (b) shows how the concentration of para-aminohippuric acid (PAH) changes. This substance is a substrate for the organic ion transport system. This means that the concentrating effect of water reab-

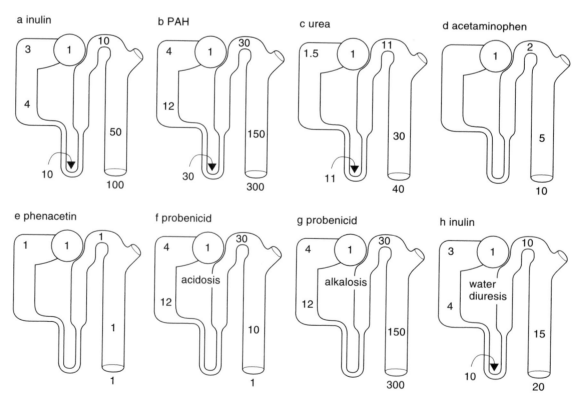

FIGURE   24.11

Comparison of the urine concentrations of a number of xenobiotics in the kidney
An explanation is given in the text.

736

sorption is reinforced by the effect of active secretion from the blood into the urine. A certain portion of urea (c) is reabsorbed in the proximal convoluted tubule, excreted again in the loop of Henle, and then again reabsorbed from the collecting tubule. Acetaminophen (d) is reabsorbed by diffusion, but the tubular membrane is not very permeable to this substance, so that its concentration does rise towards the end of the tubule. Phenacetin (e) diffuses easily across the membrane and is thus not concentrated.

*Effect of pH*

The *effect of the pH* of the tubular fluid on the concentration of probenecid (a weak acid) is shown in figures f and g. At low pH, the substance is not dissociated at all, and can easily pass the tubular membrane; at high pH, however, it is charged and cannot cross the membrane. Figure (h), to conclude, shows what happens in the absence of ADH. Much more water is excreted in this case, so that the concentration of inulin at the end of the tubule is much lower.

> ASSIGNMENT 24.4
> What properties does a substance need to have for a high concentration of it to be excreted in the urine?

## 2 Exposure to nephrotoxic substances

In industrialized countries, man is exposed to a large number of potentially nephrotoxic substances. Some of these are present in the environment. Others present a hazard only to those who work with them every day. Still other substances are administered as drugs and are therefore relevant only to patients. Several examples of substances belonging to the various categories are given below.

*Environment.* Pesticides and herbicides, e.g., 2,4,5-trichlorophenoxyacetic acid, polychlorinated biphenyls (PCBs), tetrachlorodibenzo-p-dioxin (TCDD). Heavy metals such as mercury and cadmium.

*Labor.* Haloalkanes and haloalkenes, heavy metals, herbicides and pesticides.

*Diet.* Toxins formed by fungi and bacteria, herbicides and pesticides, haloalkanes in chlorinated tap water.

*Drugs.* Antibiotics, e.g., aminoglycosides and cephalosporins. Analgesics such as acetaminophen, cyclosporin A (an immunosuppressant), cisplatin (a cytostatic) and radiographic contrast agents.

> In which branches of industry are many nephrotoxic substances used?

Many of the above-mentioned substances are used in the petrochemical industry, the paints industry, polymer chemistry and agriculture and horticulture.

## 3 Consequences of exposure—pathology and regeneration

### 3.1 DEVELOPMENT OF URINE CONCENTRATIONS IN THE KIDNEY

As described in section 1, the kidney is a well-perfused organ. If a toxic substance is present in the blood, a large quantity of it will pass the kidneys. In particular the proximal convoluted tubule, because of its location and possession of various systems of uptake, is frequently the target of toxic substances.

> By which routes can these substances enter the cell?

737

Substances may be introduced into the cell from the blood, via the capillary network, by the organic transport systems. The luminal membrane is the first to be exposed to the glomerular ultrafiltrate and this is where an important part of normal physiologic reabsorption takes place. Xenobiotics, however, are also taken up, either because a substance is recognized by one of the carriers in the membrane, or because it is taken up by endocytosis while bound to small proteins. A third possibility is that the substance diffuses through the membrane non-specifically.

*Protective mechanisms*

Like the hepatocyte, the kidney cell contains the enzymes mediating phase I and phase II biotransformation reactions. It is therefore also possible that biotransformation (or other activation mechanisms) cause reactive intermediates to be formed. The cell has *protective mechanisms* that are able to scavenge reactive intermediates, such as the tripeptide glutathione or the enzyme superoxide dismutase in combination with peroxidase. If these protective mechanisms are inadequate, however, the reactive metabolites will react with the building blocks of the cell: the lipids, proteins and nucleic acids. A more detailed account of these reactions is given in section 4.

*Degradation of transport protein*

The substance that eventually acts as the toxicant may also be released because the *transport protein* bound to which it has entered the cell is degraded. This can be observed, for example, in the case of heavy metals, which bind to small proteins and enter the cell by endocytosis. After degradation of the protein, the metal is released. Detailed information is available on the toxicity of a number of substances that enter the proximal tubular cell bound to *cysteine*. They do not become toxic until after a reactive thiol compound has been formed by mediation of $\beta$-lyase.

Many renal diseases, which develop after exposure to toxic substances are of tubular origin, but the glomerulus and the papilla may also be the target of toxicants. After exposure of the kidney to, for example, mercury, drugs with a free sulfydryl group, non-narcotic analgesics, silica and heroin, glomerulonephritis may develop, usually of the immune-mediated type. What this means is, very briefly, that immune complexes are formed on the membranes of the glomerulus, causing the filtration characteristic of the glomerulus to change.

Approximately 10 % of cases of renal insufficiency arising after exposure to xenobiotics are caused by damage to the papilla. The damage is usually the result of long-term excessive use of combinations of various analgesics. The mechanism by which this takes place is discussed later in this unit.

## 3.2 DETECTING RENAL DAMAGE

### 3.2.1 In vivo, histopathological

Information concerning the type of renal damage that has occurred after exposure to toxic substances can be obtained by microscopic examination of histological sections. Such examination can take place by light microscopy, in which case one or more stains are usually applied. In this way, any disturbance or loss of the normal arrangement of the cells within the tissue can be detected, as well as the presence or absence of enzymatic activity. By electron microscopy, it is also possible to make intracellular structures visible. This technique does however require special preparation of the sections. Some of the specific types of renal injury that may be encountered are described below.

A reaction to a disturbance of electric charge at the surface of the glomerular podocyte may be an increase in the amount of cytoplasm and retraction of the cellular processes. This is called "fusion" of the foot processes of the podocytes (see Figure 24.12).

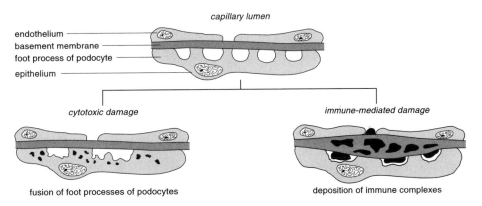

FIGURE  24.12
Two forms of glomerulonephropathy which lead to altered permeability and proteinuria

*Glomerulopathies*

Diffuse disorders of the glomerulus or *glomerulopathies* are known in forms that are characterized mainly by degeneration without inflammatory changes. Such disorders are termed *glomerulonephroses*. In contrast, glomerulopathies that are characterized by inflammatory reactions are called *glomerulonephritides*.

Degenerative changes are frequently followed by inflammation. Many glomerulopathies are moreover caused by circulating antigen-antibody complexes, which are sieved out in the glomerulus. Accumulation of these complexes is thought to cause pathological changes, probably in cooperation with complement.

Glomerulopathies may also be accompanied by the following changes outside the glomerulus.

1.  Due to their colloid osmotic activity, the proteins that have been allowed to pass through may inhibit reabsorption of dissolved substances and water from the proximal convoluted tubule; in such cases the *lumina* are *dilated*.

2.  The proximal tubular cell contains *hyaline droplets*. These are enlarged lysosomes filled with protein.

3.  The tubular cell *degenerates*: hydropic and steatotic degeneration (tubulonephrosis).

4.  The tubular change leads to *inflammation* and *fibrosis* in the renal interstitium (*interstitial nephritis*).

Conversely, tubular changes may also affect the glomerulus. Blocking of the tubular lumen, for example, results in urinary stasis in the nephron, distention of Bowman's capsule and atrophy and sclerosis of the glomerulus.

The nephroses can be classified into *glomerulonephroses* and *tubulonephroses*. Tubular changes not accompanied by clinically abnormal renal functioning, such as accumulation of pigment, fat or protein, are also regarded as nephroses (*accumulation nephroses*).

*Glomerulonephroses*

Degeneration of the glomeruli is usually called *glomerulonephrosis*. This disorder is characterized by an increase in intercellular matter. Increases encountered at the level of the basement membrane, due to deposition of immune complexes or anti-basement membrane immunoglobulins, are often considered to be glomerulonephritides.

*Renal amyloidosis*
amyloid = an accumulation of glycoproteins

In cases of *renal amyloidosis* (amyloid nephrosis), the amyloid is frequently located in the *glomeruli* (glomerulonephrosis), although it may also be found in the *interstitium* between the tubules, in which case it tends to concentrate in the renal medulla (medullar amyloidosis). Amyloidosis may occur mainly in the glomerulus, or mainly in the medulla or in both.

Glomerular amyloidosis is usually accompanied by obvious clinical symptoms (nephrotic syndrome). If the disorder is primarily in the medulla, the signs are usually less obvious; one might expect polyuria as a result of insufficient concentrating capacity.

*mesangium = intercapillary mesenchyme in the glomeruli*

*Microscopically*, a kidney affected by amyloidosis is characterized by damaged glomeruli. They are enlarged and contain hyaline material called "amyloid". Amyloid is found primarily in the mesangium and between the endothelial cells and the basement membrane, while the lumina of the capillary loops are sometimes almost entirely compressed.

*Deposition of immune complexes in the glomerulus*

The *deposition of immune complexes in the glomerulus* can be made visible by fluorescent microscopy in which the immune complexes are marked with a fluorescent substance. In Figure 24.13, these complexes are the light parts.

*Nephropathies of the proximal tubule*

Nephrotoxicity is frequently observed in the proximal tubule. Microscopically, some form of degeneration can often be observed, sometimes accompanied by inflammatory changes and/or repair, depending on the nature and extent of the disorder. Toxicologically, the inclusions, hydropic changes and tubular necrosis are important.

*Inclusions* may occur both in the nucleus and in the cytoplasm. Continuous accumulation of lead causes the formation of eosinophilic bodies in the nucleus. Usually, chemicals tend more often to produce cytoplasmic inclusions. Chronic treatment of rats with estrogens causes large brown pigment granules in the proximal tubular epithelium. The proximal tubule may also contain eosinophilic globules resulting from lysosomal accumulation of protein (hyaline droplets).

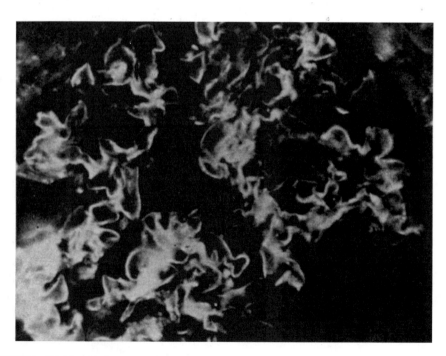

FIGURE   24.13
Immunofluorescence patterns in a glomerulus on which fluorescent antibodies have been deposited

*Hydropic degeneration* is observed in the proximal convoluted tubule in the initial stages of degenerative processes that eventually develop into necrosis. This phenomenon is also observed as a final stage in the toxicity of certain chemicals. After injection with hypertonic glucose, saccharose, inulin or gelatin, vacuolization is observed in the proximal tubule. The vacuoles are probably pinocytotic vacuoles and tend to be the result of physiological adaptation rather than of a toxic effect.

Figure 24.14 shows a light-microscopic image of a biopsy specimen taken from the kidney of a chemist who had ingested mercuric chloride. The large tubule in the center has entirely lost its epithelial cells, and the debris of these cells can be discerned in the lumen.

Figure 24.15 shows the results of renal injury caused by dehydration. The arrows indicate where cells are missing.

Figure 24.16b shows the results of treatment with gentamicin in an 18-year-old girl. The brush border has disappeared completely. The control section (a) shows normal brush border membranes.

An electron-microscopic image of tubular damage caused by ischemia is shown in figure 24.17. Between two cells that have lost their brush border but otherwise look normal (*), there is a cell with swollen endoplasmic reticulum and with a luminal membrane, which has almost completely disappeared.

Figure 24.18 shows an even more advanced stage of renal damage. Entire cells are missing, and only the virtually bare membrane is left.

The order in which morphological changes occur is generally assumed to be as follows (see also Table 24.3):

a.  decrease in the amount of glycogen, aggregation of chromatin in the nucleus, formation of intracellular vesicles, swelling of the endoplasmic reticulum and contraction of the inner mitochondrial compartment;

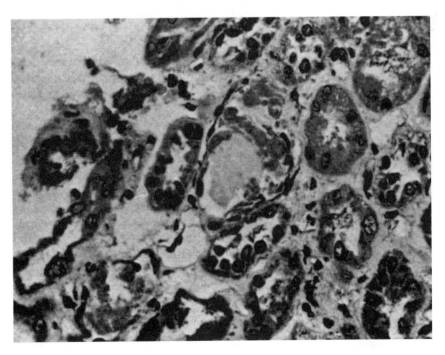

FIGURE   24.14
Microscopic image of a tubule damaged by mercury

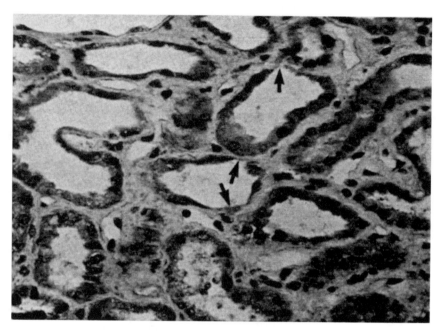

FIGURE 24.15
Damage to the tubular epithelium as a result of dehydration
The arrows indicate places where the tubular cells have disappeared altogether (HE stain, × 390)

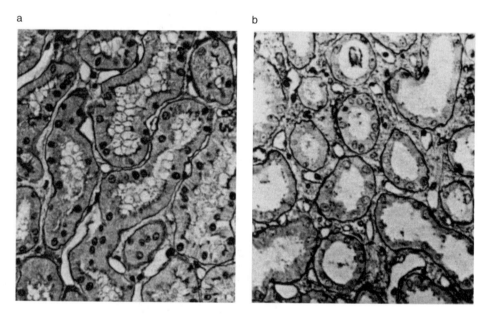

FIGURE 24.16
Damage to the tubular epithelium caused by treatment with gentamicin (PAS stain, × 390)
a. biopsy specimen of a normal kidney; the brush border is clearly discernible
b. acute tubular necrosis resulting from treatment with gentamicin. Note the absence of the brush border in the proximal tubule.

b. aggravation of the phenomena described under (a) plus loss of the brush border and formation of vesicles on the external surface of the cell, which may sometimes bud off and clog the lumen;

*Irreversible cell damage*

c. formation of aggregates in the mitochondria, probably from denatured proteins. This indicates loss of mitochondrial function. This is probably the point at which cellular damage has become *irreversible* (point of no return).

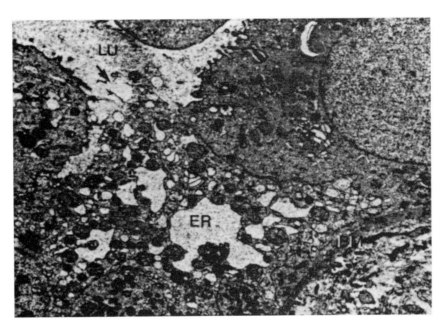

FIGURE 24.17
Electron-microscopic image of a tubule damaged by lack of oxygen

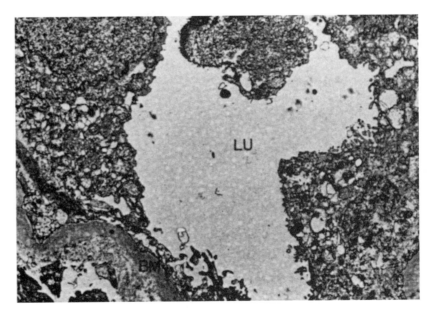

FIGURE 24.18
Electron micrograph of a proximal tubule of a patient suffering from acute interstitial nephritis
Part of the basement membrane (BM) is covered only by a thin layer originating from the adjacent epithelial cells. In fact, a complete epithelial cell of the tubule has disappeared.

From this point on, the mitochondria, nucleus and endoplasmic reticulum lose their original shape entirely. The cell itself will eventually disintegrate.

*Distal tubular nephropathy*   The tubular components of the distal nephron are the loop of Henle, the distal tubule and the collecting tubule. They are all involved in the regulation of water, electrolytes and acid/base balance. The most common microscopic alterations caused by toxic effects are renal papillary necrosis and depositions of crystals that may eventually enter the urine.

TABLE 24.3
Morphological changes accompanying cell death in the kidney

| | |
|---|---|
| A | • reduction of amount of glycogen<br>• aggregation of chromatin in nucleus<br>• formation of intracellular vesicles<br>• swelling of ER<br>• contraction of inner mitochondrial compartment |
| B | • aggravation of the phenomena under A<br>• loss of brush border<br>• budding off of vesicles (clogging of lumen) |
| C | • formation of aggregates in mitochondria from denatured protein (point of no return)<br>• loss of shape of:<br>  — mitochondria<br>  — nucleus<br>  — endoplasmic reticulum<br>• disintegration of the cell |

### 3.2.2 In vivo, clinical and experimental

*Disturbed urine production*

The presence of renal damage often becomes rapidly noticeable due to changes in two important functions of the kidney: the formation of urine and the reabsorption of substances. One of the first phenomena that can be observed following renal injury is a change in composition of the urine. The kidneys may excrete *more water* (polyuria) or *less water* (oliguria). The first condition may occur because the kidney has lost its concentrating capacity, and the second because filtrate leaks back into the blood. Interference with the reabsorptive capacity of the kidney will become manifest in the excretion of certain substances in the urine, such as glucose. If the damage is such that cellular structures are broken down, protein will be present in the urine as a result. Excretion of protein may however also be indicative of reduced reabsorptive capacity. Small proteins, for example $\beta$-microglobulins, may pass the glomerular membranes, after which (under normal circumstances) they are reabsorbed by the tubular cells. If, however, the tubular cells have been damaged to such an extent that reabsorption can no longer take place, the protein is excreted in the urine.

Conversely, the urinary excretion of substances that are normally reabsorbed, will lead to a reduced concentration of those substances in the blood, as in hypomagnesemia.

*Determination of renal function*

*Renal function* is often tested by measuring the *concentration of urea in the blood*. This concentration is increased if renal function is severely impaired. The efficiency of renal function is also assessed by measuring *creatinine clearance*.

ASSIGNMENT 24.5

Why is creatinine preferred to inulin in determining physiological clearance?

*Regeneration*

The damage caused by toxic substances does not necessarily have to lead to irreversible loss of renal function. Much depends on the particular toxic substance that has been used, the concentration and the duration of exposure. Even if proximal tubular cells have died, an intact tubule may be formed again by division of the remaining cells. This seems possible only if the basement membrane is still intact. Traces of damage may however also remain as interstitial connective tissue or degenerated tubules with flattened epithelial cells.

*3.2.3 In vitro, experimental*

*Capacity to take up organic ions*

A method commonly used to test the potential nephrotoxic effect of a substance is to measure its effect on the capacity of kidney slices to take up *organic ions*. Radioactively-labeled para-aminohippuric acid (PAH) or tetraethylammonium (TEA) are often used in these experiments. The uptake is expressed as the ratio between the radioactivity in the kidney slice and that in the incubation medium. This is a fairly coarse method by which only a first impression of the nephrotoxicity of a substance is gained, because not all cells are in contact with the toxic substance and the organic ion.

*Perfusion technique*

*Perfusion of isolated tubules* is another technique by which the potential nephrotoxic properties of a substance can be studied, but the problem here is that the highest reabsorption takes place in that part of the proximal convoluted tubule that immediately follows the glomerulus. It is technically difficult, however, to cannulate the tubule directly after the glomerulus, so that the results from tubule perfusion studies may not be completely reliable.

*Isolated cells*

A method, which does not involve these problems, is the *incubation of isolated tubular cells* or tubular fragments with the substance to be assessed. A specific function of the renal tubule is then tested.

> ASSIGNMENT 24.6
>
> Which specific tubular function or functions could be tested in this manner?

## 4 Biochemical background to cellular lesions

The nephrotoxic compounds belong to a wide range of different classes of substances. Several examples of the various types of toxic substances have already been given in section 2. Now the various classes will be described and a number of typical examples will be given. Aspects discussed are the routes of uptake used by the substance to enter the cell, and how the substance exerts its initial toxic effect.

### 4.1 MERCURY

*Mercuric chloride (HgCl₂)*
*Dimethyl mercury*
*CH₃-Hg-CH₃*

*Mercury* can occur in various forms. In inorganic form it may be found as $HgCl_2$, while in organic form it may occur as *dimethylmercury*. As a result of environmental pollution, the latter compound is found in the bodies of fish and birds. Dimethylmercury is more toxic than mercuric chloride, because it is lipophilic and can therefore more easily pass membranes. How $HgCl_2$ enters the cell has not yet been clarified; in the blood, it is transported while bound to macromolecules. Whether endocytosis of the mercury complex or simple diffusion takes place has still to be studied. It is known that the nephrotoxicity displayed by mercury in rats is reduced after preliminary treatment of the animals with cadmium. This phenomenon is attributed to the reduced surface area of the brush border in regenerating cells, which have replaced cells that had died as a result of cadmium administration. This could indicate that uptake of mercury takes place via a process of diffusion proportional to the surface area available for diffusion. The toxic mechanism of mercury is based on the affinity the thiol groups of proteins have for it, as a result of which it inhibits the action of certain enzymes such as various membrane-bound ATPases. Organic ion transport and mitochondrial respiration have been shown to fail after exposure to mercury.

Mercury used to be applied as a diuretic (organometal compound), and tended to cause glomerulonephropathies and proteinuria, especially after long-term use. These disorders can also be induced experimentally in some strains of rats.

745

If induced experimentally, the disease is biphasic. Initially, there is induction of antibodies against basement membrane components. In the second phase of the disease this is followed by deposition of immune complexes.

*Mercury as an antigen*

The role of *mercury as an antigen* is not known. Mercury may perhaps act directly as a hapten, but it is also possible that it induces endogenous molecules indirectly so that an auto-immune disease develops.

## 4.2  PLATINUM

cis-diamine-dichloroplatinum (II)
cisplatin ®

*Cisplatin*, which has platinum(II) as the central ion in a planar square with two chlorine atoms in the cis configuration and two amino groups, is often used as an antineoplastic agent. It is used to treat cancer of the testes, ovaries, head and neck. It causes excretion of proteins in the urine and a reduction in organic ion transport, which is typical of tubular necrosis. In addition, there is polyuria and increased excretion of $Mg^{2+}$. In the blood, it is hardly found in its free inorganic form at all (<5%). There are eight different low-molecular-weight components to which cisplatin has been shown to bind. The form in which cisplatin enters the cell is unknown, nor is much information available on the exact mechanism by which cisplatin exerts its toxic effect. There are indications that it is not cisplatin itself that acts as the toxicant, but a metabolite. As in the case of mercury, thiol groups have a strong affinity for platinum.

Histopathologically, cisplatin (or a metabolite) causes damage especially to the proximal and distal tubular cells. The lesions are found mainly in those regions of the cortex and medulla where its concentration is highest.

The toxicity to the tubular cells is dose-dependent. Repeated weekly injections to rats cause atrophy of the cortical portions of the nephrons and cystic dilatation of the inner cortical and the medullary tubules. The antineoplastic effect of cisplatin is due to the formation of covalent bonds with DNA, thus inhibiting the growth of rapidly dividing tissues. Clinically, cisplatin-mediated injury is now restricted to a minimum by thorough hydration of patients with saline before treatment, which reduces the concentration of cisplatin in the kidneys considerably.

## 4.3  CADMIUM

*Metallothionein*

Cadmium also causes damage primarily to the tubules. When it is given to an experimental animal, the liver reacts by producing a metal binding protein, *metallothionein*. Binding of cadmium to metallothionein reinforces its toxic effect. This has been shown by tests, which compared the toxic effect of oral doses of inorganic $CdCl_2$ with that of the metallothionein-Cd complex in rats that had not received preliminary treatment. This finding could mean that the liver passes on a toxic substance in a form that is in fact more nephrotoxic. This has also been observed for other substances. The kidney also reacts by producing metallothionein. There are indications that this might have a protective effect. One suggestion is that the Cd-metallothionein complex is easily taken up by the kidney cell, and that the metallothionein is subsequently degraded. The Cd that has been released is now free to exert its toxic effect. However, when the kidney has produced its own metallothionein, the Cd is immediately bound again, and cannot therefore exert its toxic action.

### ASSIGNMENT  24.7

One sign of the toxic action of cadmium is proteinuria, excretion of protein in the urine of low-molecular weight proteins. Proteinuria of high-molecular-weight proteins is less frequently observed. Explain why this is the case.

## 4.4 HALOALKANES

A considerable amount of information on these substances is given in the study units dealing with hepatotoxicity, for example on carbon tetrachloride ($CCl_4$) and chloroform($CHCl_3$). Activation by the mixed-function oxidase system gives rise to the formation of various free radicals. Both carbon tetrachloride and chloroform are hepatotoxic and nephrotoxic. In mice, however, $CHCl_3$ is nephrotoxic only in males, not in females. This finding may be related to the fact that the activity of cytochrome P-450 is much higher in male mice. Change of effective gender by castration and administration of female sex hormones diminishes their sensitivity to low doses of $CHCl_3$.

The precise metabolite formed which specifically causes renal damage is not known. As is the case in the liver, radioactivity covalently bound to proteins and lipids can be observed after administration of radioactive $CCl_4$. There are, however, also differences between $CCl_4$ nephrotoxicity and hepatotoxicity. Neither the damage to the endoplasmic reticulum nor the lipid accumulation which are found in the liver can be observed in the kidney. A specific renal function which is affected is the transportation of organic ions. The toxic effects of $CHCl_3$ on renal function are counteracted by glutathione. Depletion of glutathione by administration of diethylmaleate makes the kidney much more sensitive to $CHCl_3$.

## 4.5 HALOALKENES

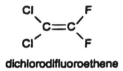

**dichlorodifluoroethene**

Examples of haloalkenes are hexachlorobutadiene and 1,1-dichloro-2,2-difluoroethene (DCDFE). When the latter substance is injected in rats, an acetylcysteine conjugate is found in the urine after a certain period of time. This is an indication that DCDFE is initially conjugated in the liver with glutathione and is then converted into a mercapturic acid, which is subsequently transported to the kidney.

> ASSIGNMENT 24.8
>
> What reactions need to take place in the kidney for a toxic compound to be formed from the DCDFE mercapturic acid? What is the difference between this conjugation reaction and the formation of the glutathione conjugate in the previous section, which was a detoxication reaction?

## 4.6 HERBICIDES

Thirty percent of the world production of herbicides consists of 2,4-dichlorophenoxyacetic acid and 2,4,5-trichlorophenoxyacetic acid (2,4-D and 2,4,5-T). At physiological pH, 2,4,5-T is in the anion form. This is one of the reasons why it used to be considered reasonably safe.

**2,4,5-trichlorophenoxy acetic acid**

> Why would an anion have been considered reasonably safe?

After all, this means that it is a good substrate for the organic anion transport system and should therefore be readily excreted, without accumulating in the body fat, like lipophilic pesticides. *In vitro* tests with kidney slices have indeed demonstrated that 2,4,5-T inhibits the uptake of para-aminohippuric acid and must therefore be transported by the same organic anion transport system. *In vivo* clearance studies in mammals, however, did not demonstrate any further excretion in addition to that by glomerular filtration. They rather seemed to indicate net reabsorption. In contrast, certain types of fish (flounder and dogfish) showed excretion 50–500 times higher than could be explained from glomerular filtration. The explanation is that *in vivo*, 2,4,5-T is bound strongly to plasma proteins; only 1–5% is present in its free form. In comparison to PAH, this bond is much stronger, and much less 2,4,5-T is therefore available in the blood for transport via the organic ion transport systems. This illustrates why the affinity of carriers is not the only factor which determines excretion in the tubule, but that the type of transport in the blood may also play a role.

The information so far available on the nephrotoxic mechanism of 2,4,5-T is only limited. However, we do know that, after uptake, intracellular values are reached *in vivo* which *in vitro* inhibit mitochondrial oxidative phosphorylation.

## 4.7 AMINOGLYCOSIDES

Gentamicin is one of the antibiotics used in clinical practice which have nephrotoxic side effects. In addition to its effect on the endothelium of the glomerulus, where it neutralizes the negative charges present, the substance also causes changes in the proximal tubular cell. Some of it binds to the negatively charged phospholipids of the brush border membrane.

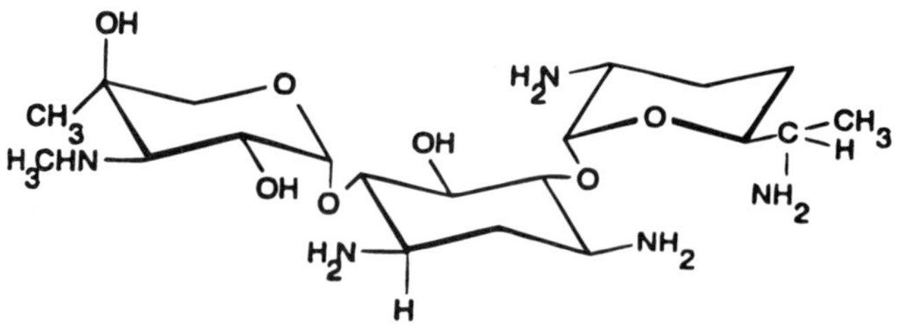

**gentamicin**

The entire complex is taken up by endocytosis and stored in the lysosomes. The biochemical changes which occur are numerous, on the one hand because the phospholipid composition of the membrane changes and the membrane-bound processes therefore also change (e.g. permeability, $Na^+/K^+$-ATPase activity, transport of cations), on the other because a complex is formed with phosphoinositol, a phospholipid which forms an important link in the relay of signals by hormones in the cell.

## 4.8 CEPHALOSPORINS

An example of this class of antibiotics is cephaloridine. This substance must be transported into the cell by the organic ion transport system, since its uptake in kidney slices is inhibited by para-aminohippuric acid and probenecid. Moreover, the substance is not toxic in very young rats, in whom the organic anion transport system has not yet developed. Once inside the cell, it is removed from it with difficulty; tubular excretion is minimal. A metabolite of cephaloridine is probably the true toxicant.

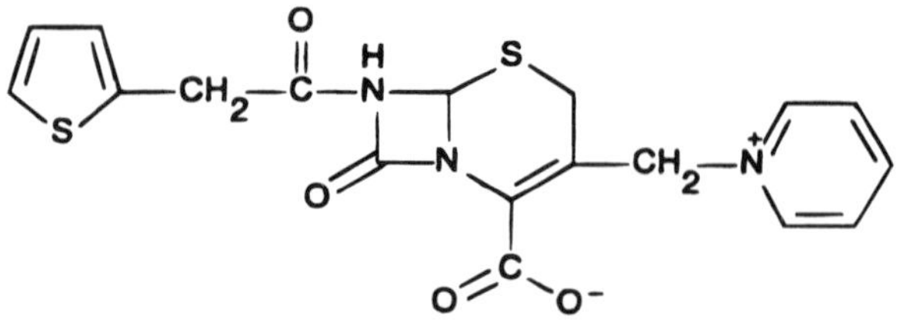

**cephaloridine**

When cytochrome P-450 is inhibited, the toxicity of cephaloridine is reduced in mice and rats. On the other hand, when cytochrome P-450 activity is stimulated by pretreatment of animals with phenobarbital, the toxicity of cephaloridine is increased in rabbits, but not in mice or rats. The formation of radicals and the resulting oxidative stress have been shown to play a role in the toxicity of cephaloridine. Reduced glutathione protects the cell against the toxic effects of cephaloridine. Animals which have received a diet low in selenium or vitamin E are more sensitive to the toxicity of cephaloridine. The selenium deficiency impairs the function of glutathione peroxidase, while vitamin E is able to make radicals innocuous.

ASSIGNMENT 24.9

What reaction is catalyzed by glutathione peroxidase?

## 4.9 CYCLOSPORIN A

This drug, which suppresses the action of the immune system, has made it possible to carry out organ transplants with a great chance of success. A disadvantage of cyclosporin A is its nephrotoxic side effect. All symptoms of renal injury have been observed in patients treated with this drug. The mechanism by which cyclosporin A exerts its toxic effects is only partly understood, since research is hampered by the very high doses that are required to induce the same effects in laboratory animals as those observed in patients. There are however indications that its toxic action is based on a reduced blood supply to the kidney and on changes in the endothelium.

## 4.10 NON-NARCOTIC ANALGESICS

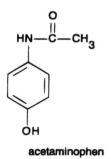

acetaminophen

When large doses of analgesics are taken for long periods of time, there is a risk of developing renal damage, as was described in the introduction to this study unit. Histologically, loss of the renal papilla, inflammation of the interstitial tissue accompanied by fibrosis and overall loss of shape of the nephron have been observed. Again, it is difficult to induce in laboratory animals the changes caused by these substances in man. Generally, the phenomena can only be observed in laboratory animals after administration of conventional analgesics in very high concentrations. This is why bromoethylamine is now used, which mimics the effects of analgesics in laboratory animals in a much more reproducible way. Researchers have not yet reached a consensus on the exact toxic effect of salicylic acid and phenacetin, or the metabolite, acetaminophen. Salicylic acid and other analgesics are effective inhibitors of prostaglandin synthetase; a lack of endogenous prostaglandins, which act as vasodilators, could lead to ischemia of the medulla and eventually to necrosis. Another possibility is that acetaminophen is activated in the kidney to form an intermediate which is able to form covalent bonds with renal macromolecules. It has been demonstrated that covalent binding of acetaminophen may take place under the influence of prostaglandin synthetase. The nephrotoxic action of acetaminophen is seen most clearly in patients suffering from hepatic insufficiency. Under normal circumstances, almost all the acetaminophen is made innocuous in the liver. The kidney is therefore usually exposed to only very low concentrations. However, in cases where the protective action of the liver is no longer present, the kidney is exposed to much higher concentrations.

## 4.11 MISCELLANEOUS

Some substances are not nephrotoxic but do influence the organic ion transport system of the kidney. One of these substances is the neuroleptic drug mepiperphenidol, which is used experimentally to inhibit organic cation transport.

H₃C

NCN
CH₃NHCNHCH₂CH₂SCH₂

**cimetidine**

Clinical studies have shown that cimetidine (the antagonist of the $H_2$ histamine receptor) inhibits excretion of the antiarrhythmic agent procainamide. This affects the plasma concentration of the latter substance. Further research has shown that cimetidine inhibits the transport of organic cations and can therefore be used to study their transport in human subjects.

## 5 Causes of cell death

It has been shown how the various substances discussed in section 4 are thought to cause their toxic effects. Some substances bind directly to thiol groups, while others form reactive intermediates which react with cellular macromolecules or cause lipid peroxidation.

Although consensus has by no means been reached on this point, and a large amount of research still remains to be performed before there is any clarity on the way in which a cell eventually dies, below it is attempted to give a survey, albeit a very modest one, of the various possibilities.

First the reactive intermediates will be discussed. These are substances whose chemical properties make them prone to react with other substances. The free radical, to begin with, is a molecule with an unpaired electron, which is suspected of playing a role in the toxicity of $CCl_4$ and $CHCl_3$. The existence of these molecules has been verified by means of electron spin resonance spectroscopy. Radicals have usually a very short life, because they are highly reactive and seek a partner for their unpaired electron, often an S or N atom. These atoms may be the S atom of a protein or glutathione molecule, or the N atom of the amino groups in proteins, DNA or RNA. A second type of reactive intermediate is the quinone, which is also thought to play a role in the toxicity of acetaminophen and cephaloridine. These reactive intermediates can form covalent bonds with cellular structures, but may also be converted into the parent compound again, in which case reactive oxygen species are produced in the process.

What enzyme system forms radicals and quinones?

*Thiol*

Specific nephrotoxic activity is also displayed by the reactive *thiol*, which is formed from cysteine conjugates by $\beta$-lyase.

The reactive oxygen compounds mentioned above, namely the $O_2^\bullet$ and the $OH^\bullet$ radicals, constitute a separate group of radicals. They may be formed in various ways: by cytochrome P-450-dependent reactions, by xanthineoxidase reactions and by prostaglandin synthetase reactions.

The oxygen radicals are highly reactive and may give rise to various toxic reactions. One of these is lipid peroxidation. This process eventually leads to degradation of unsaturated fatty acids in the cell membranes (such degradation may also be induced by other radicals, provided they are able to abstract hydrogen atoms). These changes in the composition of the cell membrane may disturb a variety of membrane-bound functions.

*Radical scavengers*

Protection against radicals and lipid peroxidation is offered by *radical scavengers*. Although vitamins E and C are also able to remove radicals, the most important radical scavenger is glutathione.

H₂NCHCH₂CH₂CONHCHCONHCH₂COOH
         |              |
        COOH          CH₂SH

**glutathione**

*Glutathione peroxidase*

Two glutathione molecules (GSH) are converted by *glutathione peroxidase* into the disulfide. The enzyme glutathione reductase subsequently converts the disulfide back into the original reduced GSH. This mechanism ensures a continuous regeneration of radical scavengers.

The number of radicals present may however be so great that the protective mechanisms are no longer able to cope, in which case covalent binding and lipid peroxidation may occur. This, of course, also happens if the cell comes into contact with substances against which the protective mechanisms are ineffective.

Binding to DNA will not have an immediate cytotoxic effect. Direct cytotoxic effects do occur when the function of a protein vital to the cell is interfered with.

To summarize, it can be said that toxic substances affect the structures of certain macromolecules in the cell, which leads to impairment or loss of function and eventually to cell death.

## 6 Summary

Both in function and in structure, the kidney is a very complex organ. Its primary function is the excretion of waste products. In addition, it plays an important role in maintaining homeostasis and produces a number of hormones and other endogenous substances. All this implies that intoxication of the kidney can have very complex consequences.

In this unit, the renal structure and function have been reviewed, and the sensitivity of the kidney to the action of toxic substances has been discussed.

The action of nephrotoxic substances may be direct or indirect. A direct action is exerted by substances which themselves have an acute effect on the functioning or structure of the kidney. Indirect action means that the toxic effect is brought about by a reactive metabolite formed in the kidney, or by an immune mechanism. The extent of renal injury due to direct toxic effects is dose-dependent. Such effects usually do not involve specific receptors, but are based on non-specific lesions of cellular structures. In the case of immunological reactions, the lesion does not occur until after a certain period of time. Such reactions are not dose-dependent. A specific immune-mediated disorder is immune complex glomerulonephritis, in which antigen-antibody complexes are accumulated in the glomerular capillaries, which secondarily leads to inflammatory reactions, resulting in damage to the glomerular membrane.

A number of methods by which renal injury can be detected has been reviewed. Histopathological methods after *in vivo* exposure were distinguished from *in vivo* clinical and experimental methods. Some experimental *in vitro* techniques were also briefly discussed.

Rather more attention was devoted to the mechanisms of nephrotoxicity of a number of xenobiotics, namely mercury, platinum, cadmium, haloalkanes, haloalkenes, herbicides, aminoglycosides, cephalosporins, cyclosporin A and non-narcotic analgesics such as acetylsalicylic acid and acetaminophen. The final section provided a brief survey of the causes of cell death.

SELF ASSESSMENT QUESTIONS

1 Table 24.4 shows the results of an experiment in which the nephrotoxicity of cephaloridine was studied in the rabbit. The rabbits were pretreated with 160 mg kg$^{-1}$ phenobarbital or a physiological salt solution (= control group) for a period of four days, followed by a single dose of cephaloridine.

TABLE 24.4
Effect of phenobarbital treatment on cephaloridine nephrotoxicity in rabbits

| Treatment | Cephaloridine mg kg$^{-1}$ | BUN (mg%) | PAH S/M | TEA S/M |
|-----------|----------------------------|-----------|---------|---------|
| control | 0 | 15 | 15 | 18 |
| phenobarbital | 0 | 17 | 19 | 18 |
| control | 150 | 32 | 9 | 14 |
| phenobarbital | 150 | 59 | 3* | 6* |
| control | 300 | 93 | 2 | 5 |
| phenobarbital | 300 | 146* | 1* | 1* |

*Significantly different from the control group receiving an equivalent dose of cephaloridine ($p < 0.05$).

Values measured were blood urea nitrogen (BUN), the accumulation of the organic anion para-aminohippuric acid (PAH) and the organic anion tetraethylammonium (TEA) in kidney slices.

What conclusion can be drawn from these results concerning the nephrotoxicity of cephaloridine in the rabbit?

2 Nephrotoxicity can be measured by means of *in vivo* and *in vitro* methods. Give examples of both and indicate the advantages and disadvantages they may be expected to have.

3 In renal physiology, extensive use is made of determination of clearance. What is meant by clearance? Indicate for each of the following substances what is the purpose/importance of measuring its clearance: creatinine, PAH, low-molecular-weight proteins, and high-molecular-weight proteins.

4 Proximal tubular cells are often the targets of toxic substances. The result may be a disturbance in physiological function, but also death of the cells. Fortunately, there is often regeneration of lost tubular epithelium. Explain how such regeneration can take place, what important structural difference the new tubular cells display in comparison with the original ones, and until what stage of damage regeneration can still take place.

5 Indicate for each of the following substances on which part of the kidney they exert their nephrotoxic effect:

- carbon tetrachloride
- cadmium
- acetylsalicylic acid.

6 Name some factors which contribute to the kidney's particular sensitivity to the toxic effect of a large number of xenobiotics.

## FEEDBACK

### 1 Answers to the assignments

24.1 No, the basement membrane also selects on the basis of the charge of the molecules (see also section 1.2.1).

24.2 Glutathione conjugates are formed in the liver and the kidney. Because the liver is the first to receive blood from the intestines, compounds which have entered the body via the oral route will first be conjugated in the liver. They are often lipophilic substances. Conjugation with glutathione makes them more water-soluble, as a result of which they are more easily transported by the blood. If such conjugation did not take place, these substances would remain in the body for a longer period of time.

24.3 The formation of hypotonic urine can occur because the wall of the collecting tubule is impermeable to water.

24.4 Low molecular weight, being a good substrate for one of the organic ion transport systems, and not being reabsorbed.

24.5 Creatinine is an endogenous substance which, unlike inulin, does not need to be introduced intravenously. A method which does not require intravenous administration is of course preferable to one which does.

24.6 The activity of the uptake mechanisms can be tested in this way, for example the uptake of glucose.

24.7 Proteinuria of low-molecular-weight proteins is an indication of damage to the tubular epithelium, in this case disturbed reabsorption of low-molecular-weight proteins. Excretion of high-molecular-weight proteins, in contrast, is indicative of damage to the glomerular membrane, since under normal circumstances this membrane does not allow any high-molecular-weight proteins to pass through.

24.8 The DCDFE glutathione conjugate is formed in the liver and subsequently converted into a mercapturic acid by a number of steps. It is then transported to the kidney, where it can be taken up via the organic ion transport system. The next step is deacetylation to the cysteine conjugate, which is converted by β-lyase into a reactive, toxic thiol. The toxicity of this thiol compound is based on its ability to bind to cellular macromolecules.

In contrast, haloalkanes arrive as such in the cell and are bioactivated into intermediates which would be able to bind to cellular macromolecules if they were to remain in that form. However, binding is prevented by the formation of a conjugate with glutathione. In this case, glutathione has a detoxicating effect. Theoretically, it is not impossible that the glutathione conjugate formed in this way is excreted by one cell and subsequently converted by another into a reactive thiol. However, no evidence of this mechanism has been found so far.

24.9 Glutathione peroxidase, a selenium-containing enzyme, catalyzes the detoxication of hydrogen peroxide.

## 2   Answers to the self assessment questions

1   From the results presented in the table, it may be concluded that cephaloridine inhibits the active reabsorption of organic anions (PAH) as well as that of organic cations (TEA). The excretion of urea is also blocked, which can be deduced from the increased BUN level. The effects in the rabbit are caused by the presence of a reactive intermediate formed by the cytochrome

P-450 enzyme system. This can be deduced from the fact that the above effects are observed only in animals treated with phenobarbital.

2 Table 24.5 shows a number of *in vivo* and *in vitro* test methods with their respective advantages and disadvantages. These advantages and disadvantages are mainly connected with how closely the situation in the living organism is approached (quite closely with *in vivo* methods) and whether a method provides information on the way in which a substance 'attacks' the cell (more information obtained from isolated cell cultures).

3 Clearance is the volume of plasma from which a particular substance is removed entirely in a certain amount of time. Creatinine is used to determine the glomerular filtration rate. Determining the clearance of para-aminohippuric acid gives an indication of the active secretory function of the kidney. Proteins of low molecular weight are filtered through the glomerulus quite easily and almost totally; their clearance may change as a result of changes in proximal tubular function, since they are reabsorbed almost entirely in the proximal tubule. If high-molecular-weight proteins are found in the urine, this indicates that the glomerular membrane has been damaged.

4 Lost tubular cells can be replaced by division of adjacent, surviving tubular cells. Structurally, these new cells are different from the original ones in that they hardly have a brush border. Regeneration can take place as long as the basement membrane underneath the tubular cells has not been damaged.

TABLE 24.5

Comparison of some *in vivo* and *in vitro* methods which may be applied in nephrotoxicity research

| Methods | Effects | Advantages/disadvantages |
|---|---|---|
| *in vivo:* | | |
| – microscopy | morphological changes | naturalistic effect; provides little or no information on mechanism of action |
| – electron microscopy | intracellular structural changes | ditto |
| – urinary determinations | functional changes | ditto |
| – plasma determinations | ditto | ditto |
| *in vitro:* | | |
| – isolated cell cultures | formation of metabolites, uptake of substances | less realistic; metabolites formed in other organs are absent; physiological regulation mechanisms are lacking |
| – kidney slices | active or passive uptake of substances, formation of metabolites etc. | more naturalistic than cell cultures, but 'less true to life' than *in vivo* experiments, minor physiological regulating mechanisms present, but major (blood, hormones, nervous system) absent |
| – organ perfusion techniques* | histological toxicity, metabolism, kinetics | with regard to naturalistic image: in between *in vivo* experiments and kidney slices |

*Organ perfusion is discussed in detail in Study unit 25.

5    Carbon tetrachloride probably exerts its nephrotoxic effect via reactive intermediates which form covalent bonds with structures of the proximal tubular cell. Cadmium binds to a metallothionein and is taken up into the proximal tubular cell in that form. Once inside the cell, the metallothionein is removed. The free cadmium then causes cytotoxicity because it engages the binding sites of other metal ions in enzymes and other proteins. Renal cytotoxicity caused by acetylsalicylic acid is probably due, on the one hand, to the action of reactive metabolites, and on the other to inhibition of prostaglandin synthesis, which may give rise to vasoconstriction, resulting in local ischemia.

6    Factors contributing to the kidney's sensitivity to the action of toxic chemicals are the following:

- high degree of perfusion
- concentration of chemicals in the tubule
- renal transport of chemicals in the tubular cells
- biotransformation of parent compound into toxic metabolites.

# Contents Study unit 25
# Organ perfusion techniques: in vitro toxicity testing

0-8493-9232-2/96/$0.00 + $.50

# Organ perfusion techniques: in vitro toxicity testing

*A. Sj. Koster*

INTRODUCTION

Several experimental methods can be used to explain the mechanisms of toxicity in various organs (target organ toxicity). Some examples of organ-directed toxicity are provided in Table 25.1. The presence of biotransformation enzymes in the organ concerned plays an important role in the induction of these effects. This is one reason why interest in extrahepatic metabolism has increased considerably in recent years. Research focusing on metabolism in subcellular fractions only is not sufficient to obtain a complete insight into the mechanisms involved in target organ toxicity.

> Why do you think this is the case? Give as many reasons as you can.

Besides metabolism other factors also play a role, such as local accumulation, transport of metabolites, local differences in covalent binding and organ-specific biochemical and physiological characteristics. There are, on the one hand, examples of metabolic activation that take place selectively in a certain organ. On the other hand, there are substances that can be metabolized in several organs, while they in combination with other factors cause toxicity in only one of them. An example of the first type of activation is the nephrotoxicity of hexachlorobutadiene; an example of the second is the pulmonary toxicity of paraquat. Hexachlorobutadiene is converted in the liver to a glutathione conjugate, which—via excretion in the bile and reabsorption in the intestine—is converted to a cysteine conjugate (by $\gamma$-glutamyltranspeptidase and aminopeptidase). The presence of C-S-lyase in the kidney leads to selective formation of a toxic thiol from the cysteine conjugate in that organ. Paraquat can undergo redox cycling in many organs, accompanied by the formation of reactive oxygen species, although it induces toxicity only in the lung because that is where accumulation occurs. This effect is reinforced by the high partial pressure of oxygen in the lung.

From the above examples it will be clear that a combination of various techniques needs to be used to explain the toxicity mechanisms of foreign compounds. Many techniques at various levels of integration can be applied (see Figure 25.1), each with its own advantages and limitations. The present study unit devotes particular attention to the possible applications of organ perfusion systems in toxicology.

TABLE 25.1

Examples of organ-specific bioactivation and toxicity

| Organ | Substance | Toxicity | Mechanism of bioactivation (enzyme involved) |
|---|---|---|---|
| liver | bromobenzene | centrilobular necrosis | epoxidation (cytochrome P-450) |
| | chloroform | centrilobular necrosis | phosgene formation (cytochrome P-450) |
| | aflatoxin | formation of hepatic tumors | epoxidation (cytochrome P-450) |
| lung | paraquat | pulmonary fibrosis | radical formation by redox cycling (NADPH-cyt. P-450-reductase) |
| | 4-ipomeanol | necrosis of Clara cells | epoxidation? (cytochrome P-450) |
| intestine | dimethylhydrazine | colon cancer | demethylation (cytochrome P-450) |
| | N-nitrosomethyl-benzylamine | formation of esophageal tumors | hydroxylation (cytochrome P-450) |
| kidney | cephaloridine | proximal tubular necrosis | accumulation + radical formation? |
| | hexachlorobutadiene | proximal tubular necrosis | cleavage of the cysteine conjugate (C-S-lyase) |

The main advantage of organ perfusion studies is that they offer the possibility of studying local processes under circumstances that approach the *in vivo* situation as closely as possible, without any interaction with other organs or influence from systemic factors (hormones, nervous system).

Why would this be an advantage?

*In vivo*, the processes in an organ are undoubtedly influenced by hormones (e.g. stimulation of cell metabolism) or the nervous system (e.g. vasodilatation or vasoconstriction). However, these effects are difficult to measure or control *in vivo*, but can be manipulated in perfusion systems. This offers the possibility of contributing to our knowledge of the mechanisms of toxicity. Potential applications are in the following three areas:

- *studying local toxicity*, e.g., covalent binding and impaired organ functions.
- *studying local metabolism of xenobiotics, possibly in combination with covalent binding and toxicity*. Uptake, conversion and release of metabolites in the organ concerned can be studied in detail.
- *studying the kinetics of local processes*, for example effects on toxicity and metabolism through changes in blood flow, protein binding and interaction with other compounds.

The present study unit discusses several examples of each of the three areas mentioned. To start with, section 1 deals with the physiological requirements that an organ perfusion system has to meet. The examples given are taken from perfusion studies with the liver, lung, kidney and intestine.

LEARNING OBJECTIVES

After having studied this unit, you should be able to:

— explain the following concepts: ischemia, edema, carbogen, single-pass perfusion, target organ, induction, elimination, excretion, absorption, clearance, extraction ratio, well-stirred model, intrinsic clearance
— give examples of substances that are metabolized in the intestine, kidney or lung

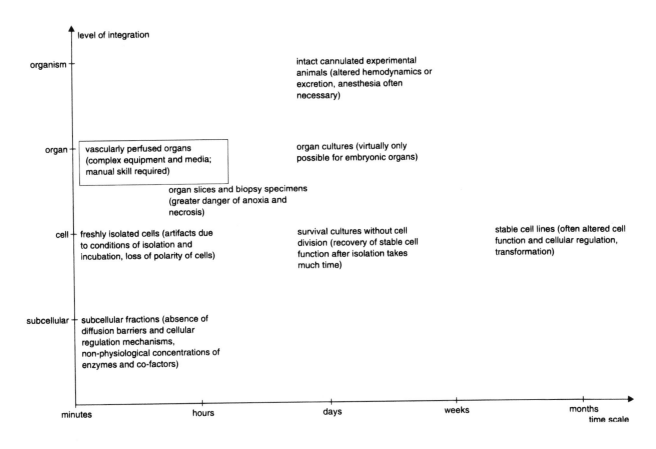

FIGURE 25.1
Model systems for the study of organ functions
The major limitations of each system are presented.

— give examples of biotransformation reactions in intestinal, renal and pulmonary tissue
— indicate the minimum requirements that a perfusion medium for an isolated organ should meet
— calculate the amount of oxygen per unit of time that a particular perfusion medium can supply under specified conditions of gas exchange and perfusion
— explain why organ perfusion systems are less suitable for direct measurement of acute toxicity
— name the ways in which biotransformation in isolated organs may differ from that in isolated cells or cell homogenates
— explain why induction of biotransformation enzymes cannot be demonstrated by exposure of a perfused organ to the inducer
— calculate the elimination rate, clearance and extraction ratio of a substance in a particular organ (at known inflow concentration, outflow concentration and perfusion rate)
— predict how the elimination rate, clearance and extraction ratio of a substance in a certain organ and under known conditions will change if either the concentration supplied or the flow is changed and/or in the case of enzyme induction or inhibition.

*Study hints*

The present study unit is in fact an integrative unit. It calls upon the subject matter of many of the preceding units to explain techniques applied in toxicology and pharmacology. You should try to understand the possibilities and limitations of the technique, what parameters are studied and what conclusions can be drawn. The study load for this unit should be between 3 and 4 hours.

## STUDY CORE

### 1    Physiological requirements

An important condition for the meaningful use of organ perfusion is that the function of the isolated organ should resemble that in the *in vivo* situation as closely as possible. Only if that condition is fulfilled qualitatively and quantitatively reliable data can be obtained, which can be extrapolated directly to the *in vivo* situation. This means that in the development stage the function of the isolated organ under experimental circumstances should be carefully defined and, if possible, compared directly with data obtained *in vivo*. The latter data will often be taken from the literature.

It is advisable to check several functional parameters from time to time, even during routine use of an organ perfusion system once it has been developed. Developing and defining an organ perfusion system is time-consuming, taking 6 months to a year. This is so, even when similar systems have been described in the literature. Increasing manual skill, routine and standardization normally lead to increased reproducibility of the experimental results.

In the following, a number of physiological requirements which an organ perfusion system should meet will be discussed. It should be borne in mind that the *in vivo* situation can only be approximated; to achieve complete similarity in all aspects is impossible and usually not even usefull. However, one should be aware which factors may have a relatively major influence on the process to be studied. It is important that this is studied in the development stage. An immediate advantage of organ perfusion systems is that these factors can be varied under carefully controlled circumstances. Changes in the effects of the autonomic nervous system and of hormones in the blood are not present in an isolated organ (unless blood is used as the perfusion medium; see below). The possibility of controlling and manipulating the experimental parameters is the most important feature of organ perfusion.

> ASSIGNMENT   25.1
>
> Make a list of the experimental parameters that can be varied in organ perfusion studies. If necessary, add to your list while reading the rest of this section.

Stability during the experimental period is an important condition for meaningful application of organ perfusion. Although there are examples of organs being used for 5–10 hours, organ perfusion is normally restricted to 1 or 2 hours.

*Oxygen*          *Supply of sufficient oxygen* is a prerequisite for all isolated organs. This is a general requirement since insufficient oxygen supply (hypoxia or ischemia) rapidly leads to disturbed organ function. This aspect will be discussed in more detail. Some standard values for blood flow parameters in the liver, lung, intestine and kidney of the rat are listed in Table 25.2. Based on the difference in arterial and venous partial oxygen pressure, the oxygen dissociation curve (see

Figure 25.2) and the blood flow rate, it is possible to calculate the oxygen consumption of the organs.

1 torr = 1 mm Hg = 133.322 Pa
(= 1/760 atm)

Values normally measured *in vivo* are given in Table 25.2. The lung has a special position in that the oxygen required for its cellular metabolism is obtained directly from the alveolar air. Under *in vivo* circumstances, the organs have at their disposal several mechanisms by which they can adapt the oxygen availability to their demand. This process of adaptation is called *autoregulation*. Vasodilatation and the factors determining the shape of the oxygen dissociation curve play a role in this process. In addition, the autonomic nervous system plays an important role in determining the blood supply to the tissues. When an organ is isolated, some of these regulatory mechanisms are maintained, such as vasodilatation.

*Autoregulation*

ASSIGNMENT  25.2

Indicate by which regulatory mechanisms the body can adapt the oxygen supply to the tissues to their oxygen demand.

In organ perfusion systems, blood is not normally used as the perfusion medium (see below). This has important consequences for the possibility of supplying enough oxygen per unit of time. The most commonly used *perfusion medium*, Krebs-Ringer bicarbonate buffer, if gassed with air, can contain only 5 $\mu l$ oxygen per ml (see Figure 25.2). It will be obvious that this is insufficient, at normal perfusion flow, to supply enough oxygen to the organs listed in Table 25.2. Under these circumstances, perfusion rapidly leads to impaired organ function as a result of hypoxia, which manifests itself in the *formation of edema* (due to increased capillary permeability) and cell death. The development of edema can be demonstrated by measuring the dry weight and the wet weight of the organ. Cell death can be quantified by monitoring the appearance of cellular enzymes in the perfusion medium (e.g. lactic dehydrogenase (LDH), or alanine aminotransferase (ALT). A sufficient oxygen supply can be guaranteed by means of a high perfusion flow and by gassing the medium with carbogen (a mixture of 95% $O_2$ and 5% $CO_2$). Another

TABLE  25.2
Blood flow/perfusion and oxygen consumption of liver, lung, intestine and kidney of the rat *in vivo* and in organ perfusion

|  | parameter (dimension) | liver | lung | intestine | kidney |
|---|---|---|---|---|---|
| in vivo | blood flow (ml min$^{-1}$) | 13–20 | 55–70 | 5–8 | 4–6 |
|  | blood pressure S/D (torr) | 150/100 | 25/10 | 150/100 | 150/100 |
|  | pO$_2$-arterial (torr) | 95 | 40 | 95 | 95 |
|  | pO$_2$-venous (torr) | 40 | 100 | 50 | 70 |
|  | O$_2$.consumption ($\mu l$ min$^{-1}$) | 500–800 | from air | 40–160 | 100–200 |
| In perfusion | perfusion flow (ml min$^{-1}$) | 30–50 | 50 | 6 | 20–35 |
|  | perfusion pressure (torr) | 100–120 | 10–20 | 100–120 | 100–120 |
|  | pO$_2$-arterial (torr) | 600 | 600 | 400 | 600 |
|  | pO$_2$-venous (torr) | 200 | ? | 180 | 400 |
|  | max. O$_2$-supply* ($\mu l$ min$^{-1}$) | 380–630 | ? | 120** | 120–220 |

These values are indications of the most common values measured for the various organs in a rat of 250 to 300 g. The data provided for the kidney apply to a single kidney. The values measured in organ perfusion may differ greatly, depending on the set-up, method of gassing, etc.

S = systolic

D = diastolic

* Calculated from pO$_2$-arterial, pO$_2$-venous and perfusion flow.

** With 20% FC-43 emulsion in KRB; other figures apply to KRB without erythrocytes or oxygen carrier.

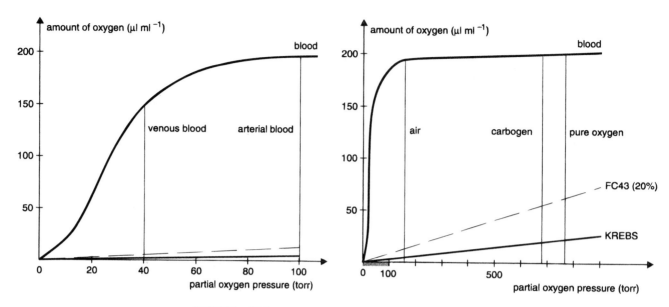

FIGURE 25.2

Oxygen dissociation curves for blood (hematocrit = 0.45), Krebs buffer (KRB) and 20% fluorocarbon emulsion at 37° C, pH = 7.4 and $pCO_2$ = 20 torr

possibility is to add *oxygen carriers* to the medium, for example fluorocarbon emulsions such as FC43. FC43 can carry three times as much oxygen per ml as Krebs-Ringer bicarbonate buffer (see Figure 25.2). Yet another possibility is to add erythrocytes; for this, washed bovine erythrocytes (from a slaughter–house) or outdated human erythrocytes (from a blood bank) are normally used.

ASSIGNMENT 25.3

Calculate the minimum perfusion flow required to supply 1 ml $O_2$ per minute to a perfused organ. Do this for studies in which blood, Krebs-Ringer bicarbonate buffer and a 20% FC emulsion, respectively, are used as perfusion mediums, all of them gassed with carbogen.

Liver and kidney perfusion studies are normally carried out with Krebs-Ringer bicarbonate buffer, gassed with 5% carbon dioxide in oxygen, at a perfusion flow higher than normal (see Table 25.2). In the isolated perfused intestine, a fluorocarbon emulsion is used, because Krebs-Ringer bicarbonate buffer cannot supply sufficient oxygen at the flow applied. In the perfused lung, sufficient oxygen supply is ensured by ventilation of the lung with air (or sometimes with carbogen) via the trachea.

*Oxygen consumption*      The *oxygen consumption* of an isolated organ is an important functional parameter. Figure 25.3 shows that a normal oxygen consumption and a normal cellular ATP level can be achieved in different ways. If the perfusion medium is Krebs-Ringer bicarbonate buffer, a flow of at least 30 ml per min is required; if a fluorocarbon emulsion is used or if erythrocytes are added, a lower flow of 20 ml per min is sufficient.

ASSIGNMENT 25.4

Figure 25.3 also shows that a further increase in flow does not lead to a further increase in oxygen consumption. Explain why this is the case.

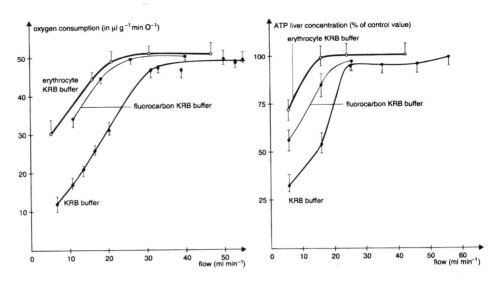

FIGURE 25.3

Oxygen consumption (left) and cellular ATP concentration (right) of perfused livers of the rat. The average weight of the livers is 12 grams.

It appears that at higher flows, the oxygen consumption is no longer restricted by the supply of oxygen but by cellular metabolism. In other words, at higher perfusion rates the liver uses approximately 0.6 ml oxygen per minute, irrespective of the amount supplied. As a result, the ATP level is kept at its normal value (see Figure 25.3). This is an important indication of normal hepatic function. However, it should be realized that although the oxygen supply and consumption in isolated organs correspond with those *in vivo* the partial pressure of oxygen at which this occurs is higher than in the physiological situation. The effects of this on biotransformation and on toxicity have hardly been studied. In general, however, this does not seem to lead to obvious problems.

*Parameters for the functional state*

As stated above, oxygen consumption, edema formation and leakage of cellular enzymes can be used as *parameters for the functional state* of the perfused organ. Various biochemical parameters can be used, such as ATP level, glucose consumption and lactate/pyruvate ratios. Morphological parameters, such as histological and electron-microscopic integrity of the tissue, can also be used to characterize an organ perfusion system. In addition to these general features, organ-specific parameters can be used to assess the functional state of the organ. To that end, active, i.e. ATP-dependent, transport functions are often used: biliary excretion in the perfused liver, absorption of [3]H-methylglucose in the perfused intestine and $Na^+$ or glucose reabsorption in the perfused kidney.

*Composition of the perfusion medium*

The *composition of the perfusion medium* is very important for success of the perfusion. *Blood* is hardly ever used, because its application causes great practical problems. The composition of blood is largely unknown and/or variable (in particular as regards the presence of proteins, hormones, neurotransmitters, vitamins and possibly xenobiotics) and therefore does not meet the requirement of controllability. In addition, blood often causes analytical problems when measuring foreign compounds and their metabolites. Finally, the use of blood would require many donor animals for each experiment (at least 8 for one liver perfusion). Some of these objections also apply to addition of erythrocytes (see above).

*Artificial media*

This is why there is a strong preference for completely *artificial media*, which contain the following components: electrolytes, buffer, an energy source, an oncotic agent, other added substances and sometimes an oxygen carrier. The Krebs-Ringer bicarbonate buffer or a variant of it normally forms the basis for the medium. The salt solution is *isotonic* with the tissues (approximately 300 mOsmol) and contains the ions normally present in the blood plasma: $Na^+$, $K^+$, $Mg^{2+}$, $Ca^{2+}$, $Cl^-$, $HPO_4^{2-}$, $SO_4^{2-}$, $HCO_3^-$. The bicarbonate, together with the $CO_2$ from carbogen, forms a *buffer system* for maintaining the pH at 7.4. Glucose and usually certain amino acids are present as *energy sources*. An *oncotic agent* guarantees the correct *colloid osmotic pressure* to prevent the formation of edema. Bovine serum albumin (BSA), dextran or various forms of modified starch are commonly used. Various other substances, such as anticoagulants, antibiotics, hormones, vitamins and trace elements have been added (sometimes up to 100 different substances). The addition of such large numbers of substances seems to be of limited use, unless an obvious functional relationship with the process to be studied has been established. An example of a useful perfusion medium for the kidney is described in Table 25.3.

*Oncotic agent*

*Isolation technique*

The last aspect, or rather the first, with which one is confronted in organ perfusion, is the *isolation technique*. After an experimental animal has been anesthetized, cannulae are inserted (for example into the common bile duct for liver perfusion, into the ureter for perfusion of the kidney and into the trachea for perfusion of the lung). The efferent blood vessels can also be cannulated. Cannulating the afferent arteries is the crucial moment that determines the success of the perfusion, because at this point the supply of oxygenated blood is briefly interrupted (ischemic period). The interruption in the oxygen supply should be as short as possible. It should certainly be less than 1 minute to prevent irreversible damage to the organ. Immediately after fixing the arterial cannula, perfusion is started. After an initial period in which the blood is rinsed out of the organ, the perfusate flowing out of the organ is usually returned to the arterial cannula. This is called *recirculating perfusion*. Another technique is *"single-pass"* perfusion, in which the perfusate passes through the organ only once.

*Constant flow or constant pressure*

Perfusion can be carried out at *constant flow* or at *constant pressure*. In the former, the flow is determined by a pump (see Figure 25.4). The pressure may be used as a functional parameter. In the latter, the pressure is determined by the difference in height between the reservoir holding the supply of perfusion medium

TABLE 25.3
Composition of a kidney perfusion medium

|  | component | concentration | |
|---|---|---|---|
| electrolytes | NaCl | 115 | mM |
| | KCl | 5.4 | mM |
| | $MgSO_4$ | 2.4 | mM |
| | $CaCl_2$ | 3.0 | mM |
| buffer | $NaH_2PO_4$ | 1.5 | mM |
| | $NaHCO_3$ | 25 | mM |
| energy source | glucose | 5 | mM |
| | glutamine | 2 | mM |
| oncotic agent | bovine serum albumin | 60 | $g^{-1}$ |
| other additions | alanine | 2 | mM |
| | glutathione | 2 | mM |

and the organ, while the flow is the functional parameter. The complete set-up is normally kept in a cabinet at 37°C.

Figure 25.4 shows a kidney perfusion experiment. The wash-out system is used to rinse out the blood during isolation. A recirculating system is then applied by which the perfusate is pumped through a 'bubble trap' into the cannula in the renal artery. The bubble trap serves to prevent any air bubbles blocking the vascular bed of the kidney. The perfusate flows out of the renal vein and is returned to the reservoir. The ureter is cannulated so that the urine formed can be collected and sampled. The values of some functional parameters with respect to duration of perfusion are provided in Table 25.4. Deteriorating of the functional parameters during perfusion is generally observed. Evaluating the acceptability of these changes and comparing them with recent data from the literature are important aspects of working with organ perfusion systems.

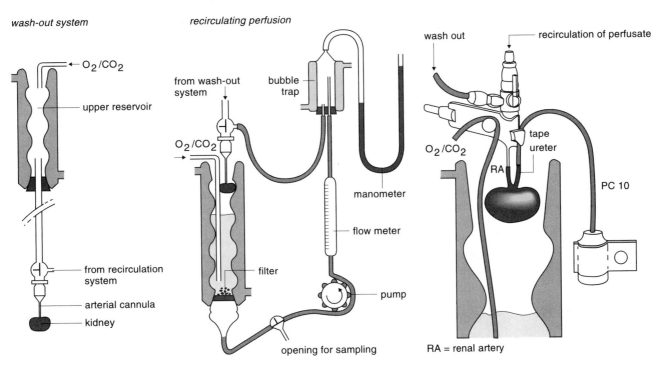

FIGURE 25.4
Perfusion of a kidney during washing out of the blood (left) and during recirculating perfusion (center)
A detail of the equipment is shown on the right.

TABLE 25.4
Functional parameters of an isolated perfused kidney

| Time | Reabsorption of glucose (%) | Glomerular filtration ($\mu l\ min^{-1}$) | Production of urine ($\mu l\ min^{-1}$) |
|---|---|---|---|
| 0–10 min | 94.5 ± 3.1 | 424 ± 42 | 73 ± 10 |
| 30–40 min | 94.1 ± 2.8 | 351 ± 35 | 64 ± 9 |
| 70–80 min | 91.5 ± 4.3 | 241 ± 36 | 37 ± 6 |

The figures show the average values ± SEM from 12 experiments.

ASSIGNMENT 25.5

Explain what may be the cause or causes of the changes in renal function shown in Table 25.4.

*Summary*

The supply of oxygen and nutrients for cell metabolism is essential for proper functioning of an isolated organ. The composition of the perfusion medium and the preparation of the organ should be optimized and checked for each individual case. Criteria which can be used are structural integrity (histological, electron-microscopic) and various organ-specific physiological and/or biochemical processes. Even under ideal circumstances, a gradual loss of organ function will occur during a perfusion experiment.

## 2 Toxicity in organ perfusion

It is sometimes possible to study the occurrence of *acute toxicity* in isolated organs. A precondition for this is that the toxicity occurs rapidly enough, in at most a few hours, and that the toxic effect is obvious enough not to be confused with the gradual deterioration in function that normally occurs in organ perfusion. So far, this approach has been used only sporadically, probably because this combination of preconditions is rarely met. In these cases, it is easier to examine acute toxicity in isolated cells. Cytotoxicity parameters include cell death, which can be established by LDH leakage or trypan blue exclusion, or indirect factors such as GSH depletion. However, it does seem likely that cell death is preceded

*Disturbance of normal cell function*

by a *disturbance of normal cell function*. Functional disturbances can be expected to occur at concentrations of the toxic substance that do not cause cell death. In such cases, the use of organ perfusion offers possibilities. An example is the use of a kidney perfusion system to study the nephrotoxicity of *gentamicin* and *cephaloridine*.

*Perfusion of the kidney*
*Accumulation*

Gentamicin and cephaloridine cause proximal tubular necrosis. For both substances, *accumulation* in the tubular cells has been shown to play an important part in their toxicity. Accumulation of cephaloridine is two to twenty-fold (relative to the perfusion medium; depending on species and experimental conditions) and disturbs the transport capacity of the tubular cells by a mechanism that is not entirely elucidated. This reduces the active transport of urea and other substances (for example para-aminohippuric acid). Eventually, cell death (necrosis) occurs. Accumulation of gentamicin in the tubular cells (5 to 10-fold relative to the perfusion medium) mainly causes a disturbance in reabsorption of low molecular weight proteins such as lysozyme; $Na^+$ reabsorption and $K^+$ excretion are also disturbed. In addition, gentamicin causes a reduction in glomerular filtration. The dose-dependent disturbance of the lysozyme reabsorption in the perfused kidney is shown in Figure 25.5.

The perfused kidney has also been used to study the mechanism underlying the accumulation of gentamicin and cephaloridine in the proximal tubular cells. To this end, use is made of the possibility of suppressing glomerular filtration in an isolated, perfused kidney. Reducing the perfusion pressure and increasing the colloid osmotic pressure by adding extra albumin to the perfusion medium cause glomerular filtration to stop (effective filtration pressure = perfusion pressure – osmotic pressure). Under these circumstances, substances present in the perfusion medium no longer enter the glomerular filtrate, so that they can no longer be reabsorbed via this route.

In a rat kidney perfused in the normal way, both gentamicin (5.5-fold) and cephaloridine (1.7-fold) are concentrated (see Figure 25.6, open bars). In a non-

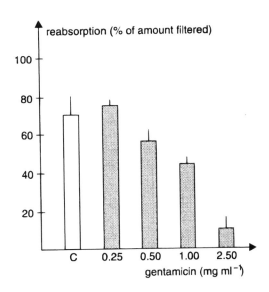

FIGURE 25.5
Influence of gentamicin on the reabsorption of lysozyme in the isolated perfused kidney of the rat
C = control

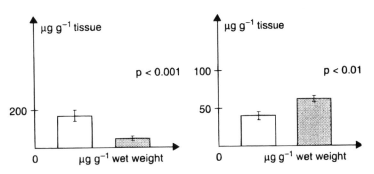

FIGURE 25.6
Accumulation of gentamicin (left) and cephaloridine (right) in the proximal tubules of filtering (open bars) and non-filtering (gray bars) isolated rat kidneys

filtering kidney (Figure 25.6, grey bars), the accumulation of gentamicin is greatly decreased (1.0-fold), while that of cephaloridine is in fact increased (2.7-fold). From these experiments it was concluded that accumulation of gentamicin takes place via reabsorption from the glomerular filtrate (via the brush border membrane), while cephaloridine is absorbed from the perfusion medium, via the basolateral membrane (see Figure 25.7). This conclusion is confirmed by the observation that accumulation and toxicity of cephaloridine can be prevented by simultaneous administration of probenecid, whereas that of gentamicin can not. Probenecid inhibits the absorption of anions via the basolateral membrane.

When a relationship between the eventual occurrence of toxicity and a preceding *biochemical change* in the cell has been established, this biochemical change (a so-called early indication of toxicity) can also be used in organ perfusions as a measure for the occurrence of toxicity.

*Perfusion of the lung*

An example is the marked decrease in reduced glutathione (GSH) level and the release of oxidized glutathione (GSSG) in the perfused lung under the influence of *nitrofurantoin*. Furthermore, by simultaneously measuring GSSG, it is possible to distinguish between toxicity caused by the formation of a covalently binding

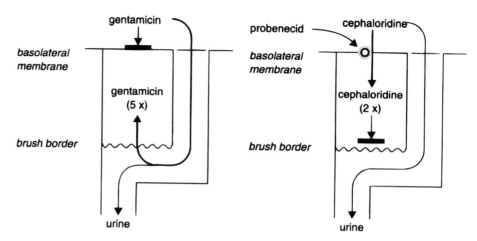

FIGURE 25.7
Accumulation of gentamicin and cephaloridine in proximal tubular cells

intermediate and toxicity caused by redox cycling. In the latter case, GSH will be oxidized to an equivalent amount of GSSG (in other words, the total amount of glutathione remains the same), while in the former case the total amount of glutathione will decrease. On administration of 420 $\mu$M nitrofurantoin to the perfused rabbit lung, the GSH level had dropped considerably after 30 minutes (from 11.5 to 7.6 $\mu$g per mg protein) and that of GSSG was found to have risen greatly (from 0.09 to 3.17 $\mu$g per mg protein). The total amount of glutathione remained unchanged. From this it was concluded that nitrofurantoin causes pulmonary toxicity via redox cycling. However, it should be noted that these changes were measured in the absence of any other indications of toxicity, such as LDH leakage and edema formation (the real parameters of toxicity).

ASSIGNMENT 25.6

Indicate why it is useful to use the levels of GSH and GSSG as an early indication of toxicity.

*Summary*

A change in organ-specific functions or biochemical parameters resulting from toxicity can be measured in isolated organs. This change must be sufficiently marked or occur rapidly enough to be distinguished from the normal deterioration of organ function during perfusion. So far, this method has only been used infrequently.

## 3   Metabolism in organ perfusion

In the development of target organ toxicity, a complex combination of metabolism, transport of metabolites, reabsorption and further metabolism often plays a role. To clarify the importance of various organs in this process, it is often necessary to use a *combination of techniques*: *in vivo* experiments, isolated cells and subcellular fractions. In this way, it is possible, to demonstrate that damage to the vascular endothelium in the lung induced by monocrotaline is not caused by bioactivation in the vascular tissue itself but by metabolism in the liver, followed by transport of a relatively stable metabolite to the lung. Similarly, it has been shown that the pulmonary toxicity of *4-ipomeanol* is caused by local formation of a reactive metabolite. A final example is the induction of urinary bladder tumors by a metabolite of 2-naphthylamine formed in the liver and excreted

*Combination of techniques*

768

via the kidney. This metabolite is unstable in the acid environment of the bladder and is hydrolyzed to the nitrenium ion of 2-naphthylamine. Covalent binding to DNA eventually leads to the development of a tumor. Isolated perfused organs can be very useful in elucidating the role played by various organs in these processes. Because in an isolated organ all diffusion barriers, intracellular enzyme and co-factor concentrations and transport functions are intact, a perfused organ gives a much more faithful representation of reality *in vivo* than isolated cells or subcellular fractions (see Figure 25.1). The formation and release of metabolites can be studied in detail, while any covalent binding to DNA, RNA or proteins can be studied in parallel experiments. It is also possible to add certain metabolites to the perfusion medium.

In the following, an example dealing with the metabolism of benzo[*a*]pyrene and benzo[*a*]pyrene-4,5-epoxide in the perfused liver and lung will be elaborated.

*Benzo[a]pyrene metabolism*

The metabolism of benzo[*a*]pyrene is very complicated (see Figure 25.8). Oxidation by cytochrome P-450 leads to the formation of epoxides, which are converted to phenols or dihydrodiols by spontaneous rearrangement or epoxide hydrolase-mediated hydrolysis. In addition, glutathione conjugates may be formed. Phenols and diols are metabolized further to glucuronides and/or sulfate conjugates. The diols can be converted again by cytochrome P-450. The diolepoxides formed can undergo hydrolysis into tetrols. The diolepoxides, and in particular the $7\beta$, $8\alpha$-dihydroxy-$9\alpha$, $10\alpha$-epoxide, are responsible for DNA adduct formation (see Figure 25.8), ultimately leading to cancer.

ASSIGNMENT 25.7

Draw the structural formulae of the intermediates that give rise to the above benzo[*a*]pyrene-DNA adduct.

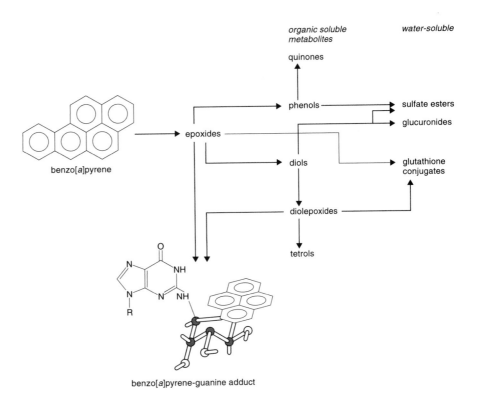

benzo[*a*]pyrene-guanine adduct

FIGURE 25.8
Metabolism and DNA adduct formation of benzo[*a*]pyrene

Although benzo[a]pyrene is metabolized in the *liver* to a significant extent, the liver is not the primary target organ of benzo[a]pyrene toxicity. It may happen, therefore, that metabolites formed in the liver eventually give rise to toxicity in other organs, possibly after further metabolism. Organ perfusions are particularly well suited to answer such questions.

Figure 25.9 shows the result of an experiment in which the bile produced by an isolated perfused liver was examined for the presence of any mutagenic benzo[a]pyrene metabolites. Mutagenic activity was examined by means of the Ames test after treatment of the bile samples with β-glucuronidase. Normally, the bile does not contain any mutagenic component; however, as soon as benzo[a]pyrene is added to the perfusate, mutagenic substances start to appear in the bile.

> What is the basis for the conclusion that the mutagenicity
> observed is caused by these metabolites?

Mutagenicity can only be demonstrated after treatment of the bile with β-glucuronidase. Therefore, the conclusion is that the glucuronides themselves are not mutagenic, but that the mutagenicity is caused by the hydrolysis products. These products are probably phenols or dihydrodiols. It should be noted that cleavage of the glucuronides may also take place *in vivo* by the glucuronidase from the intestinal wall or from the intestinal flora. Potentially mutagenic metabolites also appear in the perfusate of the isolated perfused liver (see Figure 25.10).

In this case, cleavage by β-glucuronidase is not necessary to demonstrate mutagenicity by means of the Ames test. Further metabolism by cytochrome P-450 is, however, necessary. On addition of liver homogenate and several co-factors, the S9 fraction, to the perfusate samples in the Ames test, this metabolic activation can take place *in vitro*. From this, it may be concluded that the liver releases benzo[a]pyrene metabolites into the perfusate, which could be metabolized further into mutagenic compounds in other organs. These are probably a number of different diols. If glucuronidation in the perfused liver is inhibited by salicylamide (see Figure 25.10, center), the mutagenicity of the perfusate samples is clearly higher. This finding is in accordance with the fact that under these circumstances, the concentration of diols (in particular 4,5-diol and 7,8-diol) in the perfusate is greatly increased. Glucuronidation thus clearly has a protective function.

The results in Figure 25.9 also lead to the conclusion that, under the circumstances of the study, benzo[a]pyrene has no *direct toxic effect on the liver*. This conclusion is based on the observation that the oxygen consumption of the liver during benzo[a]pyrene perfusion remains constant. The increase in oxygen consumption caused by the vehicle (0.15% albumin) results from metabolic oxidation of fatty acids bound to the albumin. Addition of albumin is necessary to keep benzo[a]pyrene in solution. The bile flow slowly decreases during the experiment because no bile salts have been added to the perfusate. This decrease cannot therefore be used as an indicator of toxicity.

The metabolism of benzo[a]pyrene and the benzo[a]pyrene-4,5-epoxide has also been studied in the *isolated perfused lung*. If the epoxide is added to the perfusate, the 4,5-diol and two thio-ether conjugates (glutathione conjugate and cysteine conjugate) appear in the perfusate (see Figure 25.11), whereas sulfates or glucuronides are not found. The thio-ether conjugates appear in the perfusate fairly rapidly and accumulate in the pulmonary tissue to only a small extent (about 2 times that of the perfusate). The 4,5-diol, however, does not readily diffuse from the pulmonary tissue to the perfusate very well, resulting in a high lung con-

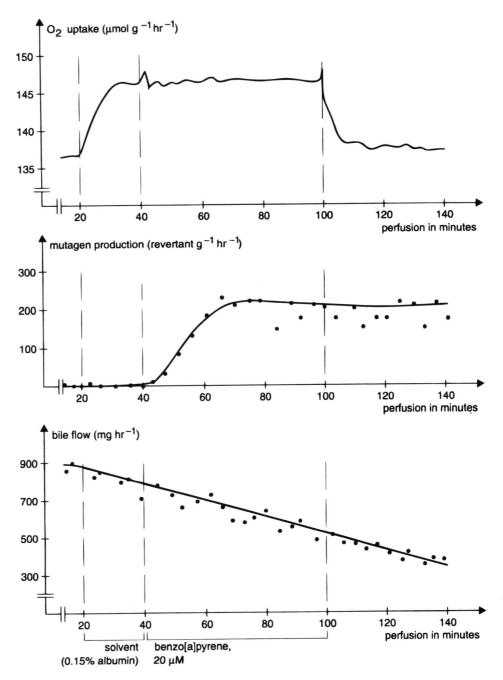

FIGURE 25.9
Oxygen consumption (top), mutagenicity of produced bile (center) and bile flow (bottom) of a perfused rat liver during infusion of 20 μM benzo[a]pyrene

centration (13 times that of the perfusate). Further metabolism of the 4,5-diol to unidentified diolepoxides is likely to be enhanced under these circumstances.

*Covalent binding of benzo[a]pyrene to DNA, RNA, proteins*

At the end of the perfusion experiment, covalent binding of benzo[a]pyrene metabolites to DNA, RNA and proteins can be demonstrated.

If isolated perfused lungs are exposed to benzo[a]pyrene, covalent binding to macromolecules takes place (see Figure 25.12, open bars). In the experiment shown in Figure 25.12, a special application of organ perfusion is used. By performing a

771

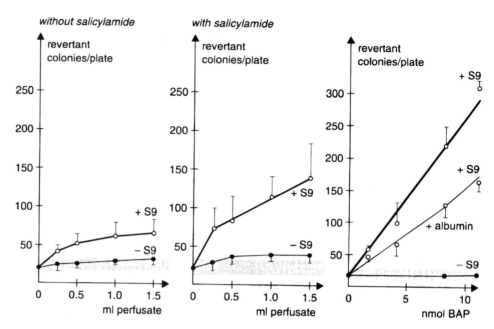

FIGURE 25.10

Mutagenicity of liver perfusate samples with (open symbols) and without (closed symbols) addition of S9 fraction

The livers are perfused without (left) and with (center) salicylamide. To allow comparison, the mutagenicity of a known quantity of benzo[*a*]pyrene is included (right).

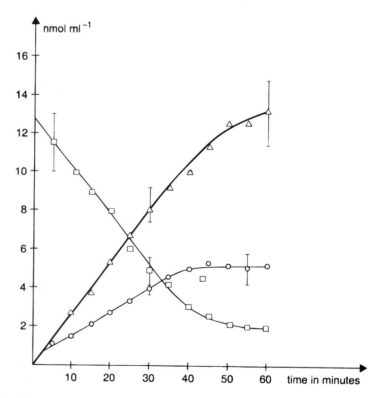

FIGURE 25.11

Decrease in benzo[*a*]pyrene-4,5-epoxide (boxes) and increase in 4,5-diol (circles) and thioether conjugates (triangles) in the perfusate of an isolated perfused rabbit lung

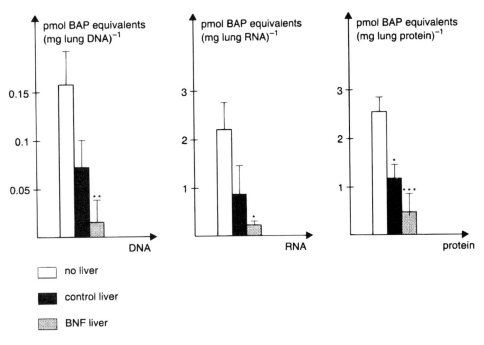

FIGURE  25.12
Covalent binding of benzo[*a*]pyrene metabolites to DNA (left), RNA (center) and protein (right) in a perfused rat lung.
The perfusion was carried out without a liver (open bars), or in combination with the liver of a control rat (black bars) or in combination with the liver of a rat treated with β-naphthoflavone (gray bars).

combined lung and liver perfusion, it was possible to demonstrate directly that the liver protects the lung against covalent binding. If a control liver or the liver of a rat that was pretreated with β-naphthoflavone is incorporated into the perfusion circuit, covalent binding in the pulmonary tissue is greatly reduced (Figure 25.12). The effect of pretreatment with β-naphthoflavone makes it likely that hepatic metabolism is responsible for the observed reduction in covalent binding in the lung.

ASSIGNMENT  25.8
What is the effect of β-naphthoflavone and why does this make it likely that hepatic metabolism is responsible for the reduced covalent binding in the lung?

*Effect of induction*

Organ perfusion also offers the possibility of studying the *effect of induction* and/or inhibition of metabolism.

Inducers should be given before the perfusion experiment as induction takes place relatively slowly. The same treatment may sometimes have different effects, depending on the moment at which it is given. This is illustrated in Figure 25.13, which shows the glucuronidation of 4-methylumbelliferone in an isolated hamster lung.

Try to explain why preliminary and simultaneous exposure to cigarette smoke have different effects on the glucuronidation of 4-methylumbelliferone in the perfused lung.

When the hamsters were exposed to cigarette smoke for 1 hour, 20 hours before isolation of the lungs, glucuronidation during perfusion was enhanced (induction). However, acute exposure to cigarette smoke during the perfusion expe-

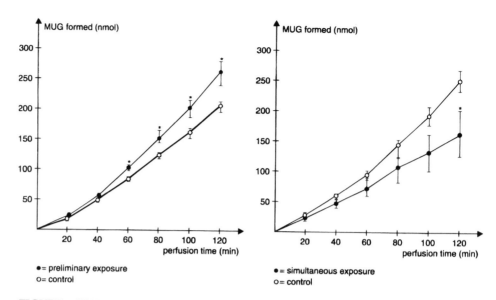

FIGURE 25.13

Metabolism of 4-methylumbelliferone in isolated, perfused hamster lungs after pre-exposure (left) or on simultaneous exposure to cigarette smoke

MUG = methylumbelliferone glucuronide

riment inhibited the metabolism of 4-methylumbelliferone. The mechanism of this inhibition is not entirely clear. Enzyme inhibition, removal of co-factors required for glucuronidation, or other mechanisms may be involved.

*Localization of glucuronidation activity*

A special application of the organ perfusion technique has been used to *localize glucuronidation activity* in the liver. The question whether the various zones of the liver sinusoids (periportal, midzonal, centrilobular; see Study unit 23) differ in metabolism of xenobiotics has been the subject of debate for a long time. Indirect measurements such as enzyme histochemistry or enzyme activity measurements carried out on fragments isolated from cryostat sections, only reflect the maximum enzymatic capacity as optimum concentrations of co-factors and substrates are used. It is very difficult to isolate cells from the individual zones of hepatic tissue. In addition, *in vivo* the oxygen partial pressure and the availability of glucose differ considerably from one zone to another. Because glucuronidation, in particular, depends on these factors to a large extent, meaningful prediction of glucuronidation activity in the various sinusoidal zones based on indirect methods is impossible. Direct measurement in an intact organ is the only possible solution. This can be carried out by using fiber optics technology to quantify the concentration of a fluorescent glucuronidation substrate in an intact liver. An example is a study of the glucuronidation of 7-hydroxycoumarin (HC). HC fluoresces at a wavelength of 366/450 nm (excitation/emission). At these wavelengths, the hydroxycoumarin glucuronide is not fluorescent. During perfusion of the liver, a pair of fiber optic light guides (one for excitation, one for emission) are placed both on the periportal and on the centrilobular zone of a liver sinusoid. The diameter of these light guides (0.07 mm) is so small that they measure fluorescence only from the periportal or the centrilobular zone. The distance between the two zones is approximately 1 mm. If 80 $\mu$M hydroxycoumarin is added to the liver perfusate (single-pass) for 15 minutes, the fluorescence increases immediately, with the increase in the periportal area being much greater than that in the centrilobular area (see Figure 25.14, left). Half an hour later, another dose of 80 $\mu$M hydroxycoumarin is administered, this time in combination with 20 mM ethanol and gassing with N$_2$. Under these circumstances, glucuronidation does not take place. The fluorescence measured in this period can be used for calibration: it corresponds to 80 $\mu$M hydroxycoumarin. The concentrations of hydroxycoumarin in the periportal and centrilobular zones in the first stage of the experiment can then be calculated; in this experiment they are 71 and 12 $\mu$M hydroxycoumarin (see Figure 25.14).

*Retrograde perfusion*

It may be concluded from the above that glucuronidation of hydroxycoumarin hardly takes place in the periportal zone but mainly in the sinusoidal areas behind it. If the direction of perfusion in the liver is reversed (so-called *retrograde perfusion*, i.e. from the hepatic vein to the portal vein), the perfusate first reaches the centrilobular part of the sinusoids. When the above experiment is repeated as a retrograde perfusion experiment, the hydroxycoumarin concentration in the centrilobular zone is 23 $\mu$M and that in the periportal zone 10 $\mu$M (see Figure 25.14, right). It was concluded from these experiments that glucuronidation in the centrilobular zone of the sinusoids is more extensive than in the periportal zone.

### Summary

The metabolism of potentially toxic foreign compounds and the possible formation of covalent bonds can be studied in detail in isolated perfused organs under circumstances in which the diffusion barriers for the substances themselves and for their metabolites are intact. In addition, metabolism can take place via a number of biotransformation routes at the same time. As a result of this, the metabolism in an isolated organ reflects the *in vivo* situation with reasonable reliability, both quantitatively and qualitatively.

### 4 Kinetics in organ perfusion

*Clearance (Cl)*
*For clearance also see Study units 5 and 6*

Isolated organs can also be used for detailed studies on the (toxico)kinetics of xenobiotics. In these studies, the concept of *clearance (Cl)* is frequently used to describe the eliminating capacity of the organ. *Cl* has been defined as the elimi-

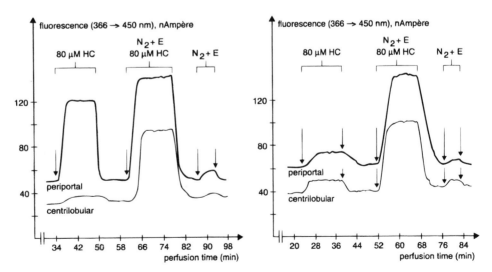

FIGURE 25.14
Fluorescence of 7-hydroxycoumarin (HC) in the periportal and centrilobular zones of liver sinusoids during anterograde (left) and retrograde (right) perfusion with 80 $\mu$M hydroxycoumarin
N$_2$ + E = nitrogen gassing + ethanol

nation rate $R$ of a substance (quantity per unit of time), in relation to the concentration $C$ (quantity per unit of volume) of that substance in blood or plasma: $Cl = R/C$. $Cl$ has the dimension volume time$^{-1}$ and ml min$^{-1}$ and l hour$^{-1}$ are the most common units. If the elimination rate of a substance is proportional to its concentration (i.e. if $Cl$ is constant), its kinetics are called linear. The clearance of an organ can be described as:

$$Cl = \frac{R}{C} = Q\frac{C_{in} - C_{out}}{C_{in}} = Q \cdot E \tag{1}$$

*Extraction ratio*

*Where,* $Q$ is the blood flow through the organ, and $C_{in}$ and $C_{out}$ are the concentrations of the substance in the liquid flowing into and out of the organ. The elimination rate $R = Q(C_{in} - C_{out})$ is here related to the concentration flowing in ($C_{in}$). The *extraction ratio* $E = (C_{in} - C_{out})/C_{in}$ represents the fraction of the concentration flowing in that is eliminated by the organ. The extraction ratio depends on the elimination capacity of the organ concerned. $E$ may vary from 0 (no elimination) to 1 (complete elimination of the substance from the liquid). The influence of physiological and biochemical parameters on $E$ can be described by models predicting the effect of a change in those parameters. The simplest model is the so-called *well-stirred model*, which assumes that the intracellular concentration of the substance is equal to the concentration in the liquid flowing out of the organ ($C_{out}$) and that there are no rate-limiting diffusion barriers between the perfusate and the cytosol. If it is also assumed that all molecules in the perfusate are available for elimination (i.e., that there is no protein binding etc.), $E$ can be described as:

*Well-stirred model*

$$E = \frac{Cl_{int}}{Q + Cl_{int}} \tag{2}$$

where $Cl_{int}$ (intrinsic clearance) is the clearance that would occur if there is no restriction by $Q$. In an organ perfusion the $Cl_{int}$ can be calculated from the $E$ measured and the flow applied, as rearrangement of (2) shows:

$$Cl_{int} = E \cdot \frac{Q}{1 - E} \tag{3}$$

In dealing with elimination by metabolism, $Cl_{int}$ can be predicted from:

$$Cl_{int} = \frac{V_{max}}{K_m + C} \tag{4}$$

Since the *in vivo* concentrations and the concentrations used in organ perfusion studies are often lower than the $K_m$ values, $Cl_{int}$ can normally be regarded as constant: $C$ is then negligible in relation to $K_m$ and $Cl_{int} = V_{max}/K_m$. Note that the $Cl$ of an organ is determined by two mutually independent parameters: the eliminating capacity $Cl_{int}$ of the organ and the blood flow $Q$ through it. Combination of (1) and (2) shows that the clearance by an organ can be described by:

$$Cl = Q \cdot E = Q \cdot \frac{Cl_{int}}{Q + Cl_{int}} \tag{5}$$

*Low-extraction substances*

When this formula is examined, it will be seen that the $Cl$ of substances with a low $Cl_{int}$ (in relation to $Q$) depends largely on this intrinsic clearance. These substances are called *low-extraction substances* ($E < 0.3$). If $Cl_{int}$ is changed (for example by enzyme induction or inhibition), $E$ and therefore $Cl$ will undergo relatively large changes.

Conversely, the $Cl$ of a *high-extraction substance* (high $Cl_{int}$ in relation to $Q$; $E > 0.7$) will depend to a relatively large extent on the blood flow $Q$ through the eliminating organ. Enzyme induction and/or inhibition will have hardly any influence. In order to be able to predict the influence of various circumstances on total body clearance, the $Cl$ of the individual organs under those circumstances must be known. Besides the $Cl_{int}$ (which can be measured *in vitro*), the $Q$ of the individual organs should also be taken into account. Organ perfusion techniques offer the possibility of measuring the effects of certain factors on organ clearance directly. A good example is the clearance of benzo[*a*]pyrene in the isolated livers and lungs of control rats and rats which were pretreated with 3-methylcholanthrene (see Figure 25.15).

The $Cl$ in the liver is entirely flow-dependent and is barely increased by pretreatment with 3-methylcholanthrene. This suggests that benzo[*a*]pyrene is a high-extraction substance in the liver in both conditions. Although the $Cl_{int}$ of benzo[*a*]pyrene is increased by a factor of 8 as a result of pretreatment with 3-methylcholanthrene (measured in liver homogenate), the organ $Cl$ is hardly increased. In the lung, however, an increase in $Cl_{int}$ (23-fold in homogenate) does lead to a clear increase in $Cl$. This suggests that in the lung, benzo[*a*]pyrene is a low-extraction substance. Considering the normal blood flow through the liver and lung (see Table 25.2), it will be seen that under control conditions the lung scarcely contributes to total clearance ($Cl_{liver} = 10$ ml/min; $Cl_{lung} < 1$ ml/min). After treatment with 3-methylcholanthrene, however, both organs contribute approximately equally ($Cl_{liver} = 12$ ml/min; $Cl_{lung} = 9$ ml/min).

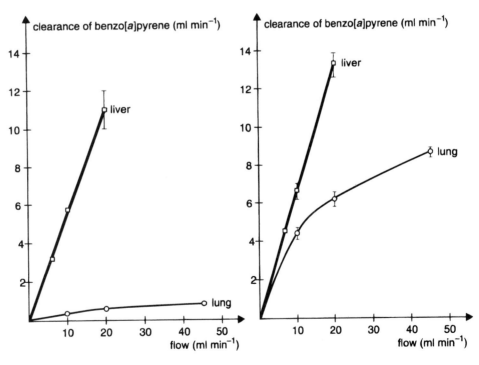

FIGURE   25.15
Clearance of benzo[*a*]pyrene in the isolated perfused liver and lung of control rats (left) and of rats treated with 3-methylcholanthrene (right)

*Absorption processes*

Besides excretion and metabolism, *absorption processes* can also be quantified in terms of clearance. This will be demonstrated in two examples. First, the absorption clearance of antipyrine and the metabolic clearance of 1-naphthol in the isolated intestine will be discussed. The influence of the blood flow will again become clear. The second example concerns the excretion clearance of 1-naphthol conjugates and the metabolic clearance of 1-naphthol in the isolated kidney.

An important advantage of the use of the concept of clearance in describing a transport process is that the process can be defined by a single figure. A limitation is, of course, that this definition applies only to those concentrations at which the kinetics are linear (see above). This requirement, however, is in fact met quite frequently.

*Absorption clearance in the intestine*

Figure 25.16 shows the absorption clearance of antipyrine in the isolated perfused intestine as a function of perfusion.

The term absorption clearance is used here because the absorption rate of antipyrine from the intestinal lumen is related to the concentration supplied. Absorption clearance is almost entirely flow-dependent, because the removal of the absorbed antipyrine is a rate-limiting factor; diffusion through the intestinal wall is very efficient. For substances that diffuse poorly through the intestinal wall, such as sorbitol, the absorption clearance is not flow dependent. Although antipyrine itself is a high absorption substance in the isolated intestine, its $Cl$ is only about 10% of the total perfusate flow. This is a consequence of

*Special construction of the vascular system of the intestine*

the special characteristics of the *vascular system of the intestine* (see Figure 25.17). The blood flowing into the organ branches out over a number of parallel vascular beds.

Figure 25.17 shows two of these vascular beds, where $Q_{muc}$ is the flow to the intestinal epithelium, the mucosa. Another part of the blood flows to the muscular layer of the intestine ($Q_{ma} - Q_{muc}$).

The absorbed antipyrine is removed exclusively by the part of the mucosal blood flow that passes along the tips of the villi. This part, the effective absorption blood flow, accounts for approximately 10% of the total flow. If the x-axis in Figure 25.16 did not show the total perfusate flow but the effective absorption blood flow, the absorption clearance of antipyrine would have been virtually equal to this flow.

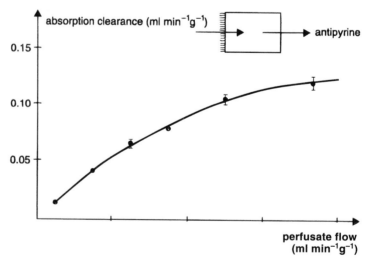

FIGURE 25.16

Absorption of antipyrine from the intestinal lumen as a function of the perfusion of the intestine

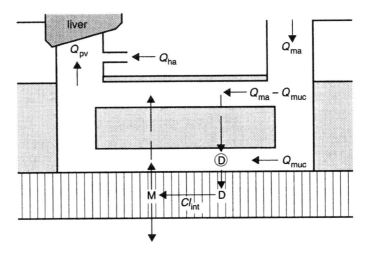

FIGURE 25.17
Schematic summary of the blood flow through the intestine
A xenobiotic D is metabolized in the intestine into a metabolite M.

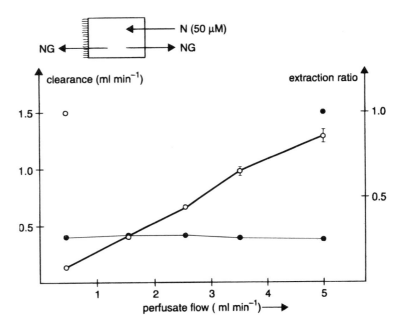

FIGURE 25.18
Clearance and extraction ratio of 1-naphthol in the isolated small intestine (rat) as a function of the perfusion flow

The distribution of the intestinal blood flow over two parallel vascular beds also has implications for the flow dependence of $Cl$ and $E$ of a substance that is metabolized. 1-naphthol (N) added to the perfusate (i.e., not in the lumen) is converted by the mucosal cells to naphthol glucuronide. The measured $Cl$ is entirely flow-dependent (see Figure 25.18). This means that N behaves as a high-extraction substance and yet $E$ is only approximately 0.25. Apparently, only 25% of the total perfusate reaches the metabolizing cells. This percentage corresponds with $Q_{muc}$. All N is removed from $Q_{muc}$ because of the very high $Cl_{int}$ ($E_{muc} = 1$). The liquid flows from the mucosa and from the rest of the intestine joining each other again at the end of the organ. The result is that for the intact organ an $E$ of only 0.25 is measured.

*Elimination in the kidney*
*Glomerular filtration*

*Elimination in the isolated kidney* can also be characterized by clearance. A number of different processes can contribute to renal elimination. Low-molecular-weight substances present in the perfusate are subjected to *glomerular filtration*, provided they are not bound to proteins. The Cl via glomerular filtration thus depends on the unbound fraction (*fu*) and the glomerular filtration rate (GFR): $Cl = fu \times GFR$. As a measure for GFR, creatinine clearance is often used.

*Active transport*

A second process that plays a role in elimination in the kidney is *active transport* via the tubular cells. Active transport processes remove substances from the blood very efficiently. One of the most important transport processes is that for anions such as para-aminohippuric acid. Active transport of this compound and of other anions can be inhibited by probenecid (see above). Para-aminohippuric acid is transported so efficiently that its extraction ratio *in vivo* is almost 1. In other words, para-aminohippuric acid is a high-extraction substance in the kidney and has a renal Cl equal to the blood flow through the kidney.

*Metabolism*
*Reabsorption*

A third process that may contribute to elimination in the kidney is *metabolism*. Metabolism can be studied by monitoring the appearance of any metabolites. The situation in the kidney is complicated by the possibility that molecules that have already been filtered out or excreted via active transport are *reabsorbed*. This leads to a decrease in the clearance measured. For some substances, therefore, the clearance measured may be even smaller than its glomerular filtration. Glucose, for example, is reabsorbed completely and is not normally excreted in the urine. The renal Cl of a substance can at most be equal to that of PAH (glomerular filtration, active secretion, no reabsorption).

Because the kidney is an important organ for the elimination of xenobiotics or their metabolites, thorough description of the elimination processes is very important. The isolated kidney presents the opportunity to study renal elimination in detail. The main metabolites of 1-naphthol, naphthol glucuronide and naphthol sulfate are efficiently cleared in the isolated kidney (see Figure 25.19).

In the presence of 0.5 mM probenecid, the Cl of naphthol glucuronide and naphthol sulfate is significantly inhibited; the Cl measured is equal to that of creatinine. Therefore, it may be concluded, that naphthol glucuronide and naphthol sulfate are cleared by glomerular filtration and active transport. This is shown schematically in Figure 25.20.

N itself is also very efficiently cleared in the isolated kidney. Its Cl equals that of para-aminohippuric acid. Detailed research has shown that this is not excretion clearance but metabolic clearance. In the isolated rat kidney, naphthol is almost entirely converted into naphthol sulfate and naphthol glucuronide. These metabolites are released into the perfusate (naphthol sulfate and half of the naphthol glucuronide formed) or excreted directly into the urine (the other half of the naphthol glucuronide; see Figure 25.20). Comparing the Cl measured for N to that of para-aminohippuric acid (see Figure 25.19), it can be seen that N is cleared as efficiently as para-aminohippuric acid. This means that a renal extraction ratio for naphthol of 1 may be expected *in vivo*. It should be noted in this context that the E of para-aminohippuric acid in the perfused kidney is not 1 but about 0.3. This results from the unphysiologically high perfusate flow needed to keep the oxygen supply of the isolated kidney at the required level (see above). This leads to a redistribution of the flow, so that only part of the para-aminohippuric acid can be eliminated.

*Estimate of total in vivo clearance*

Once the clearance of a particular substance in a number of isolated organs has been quantified, an attempt can be made to estimate the contribution of these organs to the total clearance *in vivo*. The greatest uncertainties are due to the dif-

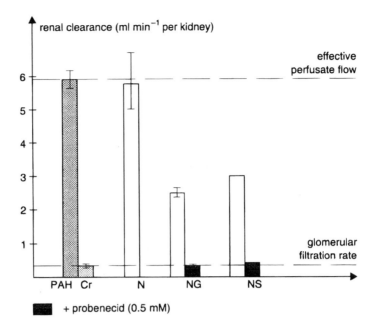

FIGURE 25.19
Renal clearance of para-aminohippuric acid (PAH), creatinine (Cr), 1-naphthol (N), 1-naphthol glucuronide (NG) and 1-naphthol sulfate (NS) in an isolated rat kidney. Dextran was used as an oncotic agent in order to avoid protein binding of the substances.

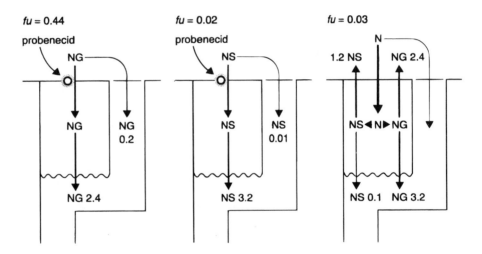

FIGURE 25.20
Clearance of 1-naphthol glucuronide (NG), 1-naphthol sulfate (NS) and 1-naphthol (N) in the isolated kidney
$fu$ is the unbound fraction in a perfusate in which albumin is used as an oncotic agent. The other figures indicate clearance (in ml min-1).

ferences between the flows *in vivo* and in perfusion (see Table 25.2). The best method is probably to extrapolate the extraction ratios measured in organ perfusion to the *in vivo* situation. By comparing the blood flow through the organs *in vivo*, the *in vivo* organ clearance can then be estimated. Another uncertain factor is the composition of the perfusion media and its influence on, e.g. protein binding. As a result, the fraction available for elimination in a perfusate may differ from that in blood. If one is aware of these complications, measurement and correction are usually possible.

*Clearance by liver, lung, intestine, kidney*

An example of the contribution of the liver and the lung to clearance has already been given above for benzo[*a*]pyrene. Another example is the calculation of the $Cl$ of 1-naphthol (N) in the liver, lung, intestine and kidney. The extraction ratio for N in the perfused liver is virtually 1. Naphthol clearance in the liver is thus equal to the hepatic blood flow: $Cl$(liver) = 13–20 ml per min (see Table 25.2). The $Cl$ of N in the perfused lung has unfortunately never been measured; however, *in vivo* data indicate an $E$ of 0.38. This implies a $Cl$(lung) of 21–27 ml per min. As mentioned, the $E$ for the kidney is 1 and that for the intestine 0.25. The $Cl$(kidney) is thus 4–6 ml per min per kidney, or 8–12 ml per min per rat. Any contribution to the total clearance of N from the intestine is not expressed *in vivo* because the intestine and the liver are connected in series and the $E$ of the liver is 1. Independently of the elimination in the intestine, therefore, 100% will always be eliminated: $Cl$(liver + intestine) = $Cl$(liver). Addition of the $Cl$s in the liver, lung, kidney and intestine results in a total $Cl$ of 1-naphthol of 42–59 ml per min. The $Cl$ measured *in vivo* is 55–85 ml per min. Thus, the $Cl$ measured *in vivo* is accounted for largely by the organ clearances of the liver, lung, kidney and intestine. This confirms that the values measured in organ perfusion studies are a reasonable reflection of those *in vivo*.

*Summary*

The elimination of foreign (potentially toxic) compounds by excretion or metabolism in an individual organ can be quantified in studies using the isolated organ. The extraction ratio measured and the effects of any enzyme induction, enzyme inhibition and/or changes in flow can be extrapolated to the *in vivo* situation.

## 5    Conclusions

Organ perfusion techniques can be applied in many areas of toxicology. They are particularly suitable for quantifying metabolism in various organs and for detailed study of kinetics under circumstances that are virtually 'true-to-life'. Organ perfusions are less suitable for the *in vitro* study of toxification processes, in particular because they do not remain viable for long after isolation. In all cases, the manipulability of the system and the absence of systemic effects are important advantages. By relatively simple means, very detailed information can be obtained on biochemically and physiologically relevant processes. To obtain the same information from intact experimental animals is almost always much more difficult and sometimes even impossible. However, there are also some limitations. The use of organ perfusion requires considerable investment in equipment, manual skill and expertise. Therefore, specialization in a laboratory or among several laboratories is advisable. Much time and attention need to be devoted to defining the system, particularly in the development stage. If certain questions can be answered by studies in subcellular systems or isolated cells, this is nearly always simpler, less time-consuming and cheaper. Isolated organ systems and intact experimental animals can then be used for experimental verification of the extrapolations made.

In summary, it may be concluded that isolated organs have a specific application in toxicology and pharmacology. On the one hand, organ-specific information on biotransformation and kinetics can be obtained, on the other, they can function as a necessary link in relating data from cellular systems to that derived from intact animals.

## SELF ASSESSMENT QUESTIONS

1   Name at least three enzymes involved in biotransformation in the lung and three enzymes involved in biotransformation in the kidney.

2   Name at least four possible reasons why the biotransformation of a certain substance in an organ perfusion system may differ qualitatively and/or quantitatively from that in isolated cells of the same organ.

3   The metabolism of 1-naphthol is studied in the isolated perfused lung (flow 15 ml min⁻¹; single-pass perfusion). On administration of 10 $\mu$M naphthol, the following concentrations are found in the perfusate leaving the organ: naphthol 8.8 $\mu$M, naphthol glucuronide 0.6 $\mu$M and naphthol sulfate 0.5 $\mu$M. Calculate the rate of glucuronidation, the rate of sulfation, the extraction ratio and the clearance of naphthol in the lung.
NB: calculate the clearance using two different methods!

4   The experiment described in question 3 is repeated at a perfusion flow of 45 ml min⁻¹. Will the values of the parameters you have calculated change? If so, calculate the new values. What will be the concentration of the perfusate leaving the organ? Explain your answers.

5   The experiment described in question 4 is repeated with a naphthol concentration of 0.2 mM. The extraction ratio measured is 0.02. What extraction ratio had you expected and what could be the reason for the difference between the measured and the expected extraction ratio?

6   The experiment described in question 3 is repeated with radio-actively labelled naphthol. After the experiment, a considerable amount of radioactivity is found in the pulmonary tissue. Does this surprise you, in view of the results you found for question 3? Explain your answer.

7   The oxygen consumption of the isolated lung in the experiments described in questions 3, 4 and 6 is normal and identical. In the experiment described in question 5, however, the oxygen consumption is 40% lower. What could be a reason for this? Explain your answer.

8   For question 3, you calculated the clearance using two different methods. The results were different. Explain why this was the case.

## FEEDBACK

1   **Answers to the assignments**

25.1   In an organ perfusion study, a large number of variables can be manipulated. For each variable, there is only a limited range within which normal organ function is maintained. The most general variables are the following:

*composition of the perfusion medium*

- ion composition and osmolarity
- nature and strength of the buffer used
- nature and concentration of the oncotic agent (e.g. protein binding)

- nature and concentration of substrates for cell metabolism
- nature and concentration of any oxygen carriers (if erythrocytes are used, also the animal species), viscosity
- partial pressures of gasses, in particular oxygen
- addition of drugs, hormones, neurohormones, vitamins, trace elements

  *method of perfusion*
- perfusion pressure and perfusion flow or both: constant pressure or constant flow, possibly pulsating
- recirculating or single-pass perfusion
- direction of perfusion: anterograde or retrograde.

25.2 The $O_2$ supply to a tissue is regulated *in vivo* by intrinsic and extrinsic mechanisms. The extrinsic mechanisms include an increase in the total blood flow because of increased cardiac output and redistribution of the blood over the tissues (regulated by the autonomic nervous system and various hormones and neurohormones). In many tissues, the blood vessels react to increased oxygen demand by dilatation (intrinsic regulation under the influence of $CO_2$ pressure and/or degradation products of cell metabolism). Finally, the oxygen dissociation curve of hemoglobin (see Figure 25.2) shifts to the right under the influence of rising temperature and lowering of the pH (Bohr effect). As a result, additional $O_2$ is released in metabolically active tissues.

25.3 From Figure 25.2, it can be seen that, if gassed with carbogen (partial $O_2$ pressure $= 95\% \times 760 = 722$ torr), blood can contain 200 $\mu$l $O_2$ per ml, Krebs-Ringer bicarbonate buffer 21 $\mu$l $O_2$ per ml and a 20% fluorocarbon emulsion 62 $\mu$l $O_2$ per ml. The minimum perfusion flow necessary to supply 1 ml $O_2$ per minute is therefore 5 ml per min for blood, 47.6 ml per min for Krebs-Ringer bicarbonate buffer and 16 ml per min for a fluorocarbon emulsion. If blood is used as the perfusion medium, gassing with carbogen is unnecessary, since gassing with air gives virtually the same $O_2$ transport capacity. If Krebs-Ringer bicarbonate buffer or a fluorocarbon emulsion is gassed with air, the flow should be increased by a factor $722/152 = 4.75$ to supply the same amount of $O_2$ per minute. NB: 152 torr is the partial pressure of $O_2$ in air.

25.4 If gassed with carbogen and at a flow of 30 ml per min, Krebs-Ringer bicarbonate buffer can transport $21 \times 30 = 630$ $\mu$l $O_2$ per minute. Figure 25.3 shows that at a flow of 30 ml per min, approximately $46 \times 12 = 552$ $\mu$l $O_2$ is used per 12 g liver. It is evident that the liver consumes almost 90% of the amount of $O_2$ supplied. Lower flows will therefore lead to oxygen deficiency.

25.5 The gradual reduction in glucose reabsorption means that the active transport process for glucose in the proximal tubule proceeds less efficiently (as a result of the changed energy metabolism of the tubular cells and/or death of some of the cells). The glomerular filtration rate gradually decreases as the pores of the glomerulus become blocked. As a result of the reduced glomerular filtration, the production of urine is also slowly decreased. The reabsorption of water (approximately 85% of the glomerular filtrate), however, is maintained.

25.6 Measuring GSH and GSSG as an early indication of toxicity is useful as in most cases studied, a marked decrease in GSH levels precedes cell death.

The GSH levels may be reduced as a result of conjugation with reactive intermediates (e.g. epoxides) or by reduction of $H_2O_2$ and/or lipid hydroperoxides. In the latter case, an equivalent quantity of GSSG is formed.

**benzo[a]pyrene**

cytochrome P-450

$7\alpha, 8\alpha$-epoxide

epoxide hydrolase

$7\beta,8\alpha$-dihydrodiol

cytochrome P-450

$7\beta,8\alpha$-dihydrodiol-$9\alpha,10\alpha$-epoxide

25.7 Besides the metabolites shown above, other stereo-isomers are also formed, depending on the experimental system used. The cytochrome P-450-mediated oxidation shows stereoselectivity.

25.8 β-Naphthoflavone induces certain forms of cytochrome P-450, UDP glucuronyl transferase and other biotransformation enzymes in a similar way to that of 3-methylcholanthrene. After binding of β-naphthoflavone to a receptor, the synthesis of enzymes is increased via a genetic regulation mechanism. This increase can be measured a few days after the start of the treatment with β-naphthoflavone.

## 2    Answers to the self assessment questions

1    Examples of biotransformation enzymes mentioned in this unit: epoxide hydrolase, glutathione transferase and cytochrome P-450 (lung); C-S-lyase, glucuronyl transferase and sulfotransferase (kidney).

2    The following factors may cause a qualitative or quantitative difference in biotransformation between isolated cells and organ perfusion:

- the isolated cells represent only a portion of the metabolizing cells of the whole organ;

- in the isolated organ, metabolism is restricted by other factors than in isolated cells. For example, restrictions due to perfusion flow (e.g., with high-extraction substances) or a smaller available diffusion surface area of the cells in the isolated organ. Isolated hepatocytes are surrounded on all sides by the incubation medium, while in the intact liver, only the sinusoidal membrane is in contact with the perfusion medium;

- the availability of co-factors for biotransformation differs as a result of differences in incubation conditions of incubation (cells) and perfusion conditions (organ);

- in one of the systems, there is enzyme inhibition as a result of differences in incubation and perfusion conditions.

3    The rate of glucuronidation $R_{gl}$ and the rate of sulfation $R_s$ are calculated from the concentrations in the perfusate leaving the organ (in $\mu M$ = nmol.ml$^{-1}$) and the perfusion rate: $R_{gl} = 0.6 \times 15 = 9$ nmol min$^{-1}$, $R_s = 0.5 \times 15 = 7.5$ nmol min$^{-1}$. The extraction ratio is calculated from the concentrations of naphthol flowing into and out of the organ: $E = (10 - 8.8)/10 = 0.12$. The clearance $Cl$ can be calculated in two ways
formula (1):

$$Cl_1 = (R_{gl} + R_s)/C_{in} = (9 + 7.5)/10 = 1.65 \text{ ml min}^{-1}$$

formula (5):

$$Cl_2 = Q \times E = 15 \times 0.12 = 1.8 \text{ ml min}^{-1}.$$

The reason why there is a difference in the results is discussed in the answer to question 8.

4    Since naphthol appears to be a low-extraction substance in the lung ($E = 0.12$), the change in flow can be expected to have hardly any effect on the clearance; therefore the extraction ratio will be decreased. So, in this case, the metabolic rate is rate-limiting. $R_{gl}$ and $R_s$ and hence $Cl_{int}$ will be equal to the values mentioned in question 3. From the $Q$ and $E$ calculated in question 3, $Cl_{int}$ can be calculated by applying formula (3):

$$Cl_{int}(\text{question 3}) = (0.12 \times 15)/(1 - 0.12) = 2.045 \text{ ml min}^{-1}$$

This value of $Cl_{int}$ does not depend on $Q$. $E$ and $Cl$ can now be calculated from $Cl_{int}$ and $Q$ by applying formulae (2) and (1):

$$E = Cl_{int}/(Q + Cl_{int}) = 2.045/(45 + 2.045) = 0.043$$

$$Cl = Q \times E = 45 \times 0.043 = 1.94 \text{ ml min}^{-1}$$

It follows from the calculated $E$ that the naphthol concentration in the out-flowing perfusate will be $(1 - 0.043) \times 10 = 9.57 \ \mu M$.

5  The concentration of naphthol supplied is 20× higher than that in question 3. With linear kinetics, one may expect the metabolic rate also to be increased by a factor of 20. From the information in question 4, one can calculate that when 10 $\mu M$ naphthol is supplied, $(10 - 9.57) \times 45 = 19.35$ nmol min$^{-1}$ is metabolized. If 200 $\mu M$ naphthol is supplied, therefore, one may expect $20 \times 19.35 = 387$ nmol min$^{-1}$ to be metabolized. At a flow of 45 ml min$^{-1}$, this results in a concentration $C_{out}$ leaving the organ of $(200 - 387)/45 = 191.4$ nmol ml$^{-1}$. The expected $E$ is then $(200 - 191.4)/200 = 0.043$. Please note that this is the same value as that found in question 4!

The extraction ratio measured, however, appears to be 0.02, which means that only $0.02 \times 200 \times 45 = 180$ nmol min$^{-1}$ is metabolized. In other words: if the concentration of naphthol supplied is increased from 10 to 200 $\mu M$ (a 20-fold increase), the metabolic rate is only increased from 19.35 to 180 nmol min$^{-1}$ (a 9.3-fold increase). This means that the kinetics are not linear. The most likely reason for this is that, at the higher concentration, the metabolism becomes saturated (concentration approaches $V_{max}$). The result is that the metabolic rate is no longer proportional to the concentration and that the clearance is not constant. At higher concentrations, the clearance is decreased (an important consequence of metabolic saturation). As a result, the $E$ in an isolated organ is also decreased (formula (1)).

6  From the figures in question 3, it is possible to conclude that not all of the amount of naphthol that leaves the perfusate is recovered as glucuronides and/or sulfates: $0.1 \times 15 = 1.5$ nmol min$^{-1}$ is lost. Apparently, this amount is still present in the tissue as naphthol and/or metabolites at the end of the experiment.

7  It is possible that the higher concentration of naphthol in the experiment described in this question is toxic. In that case, impaired cellular function or cell death of part of the pulmonary tissue may lead to a reduced $O_2$ consumption.

8  The following two values for $Cl$ were found in question 3: $Cl_1 = 1.65$ ml min$^{-1}$ (calculated from $R_{gl}$, $R_s$ and $C_{in}$) and $Cl_2 = 1.8$ ml min$^{-1}$ (calculated from $Q$ and $E$). Because $Cl_2$ is based entirely on the disappearance of naphthol itself, this $Cl$ includes all the processes that lead to the disappearance of naphthol. Metabolism into glucuronides and sulfates and accumulation in the tissue contribute to this disappearance. $Cl_1$ is based on the appearance of the conjugates which are formed. Clearance of naphthol by accumulation in the pulmonary tissue is therefore not taken into account and consequently $Cl_1$ is smaller than $Cl_2$. The difference between $Cl_1$ and $Cl_2$ (0.15 ml min$^{-1}$) is a measure for the accumulation in the tissue. This can be referred to as accumulation clearance.

# Content Study unit 26
# Cardiovascular toxicology: toxicological pathology and methodological aspects

# Cardiovascular toxicology: toxicological pathology and methodological aspects

*A. Verheyen*

## INTRODUCTION

In cardiovascular toxicology, the toxic effects of substances which are selective for the heart or vascular system are investigated. To gain a better understanding of the way in which substances can cause toxic effects, the normal relationship between structure and function of the heart and vascular system will be briefly discussed. This is followed by a general overview of the most important toxicological changes, distinguishing between functional and structural effects. Depending on the dosage and duration of the exposure to a toxic substance, *functional changes* may be less serious and of a transient nature, but they may also be irreversible.

Since functional effects are frequently of an acute nature, they may quickly lead to abnormal heart function, which may be fatal. Substances can also cause *structural*, more specifically degenerative, and inflammatory changes in the heart and blood vessels. These can, in turn, lead to functional abnormalities. The general overview is followed by a review of some cardiotoxic substances. Finally, test procedures that may be used to demonstrate cardiovascular toxicity will be discussed.

LEARNING OBJECTIVES

After studying this unit on the toxicology of the heart and vascular system, you will be expected to

— know the causes of arrhythmias in the heart
— be able to explain what is meant by abnormal automaticity
— be able to explain the concept of abnormal conduction
— be able to classify some important arrhythmias on the basis of changes in the ECG
— be able to describe chemically induced changes in the morphological structure of the heart
— be able to name some important cardiotoxic substances and explain their effects
— be able to explain circulatory insufficiency or shock
— be able to describe the phenomena which lead to arteriosclerosis and atherosclerosis
— be able to describe and explain the *in vivo* and *in vitro* test procedures for demonstrating cardiovascular toxicity.

*Study hints*

In this unit, attention is devoted to the anatomy and physiology of the heart. This is largely intended as a review of this rather complicated subject. The discussion of anatomy and physiology presented here, however, is not intended to be sufficient to remedy a lack of knowledge on your part. Other sources are available for that purpose. You should be aware that this unit is primarily concerned with the toxicology of the heart and blood vessels and that sections 1 and 5 are merely intended to refresh your memory. The study load of this otherwise fairly short unit is estimated at 2–3 hours.

## STUDY CORE

### 1 Components of the heart: relationship between structure and function

Although not all the details of the functioning of the cardiovascular system have been accounted for so far, considerable knowledge has been accumulated since the discovery of the cardiovascular system by Harvey in 1628. In the following sections the normal structure and function of the various components of the heart and blood vessels are discussed; this should help you to understand the toxicological phenomena which may occur in the cardiovascular system.

#### 1.1 ANATOMY AND GENERAL FUNCTION

Upon relaxation of the right atrium, deoxygenated blood is drawn from the superior and inferior vena cava, both of which enter the atrium from the side (Figure 26.1a). The blood then flows to the right ventricle, passing the tricuspid valve.

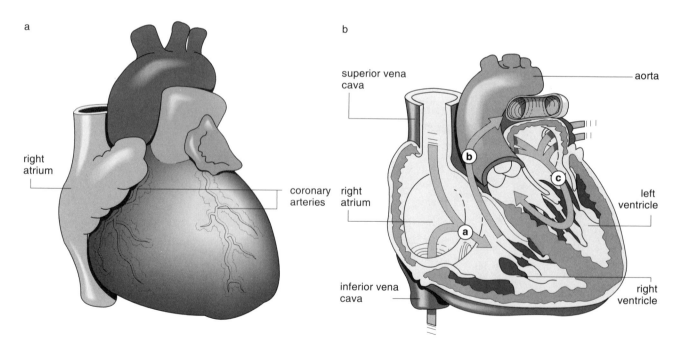

FIGURE 26.1

Schematic diagram showing the heart in its entirety and in cross-section
In Figure b, the pulmonary artery has been omitted for the sake of clarity.

From the right ventricle the blood is pumped through the pulmonary valve into the pulmonary artery (b) and from there distributed over the lungs.

The oxygenated blood flows back into the left atrium (c) and from there through the mitral valve into the left ventricle. This ventricle forces the blood through the aortic valve into the aorta and thus to the various organs of the body.

> ASSIGNMENT   26.1
>
> Are the differences in thickness of the muscle wall between the atria and ventricles on the one hand, and between the left and right ventricle walls, on the other, functionally relevant?

Inside, the ventricle wall is covered by a wide-meshed network of muscle tissue. The large muscles, called papillary muscles, are connected to the valves between atrium and ventricle by means of fibrous cords. The heart muscle itself is mainly supplied with blood by the coronary arteries, which branch from the aorta directly behind the aortic valve. The perfusion pressure of the blood in the internal part of the heart muscle is significantly lower than that in the external part. The deoxygenated blood from the heart muscle is carried to the right atrium via the coronary veins. The heart is almost entirely dependent on these coronary blood vessels for its energy supply. The heart muscle pumps out the blood by rhythmic contraction (*systole*) and dilation (*diastole*). The left and right halves of the heart work in near perfect synchronicity. When the ventricles contract during systole, the increasing pressure closes the valves between atria and ventricles and opens the valves to the pulmonary artery and aorta. During diastole, the situation is reversed.

> What initiates the contraction of the heart and how is it coordinated?

*Impulse conduction*

Study this figure carefully when reading the description of stimulus conduction.

The electrical stimulus which induces the heart muscle to contract originates from the heart itself, more specifically from the *sinoatrial (SA) node*, which is situated in the right atrium, near the origin of the superior vena cava (Figure 26.2).

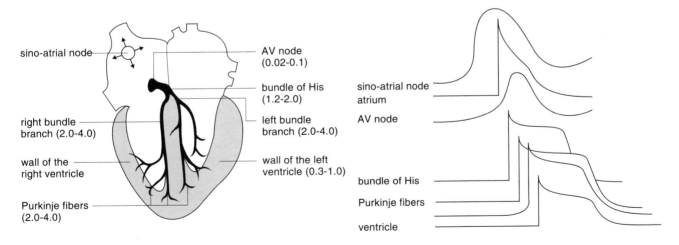

FIGURE   26.2

Conduction system of the heart

Numbers between brackets indicate the impulse conduction rate in meters per second. On the right, typical action potentials are shown which can be measured in individual cells of, from top to bottom, the SA node, the muscle tissue of the atrium, the atrioventricular (AV) node, the bundle of His, Purkinje fibers and the ventricular tissue.

This spontaneous discharge of the SA node means that there is *automaticity* in the heart muscle, as a result of which a completely isolated heart continues to beat as long as its metabolism remains intact. The SA node can be considered as the pacemaker of the heart. The electrical stimulus from the sinoatrial node spreads more or less evenly over the muscle cells of both atria. It reaches the *atrioventricular (AV) node*, which is situated at the boundary between atria and ventricles. Impulse conduction is one of the specific intrinsic properties of the heart. The impulse continues through the *bundle of His*, which splits into a left and right branch, which run on different sides of the heart septum, down to the apex of the heart. Along the way there are minor side branches, the *Purkinje fibers*, from where the impulse is distributed over the muscle cells of the two ventricles. The impulse passes the Purkinje fibers very rapidly, as compared with impulse conduction in the AV node, and reaches many sites of the inner ventricular walls almost at the same time. Because of this, the left and right ventricles contract simultaneously. As a result, ventricular contraction does not coincide with that of the atria. This ensures a well coordinated pumping action. In principle, the entire impulse conduction system has the ability to discharge spontaneously (automaticity) and can take over the function of the SA node. In that situation, however, the heart beat becomes much slower. Changes in the impulse conduction or the abnormal induction of spontaneous discharge by, for example, chemical interaction, may lead to abnormal heart contraction (see section 2).

*Nervous control*

The frequency with which the cells of the SA node normally discharge is influenced externally by the *autonomic nervous system*, which innervates the heart. These nerves ultimately determine the heart rate through their inhibiting and stimulating influences. In adults, this rate is 60–70 beats per minute at rest; in infants and young children it is 100–120 beats per minute. Depending on conditions such as stress, fever, physical exertion and substances, as well as the degree of physical training, the rate of a healthy heart can vary from 55 to 200 beats per minute.

The performance of the heart muscle is expressed as the volume of blood pumped out per unit time: the *cardiac output*. This is determined by the heart rate and by the volume of blood pumped out at each beat, the *stroke volume*.

## 1.2 FUNCTIONAL UNITY

The actual contraction of atria and ventricles is brought about by the contractile myocardial (heart muscle) tissue. The external part of the myocardium is called *epicardium*, while the internal part, which is in contact with the blood, is called *endocardium*.

The contractile apparatus is composed of striated muscle fibers or myocardial cells (Figure 26.3).

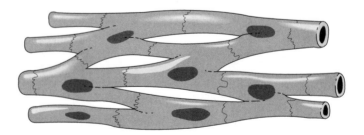

FIGURE 26.3
Schematic representation of myocardial muscle cells and their interconnections

The various cells are connected to each other by specialized intercellular junctions (called intercalated discs), which allow the rapid distribution of the impulses. Each cell contains mainly longitudinally oriented myofibrils, which are composed of repeating contractile units: the *sarcomeres*.

The specialized cells of the conduction system are much smaller than the normal myocardial cells. They can be distinguished from the fibroblasts in the abundant connective tissue by the presence of myofilaments. Although these cells can contract, their main function is to conduct the impulse to the various parts of the heart.

## 1.3 PHYSIOLOGY OF MYOCARDIAL CONTRACTION

The electrical activity of the heart originates at the level of the individual myocardial cells. The changes in electrical current which take place in these muscle cells are produced by diffusing ions: sodium, potassium, calcium and chloride. If a particular heart muscle cell is stimulated, successive changes in potential occur as a function of time.

*Action potential*

This process of changes in potential is called the *action potential*. It consists of various phases: the *depolarization phase*, the *plateau phase*, the *repolarization phase* and sometimes a *diastolic depolarization phase* (Figure 26.4).

Two different action potentials can be distinguished, depending on whether depolarization proceeds rapidly (*rapid response*) or slowly (*slow response*). Rapid action potentials occur in the atrial and ventricular myocardium, as well as in the Purkinje fibers.

Slow action potentials only occur in the so-called pacemaker tissue of the SA node and the AV node.

The characteristic shape of these action potentials is caused by specific ionic fluxes which are different for the two types.

> Which ionic fluxes occur and how do they lead to specific action potentials?

Changes in the permeability of the cell membrane result in ionic fluxes which in turn cause changes in potential. These changes in turn lead to further changes in permeability (positive feedback). This ionic movement under the influence of altered membrane potentials produces an electrical current. The ionic fluxes proceed through channels in the membrane. The permeability of these channels can be modulated by adjustment of pores which act as gates, and which may work slowly or rapidly.

*Resting potential*

The *resting potential* of myocardial cells with a rapid response (Figure 26.4a) is about –90 mV (going from the inside to the outside). This potential is primarily based on the difference in concentrations of potassium and sodium ions on either side of the cell membrane and on the differential permeability of the cell membrane for these ions. When the membrane potential reaches a critical value of about –60 to –70 mV (*threshold potential*), for example through stimulation of an adjacent cell, the rapid sodium channels in the cell membrane open up and the action potential is initiated (*phase 0*). The conduction rate of the impulse to the other cells is directly related to the rate of increase in phase 0. Cells with a rapid response conduct the impulse very quickly. At the end of phase 0, the cell is fully polarized and the internal potential is about +30 mV. During phase 1 and the early stages of phase 2 of the action potential, the influx of sodium decreases sharply and the membrane potential starts to decrease, partly because potas-

*Phase 0*

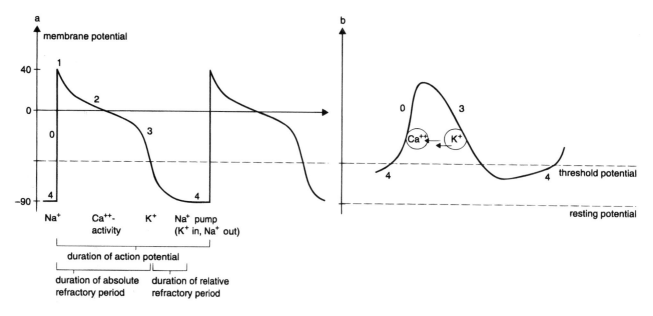

FIGURE 26.4
Sequence of electrical and ionic activities in a heart muscle cell
a, an example of a rapid response; b, an example of a slow response 0 = depolarization, 1 = rapid repolarization, 2 = plateau, 3 = repolarization, 4 = late repolarization

*Phase 1*
*Phase 2*

sium is also leaving the cell. It is assumed that the start of repolarization during *phase 1* of the action potential is attributable to a transient influx of negatively charged chloride ions. During the plateau phase (*phase 2*), calcium and sodium enter the cell through slow channels, thus counteracting the repolarizing effect of the outward potassium efflux. The influx of calcium is thought to initiate the excitation-contraction process at this moment. During *phase 3*, the permeability for potassium increases and the slow channels for calcium and sodium are deactivated. The ultimate result is repolarization of the membrane and a return to the resting potential (*phase 4*). This phase occurs between the successive action potentials during diastole.

*Phase 3*

*Phase 4*

Apart from action potentials with constant resting potential, which occur in non-automatic myocardial cells, there are also automatic heart muscle cells with a slow diastolic depolarization. These slow depolarizations, which occur during diastole, take place via the slow sodium channels, which are entirely different from the rapid sodium channels of rapid depolarization.

The resting potential in pacemaker cells or cells with a slow response is about –60 mV (Figure 26.4b). At this level, the rapid sodium channels are inactive and only the slow sodium and calcium channels are active. These are activated whenever the membrane potential reaches –40 mV. Depolarization proceeds relatively slowly.

It should also be noted that heart muscle cells do not react to external stimuli during the period of contraction itself. This *refractory period* is an important property of all heart muscle cells; without it they could be continually prompted to contract.

Activation of an individual myocardial cell in turn causes activity in the adjacent cell. This takes place via the intercalated discs, which are thought to constitute low resistance passages. In this way, the impulse is conducted from one cell to another, which, under normal conditions, results in coordinated heart contraction.

*Nervous control*

As was mentioned above, the heart is controlled by the autonomic nervous system, both the *parasympathetic* and the *sympathetic* branches.

The (parasympathetic) vagus nerve fibers innervate the SA node, the atria, the AV node and, to a limited extent, the ventricles.

*Acetylcholine*

The main effects of the neurotransmitter *acetylcholine*, which is released from the vagus nerves, include: reduced force of atrial and ventricular contraction, reduced impulse conduction in the AV node and reduced heart rate. This effect of acetylcholine mainly results from a reduction in the slope (phase 4) of the pacemaker potential and by the establishment of a lower negative diastolic potential. This hyperpolarization could be caused by an increase in potassium permeability of the external muscle cell membrane.

*Norepinephrine*

The release of the neurotransmitter *norepinephrine* through stimulation of the sympathetic nerves increases the slope of diastolic depolarization, so that the threshold potential is reached more rapidly and the release of impulses from the SA node is accelerated. The effects on the AV node and other conducting tissues are similar. They are attributed to the increased influx of calcium through the slow channels.

> How can the electrical activity be measured in a non-invasive way?

The electrical activity of the heart immediately preceding the contraction of the various parts of the heart muscle can be recorded by means of electrocardiography.

*Electrocardiogram*

The *electrocardiogram*, or ECG, provides information on the heart rhythm, impulse conduction and the state of the myocardium.

The normal ECG in Figure 26.5 shows, from left to right: the *P wave* (depolarization or contraction of the atria), a short interval without electrical activity as a result of the impulse being delayed in the AV node, the *QRS complex* (depolarization in both ventricles) and the *T wave* (repolarization in the ventricles). Like the presence and the height of the various peaks in the ECG, the various intervals and segments are also criteria for the normal functioning of the heart. Pronounced changes in the ECG have been observed after, for instance, administration of toxic concentrations of digitalis glycosides, which may lead to ventricular fibrillation or complete blockage of the AV node (see Figure 26.6: compare the ECG of *a* with those of *g* and *h*). The ECG changes will be discussed in more detail in later sections.

Ventricular fibrillation is an arrhythmia caused by disorganized electrical activity of the ventricle, leading to cardiac arrest.

## 2 Chemically induced changes in the physiology of the heart

The above description implies that the heart has various intrinsic properties that combine to ensure an ideal pump function.

ASSIGNMENT 26.2

Name these intrinsic properties.

The various mechanisms underlying each of these properties may be subject to pathological or chemical influences, resulting in abnormal heart function. The consequences may be: changes in heart rate (*chronotropism*), in conduction (*dromotropism*), in excitability (*bathmotropism*) or in contractility (*inotropism*). Each of these changes may be positive or negative with respect to the normal situation. The most significant functional abnormalities are *arrhythmias* and *contractility disturbances*.

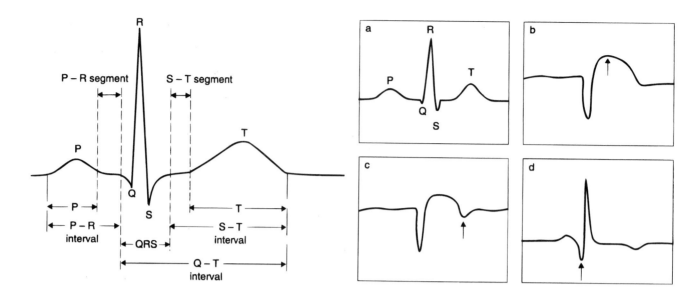

FIGURE 26.5

The normal electrocardiogram (shown left), in which intervals and segments are indicated

b, c and d are pathological ECG changes associated with myocardial infarction; b shows an increased ST interval (ischemia); c shows an inverted T wave (severe degree of ischemia); d shows a Q wave (necrosis).

## 2.1 ARRHYTHMIAS

The normal rhythm of the heart is produced by a regularly recurring impulse from the SA node, which then proceeds to other areas of the heart in a coordinated way. The rhythm of the SA node is stronger than that of the other conducting tissues. Under certain circumstances, the SA node rhythm can change or impulses can be generated in other parts of the heart (in conducting tissue as well as in contractile myocardial cells), bypassing the SA node. This influences the coordination of the heart beat and rhythm disturbances or *arrhythmias* may arise. This may occur under the influence of, for example, high fever or surgical interventions, or following a myocardial infarction, but also under the influence of certain *stimulants* (coffee, tobacco, alcohol, amphetamines) and all sorts of substances, including, paradoxically, antiarrhythmic agents. Arrhythmias are common functional disorders, which may vary from fairly harmless *extrasystoles* to *ventricular fibrillation* and total cardiac arrest. The result of arrhythmia is a heart beat that is too slow (*bradycardia* = negative chronotropism), or too fast (*tachycardia* = positive chronotropism), or just irregular.

Although a wide range of mechanisms may be involved in arrhythmias (see Table 26.1), the root causes can be traced back to two essential changes: deviations in impulse *generation*, or automaticity, and deviations in impulse *conduction*. These two may also occur simultaneously, and they are interrelated. According to where the arrhythmia occurs, it is referred to as supraventricular (above the level of the ventricles) or ventricular. Arrhythmias are usually classified on the basis of ECG changes. Figure 26.6 shows examples of the most common arrhythmias, which are discussed in the following sections.

*Arrhythmias*

### 2.1.1 Abnormal automaticity

The rate at which heart muscle cells are activated depends on the level of the resting potential, the gradient of diastolic depolarization and the level of the membrane potential at the end of repolarization. If the resting potential is shifted

796

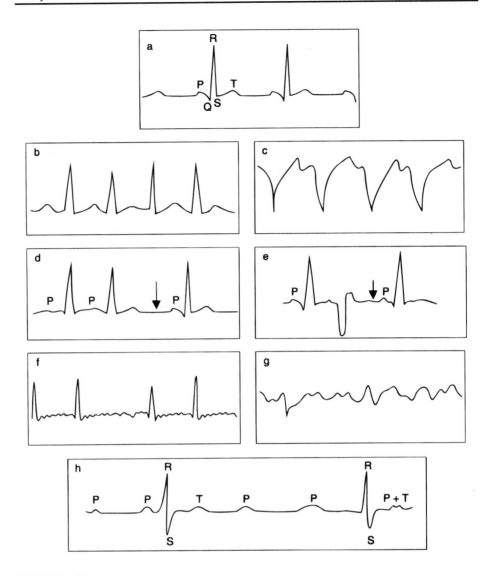

FIGURE    26.6
Some examples of the most common arrhythmias classified on the basis of changes in the ECG
a. normal rhythm
b. atrial tachycardia
c. ventricular tachycardia
d. extrasystole caused by premature excitation of the atrium
e. extrasystole caused by premature excitation of the ventricle
f. atrial fibrillation
g. ventricular fibrillation
h. complete block of the AV node
The arrows in panels d and e point to a compensatory pause which enables the heart to resume its normal rhythm

in a positive direction (towards 0), the depolarization can be mediated by the transport of ions other than sodium (via the rapid channels), particularly by the transport of calcium (via the slow channels). Myocardial cells which normally have a rapid response can then be functionally changed into pacemaker cells with a slow response.

*Ectopic impulses*

Action potentials can then be generated in other areas of the heart without the SA node being involved (Table 26.1). These are called *ectopic impulses*. They es-

TABLE 26.1
Mechanisms of cardiac arrhythmia

| I Abnormal automaticity | II Abnormal conduction | III Abnormal automaticity and abnormal conduction |
|---|---|---|
| A site of the impulse initiation<br>1 normal<br>2 abnormal<br>　a specialized atrial fibers<br>　b AV conducting fibers<br>　c His-Purkinje fibers<br>　d atrial fibers in AV valves | A causes of poor conductivity<br>1 partial depolarization<br>2 incomplete repolarization<br>3 impaired responsiveness<br>4 anatomical interruption<br>5 abnormal response | A phase 4 depolarization and poor conductivity<br>1 specialized myocardial fibers |
| B normal automaticity<br><br>1 abnormal frequency<br>　a tachycardia<br>　b bradycardia<br>2 abnormal rhythm<br>　a premature impulses<br>　b delayed impulses<br>　c no impulses | B delay and blockage<br><br>1 sinoatrial block<br>2 AV block<br>3 blockage of bundle of His<br>4 bundle-branch block<br>5 blockage of Purkinje fibers | B abnormal automaticity and poor conductivity<br>1 specialized myocardial fibers<br>　a afterdepolarization<br>　b other<br>2 other myocardial fibers |
| C abnormal automaticity<br>　1 afterdepolarization<br>　2 incomplete repolarization<br>　3 other<br>　　a oscillatory depolarization at low<br>　　　membrane potential<br>　　b other | C one-way blockage and re-entry<br>　1 regular re-entry<br>　　a SA node and conducting fibers<br>　　b AV node and conducting fibers<br>　　c His-Purkinje system<br>　　d Purkinje fiber-muscle cell linkages<br>　　e abnormal AV conducting fibers<br>　2 irregular re-entry<br>　　a atrial muscles<br>　　b ventricular muscles | C parasystole |

Chemical influence is not (necessarily) the direct cause of the mechanisms shown. Structural changes can be caused, for instance, by ischemic cell damage, surgical intervention or toxic cell damage.

cape the rhythm normally imposed by the SA node. For that reason, they are referred to as escape phenomena.

Arrhythmias attributable to an abnormal automaticity are usually caused by changes in phase 4 diastolic depolarization.

This may lead to changes in rate, in heart rhythm and also to the generation of impulses in other areas of the heart. The steeper slope of diastolic depolarization in cells of the SA node (under the influence of, for example, marked sympathetic $\beta$-adrenergic stimulation) results in sinus tachycardia (Table 26.1). This is caused by an increased calcium and sodium influx. A decreased slope (under the influence of, for example, marked vagus stimulation, which causes increased potassium efflux and decreased calcium influx) results in either sinus bradycardia (Table 26.1) or ectopic impulse generation. The latter may also arise if the normal rate is increased by catecholamines. This may lead to premature depolarizations (extrasystoles) which may occur sporadically or frequently and, in the latter case, may lead to ectopic rhythm.

*Direct influence on initiation*　　Certain substances can directly influence the *initiation* (and conduction) of electrical impulses by *causing changes in the ionic gradients and fluxes* which underlie these processes. For instance, strontium and barium ions can take the place of

798

calcium in carrying the electrical charge through the slow channels, which initially stimulates the heart. This is, however, followed by arrhythmia (ventricular extrasystoles, sometimes two or more in succession, and tachycardia; Figure 26.6) which leads to ventricular fibrillation and cardiac arrest. These effects are thought to be caused by an influence on the potassium efflux.

*Afterdepolarization*

By definition, an automatic rhythm is independent of a previous action potential. If it is not, the process is called *afterdepolarization*. Afterdepolarization may occur rapidly or slowly. In either case, the result is tachycardia.

The rapid type is due to a delay in repolarization and arises before phase 3 is concluded. It is caused by a decreased repolarization current carried by potassium efflux or by increased influx of sodium or calcium. This early afterdepolarization is observed after the administration of quinidine, for example. Delayed afterdepolarization takes place after complete repolarization of the previous action potential. This is observed in cases of, for example, digitalis intoxication and is attributable to increased calcium influx.

### 2.1.2 Abnormal conduction

Since the possibility of evoking an action potential in an adjacent cell is directly dependent on the rate of increase and amplitude of the action potential, changes in the level of the membrane potential also affect conduction. Arrhythmias caused by abnormal impulse conduction probably occur more often than those caused by abnormal automaticity.

Arrhythmias due to a delay or blockage of impulse transmission can be caused by various factors. In general, however, they are based on the *impulse being too weak* to excite successive cells, on *reduced excitability of the cells themselves*, or on there being an *interruption in the conduction route* due to a loss of living cells. Causes of decreased efficiency in the conduction of the action potential include partial depolarization, incomplete repolarization and the switch-over from a normal rapid action potential to one with a slow response. Most conduction abnormalities are found in the AV node, but they may also be seen in any other conducting tissue.

*Digitalis glycosides*

*Digitalis glycosides* prolong the refractory period in the AV node and thus decrease the rate of impulse conduction.

*Re-excitation or re-entry*

The delay or blockage of impulse conduction can in some cases lead to tachycardia, since the same impulse may result in more than one excitation (*re-excitation or re-entry*). Re-entry is caused by a very pronounced reduction in the conduction rate due to decreased sodium influx, slow calcium influx or both. This phenomenon is found in the SA node (early atrial contractions), in the atria (atrial fibrillation) and in the ventricles (early ventricular contractions, ventricular tachycardia).

Although nearly all arrhythmias are potentially dangerous, lethal disturbances are usually of the re-entry type.

### Summary

In general, it may be assumed that changes in heart rate or heart rhythm can be attributed to increased or decreased automaticity in the normal pacemaker cells or to increased automaticity in ectopic or latent pacemaker cells. On the other hand, changes in the action potential of conducting tissue bring about changes in the conduction of the impulses, leading to abnormal heart activity. Abnormal

799

automaticity and abnormal conduction often go hand in hand. Changed ion fluxes play an important role in all of these abnormalities.

### 2.1.3 Treatment of arrhythmias

The decision to commence *antiarrhythmic therapy* depends on the nature of the disturbance itself and on any possible underlying pathology.

Depending on the indication, there are three methods of treatment: by electrical stimulation (defibrillation, pacemaker), surgically (excision of the abnormally conducting branch) or by medication. The first two methods are used only in specific cases. The last method is the most frequently used.

*Treatment with antiarrhythmic agents*

The value of treatment with antiarrhythmic agents always has to be weighed against its potential dangers (see section 4). ECG criteria provide a first guideline for selecting a suitable therapy, but its effectiveness must be closely monitored.

Although the classification of antiarrhythmic agents is still controversial, the available drugs may be categorized into four groups, on the basis of their influence on the ionic fluxes that generate the action potential of the heart:

- sodium influx inhibitors (inhibit rapid sodium influx)
- $\beta$-blockers (inhibit catecholamine-induced stimulation)
- repolarization antagonists (delay repolarization, leading to an increased duration of the action potential and thus to a prolonged refractory period)
- calcium influx inhibitors (inhibit the slow calcium influx).

### 2.2 CONTRACTILITY DISTURBANCES

The specific ion fluxes which generate the action potential increase the intracellular free calcium concentration in the heart muscle cells. This free calcium activates myosin ATPase (myosin adenosine triphosphatase) which supplies the energy for the contraction of the myocardial cell. Various substances can influence the autonomic nervous system and hence the contractility of the heart. An abnormal increase (under the influence of, for example, norepinephrine, which acts on the $\beta$-adrenergic receptors) or decrease (by blocking these $\beta$-adrenergic receptors, for example, by propranolol) in the amount of free calcium in the cell causes increased or decreased heart contractility. These effects are referred to as *positive and negative inotropic effects*, respectively. Poor contractility is frequently also the result of a decrease in myocardial energy levels. A number of substances are known to influence processes such as the generation, release, accumulation and consumption of energy.

*Positive and negative inotropic effects*

Cardiotoxic substances may also change myocardial contractility by their influence on particular structures or steps in the excitation-contraction process. Differences in ion permeability at sarcolemmal level or changes in the activity of membrane-bound enzymes can change the action potential and hence influence the strength of myocardial contraction.

## 3    Chemically induced changes in the morphological structure of the heart

Morphological reactions of the heart to toxic damage can be classified into three categories: hypertrophy, cardiomyopathy, and myocardial necrosis and myocarditis.

### 3.1    HYPERTROPHY

Cardiac hypertrophy is defined as an increase in heart muscle mass which exceeds the normal mass for a particular age, sex and body weight. This increase in muscle mass (heart weight over 500 g in human adults) is predominantly due to an increase in the contractile elements and mitochondria. Hypertrophy usually develops as a means of compensation: a thicker muscular wall can generate more power. Three stages may be distinguished in hypertrophy:

*Stages of hypertrophy in the heart*

- *development*
- *stable hyperfunction*
- *cellular exhaustion with degenerative changes and cardiac insufficiency*

Abnormal heart weight is usually the result of congenital abnormalities, abnormal heart valve function or systemic hypertension, though it may also arise from long-term chemical influences (thyroid hormone, growth hormone, catecholamines).

> ASSIGNMENT 26.3
>
> To what extent is the etiology of the hypertrophic 'athlete's heart' comparable with that of chemically induced hypertrophy due to catecholamines?

Hypertrophy usually affects only part of the heart: the right half, in cases of abnormal lung function, or the left half in cases of persistent severe hypertension.

## 3.2 CARDIOMYOPATHY

Cardiomyopathies or heart muscle diseases are pathological states in which the heart muscle fails to function as it should. One of the ways in which this manifests itself is in a change in left ventricular pressure. The disorders can be subdivided into hypertrophic, congestive (or ventriculo-dilatory), and restrictive and/or obliterative cardiomyopathies.

*Hypertrophic cardiomyopathy*

In *hypertrophic cardiomyopathy*, the heart muscle tissue as a whole increases in size. The etiology of this process is unknown and is not thought to be related to toxic substances. It is pharmacologically interesting because its various, complex clinical manifestations can be considerably influenced by substances which block $\beta$-adrenergic receptors, by inotropic substances and by substances that alter the calcium transport.

*Congestive cardiomyopathy*

*Morphology*

The term *congestive or ventriculo-dilatory cardiomyopathy* is used for a heterogeneous group of myocardial diseases which are characterized by abnormal ventricular blood congestion, deficient systolic pump action and abnormal dilatation of the ventricular chambers. This disease is also known as *congestive cardiac insufficiency*. Mural thrombosis and focal thickening of the endocardium, myocytolysis and myocardial fibrosis are common morphological changes. In patients where this cardiomyopathy has developed independently of other diseases or external influences (primary or idiopathic dilatory cardiomyopathy), the actual cause is not known. But in other patients it is associated with chronic alcoholism, chronic administration of toxic substances (antineoplastic drugs) or viral infections.

*Obliterative cardiomyopathy*

*Restrictive cardiomyopathy*

*Obliterative cardiomyopathy* is characterized by fibrous thickening of the endocardium and mural thrombosis which lead to a partial obstruction or narrowing of the ventricular cavities. *Restrictive cardiomyopathy* is said to occur if infiltration processes (such as those in amyloidosis) or ventricular fibrosis reduce the ability of the myocardium to contract normally and bring about changes in ventricular filling. Endocardial fibrosis may be associated with toxic (methysergide, ergotamine tartrate, allylamine) or ischemic myocardial necrosis.

### 3.3 MYOCARDIAL NECROSIS AND MYOCARDITIS

*Acute toxic injury*

On the basis of its pathogenesis and the morphology of the lesions, *acute toxic injury* may be subdivided into *infarct-like injuries* or *myocardial necrosis* (due to circulatory disturbances), *myocarditis* as a result of hypersensitivity reactions, and *toxic myocarditis*. Drug induced myocardial necrosis can result indirectly from perfusion disturbances (ischemic damage), or directly from cytotoxic damage, or from a combination of the two. The end result is the same, though the location of the necrosis may differ. *Ischemic damage* usually affects specific sites, depending on the location of the perfusion disturbance (predominantly the endocardium) while *cytotoxic necrosis* is often scattered over the entire myocardium.

*Infarct*

*Infarct*-like necrotic damage can be caused, for instance, by high, toxic concentrations of isoproterenol. It was originally supposed that this necrosis was the result of an increased heart rate, contractility and oxidative metabolism. Recently, however, it has been established that isoproterenol also produces other complex effects, such as marked increases in calcium influx, stimulation of the adenylate cyclase system and formation of free radicals. Other sympathomimetic amines (norepinephrine, epinephrine) can also induce scattered foci of myocardial necrosis, predominantly in the ventricular endocardium. Catecholamine-induced myocardial damage also occurs in certain disorders in humans (tetanus, subarachnoid hemorrhages and damage to the central nervous system). Under these circumstances, large quantities of catecholamines are released, which can lead to local myocardial damage.

*Hypersensitivity*

*Myocarditis* caused by *hypersensitivity* to chemicals is a very common form of heart disease. The clinical criteria are: previous use of the substance without ill effects; the hypersensitivity is not dose-dependent; the reaction is characterized by classic allergic symptoms which remain until the substance is removed, and immunological confirmation. This myocarditis is characterized by infiltration of eosinophils and mononuclear cells (predominantly lymphocytes and plasma cells) into the heart muscle. The infiltration may be focal or diffuse and is associated with local myocytolysis. The absence of widespread myocardial necrosis and fibrosis distinguishes this disorder from other types of myocarditis. The hypersensitivity is thought to be due to an immunological reaction in which the substance or one of its metabolites acts as a hapten. This hapten would bind to an endogenous macromolecule and thereby become immunogenic.

*Toxic myocarditis*

Chemicals can also cause toxic myocarditis directly, resulting in extensive cell damage and cell death. This toxicity is dose-dependent. *Toxic myocarditis* is characterized by interstitial edema, multifocal necrosis and fibrosis, and infiltration by lymphocytes, plasma cells and neutrophils. Eosinophils are seldom present.

> ASSIGNMENT 26.4
>
> What are the principal 'cardiotoxic' effects which can arise from an excessive administration of catecholamine?

### 3.4 BIOCHEMICAL CHANGES

As with morphological injury to the liver and kidney, cellular injury to the heart, which releases intracellular enzymes, may be demonstrated by biochemical tests. Soon after a myocardial infarction, during the necrotic phase, increased levels of AST (aspartic aminotransferase), LDH (lactate dehydrogenase) and

CPK (creatine phosphokinase) can be observed. These plasma tests are of particular diagnostic value when combined with other techniques.

*Summary*

The morphological damage caused in the heart by toxic substances normally manifests itself as either a focal or diffuse (degenerative) change. The loss of vital myocardial tissue can ultimately lead to abnormal heart function.

4      **Some important cardiotoxic substances**

Table 26.2 summarizes the principal groups of cardiotoxic substances and their effects. Each of these groups will be briefly discussed.

*Ethanol*

*Ethanol* reduces the force of contraction of the human heart if plasma levels exceed 75 mg per 100 ml. Negative dromotropism and lowering of the threshold level for ventricular fibrillation have been observed in chronic drinkers, leading to ventricular fibrillation and sudden death. Alcoholism also decreases the myocardial capacity at increased cardiac activity, resulting in shortness of breath due to congestion in the pulmonary vessels.

*Halogenated hydrocarbons*

*Halogenated hydrocarbons* lower the heart rate, contractility and conduction. These substances include volatile anesthetics such as halothane, methoxyflurane and enflurane, even at concentrations used in surgery. They can cause cardiac depression and, in rare cases, even cardiac arrest.

*Heavy metals*

*Cadmium, lead* and *cobalt* are among the *heavy metals* involved in selective cardiotoxicity. They are negatively inotropic and dromotropic and can also cause structural changes. Cobalt, for example, has been discovered to be the cause of an endemic cardiomyopathy in heavy beer drinkers in Canada, where it was used as an additive to stabilize the froth. Although the amount of cobalt thus ingested was lower than that used in certain therapies, the poor general nutritional state that is typical of chronic drinkers (possibly in combination with an

TABLE   26.2
The most important cardiotoxic substances and their effects

| | Chronotropism | Dromotropism | Bathmo-tropism | Inotropism | Arrhythmo-genic | Structural changes |
|---|---|---|---|---|---|---|
| ethanol | | − | + | − | + | chronic cardiomyopathy |
| halogenated alkanes | − | − | + | − | + | chronic degenerative changes |
| heavy metals | | − | | − | + | chronic degenerative changes |
| digitalis | − | − | + | + | + | |
| catecholamines | + | + | + | + | + | acute focal necrosis, hypertrophy |
| antiarrhythmic agents | − | − | | − | + | |
| centrally active substances | | | | | | |
| - tricyclic antidepressants | + | − | + | | + | |
| - neuroleptics | − | | | − | + | |
| antineoplastic anthracylines | | | | | + | chronic cardiomyopathy |

Not all substances in a particular group have cardiotoxic effects. For example, not all neuroleptic agents induce arrhythmias.

− = decrease
+ = increase

as yet unidentified factor) made these people more susceptible to the cardiotoxicity of cobalt. The cardiotoxicity is thought to be principally attributable to inhibition of the mitochondrial energy metabolism.

ASSIGNMENT 26.5

Explain how inhibition of mitochondrial energy metabolism can lead to cardiotoxicity.

*Digitalis glycosides*

*Digitalis glycosides* (particularly digoxin and digitoxin) and glycosides of strophanthin and oleandrin are prescribed for patients with congestive cardiac insufficiency and arrhythmias. Because these patients are usually seriously ill and the therapeutic ratio of these substances is rather low, cardiotoxic side-effects occur quite frequently. These glycosides inhibit the sarcolemmal $Na^+/K^+$-ATPase, resulting in an increased intracellular $Na^+$ concentration. This in turn leads to an increased intracellular $Ca^{2+}$ concentration via the $Na^+/Ca^{2+}$ exchange mechanism, and hence to increased cardiac contractility.

In addition, the increased intracellular calcium levels result in increased automaticity, which together with other effects of digitalis glycosides (such as increased vagal activity and delayed AV conduction) can lead to arrhythmia. Ventricular extrasystoles can produce ventricular fibrillation, decreased AV conduction and complete cardiac arrest. Humans, dogs and cats are most sensitive to digitalis, while rats are least sensitive.

*Epinephrine*

*Epinephrine and its synthetic analogs,* primarily $\beta$-adrenergic receptor agonists such as isoproterenol, have positive chronotropic and inotropic effects. The side-effects of these substances are related to these pharmacological activities. An overdose of such substances can lead to changes in the ECG which resemble those due to hypoxia (i.e. changes in the ST segment, see Figure 26.5, and ectopic heart beats) and also endocardial necrosis. $\beta$-Adrenergic receptor antagonists (such as sotalol) and antihypertensive agents which inhibit the adrenergic function (reserpine, guanethidine) decrease cardiac contractility and may cause AV blockage, which can lead to cardiac insufficiency.

*Antiarrhythmic agents*

In principle, all *antiarrhythmic agents* are toxic, at least when administered in unduly high concentrations. They reduce the conductivity and excitability of the myocardium, which in fact constitutes the basis of their therapeutic use. Quinidine and procainamide prolong the QRS and QT intervals. This condition increases the susceptibility to arrhythmia by, for instance, the "re-entry mechanism" (see section 2.1.2). Overdoses of lidocaine and phenytoin cause sinus bradycardia and cardiac arrest. Local anesthetics of the amide type cause ventricular fibrillation and cardiac arrest if injected intravenously without due caution.

*Tricyclic antidepressants*

*Tricyclic antidepressants,* such as imipramine and amitriptyline, have quinidine-like effects on the heart.

An overdose causes extension of the P-R, QRS and Q-T intervals and blockage of the impulse conduction in the bundle of His. This results in supraventricular or ventricular arrhythmia.

*Neuroleptic substances*

*Neuroleptic substances,* such as *phenothiazine* and *butyrophenone derivatives* can induce dose-dependent tachyarrhythmias, as well as changes similar to those described above for tricyclic antidepressants, though the incidence is lower. Older patients with an existing heart disease are at highest risk.

*Psychoactive substances*

The non-medical use of *psychoactive substances*, such as amphetamine, cocaine, ecstasy and marijuana, may evoke a cardiac crisis. These substances increase the workload imposed on the heart by raising the heart rate and blood pressure. They are especially dangerous for people with angina, hypertension, coronary arteriosclerosis or cerebrovascular disorders.

*Anthracyclines*

*Anthracyclines* are antibiotics which are among the most effective antitumor agents in clinical use. They are, however, potent cardiotoxic compounds (daunorubicin, doxorubicin). The lowest therapeutic doses can cause arrhythmia, which is thought to be due to the release of histamine. Chronic treatment results in congestive cardiomyopathy. The development of this myopathy is slow, and depends on the cumulative doses. It may not become manifest until several months after treatment.

The pathogenesis of this myocardial injury is thought to be linked to the formation of oxygen radicals and the peroxidation of membrane lipids, followed by changes in permeability and cellular homeostasis.

## 5    Blood vessels

### 5.1    ANATOMY AND GENERAL FUNCTION

The vessels of the cardiovascular system can be divided into arteries and veins. A cross-section of the vessel wall shows three layers starting from the inside: the *tunica intima* (which in normal blood vessels usually consists of only one cell layer, the endothelium), the muscular *tunica media*, and the connective tissue layer called *tunica adventitia*.

*Elastic and muscular arteries*

The arteries may be subdivided into two categories: *elastic and muscular arteries*. In the large elastic arteries, such as the aorta and the carotid arteries, the tunica media consists of smooth muscle cells, a small amount of connective tissue, and large amounts of elastic material, which may be present in various layers. The smaller the diameter of the arteries, the smaller the amount of elastic material. This means that the tunica media consists largely of smooth muscle cells: these are the muscular arteries. If the tunica media of the vessel wall contains only one or two layers of smooth muscle cells, the muscular arteries are called *arterioles* or *resistance vessels*.

*Arterioles*

The arterioles ultimately distribute the blood to the *capillaries*, which consist largely of one endothelial cell layer.

Since the movement of blood in the arteries is caused by contractions of the heart, it is a pulsed movement. If the arterial walls were not flexible, the blood supply to the capillaries would be regularly interrupted. Since the large arteries close to the heart have a dilatable, elastic wall, only part of the power of the heart's contraction is used to force the blood through the blood vessels; the remainder is used to dilate the elastic arterial wall. The potential energy thus stored in the elastic vessel walls during systole is released during the heart's inactive period (diastole). This release of vessel-wall tension provides an additional pump action, which means that the blood is also forced onwards during diastole, thus ensuring continuous perfusion of the capillaries. The muscular arteries can contract and relax and thus influence the distribution of blood to the various tissues and organs. Contraction and relaxation of arterioles produces changes in the peripheral resistance to perfusion, which in turn influences blood pressure. The permeability of the capillaries to macromolecular substances varies from one organ to the next and depends on the structural variations in the endothelial cells.

*Veins*

From the capillaries the blood returns to the heart via the *veins*. These usually run parallel to the corresponding arteries. The cross-sections of the individual veins are larger than those of the corresponding arteries. The venous walls are thinner, more flexible and less elastic than those of the arteries. The small veins, or venules, which receive blood from the capillaries, contain relatively few smooth muscle cells. Together with capillaries, these venules play an important role in the exchange between tissue and blood, especially in *inflammatory phenomena*. Closer to the heart, the diameter and thickness of the venous walls gradually increase. The ratio between the amount of connective tissue and the amount of smooth muscle cells is much higher for veins than for the corresponding arteries. Many medium-sized veins, particularly those in the extremities, possess valves which prevent reflux of blood. The most important function of the veins is to regulate the blood supply to the heart. This is achieved by both active and passive changes in capacity. The active expulsion of blood is established by contraction of the smooth muscle cells, while passive changes in capacity result from decreased venous pressure. The latter process is caused by contraction of the resistance vessels.

*Innervation*

Except for the capillaries, virtually all arteries and veins are innervated by the autonomic nervous system.

This innervation varies greatly between blood vessels and is most pronounced in the arterial vascular bed. The contraction and relaxation of blood vessels is regulated in this way.

## 5.2   CIRCULATORY REGULATION

Normal functioning of the cardiovascular system requires at least two important parameters to be accurately regulated: the mean *blood pressure* and the *cardiac output*. The mean blood pressure is normally kept within fairly narrow limits. The cardiac output is controlled by the oxygen consumption of the organism as a whole and can therefore show considerable variations.

How is the blood pressure regulated?

*Blood-pressure regulation*

In the *short term*, the blood pressure is controlled by the arterial *baroreceptors*. These pressure-sensitive receptors are situated in the aortic arch and in a particular site in the carotid arteries. They are connected via nerve fibers to the blood pressure regulating centers in the brain. These centers are in their turn connected to the heart and to the muscle cells of the arterioles and venules. Excessive blood pressure increases the stimulation of the baroreceptors and hence of the centers in the brain. These centers in turn decrease the stimulation of the heart and blood vessels. The heart beat decreases in strength and frequency, arteriolar resistance decreases and the venous capacity increases. This combination of effects causes the peripheral resistance to be reduced and the blood pressure to be lowered. Too low a blood pressure produces the opposite effects, ultimately causing the blood pressure to rise again.

In the *long term*, the regulation of blood pressure is achieved by adjustment of the blood volume. This adjustment is achieved through hormonal action (renin-angiotensin system, antidiuretic hormone, aldosterone).

*Cardiac output*

The *cardiac output* can vary by a factor of 5–6 and is dependent on the oxygen consumption, as was mentioned above. The changes in cardiac output ultimately result from changes in the amount of venous blood returning from the periphery, in combination with changes in myocardial contractility and heart rate. The distribution of the total cardiac output to the various organs is determined by neuronal and local regulation.

*Neuronal control*

*Neuronal control* consists primarily of an increase or decrease in sympathetic stimulation. These effects are tissue-specific and are largely dependent on the density and proportions of $\alpha$-adrenergic and $\beta$-adrenergic receptors in the blood vessels. Stimulation of the $\alpha$-receptors usually causes contraction. This stimulation increases the influx of calcium ions through the slow channels. The cytoplasmic calcium activates an enzyme that catalyzes the interaction between myosin and actin, which leads to contraction of the smooth muscle cell. Stimulation of $\beta$-receptors causes relaxation. This is achieved through the efflux of calcium ions from the cell under the influence of certain intracellular mechanisms.

The local control of blood supply, the so-called autoregulation, is mediated by products of the cell metabolism.

## 6  Toxic changes in the blood vessels

### 6.1  BLOOD-PRESSURE CHANGES

From section 5.2, it has become clear that an optimal function of the cardiovascular system requires two parameters to be accurately regulated, namely the mean arterial blood pressure and the cardiac output. If either of these two parameters drops sharply the blood supply to vital organs is reduced.

> ASSIGNMENT  26.6
>
> How is it possible that in a general ischemic crisis of the heart the endocardium is damaged sooner than the epicardium?

*Hypotension*

Acute intoxication, for example, by sedatives which act on the central nervous system or by an overdose of certain antihypertensive agents may lead to *hypotension*. This acute low blood pressure can usually be compensated for by sympathico-adrenal activity.

> What will happen if the low blood pressure is not compensated for?

*Shock*

If (too) much fluid is lost from the body due to frequent vomiting or diarrhea, for example as a consequence of severe gastrointestinal infection or poisoning, the intravascular blood volume falls significantly. This leads to a sharp decrease in cardiac output and ultimately to *circulatory insufficiency* or *shock*. The blood volume is so low that the capillary system can no longer be filled, so that hypoxia or acidosis set in, ultimately leading to cell death. In such a state of shock, all physiological parameters involved in tissue perfusion are disturbed, often with fatal consequences. Other causes of shock are serious arrhythmias, cardiomyopathies and poor perfusion under the influence of certain mediators (histamine, leukotrienes and kinins). These mediators produce the anaphylactic reactions, so that the intrinsic tonus of the blood vessels is altered to such an extent that sufficient tissue perfusion becomes impossible. The most critical effect of shock thus takes place at the level of the microcirculation.

*Hypertension*

In contrast to what has been described previously, certain substances can raise blood pressure, acutely or chronically. *Hypertension* can take place acutely following an overdose of sympathomimetic and anticholinergic substances.

> ASSIGNMENT  26.7
>
> How do such sympathomimetic and anticholinergic substances cause hypertension?

807

Mineralocorticoids, administered together with sodium chloride, cause sodium retention and hence an increased blood volume, resulting in hypertension. Oral contraceptives with high estrogen concentrations also cause hypertension, by stimulating angiotensinogen synthesis. Angiotensin II, which results from the conversion of angiotensinogen (via angiotensin I), is a highly potent vasoconstrictor, which makes the resistance vessels contract, causing increased peripheral resistance. This ultimately leads to an increased blood pressure.

*Effect on blood coagulation*

Finally, it should be noted that some substances (independent of structural damage) can evoke *intravascular coagulation phenomena*, which may result in blockage of arteries or veins. This can occur due to the influence of these substances on factors involved in coagulation or through changes in the contraction state of arteries or veins.

## 6.2    STRUCTURAL CHANGES

Substances can cause degenerative and/or inflammatory changes in blood vessels. These may result from an excessive pharmacological effect or from interactions with the vascular structure or functional macromolecules.

Ergotamine intoxication leads to prolonged arterial constriction, which causes damage to the vessel walls.

*Edema formation*

Mediators such as histamine, serotonin and bradykinin cause contraction of the endothelial cells in the postcapillary venules. This contraction results in openings between the endothelial cells, which allow plasma and other blood components to leak into the surrounding tissue, leading to *edema formation*. Such edema can have a negative effect on tissue perfusion by compressing the capillaries.

*Thrombosis*

Some substances cause direct endothelial damage, exposing the underlying connective tissue. The subsequent coagulation phenomenon with which the system tries to repair the damage may lead to *thrombosis*. Pieces of these thrombi may break off and obstruct the smaller blood vessels (emboli). A definite correlation has been shown to exist between the use of contraceptive steroids and the development of thrombo-embolism. A more comprehensive direct toxic effect has been observed for the industrial substance allylamine. Allylamine is an unsaturated aliphatic amine used in the production of drugs, antiseptics and plastics. It is the active metabolite of the amine, acrolein, which damages vessel walls. This results in arteriosclerosis especially of the aorta and the coronary arteries.

### Intermezzo

*Arteriosclerosis* is a general term including a group of vascular diseases of the arteries which can be caused by a wide range of forms of vessel wall damage. This pathology is characterized by thickening of the tunica intima (caused by the proliferation of smooth muscle cells from the tunica media) and by degeneration of smooth muscle cells migrated in the tunica intima and/or tunica media, with excessive formation of connective tissue and accumulation of complex hydrocarbons. It is often accompanied by infiltration of various blood components and by calcification. The changes described can occur in varying proportions. *Atherosclerosis* is the most common form of arteriosclerosis and is, in its later stages of development, characterized by the accumulation of large quantities of lipids and by fibrosis. Thrombotic phenomena are frequently seen due to the damage to the vessel wall. The main consequences of arteriosclerosis are loss of elasticity and narrowing of the arteries (Figure 26.7).

ASSIGNMENT   26.8

What may be the consequences of loss of elasticity in the vessel wall?

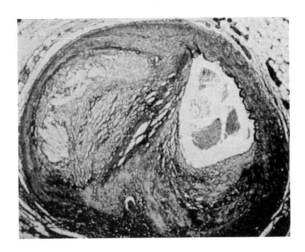

FIGURE 26.7
Atherosclerotic coronary artery of a middle-aged man
The lumen is reduced to 20% of its original size.

The organs (such as the brain or the heart) which are supplied by these arteries often receive too little blood, resulting in a stroke or myocardial infarction.

*Hypervitaminosis D*

Arterial blood vessels appear to be highly susceptible to an excess of vitamin D (*hypervitaminosis D*). The elastic tissue and surrounding matrix begin to accumulate large quantities of calcium, leading to calcification and serious cell damage in the arteries. Together with other risk factors (hypertension, stress, hypercholesterolemia), this calcium excess can accelerate the process of arteriosclerosis. Other substances, such as carbon monoxide, carbon dioxide and homocysteine can also accelerate this process. *Inflammation* of the blood vessels (usually the arterioles, capillaries and venules) can arise under the influence of certain substances (drug-induced vasculitis, for instance by gold salts, methyldopa, penicillin, sulfonamides) or may be associated with serum sickness or systemic bacterial or protozoic infections (hypersensitivity angitit).

*Hemorrhage*

*Hemorrhagic spots or petechiae*

In addition to the formation of edema caused by changes in the permeability of the endothelial cell layer, the affected blood vessels may be so severely damaged that red blood cells also escape from the blood vessels. This is referred to as internal bleeding or *hemorrhage*. Serious hemorrhages can occur following poisoning by heavy metals. If this happens in combination with serious loss of fluid from the inflamed and hemorrhagic areas, it can lead to circulatory shock. Less serious, local hemorrhages caused by other types of acute poisoning usually occur at the capillary level: these are *hemorrhagic spots or petechiae*. Lathyrus (sweet pea) alkaloids affect the vascular connective tissue of large arteries. This results in weakening of the vessel walls, and ultimately in dilation or aneurysms. The arterial wall can become so severely weakened that even the normal propulsion of the blood can cause rupture of the vessel walls.

*Summary*

Substances can affect both the function and the structure of anatomically different types of blood vessels. The result is usually disturbed tissue perfusion.

## 7 Test procedures for detecting cardiovascular toxicity

The goal of much experimental toxicological research is the characterization of functional and morphological effects or side effects of a substance on various organ systems. This includes determining cardiovascular toxicity and establishing its dose-response relationship. Morphological side-effects are usually established after chronic administration, using light microscopy and possibly electron microscopy. Most research is, however, carried out to study acute functional effects. The cardiotoxic or vasculotoxic effects of a (new) drug and the predictability of these effects are frequently correlated with the pharmacological activity of the substance and usually manifest themselves after an overdose. Such toxic effects are most frequent in substances used in the treatment of cardiovascular disease.

Acute cardiovascular toxicity may be studied by *in vivo* and *in vitro* experiments.

### 7.1 IN VIVO

Most experiments are performed on anesthetized or conscious dogs. One advantage of doing experiments on an *anesthetized dog* is that the animal is kept in a stable state by the anesthesia. This allows simultaneous measurement of all kinds of parameters, such as ventricular, aortic and arterial pressure, ECG, and flow measurements. (Figure 26.8).

The disadvantages include the risk of acute surgical trauma, possible interference of the anesthetic with the substance being examined, the fact that the substance can only be administered intravenously, and that behavioral parameters cannot be investigated. In the *conscious dog*, by contrast, behavior can be observed and substances can be administered orally, if necessary chronically. Depending on the place where the catheter or flow meter is implanted, it is possible to measure the arterial or ventricular blood pressure, the blood supply to the heart, brain, kidney, intestine and skeletal muscle, or other ventricular and vascular parameters. However, since only one or two implants can normally be used at the same time, only a few parameters can be measured concurrently. Another disadvantage is that the dog may be influenced by its surroundings and thus may be less stable.

### 7.2 IN VITRO

The isolated perfused heart is often used to measure the effect of substances on the electrical and mechanical activity of the heart and on coronary perfusion. Isolated Purkinje fibers and cultivated heart cells are used to study the influence of substances on the course of electrically induced action potentials.

The isolation makes it possible to determine these parameters independently of systemic influences and innervation. These *in vitro* systems enable further testing of several substances or various concentrations of the same substance over a short period of time.

Although extreme pharmacological (toxic) effects can usually be detected with these test systems, there may be differences between species. It should also be noted that preclinical toxicity studies are usually carried out on healthy, well-fed, juvenile or adult animals. This may mean that facultative toxicity due to particular predisposing conditions or factors is overlooked. It is known that factors such as existing cardiovascular disease, overweight, poor nutritional state and old age make the cardiovascular system more susceptible to potentially toxic substances. Moreover, interactions between various chemicals may play an impor-

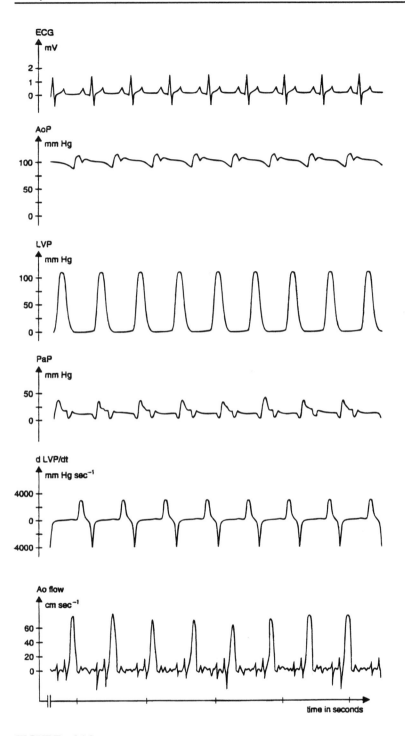

FIGURE   26.8
time in seconds
Normal hemodynamic parameters measured in an anesthetized dog
Time: in seconds
ECG: electrocardiogram
AoP: aortic pressure
LVP: left ventricular pressure
PaP: pulmonary arterial pressure
dLVP/dt: changes in left ventricular pressure as a function of time
AoF: aortic flow or stroke volume

tant role in the development of severe, acute toxicity. This may necessitate the use of additional models, such as the experimental induction of a myocardial infarction, cardiomyopathic hamsters, obesity and drug-interaction models.

## 8    Summary

The heart is not often the target organ for toxic substances. Nonetheless, a wide variety of xenobiotics may have a negative effect on the physiology and/or anatomy of this organ. The conduction of electrical signals and the cellular metabolism are particularly susceptible to toxicological effects by virtue of their specific functions.

Cardiotoxic substances can be divided into those substances which primarily interfere with the heart function and those that primarily affect the structure of the organ. These effects can, of course, not be completely separated: changes in the anatomy of the heart will influence its conduction and hence its function. On the other hand, prolonged functional disturbance may leave its mark on the structure.

Notable functional disturbances include arrhythmias and decreased contractility. Antiarrhythmic agents administered in non-therapeutic doses are notorious for their arrhythmogenic effect. Well known examples are the digitalis glycosides. Pathological cardiac abnormalities induced by xenobiotics can be subdivided into hypertrophies, cardiomyopathies, necrosis and myocarditis, and pericarditis. Hypertrophy is usually an adaptive process.

In this study unit the toxicology of blood vessels is also briefly discussed. Important pathological/pathophysiological phenomena here include edema formation, thrombosis, hemorrhage, hypotension and hypertension, and shock. The final section presented some information on the use of *in vivo* and *in vitro* experiments to determine cardiovascular toxicity.

SELF ASSESSMENT QUESTIONS

1    List the successive parts of the conducting system of the heart. Explain briefly how the coordination of the heart contraction is achieved.

2    Which phases can be distinguished in the action potential of a rapid-response myocardial cell and which ions play a role in each of them? What is the difference between an action potential with a delayed response and an action potential with an early response?

3    Give a brief description of a normal electrocardiogram (see Figure 26.5). What information does an ECG provide?

4    How is the blood pressure regulated?

5    Name the essential changes which cause arrhythmias.

6    What is meant by the term automaticity and where in the heart does it occur? What are the consequences of this automaticity?

7    Which abnormality is shown by the ECG below? What characterizes this abnormal ECG?

8   What is the potential danger of treating arrhythmias with antiarrhythmic agents?

9   Which categories of chemically induced changes in the morphological structure of the heart can be distinguished?

10   What is meant by circulatory insufficiency or shock?


FEEDBACK

1   **Answers to the assignments**

26.1 Yes. This is directly related to the force that the individual sections have to provide to fulfil their function. The atria with their weak musculature only need to pump the blood to the ventricles. The slightly thicker right ventricle pumps blood to the lungs in the lesser blood circulation; the very muscular left ventricle pumps blood to all the body organs in the greater blood circulation.

26.2 Intrinsic properties of the heart which are responsible for the pump function:

   • automaticity
   • excitation
   • conduction
   • contractility

26.3 They are both caused by excessive stimulation of β-adrenergic receptors: the athlete's heart results indirectly, because of the higher load, while the catecholamine has a direct influence.

26.4 The most important cardiotoxic effects of excessive administration of catecholamine are:

   • increased heart rate
   • increased automaticity, leading to irregular rhythm
   • myocardial necrosis.

26.5 Since the heart muscle has to work continuously, it continuously requires large amounts of energy, which are provided largely by the mitochondrial metabolism in the myocardium. Inhibition of this metabolism may thus lead to a lack of energy resources and hence to abnormal heart function.

26.6 Because the capillary pressure is lowest in the endocardial tissue. This means that, compared to the epicardium, the restriction of blood supply can occur more rapidly in the endocardium.

26.7 Sympathomimetic agents and anticholinergic substances increase the contraction state of the resistance vessels.

26.8 The potential energy that may be stored in the elastic vessel wall during systole is reduced. As a result of a decreased release of vessel-wall tension during diastole this may affect the additional pump function, leading to discontinuous perfusion of capillaries.

## 2    Answers to the self assessment questions

1    • SA node, atrioventricular (AV) node, bundle of His, Purkinje fibers.

   • The electrical stimulation to contract arises in the SA node, which sends stimuli to the muscle cells of both atria, inducing them to contract. The stimuli then reach the AV node. Here they are conducted rather slowly, until they reach the bundle of His. This passes them on via its two branches, to the Purkinje fibers and then to the two ventricles. Because of the relatively slow conduction of impulses in the AV node, the ventricles contract evenly. Another effect is that the contraction of the ventricles does not coincide with that of the atria. This ensures a well-coordinated pump function of the heart.

2    • Depolarization phase, plateau phase, repolarization phase and diastolic depolarization phase.

   • Sodium, calcium, chloride, potassium.

   • The resting potential in the pacemaker cells or cells with a delayed response is less negative than that in cells with an early response, the difference being 30 mV. At this level, –60 mV, the rapid sodium channels are inactive and only the slow sodium and calcium channels are active. The depolarization therefore proceeds rather slowly. There is no obvious plateau phase.

3    • The ECG reflects the electrical activity of the heart. The P wave represents the depolarization or the contraction of the atria. This is followed by a short interval without electrical activity, due to the rather slow impulse conduction in the AV node. The QRS complex which then follows shows the depolarization of the two ventricles, and the T wave reflects the repolarization of the ventricles.

   • The ECG provides information on the heart rhythm, the impulse conduction and the condition of the heart muscle.

4    In the short term, blood pressure is regulated by arterial baroreceptors, which are connected via nerve fibers with the blood-pressure regulating centers in the brain. These centers are in turn connected with the heart and the vessel walls of the peripheral arterioles and venules. The release of specific neuronal substances in heart and blood vessels ensures a combination of effects which raises or lowers the blood pressure. Long-term blood pressure regulation is established by adjustment of the blood volume by hormones.

5    Abnormal impulse generation or automaticity and abnormal impulse conduction. The two may coincide and are interrelated.

6    Automaticity is the capacity of heart muscle cells to discharge spontaneously without external influence. Thus, the electrical stimulus for a contraction of the heart muscle arises in the SA node itself. This property is not restricted to cells in the SA node. In principle, the entire impulse conduction system has the ability to discharge spontaneously. The consequence is that other parts of the impulse conduction system can take over the function of the SA node or can influence it, possibly resulting in functional disturbances.

7   •   Atrial fibrillation.

    •   This appears from the occurrence of several electrical activity peaks in rapid succession in the atria, interspersed between the fairly normal QRS complexes. (The latter indicates a more or less normal ventricular contraction.)

8   Since therapeutic use of these substances is based on a reduction of the conductivity and excitability of the heart, incorrect dosage or use of the wrong substance can lead to arrhythmias.

9   •   Hypertrophy: an increase in heart muscle mass which exceeds the amount considered normal for a particular age, sex and body weight.

    •   Cardiomyopathy: a pathological state of the heart muscle, leading to imperfect cardiac function.

    •   Myocardial necrosis: infarction-like injuries.

    •   Myocarditis: inflammation of the heart muscle.

10  Circulatory insufficiency (shock) is a state in which the intravascular blood volume is so greatly reduced that the capillary system can no longer be filled. This produces hypoxia or acidosis, which may lead to cell death. In such a state of shock all physiological parameters of tissue perfusion are disturbed, which often results in death.

# Contents Study unit 27
# Toxicology of the blood: pathophysiology, toxicological pathology and mechanistic aspects

0-8493-9232-2/96/$6.00 + $.50
© 1996 by CRC Press, Inc.

# Toxicology of the blood: pathophysiology, toxicological pathology and mechanistic aspects

## J. J. M. Marx

### INTRODUCTION

Compared to most other cells in the body, blood cells have a short life-span. In the toxicology of blood, therefore, not only are the effects on the metabolism and function of mature blood cells extremely important, but also the effects on hemopoiesis. The response to toxic influences manifests itself primarily in a reduction in the numbers of circulating blood cells, in functional and structural abnormalities of the blood cells and, to a much lesser extent, by morphological changes. Exposure may occur, in chronic as well as in acute form, due to poisonous compounds in the environment, at the workplace and in the household, due to drugs and sometimes even due to endogenous substances. Sometimes, an acute intoxication may, after a long interval, induce new abnormalities. These interactions may become complicated by injurious effects of necessary treatment. The following case study may serve as an example.

### CASE STUDY

At the beginning of July 1965, Mr. R, born in 1917, had problems with mosquitoes. He closed all his doors and windows and made extensive use of an aerosol pesticide which contained lindane (hexachlorocyclohexane). The next day he felt tired and apathetic, as did his daughter. He also suffered from diarrhea, muscular spasms and dilated pupils. His gait became unsteady and he felt progressively more tired and dizzy. Four weeks later he was admitted to a hospital showing bruises, petechia and tightness of the chest during exertion. He was found to have not only severe anemia (Hb 4.2 mmol l$^{-1}$) but also a serious granulocyte and thrombocyte deficit. Bone marrow obtained by sternal puncture showed significantly decreased production of granulocytes and thrombocytes and a pathological production of erythrocytes. This bone marrow aplasia was attributed to lindane. Treatment with corticosteroids (adrenocortical hormone) had to be supplemented with regular transfusions of erythrocytes and thrombocytes. During this period, the patient developed antibodies against blood products, which resulted in cold shivers during the transfusions. He gradually improved, however, and 1 year later his blood count had returned to normal. At the end of 1968, the patient was readmitted. He once again felt tired and regularly passed red urine. The production of red blood cell precursors in his bone marrow was now greatly increased.

Further investigation showed a paroxysmal nocturnal hemoglobinuria (PNH).

In this condition there is increased sensitivity of blood cells, in particular erythrocytes, to complement. Large numbers of erythrocytes are degraded in the bloodstream. This happens periodically and often at night. The hemoglobin released is mainly found in the urine. Some of it, however, is reabsorbed and degraded in the kidney cells. The iron released causes local iron accumulation. Meanwhile, kidney function deteriorates. The need for transfusions increases, which leads to hemochromatosis (general iron accumulation) and liver damage, owing to the toxicity of iron.

Due to the increased excretion of bilirubin via the biliary tract, the patient developed gallstones with occlusion symptoms and inflammation of the pancreas. The operation to remove the gall bladder presented some complications, as often happens in cases of PNH. In 1988, the general condition of the patient was mediocre, though intensive hematological monitoring enabled Mr. R to lead a reasonably normal life.

> Describe, in chronological order, the abnormalities which the patient developed after lindane intoxication.

This study unit deals with the toxic effects of compounds on hemopoiesis and on the functioning of the various types of blood cell, such as erythrocytes, leukocytes and blood platelets. In discussing the toxic effects of compounds, priority will be given to the disturbances in the functioning of blood.

LEARNING OBJECTIVES

After studying this unit, you will be expected to

— be familiar with the most important normal values for blood cells, relevant plasma proteins and iron metabolism
— be able to give a description of the morphology, function, production and degradation of blood cells
— be able to indicate which (groups of) chemicals are harmful to the blood and hemopoietic organs
— be aware of the hazards of ionizing radiation for hemopoiesis
— know which mechanisms underlie acute and chronic injury to blood cells and hemopoiesis
— be able to describe the function and hazards of iron and oxygen metabolites.

*Study hints*

In this unit subjects in hematology are referred to which are normally discussed in courses and handbooks in biochemistry. Only those aspects of hematology will be dealt with that are essential for an understanding of common toxic influences and phenomena. The study load should be about 3–4 hours.

> While studying this unit, make a list of all the toxic compounds discussed. For each of these, note the pathological effect and, where possible, the mode of action.

## STUDY CORE

### 1 Physiology and morphology

In order to understand the mechanisms of toxicity on blood and hemopoietic tissues it is necessary to have some insight into their physiology and morphology. Furthermore, the interpretation of abnormal findings requires some knowledge of the normal values.

## 1.1  BLOOD CELLS

Blood comprises about 50% liquid (plasma) and 50% cells: red blood cells (erythrocytes), white blood cells (leukocytes) and blood platelets (thrombocytes). The numbers of these cells in peripheral blood are given in table 27.1.

> ASSIGNMENT  27.1
>
> Which blood values are different for men and women?

### 1.1.1  Examination of blood cells

The diagnosis of all blood abnormalities is based on quantitative and qualitative examination of peripheral blood cells. Quantitative examination is now practiced virtually everywhere by means of advanced electronic counting devices, which work quickly and accurately. The results for leukocytes and thrombocytes, however, are unreliable at both extremely high and low values. In such cases, a second check is carried out 'manually', that is, under the microscope. To differentiate leukocytes and for the qualitative morphological examination of blood cells a blood smear is made on a microscopic slide. This smear is then stained with a mixture of acidophilic and basophilic dyes (for example May-Grünwald-Giemsa stain). This results in the acidophilic and basophilic cell components being stained red and blue, respectively. Figure 27.1 shows some characteristics of normal blood cells.

### 1.1.2  Functions of blood cells

*Erythrocytes*

The most important task of the *erythrocytes* is to transport oxygen to the tissues and carbon dioxide to the lungs. Erythrocytes do not have a nucleus and are no

TABLE  27.1
Quantitative data on blood cells in healthy adults

|  | Men | Women | Percentage |
|---|---|---|---|
| hemoglobin (mmol $l^{-1}$) | 8.6–10.7 | 7.4–9.4 |  |
| erythrocytes ($\times 10^{12}$ $l^{-1}$) | 4.2–5.5 | 3.7–5.0 |  |
| hematocrit (1/1) | 0.41–0.55 | 0.36–0.46 |  |
| MCV (fl) | 85–105 | 85–105 |  |
| MCH (fmol) | 1.75–2.23 | 1.75–2.23 |  |
| MCHC (mmol $l^{-1}$) | 20–23 | 20–23 |  |
| thrombocytes ($\times 10^9$ $l^{-1}$) | 150–400 | 150–400 |  |
| leukocytes ($\times 10^9 l^{-1}$) |  |  |  |
| total | 4.0–11.0 | 4.0–11.0 | 100 |
| lymphocytes | 1.5–3.5 | 1.5–3.6 | 20–40 |
| monocytes | 0.2–0.8 | 0.2–0.8 | 1–6 |
| neutrophilic granulocytes* | 2.5–7.5 | 2.5–7.5 | 50–75 |
| eosinophilic granulocytes | 0.04–0.44 | 0.04–0.44 | 1–3 |
| basophilic granulocytes | 0.01–0.1 | 0.01–0.1 | 0–1 |

$$MCV = \text{mean cell volume} = \frac{\text{hematocrit } (1/1)}{\text{number of erythrocytes } l^{-1}} \times 10^{15}$$

$$MCH = \text{mean cell hemoglobin} = \frac{\text{hemoglobin (mmol } l^{-1})}{\text{number of erythrocytes } l^{-1}} \times 10^{12}$$

$$MCHC = \text{mean cell hemoglobin concentration} = \frac{\text{hemoglobin (mmol } l^{-1})}{\text{hematocrit } (1/1)}$$

*cells with rod-shaped nuclei: 1–5%, cells with segmented nuclei: 50–70%

| cell | characteristics | |
|------|----------------|---|
| erythrocyte | flat disc with 7 μm diameter; pink color, lighter in the center; no nucleus | |
| thrombocyte | irregularly shaped cell without a nucleus, with light and dark granules | |
| lymphocyte | slightly larger than an erythrocyte; round, coarse-structured nucleus; very narrow border of cytoplasm (1). In activated cells, 'atypical' lymphocytes (2), the light blue stained cytoplasmic border may be much wider | |
| monocyte | the largest blood cells, with a large, lobed nucleus and light blue stained cytoplasm, with a few light granules and sometimes vacuoles | |
| neutrophilic granulocytes | round cell with a rod-shaped (1) or segmented (2) nucleus; the cytoplasm contains light pink to light purple stained granules | |
| eosinophilic granulocytes | nucleus contains a maximum of two segments; numerous smooth, round, red stained granules in the cytoplasm | |
| basophilic granulocytes | segmented nucleus; cytoplasm filled with large, dark blue stained granules | |

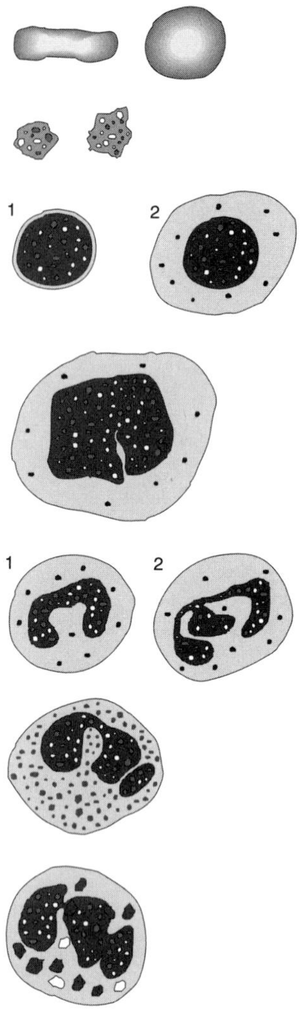

FIGURE 27.1

Some characteristics of normal blood cells (stained with May-Grünwald-Giemsa)

longer capable of synthesizing proteins. They lack mitochondria and do not have oxidative phosphorylation. Their energy supply is totally dependent on the enzyme-controlled glycolytic system in which glucose is converted to lactic acid.

The ATP formed during glycolysis is sufficient to maintain shape, volume and flexibility of the red blood cells. In the hexose-monophosphate shunt, GSH (glutathione), is generated which serves to eliminate the endogenous and exogenous oxidants which are continuously formed, particularly hydrogen peroxide. In addition, 2,3-diphosphoglycerate (2,3-DPG) is formed during glycolysis. This compound plays an important role in oxygen dissociation. After releasing oxygen, 2,3-DPG assumes a position in between two $\beta$-chains of the hemoglobin molecule, and by doing so reduces the affinity for oxygen and facilitates the release of oxygen to the tissues.

*Granulocytes*

All *granulocytes* have important roles in the defence against infections. After having been loaded with antibodies or complement (a process known as *opsonization*), microorganisms are bound to specific receptors on the granulocyte. This binding initiates a complex mechanism which results in *phagocytosis* (the inges-

820

tion of microorganisms by the formation of phagosomes), activation of *superoxide production* (resulting in the production of toxic oxygen metabolites, see section 6.2) and in the *killing* of the phagocytosed microorganisms. In addition to the toxic oxygen metabolites formed in the phagosomes (superoxide, hydrogen peroxide and hydroxyl radicals), substances stored in the primary granules (lysosomes) and the secondary (specific) granules play a part in the killing. The protein *lactoferrin*, which is produced by granulocytes, inhibits bacterial growth due to its high affinity for iron. This means that the iron is not available for the bacterial metabolism.

After their release from the bone marrow, *neutrophilic granulocytes* remain in the circulation for only 6–12 hours. They then migrate through the vessel wall to the tissues, where they carry out their function of phagocytosis and killing. After 2–4 days, the granulocyte itself is destroyed in the tissues. It is assumed that the *mast cells* in the tissues derive from the *basophilic granulocytes*. Both cell types contain granules in which *histamine* and *heparin* are stored and leukotrienes are formed *de novo*. These compounds are released in response to the formation of allergenic-IgE complexes which bind to the cell surface via the Fc receptors for IgE. Mast cells play an important role in the defence against parasites. The release of these three substances is also responsible for the symptoms observed in allergic and anaphylactic reactions.

*Eosinophilic granulocytes* also possess the capacity for phagocytosis. Their specific function, however, is to discharge the contents of their granules when encountering certain parasites, such as worms. The granules contain histaminase and aryl sulfatase, which inactivate histamine, respectively, and consequently are important in the neutralization of allergic reactions.

ASSIGNMENT 27.2

Where does the production of superoxide in the granulocyte take place?

*Monocytes*

*Monocytes* are phagocytes which only remain in the blood for a few hours. They then migrate to the tissues, where they mature into macrophages with a life-span of months or years. They are part of the reticulo-endothelial system (RES) which is situated, for instance, in the bone marrow, spleen, liver (Kupffer cells), pulmonary alveoli and the peritoneum. They remove macromolecular and corpuscular antigens from the circulation, and phagocytose and digest blood cells, especially in the spleen and liver, as soon as these cells have reached the end of their natural life-span. Another important task of monocytes and macrophages is the production of interferon, tumor necrosis factor (TNF) and monokines (interleukin 1, for example). These are so-called *biological response modifiers*, which play an essential part in the functioning and formation of other blood cells, including lymphocytes.

Antigen-presenting cells are specialized macrophages which can bind antigens to their surface and subsequently present them to T-lymphocytes which have a memory for that antigen. These cells then proceed to multiply and produce substances which can destroy the antigens.

*Lymphocytes*

In principle, phagocytes have a non-specific role in the defence system. However, they cooperate in various ways with *lymphocytes* which do react specifically with antigens. There are two main groups of lymphocytes: *T-cells* (which are dependent on the thymus for their development) and *B-cells* (which in birds derive from the bursa of Fabricius; in mammals, which do not have a bursa, they are made in a 'bursa equivalent', which has not been precisely located). T-and B-lymphocytes in the blood cannot be distinguished morphologically, but they can be recognized by using certain techniques. Nowadays, reactions of monoclonal antibodies with

*Cytotoxic T-cells and T-helper cells*

lymphocyte membrane antigen which are specific for a particular phase of development or subpopulations are particularly used for this purpose. Meanwhile, a great many different types of lymphocyte have been described, each with a specific task. The T-cells, which constitute 60–80% of the circulating lymphocytes, provide *specific cellular immunity*. There are *cytotoxic T-cells*, which can directly destroy cells recognized as foreign, and *T-lymphocytes* which have a *regulatory function* in the production of antibodies (immunoglobulins) by B-lymphocytes, the *T-helper* and *T-suppressor* cells. When presented with antigen, the B-cells which recognize this antigen develop into plasma cells with the assistance of T-cells. B-cells as well as plasma cells produce immunoglobulins.

*Thrombocytes*

*Thrombocytes* play an essential part in hemostasis, the stopping of hemorrhages. This requires interaction between the blood-vessel wall (endothelial cells), the thrombocytes and coagulation factors. Under normal circumstances, coagulation does not take place in the circulation. As soon as a defect appears in the protective endothelium, however, the blood platelets and coagulation factors come into contact with the underlying collagen (connective tissue). The platelets then stick to the collagen (adhesion) and a vast number of substances, most of which were stored in certain intracellular granules, are released from them (release reaction). These substances attract other thrombocytes, together forming a thrombus (aggregation), which seals the defect in the blood vessel. At the same time, a network of fibrin threads is formed by activation of circulating coagulation proteins. This reinforces the thrombus and puts a definitive stop to the bleeding.

## 1.2 HEMOPOIESIS

*Hemopoietic organs*

Before birth, the production of blood cells takes place in, successively, the liver, spleen and bone marrow. By the time of birth, this function has entirely been taken over by the 'red' bone marrow, which is situated in the flat bones (skull, sternum, ribs, vertebrae, pelvis).

If the hemopoietic bone marrow is injured, and in certain blood diseases, the formation of blood cells can be taken over by the long bones, the liver and spleen, organs which already had this capacity at the fetal stage. This phenomenon is known as extramedullary hemopoiesis.

### 1.2.1 Development of blood cells

*Pluripotent stem cells*

The parent cell of all blood cells is the *pluripotent stem cell*. The stem cells continuously duplicate themselves, and at the same time some of them differentiate to form the next generation of (unipotent or committed) stem cells, under the influence of specific growth factors. If the stem cells are destroyed, especially the pluripotent variety, blood formation is no longer possible.

Figure 27.2 shows the production of blood cells in schematic form. This production involves various processes: cell division, differentiation and maturation. The growth and division of stem cells require a finely tuned micro-environment, involving a matrix which includes endothelial cells, fat cells, fibroblasts, reticular cells and macrophages. If this matrix is destroyed, for example by high doses of radiation, no further stem-cell division can take place.

**Intermezzo**

Morphologically, the various stem cells cannot be distinguished from lymphocytes. It is possible to induce committed stem cells in bone-marrow cultures to divide and mature. The progenitor cells are known as *colony-forming units (CFU)* and can be recognized by the composition of the colonies that are formed. The first stem cell to become recognizable is the CFU-GEMM (Granulocytes, Erythroblasts, Monocytes, Megakaryocytes). Other specialized stem cells include CFU-GM (Granulocytes,

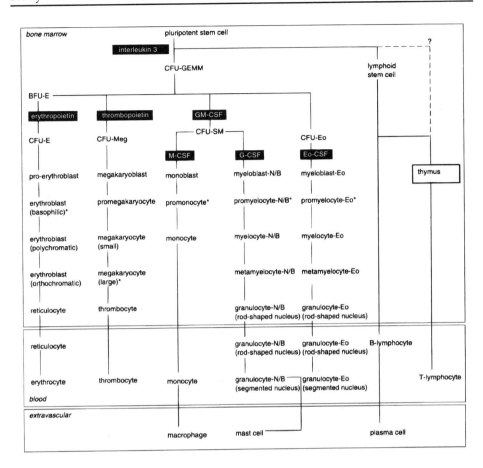

FIGURE   27.2

Formation of blood cells in the bone marrow and migration to the blood and extravascular tissues

CFU = colony-forming unit (GEMM = granulocyte, erythroid, monocyte, megakaryocyte; E = erythroid; Meg = megakaryocyte; GM = granulocyte, monocyte; Eo = eosinophilic), BFU = burst-forming unit, N/B = neutrophil/basophil. The growth factors have been highlighted in black boxes. The intermediate stages of lymphoid cells are not shown. Cell or nucleus division is possible up to the stage marked*.

Monocytes), CFU-Eo (Eosinophil granulocytes), CFU-E (erythroids) and CFU-Meg (Megakaryocytes). *BFU-E (Burst-Forming Units, Erythroids)* are the precursors of CFU-E.

To grow stem cells *in vitro*, carefully composed culture media are needed, to which specific growth factors are added. These techniques are especially useful in the diagnosis and therapy (including bone-marrow transplants) of abnormalities in hemopoiesis caused by toxic influences.

### 1.2.2 Regulation of hemopoiesis

Hemopoiesis is hormonally controlled by growth factors. These growth factors bind to receptors on the membrane of various stem cells. This signal is then transduced to the cell nucleus in a way that has not yet been completely elucidated. Compounds such as cyclic AMP and tyrosine kinase are involved.

*Interleukin 3*

Growth of the pluripotent stem cell is stimulated by *interleukin 3*. In the next phase, there are specific growth factors (CSF = colony-stimulating factor) which stimulate the unipotent stem cells: GM-CSF, G-CSF, M-CSF, Eo-CSF, erythropoietin and thrombopoietin. Figure 27.2 shows the role of these growth factors in hemopoiesis. Most growth factors are produced by macrophages. A special case

*Erythropoietin*

is *erythropoietin*, which is mainly produced in the kidneys. Hence severe kidney damage will always lead to serious anemia due to a shortage of erythropoietin.

## 1.3 HEMOGLOBIN

*Anemia*

The function of hemoglobin is to transport oxygen from the lungs to the tissues and carbon dioxide from the tissues to the lungs. A shortage of circulating hemoglobin is referred to as *anemia*.

### Intermezzo

Hemoglobin, the red blood pigment, has a molecular weight of 68,000 and consists of four polypeptide chains, two $\alpha$ and two $\beta$ chains ($\alpha_2\beta_2$ = HbA; See Figure 15.10b). Each polypeptide chain contains a heme group. Prior to birth the hemoglobin has a different structure. This is because there is hardly any production of $\beta$ chains at the fetal stage. Instead, $\gamma$ chains are formed, which, incidentally, have a normal affinity for oxygen. Five months after birth, the fetal hemoglobin (HbF) has been almost entirely replaced by mature hemoglobin. The most important hemoglobin molecule after birth is HbA. If the production of $\beta$ chains is disturbed, the body compensates for this by producing HbF.

*Heme synthesis*

*Heme synthesis* occurs partially in the mitochondria and partially in the cytosol of the erythroblast. The first step, in which $\delta$-aminolevulinic acid (ALA) is formed from glycine and succinyl coenzyme A, takes place in the mitochondria. The reaction is catalyzed by ALA synthetase and vitamin $B_6$ and inhibited (feedback mechanism) by the end-product heme. The ALA migrates to the cytosol. The protoporphyrin ring is synthesized via a chain of enzyme-mediated reactions. Subsequently, an iron atom is built in to form heme. This takes place in the mitochondria again. In the meantime, the ribosomes have synthesized the globin chains. The heme is transferred to the cytosol and becomes incorporated in a globin chain, after which two $\alpha$ and two $\beta$ polypeptide chains form a stable hemoglobin molecule.

*Abnormalities in hemoglobin synthesis*

Abnormalities in hemoglobin synthesis can arise from:

a.  a disturbed heme synthesis: for example, due to a shortage of iron or an abnormal porphyrin synthesis;

b.  disturbances in the $\alpha$ or $\beta$ chains. These result in, respectively, $\alpha$ or $\beta$ thalassemia.

> ASSIGNMENT 27.3
>
> What is the difference between anemia and ischemia?

## 2 Toxic effects on hemopoiesis

Because of the high turnover in blood cells, there is an intensive production of cells in the bone marrow, which is highly sensitive to toxic influences. The proliferation of cells in the bone marrow is affected by nutritional deficiencies, direct toxic effects and immunological factors. This may result in abnormal production (*dysplasia*), decreased production (*hypoplasia*), complete inhibition of production (*aplasia*) or the production of malignant cells due to changes in the DNA. Sometimes only one cell line is affected by the toxic effect, sometimes all of them are.

## 2.1 INHIBITION OF HEMOPOIESIS

*Aspiration of the bone marrow*
aspiration of bone marrow is the sucking out of the bone marrow by means of a bone puncture
*Bone marrow biopsy*

Although the effect of inhibition of hemopoiesis can be established by the decline in numbers of the circulating blood cells, investigation of the bone marrow is necessary for diagnosis. This requires *aspiration of the bone marrow*, usually from the sternum. For a good, quantitative impression, however, *bone marrow biopsy* usually has to be performed in the pelvic crest. An aspirate is highly suitable for studying the morphology of individual cells, while a biopsy specimen is necessary to evaluate the relationship between the cell lines and the absolute decline in the number of cells of each cell line.

### 2.1.1 Types of hemopoiesis inhibition

The inhibition of hemopoiesis can affect all or only one of the cell lines:

a.  *aplastic anemia*: although the term suggests that this only concerns a disturbance in the production of erythrocytes, the disturbance actually affects all cell lines;

b.  *pure red cell aplasia*: only the production of the red cell line is disturbed;

c.  *agranulocytosis, leukopenia*: disturbed production of white cells;

d.  *amegakaryopoiesis, thrombocytopenia*: disturbed production of blood platelets.

*Inhibition of red cell line*

The complaints and abnormalities which arise depend on the cell line that is disturbed.

*Inhibition of the red cell line* usually results in severe anemia which necessitates the administration of regular blood transfusions.

*Inhibition of white cell line*

*Inhibition of white cell lines* generally causes a sharp reduction in the number of granulocytes, leading to increased sensitivity to infections. These are not primarily infections from external sources, but rather infections by microorganisms from the body's own intestinal or skin flora, which may be fatal. Prophylactic treatment by "selective intestinal decontamination" (eradication of pathogenic microorganisms while preserving the non-pathogenic flora) is often successful. All infections require aggressive antibiotic treatment in view of the patient's own defective immune system.

*Absence of megakaryopoiesis*

*Absence of megakaryopoiesis* leads to thrombocytopenia, accompanied by a highly increased tendency to hemorrhage, for instance in the skin, kidneys, retina and brain. Treatment with blood platelet transfusions is possible, but is often complicated by the formation of antibodies, which may rapidly break down the blood platelets administered.

### 2.1.2 Severity of hemopoiesis inhibition

The severity of hemopoiesis inhibition depends on the cell line which is disturbed, on the severity of the inhibition (hypoplasia or aplasia) and the duration of the inhibition (reversible or irreversible).

An irreversible inhibition, particularly aplastic anemia or agranulocytosis, is a very serious disorder, and usually fatal. Provided a suitable donor is available, a bone marrow transplant may sometimes constitute successful treatment.

### 2.1.3 Causes of hemopoiesis inhibition

Hemopoiesis can be inhibited by a multitude of compounds. This is sometimes done intentionally, in particular in the treatment of malignant neoplasms, with so-called *cytostatics* (see also section 2.2). Therapy for acute leukemias requires particularly high doses of these compounds, so that normal hemopoiesis is completely inhibited for prolonged periods. It is then hoped that regeneration will start from the healthy stem-cell compartment. For many other drugs and chemicals which inhibit the formation of bone marrow cells, the mechanism is unknown. The antibiotic chloramphenicol and the antirheumatic agent phenylbutazone and chemically related compounds are particularly notorious for causing agranulocytosis or aplastic anemia. Chlorpromazine, thiouracil and sulfonamides can induce leukopenia.

ASSIGNMENT 27.4

In which cases is a bone biopsy preferred over an aspirate when carrying out morphological research on hemopoiesis?

## 2.2 MEGALOBLASTIC CHANGES

Inhibition of DNA synthesis leads to megaloblastic changes in all cell lines. Erythroblasts, (meta)myelocytes and megakaryocytes are all relatively oversized in such cases. Since protein synthesis is not affected, the nuclei are immature compared to the cytoplasm (asynchrony between nucleus and cytoplasm). In the peripheral blood, the number of circulating cells is reduced, the erythrocytes are too big (macrocytes) and the neutrophilic granulocytes show hypersegmentation (five lobes or more).

*Cofactors in DNA synthesis*

Important *cofactors in the DNA synthesis* are folates, vitamin $B_{12}$ (cyanocobalamine) and purine and pyrimidine nucleotides. A shortage of these compounds leads to disturbances in cell division, with morphologically megaloblastic changes.

*Folates*, in the reduced form of tetrahydrofolate, serve as coenzymes in purine and pyrimidine synthesis. Certain chemicals can interfere with folate uptake from the intestines (diphenylhydantoin, barbiturates, ethyl alcohol). Other chemicals can prevent folate uptake by the cell. For instance, methotrexate (a commonly used cytostatic) competes with the receptors for reduced folate and inhibits dihydrofolate reductase. As a result, the production of thymidylate is reduced, which in turn inhibits DNA synthesis. *Cyanocobalamine (vitamin $B_{12}$)* acts as a coenzyme, together with 5-methyltetrahydrofolate, in the methylation of homocysteine to methionine. Chemicals interfering with the action of cobalamine do so mainly by negatively influencing the uptake of this compound (examples include the antituberculosis agent para-aminosalicylic acid and the antibiotic neomycin). Cobalamine is absorbed in the last portion of the ileum. This is only possible, however, if the cobalamines are bound to the protein "intrinsic factor", which is produced in the stomach. The protein-vitamin complex is not sensitive to proteolysis in the intestine and binds to specific receptors on mucosa cells in the final ileal coil.

Other *inhibitors of DNA synthesis* include pyrimidine antagonists (such as the cytostatics hydroxyurea, 5-fluorouracil and cytosine arabinoside) and purine antagonists (for instance the cytostatics azathioprine and 6-thioguanine).

## 2.3 SIDEROBLASTIC ANEMIA

*Heme synthesis* can be interrupted at several levels. Pyridoxine is a necessary cofactor in the first step of heme synthesis, the formation of δ-aminolevulinic acid. This step is inhibited by the antituberculosis drug isoniazid. This causes the iron, which is incorporated in the porphyrin ring during the last step of heme synthesis, to accumulate in the mitochondria instead.

*Ring sideroblasts*
*Lead intoxication*

This can be clearly seen in a bone marrow puncture stained for iron. More mature erythroblasts clearly show a ring of iron deposit around the nucleus. These cells are known as *ring sideroblasts*, and are typical for sideroblastic anemia. The same phenomenon is observed in *lead intoxication*. In this case, however, the interference with heme synthesis occurs at several levels. In addition to sideroblastic anemia, patients with lead intoxication also suffer from stomach cramp, constipation and neurological abnormalities. They show a characteristic gray lead border around the teeth.

## 2.4 INDUCTION OF MALIGNANT BLOOD DISEASES

Epidemiological research has shown that malignant blood diseases can arise from long-term exposure to certain chemicals. Clusters of patients with blood cancer are often associated with a particular occupational group.

### 2.4.1 Classification of blood cancers

There are many forms of blood cancer. Their classification is complicated by the ever-changing classification system of these disorders. Table 27.2 shows a general overview of malignant blood diseases.

*Acute leukemia*

In *acute leukemia* there is an accumulation of young bone marrow cells (myeloblasts, promyelocytes, monoblasts, lymphoblasts) in the bone marrow, and usually also in the blood, and sometimes in other organs. They arise from a mutation in a single young hematological cell in the bone marrow or thymus. Acute leukemia often ensues from another, basically more benign, hematological disease. The proliferation of leukemic cells in the bone marrow has a repressive effect on the normal hemopoiesis. Hence, acute leukemia often manifests itself in anemia, in increased sensitivity to infections (often throat infection) and in increased tendency to hemorrhage (spontaneously appearing bruises, petechia). Without adequate treatment, acute leukemia usually has a fatal outcome within a few weeks.

*Chronic leukemia*

A *chronic leukemia* has a much milder course. Patients with chronic lymphatic leukemia, which usually presents at an advanced age, can survive for more than 10 years without any therapy.

Likewise, a chronic myeloid leukemia can also be relatively non-problematic for several years. Nevertheless, it is almost invariably fatal, since the chronic form changes to an acute leukemia.

*Malignant lymphomas*

In *malignant lymphomas*, there is a proliferation of lymphatic cells in the lymph nodes or extranodal lymphatic tissue (that is, outside the lymph nodes, for example in the intestine). The pathologically proliferating cells show the characteristics of B- or T-lymphocytes at various stages of development. Depending on the cell type and the relation between the cells (diffuse or nodular, for example) the prognosis can vary from rapidly progressive, with a fatal outcome within a few months, to no symptoms at all over periods up to 20 years. Malignant lymphomas may result in infiltrations in almost all organs. The first sign of these diseases is usually a painless swelling in a peripheral lymph node.

TABLE   27.2
Overview of the most important malignant blood diseases

---

1. leukemias

definition: malignant disorders of cells occurring in the blood circulation and originating from the bone

*myeloid leukemias*
—acute myeloid leukemia (AML)
—acute monocytic leukemia (AMoL)
—chronic myeloid leukemia (CML)
—erythroleukemia

*lymphatic leukemias*
—acute lymphatic leukemia (ALL)
—chronic lymphatic leukemia (CLL)

2. lymphomas

definition: malignant disorders of cells found in lymph nodes
*Hodgkin's disease* (Sternberg-Reed giant cells present in lymph nodes and other organs)

*multiple myelomas* (proliferation of plasma cells, particularly in the bones)

*non-Hodgkin's lymphomas* (heterogeneous group of malignant proliferations of lymph cells)

---

*Hodgkin's disease*

Unlike non-Hodgkin lymphomas, *Hodgkin's disease* usually starts in a single lymph node. Subsequently, the disease spreads throughout the body, in a more or less fixed pattern.

*Multiple myelomas (Kahler's disease)*

*Multiple myelomas (Kahler's disease)* involve proliferation of plasma cells. High concentrations of monoclonal antibodies produced by these cells are often found in the plasma.

ASSIGNMENT 27.5

Describe some disease symptoms with which a leukemia patient could present to the doctor.

### 2.4.2 Toxicological causes of hematological malignancies

Although epidemiological research can often indicate which trades are most at risk of hematological malignancies, it is not always possible to identify the toxic agent. The reason often is that prolonged induction is necessary, or that the induction of the malignancy has taken place so long ago that a relationship between cause and effect can no longer be established. Often, exposure to several toxic compounds has taken place.

*Benzene*

pancytopenia is a deficit of all types of blood cells

The best known and most notorious agent is *benzene*. It has been established that exposure to benzene results in a high frequency of acute myeloid leukemias, often preceded by pancytopenia. Benzene is an ingredient of numerous organic solvents, which are used not only in industry but also in households.

All of these solvents have identical toxic effects. Malignant lymphomas and multiple myelomas following exposure to benzene have been described. Some other compounds which can cause malignant hematological diseases include asbestos, ethylene oxide, heavy metals, pentachlorophenol, chlorophenol, phenoxy acids, styrene, polystyrene and vinyl chloride. Leukemias as well as lymphomas have been reported after exposure to all of these compounds. Trades at risk include workers in the electricity industry, farmers, painters in the building/construction industry, printers, woodworkers, and workers in the petrochemical industry, metal industry and footwear industry.

*Cytostatics*

Drugs intended to fight cancer, *cytostatics*, can also be carcinogenic themselves. A greatly increased frequency of acute leukemia is seen in patients who have been successfully treated for other forms of cancer, particularly if a combination of cytostatics and radiotherapy has been used. These so-called secondary leukemias are highly resistant to therapy.

### 2.5 EFFECTS OF IONIZING RADIATION

Exposure to high doses of ionizing radiation (X-rays, neutrons, beta and gamma) may occur accidentally in the laboratory, in or around (nuclear) reactor centers (Chernobyl) and through nuclear explosions. A much more frequent source of exposure, however, is the use of therapeutic doses of radioactivity in radiological treatment of malignant tumors.

Which tissues could be damaged by this?

All rapidly dividing tissues are at risk of damaging effects: the gonads, intestinal epithelium and hemopoietic cells in the bone marrow. High doses of radiation kill the cells in all of these tissues, resulting in, for instance, bone-marrow aplasia (complete inhibition). At lower doses, the stem cells are able to regenerate, after which the blood cell production gradually returns to normal. This regeneration, however, is often incomplete, since large numbers of stem cells, along with the microvascular bone-marrow matrix required for their division, are destroyed.

In addition, ionizing radiation can cause severe damage to the chromosomes. After accidents, a remarkable rise in the frequency of acute and chronic myeloid leukemias is observed, sometimes many years later.

ASSIGNMENT 27.6

Can exposure to low doses of ionizing radiation be fatal?

## 2.6 CYTOGENETICS

Human somatic cells contain 23 chromosome pairs. The first 22 have been given numbers, while the sex chromosomes are known as XX in women and XY in men. In cell cultures, mitotic cells are easily recognized and analyzed. A photomicrograph of all chromosomes is called a karyotype. For each chromosome the short (p) and long (q) arms can be distinguished. Improvements in staining techniques have revealed more and more details of chromosomes.

Severe and recognizable injury to chromosomes can result from exposure to toxic compounds, such as benzene, as well as from ionizing radiation. The effects may become manifest in a number of ways:

- aneuploidy
- chromosomal aberrations
- formation of micronuclei
- chromatid exchange with other chromosomes
- abnormalities in cell cycle kinetics.

ASSIGNMENT 27.7

Define the terms aneuploidy, chromosomal aberrations and micronuclei.

See also Study unit 11

All these abnormalities may induce hematological malignancies, especially leukemias. The best-known of these is the typical chromosomal abnormality found in patients with chronic myeloid leukemia: the Philadelphia (or Ph[1]) chromosome. This involves translocation from the long arm of chromosome 22 (22q–) to the long arm of chromosome 9 (9q+). In a transition from chronic to acute leukemia, further chromosomal abnormalities are usually seen.

## 3 Influence of toxic compounds on erythrocytes

Circulating blood cells are subject to direct or indirect damage by chemicals. These may cause accelerated degradation of blood cells or have a negative influence on cellular metabolism, resulting in loss of function.

### 3.1 HEMOLYSIS BY ANTIBODY FORMATION AND OXIDATIVE DAMAGE

Hemolysis is an accelerated degradation of erythrocytes in the circulation. The degradation can take place in the bloodstream (intravascular) or in the RES (extravascular). This may considerably reduce the normal life-span of erythrocytes (120 days). The cause of this reduced life-span may be disturbed production (abnormal hemoglobin, abnormal membrane structure or a deficiency of one of the glycolytic enzymes) or may arise in the circulation (as a result of antibodies or physical or chemical injury).

### 3.1.1 Immunological causes of hemolysis

Drug-induced hemolysis is generally benign and reversible. Low-molecular-weight compounds, such as most drugs and chemicals, are not immunogenic themselves. To stimulate the formation of antibodies, conjugation to a protein carrier is needed. Three mechanisms of drug-induced immunohemolysis are known:

a. auto-antibody induction

b. hapten-related immunohemolysis

c. immune complex or 'innocent bystander' reactions.

These concepts can be illustrated by the following examples.

*Auto-immune hemolytic anemia*

The antihypertensive agent methyldopa can cause an *auto-immune hemolytic anemia*, in which the antibodies (usually of the IgG type) are aimed at Rh determinants on the erythrocyte membrane. This phenomenon is observed in about 10% of the patients treated with this drug.

Manifest hemolysis, however, occurs in only 1% of patients. It is assumed that methyldopa interacts with T-lymphocytes, resulting in the loss of suppressor-cell functions and hence in the production of antibodies by B-lymphocytes.

*Hapten-related immune mechanisms*

*Hapten-related immune mechanisms* involve a covalent bond between a low-molecular-weight chemical and a protein which may, for instance, be located on the surface of erythrocytes. Penicillin is the prototype of this form of immuno-hemolysis. Most patients treated with high doses of penicillin develop IgM antibodies. The antibody responsible for hemolysis, however, belongs to the IgG class and is much less common. Erythrocytes loaded with penicillin and anti-penicillin IgG are destroyed in the spleen. Cephalosporins and tetracyclines can cause identical forms of immunohemolysis.

*Immune-complex mechanism*

The *immune-complex mechanism* differs from the hapten mechanism in that the drugs involved have little affinity for erythrocytes. Unlike the hapten mechanism, only small doses are required to initiate hemolysis. Finally, cell damage occurs primarily through the complement system. Examples of this mechanism include quinine and quinidine. The drug binds to circulating antibodies. The resulting immune complexes bind reversibly to erythrocytes and induce activation and binding of complement components to the cell membrane. The immune complexes themselves can migrate from one cell to another. Cell destruction may occur intravascularly after the entire complement cycle has been completed. Alternatively, cells which have not been destroyed can bind to C3b receptors on the macrophages, followed by digestion in the liver or spleen. This latter process is also known as the 'innocent bystander' mechanism, since the antibodies themselves show hardly any affinity for the erythrocyte and the immune complexes react only reversibly with the erythrocyte membrane.

### 3.1.2 Oxidative causes of hemolysis

Severe oxidative stress can lead to hemolysis. In principle, the erythrocyte is very sensitive to peroxidative reactions, given the abundant presence of the ingredients required: oxygen, transition metals and unsaturated fatty acids (see also section 6). Under normal circumstances, the erythrocyte is very well protected against peroxidative reactions, for instance, by the presence of catalase and glutathione, both of which are hydrogen peroxide scavengers.

This balance, however, can be disturbed by aromatic compounds containing amino, nitro or hydroxy groups. Oxidative damage can result in direct injury to the cell membrane, due to lipid peroxidation, and bring about changes in membrane proteins. Structural changes can also take place in the hemoglobin molecule, leading to its denaturation and precipitation. The precipitates, the so-called *Heinz bodies*, can become attached to the cell membrane. As a consequence, changes in permeability and cell lysis may occur, as well as deformations leading to the premature removal of the cells by macrophages in the spleen.

*Heinz bodies*

### 3.2    METHEMOGLOBINEMIA AND SULFHEMOGLOBINEMIA

In the erythrocytes, small amounts of *methemoglobin* (Hb-$Fe^{3+}$, also known as ferrihemoglobin or hemiglobin) are spontaneously formed by endogenous oxidants. Due to the presence of reducing systems, particularly *methemoglobin reductase* (cytochrome $b_5$ reductase), the production of this brown-colored pigment is, however, reversible. The enzymatic reduction of methemoglobin is linked to the oxidation of NADH to NAD. Figure 27.3a shows the reaction chain.

*Methemoglobin*

Some compounds, however, can drastically reduce the oxygen-transporting capacity of erythrocytes by oxidizing the heme iron from the ferro to the ferri form. The resulting *methemoglobin* is incapable of binding oxygen reversibly. Compounds with such an effect include nitrates in mineral water (which are reduced to nitrites by the intestinal flora), chlorates, quinones, aniline and sulfonamide. In normal erythrocytes, the methemoglobin content is not more than 1%. If the percentage of methemoglobin reaches 10%, the patient's skin turns blue (cyanosis); at 35%, headaches and tightness of the chest occur. Concentrations of more than 70% are fatal.

If the intoxication is moderate, it can be quickly remedied with methylene blue. This acts via NADPH-dependent methemoglobin reductase, as shown in Figure 27.3b. If the intoxication is severe, replacement transfusion with fresh blood and kidney dialysis may be necessary. Methemoglobin has a characteristic absorption spectrum that is easily distinguished from those of oxyhemoglobin and deoxyhemoglobin. The same is true for *sulfhemoglobin*, a poorly characterized hemoglobin derivative which can arise following exposure to a number of oxidants, such as sulfonamides, phenacetin and acetanilide. Unlike methemoglobin, sulfhemoglobin cannot be converted back to hemoglobin. The erythrocyte will therefore carry this pigment for the rest of its life-span.

*Sulfhemoglobin*

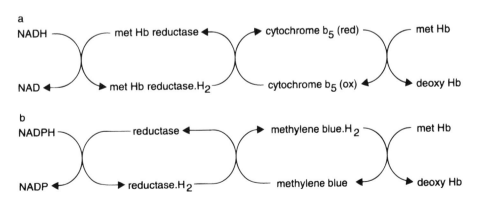

FIGURE    27.3
Reduction of methemoglobin (metHb)
Normal route is shown by (a), methylene blue route by (b).

## 3.3   CARBON MONOXIDE POISONING

*Carboxyhemoglobin*

The heme group of the hemoglobin molecule has an affinity for carbon monoxide (CO) which is 210 times higher than that for oxygen. The reaction produces *carboxyhemoglobin* (HbCO), resulting in a significantly decreased oxygen-transporting capacity of the erythrocyte. This causes an increased affinity for oxygen in the remaining heme groups. The result is a shift to the left in the oxygen dissociation curve, accompanied by a decreased release of oxygen in the tissues.

Carbon monoxide is produced by incomplete combustion of organic materials, particularly hydrocarbons. It is an important component of cigarette smoke. Consequently, heavy smokers have high levels of CO in their blood, in the form of HbCO.

Carbon monoxide intoxication often occurs as a result of suicide attempts (exhaust gases from cars), the use of coal-fired stoves or heaters in badly ventilated areas or in smoke poisoning from fires. Under normal circumstances, the amount of HbCO is less than 2% of the total hemoglobin. At 6–10% HbCO, the patient feels disoriented and visual capacity is impaired. At 40–60%, the patient loses consciousness and dies. HbCO is a cherry-red pigment, which can be seen in the skin color of intoxicated patients. Victims need to be supplied with sufficient oxygen as soon as possible, which means that artificial respiration is often necessary.

## 3.4   CYANIDE POISONING

Intoxication by cyanide ($CN^-$) severely disrupts oxidative metabolism. Electron transport from cytochrome oxidase to molecular oxygen becomes blocked, peripheral oxygen tension increases and the release of oxygen by the hemoglobin decreases. At the same time, cyanide stimulates the chemoreceptors in the carotid artery, resulting in hyperpnea (unusually rapid breathing).

Although arrhythmias occur, the patient actually dies from central respiratory failure. This may occur within seconds or minutes following the inhalation of hydrocyanic acid (HCN).

Oral intoxication with cyanide is fatal within 1 hour. Cyanide can be released from amygdalin in the intestine by $\beta$-glucosidase containing bacteria. The amygdalin is present in sweet almonds, in apricot and peach stones and in Laetril®, a controversial alternative cancer treatment.

*Treatment*

The drug sodium nitroprusside can also cause cyanide poisoning when administered in very high doses. The intoxication can be *treated* by intravenous administration of sodium nitrite, resulting in the production of methemoglobin. The latter releases the cyanide from the cytochrome oxidase. If thiosulfate is administered as well, this acts as a substrate for the enzyme rhodanese, which catalyzes the biotransformation of cyanide to thiosulfate.

## 3.5   BENZENE

Benzene is present naturally in the atmosphere but is also released by industrial activities (printing works, petrochemical industry) and the combustion of petrol (exhaust gases from cars). Uptake takes place mainly through the lungs. Fifty percent of the benzene inhaled is absorbed by the lungs; the rest is exhaled again.

*Benzene epoxide*

The toxicity of benzene is caused particularly by the formation of a reactive intermediate, *benzene epoxide*, in the liver and, to a lesser extent, in the bone marrow and spleen.

Prolonged exposure to benzene first causes anemia and, in later stages, thrombocytopenia and granulocytopenia as well. In some cases, the first symptoms consist of leucocytosis or the presence of macrocytes (deformed red blood cells) in blood and bone marrow. Epidemiological data indicate that benzene also causes leukemia.

Exposure of test animals to benzene caused the following four abnormalities:

- reduced number of erythrocytes in the blood, later on often followed by reduced numbers of white blood cells and blood platelets;
- reduced numbers of bone-marrow cells and spleen cells;
- inhibited development of the rapidly dividing precursors of erythrocytes (normoblasts and pronormoblasts);
- damage to the membrane of erythrocytes, resulting in changes in their shape, staining properties and size, ultimately resulting in lysis of the erythrocytes.

On the basis of observations in humans and test animals, it is assumed that the toxicity of benzene arises from one of the following modes of action:

1. an effect on the membrane of red blood cells, resulting in cell lysis and hence a reduced life-span of the cell;
2. a direct effect on the stem cell, leading to a reduced number of red blood cells if differentiation is inhibited; or to an uninhibited production of blood cells;
3. benzene influences the rapidly proliferating stages of blood-cell formation and could therefore inhibit the development of all types of blood cell.

There is no conclusive evidence at this time to support any of the three postulated mechanisms, partly because there is no suitable animal model.

## 3.6 LEAD

Although lead is used in numerous industrial processes, the greatest emission into the atmosphere is in the form of tetraethyllead, which is used as an anti-knock agent in gasoline.

*Target organs*

Man absorbs lead from the environment through food, drinking water and air. Ten percent of the amount of lead that enters the body is absorbed. The majority of this (more than 90%) accumulates in bone tissue. Prolonged exposure to lead leads to abnormalities in the central nervous system (see Study units 33, 34 and 35), the gastrointestinal tract, the kidneys and blood. The lead in blood is largely found in red blood cells. Its consequences include anemia, decline of enzymes involved in heme synthesis and accumulation of heme precursors such as protoporphyrin.

*Erythropoietin stimulates the differentiation of stem cells to erythrocytes*

The anemia caused by lead is the result of the expulsion of potassium ions from the red blood cell, which considerably reduces the erythrocyte life-span. This anemia is further exacerbated by the fact that lead causes kidney damage, resulting in decreased production of erythropoietin.

Although the erythrocyte is not capable of hemoglobin synthesis (a red blood cell, after all, has no nucleus or mitochondria), it still contains cytoplasmic enzymes such as $\delta$-aminolevulinic acid (ALA). Since lead inhibits the activity of this enzyme in the blood, the ALA activity is considered a sensitive parameter for establishing lead exposure. Since heme synthesis takes place in the bone marrow, there can be no relationship between decreased ALA activity and disruptions in heme synthesis.

If exposure to lead is prolonged, the metal accumulates mainly in the bone marrow and then there will probably be a direct effect on heme production. Apart from its effect on red blood cells, lead also shortens the life-span of white blood cells, and causes a reduction in the number of pluripotent stem cells as well as plasma cells. Hence, it is also responsible for decreased resistance of the body to infections.

## 4    Influence of toxic compounds on leukocytes

*Increased degradation of leukocytes*

In principle, the processes which can lead to hemolysis can also cause *increased degradation of leukocytes*. The agranulocytosis (neutropenia) which results from aminopyrine treatment is caused by hapten formation. A complex of this drug and a protein on the leukocytes constitutes an antigen. This induces the production of antibodies, which can cause massive *leuco-agglutination*. These agglutinates are removed from the blood in the pulmonary circulation. To compensate, hyperplasia of the myeloid system occurs in the bone marrow. If the intake of aminopyrine continues, the bone marrow becomes exhausted, although the other cell lines continue to function normally. The enormous destruction of granulocytes in the circulation causes a high fever.

*Pseudoneutropenia*

Histamine, dextran, glucocorticoids and inorganic iron can cause *pseudoneutropenia* by inducing adhesion of granulocytes to the endothelium of the vessel wall. This increases the marginal pool at the expense of the circulating pool. The total number of leukocytes in the blood, however, remains the same. The opposite is true for epinephrine, which causes a rapid increase in circulating granulocytes through demargination.

*Decreased leucocyte function*

Any step of leucocyte function (adhesion, chemotaxis, phagocytosis, lysosomal degranulation and microbial killing) may be affected. Various antiinflammatory drugs inhibit chemotaxis. Compounds like colchicine inhibit chemotaxis by their effect on the microtubules. Increased plasma concentrations of galactose and glucose inhibit phagocytosis. Degranulation of lysosomes is inhibited by glucocorticoids and chloroquine.

Ethanol inhibits the function of granulocytes at several levels by decreasing adhesion, chemotaxis and phagocytosis.

## 5    Influence of toxic compounds on blood platelets

If there is a shortage of circulating blood platelets and impaired function of these cells, bleeding is prolonged. This is not the case for disturbances of the coagulation cascade. In that case, primary hemostasis is normal, but the thrombus formed remains vulnerable since no stable fibrin network can be formed.

### 5.1    INFLUENCES ON THE LIFE-SPAN OF THROMBOCYTES

Hapten formation in blood platelets can occur, for instance, as a result of binding by rifampicin, chlorothiazide and various sulfa drugs to the thrombocyte membrane. The subsequent binding of antibodies causes the blood platelets to be degraded more rapidly. The immune complex-mediated destruction of thrombocytes in patients who have been sensitized to quinine and quinidine may be very severe. Together with these drugs, the circulating antibodies form immune complexes, which bind to the platelet membrane and cause complement-mediated destruction of thrombocytes. After discontinuing the drug, the number of thrombocytes usually starts to rise again within seven days. Normalization is much slower after intoxication by gold thiomalate (injections in rheumatic patients) and diphenylhydantoin, compounds which are eliminated only slowly. Heparin, a drug that prevents coagulation, can cause throm-

834

bocytopenia by (a) an immune mechanism or (b) a direct effect on the blood platelets.

## 5.2   EFFECTS ON THROMBOCYTE METABOLISM

A large number of chemicals have an adverse effect on the functioning of circulating blood platelets. Dipyridamole, for example, inhibits adhesion. The antibiotic carbenicillin interferes with aggregation. Chloroquine accumulates in the serotonin granules. Aspirin causes an irreversible acetylation of platelet cyclo-oxygenase, which results in disturbed synthesis of cyclic endoperoxides and thromboxane $A_2$, a potent platelet aggregator and vasoconstrictor. The blood platelets retain this defect until they are degraded in the RES.

## 6   Toxic interactions between iron and oxygen

### 6.1   IRON METABOLISM

Iron is an indispensable element in virtually all biological systems. Since iron can occur in two stable oxidation states in aqueous environments, viz. ferro ($Fe^{2+}$) and ferri ($Fe^{3+}$), it plays an important role in numerous redox reactions. In biological fluids at a neutral pH and normal atmospheric oxygen tension, $Fe^{2+}$ is very rapidly oxidized to $Fe^{3+}$, with formation of polynuclear ferrihydroxide complexes. This $Fe^{3+}$ will precipitate almost immediately, since its maximum concentration under the conditions stated is only $10^{-17}$ M. Since the precipitated iron is not suitable for biological reactions, nature has devised a number of proteins which maintain the iron in its soluble form. The iron in the human body may be divided into three main groups, depending on the ligand:

a.   *functional iron*: hemoglobin (in blood), myoglobin (muscles), other heme proteins, such as cytochromes and catalase, and non-heme proteins, such as aconitase, Fe-S proteins, xanthine oxidase (all cells);

b.   *non-functional iron*: ferritin and hemosiderin. These are formed in all cells where more iron is available than is necessary for the cell's own metabolism;

c.   *transport iron*: bound in the form of transferrin and lactoferrin.

The iron in the body is contained in a virtually closed system. Its total amount in adult human beings is about 4000 mg. Every day 1 mg is lost, largely through the renewal of epithelial cells (intestine, urinary tract, skin) and perspiration. Menstruating women lose on average 1 mg extra daily during menstruation. This loss is compensated for by iron uptake in the diet. The iron balance in the body is maintained by regulation of its uptake. If there is a need for more iron (as after blood loss or donation), the intestinal mucosa cells take up more iron. In healthy men, an average of 10% of the iron content of the diet is taken up in the blood. In women who are menstruating, or in cases of iron deficiency, this percentage is often significantly higher.

The iron taken up becomes bound to transferrin, a glycoprotein (molecular weight 80,000) which can bind a maximum of two iron atoms at two specific binding sites. The transferrin transports iron to all the cells which require it. Most of the iron goes to the erythroid system in the bone marrow, where it is incorporated to form hemoglobin. Of the total amount of iron in the body, more than half is found in hemoglobin.

*Iron uptake by erythroblasts*

*Iron uptake by erythroblasts* (and other cells requiring iron) is achieved by receptor-mediated endocytosis. Transferrin loaded with iron binds to the transferrin receptor. The entire complex is taken up into the cell by the formation of endocytotic vesicles. A proton pump causes the pH in the vesicles to decrease, so that the iron is released from the transferrin. This iron is transported via the cytosol to the mitochondria. The transferrin is returned to the outside surface of the cell by exocytosis. There, it is released from its receptor and can bind more iron elsewhere. It will be obvious that only a small proportion of the iron in this feedback cycle comes from uptake in the gastrointestinal tract.

The vast majority of the iron which is bound by transferrin in the course of the day comes from the *reticulo-endothelial system (RES)*, in which the iron released from the degradation of old erythrocytes is stored for a shorter or longer period of time.

*Depot iron*

The *depot iron* is located inside the protein ferritin. This is a ball-shaped protein (molecular weight 400,000), consisting of 24 subunits, and can store more than 4000 iron atoms in its lumen. In cells which contain substantial amounts of iron, degeneration of the protein envelope of ferritin takes place, followed by formation of an aggregate, the water-insoluble protein *hemosiderin*. This can be visualized under the microscope (for example, in bone marrow and liver preparations) using Berlin blue stain. Transferrin and the closely related protein lactoferrin (which occurs in granulocytes, milk and almost all secretions) have a strong bacteriostatic action, as long as they have not bound any iron yet. The reason is that they are capable of binding the iron which is necessary for the growth of bacteria. The iron cycle in the body is shown schematically in Figure 27.4.

### 6.2 OXYGEN RADICALS

The oxygen molecule can be reduced in two ways. The tetravalent reduction to water takes place in the mitochondria. Alternatively, a univalent reduction of $O_2$ can occur, whereby one electron is accepted in each step. Ultimately this too results in the formation of water. Figure 27.5 shows a schematic representation of this reaction chain.

*Univalent reduction of oxygen*
See also Study unit 10

During the *univalent reduction of oxygen*, radicals are formed such as the superoxide anion radical and the extremely reactive hydroxyl radical.

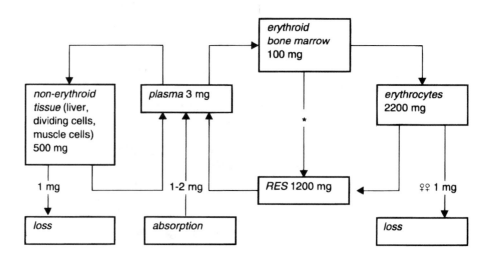

FIGURE 27.4
Schematic representation of the iron cycle in the body
*Denotes ineffective erythropoiesis: some erythroblasts are already degraded in the bone marrow; this iron is transported quickly to the RES (reticulo-endothelial system).

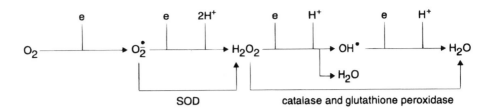

FIGURE 27.5
Univalent reduction of oxygen
Four electrons are transferred one by one to the oxygen molecule, leading to the formation of, successively, the superoxide anion radical ($O_2^-$), hydrogen peroxide ($H_2O_2$), hydroxyl radical ($OH^\bullet$) and water. SOD = superoxide dismutase.

Toxic oxygen metabolites are essential for the function of phagocytosing cells. They are responsible for killing phagocytosed microorganisms and the degradation of other particles that are taken up. For this purpose, phagocytes have a superoxide-generating system which is situated in the cell membrane: the NADPH-oxidase complex. When this complex is activated, for example by binding to a microorganism loaded with immunoglobulin or with complement, superoxide is immediately formed. This in turn causes the formation of a hydroxyl radical. At the same time, the cell membrane surrounds the microorganism and a phagosome is formed. This intracellularly fuses with primary and secondary granules. The lysosomal enzymes present in these granules and the enzyme myeloperoxidase assist in the killing of the microorganism.

*Myeloperoxidase is a peroxidase present in human leukocytes*

### 6.3 TOXIC EFFECTS OF IRON AND OXYGEN

*Oxidative hemolysis*

In normal circumstances, the defence mechanism of cells against autodestruction by oxygen metabolites and iron is quite adequate, but it may fail. This may be caused by congenital deficiencies of glycolytic enzymes in the erythrocyte, particularly of the enzymes which influence the hexose-monophosphate shunt (hexokinase, glucose-6-phosphate dehydrogenase, glutathione reductase). As a result, glutathione production may be reduced. This then leads to *oxidative hemolysis*. Oxidative cell injury also occurs if granulocytes are activated in the wrong places, for example in the joints of rheumatic patients, as well as in numerous other disorders. The toxic oxygen metabolites, that are intended to destroy microorganisms, then damage the surrounding cells instead. The presence of iron is essential for these processes, as is shown by the fact that the toxicity of oxygen can be entirely prevented by the presence of deferoxamine, a strong iron chelator. If hydroxyl radicals are formed close to cell membranes, this will lead to lipid peroxidation. The more double bonds there are in the phospholipids, the more severe the injury.

*Iron poisoning*

In *iron poisoning*, which is especially common in children, large amounts of toxic oxygen metabolites are generated. This results in severe abnormalities of the gastrointestinal tract, with a corrosive effect on the intestinal epithelium. In this way, much more iron enters the circulation than can be bound to the circulating transferrin. Hence, oxidative damage develops in virtually all organ systems, resulting in permanent damage or, in very severe intoxications, shock and death of the patient. Swift oral and parenteral treatment with the iron chelator deferoxamine can prevent these severe phenomena.

### 7 Summary

Since blood plays an important role in the functioning of the body, blood loss and changes in blood composition frequently have fatal consequences for the well-being of the organism. This study unit has dealt with the toxic effects of compounds on hemopoiesis and on the functioning of the various types of blood cell, such as erythrocytes, leukocytes and blood platelets. In discussing the toxic effects of compounds, priority has been given to the disturbances in the functioning of blood.

## SELF ASSESSMENT QUESTIONS

1    Which bone-marrow cells are changed in megaloblastic anemia?

2    Where is the iron localized in ring sideroblasts?

3    What kind of patients often show secondary leukemia?

4    Why are high concentrations of methemoglobin toxic?

5    Supposing that someone has a prolonged bleeding time as a result of taking aspirin. How long could this effect last?

6    How is the superoxide-generating system of a granulocyte activated?

## FEEDBACK

1    **Answers to the assignments**

27.1  See Table 27.1.

27.2  The production of superoxide in the granulocytes takes place in the cell membrane. Its physiological function and high reactivity require the reactive oxygen radical to be formed at the site of action.

27.3  Anemia (literally, bloodlessness) is a shortage of circulating hemoglobin. This disorder may cause certain regions to be inadequately supplied with oxygen. Ischemia is a local lack of blood, caused by obstruction of the blood supply. See also Study unit 15.

27.4  It is preferable to take a bone biopsy specimen when quantitative aspects of the disorder are at issue.

27.5  Clinical symptoms of leukemia include:
- *acute leukemia*: infections (of the mouth and throat), fever, ulcers on the lips and mouth, bruises and hemorrhages, sometimes general symptoms of anemia; the symptoms arise suddenly and rapidly increase in severity;
- *chronic leukemia*: usually no symptoms at first; sometimes the first symptoms are enlarged lymph nodes in the neck and armpits and possibly an enlarged spleen; the symptoms may be the same as those of anemia or infections.

27.6  Yes, not only because regeneration is often incomplete (infectious diseases, etc.), but also because the chromosomes may be damaged (mutagenesis, carcinogenesis).

27.7 *Aneuploidy*: changes in the number of chromosomes per cell.

*Chromosomal aberrations*: changes in the morphology of chromosomes.

*Micronuclei*: cytoplasmic nucleoli resulting from exclusion of acentric chromosome fragments.

## 2    Answers to the self assessment questions

1    Megaloblastic anemia is associated with inhibition of DNA synthesis in all cell lines. Erythroblasts, myelocytes and megalocytes are affected (see section 2.2).

2    In ring sideroblasts, the iron is localized in the mitochondria.

3    Patients who have been treated with cytostatics.

4    Methemoglobin cannot enter into a reversible bond with oxygen, as a result of which the cellular oxygen supply is compromised by high concentrations of methemoglobin.

5    The prolonged bleeding time is caused by the effect of aspirin on the metabolism of thrombocytes. The exposure to aspirin results in inhibition of the synthesis of cyclic endoperoxides and thromboxane $A_2$. Only after aspirin has been eliminated and the affected blood platelets have been degraded by the RES will the bleeding time return to normal.

6    In a granulocyte, the NADPH-oxidase complex is activated to generate superoxide anions when it comes into contact with immunoglobulin or with a microorganism packed with complement.

# Contents Study unit 28
# Immunotoxicology: determination of immunotoxic effects and immunotoxicity mechanisms

0-8493-9232-2/96/$0.00 + $.50

Study unit 28

# Immunotoxicology: determination of immunotoxic effects and immunotoxicity mechanisms

*J. G. Vos and H. van Loveren*

## INTRODUCTION

The past decade has seen an increasing number of indications that human exposure to substances suppressing the immune system results in an increased incidence of infections and certain neoplastic disorders. This has become clear in particular from studies on the effects of certain pharmaceuticals. Chemicals occurring in the environment have also been found to influence the immune system. Several examples of such substances are listed in Table 28.1.

For these chemicals it is less clear than for pharmaceuticals that exposure to them causes an increased risk of infection or neoplastic disorder. It should however be emphasized that little epidemiological research has been carried out so far on these substances, although a few examples have been described. Dairy

TABLE 28.1
Examples of substances causing immunotoxicity in rats or in humans

| Toxic agent | Disturbance of immune system | |
| --- | --- | --- |
| | **Rat/Mouse** | **Man** |
| 2,3,7,8-tetrachlorodibenzo-p-dioxin and furan | + | + |
| polychlorinated biphenyls | + | + |
| polybrominated biphenyls | + | + |
| hexachlorobenzene | + | not known |
| lead | + | not known |
| cadmium | + | not known |
| methylmercury | + | not known |
| 7,12-dimethylbenzo[a]anthracene | + | not known |
| benzo[a]pyrene | + | not known |
| di-n-octyltindichloride | + | not known |
| di-n-butyltindichloride | + | not known |
| benzidine | + | + |
| nitrogen dioxide and ozone | + | + |
| benzene, toluene and xylene | + | + |
| asbestos | + | + |
| dimethylnitrosamine | + | not known |
| diethylstilbestrol | + | + |

farmers and workers in the dairy industry in Michigan, who were exposed to polybrominated biphenyls (PBBs), as well as people in Taiwan who were accidentally exposed to rice oil contaminated with polychlorinated biphenyls (PCBs) and polychlorinated dibenzofurans (PCDFs), showed obvious changes in the functioning of their immune system. This could be established in the laboratory using several immunological parameters. Clinically, these patients showed an increased incidence of infections of the upper respiratory tract, especially during the initial period of PCB or PCDF poisoning. Some researchers have suggested that long-term exposure to 2,3,7,8-tetrachlorodibenzo-p-dioxin (TCDD, dioxin), as happened in a certain area of Missouri, in 1971, correlated with reduced cellular immunity.

In 1981 there was an outbreak of pneumonia in Spain among people who had consumed chemically treated rape seed oil, which had been sold as olive oil. This so-called "Toxic Oil Syndrome", as the disorder has come to be known, possibly can be attributed to imidazoline-thiol components, derivatives of isothiocyanate, present in the rape seed oil. These components are thought to cause disorders resembling the "graft-versus-host" condition, which has an immunologic background. A final example of the effects of environmental contaminants on the immune system is provided by the increased incidence of respiratory infections in people exposed to air-polluting gases or aerosols. As far as pharmaceuticals are concerned, an increased incidence of infections and neoplastic disorders has been observed in patients who had been treated therapeutically with immunosuppressants. Transplant patients who had received long-term treatment with immunosuppressants such as glucocorticoids or azathioprine in order to prevent rejection, showed a marked increase in the incidence of tumors (rising from 26% 1 year after the transplantation to as much as 47% 10 years after the operation).

The dramatic consequences of suppressing the body's resistance to infections and neoplastic disorders and thus implicitly the potential consequence of exposure to immunotoxic substances can probably be best illustrated by examining the increased incidence of lymphomas and leukemias, Kaposi sarcomas and opportunistic infections observed in patients suffering from AIDS (acquired immune deficiency syndrome). Actually, AIDS patients do not have a reduced resistance due to exposure to toxic substances but because of infection with the human immunodeficiency virus (HIV), which destroys the immune system.

In experimental animals, the toxic effects of substances on the immune system can manifest themselves in various ways. Changes in weight and histology of lymphoid organs are often important signs. Quantitative and qualitative changes in the cellularity of the lymphoid organs and bone marrow are also frequently observed, as are changes in the white blood cell count in the peripheral blood. The immunologic functions can be altered by exposure to toxic substances. The same is true of resistance to experimentally induced infections or transplantable tumors.

Immunotoxicology is the discipline which studies the events that may lead to unwanted effects caused by interactions between substances and the immune system. These effects may be caused by:

1.  the direct and/or indirect interaction between the substances or their metabolites and the immune system;

2.  an immunological response on the part of the host to the substances or their metabolites, or to host antigens which have been modified by the substance or their metabolites.

The term "immune system" is used here in a fairly broad sense. It includes not only effects on acquired or specific immunity, in other words processes which are mediated by T-cells, B-cells, antibodies etc. Here it also includes processes mediated by non-specific or natural resistance. These may be mediated by macrophages, polymorphonuclear granulocytes, natural killer cells, etc. and which are of significant importance to the body's resistance to infections and neoplastic disorders.

Immunotoxicology can be divided into four subdisciplines:

a. study of the changes in immunologic responses after exposure of humans and animals to toxic substances, including drugs developed for purposes other than modulating immunity;

b. study of changes in immune functions after exposure to immunotherapeutic drugs, i.e. substances which are in fact produced for the purpose of modulating immunity;

c. study of allergy and autoimmunity caused by exposure to toxic substances, including pharmaceuticals;

d. development of immunologic techniques and approaches in toxicology.

The present study unit focusses on determining the changes in immunological functioning after exposure to chemical substances. Section 3 will deal with allergy and autoimmunity caused by exposure to xenobiotics.

Routine toxicity studies are aimed at determining the toxicological profile of a substance, i.e. they are carried out using a variety of dosages, ranging from those with little effect to high dosages. With this method the target organ of the toxic substance can be determined.

The target organ is defined as the organ in which a certain dosage still causes changes without there being toxicity elsewhere in the body. Determination of immunotoxicity is therefore best carried out in the context of conventional toxicology, examining whether the immune system is perhaps the target of the toxic substance. Since conventional toxicological studies are carried out on rats, it is natural enough to use the same animal for immunotoxicological purposes.

ASSIGNMENT 28.1

What are the advantages for toxicology of choosing the rat as animal model?

LEARNING OBJECTIVES

After studying this unit, you should be able to:

— explain the following concepts in your own words:

immunotoxicology

immunosuppression

immunostimulation

allergy

autoimmunity

— mention how the various immunotoxicological effects of chemicals can be studied

— give examples of substances that can cause immunosuppression, allergy or autoimmunity, and indicate the underlying mechanism (in so far as these are known)

— indicate and explain the possibilities and limitations of general toxicological research for the detection of immunotoxic properties of chemicals

— describe the importance of specific immunotoxicological tests and the mechanisms by which they work

— indicate differences and similarities between substances that stimulate the immune system and those that suppress it

*Study hints*

The structure of the immune system is extremely complex and at the same time extremely well balanced. An extensive explanation of the immune system and its related defence mechanisms can be found in textbooks on immunology. Although the present unit gives a short description of the immune system, it assumes that you have a good knowledge of the anatomy and functioning of that system. The units dealing with the toxicology of the skin (Study unit 17) and of the respiratory system (Study unit 18) have also touched upon a certain aspects of the toxicology of the immune system. It might be useful to reread the relevant sections. The study load for the present unit is estimated at 3 hours. The optionally available CD-I program "Toxicological Histopathology" gives a few microscopic-anatomical examples of immunopathological processes.

## STUDY CORE

### 1 Immunological and non-specific defence mechanisms

The purpose of the specific immune system and its related non-specific defence mechanisms can be summarized as protecting the host against infections and tumors. The nature of the immune system is a special one when compared with other organ systems, such as the kidneys or lungs, in that these systems carry out their functions continuously, while the immune system is called into action to deal with a developing infection. It will be obvious that this characteristic of the system bears repercussions for the method of determining the immunotoxicity of substances. It should also be emphasized that the host is continually exposed to a wide range of antigens, in particular antigens that reach the host via the gastrointestinal tract and the respiratory organs. The immune response displayed by the host after contact with an antigen is determined to a significant extent not only by the type of antigen but also by the route by which the host comes into contact with it. Figure 28.1 gives a survey of the various cell types involved in the immune response and in defence mechanisms. The following only briefly summarizes the most important aspects.

*Primary lymphoid tissues*
*Secondary lymphoid organs*

The immune system consists of the central or *primary lymphoid organs*, such as bone marrow and thymus, and the peripheral or *secondary lymphoid organs*, such as spleen, lymph nodes, Peyer's patches in the intestine, and bronchus-associated lymphoid tissue. The blood can also be included in the latter category. The primary tissues are the site of proliferation of lymphocytes, independent of antigens. T-lymphocytes, originating from the bone marrow, mature in the thymus to functional cells. These T-cells are responsible for the *cellular immunity* and regulate the humoral immunity for certain (T-cell dependent) antigens.

*Cellular immunity*

ASSIGNMENT 28.2

It has been shown that in birds B-cells, which also originate in the bone marrow, mature in the bursa of Fabricius, which, like the thymus, is a primary lymphoid tissue. Where does maturation of the B-cells take place in mammals?

844

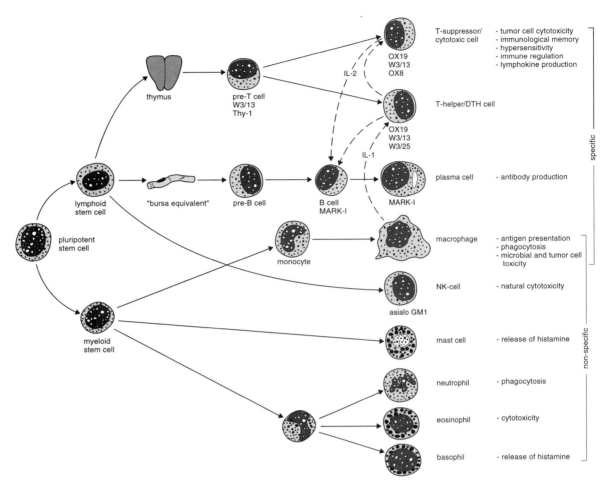

FIGURE 28.1
Cells involved in specific and non-specific resistance in rats
Examples of monoclonal antibodies against various subpopulations are indicated underneath the cells (IL = interleukin).

*Humoral immunity*

B-cells are responsible for *humoral immunity*, in other words they can mature to plasma cells which produce immunoglobulins. The maturation of B-cells (*plasma cells*), but also of *T-cells*, is induced in the secondary lymphoid tissue. A group of T-cells are the T-helper cells, that help regulate the synthesis of antibodies by plasma cells. There are also T-cells that produce chemoattractants, macrophage-activating lymphokines or interferon. These substances, called cytokines, can influence the activity of non-specific cells such as macrophages and natural killer cells. Finally, there are the *cytotoxic T-cells*, capable of killing e.g. tumor cells and T-suppressor cells, suppressing the activity of other lymphocytes.

Like maturation of B-cells to plasma cells, the maturation of these types of T-cells takes place in the secondary lymphoid tissue under the influence of antigens. This induction is generally effectuated by the antigen's entry into the organism, and its subsequent presentation (by antigen-presenting cells such as macrophages) to the lymphocytes which then show a primary response. This initial interaction can also cause the development of a "memory" for this particular antigen, so that renewed contact between the organism and the antigen will lead to a rapid and more vehement reaction intended to eliminate the agent as quickly and effectively as possible.

*Proliferation of lymphocytes*

An important phenomenon occurring when an immune response is first induced (primary response) or is once more generated (secondary response) is the *proliferation of lymphocytes*. This involves both T-and B-lymphocytes, and brings about a significant increase in the potential (which the immune system is able to mobilize) to deal with a particular antigen. Lymphocytes are therefore particularly sensitive to substances that can interfere with the mechanism of proliferation.

The immune system is not restricted to the primary and secondary lymphoid organs mentioned above. Via the blood and the lymph, lymphoid cells recirculate into and out of the lymphoid organs throughout virtually the whole body. They can also leave the blood and lymph vessels and enter the extravascular tissues. The same is true of antibodies and cytokines, which are produced by the B-and the T-cells, respectively. Antibodies, more specifically those with a specialized function, such as immunoglobulin A (IgA), are also secreted in the intestinal and respiratory mucus and in tears and saliva. Induction of this latter type of antibody takes place to a large extent in lymphoid tissue associated with mucous membranes, such as Peyer's patches and the bronchus-associated lymphoid tissue. It is presumed that the production of these antibodies is regulated more or less independently of the regulation of the systemic immune responses. This is one of the reasons why the mucosal immune system is also referred to as the 'local immune system'.

ASSIGNMENT 28.3

Why is the local immune system particularly interesting from the point of view of immunotoxicology?

Many cell types are involved in the immune response. Strictly speaking, they do not themselves belong to this system, as they do not have the ability to recognize antigens. These cells function as *amplification, effector* or *initiator cells*, and as such are of great importance to the ultimate efficacy of the immune system.

*Non-specific defence mechanisms*

Together with the immune system, these so-called *non-specific defence mechanisms* provide resistance to infections and tumors. They include non-specific cells such as macrophages, natural killer cells, neutrophilic, eosinophilic and basophilic granulocytes, mast cells and probably even endothelial cells.

Macrophages, neutrophils and natural killer cells are particularly important 'front-line' effector cells in non-specific defence mechanisms which are independent of specific immune responses. Research in the field of immunotoxicology will therefore also involve the study of these types of cell.

Resistance to opportunistic infections and neoplastic disorders requires functionally immunocompetent cells. These cells should proliferate and differentiate, in order to carry out their task and are therefore sensitive to agents that can influence the processes involved. The immune system is a tightly organized system with continuous intensive communication between the various cell types via soluble mediators and direct cell contact. Each agent capable of intervening in these complex regulatory systems is therefore also potentially capable of disturbing the balance which the system tries to maintain. This can lead to altered

*Immunostimulation and immunosuppression*

immune functions, such as *immunostimulation* (possibly resulting in autoimmunity or hypersensitivity) or *immunosuppression* (possibly causing deficient resistance in the host).

## 2    Determining immunotoxicity

The following section considers the reasons why the immunotoxicity of substances is determined within the setting of routine toxicological determinations, and the problems met when following such an approach. As will become apparent, in practice, screening for immunotoxity can be incorporated into routine toxicity studies. Follow-up studies can then establish what part of the immune system and the defence mechanisms related to it, are affected by the immunotoxic substance. This so-called tiered test system as well as methods investigating the mechanisms underlying immunotoxic effects.

## 2.1 IMMUNOTOXICOLOGY VERSUS ROUTINE TOXICOLOGICAL RESEARCH

See also Study unit 14

Carrying out routine toxicological research includes establishing the toxicological profile of the substance involved. The authorities in most industrialized countries have laid down that, in addition to acute toxicity tests, 28-day and 90-day toxicity tests must be carried out in which at least three different dosages of the substance must be administered: a high dosage (which can be expected to induce a clear toxic effect), a low dosage (from which no effect is expected) and an intermediate dosage. The same approach is applied for determining immunotoxicity. Immunological research has developed a vast number of immunological tests. For many of these methods the relevance to the determination of immunotoxicity has been established. This is true particularly of mouse models, and to a lesser extent for rat models.

Partly because the number of substances that qualify for immunotoxicological research is continually increasing, it is in practice impossible to test all substances for their potential effects on all aspects of the immune system and related non-specific defence mechanisms. Testing is therefore of necessity restricted firstly to the screening of a number of important and relevant parameters that will give a rough picture of the various defence mechanisms. If immunotoxicity is indicated, other tests are subsequently carried out to obtain more detailed information. Such a tiered system thus comprises several panels of immunological tests. If the outcome of the primary panel indicates immunotoxicity of a substance, a secondary panel of tests can be carried out. Which tests make up the secondary panel is determined on the basis of the results of the first set. The immunological tests included in these panels are shown in Table 28.2. The individual tests are discussed in later sections.

*Tests not compromising the immune system*

It should be noted that the primary panel of immunological assays carried out to determine immunotoxicity measures a number of general parameters of the host's specific and non-specific resistance. These tests *do not compromise the toxicity study*. This means that the rats are not exposed to antigens by means of immunization or infected with bacteria or parasites to determine how well the immune system works. In other words, no so-called function tests are carried out. The advantage of this approach is that these general parameters can all be incorporated quite easily into the routine 28-day or 90-day toxicity studies. Combination of the toxic substance to be tested with administration of infectious antigens or immunization with antigens while carrying out these measurements might well interfere with the results found for the general toxicological parameters and would make the routine toxicology study invalid. A problem when following the above-described approach is that probably not all immunotoxic substances are detected unless the function tests are included in the study.

To what type of error might this give rise?

In other words, this approach might give rise to false-negative results. However, the immune system appears to be highly sensitive to damage by toxic substances. It is therefore not surprising that the method described above using a hierar-

TABLE 28.2
Methods of determining immunotoxicity in rats.
  For further information see text.

| | parameter | procedure |
|---|---|---|
| primary panel | immunopathology | — routine hematology (differentiation of white blood cells)<br>— serum IgM, IgG, IgA levels<br>— bone marrow cellularity<br>— weight and histology of organs (thymus, spleen, lymph nodes, Peyer's patches, BALT)<br>— (possibly) immunocytochemistry and flow cytometry of lymphoid tissues |
| secondary panel | cellular immunity | — sensitization with T-cell-dependent antigens (ovalbumin, tuberculin, *Listeria*) and skin tests<br>— *in vitro* lymphoproliferative responses to antigen (*Listeria*), and to T-cell mitogens (Con A, PHA) |
| | humoral immunity | — serum titres of IgM, IgG, IgA and IgE against T-cell-dependent antigens (ovalbumin, tetanus toxoid, *T.spinalis*)<br>— serum titres of IgM against T-cel-independent antigen (*E.coli* lipo-polysaccharide, LPS)<br>— *in vitro* lymphoproliferative response to LPS |
| | macrophage function | — *in vitro* phagocytosis and killing of *L.monocytogenes* |
| | NK-cell activity | — *in vitro* cytolysis of YAC lymphoma cells by non-adherent cells |
| | resistance to infectious diseases | — challenge with *T.spiralis* (rejection of adult worms, yield of muscle larvae)<br>— challenge with cytomegalovirus (virus determination in salivary gland) |
| | influence on autoimmunity | — adjuvant arthritis<br>— experimental allergic encephalomyelitis |

chical system of panels of immunological assays has, in practice, proved to be suitable for establishing the immunotoxicity of many substances.

Changes in immune functions as observed in immunotoxicity studies, should be viewed critically as regards the origin of the effect: are the changes actually the result of direct effects of the substance on the immune system, or are they indirect effects, e.g. resulting from malnutrition, disturbed protein synthesis, stress or hormonal imbalance after exposure to the substance concerned?

## 2.2    IMMUNOTOXICOLOGY AS PART OF GENERAL TOXICOLOGY

Figures 28.2 and 28.3 show examples of effects that may be found with the aid of the tests in the primary immunotoxicity screening panel (see Table 28.2). The figures refer to the effects of exposure to two types of immunotoxic substances, namely bis(tri-n-butyltin)oxide (TBTO) (see Figure 28.2), and hexachlorobenzene (HCB) (see Figure 28.3).

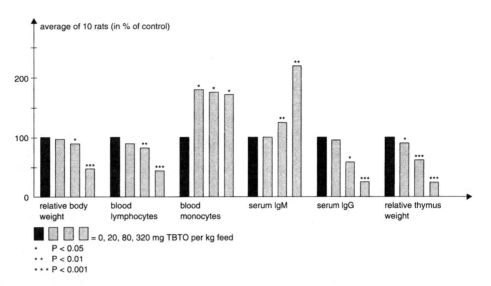

FIGURE 28.2

Effects of exposure to TBTO on various immunologic parameters

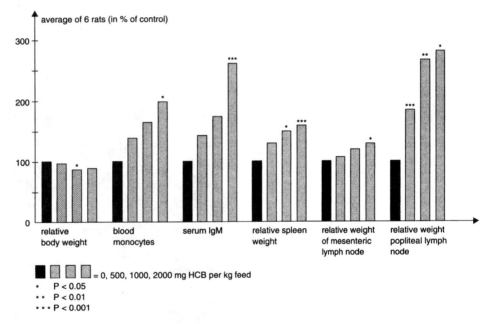

FIGURE 28.3

Effects of exposure to HCB on different immunologic parameters

*Weight of lymphoid organs*

In addition to the serum levels of the immunoglobulins M, G, A and E, another important immunotoxicological parameter for the screening of potentially immunotoxic substances is the *weight of the lymphoid organs*.

ASSIGNMENT 28.4

Both TBTO and HCB are immunotoxic. Can you conclude from the data available whether the two substances cause the same immunotoxicity?

*Histopathology*

In routine toxicological research, *histopathological examination* is carried out primarily in hematoxylin-eosin(HE)-stained paraffin sections. In many studies this

849

histopathological assessment appears to be very useful for the establishment of immunotoxity, especially if the histopathological information is combined with data on the weight of the lymphoid organs.

*Lymph nodes and spleen*

The *lymph nodes and spleen* are divided morphologically into thymus-dependent and thymus-independent areas. Hence, this division can provide information regarding the relative effects of the substances under study on the T-cell and B-cell compartments (see Figures 28.4 and 28.5). Depending on the route of exposure, it may be relevant to include the bronchus-associated or the intestine-associated lymphoid tissue in the study. These tissues also display a T/B-cell compartmentalization.

*Bone marrow*

The *bone marrow* is an integral part of the immune system and contains pluripotent stem cells, which can differentiate to, among others, B-cells, T-cells, macrophages, granulocytes (see also Figure 28.1).

Morphological examination of the bone marrow is therefore essential in establishing possible immunotoxity. Microscopic analysis can be carried out using sections, but also smears or cytocentrifuge preparations of cells collected from the bone marrow. The *cellularity* of bone marrow, i.e. the quantity of cells as determined after flushing the (femoral) bone marrow and counting the number of nucleated cells, found in it, has proved a valuable parameter for determining immunotoxity.

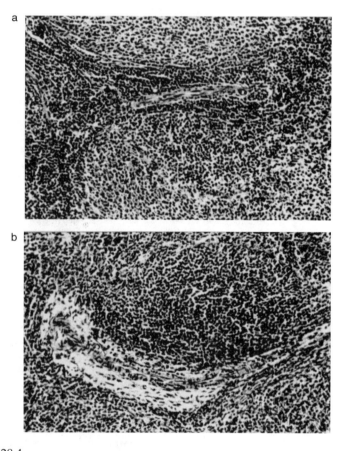

FIGURE 28.4
Spleen of a normal rat (a) and an immunodeficient ('nude') rat (b)
The immunodeficiency in this rat is based on a congenital anomaly, causing the thymus to be only rudimentary. As a result, the T-cell-dependent areas in the spleen are depleted.

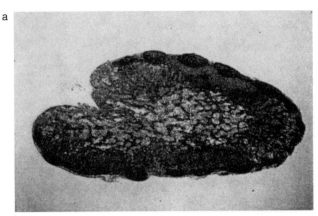

FIGURE   28.5
Lymph node of a normal rat (a) and of an immunodeficient rat (b)
The animals are the same as those in Figure 28.4.

*Broncho-alveolar lavage*

After exposure to toxic substances by inhalation, characterization and quantification of cells obtained from *broncho-alveolar lavage* has proved to be a very useful method.

An immunologic parameter which can easily be incorporated into conventional toxicity experiments (already referred to above) is the determination of *serum immunoglobulin levels*. The changes in serum levels of IgM, IgG and IgA appear to be a particularly useful parameter in determining immunotoxicity.

*Immunoglobulin levels in serum*

If any indications of immunotoxicity are found in this primary screening panel, these findings can then be confirmed and studied in greater detail with more advanced techniques, while still remaining within the bounds of general toxicological experiments. One of these techniques is immunocytochemistry.

Cytoplasmic components, such as immunoglobulin in plasma cells, or lysozyme in macrophages, can easily be demonstrated in paraffin sections of fixed material using the *immunoperoxidase technique* (see Figure 28.6).

*Immunoperoxidase technique*

**Intermezzo**

Determinants occurring on the cell membrane, are generally only small in number. Fixation tends to change the structure of various determinants somewhat, so that the antibodies applied in the immunoperoxidase technique no longer recognize these determinants, certainly not if there are only few of them. For that reason surface markers, for example on macrophages, helper T-cells or suppressor T-cells, can be demonstrated much better in frozen sections.

This qualitative method may be followed by a quantitative method, in which flow cytometric analysis can be applied to quantify T-cells and B-cells in cell suspensions of the lymphoid organs of rats exposed to toxic substances. To this end, monoclonal antibodies have been developed,

851

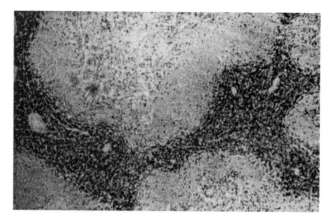

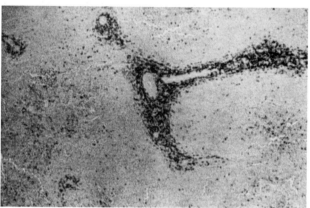

FIGURE 28.6

Example of an immunoperoxidase stain for T-cells in the spleen of a rat exposed to TBTO
Depletion of the T-cell area is clearly visible; upper panel shows the spleen of control rat.

with which specific markers on the membranes of subpopulations of rat lymphocytes or on other leukocytes can be demonstrated (see Figure 28.1).

## 2.3  IMMUNOTOXICOLOGY ON THE BASIS OF IMMUNE FUNCTION TESTS

*Immune function tests*

If the outcome of the primary panel of immunotoxicity tests incorporated into a routine toxicity study, suggests that the substance under study is immunotoxic, the research enters the following phase. This second stage includes the use of *immune function tests*. These involve immunogenic stimuli to which the immune system is expected to respond. The effect of exposure to the substance involved on the response of the immune system is then studied. This second stage of the examination consists of a set of immune function tests, composed on the basis of the results of the primary phase. For example, if any changes in serum immunoglobulin levels were observed in the primary test panel, the second stage will certainly include B-cell function tests. If, on the other hand, changes in the thymus or the T-cell-dependent areas of the lymph nodes were found, cellular immune function tests will be carried out in the second phase.

The following sections will elaborate on how to determine whether immunotoxic substances affect humoral or cellular aspects of the immune system, or non-specific defence mechanisms. Next, methods for examining the possible effects of toxic substances on these aspects of the body's defence with regard to the course of infections will be described.

### 2.3.1 Cellular immunity

*Cellular immunity in vitro*

Delayed-type hypersensitivity correlates well with an *in vitro* parameter of cellular immunity, namely *proliferation of sensitized lymphocytes* which are cultured *in vitro* together with the specific antigen. The extent of proliferation is determined by measuring the incorporation of tritiated thymidine into DNA. The ability of rat T-cells to transform and proliferate can also be tested *in vitro* by *adding T-cell mitogens to the culture medium*, such as phytohemagglutinin (PHA) or concanavalin A (Con A).

*Addition of T-cell mitogens to a culture medium*

In contrast to specific antigens, these mitogens activate a relatively high percentage of the lymphocytes.

Although this parameter is often used, it corresponds far less well with *in vivo* resistance to infection and tumors than antigen-induced lymphoproliferation. Therefore, data obtained from mitogen stimulation and antigen-induced stimulation are not interchangeable. Rather, they should be seen as complementary.

*Rejection of allogeneous skin transplants*
*Cellular immunity in vivo*

*Rejection of allogeneous skin transplants* is a T-cell-mediated process which can be used as a parameter in determining immunotoxicity. This *in vivo* technique, however, is not very sensitive; considerable immunosuppression is required to delay rejection of the graft by one to two days. An important aspect of T-cell-dependent cellular immunity, which is directed largely against viral infection, is the activity of *cytotoxic T-cells (CTL)*. Measurement of CTL activity should therefore in fact be included in the standard immunotoxicity test panels. It is difficult, however, to induce CTL activity in cell populations. Moreover, this type of research requires inbred strains, while protocol-toxicity research is usually carried out on non-inbred strains.

*Cytotoxic T-lymphocytes, CTL*

*Delayed-type hypersensitivity*

Other function tests of cellular immunity are measurements of *delayed-type hypersensitivity* to antigens such as *Listeria*, ovalbumin or tuberculin. In previously sensitized animals, increased *thickness of the skin* at the site where the antigen is administered is a reasonably sensitive parameter. In rats, antigens are administered mainly in the sole of the foot or in the ear, as that is where changes in thickness are easiest to measure with a micrometer (see Figure 28.7).

### 2.3.2 Humoral immunity

For most antigens, humoral immunity, i.e. immunity depending on antibody synthesis, is controlled by T-cells. For a few antigens (primarily lipopolysaccharides) such responses are independent of T-helper cells. Immunotoxicity of

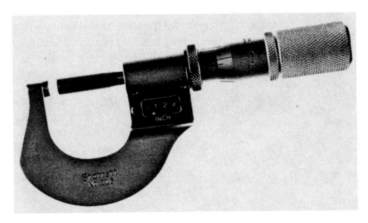

FIGURE 28.7
Micrometer with which the thickness of delayed-type hypersensitivity reactions in the ear can be measured

*Sheep red blood cells (SRBC)*

substances to thymus-dependent antibody synthesis (by B-cells differentiated into plasma cells under the influence of T-helper cells) can be tested using the T-cell-dependent antigens tetanus toxoid, sheep red blood cells (SRBC), ovalbumin, or antigens derived from the parasite Trichinella spiralis. These four antigens all induce the synthesis of IgG and IgM antibodies, while T.spiralis and ovalbumin induce IgE synthesis as well. IgA antibodies are also induced by T.spiralis and can also be induced against SRBC and ovalbumin, provided the animals are first immunized locally in the small intestinal Peyers patches.

**Intermezzo**

*ELISA technique*

Antibody titers in the serum can be demonstrated by means of the *ELISA technique* (enzyme-linked immunosorbent assay). In this technique, antigen is linked to a solid phase, namely the bottom of a polystyrene microliter plate. Incubation then takes place with serial dilutions of the serum to be tested. The IgG, IgM or IgA antibody levels are then titrated by further incubation with anti-IgG, anti-IgM or anti-IgA antibodies to which the enzyme peroxidase has been linked and which in this way bring about the conversion of a substrate to a colored reaction product.

*Hemagglutination test*

Antibody levels against SRBC can be measured by means of the *hemagglutination test*. Treatment of serum with 2-mercaptoethanol to denature the pentamer IgM could make the assay suitable for differentiating between IgG and IgM, but this is not a very reliable method. Therefore, an ELISA has recently been developed which uses antigens extracted from sheep erythrocytes. The procedure is otherwise identical to that described above.

Immunoglobulin A, an antibody whose production is controlled by T-helper cells, plays a major role in the protection of mucosal surfaces, for example in the local immune responses in the mucosa of the intestinal and respiratory tracts. Immunotoxic effects of substances on the IgA response in the respiratory or the gastrointestinal tract can be studied after injection of SRBC via the intratracheal route or into Peyer's patches. Likewise, such effects can be studied after oral infection with *Trichinella spiralis* or after immunization of rats against ovalbumin by injection into Peyer's patches. IgA antibody levels in serum, in lymph obtained by cannulation of the thoracic duct, or in intestinal lavages can be determined in an ELISA test by using these monoclonal antibodies.

*Thymus-independent antibody synthesis*

*Thymus-independent antibody synthesis*, i.e. the synthesis of immunoglobulins by plasma cells, which can be activated independent of T-helper cells, can be observed after immunization of rats with *E.coli* lipopolysaccharide (LPS).

Although LPS is a weak immunogen in rats, reasonable anti-LPS IgM titers can be observed in the serum using the ELISA technique.

The ability of B-lymphocytes to transform and proliferate can be tested *in vitro* by measuring the incorporation of tritiated thymidine into DNA induced by the addition of LPS to the culture medium.

### 2.3.3 Non-specific defence mechanisms

Non-specific defence mechanisms are of vital importance for the resistance to infections and neoplasms. They play an important role in the front-line defence against infections before a specific immune response has been triggered.

*Phagocytosis and lysis*

Important aspects of non-specific resistance are *phagocytosis* and *lysis* of bacteria by macrophages and natural cytotoxic activity to tumor cells and virally infected cells. These processes can be tested both *in vitro* and *in vivo*.

*Cytotoxicity by macrophages and natural killer cells*

Important non-specific defence mechanisms which must also be mentioned here are *cytotoxicity by macrophages or natural killer (NK) cells* (non-adherent lymphoid cells). These cells play an important role in the body's resistance to tumor cells and depend on a process of exocytosis. The activity of this type of cell can be determined *in vitro* by measuring the release of radioactive chromium from labelled so-called YAC-1 lymphoma target cells cultured together with the cytotoxic effector cells. Although assays of phagocytosis and lysis by macrophages and of cytotoxicity by macrophages and NK-cells are function tests, they can be made even more sensitive by stimulating the activity of these types of cell with the aid of certain mediators. A well-known mediator for NK-cells is, for example, *interferon*. The increased activity of the effector cells resulting from treatment with such a stimulating agent, makes a much greater demand on the cells's potential for mechanisms with which they fulfil their task than is the case for non-stimulated cells. Hence, interaction of toxic substances with these mechanisms may sooner cause an altered function, which may also be more easily measurable than if the cells had not been stimulated.

A number of immunologic test methods have been described above which are used to determine in greater detail the nature of the immunotoxicity of substances of which in a previous stage of toxicity research possible immunotoxicity had been established. The methods described are all based on *in vivo* exposure to the toxic substance and *in vivo* or *ex vivo* measurement of the immune responses.

The relevance of changes in immune responses measured using these tests can be studied by means of so-called infection models.

### 2.3.4 *In vivo resistance models*

A number of infection models are available for rats. They generally assess more than one immune mechanism, as well as non-specific defence mechanisms. Three models will be described here.

The resistance model in which animals are infected with *Listeria monocytogenes* examines the non-specific activity of macrophages and the cellular T-cell-dependent (in particular T-helper cell-dependent) immunity. Animals may be infected either intravenously or intratracheally, in order to test the systemic or respiratory resistance respectively. Depending on the route of infection, bacteria can then be cultured either from the spleen or from the lung as a measure of the animal's resistance to the infection. The bacteria can grow both outside and inside cells, especially in macrophages. On the other hand, these macrophages can eventually kill the bacteria. Resistance to *Listeria*-infection is to a large extent dependent on *macrophage activity*. Clearance of the bacteria is measured by bacteria counts 1–2 days after infection, when no specific T-cell response has developed yet.

These bacteria counts 1–2 days after a primary infection, when no immune response against the bacterium has yet developed, give an impression of the rats' *non-specific, macrophage-dependent resistance*.

The number of bacteria in the lung or spleen is determined by conventional bacteriological methods.

Also *in vitro* phagocytosis and intracellular lysis of bacteria by the macrophages can be measured. To do so, monolayers of macrophages are incubated with the bacteria for different periods of time. The eventual fate of the bacteria is then used as an indicator of macrophage activity.

During an infection, *Listeria*-specific *T-cells* are induced. These T-cells can produce cytokines, which direct macrophages to the focus of infection and further stimulate macrophage activity. Therefore, in addition to macrophages, T-cells are of great importance in the resistance to this type of infection.

*Determination of the numbers of bacteria* in homogenates of the spleen or lung 4 to 6 days after infection with a sublethal dose of *Listeria* is a reliable parameter to establish the cellular immune response to *Listeria*.

*Interferon*

*Model 1: Infection with Listeria monocytogenes*
*Listeria model, in vivo*

*Non-specific, macrophage-dependent resistance*

*Listeria model, in vitro*

*T-cells*

855

Rats can also be immunized, for example subcutaneously or intratracheally, after which they can be exposed to secondary infection by intravenous or intratracheal administration respectively. Again, bacteria counts in spleen and lung homogenates can be used as parameters of immunity against *Listeria*. The above procedure can be very helpful in answering the question where the immune response is affected by the toxic substance, i.e. in the induction of *Listeria*-specific T-cells (the *afferent phase*), or the phase in which the T-cells do their work (the *effector* or *efferent phase*).

Another useful parameter in the *Listeria* model is constituted by the changes in lymphocyte subpopulations in draining lymph nodes. If rats are infected intratracheally, the ratio of T-cells/B-cells in the bronchial lymph nodes shifts in favor of the T-cells. This effect has been demonstrated by means of flow cytometric analysis of lymph node suspensions. Such a shift is not surprising, as *Listeria* mainly induces a cellular, T-cell-dependent immune response.

*Model 2: Infection with Trichinella spiralis*
*Parameters in the T.spiralis model*

The infection model which makes use of the intestinal nematode *Trichinella spiralis*, is interesting because it allows even more parameters of the body's resistance to be measured. After oral infection of rats with *T.spiralis* larvae by the oral route, the larvae develop to maturity in the small intestine. Fertilized female worms then penetrate into the mucosa. Locally, T-cell-dependent processes can be observed in the intestine, such as the development of an inflammatory infiltrate characterized by mononuclear cells, mast cells and eosinophilic granulocytes. T-cell-dependent humoral immune responses also occur, i.e. production of immunoglobulins M, G, E and A. Although the precise mechanism is not known, the interaction of these processes is believed to lead to the expulsion of the worms from the intestine. During this intestinal phase of the infection, so-called newborn larvae migrate from the intestine via blood and lymph to muscle tissue elsewhere in the body. Inflammatory infiltrates develop around these larvae as well, and these responses are also T-cell-dependent.

*Model 3: infection with the cytomegalovirus*
*Parameters in the cytomegalovirus model*

The most important defence mechanisms in the infection model in which animals are infected intraperitoneally with the *cytomegalovirus* are natural-killer cell activity, cytotoxic T-cell activity and humoral immunity. A target organ of this virus is the salivary gland. Determination of the quantity of the virus present in that gland provides a measure of the animal's resistance to the virus.

*Thymus dependency*

The *thymus dependence* of these models (*T.spiralis*, *L.monocytogenes* and cytomegalovirus) has been validated in rats lacking a thymus. As a result of a genetic defect, these rats have only a rudimentary thymus, and consequently do not exhibit any T-cell-dependent immune responses (see Figure 28.8).

As an example, Figure 28.9 shows the effect of exposure to bis(tri-n-butyltin)oxide (TBTO) on resistance, as measured with one of the infection models described above.

In addition to the infection models mentioned above, rat tumor models can also be used. Compared to mouse models, however, not many rat tumor models are available. Moreover, rat tumor models suffer the same drawback as cytotoxic T-cell tests and mixed lymphocyte reactions, namely that they require the use of inbred rat strains.

ASSIGNMENT 28.5

At what aspects of resistance should infection models to be developed in the future (or already in development) be aimed?

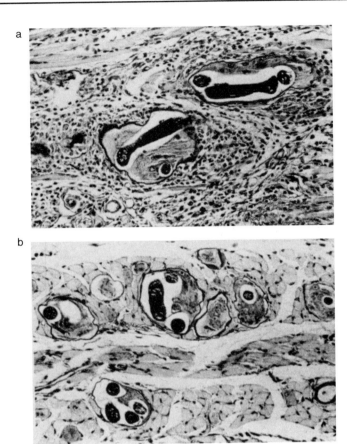

FIGURE 28.8
Inflammatory infiltrate around *T. spiralis* muscle larvae in a normal (a) and absence of infiltrate in an athymic rat (b)

Infection models involve more than one aspect of immunity and related defence mechanisms. These "real world" tests are of great significance in assessing the relevance of changes in immune responses observed after exposure to foreign compounds.

## 2.4 ADVANTAGES AND DISADVANTAGES OF THE IMMUNOTOXICITY RESEARCH DESCRIBED

For practical reasons, rats are chosen to an increasing extent as the experimental animals for use in immunotoxicological research.

Although the immunotoxicological research carried out so far was mainly concerned with subacute exposure studies, the routine toxicological parameters tested in studies in rats could also include immunologic parameters if exposure is semichronic, chronic or perinatal. It is known that the most obvious effects of substances on the immune system can be demonstrated if animals are brought into contact with the substance involved during the ontogenesis of the lymphoid system. Consequently, *in utero* exposure and neonatal exposure seem to be the most sensitive ways of exposure with which the immunotoxicity of substances can be examined. This is particularly true for substances that can influence the proliferation and differentiation of thymocytes in the thymus. Examples are TCDD and several dialkyltin substances (see also Study unit 29). An example of such a change is the effect of benzene on so-called granulocyte-colony-forming cells. For non-specific defence mechanisms, *in*

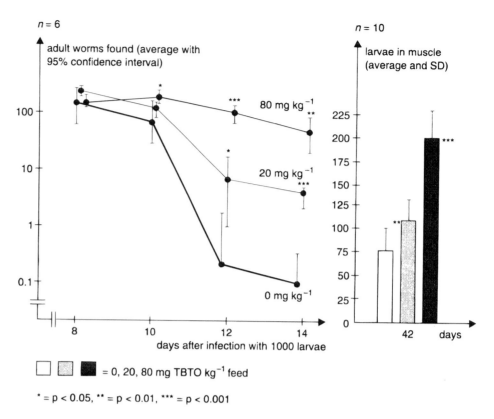

FIGURE 28.9
Effects of TBTO on resistance to *Trichinella spiralis*

*utero* exposure seems to be able to give rise to changes that can be observed in adult subjects.

A number of tests now used in mouse studies have been scientifically validated by limited interlaboratory comparative research and by frequent use in many laboratories. In the meantime, attempts have been made to establish which of these tests are truly relevant to assess the potential immunotoxic properties of a substance. The best way of demonstrating changes in the functioning of the immune system resulting from exposure to foreign substances, for example, is when the system is stimulated by an infection. For this reason, tests studying the various parameters of resistance in the rat should be evaluated in the light of their relevance to the eventual resistance to the infection shown by the host. This approach, which has already been followed in mice, is currently implemented in immunotoxicologic research in rats.

Organotin compounds are toxic metal compounds, characterized by covalent tin-carbon bonds

Using the rat as experimental animal and hierarchically structured test systems, a number of substances have now been shown to be immunotoxic. Examples are TCDD and various organotin substances (characterized by at least one carbon-tin bond). The screening method described in this study unit and summarized in Table 28.2 has also been used to determine the immunotoxicity of 18 pesticides. Five of them proved to be definitively immunotoxic, the most sensitive indicators of their toxicity being such immunologic parameters as the thymus weight and lymph node weight and serum immunoglobulin levels. Some of these substances will be dealt with in greater detail in Study unit 29.

Research has shown that changes in the weight of lymphoid organs or in their histology or cellularity do not always correlate with effects on immune functions. Recently, thymic atrophy has been found in mice exposed to ethylene glycol monomethyl ether and its metabolite methoxyacetic acid, although no functional immune defect was observed. Exposure of rats to diethylstilbestrol was also found to cause thymic atrophy, while the rats' thymus-dependent immunity remained intact. In mice, however, immunosuppression was in fact found. It is therefore too early to conclude definitively that the procedure described above is a completely adequate basis for confirmation or rejection of immunotoxicity.

Species differences might explain the fact that TCDD causes thymic atrophy in all species studied, while pre- and postnatal exposure (which implies exposure during the ontogenesis of the immune system) seems to be a *conditio sine qua non* for immunosuppression to occur in rats. In contrast to this finding are the results of studies on certain organotin substances. These substances induce thymic atrophy in young adult rats, but not in mice or guinea pigs. In rats, T-cell-dependent immunosuppression is observed. In this case, then, exposure during ontogenesis of the immune system is not at all a prerequisite for immunosuppression. Differences in thymotoxic effects between TCDD and organotin substances probably are a reflection of the different mechanisms underlying the effects of these substances.

An important development that might allow an increase in sensitivity of the screening stage of immunotoxicity studies is the introduction into immunotoxicology of methods by which the expression of interleukins can be determined. Interleukins are molecules which act as messengers between the various components of the immune system. A change in interleukin expression can be regarded as an early parameter of altered immune functioning, for example, caused by immunotoxic substances. It might be relatively easy to incorporate into the primary panel of immunotoxicity tests included in (routine) toxicity experiments, the measurement of interleukin expression at the level of messenger RNA, using molecular-biological probes (DNA probes) and dot blot techniques, or *in situ* hybridization techniques.

## 3    Substances inducing immunostimulation

In addition to the substances discussed in the preceding sections, which suppress the immune system, there are also substances that evoke an allergic reaction or autoimmune disease, i.e. activate the immune system. Substances may either stimulate the immune system, thus promoting allergy or autoimmunity, or they may themselves act as antigens, or alter endogenous determinants in such a way that these act as antigens.

Of course, not all substances that activate the immune system are in fact immunotoxic. After all, the physiological function of the immune system is to react to any foreign substances and render them harmless. For example, there are drugs with an immunostimulatory effect which are used in the treatment of tumors to restore or improve the antitumor response. Only in the case of a disturbance of the immune system, such as the induction of an allergic reaction or an autoimmune disease, the term toxic effect is justified. Incidentally, there are also immunostimulatory substances which do not stimulate the immune system directly but indirectly by inhibiting feedback mechanisms. An example of this latter group of compounds is formed by the bacterial endotoxins.

*Allergy*

One of the important side effects of immunity is the development, under some conditions, of allergy. There are at least three different types of allergy, two of which can occur in any person, and a third that occurs only in persons who have a specific allergic tendency. In the condition known as allergy, an antigen referred to as an allergen enters the body, and the defense systems respond to it. Examples of substances that can act as allergens are pollen, insect venom, food components and drugs. Unfortunately, in eliminating the allergen, the defense systems produce undesirable side effects. Often, these side effects result from an excessive inflammatory response. In most allergies, the allergen is not a major threat to the body, and the individual would be better off if the allergen would be ignored by the body. Several allergies exist, the most important of which are immediate hypersensitivity and delayed hypersensitivity.

The clinical classification into various types of allergic reaction is discussed in Study unit 18

**Intermezzo**

In an *immediate hypersensitivity* (type I), the allergic reaction occurs within minutes of exposure to the allergen. The allergic reaction is triggered when the allergen binds to antibodies attached to mast cells. The binding of allergen to these antibodies, which are of the immunoglobulin E class, triggers mast cells to release histamine and other chemicals that lead the inflammatory response. Hives, hay fever, some types of asthma, and anaphylactic shock are produced by immediate hypersensitivity reactions.

*Delayed hypersensitivity* (type IV), frequently causes skin eruptions in response to certain drugs or chemicals, particularly some cosmetics and household chemicals, to which one's skin is often exposed. Delayed hypersensitivities appear more slowly than do immediate hypersensitivities; here, the symptoms appear 2 to 14 days after exposure to the allergen. Delayed-reaction allergy is caused by sensitized lymphocytes and not by antibodies. This type of allergic reaction is triggered when the allergen encounters a T-lymphocyte and stimulates it to release cytokines. The cytokines attract and activate monocyte macrophages, which release yet other chemicals that lead to the inflammatory response. Examples of substances that produce delayed hypersensitivity are poison ivy and certain substances in cosmetic products.

A method used to investigate whether a substance induces a hypersensitivity reaction is the Draize test discussed in Study unit 17. The substance involved is administered intradermally, while a challenge is given at a different site. The extent to which erythema and edema develop are a measure of the allergic response. Several other tests are based on the Draize test.

Hypersensitivity in man can be tested by means of a skin test. Intradermal injection or epicutaneous application of the substance under investigation is used. In the case of tuberculine (TB), a small scratch is made in the skin at a certain site, and tuberculin is applied at that site. Any allergic reaction which may occur is then assessed.

By studying both the time course and nature of the reaction, this test and variations of it can be used to distinguish between type I and IV allergic reactions.

Since immediate hypersensitivity reactions are mediated by IgE, the existence of hypersensitivity may also be established by means of plasma determination of this immunoglobulin.

*Systemic allergic disorders and autoimmune disorders*

Another group of disorders of the immune system in which the system reacts inappropriately is that of *systemic allergic disorders and autoimmune disorders*.

**Intermezzo**

*An autoimmune disorder* is a disease resulting from an inappropriate reaction of the immune system to endogenous components. Different substances can induce the development of auto-immune disease. A common mechanism is that in which the xenobiotic acts as a hapten and binds to an endogenous (protein) component, so that the latter is perceived as foreign by the immune system. The body reacts by producing antibodies and/or cytotoxic T-cells directed against the entire molecule. It is not clear yet whether this process is due to induction of new T-helper cells or to inhibition of T-suppressor cells. Examples of this kind of substances are toluene diisocyanate (TDI) and β-lactam antibiotics such as penicillin. Apart from via this so-called "haptenization", certain substances are capable of changing endogenous molecules in such a way that they are recognized as foreign, without binding to the endogenous molecule. An example is the antihypertensive drug α-methyldopa, which modifies a molecule at the surface of the erythrocyte in such a way that it becomes an antigen.

Table 28.3 lists biologically active substances which occasionally give rise to systemic allergic reactions or autoimmune reactions in susceptible individuals.

In practice, chemically- or drug induced systemic allergic reactions or autoimmune disease do not become manifest until after human exposure to this kind of substance. Systemic allergic reactions and autoimmune reactions are generally not recognized in toxicity studies. It is therefore important that predictive testing methods become available which will enable recognition of these potentially immunotoxic effects of drugs and other chemicals.

A specific problem occurring when developing new tests for this type of immunotoxic effect is that various endogenous and exogenous factors play a role in the establishment of autoimmune disease. The diagram in Figure 28.10 shows which factors may be involved in the development of an auto-immune disorder.

For adequate risk assessment, the relative contributions of genetic predisposition and exogenous factors which may contribute to the induction and development of auto-immune diseases must be analyzed.

*Popliteal lymph node*
popliteal = pertaining to or near the ham, or that part of the leg behind the knee
*Biopterin*
Biopterin, one of the pterins, is a substance which is released after activation of macrophages and T-cells in a graft-versus-host (GVH) reaction; it is a metabolite of guanosine triphosphate (GTP)

Recent research has shown that the increase in weight of the *popliteal lymph node* in mice after injection of the substance to be tested into the foot pad, can be correlated to the capacity of some drugs to cause autoimmune disease in man. It has also been suggested that *biopterin* (in mouse urine) could be a useful biomarker for deregulation of cellular immunity. Further study of these findings seems likely to lead to the development of methods by which substances causing autoimmune disease can be tested. Examination of structure–activity relationships may also indicate substances that are responsible for inducing autoimmune reactions.

TABLE 28.3
Substances which have been demonstrated to induce autoimmune disease or systemic allergic disorders in some individuals

| toxic agent | reported autoimmune disease |
|---|---|
| zimeldine (antidepressant) | Guillain-Barré-like neuropathy |
| halothane (anesthetic) | hepatitis |
| vinyl chloride | scleroderma-like syndrome |
| trichloroethylene | scleroderma-like syndrome |
| practolol (β-adrenergic receptor blocker) | SLE* |
| chlorpromazine (antipsychotic) | SLE |
| hydralazine (antihypertensive) | SLE |
| isoniazide (antibacterial agent) | SLE |
| diphenylhydantoin (anticonvulsant) | SLE |
| ethosuximide (anticonvulsant) | SLE |

* SLE = systemic lupus erythematosus

861

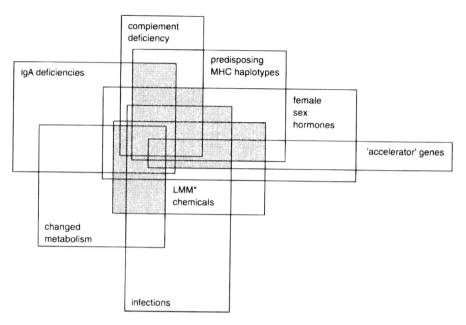

[ ] = individuals with a high risk of auto-immune disease

\* LMM = low molecular mass

FIGURE 28.10

Diagram of individual and environmental factors that may play a role in the development of autoimmune disease

The gray areas represent persons with a high risk of developing autoimmune disease. Although a combination of factors will increase the risk, not all factors need to be present for an auto-immune disorder to develop.

## 4    Sites of action of immunotoxic substances

### 4.1    IMMUNOTOXIC MECHANISMS

Study unit 29 will describe the immunotoxic action of several specific substances in greater detail. The present unit restricts itself to a brief, more general deliberation on the (presumed) sites of action of immunotoxic chemicals.

The effects of immunotoxic substances may be realized in various ways. Unfortunately, very little experimental information is available on the exact mechanisms of immunotoxic effects. This is explained in part by the fact that the physiological functioning of the immune system has not yet been completely clarified either.

As described in section 2, the complexity of the immune system makes the examination of immunotoxic substances far from easy. Figure 28.11 shows schematically at which sites of the immune system the chemicals might theoretically act.

It should be noted that, theoretically, a substance could exert its effect at various sites within the immune system. To illustrate this, a fictitious antibiotic can serve as an example. As a substance acting as an antigen, the antibiotic could sensitize the immune system and thus evoke an immune response. At the same time, the protein-inhibiting effect of that same antibiotic could have precisely the opposite effect, i.e. inhibition of the immune response. It is therefore not surprising that, in practice, different dosages often lead to opposite effects. Moreover, the great variety of testing methods may lead to the situation in which a substance is a suppressor according to one method, and a stimulator according to another, and not immunotoxic at all according to a third.

Earlier on it became evident that hypersensitivity and the development of autoimmune disease are based on sensitization of the immune system. In both cases, the genetic constitution of the individual involved plays a very important role.

Figure 28.12 shows the various components of the immune system that are particularly sensitive to the effects of chemicals.

The first phase in the immunologic process is constituted by the first contact with the antigen, the phase of antigen recognition (a). This is followed by an adaptive phase in which proliferation and differentiation of lymphocytes take place (b), which in turn is followed by a phase of clonal replication (c). In the final phase, the immune reactivity becomes manifest. At that stage, the B-cells produce and release proteins (antibodies), the T-cells produce cytokines and the macrophages synthesize proteolytic enzymes (d).

*Sensitivity to antiproliferative substances*

In some of these phases, mitotic activity is high. It is therefore in these phases that the immune response is very sensitive to cytotoxic substances such as alkylating agents and purine and pyrimidine antimetabolites.

Presumably, the immunosuppressive effect of some substances is due to their anti-proliferative effect. Apart from the selective sensitivity of the immune system caused by disturbance of cell proliferation, the lymphocytes are probably more restricted in their ability to provide detoxication than other cells.

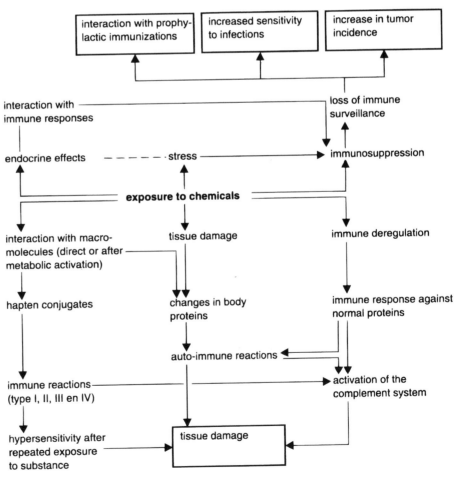

FIGURE   28.11
Diagram of the targets of immunotoxic substances within the immune system

ASSIGNMENT 28.6

How is it to be explained that lymphocytes have a more restricted detoxication system and are yet easily exposed to toxic xenobiotics?

*Effects via the endocrine system*

In addition to the direct effects on the immune system mentioned above, a large number of substances appear to have an indirect effect on the immune system. In particular, effects via the endocrine system are frequently observed.

The release of glucocorticoids as a result of stress, can lead to immunosuppression. For example, the involution of the thymus commonly observed in immunotoxicity research can often be attributed to effects on the immune system via the endocrine system.

*Nutrition*

Nutritional deficiencies sometimes also cause selective immunotoxic effects. Vitamin $B_6$ or zinc deficiency may be the cause of suppression of cell-mediated immunity. Malnutrition is also known to lead to thymic atrophy in experimental animals.

## 4.2 THE USE OF *IN VITRO* MODELS

Immunotoxicologic examination of substances, such as those in the primary and secondary panels of tests, should provide an answer to the question whether a substance is immunotoxic or not. In the past few years, *in vitro* models for the determination of toxicity have received considerable attention, among other reasons in the context of attempts to reduce the number of test animals and to find alternatives to animal experiments. The *in vitro* approach is particularly successful in screening substances for genotoxicity. For immunotoxicity screening, however, the value of *in vitro* tests is limited. This is caused by the necessity for critical evaluation of the results of *in vitro* immunotoxicity studies in view of the *in vivo* relevance of the findings, particularly because the immune system is so very complex.

*Plaque Forming Cell test*

One *in vitro* system which has been used for determining immunotoxicity is the *in vitro* immunization/antibody 'Plaque Forming Cell' test. Various food additives

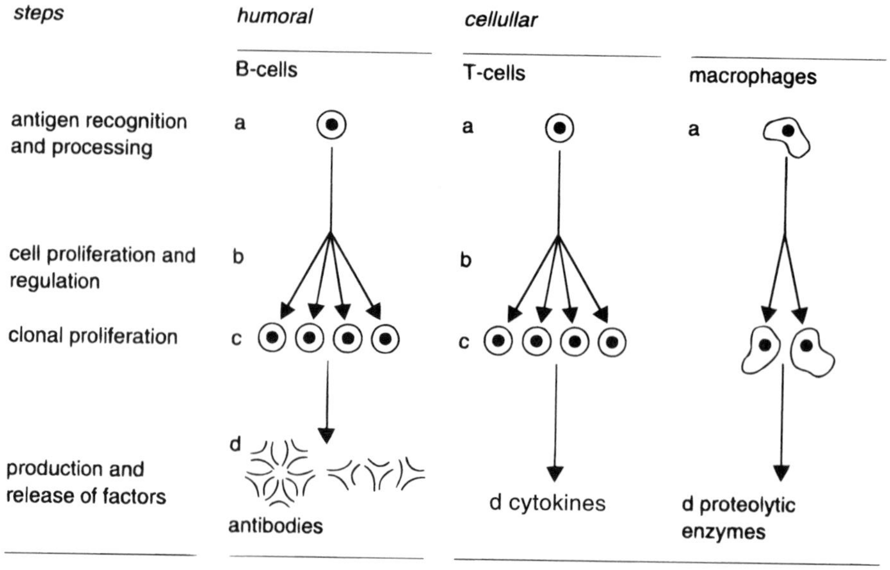

FIGURE 28.12

Stages of the immunologic process that are particularly sensitive to the effects of chemicals

and their metabolites have been studied in this test, in which the potential immunosuppressive capacity of a substance, as determined by antibody production in a 'Plaque Forming Cell assay', was related to the cytotoxic dose of the substance. The same approach has been followed to examine organometallic compounds and polychlorinated biphenyls. A remarkable finding, which unfortunately counts against this method, was that many chemicals which *in vitro* caused immunosuppression, had no effect in the "Plaque Forming Cell" test. In order to improve their applicability, the *in vitro* models such as the "Plaque Forming Cell" test, lymphocyte transformation test and bone marrow culture have been modified by the addition of microsomal fraction S9 to the system.

> ASSIGNMENT 28.7
>
> Why should addition of microsomal fraction S9 to these in vitro tests increase their usefulness?

There are examples in which *in vitro* exposure to certain compounds has proved to be important in establishing immunotoxicity. Thus, *in vitro* induction of cytotoxic T-cells can be inhibited by addition of certain polycyclic aromatic hydrocarbons to the culture medium. *In vitro* tests have also been applied to determine effects on macrophage activity. It was demonstrated, for example, that *in vitro* exposure of macrophages to cadmium reduced their phagocytic capacity. These results were in agreement with *in vivo* findings. Apart from some value of the *in vitro* approach to determine immunotoxicity, its main value comes to light in studies on the mechanisms underlying the immunotoxicity of substances, and in the application of *in vitro* methods in immunotoxicologic research using human material. Relevant examples are the research on TCDD and thymic epithelium, and on organotin substances and thymocytes (see Study unit 29).

*In vitro* tests can also be applied to find out what stage of the immune response is influenced by the toxic substances. This may be done by treating certain cells with the substance under investigation in depletion and reconstitution experiments. An example could be the reduced antigen-induced proliferation of lymphocytes in the bronchial lymph nodes of rats infected intratracheally with *Listeria* and subsequently exposed to ozone (see Study unit 29). *In vitro* experiments might throw light on the question whether antigen presentation is influenced, as a result of which a reduced T-cell response is measured, or whether the T-cells themselves are affected, which would cause them to react less well. Here too, the *in vitro* approach to answer immunotoxicologic questions may contribute to the unraveling of mechanisms of immunotoxic action.

In conclusion, it can be stated that in general only little is known about the toxic effects of substances on the immune system. Especially *in vitro* research may be suitable in a number of cases to clarify the modes of action.

A second important function of *in vitro* research may be to increase the possibilities of extrapolation of data obtained from animal studies to man. Di-n-butyl-tindichloride, for example, a substance that has a cytotoxic effect on rat thymocytes but not on mouse or guinea pig lymphocytes, was found *in vitro* to be cytotoxic also in human T-cells. An important contribution to this field may be made in particular by the possibilities that are now available and still being developed further, of expressing the effects of *in vitro* exposure of various components of the immune system on their functioning in terms of production of interleukins, cell surface determinants etc.

Research has also been started on the use of *in vitro* immunotoxicity tests as a prescreening method. This would allow reduction of the use of experimental animals.

## 5    Summary

Obvious omissions can be pointed out in current immunotoxicologic research. The emphasis of research is on T-cells, B-cells and macrophages and their respective functions. With a few exceptions, mast cells, neutrophilic, eosinophilic and basophilic granulocytes are hardly included in immunotoxicologic research.

Moreover, what is studied is mainly systemic immunity. Exposure to toxic substances will, however, tend to take place primarily via the oral or respiratory routes. So far, the local immune response has hardly received any attention.

The immune system, in close relation to the non-specific defence mechanisms, forms an entity which is of crucial importance to the maintenance of the organism's integrity. The system protects the host against exogenous invaders, in particular infectious agents, but also against attacks from within, mainly by tumor cells. This means that toxic substances influencing this system potentially affect the integrity of the organism. The discipline which is concerned with the determination of immunotoxicity therefore needs to be developed further so as to be better able to assess the risk of exposure to substances. Components of the immune system that toxic agents may act upon are the following:

- development of stem cells in the bone marrow;
- interaction of macrophages, T-cells and B-cells with antigens;
- differentiation and proliferation of T-cells and B-cells;
- complement system;
- phagocytosis and cytotoxicity.

In addition to substances causing immunosuppression, there are also xenobiotics that cause immune stimulation, as a result of which allergy or autoimmune disease may be promoted. Moreover, xenobiotics may themselves act as antigens or alter endogenous determinants in such a way that these act as antigens.

## SELF ASSESSMENT QUESTIONS

1    Define the discipline of immunotoxicology.

2    Should immunotoxicology be regarded as a subdiscipline of immunology, toxicology, or both?

3    Give arguments for and against the use of rats as experimental animals in immunotoxicologic studies.

4    Exposure to a particular substance causes thymic atrophy, but only when the animal also displays distinct growth retardation. Is this a case of immunotoxicity?

5    Exposure to a particular substance stimulates the immunoglobulin response after sensitization to ovalbumin, at a dosage at which general toxicologic parameters are not influenced. However, the resistance to infections has not been affected either. Is the substance involved immunotoxic?

6    A substance is cytotoxic to lymphocytes *in vitro* at a concentration not cytotoxic to fibroblasts. Is this an immunotoxic substance?

7    *In vitro* exposure of lymphocytes to a certain substance results in inhibition of antigen-induced proliferation at a concentration at which the substance is not cytotoxic. Is this a case of immunotoxicity?

8    Indicate what obvious omissions there still are in immunotoxicity research.

9    Does Figure 28.2 allow a conclusion on whether TBTO causes immunostimulation or immunosuppression? Does Figure 28.9?

FEEDBACK

1    **Answers to the assignments**

28.1  Toxicologic studies use mainly rats. The necessity of again establishing dose–response relationships for new animal models (mouse) is avoided if routine toxicity or immunotoxicity studies are carried out in the same experimental animal. The immunotoxic effect found can thus be assessed in the light of the toxicologic profile of the substance.

28.2  In mammals, the primary lymphoid tissue in which maturation of B-cells from precursor B-cells takes place, is not restricted to one particular site, as is the case in birds (bursa of Fabricius), but is probably distributed over various organs in the body. Of these, bone marrow is considered to be the most important location.

28.3  Exposure to toxic substances takes place to a large extent via the gastrointestinal tract and the respiratory organs. The local immune system is crucial to the immunologic surveillance of these organs, and effects of toxic substances on this system might therefore be of major importance.

28.4  HCB seems to stimulate all the parameters, and may be an immunostimulatory substance. The effects of TBTO are less obvious. Reduced levels of lymphocytes and IgG occur, as well as reduction in thymic weight, but the number of blood monocytes and the levels of IgM are increased. The exact nature of the immunotoxicity of both HCB and TBTO needs to be established in follow-up studies, using tests which form part of the secondary panel presented in Table 28.2.

28.5  A new category of infection models to be developed should be aimed at the functioning of aspects of resistance which are not assessed in existing models, for example the population of non-specific effector cells such as granulocytes. Possible candidates might be bacterial models in which infection with streptococci or staphylococci takes place. Since, in the resistance to these pathogenic agents, phagocytosis is promoted by opsonizing antibodies, such a model would test both the activity of granulocytes and a related humoral immune response.

28.6  The large nucleus takes up approximately 60% of the volume of a lymphocyte. As a result, much less space remains for other organelles. It is assumed that lymphocytes have only a very limited biotransformation system at their disposal with which they can process xenobiotics. Moreover, lipophilic toxic substances which are absorbed via chylomicrons and via the thoracic duct can come into direct contact with lymphocytes, i.e. before the liver has had a chance to detoxicate them.

28.7  Metabolic activation by the microsomal fraction enables the examination of substances for immunotoxicity if they have no direct effects, but exert their effects via reactive metabolites. This approach has had particular success in the case of cyclophosphamide.

## 2 Answers to the self assessment questions

1   Immunotoxicology is the toxicologic discipline concerned with the study of interactions of substances with the immune system, which may lead to adverse effects.

2   Although immunotoxicologic findings may be useful to gain understanding of the immune system, immunotoxicologic research is not primarily aimed at unraveling immunologic mechanisms, but at establishing the potential toxicity of substances. It should therefore be regarded as part of toxicology.

3   An important advantage of the use of rats in immunotoxicology is that it allows immunotoxicity tests to be incorporated into general (routine) toxicity tests. A disadvantage is that assays for immunologic parameters in rats are operational only to a limited extent, when compared to the mouse.

4   Although immunotoxicity may be involved, one must in this case consider whether the thymic atrophy might not be caused by the growth retardation, and thus represent an indirect effect.

5   Stimulation of immunologic processes may have detrimental effects, such as deposition of antigen-antibody complexes, hypersensitivity, or autoimmunity. In other words, such a substance is very likely to be immunotoxic.

6   This information does not permit any conclusion on whether the substance is immunotoxic. This will have to be left to *in vivo* immunotoxicity tests.

7   Although the chance of immunotoxicity is greater than in the preceding question, the same answer applies.

8   Apart from the blood picture and possibly the histology of lymphoid organs, there are no good general parameters of non-specific resistance. Immune function tests still pay little attention to mucosal immunity.

9   This can in fact not be concluded from either of the figures. Figure 28.2 shows that some components of resistance (monocytes in the circulation, serum IgM levels) have been stimulated while others have been suppressed. Figure 28.9 shows the resistance to *T.spiralis* to be suppressed. This means that some, but not necessarily all, immune functions have been suppressed. Immunotoxicity includes a disturbance of the normal functioning of the immune system and the defence mechanisms related to it. In that sense immunotoxicity can be concluded from both figures.

# Contents Study unit 29
# Immunotoxicology: examples of immunotoxic substances

0-8493-9232-2/96/$0.00 + $.50
© 1996 by CRC Press, Inc.

# Immunotoxicology: examples of immunotoxic substances

*J. G. Vos and H. van Loveren*

INTRODUCTION

The preceding study unit described how the immunotoxic properties of xeno-biotics can be determined. First, a number of general immunological parameters can be incorporated into the routine toxicity studies that are carried out in rats. These parameters are chosen in such a way that additional experimental conditions do not necessitate adaptation of the set-up of the toxicological experiment. This means that only immunological parameters are measured that do not com-promize the toxicity study as is the case when animals are immunized or injected with bacteria to yield information on the immunotoxic properties of the sub-stance involved. In other words, at this stage no function tests are carried out. If, in this first phase, any indications of potential immunotoxicity are found, a new phase of research is entered. In this phase, immune function tests are carried out, in order to examine in much more detail the non-specific resistance and the im-munological processes that are affected. A final phase includes the mechanisms by which immunotoxic substances exert their harmful effects.

The present study unit reviews several immunotoxic substances. Immuno-toxicologic research into organotin compounds is discussed first. This research has followed very closely the procedure outlined in Study unit 28. A second group of substances that will be discussed is that of the polychlorinated biphenyls, dibenzofurans and dibenzo-p-dioxins. To a large extent, the im-munotoxicity of these substances had already been recognized before the lines along which immunotoxicologic research should be carried out, were agreed upon. The mecha-nism of the immunotoxicity of this group of substances has now been partly elucidated. Immunotoxicologic research into hexachloroben-zene (HCB) is discussed in the third section of this study unit. Unlike the sub-stances mentioned above, which seem to suppress the immune system, HCB seems to stimulate a number of immunological parameters in rats. Finally, this unit discusses the immunotoxicologic research into the effects of oxidizing gases on the resistance to respiratory infections. In contrast to the three other exam-ples, exposure to these gases takes place via the respiratory rather than the oral route.

The aim of this study unit is not to achieve comprehensiveness in discussing these examples, but to draw the lines along which immunotoxicologic research into these groups of substances has been carried out.

LEARNING OBJECTIVES

After studying this unit, you should be able to:

— describe how toxicologic research into the immunotoxicity of organotin compounds, polychlorinated biphenyls, dibenzofurans, dibenzo-p-dioxins, hexachlorobenzene and oxidizing gases has taken place

— indicate what is currently known about the components of the immune system these substances act upon and the mechanisms by which they do so, and on what findings this knowledge is based

— describe and (if possible) explain the differences and similarities of approach in immunotoxicologic research into these substances

*Study hints*

Several immunotoxic substances and groups of substances are discussed in the present study unit. You are recommended to write down, while you are reading the various sections, what tests were carried out, what was concluded from them and why. After studying this unit, compare the results of research into the various substances. The study load of this unit is approximately 2 hours.

## STUDY CORE

### 1   Immunotoxicity of organotin compounds

As mentioned in the previous study unit, organotin compounds are characterized by at least one tin carbon-bond. The major groups found in this series of substances are $R_2SnX_2$ and $R_3SnX$. R usually represents an alkyl or aryl group and X chloride, fluoride, oxide, hydroxyl, carboxylate (e.g. acetate) or thiolate anion or =O.

Organotin compounds have various applications. Di-n-butyltin dichloride (DBTC), for example, is used as a stabilizer in plastics or PVC and as a catalyst in the production of urethanes. Bis(tri-n-butyltin)oxide (TBTO) is used as a biocide in wood preservatives to prevent damage by fungi and insects, and in paints for ships to prevent fouling by algae, mussels etc.

The first indications of organotin compounds having immunotoxic properties came from toxicity studies in which guinea pigs and rats were exposed to triphenyltin hydroxide and to triphenyltin acetate. In both species, the numbers of circulating lymphocytes and the weight of the spleen were reduced, while, particularly in the guinea pig, the weight of the thymus was also reduced. *Thymic atrophy* was also observed in rats which had been given diphenyltin dichloride and triphenyltin chloride in their diet.

*Thymic atrophy*

Dialkyltin and trialkyltin compounds, in particular di-n-butyltin and di-n-octyltin dichlorides, as well as tri-n-butyltin oxide and tri-n-propyltin chloride, can also display immunotoxicity. They induce a remarkable reduction in the weight of the thymus in rats.

Furthermore, lymphopenia has been observed, as well as depletion of lymphocytes in T-cell-dependent areas of the lymph nodes and spleen (see Figures 29.1, 29.2 and 29.3).

Increased IgM and decreased IgG levels were found in the serum of rats exposed to TBTO (see Figure 29.3).

Immune function tests were subsequently carried out on the basis of these findings, all of which concerned immunologic parameters tested within the framework of general toxicity studies. To illustrate this, the research into the immunotoxicity of TBTO carried out by means of immune function tests will serve as an example.

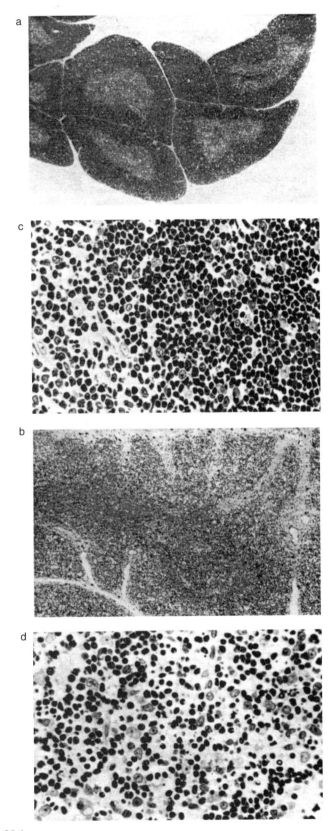

FIGURE 29.1

Thymus of a control rat (a: 37×, c: 590×) and a rat exposed to TBTO (b: 93×, d: 590×)
The lymphocyte depletion in the thymus of the exposed rat is clearly visible, as well as a slight indication of cell death (Giemsa stain).

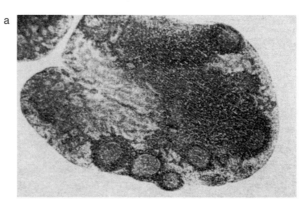

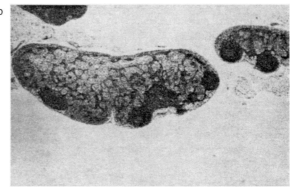

FIGURE 29.2
Lymph node of a control rat (a) and a rat exposed to TBTO (b)
Lymphocyte depletion is clearly visible, particularly in the cortical areas (hematoxylin-eosin stain, 37×).

*Reduced thymus weight*

TBTO was found to cause a reduction in thymus weight, one of the most sensitive toxicologic parameters. Rats were therefore exposed to 20 or 80 mg of this substance per kg feed for a period of 6 weeks after weaning (At 80 mg per kg, the animals display only slight growth retardation). They were then immunized with a mixture of ovalbumin and H37Ra complete adjuvant, after which the delayed type

*Hypersensitivity response*

*hypersensitivity responses* to an injection of ovalbumin or tuberculin were measured, respectively. These responses had decreased depending on the dose. The *prolife-*

*Proliferative response*

*rative response* of thymic and splenic cell suspensions to *in vitro* cultures with T-cell mitogens was also reduced. This phenomenon can be explained by the reduced number of T-cells in splenic cell suspensions, which was confirmed by cytofluorometric determination of T-lymphocytes with the aid of their surface markers.

ASSIGNMENT 29.1

Can you draw a conclusion from the above data and those presented in Figure 29.3 as to what component of resistance is affected by TBTO?

*Macrophage activity and natural killer cell activity*

In addition to the parameters of specific immunity mentioned above, *macrophage activity and natural killer cell activity* are also reduced in rats exposed to TBTO. The resistance of the rats to infections was also found to be reduced as a result of the immunotoxicity observed.

*Trichinella test*

The expulsion from the intestine of adult worms after oral infection with the nematode *Trichinella spiralis*, for example, was also significantly reduced in rats exposed to TBTO. In comparison to non-exposed animals an increase in the number of larvae was found in muscle tissue after infection. The inflammatory infiltrate

874

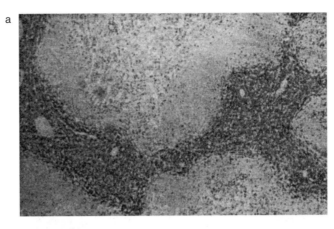

FIGURE   29.3

Spleen of a control rat (a) and a rat exposed to TBTO (b)

Lymphocyte depletion can be observed in the periarterial lymphocyte sheath (PALS) (immunoperoxidase stain, with T-cells stained using monoclonal antibodies against T-cell determinants (93×).

around the cysts in which the larvae were encapsulated was also greatly reduced, as was the serum IgE level. The IgG and IgM titers against *T.spiralis* (as well as antiovalbumin and antitetanus toxoid IgG and IgM titers in animals immunized against these antigens) were not affected in exposed rats. Although these humoral immune responses are certainly influenced by T-cells, these results confirm that the humoral immune response is much less dramatically affected by exposure to TBTO than the cellular, T-cell-mediated immune response. Finally, it should be noted that anti-*T.spiralis* IgA titers, which give an indication of humoral resistance, are in fact increased in rats exposed to TBTO and infected with *T.spiralis*. The expulsion of worms is slower in exposed animals. This probably causes the stimulus for IgA production, i.e. the presence of the worms in the mucosa, to persist for a longer period of time in rats infected after exposure to TBTO. This then leads to the paradoxic situation that immunotoxicity seemingly takes the form of immunostimulation.

ASSIGNMENT   29.2

The hypothesis that the prolonged presence of worms resulting from exposure to TBTO might cause an increased IgA response has not yet been confirmed. An argument against it is that, despite the longer presence of the stimulus, another immunologic parameter, namely the IgE titer, is in fact suppressed. Provide an alternative hypothesis.

*Mechanism*

Research into the *mechanisms* underlying the immunotoxic effects of organotin compounds have been carried out mainly on dialkyltin compounds, namely dibutyltin dichloride and dioctyltin dichloride. One way in which these compounds might indirectly cause immunotoxicity is by disturbing the hormonal balance. Serum levels of glucocorticoids, which can influence the immune system and more particularly cause thymic atrophy, were not measured in rats treated with dialkyltin.

> ASSIGNMENT 29.3
>
> Highlight other ways in which the influence of glucocorticoids or growth hormones can be established in the observations made.

The possibility of dialkyltin compounds influencing bone marrow stem cells has also been examined. Neither the vitality nor the mitotic activity of the bone marrow of treated animals differed from those of normal animals. However, it cannot be concluded from this information that the precursor cells of T-cells, so-called prothymocytes, which form a small minority of the bone marrow cells, are not influenced by dialkyltin compounds either. Finally, distribution studies have shown that the selective effect of dialkyltin compounds on the thymus cannot be explained from their accumulation in the thymus.

Although the findings presented here cannot entirely rule out the possibility that an indirect mechanism is involved in the observed immunotoxicity of dialkyltin compounds, important information is available which suggests that these substances have a direct effect on thymocytes.

*In vitro cytotoxicity*

*In vivo cytostasis*

Dialkyltin compounds display *in vitro cytotoxicity* or growth inhibition of various types of cell, including lymphocytes. Since *in vivo* cytotoxicity is seen only at relatively high concentrations, it would seem obvious that the *in vivo* effect at low dosages is more likely to be *cytostasis* than lysis. This is in agreement with the histologic picture presented by thymuses which have undergone involution following exposure to dialkyltin compounds (see Figure 29.1).

These findings are supported by the fact that the compounds are able to inhibit DNA synthesis both *in vitro* and *in vivo*, without a general reduction of cellular metabolism to explain this. Dialkyltin compounds display a strong affinity for dithiols, and they are therefore thought to be capable of interacting with sulfhydryl groups at the level of the plasma membrane and/or in the cytoplasm, in particular the cytoskeleton. In other words, they might impede blastogenesis, i.e. the initial impetus for proliferation of lymphocytes. The studies described here suggest that, in rats, these compounds may have an antiproliferative effect, leading to thymic atrophy and eventually to suppression of thymus-dependent immunity.

> ASSIGNMENT 29.4
>
> Describe briefly what is known about the mechanism of TBTO immunotoxicity.

## 2 Immunotoxicity of polychlorinated biphenyls, dibenzofurans and dibenzo-p-dioxins

*Polychlorinated biphenyls*

*Polychlorinated biphenyls* (PCBs) are very stable. Because they are not flammable, good conductors of heat and poor conductors of electricity, they used to find wide application as a coolant in transformers. During the production and also during the combustion of these compounds, chlorinated dibenzofurans may be released. Chlorinated dioxins may be contaminants of chlorophenols and may also be formed from them if combustion takes place at insufficiently high temperatures. As in the case of organotin compounds, the first indication of possible immunotoxicity of PCBs was found in the decrease in weight and altered histology of lymphoid organs. These were observed in various animal models. In the early phase of immunotoxicologic research into this type of substance, ducks exposed to the PCB mixture Aroclor® at a dosage which did not give rise to clearly observable toxicity, were found to develop increased sensitivity to the duck hepatitis virus.

More direct evidence of immunotoxicity was derived from immune function tests carried out on various experimental animals, especially guinea pigs, rats, mice, rabbits and monkeys. For example, the antibody response after immunization with tetanus toxoid, pseudorabies virus or sheep red blood cells (SRBC) was found to be impaired in exposed animals. In contrast, the response to SRBC in rabbits and that to tetanus toxoid in monkeys was not affected in any way. Less clear are the effects of exposure to PCBs on cellular immunity. Although a reduction in delayed-type hypersensitivity to tuberculin could be diagnosed in guinea pigs, this effect was not seen in rabbits, while the *in vitro* response of rat lymphocytes to T-cell mitogens was even enhanced, and the effects on the mitogen response, mixed-lymphocyte response, graft-versus-host response and cytotoxic T-cell response in mice was negligible.

ASSIGNMENT 29.5

Summarize the effects of PCBs on the immune system.

*Suppression of humoral response regulated by T-helper cells*

Although the results are not always unambiguous, PCBs seem to be able to cause thymic atrophy, and thus induce suppression of the humoral response, in particular that regulated by *T-helper cells*. T-helper cell activity was in fact demonstrated to be reduced in a number of cases. T-helper cells which regulate the synthesis of antibodies, are considered to belong to the same population as the cells that, by producing cytokines, attract mononuclear cells to sites where delayed-type hypersensitivity responses take place. It is remarkable, therefore, that not all such hypersensitivity responses are suppressed.

As a result of PCB-induced immunosuppression, the resistance to infections of animals exposed to PCBs is reduced. Examples are the reduced resistance of mice to *Plasmodium bergei* (the parasite which causes malaria), *Listeria monocytogenes* (a bacterium), *Salmonella typhimurium* (another bacterium), *Herpes simplex* (a virus) and ectromelia virus. Note that resistance to such infections does not exclusively rely on humoral immunity. This means that other defence mechanisms may also be affected by PCBs, which agrees with the effects on cellular immunity (although these are rather unclear). Effects on other defence mechanisms, for example on the non-specific resistance dependent on phagocytosis by macrophages, or on that dependent on cytotoxicity by natural killer cells, might also play a role in the effects of PCBs in resistance models. However, research has not yet been able to give a clear answer to this question.

*Tetrachlorodibenzofuran (TCDF)*

*2,3,7,8-Tetrachlorodibenzofuran (TCDF)*, like PCBs, can induce thymic atrophy in guinea pigs and chickens. Accidental exposure of humans to PCBs and TCDF has occurred in a number of cases. This happened, for example, in Taiwan in 1979, through the consumption of contaminated rice oil. The most important clinical signs observed in the victims were a particular type of skin disease (chloracne), pigmentation of skin and nails, liver injury and abnormal immune function. In particular the patients' serum IgA and IgM levels were decreased, in

877

contrast to their IgG levels. The number of T-helper cells in the lymphocyte population in the circulation had dropped. Delayed-type hypersensitivity responses were clearly reduced in these patients, while in some of them the mitogen response had in fact increased. A similar accident had also taken place in Japan in 1968. The signs observed at the time were in general very similar to those observed later in Taiwan. Many of the patients in Japan suffered moreover from respiratory disorders such as bronchitis, in which, mainly during the initial period, there were often bacterial and viral infections (see Table 29.1).

> ASSIGNMENT 29.6
>
> Do the findings for PCB and/or dibenzofuran intoxication in man (see Table 29.1) agree with the data derived from animal experiments?

*Tetrachlorodibenzo-p-dioxin (TCDD)*

Like the immunotoxic compounds mentioned above, 2,3,7,8-tetrachlorodibenzo-p-dioxin *(TCDD)* induces thymic atrophy. This is the substance whose immunotoxic effects have been studied best. As a result, extensive knowledge is at hand of the immunotoxic effect of *in vivo* exposure to TCDD of adult test animals and of exposure during the perinatal period. In addition to depletion of lymphocytes in the cortex of the thymus and lymphopenia in the circulation, guinea pigs exposed via the oral route to only 40 ng TCDD per kg body weight per week for 8 weeks displayed reduced delayed-type hypersensitivity responses to injection with tuberculin. Other cellular immune responses can also be affected by TCDD, such as the T-cell mitogen response and the cytotoxicity of T-cells. The effects of TCDD on T-cell-dependent immune responses can be observed particularly well if exposure has been *perinatal*, i.e. during the ontogenesis of the immune system. In rats, perinatal exposure even seems to be a prerequisite for this immunosuppression to occur.

*Perinatal exposure*

*Humoral immune responses*

TCDD also affects the *humoral immune response*, although it does so at higher dosages than those affecting cellular immunity. The effect of TCDD on T-cells is known to be selective, and leaves in particular T-helper cell function unaffected. It therefore seems likely that its effect on the humoral immune response is not exerted via an effect on T-helper cell function alone. A direct effect of TCDD is in agreement with a reduced lymphocyte response to B-cell mitogens (lipopolysaccharides). Effects of TCDD on macrophages have not been observed. As a result of interference with various immune functions, the resistance of exposed animals may be affected. This is the case, for example, for the resistance of exposed mice to the intestinal bacterium *Salmonella bern* and to *Listeria monocytogenes*. Resistance to the virus *Herpes suis* appeared unaltered. It is possible that, in the first case, the increased mortality after infection was due to increased

TABLE 29.1
Comparison of delayed-type hypersensitivity responses in healthy persons and in persons exposed to polychlorinated biphenyls and dibenzofurans in Taiwan

| | Streptodomase/streptokinase hypersensitivity | | Tuberculin hypersensitivity | |
|---|---|---|---|---|
| | positive (%) | negative (%) | positive (%) | negative (%) |
| healthy | 40 (80%) | 10 (20%) | 28 (74%) | 10 (26%) |
| exposed | 13 (43%)* | 17 (57%)** | 40 (40%)* | 43 (52%)** |

* $P < 0.005$, $\chi^2$ test
** $P < 0.01$, $\chi^2$ test

sensitivity to endotoxin; such increased sensitivity is known to be induced by TCDD. Being a virus, *Herpes suis* does, of course, not produce any endotoxin, nor does *Listeria monocytogenes*. Increased mortality due to *Listeria*, however, was found only at a relatively high dose of TCDD.

*Human data*

A number of instances of *human exposure* to TCDD are known. One example is that of the disaster in Seveso, Italy; another occurred in an area of Missouri. In the latter area in particular, people who had been exposed to TCDD for longer periods displayed alterations in the functioning of their immune system, without showing clinical symptoms. These changes involved mainly a reduced delayed-type hypersensitivity response to antigens to which humans normally have already developed this response.

*Mechanisms*

Extensive research has been carried out into the *mechanisms* by which TCDD induces its immunotoxic effects. Histologically, the lymphocyte depletion in the cortex resulting from exposure to TCDD is not accompanied by thymocyte necrosis. Also, since TCDD is not cytotoxic when various cell types are exposed to it, a direct cytotoxic effect of TCDD does not seem likely. Indirect mechanisms, such as induction of glucocorticoids or disturbance of the production of growth hormone, also seem unlikely as adrenalectomy, or hypophysectomy and treatment with growth hormone have been found not to influence the thymotoxic effects of TCDD.

The immunotoxic effects of TCDD and the structurally related TCDF are very similar to those observed after exposure to certain PCBs. Examples are the planar PCBs 3,4,5,3′,4′,5′-hexachlorobiphenyl and 3,4,3′,4′-tetrachlorobiphenyl, in contrast to the non-planar compounds such as 2,3,4,2′,4′,5′-hexachlorobiphenyl (see Figure 29.4).

*Binding to Ah receptor*

Considering these similarities, the explanation for the immunotoxicity of these compounds probably lies in their structure, which allows them to bind to the so-called *Ah (aromatic hydrocarbon) receptor*, which has been found in various mammalian cells, particularly in the thymus.

*Genetically determined sensitivity*

The *sensitivity* to dioxin toxicity appears to be *genetically determined*. The *Ah* gene, which encodes for the receptor for TCDD in the cytosol, is inherited together with TCDD sensitivity. This shows that the *Ah* gene and genes determining sensitivity to TCDD are located on the same chromosome and may perhaps even be identical. It looks as if TCDD and related structures, by binding to the *Ah* receptor on thymic epithelial cells, induce the latter to differentiate faster. As a result, their function of supporting the maturation of thymocytes to adult T-cells is disturbed. An effect of TCDD on precursor cells in bone marrow has also been described. This effect might lead not only to a deficient supply of precursor cells to the thymus, but also to suppression of B-cells. Suppression of B-cells might also occur via the *Ah* receptor, but in this case via *Ah* receptors on the B-cells

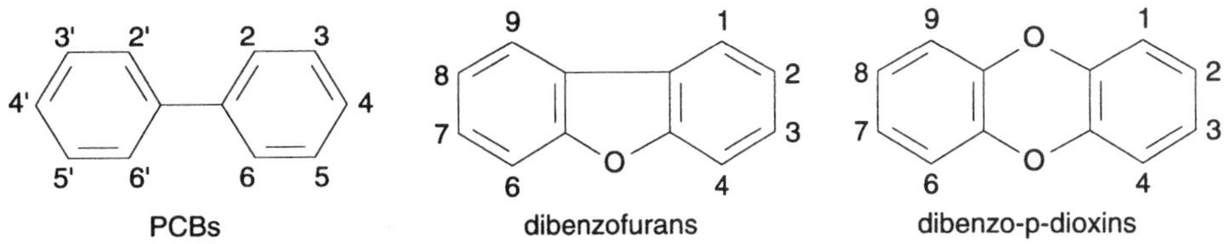

FIGURE 29.4
General structure of polychlorinated biphenyls, dibenzofurans and dioxins
The numbers indicate where chlorine can be substituted.

themselves, rather than via receptors on the thymic epithelium, as is the case for T-cells.

Summarizing, TCDD, TCDF and structurally related PCBs can induce a distinct suppression of T-cell-dependent immunity. This suppression probably results from interaction between the compounds and the thymic epithelial cells, which are of vital importance to the development of immunocompetence. Hence, these compounds exert their greatest effect if exposure takes place during the period in which the thymic epithelium is the most active, i.e. at an early age. Perinatal exposure to this type of compound has the most distinct effects.

### 3    Immunotoxicity of hexachlorobenzene

Hexachlorobenzene used to be applied as a fungicide to protect seeds meant for sowing. It is now still used in the chemical industry as a starting material for the synthesis of organic compounds. Like the immunotoxic compounds mentioned above, simple toxicologic parameters provided the first indications that HCB has immunomodulatory properties (see Figure 28.3). After oral exposure of rats to HCB, increased IgM levels were found in the serum, while the numbers of neutrophilic, basophilic and mononuclear cells in the circulation were significantly increased. On dissecting the rats, the weights of spleen and lymph nodes were found to be increased. Histologically, an increase in the quantity of white pulp could be observed in the spleen, a result of hyperplasia of the marginal zones and the follicles (see Figure 29.5).

A remarkable finding in the lymph nodes and Peyer's patches was the proliferation of so-called high-endothelial venules in the paracortex (see Figure 29.6).

This type of endothelium plays an important part in the immune response by binding and passing on lymphocytes from the blood to the lymphoid tissue. If there is antigen stimulation, the endothelium proliferates, and lymphocytes home to the lymph nodes. Furthermore, the lungs were found to contain intra-alveolar accumulations of macrophages (see Figure 29.7).

Considering the increase in the weight of lymphoid organs, hyperplasia of lymphoid tissues, proliferation of the high-endothelial venules and accumulation of macrophages in the alveoli, HCB seemed to be a potential stimulator of the immune system, at least in rats.

*Function tests*

*Function tests* demonstrated that this was not the case as far as macrophage activity was concerned, while delayed-type hypersensitivity responses and rejection of allogenic transplants were not altered in animals exposed to HCB. The primary and secondary antibody response to the thymus-dependent antigen tetanus toxoid was greatly increased, in contrast to the IgM response to the thymus-independent antigen *E.coli* lipopolysaccharide (LPS). If rats were exposed perinatally, delayed-type hypersensitivity was also stimulated. The reinforcement of immune responses, as observed in rats exposed to HCB, did not affect resistance to *Listeria monocytogenes* or *Trichinella spiralis*. A possible result of immunostimulation by HCB might be an increased or more intense susceptibility to *auto-immunity*. Exposure of rats and dogs to high dosages of HCB is known to give rise to vasculitis, which is possibly an autoimmune phenomenon. In a rat model in which experimental allergic encephalomyelitis, an autoimmune disease in which autoreactive T-cells are directed against myelin and which causes paralysis, was artificially induced, exposure to HCB considerably aggravated the condition. Contrasting results were obtained in experiments using a model in which adjuvant arthritis, an autoimmune disease in which autoreactive T-cells are directed against endogenous cartilage, was induced artificially. HCB appeared to be able to inhibit this disorder quite considerably. The mech-

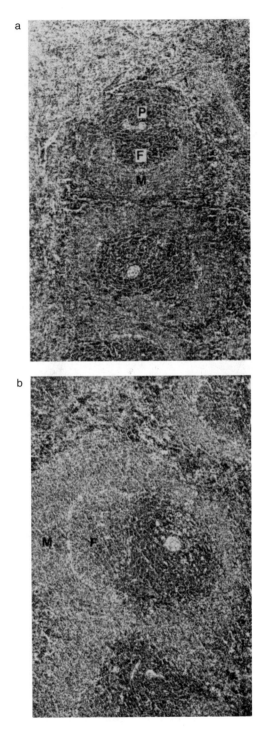

FIGURE   29.5
Spleen of a normal rat (a) and of a rat exposed to HCB (b)
An increase in the extent of the marginal zone (M) and the follicles (F) can be observed (hematoxylin-eosin stain, 100×).

anism of inhibition, which seems to resemble immunosuppression rather than immunostimulation, still needs elucidation. A remarkable finding is that in mice exposure to HCB often leads to immunosuppression.

In summary, it can be stated that, in rats, HCB mainly stimulates the synthesis of antibodies against thymus-dependent antigens and also delayed-type hy-

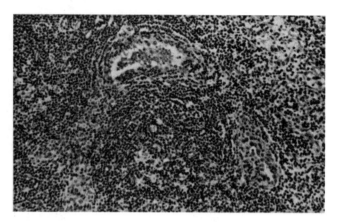

FIGURE    29.6
Proliferation of high-endothelial venules in the mesenteric lymph node of a rat exposed to HCB
(hematoxylin-eosin stain, 100×).

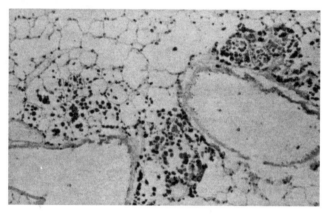

FIGURE    29.7
Increased number of macrophages in the lung of a rat after oral exposure to HCB
Immunoperoxidase stain using antibodies against rat lysozyme (in the macrophages) (100×).

persensitivity responses if exposure takes place perinatally. In the infection models used, this stimulation does not affect resistance. In autoimmune models, on the other hand, there certainly is some influence, although it is not yet completely understood. The manner in which HCB affects components of the immune system has not yet been fully elucidated.

## 4    Immunotoxicity of oxidizing gases

*Ozone*
*Nitrogen dioxide*

*Ozone* is formed in the air from oxygen and nitrogen dioxide on irradiation with ultraviolet light. *Nitrogen dioxide* is a product of industrial combustion processes. Relatively high ozone concentrations in the atmosphere are consequently measured on sunny days, with the maximum values being reached in the afternoon. Epidemiologic findings suggest that there is a relationship between exposure to oxidizing gases such as ozone and nitrogen dioxide and the occurrence of infections.

Of all the examples mentioned so far, the examination of the effects of exposure to this type of gas has conformed least of all to the tiered design for immunotoxicologic research. The experimental animal approach chosen here concentrated mainly on testing with infection models. In this type of research, animals are generally exposed to the gases to be tested and are subsequently infected with a particular pathogenic agent which in non-exposed animals causes only minimal mortality. In this approach, increased mortality or changes in the clearance of the infectious agents from the exposed animals are used as a measure of the harmfulness of the gases. Various animal models have been used in these studies, such as mice, hamsters, rats and squirrel monkeys. Infections were induced with bacteria, such as *Streptococcus pyogenes*, *Klebsiella pneumoniae*, *Listeria monocytogenes* and *Haemophilus influenzae*.

*Mechanical resistance*

Research has demonstrated unambiguously that exposure to oxidizing gases may affect the host's resistance to respiratory infections. The infection models can not, however, discriminate between the various aspects of resistance in the respiratory tract on which oxidizing gases may have an adverse effect. An important component of respiratory resistance is that of *mechanical resistance*, consisting of ciliated epithelium covered with a layer of mucus. This ciliated epithelium forms a kind of escalator reaching from the terminal bronchioles to the nasal cavity. A large proportion of the particles (including infectious agents) is transported, trapped in the mucus, from the airways to the pharynx, where it is then swallowed. The cilia are especially sensitive to toxic damage caused by oxidizing gases, and this is certainly an important factor in the reduced resistance.

ASSIGNMENT 29.7

Does the study of defence mechanisms in the respiratory tract based on ciliated epithelium and mucus belong to the field of immunotoxicology?

*Natural killer cell activity*

A second important defence mechanism that may be affected, is the non-specific *activity of natural killer cells*. The cytotoxic action of natural killer cells is directed against various types of tumor cells as well as virus-infected endogenous cells. Ozone can affect this activity, which might in part explain the changes in resistance to both tumors and viral infections which have been observed in animal models.

*Phagocytic activity*

A third important defence mechanism is the *phagocytic activity* of alveolar macrophages. Infectious agents which reach the deeper airways and the lungs are phagocytosed by these macrophages. The macrophages degrade bacteria in the so-called phagolysosomes by means of lysosomal enzymes. Many of these macrophages, which display motility, can moreover reach the mucociliary 'escalator' and so remove bacteria from the respiratory tract. Ozone and nitrogen dioxide are able to inhibit the phagocytic and cytotoxic activity of macrophages.

*Initiation of the immune response by macrophages*

Like elsewhere, macrophages can initiate immune responses in the respiratory organs. They may do so, for example, in bronchus-associated lymphoid tissue or in draining lymph nodes. They can process ingested bacteria and present bacterial or other antigens to lymphocytes. This gives rise to a *primary immune response*, which, on repeated contact with the same antigen, will usually be more rapid and more intense. This subsequent response is called a *secondary immune response*. An important immune response is of course the humoral immune response, constituted by B-cells maturing to form plasma cells, which then start to produce antibodies. This process is controlled by T-helper cells. In various experiments in which sheep erythrocytes were used as antigens, nitrogen dioxide was shown to influence such responses. So far, it has not been possible to detect a clear trend in the results: depending on the timing of the experiment, both stimulation and suppression of these responses have been observed. The relevance of these findings for actual resistance to infections has not been studied.

*Cytokines*

In addition to their control of B-cell activity, T-lymphocytes induced by antigen-presenting macrophages can also produce *cytokines*, which in their turn recruit and activate macrophages. This leads to more efficient macrophage activity. The effects of exposure to oxidizing gases on cellular immune responses have been the subject of only very little research. Increased activity of thoracic duct lymphocytes after immunization with SRBC was reported in mice exposed to $NO_2$. Suppressed antigen-specific proliferative responses of the bronchial lymph nodes and spleen were found in rats immunized intratracheally with *Listeria* and which had been exposed to ozone. The non-antigen-specific lymphoproliferative responses induced by T-cell mitogens, on the other hand, did appear to be stimulated. Delayed-type hypersensitivity to *Listeria* was also suppressed in these rats.

*Intratracheal infection with Listeria*

In a model in which rats were *infected intratracheally with Listeria* and were or were not exposed to ozone, the following can be observed. Infection with *Listeria* induces an influx of macrophages into the lung which phagocytose the bacteria. As a result, specific T-cells are induced, which produce cytokines, thus causing recruitment of more macrophages and further activation. This puts an end to the infection. In animals exposed to ozone, the macrophage activity is affected. There is an influx of macrophages, particularly in the transitional area between the air passages and the alveoli (see Figures 29.8 and 29.9).

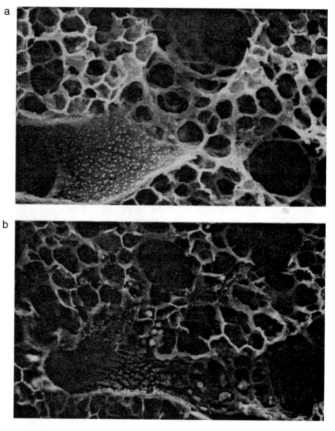

FIGURE 29.8
Scanning electron micrograph of pulmonary tissue in the transitional area between the air passages and the area where gaseous exchange takes place (alveoli) in a normal rat (a) and in a rat exposed to ozone (b)
The influx of macrophages is clearly visible.

In the exposed animals, however, the phagocytic and lytic action of macrophages on bacteria is reduced. As a result, the development of cellular immunity is also reduced.

> ASSIGNMENT   29.8
> Explain why the development of immunity is reduced in the exposed animals.

Thus, the numbers of bacteria found in the lungs of exposed animals remain for a long time higher than those of the control group. This causes an even more excessive attraction of inflammatory infiltrate, consisting mainly of macrophages and lymphocytes, of which the functions are in fact deficient. Such inflammatory infiltrates which can not efficiently terminate the infection have a granulomatous character. This means that the foci of infection have a more or less well-circumscribed structure, in which lymphocytes and macrophages are prominent, and that the normal structure of the lung is disturbed. Such structures are much more pronounced in animals exposed to ozone than in infected but non-exposed animals (see Figure 29.10).

a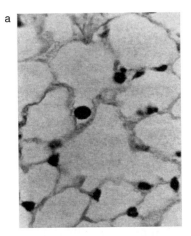

b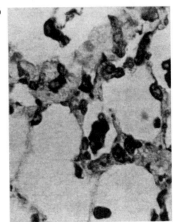

FIGURE   29.9
Immunoperoxidase stain of pulmonary lysozyme-containing cells in a normal rat (a) and in a rat exposed to ozone (b)
The increased presence of macrophages in the lung is clearly visible (100×).

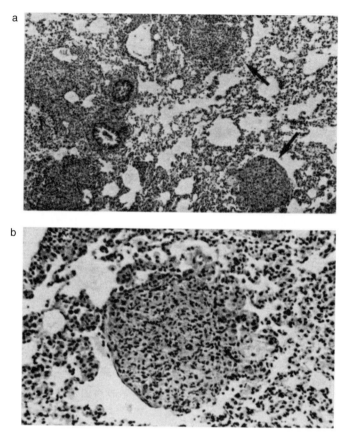

FIGURE  29.10
Granuloma formation (arrows) in the lung of a rat following combined exposure to ozone, and infection with *Listeria monocytogenes* (hematoxylin-eosin stain, a: 100×, b: 400×)

The data indicate that exposure to oxidizing gases causes increased sensitivity to respiratory infections. This will partly be the result of interference of these gases with specific and non-specific defence mechanisms, although other, especially mechanical defence mechanisms may also play an important role. The immunotoxicity of the gases seems to reinforce considerably the pathologic effects of respiratory infections.

In summary, exposure to ozone reduces the resistance to bacterial infections. An important route by which this reduction is effected is the suppression of non-specific defence mechanisms, particularly of the phagocytic and lytic activity of alveolar macrophages. In addition, the development of specific immune responses to the infectious agent is affected. The question of how ozone is capable of influencing the activity of the cells involved in the body's specific and non-specific resistance has not yet been answered.

## 5  Summary and conclusions

Ideally, research into the potential immunotoxicity of a substance should be initiated within the framework of routine toxicologic research. If in this phase general immunotoxicologic parameters provide indications of immunotoxicity, immune function tests and infection models may confirm or disprove the earlier findings and, moreover, provide insight into the question of which aspects of immunity are affected. Studies into the underlying mechanism can then make it easier to understand the processes observed.

Although the results of immune function tests show that the immunotoxicity found in a screening test does not necessarily imply impairment of the immune function, this phased system of research does however seem a suitable procedure for detecting immunotoxicity.

Research into dioxin, polychlorinated biphenyls and related compounds had already been started before this immunotoxicologic procedure (described in Study unit 28) was formulated. In retrospect, this main methodological line can still be recognized, albeit that various different test animals are used.

Research into the immunotoxicology of oxidizing gases has not followed this methodological path at all. In fact, it started at the end of the standard procedure by establishing effects using a variety of infection models, while these models had not yet been fully characterized immunologically. It was not until the effects of these gases in infection models had been studied in detail that occasionally more fundamental experiments were set up to answer the question whether the increased sensitivity to infections was in fact based on immunotoxicity. Very little histologic research has been carried out into these gases within the framework of immunotoxicologic studies. This is particularly true of the histopathology of the bronchus-associated lymphoid tissue and of draining lymph nodes. The non-specific component of resistance in the lungs, in this case macrophages, however, has been studied in reasonable detail. It would be advisable to modulate future research into gases rather more in the direction of the methodology described in Study unit 28. It should be noted that the route of exposure to harmful compounds often has consequences for the way in which studies are carried out.

## SELF ASSESSMENT QUESTIONS

1 Name the general immunologic parameters that are changed in rats exposed to bis(tri-n-butyltin)oxide.

2 Give functional immunologic parameters that are changed in rats exposed to bis(tri-n-butyltin)oxide.

3 Compare the mechanisms by which organotin compounds on the one hand and dioxins and planar polychlorinated biphenyls on the other seem to exert their immunotoxic effect.

4 HCB leads to immunostimulation in rats. Is HCB immunotoxic?

5 If inhalation of a harmful gas by rats results in increased sensitivity of the rats to respiratory infections, does this mean that the gas is immunotoxic?

## FEEDBACK

1 **Answers to the assignments**

29.1 The findings suggest that thymus-dependent immunity in particular is influenced by TBTO.

29.2 An alternative explanation might be twofold. If this substance is toxic to T-cells, especially the activity of T-suppressor cells is inhibited. Also, the balance that normally regulates the production of IgA is shifted towards increased IgA production, while at the same time the balance regulating IgE production in the same animal is disturbed in the sense that IgE production is reduced.

29.3 There are important indications that glucocorticoids are not involved in the effect of these compounds. These compounds are in fact not capable of inducing changes in the *weight of the adrenal glands* or in the *histology of the adrenal cortex*. In rats whose *adrenal cortex* had been *removed*, dialkyltin compounds were still able to induce thymic atrophy. Nor does an effect on growth hormone seem to play a significant role. *Hypophysectomy* leads to thymic atrophy, and administration of growth hormone reverses this effect. Growth hormone did not, however, influence the thymic atrophy resulting from treatment with dioctyltin dichloride.

29.4 Summarizing, it can be stated that bis(tri-n-butyltin)oxide and di-nbutyltin chloride can inhibit especially the T-cell-dependent immune response. In addition, components of non-specific resistance are also influenced by this type of substance, in particular macrophage and natural killer cell activity. As a result, the resistance to *Listeria monocytogenes* and that to *Trichinella spiralis* are reduced. There are indications that these compounds bind to the sulfhydryl groups in, for example, components of the cytoskeleton, thus inhibiting proliferation of thymocytes.

29.5 Refer to the text of section 2.

29.6 Although the patient data may be rather more fragmentary, they are certainly not in contradiction with data from animal experiments.

29.7 Strictly speaking, no. Immunotoxicology is in fact concerned with specific and non-specific resistance, for which the cell types mentioned in Figure 28.1 are responsible, and with products synthesized by these cells. It is true, however, that in interpreting the results of experiments, one should take into account the resistance based on the ciliated epithelium and mucus. The capacity of the lungs to clear bacteria, which is regarded as an immunotoxicologic parameter, is certainly influenced by this mucociliary 'escalator'!

29.8 Various explanations are possible:

1  since macrophages do not phagocytose and lyse as well as they normally do, they present antigens to the lymphocytes less efficiently, thus causing the induction of specific T-lymphocytes to proceed less efficiently;

2  lymphocytes react less well, because they themselves have incurred damage from interaction with ozone.

## 2    Answers to the self assessment questions

1  Reduced thymus weight, depletion of T-cell-dependent areas in lymphoid organs, and lymphopenia; increased serum levels of IgM, reduced IgG serum levels.

2  Reduction of delayed-type hypersensitivity responses to ovalbumin and tuberculin, reduction of *in vitro* proliferative responses of lymphocytes to T-cell mitogens. Reduction of resistance to *Trichinella spiralis*, measured as

the expulsion of worms from the intestine and the number of larvae present in muscular tissue. Reduced IgE response and increased IgA response in animals infected with *T.spiralis*.

3     Organotin compounds seem to disturb thymocytes by binding to sulfydryl groups. This is believed to block the proliferation of this type of cell. Dioxin and planar polychlorinated biphenyls are believed to induce accelerated differentiation of thymic epithelial cells following interaction with an *Ah* receptor on these cells. As a result, the cells loose their function of supporting the maturation of thymocytes into mature T-cells.

4     HCB affects the immune system and hence is immunotoxic. This immunotoxicity is manifested in rats through immunostimulation of several immunologic parameters, while the expression of adjuvant arthritis, which is an immunologic phenomenon, is suppressed. In mice, exposure to HCB generally leads to suppression of immune responses.

5     This fact in itself forms insufficient evidence. If the gas suppresses the mechanical resistance presented by the ciliated epithelium, it may have a negative effect on resistance to infections, without necessarily having any effect on specific and non-specific resistance.

# Contents Study unit 30
# Endocrinotoxicology: methodological aspects

0-8493-9232-2/96/$0.00 + $.50
© 1996 by CRC Press, Inc.

Study unit 30

# Endocrinotoxicology: methodological aspects

*F. X. R. van Leeuwen, M. A. M. Krajnc-Franken, and J. G. Loeber*

## INTRODUCTION

The most important function of the organs that form part of the endocrine system is to regulate the various metabolic processes in the body. By secreting hormones, they regulate the rate of chemical reactions in the body, the transport of nutrients and other substances across cell membranes, the secretion of other hormones, sometimes by other endocrine glands, and the maintenance of homeostasis. They also regulate growth and the processes involved in reproduction. Moreover, some endocrine organs are able to react to external stimuli.

All these processes take place via a complex network of finely regulated hormonal interactions, responses and feedback mechanisms. Such fine-tuned regulation makes the endocrine system highly sensitive to toxic substances. By disturbing endocrine regulation, toxicants may produce a wide variety of effects in an intact organism. *Endocrinotoxicological research* studies the effects of harmful substances on the activity of organs involved in the endocrine system.

*Examples*

*Examples* of effects that are frequently encountered in endocrine toxicity experiments are the following:

- impaired growth or decreased basal metabolism, which may be caused by reduced thyroid function
- changes in sugar metabolism, which originate in a disturbance of pancreatic function
- disturbances of renal function, such as reduced sodium and water retention, which may be caused by the effect of toxic substances on the adrenal gland
- reduced fertility, caused by effects on the gonads.

*Hormonal regulation and induction of tumors*

In addition to the effects of toxic substances mentioned above, there is another important phenomenon in the assessment of the toxicity of substances. Increased *hormonal stimulation of endocrine organs*, such as the pituitary gland, thyroid gland, pancreas and gonads, can produce cellular deviations that may sometimes *induce tumors*. In other cases, increased hormonal stimulation may promote the growth of tumor cells in target organs.

This means that toxicologists assessing the potential carcinogenicity of a substance must also take into account the fact that both exogenous (fo-reign) substances, such as certain pesticides (e.g. dithiocarbamates) and endogenous compounds, for instance sex hormones, can promote tumor growth by the mechanism described above.

Knowledge of potential disturbances of the endocrine system by toxic compounds is therefore not only of importance to understand their mode of action,

891

but may also be essential in deciding whether or not a substance should be considered a 'direct' carcinogen.

ASSIGNMENT   30.1

Why is it important to distinguish between substances which are and those which are not carcinogenic in toxicological risk assessment?

Routine toxicity research is aimed at establishing a no-effect level for a toxic substance, which can be used in risk assessment to calculate an *acceptable daily intake (ADI)* for human beings. On the basis of this ADI, the residue tolerance for a particular substance in foodstuffs can be determined.

*No-hormonal effect level (NHEL)*

For the assessment of the toxicity of anabolic steroids, which are used in the livestock industry, the term *no-hormonal effect level (NHEL)* was introduced. The term was used to define the dose of a compound with hormonal activity which remains without effect, in particular if that compound were to have a direct effect at the level of hormone-receptor interaction and the subsequent physiological response.

*Use of the NHEL*

It is possible, to give the term NHEL a much wider application within toxicological research. In general, the NHEL can be used for all substances for which animal experiments have shown that their endocrine effects are the most sensitive criterion. In such cases, the NHEL is defined as 'the dose at which no disturbance of the functioning of the endocrine system can be established'. If this definition is adopted, it does not matter whether we are dealing with

- substances with a *direct hormonal effect*, such as interaction with hormone receptors, or
- substances with an *indirect hormonal effect*, such as:

  1  a change in the biosynthesis of hormones
  2  disturbance of the uptake of hormones or their precursors in tissues
  3  disturbance of the release of hormones
  4  disturbance of the metabolic conversion and excretion of hormones
  5  interaction with the second-messenger system.

If a toxic substance causes a change in the functioning of the endocrine system by one of these mechanisms, this may lead to the occurrence of clearly observable, harmful effects.

*Endocrinological parameters in toxicity research*

From what is stated above, it follows that it is necessary to include endocrinological parameters in toxicity research, in addition to the usual parameters, such as those described in directives, e.g. those drawn up by the Organization for Economic Cooperation and Development (OECD). These parameters are both morphological and biochemical in nature. A logical strategy to involve *endocrine parameters in toxicity research* step by step is the following. At the start of a toxicological experiment, the *weight of the endocrine organs* is determined and sections of these organs are *histologically assessed*. If there are any indications of a potential endocrine effect, the *concentrations* in body fluids (e.g. blood) of hormones involved in the potential effect are determined, if possible in combination with specific morphological or immunocytochemical parameters.

*Ectomy*

As a next step in elucidation the mechanism and accurately establishing a no-effect dose, *specific function tests* of endocrine organs can be carried out. The involvement of certain endocrine organs in the effect which has been measured can, if necessary, be determined by removing the organs from an intact organism (*ectomy*). To conclude, *in vitro* experiments can be carried out to establish the mode of action at cellular level (see Table 30.1).

Once they have been validated *in vivo*, *in vitro* tests can also be used as screening tests to detect the potential capacity of a substance to disturb certain endocrine processes. This strategy, which forms the foundation of the subject matter discussed in the present study unit, makes it possible to gain a clear insight into the potential interactions of xenobiotics with endocrine processes.

LEARNING OBJECTIVES

After studying this unit, you should be able to:

— describe morphological and physiological aspects of some endocrine organs, insofar as they are relevant to toxicology
— indicate the position of endocrinotoxicological research within general toxicological research
— describe the various steps in endocrinotoxicological research
— describe and explain the use of specific techniques, illustrated by an example
— describe and, if possible, explain the hormonal toxicity of a number of substances used as examples (bromide, TBTO, β-HCH)
— describe specific problems encountered in endocrinotoxicity research.

*Study hints*

The present study unit provides an overview of the endocrine system. Although, in a quantitative sense, this overview accounts for a large part of the text, it is intended only to help you brush up on your knowledge of the hormone system. The most relevant part of this unit is that which deals with disturbances of the endocrine system by xenobiotics. It is important to know how foreign substances can disturb the endocrine system, where the interaction with the endocrine system can take place and how this can be measured in practice. While reading, make a list of the substances discussed, of the effects they cause and how these can be measured. If you have sufficient previous knowledge, the study load of this unit should be approximately 3 hours. The optionally available CD-I program provides examples of an atrophied and a necrotic pancreas, and of a hyperplastic adrenal cortex.

TABLE 30.1
Methods for tracing endocrine change in toxicity experiments

| screening | — weight of endocrine organs |
| | — morphology (light microscopy) |
| specific determinations | — immunochemical methods |
| | — enzyme chemistry and immunocyto-chemistry (light and electron microscopy) |
| | — function tests (tests of uptake, release, inhibition) |
| | — ectomy (adrenalectomy, gonadectomy) |
| | — *in vitro* methods (receptor interactions) |

STUDY CORE

## 1 Introduction to the endocrine system

What is actually meant by the term "hormone"? According to the classical definition, which is still largely valid, hormones are "substances which are produced by endocrine glands and secreted into the circulation, and which exert a regulatory effect elsewhere in the body". Hormones can be classified according to various chemical types:

- proteins or products derived from proteins and amino acids
- steroids
- catecholamines
- prostaglandins.

The pituitary gland and the pancreas, for example, secrete polypeptides or protein hormones, whereas the thyroid secretes a number of hormones derived from amino acids, the gonads and adrenal glands secrete steroid hormones, and the adrenal glands secrete catecholamines.

### 1.1 HORMONAL ACTION

How do hormones exert their specific effects in the target organs in the body? Although hormones may act in various ways, there are two important basic mechanisms by which a hormonal stimulus can be transmitted.

*Mechanisms of transmission of hormonal stimuli*

1. Activation of the cyclic AMP system via *extracellular receptors*, regulating specific functions inside the cell, and
2. direct *activation of the DNA in the cellular nucleus*, initiating protein synthesis, which subsequently gives rise to stimulation of specific processes in the cell.

These two mechanisms have in common that the hormone can only exert its effect after binding to a *specific receptor protein*. This binding is responsible for the specific effect of the various hormones and determines which organs are affected. The *protein hormones* act by the first mechanism, which is also called the second-messenger system, the first messenger being the hormone itself. The receptors for the protein hormones are located on the cell membrane, at the outside of the cells. After binding with the receptor, the receptor-hormone complex activates the enzyme adenylate cyclase (located in the membrane). As a result, that part of the enzyme which is in contact with the cytoplasm initiates the conversion of the adenosine triphosphate (ATP) present in the cell, to cyclic adenosine monophosphate (cAMP). The latter subsequently causes a number of intracellular processes to be initiated. What process is started is determined by the properties of the cell. Thyroid cells, for example, will be stimulated by cAMP to produce thyroid hormones, while cells in the adrenal cortex are stimulated to synthesize adrenal cortical hormones.

*Protein hormones*

*Steroid hormones*

The receptors for *steroid hormones*, which, unlike protein hormones, can pass through the cell membrane, are located in the cytoplasm or on the nuclear membrane. When a steroid hormone binds to its receptor, the resulting hormone-receptor complex is moved (translocated) to the nucleus. The complex is the active factor, that induces specific genes in the nucleus to produce RNA. This subsequently initiates *de novo* synthesis of proteins by the ribosomes. In the course of this cascade of events after the steroid hormone has bound to the receptor, it takes a while before the production of proteins starts. This is in contrast with the often instantaneous reaction which occurs after a protein hormone has bound to its receptor on the cell membrane.

## 1.2    REGULATION OF THE SYNTHESIS AND RELEASE OF HORMONES

*Neuro-endocrine regulation*

The endocrine system and the nervous system are closely connected via the hypothalamus, which forms the link between the pituitary gland and centers located higher in the brain. In the hypothalamus, a number of so-called releasing or inhibiting hormones are synthesized. This production is influenced by neurotransmitters that may have either an inhibiting or a stimulating effect. These are transported to the pituitary gland via the capillary sinusoidal network of the portal vascular system. Under the influence of these hormones, the pituitary in its turn produces a large number of hormones, each of which has a specific effect on endocrine glands elsewhere.

*Feedback control*

Another important phenomenon in the regulation of the physiological activity of a hormone is the so-called feedback control. Each endocrine gland basically tends to secrete too much of the hormone, which would give rise to too large a physiological stimulus. However, at the moment a hormone has achieved its normal physiological effect, i.e. when a sufficiently high concentration is present in the circulation and therefore also in the target organ, the secretory gland is informed of this either directly or indirectly, and further secretion of the hormone is inhibited. Conversely, if an endocrine organ is producing too little of the hormone, it receives a stimulus to step up its production and secretion. In this way, the feedback mechanism precisely regulates the rate at which hormones are produced and secreted, thus maintaining a fine balance. For a number of endocrine organs, the pituitary plays an important role in this feedback control. Therefore the following sections describe three endocrine glands controlled by the pituitary, namely:

1    the thyroid gland

2    the adrenal glands

3    the gonads

### 1.2.1 Thyroid gland

In mammals, the thyroid is located in the pharynx, immediately adjacent to the trachea. In man, it is the largest endocrine gland. Its weight in adults is approximately 20 g. In the experimental animal commonly used in toxicology, the rat, it is one of the smaller endocrine glands, weighing no more than 15–25 mg. The thyroid produces mainly thyroxine and triiodothyronine, as well as smaller amounts of related iodinated compounds. The thyroid hormones regulate the basal metabolism of the body. The production of thyroid hormones is controlled by thyroid-stimulating hormone (TSH), which is secreted by the pituitary.

The thyroid is composed of a large number of *follicles*, spherical structures formed by a single layer of *epithelial cells* (see Figure 30.1). The latter consists largely of the macroprotein *thyroglobulin* (molecular weight 670,000 daltons), which is rich in tyrosine and contains the thyroid hormones and their precursors.

*Synthesis of thyroid hormones*

The thyroid hormones are formed from the amino acid tyrosine and iodide. The main source of iodide is food. After oral ingestion, iodide is absorbed in the gastrointestinal tract, where it enters the bloodstream, and is transported to the thyroid.

*Iodide uptake*

The first step in the synthesis of thyroid hormones is the uptake of iodide from the extracellular fluid by thyroid cells. The iodide is concentrated in the thyroid

895

cells (300 to 400 times) by an active transport mechanism in the cell membranes, the so-called *iodide pump*. This is an energy-consuming mechanism because iodide is transported across the membrane against a steep concentration gradient. The mechanism by which this iodide pump works is not exactly understood, but there are indications that it is connected to a $Na^+/K^+$-ATPase system in the cell membrane. This active uptake of iodide can be stimulated by TSH.

*Biosynthesis*

If iodide is taken up by the epithelial cells of the thyroid, it needs to be converted into a form that can react with tyrosine. For this purpose, iodide is oxidized to iodine. The thyroid contains the enzyme iodide peroxidase, which, together with hydrogen peroxide produced in the thyroid, catalyzes this oxidation reaction. The next step is the iodination of the tyrosine molecules in thyroglobulin. The mechanism is not precisely understood, but the peroxide probably causes radicals of both iodine and tyrosine to be formed, which then react with one another to monoiodotyrosine or diiodotyrosine (see Figure 30.2a).

The iodinated tyrosine molecules in the thyroglobulin are subsequently linked together to form triiodothyronine ($T_3$) and tetraiodothyronine ($T_4$), the physiologically active thyroid hormones (Figure 30.2b). This coupling reaction also involves the peroxidase mentioned above. This membrane-bound enzyme is located on the boundary between the cell and the colloid. For this reason, the reactions described above probably take place in the colloid, in the vicinity of the apical membrane (see Figure 30.3).

FIGURE 30.1

Thyroid gland of an adult control rat (HE; 200 ×)

The follicles are covered with squamous epithelium and the lumen is filled with colloid.

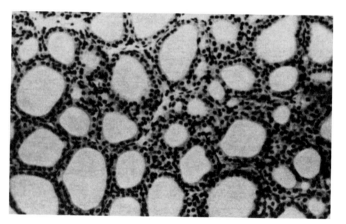

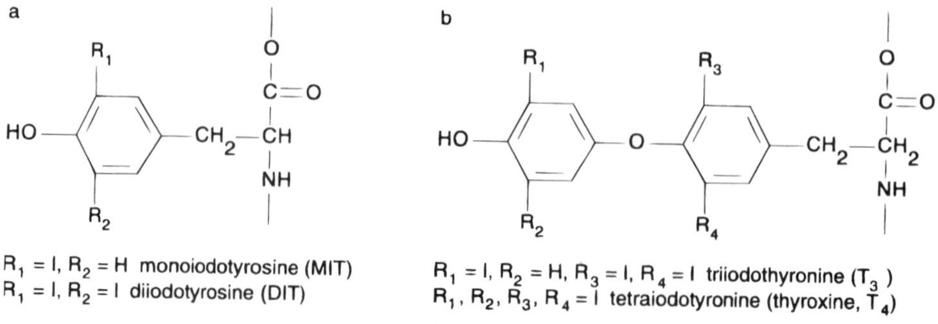

$R_1 = I, R_2 = H$ monoiodotyrosine (MIT)
$R_1 = I, R_2 = I$ diiodotyrosine (DIT)

$R_1 = I, R_2 = H, R_3 = I, R_4 = I$ triiodothyronine ($T_3$)
$R_1, R_2, R_3, R_4 = I$ tetraiodothyronine (thyroxine, $T_4$)

FIGURE 30.2

Structural formulae of monoiodotyrosine and diiodotyrosine (a) and of triiodothyronine and tetraiodothyronine (b)

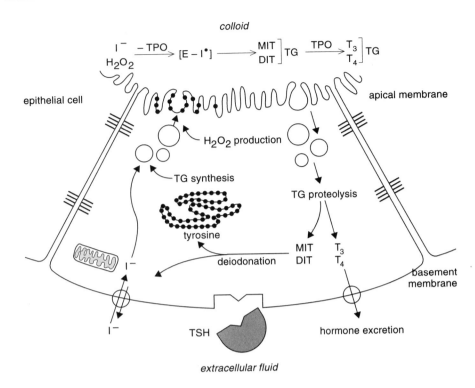

FIGURE 30.3
Schematic representation of the functioning of thyroid cells

The iodinated thyroglobulin forms a store for thyroid hormones in the colloid. Thyroglobulin is subsequently taken up by means of endocytosis into the epithelial cells, where it is broken down by lysosomal enzymes, after which the thyroid hormones $T_3$ and $T_4$ are released into the bloodstream.

*Thyroxine-binding globulin (TBG)*

In the blood, the thyroid hormones bind to proteins, and in that form they are transported through the body. The human body has a special *thyroxine-binding globulin (TBG)*, to which approximately two-thirds of the thyroid hormone bind. Most of the remainder binds to prealbumin, while a small amount binds to albumin. Rats do not have this TBG, and their thyroid hormones bind only to prealbumin and albumin.

*Regulation of thyroxine and triiodothyronine release*

To maintain a normal basal metabolism, the release of hormones by the thyroid must be regulated. Under normal circumstances, the synthesis of thyroxine and triiodothyronine and their release into the bloodstream are controlled by a hypophyseal hormone called *thyroid-stimulating hormone (TSH)*. The release of TSH by TSH-producing cells in the pituitary, in its turn, is regulated in part by a so-called releasing factor, *TSH-releasing hormone or TRH*, which is secreted by the hypothalamus. The release of TRH is inversely proportional to the concentration of thyroid hormones in the circulation: an increase in the concentration of thyroxine and triiodothyronine in the blood causes a decrease in the release of TRH by the hypothalamus, and thus in the release of TSH by the pituitary. Low thyroxine and triiodothyronine concentration in the blood, on the other hand, leads to an increased release of TRH and therefore also of TSH. In a similar way, the release of TSH by the pituitary is also linked directly to the concentrations of thyroid hormones in the blood, so that there are two mechanisms controlling the release of thyroid hormones.

*Negative feedback mechanism*

This mechanism is called a *negative feedback mechanism* because of the inverse relationship between concentrations of thyroid hormones and the amount of TSH released. In this regulation mechanism, the liver also plays an important part. As the primary metabolic organ, the liver is responsible for the deiodination of thyroid hormones and for the conjugation with glucuronic acid, so that the resulting conjugates can be excreted. The liver thus effects a change in the concentration of circulating hormones. The feedback mechanisms described above will react by changing the TSH release by the pituitary. This causes the thyroid to produce either more or less hormone.

## Hyperthyroidism and hypothyroidism

*Hyperthyroidism*

The condition in which a thyroid gland is overactive, i.e. if it produces and secretes *a surplus of thyroid hormones*, is referred to as *hyperthyroidism*. Hyperthyroidism may be diffuse, which means that the entire gland is hyperplastic (increase in cell number) and has a clearly increased weight. Such cases are known as Graves' disease. The changes in the thyroid are the same as those associated with an increased TSH stimulus. The difference is, however, that in diffuse hyperthyroidism (with an increased release of thyroid hormones) the TSH concentration in the circulation is greatly decreased because of negative feedback. This suggests that there must be a different cause for the hyperplasia of the thyroid gland. It is possible that an immunoglobulin of the IgG type, the so-called LATS or long-acting thyroid stimulator, plays an essential role here. This would mean that an autoimmune phenomenon is involved that influences the endocrine system (in this case the thyroid).

Another type of hyperthyroidism is caused by hyperfunctioning adenomas (tumors) in the thyroid, while the surrounding tissue still functions normally.

*Hypothyroidism*

*Hypothyroidism* involves a poorly functioning thyroid, i.e. a thyroid which produces or secretes *insufficient hormones*. This may be caused by:

1. a lack of iodine in the diet, so that an essential component for the biosynthesis of hormones is lacking;
2. changes in the enzymatic reactions that play a role in the biosynthesis of thyroid hormones, or in the breakdown of thyroglobulin into the thyroid hormones $T_3$ and $T_4$ and their secretion into the circulation;
3. insufficient production or secretion of TSH.

Like hyperthyroidism, hypothyroidism may also be associated with an enlarged thyroid gland. However, the enlargement is caused by an increased TSH stimulus resulting from the decreased concentration of thyroid hormones in the blood. Many toxic substances that have an effect on the thyroid will give rise to hypothyroidism, while the morphological picture (stimulated epithelial cells) is in fact more reminiscent of hyperthyroidism. Well-known examples of such substances are the following:

- thiocyanate, which stops iodide being concentrated in the thyroid cells by affecting the iodide pump, and thus inhibits the biosynthesis of thyroid hormones;

- thioamides, such as propylthiouracil and methimazole, which inhibit thyroid iodide peroxidase (TPO) and thereby the biosynthesis of hormones, with the effects described above. Dithiocarbamates and their degradation product ethylene thiourea (ETU) probably work in the same manner.

- lithium, a cation that inhibits adenylate cyclase, thus preventing TSH from stimulating the uptake of iodide and the release of thyroid hormones.

ASSIGNMENT   30.2

How will the organism react to inhibition of the iodide pump by thiocyanate?

### 1.2.2 Adrenal glands

The adrenal glands are paired organs located on or in the vicinity of the superior pole of the two kidneys. They are flattened semilunar structures, which are enclosed in a capsule of connective tissue rich in cells, and embedded in the perinephric and retroperitoneal adipose tissue. The most striking feature of the adrenal glands is that they consist of two concentric layers: a yellow peripheral *cortex* and a grey central *medulla*. The cortex and the medulla can be regarded as two glands which are both morphologically and functionally completely different. They also originate from different embryonal tissues. The cortex develops from the mesodermal coelomic epithelium, and is thus of mesodermal origin. The medulla is an ectodermal structure consisting of modified sympathetic ganglion cells deriving from the neural crest.

### Histology and histophysiology

*Adrenal cortex*

On histological examination, the *adrenal cortex* appears to consist of three zones:

1. an outer, very narrow *zona glomerulosa*, consisting of small cells arranged in circular or arch-shaped clusters and surrounded by capillaries;
2. a broad *zona fasciculata*, consisting of large cells arranged in columns, which are perpendicular to the surface of the gland; wide capillaries run between the columns;
3. an innermost, narrow *zona reticularis*, consisting of smaller cells arranged in disorderly cords and forming a sort of network, interspersed with capillaries.

These cells are often found to contain lipofuscin. The cells of the adrenal cortex display the characteristics of steroid-synthesizing cells. In particular, those in the zona fasciculata contain a large number of lipid droplets in their cytoplasm. This makes them appear highly vacuolated in normal histological sections. The fat in the vacuoles contains the precursors of steroid hormones, of which cholesterol is an important component. Although the boundaries between the various layers of the adrenal cortex are often not well demarcated, there is a distinct functional difference between the zona glomerulosa on the one hand and the zonae fasciculata and reticularis on the other. The production of *mineralocorticoids* (in particular aldosterone) takes place in the zona glomerulosa, that of *glucocorticoids* (in particular cortisol and corticosterone) and the *sex steroids* (androgens, estrogens and progesterone) in the zonae fasciculata and reticularis.

*Mineralocorticoids*

The most important action of the *mineralocorticoids* is to stimulate the reabsorption of sodium from the distal convoluted tubules of the kidneys. By doing so, they cause an increase in the sodium concentration and a decrease in the potassium concentration of the blood, thus promoting the retention of fluids.

*Glucocorticoids*

The *glucocorticoids* primarily influence protein, lipid and carbohydrate metabolism. They promote the degradation of proteins and, parallel to that, the synthesis of glucose from amino acids. They also suppress the immune system (e.g. inflammatory processes and allergic reactions). Under normal circumstances, the synthesis of sex steroids in the adrenal glands, of which that of androgens is the most important, hardly contribute to that in the gonads.

*Adrenal medulla*

The *adrenal medulla* comprises large epithelioid cells arranged in cords, forming a network surrounded by capillaries and veins. These cells are considered as modified ganglion cells. As such, they are innervated by nerve fibers located at the same side as the capillaries. At the other side, the cells are in contact with the veins, into which they release their products. The function of the adrenal medulla is to secrete the *catecholamines epinephrine* and *norepinephrine*. By the action of these hormones, the organism can adapt to an abrupt 'fright, flight or fight' reaction by increased blood pressure through vasoconstriction and greater cardiac activity, a raised blood glucose level, reduced peristaltic movements of the intestines, and stimulation of oxidative metabolism. In contrast to the cortex, whose products are released into the blood continuously, the medulla accumulates its hormones in the form of granules. A certain histological reaction causes the granules to stain brown by the reduction of chromium salts. Because of this, these cells are also known as chromaffin cells. In normal conditions, only small amounts of hormone are released. It is only in situations such as described above that large quantities are secreted.

### Regulation of adrenal cortical activity

*Aldosterone*

If the blood volume is reduced by a low sodium uptake or by blood loss, the secretion of *aldosterone* will be increased, which in turn will lead to increased retention of sodium and water. Regulation of aldosterone secretion takes place primarily by the *renin-angiotensin system* (see Figure 30.4) and only secondarily by the hypophysial *adrenocorticotropic hormone (ACTH)* and the concentrations of sodium and potassium in the blood. Renin is produced by the juxtaglomerular cells, which surround the afferent arterioles near the glomeruli in the kidney.

Once released into the blood, renin induces the conversion of angiotensinogen (an $\alpha$-globulin from the liver) to the decapeptide angiotensin I, which is subsequently converted by the 'angiotensin-converting enzyme' into angiotensin II. Angiotensin II finally stimulates the zona glomerulosa to synthesize aldosterone (see Figure 30.4).

*Glucocorticoids*

The secretion of *glucocorticoids* in the adrenal cortex is regulated by ACTH. The production of ACTH in the pituitary is controlled by the *corticotropin releasing*

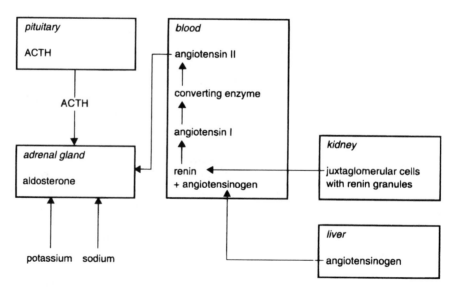

FIGURE  30.4
Regulation of aldosterone secretion by the renin–angiotensin system

*hormone (CRH)* from the hypothalamus. CRH secretion increases if the concentration of glucocorticoids in the blood falls (see introduction to section 1.2, Feedback control). It also increases as a reaction to a variety of circumstances which influence the central nervous system, such as stress, cold, infections, great physical effort, etc. This means that in such situations, the secretion of glucocorticoids will eventually increase.

### Regulation of adrenal medullar activity

In the case of physical effort and in highly emotional situations (in which hypoglycemia, fear, pain, anger, excitement etc. occur), the adrenal medulla is stimulated to immediately secrete the catecholamines epinephrine and norepinephrine. The cells of the adrenal medulla are innervated by preganglionic nerve fibers. This means that regulation of catecholamine secretion takes place via the central nervous system.

### Feedback mechanisms

Conversely, the hormones in the endocrine glands also influence their own production and/or secretion. Relatively little is known about feedback mechanisms to the central nervous system. More is known about the feedback from the periphery to the hypothalamus-pituitary system. With respect to the adrenal glands, this applies in particular to the glucocorticoids (see Figure 30.5).

The glucocorticoids inhibit ACTH secretion by the pituitary not only directly, but also indirectly, namely by inhibiting CRH release by the hypothalamus. In general, a distinction can be made between:

- rapid feedback: peripheral hormones inhibit the *secretion* of hormones by the pituitary or by the hypothalamus (in this case glucocorticoids, and ACTH or CRH, respectively);

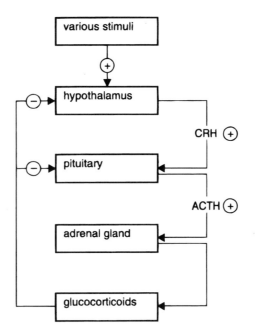

FIGURE   30.5
Feedback mechanism of ACTH and glucocorticoid secretion
+ = stimulation
− = inhibition

- slow feedback: peripheral hormones inhibit the *synthesis* of hormones in the pituitary or in the hypothalamus (in this case glucocorticoids, and ACTH and/or CRH, respectively).

### Hyperfunction and hypofunction of the adrenal glands

*Adrenal cortex*
*Hyperfunction*

If the feedback mechanism is disturbed, the continuous supply of ACTH will lead to hyperplasia of the adrenal cortex. This process, which usually affects the zona fasciculata, is called progressive transformation. Such *hyperfunction* of the adrenal glands, resulting in excessive production of glucocorticoids, is often caused by ACTH-producing tumors of the pituitary. This disorder is known as Cushing's syndrome (ACTH-dependent or pituitary Cushing's syndrome). Tumors of the adrenal cortex (non-ACTH-dependent or adrenal Cushing's syndrome) and long-term administration of corticosteroids (iatrogenic Cushing's syndrome) may give rise to the same symptoms. Deficiency of enzymes involved in the biosynthesis of glucocorticoids may sometimes lead to excessive production of, in particular, androgens. As the concentration of glucocorticoids remains low, the ACTH production increases, leading to even more androgens and resulting in the so-called androgenital syndrome.

*Hypofunction*

*Hypofunction of the adrenal cortex* (regressive transformation) may occur as a result of long-term administration of glucocorticoids, through causes related to the cortex itself or by a reduction of ACTH production in the pituitary gland.

*Influence of xenobiotics*

*Toxic substances* may also have direct or indirect effects on the adrenal cortex:

- in pigs, the antimicrobial veterinary drugs carbadox and olaquindox lead to a decrease in the concentration of aldosterone, as a result of which reabsorption of sodium in the kidney is reduced, leading in turn to a reduced sodium concentration and an increased potassium concentration in the blood;
- in rats, the flavoring glycyrrhizin, derived from the liquorice root and used in certain types of liquorice, causes hypertension, a reduced potassium concentration and reduced plasma renin activity. These phenomena are caused by the fact that glycyrrhizin mimics the action of aldosterone.

  (NB: It is this substance in liquorice, rather than salt, which may give rise to high blood pressure in persons who eat large amounts of liquorice. Liquorice itself contains very little salt, but does contain salammoniac (ammonium chloride, $NH_4Cl$)).

  ASSIGNMENT 30.3

  What morphological changes in the adrenal gland can be expected in lithium intoxication, given that the substance has the following effects:

  - it inhibits the response of antidiuretic hormone and aldosterone in the kidney, resulting in decreased sodium absorption and loss of fluid;
  - it increases plasma renin activity in the blood;
  - it increases the aldosterone concentration in the blood.

  If necessary, refer to Figure 30.4 to answer this assignment.

*Adrenal medulla*

Abnormalities of the adrenal medulla are usually hyperplasias and, in older people, tumors deriving from the chromaffin cells, known as pheochromocytomas.

In man, and probably also in rats, these display functional activity, i.e. they produce catecholamines. In rats, hyperplasias and neoplasms in the adrenal medulla can also be induced by administration of growth hormone and substances such as nicotine, thiouracil and reserpine.

### 1.2.3 The gonads

Unlike the thyroid and adrenal glands, the gonads are clearly different in males and in females. In both sexes, the gonads serve on the one hand to produce gametes (spermatozoa and ova respectively) and on the other to produce hormones which give rise to the typically male or female characteristics in the animal as it reaches adult life.

### Morphology

*Testis*

Most of the *testis* consists of intertwined seminiferous tubules, in which the earliest stages of the spermatozoa are produced. In between these tubules are the interstitial cells or Leydig cells, which produce the male sex hormone testosterone and release it into the bloodstream. In addition, there are also the *Sertoli cells*, which play a role in the further growth and maturation of the spermatozoa. The Sertoli cells also produce a protein hormone, *inhibin*, which has a negative feedback effect on the production of *follicle-stimulating hormone* (FSH) in the pituitary gland (see Figure 30.6). Testosterone is formed from cholesterol via pregnenolone and progesterone (see Figure 30.7). It is responsible for the development and maintenance of the male characteristics and plays a role in the development of the spermatozoa. The production of spermatozoa starts during puberty and continues into old age.

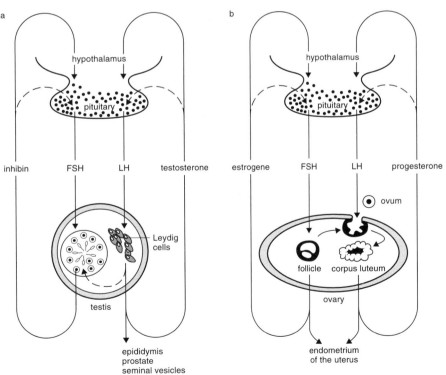

FIGURE 30.6

Regulation of the formation of male (a) and female (b) sex hormones

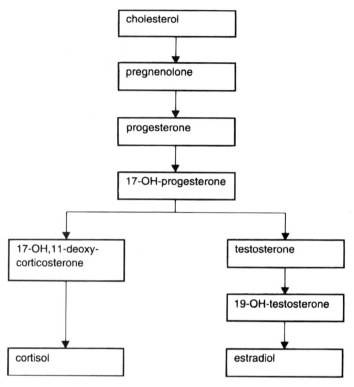

FIGURE 30.7
Biosynthesis of steroids

*Ovary*

The *ovary* consists of follicles and stroma cells. The latter form a sort of supporting tissue in which the follicles are embedded. The follicles are globular units, containing an ovum surrounded by two types of cells, namely granulosa cells and theca cells. Both types of cell can produce female sex hormones. The ovaries produce a large number of oocytes, up to a certain stage of development. This takes place before birth and the supply of oocytes is never replenished. This procedure is therefore completely different from the production of spermatozoa. At the start of sexual maturity, the follicles start to develop under the influence of the hypophysial hormone FSH. Once they have reached a certain size, the theca cells on the outside of the follicle become sensitive to LH or *luteinizing hormone* (they develop LH receptors) and start to produce steroids, mainly androgens. The granulosa cells, which are located more on the inside of the follicle, mature under the influence of FSH and develop an enzyme system which converts the androgens into estradiol-17β. Positive feedback to the pituitary leads to the production of more FSH and thus of more estrogens (see Figure 30.6b).

In the course of time, the granulosa cells also develop LH receptors so that, after ovulation, LH is able to make them luteinize. Depending on the species, one or more follicles ovulate in each cycle; the others perish. After ovulation, the production of estrogens is ceased, as a result of which the negative feedback to FSH is stopped and a new cycle can begin.

*Regulation*

Two hypophyseal protein hormones play a role in both sexes, namely follicle-stimulating hormone (FSH) and luteinizing hormone (LH), which in the older literature is also called *interstitial-cell-stimulating hormone* (ICSH) with reference to males. In the female sex, a third protein hormone also plays a role, namely *prolactin* (PRL). LH and FSH are closely structurally related. Both are glycoproteins, which means that they are made up of protein chains to which carbohydrate chains are attached. Both hormones consist of two subunits. One of these, the $\alpha$-subunit, is virtually identical in LH and FSH and in TSH, which has already been discussed. The other subunit is different for each hormone, and is called the $\beta$-subunit. LH and FSH have a molecular mass of approximately 30,000 Da. Prolactin is very different in structure. It consists of one protein chain, does not contain carbohydrate chains and has a molecular mass of about 24,000 Da.

In the *human male*, FSH stimulates the growth of the seminal vesicles and the first stages of spermatogenesis. LH is responsible for the synthesis and secretion of testosterone by the interstitial or Leydig cells. It is also involved in the maturation of the spermatozoa. The roles of both hormones can be demonstrated by removing the pituitary of a rat. The resulting lack of LH and FSH leads to degeneration of the testes and cessation of spermatogenesis. Although LH and FSH perform their tasks together, FSH is probably more important for the initiation and development of gonadal function, while LH is more important in maintaining that function. This is suggested by the fact that the effect of hypophysectomy before puberty can be alleviated by administration of FSH without LH, while the reverse is found after puberty. A further difference is that, via the production of testosterone by the Leydig cells, LH has an indirect effect on spermatogenesis in the Sertoli cells, whereas FSH does not play a role in the production of testosterone.

*Toxic compounds*

Tetrahydrocannabinol is the psychoactive component of cannabis products.

*Toxic compounds* may have an effect on the Leydig cells or the sperm-cell-producing Sertoli cells in the testis. Examples of such compounds are the following:

- cannabinoids, in particular tetrahydrocannabinol, which inhibit the synthesis of steroids in the Leydig cells, probably by inhibition of the enzyme cholesterol esterase;
- $\beta$-hexachlorocyclohexane ($\beta$-HCH), a contaminant of the pesticide lindane, which causes a reduction of the number of Leydig cells and thus leads to a reduced testosterone concentration in the blood;
- n-hexane and its major metabolite 2,5-hexanedione, which cause testicular atrophy via reduced spermatogenesis;
- phthalate esters, which are used as plasticizers in the plastics industry, and which cause atrophy of the Sertoli cells, thus leading to reduced spermatogenesis.

In the *human female*, FSH stimulates the growth and development of follicles in both ovaries from the antral stage to the preovulatory stage. As is the case in males, LH has two different functions, namely the induction of ovulation followed by luteinization of the granulosa cells, and the production of estrogens, and, primarily progestogens. As in men, FSH and LH cooperate very closely in women, namely in the development and maintenance of the female cycle. Although the description of one cycle could in fact start at any point, the beginning of the follicular phase is usually taken as the starting point. The secretion of LH and FSH increases and one of the medium-sized follicles starts to develop into a preovulatory follicle, also called Graafian follicle after the Dutch physician and anatomist Reinier de Graaf. The production of steroids in the theca cells is initiated, particularly that of estradiol-17$\beta$, androstenedione and 17$\alpha$-hydroxyprogesterone.

The rising estrogen concentration initially leads to inhibition of the secretion of FSH (negative feedback), and is later followed by simultaneous outbursts of both LH and FSH secretion (positive feedback). Approximately 24 hours after the LH peak, ovulation takes place, and the ovum passes through one of the Fallopian tubes to the uterus. Luteinization of the granulosa cells and to a somewhat lesser degree of the theca cells of the ovulated follicle then takes place.

## 2    Techniques applied in endocrinotoxicological research

### 2.1    HISTOLOGICAL METHODS

The first indications of chemically induced changes in the endocrine system are usually derived from changes in the weight and the morphological picture of the endocrine organs. The routine staining methods applied in histopathology, such as hematoxylin-eosin staining, are very useful to trace a substance with a toxic effect on the endocrine system. However, they do not give sufficient information on the exact site of action. Toxicants may, for example, affect the biosynthesis of hormones, the number of cells that produce a specific hormone or the quantity of hormone present in the cells. The progress made in the fields of enzyme histochemistry, immunocytochemistry and electron microscopy has led to the development of very sensitive and specific techniques by which a large number of enzyme activities and hormones can be demonstrated in histological sections.

*Enzyme histochemistry*

Using *enzyme histochemical methods*, the site of enzyme activity can be visualized by an insoluble stained deposit. Sections are incubated in a medium containing not only the correct substrate but also the necessary co-enzymes and cofactors. In endocrinological studies, enzyme histochemistry has proven to be useful in demonstrating the activities of important steroid-synthesizing enzymes or of enzymes which provide an indication of where steroid synthesis takes place.

*Immunocytochemistry*

*Immunocytochemical methods* allow specific demonstration in sections of many antigens, such as hormones, by means of an antigen-antibody reaction. In these techniques, the antibody is labelled. The purpose of these methods is to produce an intense staining reaction, to achieve the lowest possible non-specific background staining and to make the reaction so sensitive that only very little antiserum is needed. Immunofluorescence methods use frozen sections and *fluorochromes*, which are visible directly under the fluorescence microscope, for labelling. *Enzyme labels*, such as horseradish peroxidase, glucose oxidase and alkaline phosphatase, are used extensively in paraffin sections of tissue fixed in formalin. These labels are made visible by adding a substrate solution, which reacts with the enzyme label to form an insoluble stained product. At the ultrastructural level, *electron-dense labels* such as ferritin and colloidal gold enable localization of antigens.

*Horseradish peroxidase*

Of the enzyme labels mentioned, *horseradish peroxidase* is by far the most commonly used. A large number of chromogenic substrates, such as diaminobenzidine, are also available for peroxidase. Chromogenic substrates lead to the formation of an insoluble stained product.

*Immunoperoxidase methods*

If a substance is found to influence the endocrine system, *immunoperoxidase methods* are often applied in toxicity experiments in rats. In the endocrine system, the pituitary holds a key position because it produces a number of tropic hormones. The conventional histological *hematoxylin-eosin stain* allows three types of cell to be distinguished in the rat pituitary, namely acidophilic, basophilic and chromophobic cells.

*Hematoxylin-eosin stain*

*HE-staining of pituitary cells*

Cells producing growth hormone (GH) and prolactin (PRL) are acidophilic. Cells producing TSH, FSH and LH are basophilic, and those producing ACTH are chromophobic.

ASSIGNMENT 30.4

Indicate which component of the hematoxylin-eosin stain is bound by acidophilic, basophilic and chromophobic cells, respectively.

It will be obvious that any changes in the number of specific hormone-producing cells and in the quantity of hormones will be very difficult to detect by the HE staining method. This is why immunoperoxidase methods are applied. With 3,3'-diaminobenzidine and hydrogen peroxide as substrates for peroxidase, a selective immunocytochemical staining reaction for the various different hormones in the adenopituitary of rats can be obtained (see Figures 30.8a and b and 30.9 a to f).

The number of immunopositive cells or the intensity of a staining reaction is correlated with the quantity of the hormone concerned. Endocrinotoxic effects of substances such as bromide, β-HCH and tributyltin oxide (TBTO) can be detected in these ways. Before immunocytochemical methods can be applied at the light microscopy level, the tissues are usually subjected to a histological pro-

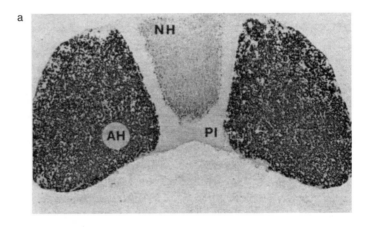

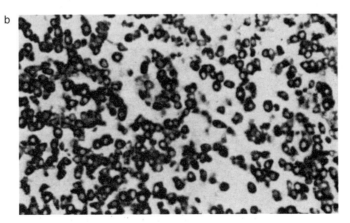

FIGURE 30.8

Immunoperoxidase reaction for GH in the pituitary of an adult control rat

a) Overview (30 ×), in which the immunoreactive GH cells are seen to be located specifically in the adenohypophysis (AH), compared with the neurohypophysis (NH) or the pars intermedia (PI).

b) Detail of a); the immunoreactive GH cells form small clusters or strings and are round or oval (300 ×).

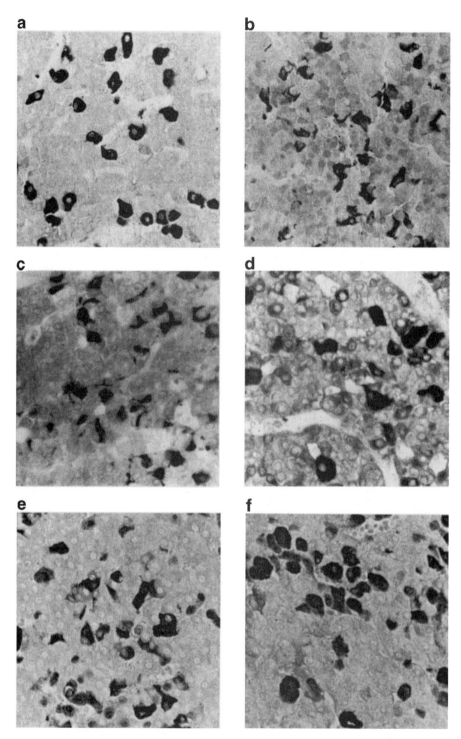

FIGURE    30.9
Immunoperoxidase reaction for PRL, ACTH, TSH, LH and FSH in the pituitary of adult
control rats (300 ×)
The immunoreactive PRL cells are cup-shaped in the female rat (a) and star-shaped in the male rat (b); the ACTH-positive cells are also star-shaped (c); the TSH-producing cells are polygonal (d); the immunoreactive FSH cells (e) and LH cells (f) are round to polygonal in shape.

cedure aimed at preserving the cellular detail. In general one can state that the more one attempts to preserve the histological structures, the more the immunoreactivity of many antigens is lost.

*Fixation of tissue*

This is why *fixation of tissue* is the most critical step in the process. In preparing material for electron microscopy, the antigen structures may be destroyed during dehydration and embedding in plastic.

A solution to this problem has been provided by cryo-ultramicrotomy, a method by which a cryotome is used to cut "ultrathin" sections. The immunocytochemical reaction concerned is carried out in these sections, after which they are embedded in plastic.

## 2.2    IMMUNOCHEMICAL METHODS

For ELISA see Study unit 28

The effects of toxic substances on the endocrine system often become manifest in subtle changes in the concentrations of hormones in body fluids. These changes can be detected using sensitive and specific methods such as the *radioimmunoassay (RIA)* and the enzyme-linked immunoassay (ELISA). Both methods are based on the principle of competition between on the one hand the antigen to be determined and, on the other, an antigen labelled with a radioisotope (RIA) or an enzyme-linked antigen (ELISA) for the specific antibody. After separation of linked and free antigen, the concentration of the label is determined in the RIA by a scintillation counter, while in the ELISA a substrate for the linked enzyme (peroxidase) must be added, which is converted to a stained product and which can then be determined by spectrophotometry.

*Radio-immunoassay*

Since its introduction in 1959 by Yalow and Berson, who developed a RIA for insulin, and since Elkins more or less at the same time managed to determine thyroxine, RIA has become a standard technique which is applied in a wide variety of scientific studies. In recent years, the technique has been improved in various ways.

*Alternative radiolabels*

In the first place, a number of alternatives for the radiolabel have been developed. In addition to the ELISA method, which uses enzyme labels, current alternatives for the radiolabel include fluorescence and chemiluminescent probes and metals, each with their distinctive pros and cons as regards safety, cost, sensitivity and stability. Secondly, the development of *monoclonal antibodies* has contributed to greater specificity. The availability of very specific antibodies means that it is now possible to use a labelled antibody instead of a labelled antigen in determinations. An example of such an immunometric method is the sandwich assay, in which the antibody is linked to a fixed carrier. Advantages of such a method are the lower detection limit and the fact that a balance between antibody and antigen is rapidly established, which shortens the time necessary for determination. Nevertheless, it may be assumed that the original RIAs will remain in use for some time because they are relatively easy to perform and have a good signal/noise ratio.

One or more radioimmunoassays or other immunoassays are currently available for virtually every endocrine variable. Determinations in experimental animals of species-specific hormones, such as protein hormones, are carried out using methods which researchers develop themselves based on species-specific antibodies. For determination of non-species-specific hormones, such as thyroid hormones or steroids, kits developed for human medicine, which are available commercially, can also be used. In the latter case, the method may need to be adapted with respect to the quantity of sample required, which is usually smaller in experimental animals. Differences between animals and man in the metabolic pattern of steroids may also cause unexpected disturbances to occur in the determination process as a result of cross-reacting metabolites.

## 3　Function tests

In addition to comparison of hormone concentrations in single blood samples from control animals and from animals treated with a test substance, there are more refined methods for obtaining information on the effects of toxic substances on the endocrine system.

*Frequent blood sampling*
*Changes in concentration of related hormones*

One option is *frequent blood sampling*, e.g. several times per hour, in order to detect minor fluctuations in hormone concentrations. Secondly, comparing the *changes in concentration* of two or more *related hormones* provides additional information. If, for example, the level of TSH is increased and that of $T_4$ is not, this might be an indication of inhibition of thyroid function. Thirdly, function tests have been developed for almost all endocrine organs.

*Function tests*

*Function tests* are specific tests aimed at determining the potency of a substance with respect to its specific action. Within the framework of endocrine toxicological research, they focus primarily on substances with direct hormonal action, or on substances which may cause changes in hormonal modes of action. Because of its complexity, there is no single test for the entire endocrine system, but there is a specific test for each endocrine organ. These tests are sometimes based on measurement of the uptake of hormone precursors, usually in the form of radioisotopes, or on determining the reaction of an endocrine organ to the administration of additional physiological stimuli. In endocrine toxicological research, these tests are applied if changes in weight or morphology of endocrine organs or changes in the concentrations of hormones in the blood have provided an indication of the target organ of a particular toxic substance. A well-known practical example is the *uterotropy test* (Tiecco test). In this test, young mice or rats are injected with the substance under investigation. After a certain length of time, the increase in uterine weight is determined. In this way, the estrogenic action of substances such as diethylstilbestrol (DES), or the fungus toxin zearalenone and its anabolic derivative zearalenol, and of pesticides such as DDT and methoxychlor can be compared with that of the positive control substance, ethinylestradiol. The following subsections discuss a number of function tests in somewhat greater detail.

### 3.1　RELEASE TESTS

Many function tests can be performed in an intact organism (test animal) after it has been experimentally exposed (whether by oral, inhalational or parenteral administration) to a toxic substance. The functioning of the various types of pituitary cells which produce tropic hormones can be studied after *stimulation of the organ with "releasing factors"*, substances that are released by the hypothalamus in physiological conditions.

*Stimulation of the organ by "releasing factors"*

For example, after intravenous administration of luteinizing-hormone-releasing hormone (LH-releasing hormone or LHRH), the release of LH and FSH by the pituitary can be determined by measuring the serum concentrations of these hormone, using RIA techniques.

In the same way, it is possible to determine the release of TSH (see Figure 30.10) and PRL in the serum after administration of TSH-releasing hormone (TRH), and the level of ACTH after administration of CRH (corticotropin-releasing hormone). In a different way, one level "lower", the functioning of the target organ can be studied. After administration of ACTH, for example, the corticosterone concentration can be determined as a measure for the functioning of the cells in the zona fasciculata of the adrenal cortex.

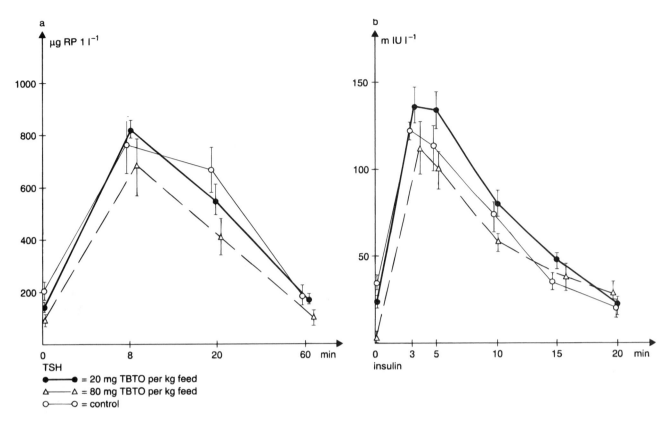

FIGURE 30.10
Time-dependency of the TSH concentrations (a) and insulin concentrations (b) in the serum of cannulated rats after i.v. administration of TSH-releasing hormone (TRH) in (a) and glucose in (b)
Measurements were carried out in the serum of rats which had received TBTO in their feed for 6 weeks
R1 = Reference Preparation 1, published by NIDDK (National Institute for Diabetic, Digestive and Kidney Diseases)
IU = international unit

*Glucose tolerance test*

A common method of measuring pancreatic function is the determination of immunoreactive insulin after administration of glucose, which is referred to as the *glucose tolerance test* (see Figure 30.10b). It should be noted, however, that oral administration of glucose leads to a stronger insulin response than parenteral administration, at equal hyperglycemia.

For these determinations, it is necessary that blood is sampled from the animals at set times after administration of the releasing hormone. This can be done by stress-free decapitation of the animals, but a more elegant (although much more elaborate) method is to use cannulated animals.

*Cannulation*

A *cannula of silicone rubber* is inserted via the external jugular vein and pushed as far as the right atrium. The loose end of the cannula is led subcutaneously to the head, and is attached there to a metal tube which is fixed to the skull by means of small screws and dental cement. This cannula can serve both for i.v. administration of releasing factors and for blood sampling.

EXAMPLE

A practical example will now be described. Two or 3 days after introduction of the cannula, the animals are fasted for 1 night. The following morning, they receive an intravenous dose of glucose (4 mmol per kg body weight). To determine the insulin blood concentration, samples are taken via the cannula at 3,

5, 10, 15 and 20 minutes after administration. Pituitary function can be tested in the same animals after a 48-hour period of rest following the glucose tolerance test. To do so, dosages of TRH and LHRH of 1 $\mu$g per kg body weight are administered intravenously at intervals of 48 to 72 hours. Before each administration, as well as 8, 20 and 60 minutes after administration, blood samples are taken for determination of hormone concentrations. In this way, a great deal of information can be obtained from a relatively small number of animals.

*Inhibition tests*

metyrapone

In addition to the release tests described, in which administration of one substance causes the release of one or more hormones, thus increasing their concentrations, there are also *inhibition tests*, in which exactly the reverse takes place. Earlier in this unit, some of the various feedback mechanisms were discussed. Fasting animals reduces their glucose levels and therefore also insulin levels. Administration of a surplus of, for example, corticosteroids gives rise to a reduction in ACTH concentration.

Another useful function test of the adrenal gland is to determine the influence of toxic substances on the inhibition by *metyrapone* of the production of corticosteroids.

*Non-invasive hormone determination*

In addition to the invasive method of measuring hormone concentrations in the blood, there are also *non-invasive* function tests. For example, adrenal cortical activity can be measured by determining the concentration of 17-hydroxycorticosteroids in the urine.

### 3.2 UPTAKE TESTS

The previous section discussed *release* tests. Another type of function test determines the *uptake* of hormone precursors by endocrine organs. Such tests generally make use of radioisotopes. For example, the adrenal cortical activity can be determined by measuring the uptake of labelled cholesterol, which is a precursor of steroid hormones. Another well-known example is the test for thyroid function in which the uptake of radioactive iodine by the thyroid is measured.

For this purpose, a dose of 2 $\mu$Ci $^{125}$I or $^{131}$I per kg body weight is administered parenterally to test animals. The quantity of the radioisotope can then be determined in isolated thyroid glands, but a more elegant method is to determine the amount of radioisotope in the thyroid of an anesthetized animal. In that way, both the uptake and the release of the iodine radioisotope can be established in individual animals by, for example, measuring the amount of label in the same animal 6, 24, 48 and 72 hours after administration. By doing so, it is possible to obtain a complete uptake/release curve from one individual animal. Figure 30.11 shows the result of such a test, in which male rats were given sodium bromide in their diet.

### 3.3 ORGAN REMOVAL (ECTOMY)

Another way to determine whether toxic substances have any effect on hormonal functioning is to remove one or more target organs from an experimental animal.

*Adrenalectomy*

Removal of the adrenal gland (*adrenalectomy*), for example, causes a reduction in the concentration of corticosteroids and, by feedback control, to an increase in the ACTH concentration. After treatment of the animal with a test substance, this increase may be found to be less. Such a finding would give an indication of the extent to which the substance to be tested mimics the action of corticosteroids.

*Gonadectomy*

*Gonadectomy* (castration; removal of the testes or ovaries) provides a very sensitive biological system which can be used to determine whether and how hor-

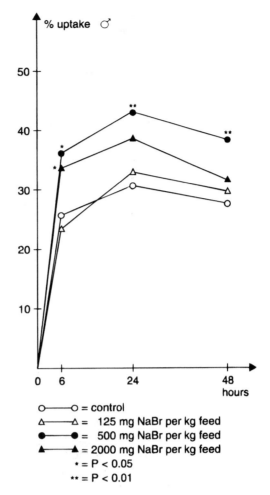

FIGURE   30.11
Uptake of [131]I in the thyroid of rats after administration of NaBr in a chloride-free diet

monally active substances inhibit the secretion of gonadotropic hormones by the pituitary. After removal of the testes, feedback will cause the pituitary to secrete more LH and FSH. Simultaneous administration of a potentially androgenic compound suppresses the increased secretion of tropic hormones. The extent of this is an indication of the potency of the androgenic compound studied in relation to, for example, testosterone.

EXAMPLE

An example is provided in Table 30.2, which shows the results of an experiment establishing the effect of 17$\beta$-trenbolon acetate, an anabolic with androgenic action, on the increase in LH secretion which occurs when adult pigs are castrated.

The substance was administered orally for 14 days after removal of the testes. It is obvious that, from a dose of 16 $\mu$g per kg body weight per day, 17$\beta$-trenbolon acetate suppresses the increase in the amount of LH. It therefore has a direct androgenic effect (mimicking testosterone). Similarly, administration of synthetic estrogen after ovariectomy will suppress the secretion of LH and FSH, thus making it possible to determine its relative potency in relation to estradiol.

TABLE 30.2
Effect of trenbolon acetate in castrated pigs

| 17 β-trenbolon acetate (µg per kg body weight per day) | Difference (ng) LH per ml between days 0 and 14 |
| --- | --- |
| 0–1 | 0.29 |
| 1 | 0.45 |
| 10 | 0.28 |
| 16 | 0.10* |
| 24 | 0.11* |
| 36 | 0.01* |

\* = $P < 0.05$
\*\* = $P < 0.01$

*Hypophysectomy*

Removal of the pituitary (*hypophysectomy*) will in general lead to degeneration of the peripheral endocrine organs due to a lack of tropic hormones. Degeneration can be prevented by simultaneous administration of hypophyseal hormones. This is how the hormonal action of a substance obtained by, for example, biotechnological means (genetic manipulation, e.g. bovine growth hormone) can be tested.

## 3.4 IN VITRO METHODS

After the toxic effect of a substance on the endocrine system has been established *in vivo*, *in vitro* test systems can be used to investigate the mode of action of the substance in greater detail. *In vitro* methods can also be applied to determine the *potency* of toxic substances with respect to specific interference with endocrine mechanisms. In other words, *in vitro* methods can be used as screening methods.

In short, every aspect of endocrine regulation which has been tested *in vivo* can also be investigated in cell or tissue cultures, with the exception of feedback mechanisms. The fact that physiological feedback is lacking is also, in a way, an advantage over the *in vivo* situation. It allows closer study of interactions at the cellular or molecular level, which is essential to determine the mode of action of a toxic substance.

*Examples of in vitro methods*

*In vitro* test methods include studies of the uptake of hormone precursors or the release of hormones, determination of the activity of enzymes involved in the biosynthesis or degradation of hormones, and studies of the interaction with *binding* to hormone receptors.

*Interaction with binding to hormone receptors*

The latter is a particularly important subject of *in vitro* studies. Toxic substances may influence the binding of tropic protein hormones to hormone receptors on the cell membrane, or of steroid hormones to receptors in the cytosol or on the nuclear membrane. They may even themselves bind to these receptors. In the latter case, they may either have a direct hormonal action (agonist) or block the binding of the hormone for which the receptor is intended (antagonist). To establish whether and how toxic substances bind to hormone receptors, it is also necessary to determine the biological response to receptor binding, to enable differentiation between an agonistic and an antagonistic effect.

---

EXAMPLE

An example of an *in vitro* system is an estrogen-sensitive human breast cancer cell line. Using these cells, it is possible not only to determine the binding characteristics of substances with estrogenic activity for the receptor by displacement of radioactively labelled estradiol, but also to measure the subsequent physiological response, i.e. induction of progesterone receptor protein. Figure 30.12 shows the concentration-dependent increase in the quantity of progesterone receptor under the influence of $\beta$-HCH and its main metabolite trichlorophenol.

A totally different example is an *in vitro* system using a thyroid cell line, with which the effects of toxic substances on the uptake of iodide (radioactively labelled) and organification can be assessed.

### 4    Practical problems

*Choice of experimental animal*

Researchers in the field of endocrine toxicology are confronted with a number of problems which may influence the results of experiments and the conclusions to be drawn from them. To begin with, of course, the choice of the *experimental animal* is important. The rat is the most commonly used laboratory animal in toxicology, but for studies of certain compounds, other species might well be more relevant in assessing the risk posed to humans. This is particularly true of the estrogenic substances, which are discussed above. The estrus cycle of the rat differs from that of humans, and for this reason rats are not as suitable for risk assessment of estrogenic substances as, for example, rhesus monkeys or cynomolgus monkeys, which have an estrus cycle similar to humans.

The developing endocrine system in young animals is also known to be more sensitive than the mature endocrine system in adult animals.

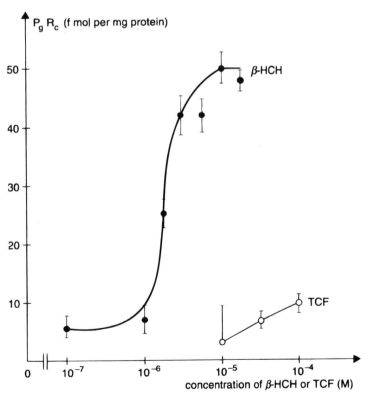

FIGURE    30.12
Dose-response curves of the induction of the cytoplasmic progesterone receptor (PgRc) by $\beta$-hexachlorocyclohexane ($\beta$-HCH) and its metabolite 2,4,6-trichlorophenol (TCP) in human breast cancer cells (MCF-7) after 6 days' incubation

*Food of experimental animals*

Another important factor is the *food* administered to experimental animals. As we have seen, sodium and potassium are important in the regulation of adrenal function, as is iodide with respect to the thyroid gland.

The amount of carbohydrates and lipids (such as cholesterol) in the diet may also affect the function of the pancreas and the adrenal glands in particular. A known, constant quantity of these minerals and nutrients in the diet is therefore important if reproducible and reliable results are to be obtained. In general, low concentrations of these minerals and nutrients in the diet of the experimental animals will reinforce the effects of toxic substances on the endocrine system, while higher concentrations will mask them. The diet of laboratory animals may also contain *contaminants*, which may affect the results of the experiment. Depending on the origin of the various dietary components, the diet may, for example, contain natural goitrogens, which affect thyroid function, or estrogenic compounds, such as zearalenone. For this reason, adequate information on the composition of the experimental diet is essential in order to carry out endocrino-toxicological studies appropriately.

*Stress*

The most important factor influencing the results of an experiment is, however, *stress*. Accurate measurement of hormone concentrations in the circulation requires a method of blood sampling which subjects the animal to as little stress as possible. Pain or fright cause an instantaneous change in a number of endocrine systems, particularly the hypothalamic-pituitary-adrenal axis. This system is affected even when an animal is lifted or when its cage is moved. Unexpected sounds, in particular those of rustling paper and running water, cause the release of CRF. A few minutes later, the concentrations of ACTH and adrenal cortical hormone rise. The levels of growth hormone and prolactin and, to a lesser degree, of the thyroid and sex hormones can also be influenced by stress.

Handling animals regularly over the course of days or even weeks will accustom them to the experimental circumstances and will greatly reduce the stress stimuli.

*Sampling*

Sampling of blood is also stressful for the animals. Decapitation is the simplest method by which blood can be sampled from rodents. For ethical reasons, the animals are usually lightly anesthetized with ether before decapitation. However, ether itself causes the release of a large quantity of CRF, which makes this method totally unsuitable for endocrine toxicological studies. Decapitation must therefore be performed without previous anesthesia, something which requires great manual skill and gentleness on the part of the researcher. A much more elegant method is the use of a cannula in one of the large vessels, as described previously. In this way, blood can be sampled from an animal without causing stress and without the administration of anesthetics.

5    Examples of endocrinotoxic substances

This section describes the results of *in vivo* and *in vitro* experiments using a number of substances which exert effects on the endocrine system.

*Bromide*

*Bromide* is a natural component of all plants and animals and is therefore naturally present in food. Toxicological interest in this anion came about following the use of bromide-containing pesticides and soil sanitation agents (ethylene dibromide, methyl bromide), which might constitute an additional burden for man. Animal experiments have shown that bromide added to the diet in the form of sodium bromide has effects primarily on endocrine organs. The relative weight of the thyroid compared with body weight was increased in rats, and histological examination of the gland revealed activation, characterized by smaller follicles and higher epithelial cells (see Figure 30.13).

ASSIGNMENT   30.5

What (two) mechanisms may be involved in this effect of NaBr, and how can they be distinguished?

Sodium bromide caused a dose-dependent reduction in the concentration of $T_4$ and an increase in TSH. Immunocytochemical studies of the pituitary showed an increase in the number of immunoreactive TSH cells.

Figure 30.11 shows uptake of radioactive iodide by the thyroid in an experiment in which rats receiving a low-salt diet (less chloride means greater bromide toxicity) were given sodium bromide.

Explain the results shown.

In the higher dosage groups, iodide uptake is increased following the enhanced TSH stimulus. In the highest dosage group, however, inhibition by bromide is so great that the increase in iodide uptake is partly masked.

In addition to its effect on the thyroid, bromide also influences the adrenal glands. It causes:

- reduced vacuolation in the zona fasciculata;
- reduced concentration of corticosterone in the blood.

ASSIGNMENT   30.6

What effect will this have on the pituitary?

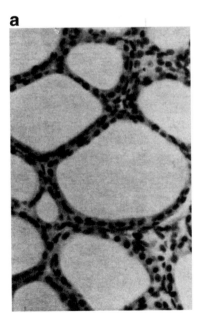 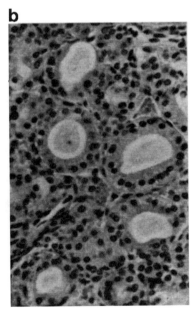

FIGURE   30.13

Thyroids of adult rats (HE; 300 ×)

a) Control rat. The follicles are lined with flat epithelial cells and the lumen is filled with colloid.

b) Rat pretreated with NaBr (4 weeks of exposure). Highly activated thyroid: the follicular epithelium is much taller, the amount of colloid is reduced and has a granular aspect.

The gonads are also influenced by bromide. Atrophy of the seminiferous tubules and reduced spermatogenesis were observed in the testes of male rats (see Figure 30.14). The number of corpora lutea in the ovaries of female rats was reduced.

This atrophy in the testes and ovaries may be the result of bromide-induced inhibition of FSH production in the pituitary. Bromide might also have a direct effect on the gonads. Studies have shown that FSH levels are increased under the influence of bromide. This suggests that, as well as having a direct effect on the thyroid, bromide also has a direct influence on the adrenal glands and the gonads.

*Bis(tri-n-butyltin) oxide (TBTO)*

Trialkyltin compounds are used on a large scale as wood preservatives and in antifouling paints. *TBTO* is used in particular in tropical countries to kill snails, which, as the secondary host, play a role in *Schistosoma* infection in man.

For immunotoxic effects of TBTO, see Study unit 29

In addition to the immunotoxic effects of TBTO, a number of effects on the endocrine organs have been observed. A considerable reduction in the serum concentration of $T_4$ was found in rats, as well as a reduction in the weight of the thyroid. Morphologically, flattening of the epithelial cells was observed, indicating inactivation of the thyroid.

ASSIGNMENT 30.7

In what different ways can these effects be caused, and how can these be distinguished from each other?

Serum levels of TSH are reduced under the influence of TBTO, as is the immunoreactivity of TSH-producing cells in the pituitary (see Figure 30.15). A release test using TRH also shows a reduced TSH release at higher doses of TBTO (see Figure 30.10). It can be concluded that, unlike bromide, TBTO causes a reduction of $T_4$ by inhibiting production of TSH in the pituitary. Serum LH concentrations increase.

a
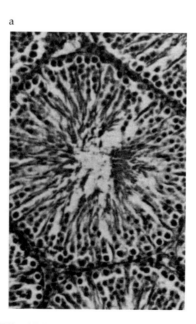

b
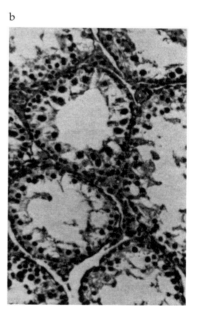

FIGURE 30.14
Testis of adult rats (HE; 190 ×)
a) Control rat
b) Rat from the group receiving the highest dose of NaBr (after 12 weeks of exposure); there is reduced spermatogenesis and a reduction in the diameter of the seminiferous tubules.

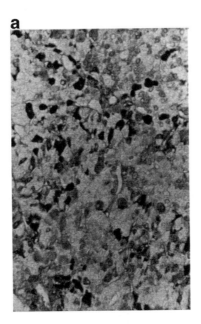 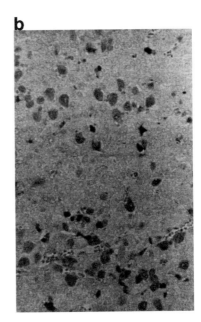

FIGURE   30.15
Immunoperoxidase reaction for TSH in the hypophysis of adult rats (190 ×)
a) Control rat
b) Rat after 6 weeks of exposure to 80 mg TBTO per kg food; the number of cells with high immunoreactivity to TSH is reduced.

ASSIGNMENT   30.8

After exposure to TBTO, what will be the immunocytochemical picture of the LH-producing cells in the pituitary, and what will be the result of a pituitary function test using LHRH?

β-HCH

Like other isomers of HCH, *β-hexachlorocyclohexane (β-HCH)* is formed during synthesis of the insecticide lindane, or γ-HCH. Technical, i.e. contaminated, lindane was used as an insecticide on a large scale. Despite the fact that, since the 1970s, most countries have allowed only the use of pure γ-HCH, the environment and the food chain are still contaminated with, in particular, β-HCH. This is due not only to the persistence of this substance but also to earlier large scale dumping of α-HCH and β-HCH.

Toxicity research in rats given β-HCH in their food has shown the endocrine system to be a selective target. The ovaries of female animals from a high dosage group contained follicles but, in contrast to control animals, did not contain any (young) corpora lutea (see Figure 30.16). This suggests that no ovulation had taken place.

ASSIGNMENT   30.9

The plasma concentration of what hormone could be affected by the absence of ovulation?

A clear reduction in progesterone levels was observed in the serum of animals from the highest dosage group. Histological examination of the vaginal epithelium revealed a disturbance in the rats' cycle. The various stages of the cycle can be recognized by their distinctive morphology. The cycle of the rat covers 4–5 days and can be subdivided into 4 stages, including estrus (ovulation). All stages of the cycle were found in the control animals, whereas the rats from the highest dosage

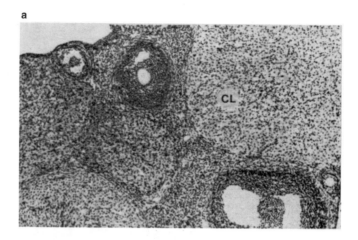

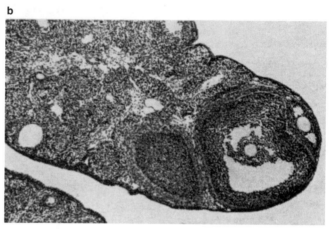

FIGURE 30.16

Ovaries of adult rats (HE; 95 ×)

a) Control rat; all stages of follicular maturation are present, as are corpora lutea (CL).

b) Rat after 13 weeks of exposure to β-HCH; there are no corpora lutea.

group were all in the estrus stage. The endometrium of the uterus of these animals also displayed focal metaplastic changes in the epithelium (see Figure 30.17).

This may of course give rise to a disturbance of reproductive function. After administration of β-HCH to male rats, hyperplasia of acidophilic cells with a lighter paranuclear zone was observed in HE sections of the pituitary (see Figure 30.18a,b). Using immunocytochemical techniques, an increase in immunoreactivity to prolactin was observed in the pituitary glands of the highest dosage group (see Figure 30.18c,d). In contrast, the serum concentration of prolactin was not increased. β-HCH is therefore thought to stimulate the production of prolactin in the pituitary, but inhibit its release into the blood.

Literature studies have confirmed that estrogenic substances may cause prolactin tumors in the pituitaries of rats.

ASSIGNMENT 30.10

What hypothesis regarding the mode of action of β-HCH do the above findings suggest?

Effects which can be ascribed to an estrogenic action of β-HCH or one of its metabolites were also observed in male rats. The number of Leydig cells in the testes was reduced and a decrease in serum testosterone was found.

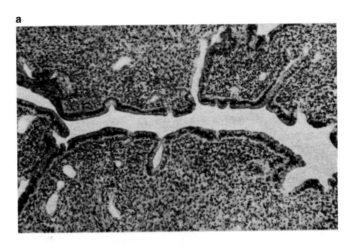

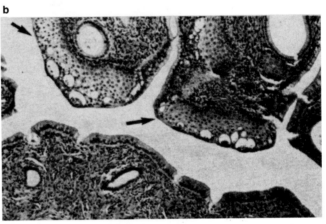

FIGURE   30.17
Uterus of adult rats in the estrus stage (HE; 95 ×)
a) Control rat; the endometrial epithelium is high.
b) Rat after 13 weeks of exposure to β-HCH; there is focal metaplasia of the endometrial epithelium (arrows).

ASSIGNMENT   30.11

To what further effects might this lead?

It can be concluded that *in vivo* studies gave clear indications of estrogenic action. A classic method used in toxicology to trace compounds with estrogenic action is the Tiecco test or uterotropy test mentioned previously. After administration of β-HCH, a dose-related increase in uterine weight was found in both rats and mice. This increase was parallel to the effect of ethinylestradiol. These parallel dose-response relationships did provide evidence of uterotropic activity, but merely suggested a direct estrogenic action of β-HCH.

ASSIGNMENT   30.12

How can evidence of direct estrogenic action of β-HCH or one of its metabolites be obtained?

The action of β-HCH has been further investigated in a human estrogen-sensitive breast cancer cell line (MCF-7). The estrogen receptor works in the same manner in these cells as it does in normal estrogen-sensitive tissue. An estrogenic substance will bind to the estrogen receptor, causing several specific in-

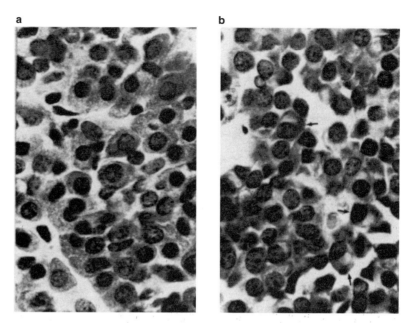

FIGURE    30.18a,b
Pituitaries of adult male rats (HE; 700 ×)
a) Control
b) Rat after 13 weeks of exposure to β-HCH; there is hyperplasia of acidophilic cells with a lighter paranuclear zone (arrows).

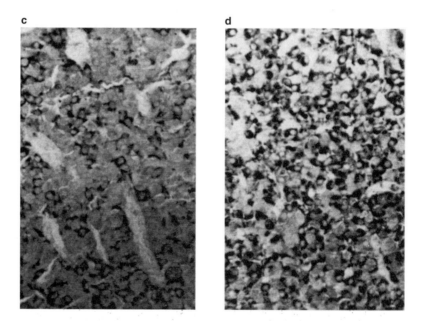

FIGURE    30.18c,d
Immunoperoxidase reaction for PRL (275 ×)
c) Control; the immunoreactive PRL cells are star-shaped.
d) Rat after 13 weeks of exposure to β-HCH; the PRL-positive cells are cup-shaped and much more immunoreactive

tracellular effects, such as induction of the cytoplasmic progesterone receptor. This is considered a specific biological effect caused by estrogens. β-HCH binding to the estrogen receptor was demonstrated because dose-dependent displacement of $^3$H-estradiol binding to the receptor was found after addition of various concentrations of β-HCH to an *in vitro* test system. Dose-dependent induction of the progesterone receptor was also found for $\beta$-HCH, while its main metabolite, trichlorophenol, had little or no effect (see Figure 30.12). It was concluded from these *in vitro* results that the mode of action of $\beta$-HCH is identical to that of estradiol and that $\beta$-HCH itself has an estrogenic action.

$\beta$-HCH also has an estrogenic effect in animals other than mammals. This became apparent from studies in two species of fish, namely *Poecilia reticulata* (guppy) and the oviparous species *Oryzias latipes*. *P. reticulata* in particular displayed greatly increased staining intensity of the blood plasma, lymph and peritoneal fluid. This finding could be ascribed to a circulating yolk protein, vitellogenine.

Hypertrophy of the rough endoplasmic reticulum was found in the liver, which is indicative of greatly increased synthesis of this protein. Increased synthesis of vitellogenine in the liver is normally caused by estrogens. In the guppy, other findings were decelerated development of the testis and stimulation of the gonadotropic cells in the pituitary. $\beta$-HCH also induced hermaphroditism in the male *O. latipes*. All these effects can be explained from the direct estrogenic action of $\beta$-HCH.

## 6    Summary

The present study unit has provided a brief description of the morphology and function of a number of endocrine glands which are important in endocrinotoxicological research. Particular attention was paid to their individual functions and the way in which they are interrelated. Determination of changes in the endocrine system can involve histological, histochemical and immunochemical techniques on the one hand, and function tests on the other. The possibility of measuring small changes is often of great importance, and existing methods have been adapted in various ways for this purpose. Endocrinotoxicological research makes use of a number of different techniques, ranging from simple histological staining methods to advanced immunocytochemical methods using a variety of labels for antibodies, such as fluorochromes (fluorescence microscopy), enzyme labels and electron-dense labels. Important immunochemical methods used are radioimmunoassay (RIA) and enzyme-linked immunosorbent assay (ELISA). These methods can highlight very specifically any changes in the endocrine system.

In addition to methods of determination, so-called function tests are also used. Important examples of these are release tests, which assess the effects on the artificially induced release of hormones by endocrine glands, and uptake tests, which study the influence of compounds on the uptake of hormone precursors by endocrine glands. Another important way in which changes in the endocrine system can be studied is to remove endocrine target organs from an experimental animal. Examples are removal of the pituitary (hypophysectomy), of the adrenal glands (adrenalectomy) and of the gonads (castration or gonadectomy). In addition to *in vivo* studies, endocrine toxicological research also makes use of *in vitro* methods. An important topic in this connection is the disturbance by xenobiotics of hormone binding to specific hormone receptors.

The final section discussed the modes of action by which bromide, tributyltin oxide and $\beta$-hexachlorocyclohexane exert their toxic effects on the endocrine system.

SELF ASSESSMENT QUESTIONS

1    What is meant by endocrinotoxicology?

2    Are substances which give rise to the formation of tumors by disturbing

hormonal mechanisms considered to be direct carcinogens?

3    What possibilities does a substance with indirect hormonal action have to exert its effect?

4    a)   How does thiocyanate exert its toxic effect?
     b)   What is the result of this?

5    Lithium causes hypertrophy of the zona glomerulosa in the adrenal glands. Which hormone is affected by this?

6    Carbadox decreases aldosterone levels. What is the result of this?

7    What function tests are used in endocrine toxicological research?

8    Describe some practical problems which may influence the results of endocrine toxicological studies.

9    How may stress be prevented in experimental animals?

10   What is the effect of bromide on the pituitary, and how can this be explained?

11   How does TBTO lead to decreased thyroid hormone levels in the blood?

12   How has it been shown that $\beta$-HCH *itself* has direct estrogenic action?

## FEEDBACK

### 1    Answers to the assignments

30.1 This is an essential distinction in risk assessment and in drawing up regulations pertaining to substances, because it is *not* possible to establish a no-effect level for genotoxic carcinogenic substances, although this *is* possible for non-carcinogenic substances.

30.2 The organism will react with an increased stimulation of the thyroid by TSH, so that the size of the thyroid is increased, as is the height of the epithelial cells (activation). However, thyroid function is impaired.

30.3 The organism attempts to compensate for the loss of sodium by stepping up aldosterone production, under the influence of renin and other factors. The cells in the zona glomerulosa, where aldosterone is synthesized, will show signs of stimulation (they will be swollen).

30.4 Acidophilic cells bind acid components of the HE stain, i.e. eosin. Basophilic cells bind alkaline components, i.e. hematoxylin. Chromophobic cells bind neither eosin nor hematoxylin.

30.5 1.   Direct stimulation of the thyroid by bromide.
     2.   Inhibition of thyroid functioning, which, by means of the feedback mechanism via the pituitary, is compensated for by increased stimulation of the thyroid by TSH.

These two mechanisms can be distinguished by measuring the blood concentrations of thyroxine ($T_4$) and TSH, and by immunocytochemical examination of the TSH-producing cells in the pituitary.

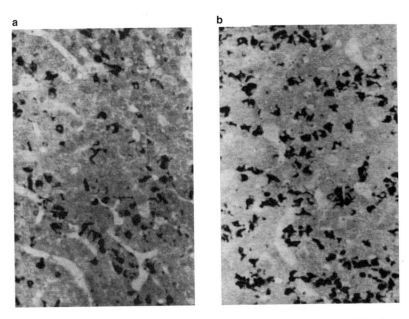

Immunoperoxidase reaction for ACTH in the hypophysis of adult rats (190 ×)
a) Control rat; the cells displaying immunoreactivity for ACTH are star shaped, with cytoplasmic projections between other cells.
b) Rat from the group having received the highest dosage of NaBr (after 12 weeks of exposure); the number of cells with high immunoreactivity for ACTH has increased.

30.6 It will lead to an increase in the activity of ACTH-producing cells, as is shown by the figure below.

30.7 TBTO may have a direct inhibiting effect on stimulus transmission by TSH, or it may inhibit the production of TSH in the pituitary. It is therefore important both to determine the concentration of TSH and to examine the pituitary using immunocytochemical methods.

30.8 An increase in the number of immunopositive cells was found for LH. A pituitary function test using LHRH reveals an increase in the release of LH under the influence of TBTO.

30.9 On the plasma concentration of progesterone.

30.10 β-HCH, or one of its metabolites, has direct estrogenic action.

30.11 Reduced spermatogenesis and atrophy of the accessory sexual glands. These effects have been observed for β-HCH.

925

30.12 This evidence could be provided by determining binding to the estrogen receptor in an *in vitro* test system, and measuring the subsequent physiological response.

## 2 Answers to the self assessment questions

1 The study of the adverse effects of substances which influence the endocrine system via direct or indirect hormonal action.

2 No. It is possible to establish a dose for these substances at which disturbance of hormonal regulation does not occur.

3 Disturbance of: uptake of hormone precursors, biosynthesis, release, degradation, excretion, and second-messenger systems.

4 a) Thiocyanate inhibits the uptake of iodide by the thyroid.
   b) The result is reduced biosynthesis and therefore a lower concentration of thyroid hormones in the blood. Feedback via the pituitary subsequently leads to increased stimulation of the thyroid by TSH.

5 Aldosterone; the effect is an increase in its blood concentration.

6 Decreased sodium and increased potassium blood levels.

7 1. release tests
   2. uptake tests
   3. inhibition tests
   4. ectomies

8 Species of experimental animal, age of animals, diet given, stress caused by handling and by blood sampling.

9 By handling the animals frequently and thus allowing them to become accustomed to it, by carrying out the experiment in a quiet environment, and by sampling blood by means of a cannula.

10 Bromide causes increased activity of TSH-producing cells in the pituitary and thereby leads to an increased blood concentration of TSH. This is due to a feedback mechanism. Bromide reduces the synthesis of thyroid hormones, which in turn causes increased activity of TSH cells in the pituitary.

11 TBTO is responsible for reduced activity of the TSH-producing cells in the pituitary. A reduced TSH stimulus will cause the thyroid to produce smaller amounts of thyroid hormones.

12 $\beta$-HCH displaces estradiol from the estrogen receptor, i.e. $\beta$-HCH itself binds to the receptor and gives rise to a positive response, namely induction of progesterone receptor protein. The most important metabolite of $\beta$-HCH, trichlorophenol, does not have this effect.

# Content Study unit 31
## General reproductive toxicology

0-8493-9232-2/96/$0.00 + $.50

Study unit 31

# General reproductive toxicology

*P. W. J. Peters and J. M. Garbis-Berkvens*

## INTRODUCTION

*History of teratology*

teras (Gr.) = monster

The word *teratology* was first used in 1832 by Geoffroy St. Hilaire in his book *Histoire générale et particulière des anomalies de l'organisation chez l'homme et les animaux*, which was subtitled *traité de tératologie*. Monsters and congenital abnormalities have fascinated man for a long time. In Catal Hüyük, in Turkey, a two-headed goddess from circa 6500 BC was found, and Egyptian wall paintings which are about 5000 years old show pictures of clubfoot and achondroplasia. The Babylonians regarded the birth of abnormal offspring as having predictive value for the economic and political affairs of the country. In Greek culture, congenital abnormalities and monstrosities were the models for some mythological figures, such as the one-eyed Polyphemus and the two-faced Janus. The Egyptian god Ptah was an *achondroplastic dwarf*. In his *Natural History*, Pliny the Elder describes abnormal individuals and races, but it is uncertain whether all of these actually existed. The sixteenth century in particular provides many descriptions of monsters.

achondroplasia = abnormalities in bone growth

*Congenital abnormalities*

Over the centuries, many explanations have been advanced for the development of *congenital abnormalities*. The ancient Greeks, for example Aristotle, ascribed them to natural causes, mishaps of nature. Hybridization between species was thought to give rise to monsters such as sphinxes, satyrs and centaurs. In the Judaeo-Christian world, congenital abnormalities were primarily seen as a punishment from God, resulting from intervention by the devil or witches, or as the product of sodomy. There has always been great interest in the influence of the spiritual experiences and the emotions of pregnant women on the development of the embryo. The Greeks advised pregnant women to look at beautiful things so as to have a beautiful child.

A more scientific theory was introduced by Harvey in 1651. He postulated that a number of abnormalities could be explained by a sudden arrest in certain processes of development (e.g. cleft palate, umbilical hernia). Mechanical causes, such as an abnormally shaped uterus and fetal diseases, have also been mentioned as explanations for the development of congenital abnormalities.

*Experimental embryology*

At the beginning of the nineteenth century, the development of *experimental embryology* made it possible to gain further insight into the origin of congenital abnormalities and to study abnormal development. Great interest in morphology and taxonomy arose. The late nineteenth century saw the publication of encyclopedic studies describing congenital abnormalities and classifying them according to anatomical criteria.

*Teratology*

At the time, *teratology*, which was usually considered to be part of the field of anatomy and embryology, was largely *descriptive* in nature and had little clinical significance, as abnormalities could not be prevented or treated. Moreover, there were no methods by which internal abnormalities of, for example, the lungs or the intestinal tract could be established during life. Early in the twentieth century, interest in teratology slackened, largely because of the development of bacteriology, and the subsequent discovery of the causes of infections. The emphasis shifted to research methods by which infectious diseases could be treated and prevented.

The rediscovery of Mendel's laws and the knowledge that some congenital abnormalities were passed on from parents to children led to attempts to explain abnormalities on the basis of genetics.

*Nutritional deficiency*

In 1933, Hale noticed that piglets born to sows which were fed on a vitamin A deficient diet were born without eyes. His conclusion was that a *nutritional deficiency* leads to a marked disturbance of the internal factors which control the mechanism of eye development. During a rubella epidemic in 1941, Gregg observed that embryos which had been exposed to the rubella virus often displayed abnormalities, such as cataract, cardiac defects, deafness and mental retardation. Soon after this, it was discovered that *Toxoplasma*, a unicellular parasite, can induce abnormalities in the fetus.

> What can you conclude from these observations with regard to the placenta as a barrier against foreign agents?

These observations proved undeniably that the placenta is not an absolute barrier against external influences.

*Clinical teratology*

In the early 1960s, a mild sedative, thalidomide, appeared to be causing characteristic congenital abnormalities, in particular a significant shortening or even absence of the limbs. This discovery led to a world-wide interest in *clinical teratology*. In 1964, the first conference on teratology was organized in the United States. The proceedings of this conference have had a major influence on the development of methods for studying teratogenicity of substances in animal experiments.

*Clinical genetics*
*Prevention*

Over the past few decades, medical technology has made such progress that prenatal diagnosis by means of ultrasonography and biochemical methods, but especially chromosome studies, has led to the development of *clinical genetics* as a subject area. *Prevention* of the birth of a child suffering from developmental defects has now become possible (secondary prevention). Teratology has developed into a multidisciplinary science.

ASSIGNMENT 31.1

Which medical-biological subject areas would you think are closely related to teratology?

LEARNING OBJECTIVES

After studying this unit, you should be able to
— describe the historical development of research on teratogenicity
— explain the role of thalidomide in the development of research on teratogenicity
— explain and use time-response and dose-response relationships in teratology and reproductive toxicology

930

— discuss the effects on organ formation of exposure to certain teratogenic compounds in various periods of fetal development
— explain the similarities and differences between research on teratogenicity and research on reproductive toxicity
— describe the mode of action of teratogenic substances
— describe the various teratogenic effects and, if possible, explain the underlying mechanisms
— highlight the difference between direct and indirect teratogenic effects
— describe the teratogenic mechanisms and/or effects of a number of compounds.

*Study hints*

This study unit assumes a certain knowledge of embryology and reproductive biology. If your knowledge of these fields needs brushing up, you are advised to study the relevant theory in a biology or embryology handbook. The study load for this unit is estimated at approximately 3 hours.

STUDY CORE

1    **Subject area and definitions**

*Reproductive toxicology*

*Reproductive toxicology* is the subject area dealing with the causes, mechanisms, effects and prevention of disturbances throughout the entire reproductive cycle induced by chemicals (Figure 31.1).

*Teratology*

*Teratology* is the science which concerns itself with birth defects of a structural nature.

*Reproductive toxicity*

*Reproductive toxicity* represents harmful effects by agents on the progeny and/or impairment of male and female reproductive functions.

*Developmental toxicity*

*Developmental toxicity* involves any adverse effect induced prior to attainment of adult life. It includes effects induced or manifested in the embryonic or fetal period and those induced or manifested postnatally.

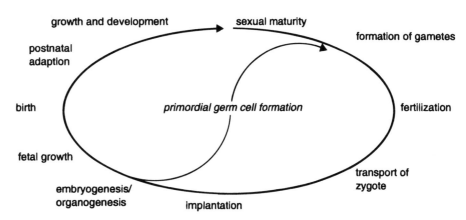

FIGURE   31.1
Different stages in the reproductive cycle

*Embryo/fetotoxicity*

*Embryo/fetotoxicity* involves any toxic effect on the conceptus resulting from pre-natal exposure, including structural or functional abnormalities or postnatal manifestations of such effects.

*Teratogenicity*

*Teratogenicity* is a manifestation of developmental toxicity, representing a particular case of embryo/fetotoxicity, by the induction or the increase of the frequency of structural disorders in the progeny.

ASSIGNMENT 31.2

Does the field of developmental toxicology constitute an integral part of reproductive toxicology?

The various stages of the reproductive cycle are part of a continuous process. They represent different stages of development, each with its own specific sensitivity to compounds. The most obvious starting point for the cycle would be the earliest moment in the development of an individual (Table 31.1).

TABLE 31.1

Specific sensitivity during the various stages of development in men and women

| developmental stage | organs and functions possibly affected in women | organs and functions possibly affected in men | possible effects |
|---|---|---|---|
| primordial germ cell formation | oogenesis | spermatogenesis | (partial) sterility, damaged sperm cells or ova |
| formation of gametes | oogenesis (takes place during fetal development) — gene duplication — cell division maturation of the ovum — hormonal influence on ovary ovulation — hormonal influence on ovary | spermatogenesis — gene duplication — cell division maturation of sperm — influence on Sertoli cells — hormonal influence on testes | sterility, partial fertility, damaged sperm cells or ova, chromosomal aberrations, effects on menstruation, onset of menopause, disturbance of hormonal balance, changes in sex ratio |
| fertilization | oviduct — contractility — secretion — hormonal influence on secretory cells and muscle cells uterus — contractility — secretion — hormonal influence on secretory cells and muscle cells | secondary reproductive organs — motility and quantity of sperm — hormonal influence on glands nervous system — erection — ejaculation — behavior — libido | impotence, sterility, partial fertility, chromosomal aberrations, changes in sex ratio, impaired function of sperm cells |
| implantation | uterus — changes in epithelial lining — secretion — hormonal influence on secretory cells | | spontaneous abortion, resorption of fetus, chromosomal aberrations, partial fertility, stillbirth, low birth weight |
| embryogenesis | uterus — development of placenta embryo — cell divisions — tissue differentiation — hormone production — growth | | spontaneous abortion, fetal death, congenital abnormalities, chromosomal aberrations, changes in sex ratio, stillbirth, low birth weight |

TABLE   31.1 Continued

| organogenesis | placenta | | congenital abnormalities, spontaneous abortion and fetal death, chromosomal aberrations, retarded growth and development, transplacental carcinogenesis |
|---|---|---|---|
| | — transport of nutrients | | |
| | — hormone production | | |
| | — protection against toxic compounds | | |
| | embryo | | |
| | — organ formation | | |
| | — growth | | |
| | maternal nutrient supply to the embryo | | |
| fetal development/ perinatal | fetus | | premature birth, congenital abnormalities (mainly functional defects), stillbirth, death at birth, low birth weight, toxic and |
| | — growth and development | | |
| | uterus | | |
| | — contractility | | withdrawal symptoms in the neonate |
| | — hormonal effects on muscle cells | | |
| | maternal nutrient supply to the fetus | | |
| postnatal | survival of child | | mental retardation, infant mortality, developmental retardation, metabolic and other functional disorders |
| | lactation | | |

Primordial germ cells are present in the embryo as early as 1 month after the first day of the last menstruation. They originate in the yolk sack outside the embryo and migrate to the as yet undifferentiated initial stages of the gonads. During the fetal period, the primordial germ cells differentiate into oocytes or spermatogonia (Figure 31.2).

The *oocytes* remain in the resting stage of the reduction division (meiosis), which is not continued until much later, after birth, shortly before ovulation. Meiosis is only completed after fertilization by expulsion of the second polar cell. Hence, the female germ cells are formed during the prenatal period; after birth no new germ cells are formed. The lifespan of the approximately 400 oocytes that take part in ovulation lasts from the moment they are formed until at least puberty and at most the last ovulation.

ASSIGNMENT   31.3

What is the approximate age of an oocyte taking part in ovulation at a woman's 23rd birthday?

The embryonic *spermatogonia* progressively increase in number. No meiosis takes place until birth; in fact, meiosis does not start until at puberty.

ASSIGNMENT   31.4

How old is a sperm cell of a 23-year-old man?

From puberty on, sperm is continuously formed.

After *fertilization* of the ovum by one of the spermatozoa in the oviduct, cell division starts and the blastocyst is transported to the uterine cavity.

933

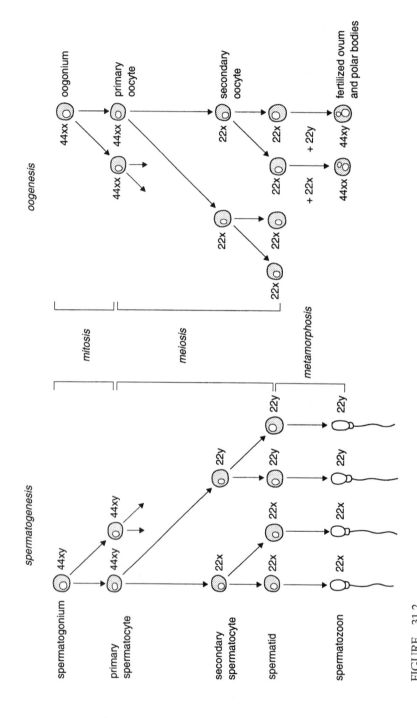

FIGURE 31.2
Cell division and reduction division in spermatogenesis and oogenesis.

*Embryogenesis*
embryo = the conceptus of
mammals in the period starting
with fertilization and ending
when the main parts of the body
and the internal organs have
been formed


*Organogenesis*


*Fetal development*
*Postnatal adaptation*
fetus = the conceptus of
mammals in the period starting
from the point where the organs
are formed and ending with
birth

Meanwhile, hormones have prepared the uterine mucosa for implantation. After *implantation*, or nidation, a bilaminar embryonic disc is formed and *embryogenesis* starts. During the following 7 weeks, numerous cell divisions take place in a carefully coordinated manner.

This is the period of proliferation, migration, cell +association, differentiation and programmed cell death. Together, these processes ensure tissue and organ formation according to the genetically determined programme already laid down at the time of fertilization. This so-called period of *organogenesis* is characterized by rapid cell divisions.

During the later stages of organogenesis the complex processes of cell migration, pattern formation and ingrowth of one group of differentiated cells into another take place. Finally, there is morphological and functional development at various stages during the 7-month period of *fetal development*, which for certain organs extends beyond *birth*. The period of *postnatal adaptation* encompasses the transition from intrauterine to extrauterine life and is characterized by considerable changes in, for example, the cardiovascular system and the physiology of respiration. After puberty the reproductive cycle is completed.

## 2    Basic principles and mechanisms

The following sections deal with some general principles and briefly discuss the underlying mechanisms of embryo/fetotoxicity and teratogenicity.

### 2.1    BASIC PRINCIPLES

Some general toxicological concepts have a special meaning within the context of teratology and reproductive toxicology.

*Expression depends on the stage of development*

#### —The expression of effects depends on the stage of development

The expression of reproductive toxicity depends on the stage of the reproductive cycle at which the agent causes damage. A clear distinction can be made between various 'critical periods'. In general, teratogenic agents may cause *structural* developmental defects if exposure has taken place during organogenesis. This period, which is part of the embryonic period, can be subdivided into periods marking the formation of individual organs (Figure 31.3).

An agent interfering with the closure of the neural tube, for example, will only induce a teratogenic effect in man if exposure occurs before day 42 after the last menstruation. Figure 31.4 shows how developmental defects caused by thalidomide depend on the stage of organogenesis at which it is administered.

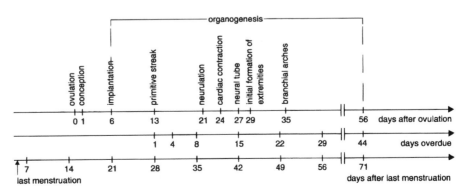

FIGURE    31.3
Various stages of organogenesis

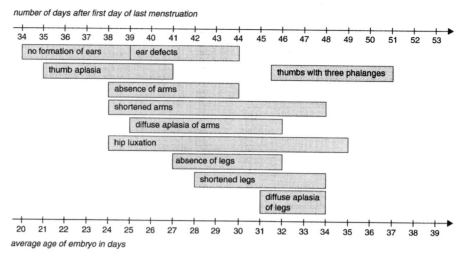

FIGURE 31.4
Developmental stages susceptible to thalidomide

ASSIGNMENT 31.5

When does administration of thalidomide cause birth defects of the ear?

*Genotype determines response*

—*The genotype determines the response*

The sensitivity to teratogenic and adverse reproductive effects depends on the genotype of the fertilized ovum and the subsequent stages in development. Individuals may react differently to the same harmful substance, depending on variations in biochemical and morphological characteristics, which are determined by genetic factors. For example, adrenocortical hormones are highly teratogenic in mice, but hardly at all in rats. The thalidomide tragedy could not have been prevented by extensive testing in mice and rats, since the agent does not produce the same defects in these species as in man. It is, however, teratogenic in rabbits, albeit at much higher concentrations and with less extensive developmental abnormalities than in man. In the case of thalidomide, man has turned out to be the most sensitive species.

*Effects are dose-dependent*

—*The effects are dose-dependent*

Dose-response relationships play an important role in general toxicology. This is also true for teratology and reproductive toxicology. A sufficiently high dose of a compound, administered at the appropriate moment, may induce toxic effects on reproduction or developmental defects of a structural or functional nature in experimental animals sensitive to that compound. The threshold (lowest effective) dose in man and experimental animals has been determined for a number of compounds (Table 31.2).

ASSIGNMENT 31.6

Use Table 31.2 to determine the ratios between experimental animals and humans. What can you say about the susceptibility of man to these compounds?

*Direct versus indirect effects*

A complicating factor is that a compound often also induces adverse effects in the mother animal. In such cases, it is sometimes difficult to distinguish *indirect effects* from *direct effects* in the developing organism. The combination of indirect and direct effects may in particular lead to embryonic or fetal death, fetal growth retardation or delayed bone formation.

936

TABLE 31.2
Comparison of the threshold doses of a number of substances in man and some experimental animals.

| chemical | threshold dose in man | threshold dose in experimental animals | animal species |
|---|---|---|---|
| thalidomide | 0.5–1.0 mg kg⁻¹d⁻¹ | 2.5 mg kg⁻¹d⁻¹ | *rabbit* |
| polychlorinated | 70 $\mu$g kg⁻¹d⁻¹ | 125 $\mu$g kg⁻¹d⁻¹ | rhesus monkey |
| biphenyls | | 1000 $\mu$g kg⁻¹d⁻¹ | dog |
| alcohol | 0.4–0.8 g kg⁻¹d⁻¹ | 1.5 g kg⁻¹d⁻¹ | rat |
| aminopterin | 50 $\mu$g kg⁻¹d⁻¹ | 100 $\mu$g kg⁻¹d⁻¹ | rat |
| methotrexate | 42 $\mu$g kg⁻¹d⁻¹ | 200 $\mu$g kg⁻¹d⁻¹ | rat |
| methylmercury | 5 $\mu$g kg⁻¹d⁻¹ | 250 $\mu$g kg⁻¹d⁻¹ | cat, rat |
| diethylstilbestrol | 20–80 $\mu$g kg⁻¹d⁻¹ | 200 $\mu$g kg⁻¹d⁻¹ | rhesus monkey |
| diphenylhydantoin | 2 mg kg⁻¹d⁻¹ | 50 mg kg⁻¹d⁻¹ | mouse |

## 2.2 MODES OF ACTION

*Mechanism → pathogenesis → dysmorphogenesis → developmental defects (= effect)*

Since little is known as yet about the basic processes regulating development, the exact mode of action of reproductive toxicants, embryo/fetotoxic agents or teratogenic compounds is seldom known. This section deals with a number of ways in which compounds may theoretically interfere with reproduction and development. In general, reproductive toxicants, embryo/fetotoxic agents or teratogenic compounds cause their harmful effects via a number of successive pathways.

*Mechanisms*

### —Mechanisms

Reproductive toxicants may cause one or more of the following types of changes:

- mutations
- chromosomal aberrations
- disturbances in cell division
- changes in nucleic acid composition and protein synthesis
- reduction in the amount of essential constituents for biosynthesis
- reduction of the energy supply for embryonic and fetal development
- disturbance of enzyme systems
- disturbances in the regulation of water and electrolyte balances
- changes in membrane characteristics

*Pathogenesis*

### —Pathogenesis

The above-mentioned disturbances, or mechanisms, may lead to abnormal embryogenesis, which may become manifest in the following ways:

- increased or decreased cell death
- disturbed cell-to-cell contact
- reduced biosynthesis
- increased morphogenetic pattern formation
- mechanical disruption of tissue structure

*Dysmorphogenesis*

### —Dysmorphogenesis

If the damage caused is so great that the repair processes available during embryonic development are no longer able to cope, dysmorphogenesis will occur because too few cells or cell products are formed to effect structural and functional maturation of the developing individual (Figure 31.5).

937

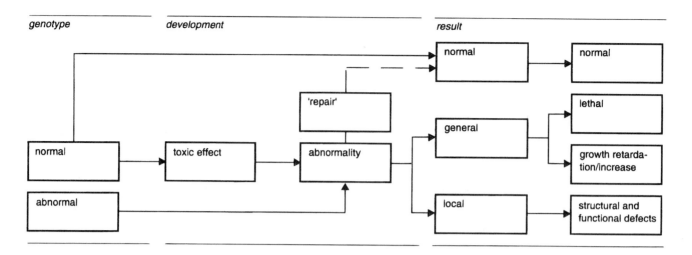

FIGURE 31.5
Normal and abnormal development

## 3 Effects

The following sections discuss a number of effects of teratogenic compounds and reproductive toxicants: functional disorders, fertility disorders, structural developmental defects (malformations), growth retardation and intrauterine death.

### 3.1 FUNCTIONAL AND POSTNATAL DISORDERS

For organisms to be adapted to life after birth, the formation and differentiation of organs and organ systems should proceed normally *in utero*. While these processes take place, organisms are susceptible to the harmful effects of, for example, chemicals such as alcohol and infections by the rubella virus or *Toxoplasma*. The consequences of these effects are not necessarily immediately evident at birth (i.e. as malformations). They may become manifest in the course of the first years of life or even in adulthood, in the form of functional disorders of organs.

*Sensitive period*

Unlike the *sensitive period* for induction of structural defects, which is relatively short and coincides mainly with the period of organ formation and development, the sensitive period for the induction of functional disorders lasts much longer, continuing even after birth. This is especially true for the development of the nervous system and the reproductive organs, which continue long after birth.

Functional disorders comprise metabolic, immunological, reproductive and behavioral disorders. Certain compounds interfere with the formation of enzyme systems, leading to disturbances in biochemical processes. This may, for example, cause changes in the metabolism and excretion of nutrients.

Immunological disorders often do not become evident until some time after birth. Again, the stage of development at the time of exposure determines the nature, extent and duration of the defect. Reproductive disorders do not manifest themselves until after puberty.

Over the past few years evidence has mounted that exposure to certain compounds during critical periods of development may cause specific behavioral changes. Behavioral disorders may be caused by disturbances in the morphogenesis and functional maturation of the central nervous system, but also through disturbances in the formation of the endocrine system.

### 3.2 FERTILITY DISORDERS

The formation and development of the reproductive system is a complex process comprising gametogenesis and the development of reproductive organs, sex hormones and sexual behavior. Due to the long period between formation and functional maturity, it takes a long time before prenatally induced defects become manifest. There are a number of sensitive periods during which chemicals may exert their harmful effects. The most evident effect is that of reduced fertility.

During the prenatal period, the formation or migration of the primordial germ cells may be disturbed. The female fetus is especially susceptible to such interference, since all oocytes are formed before birth. No primordial germ cells are formed after birth, so that the effects of compounds interfering with oogenesis are permanent. Spermatogenesis does not start until after birth, at puberty. Nevertheless, prenatal exposure to chemical agents may also affect male fertility, either directly through interference with germ cell formation, or indirectly via the hormonal control of spermatogenesis and sexual potency.

*Hormones*

*Hormones* also play a role in the development, differentiation and function of the reproductive organs. The synthesis of steroid hormones may be affected through effects on the enzymes involved or through interference with hormonal receptors. Lack of androgens during the development of the reproductive organs may lead to feminization of the male embryo. Conversely, an excess of androgens will lead to masculinization in the female embryo.

Certain effects in the liver are known to interfere with the metabolism of sex hormones, resulting in reduced fertility. Examples of compounds inducing such liver effects in the prenatal period are TCDD and PCBs. After birth, spermatogenesis in the male may be affected, so that insufficient or abnormal sperm is produced. Motility and penetrative and fertilizing capacity may be reduced or absent. Anatomical defects of the germinal epithelium may lead to sterility.

In the female, the ovulation process, menstrual cycle, fertilization, implantation, duration of pregnancy, parturition, lactation and maternal behavior may be affected.

### 3.3 STRUCTURAL DEFECTS OR MALFORMATIONS

Structural defects comprise all abnormalities that are immediately visible or demonstrable at birth or at abortion. To date, they are the main parameters for determining the teratogenicity of chemicals in animal experiments.

Structural abnormalities are usually permanent and are characterized by anatomical changes.

*Structural vs functional*

As described previously, *structural defects* are mainly induced in the embryonic period, whereas *functional defects* are established during the fetal period and later stages of development. Morphogenesis is a complex process, involving cellular proliferation, migration and interaction, ultimately leading to the differentiation and organization of the individual.

In man, most organ systems are formed in the period between week 3 (1 week after fertilization) and week 10 after the first day of the last menstruation.

*Syndrome*

A distinction can be made between single and multiple abnormalities. The term *syndrome* is used to refer to a recognizable pattern of malformations which are

*Anomaly*
*Association*

craniofacial = pertaining to the skull and face

*Anencephaly*

*VATER association*
VATER = *v*ertebral, *a*nal, *t*racheal, *e*sophageal, *r*enal

spina bifida = congenital abnormality of the spinal cord, vertebral column and skin

assumed to have the same cause. An *anomaly* is a malformation together with its resultant structural changes, and an *association* is a recognizable pattern of malformations that do not constitute a syndrome or an anomaly. An example of a syndrome is the fetal alcohol syndrome (named after the causative agent). It is characterized by the concurrence of craniofacial defects, abnormalities of the extremities, effects on the central nervous system and cardiovascular defects.

An example of an anomaly is *anencephaly*, which is the virtually complete absence of brain tissue, in combination with abnormalities of the ears, eyes and neck.

An example of an association is the *VATER association*, characterized by abnormalities of the vertebrae, anus, trachea, esophagus and kidneys. In man, geographical variations (possibly genetically determined) and sex-linked variations in the occurrence of malformations have been observed. Anencephaly, for example, occurs frequently in Ireland and Scotland, while being rare in other countries. Polydactyly (the presence of extra fingers or toes) and syndactyly (fusion of fingers or toes) occur more frequently in men than in women, while the opposite is true of anencephaly and spina bifida.

The frequency (prevalence) of spontaneous malformations in man which are visible at birth is about 2%.

## 3.4   GROWTH RETARDATION

Growth retardation in man may be the expression of the general effect of toxic or teratogenic compounds. Fetal growth is an important parameter in the determination of the teratogenicity of compounds. Administration of a compound in doses that are toxic to the mother may cause intrauterine growth retardation. This manifests itself in changes in the body or organ weight of the fetus or neonate. Growth retardation may be reversible or permanent, or it may be compensated for.

Warfarin is an anticoagulant

Examples of compounds causing growth retardation in man are alcohol, warfarin and narcotics. Children of mothers who smoke during pregnancy also often have a low birth weight. Another cause of growth retardation is an insufficient supply of oxygen and nutrients to the fetus. Toxemia of pregnancy may lead to a reduced capacity of the placenta, resulting in fetal growth retardation. This will be discussed in more detail in section 3.8. In contrast growth increase is seen in children of diabetic mothers.

## 3.5   INTRAUTERINE DEATH

In man, a large number of products of conception are lost before the pregnancy has been carried to full term. This may happen in the period between fertilization and implantation, at the time of implantation, and at various stages after implantation. The majority of the fertilized ova are lost in early pregnancy, in the period between fertilization and implantation (30–80%) and at the time of implantation (20–60%). It is generally assumed that only about one quarter of all fertilizations lead to the birth of a child. Abortion has been defined in different ways. The World Health Organization (WHO) uses the weight of the conceptus as a criterion and defines *abortion* as the expulsion of a product of conception weighing 500 g or less (this may be after 20 weeks). The birth of a child weighing over 500 g before the 37th week of pregnancy is defined as *premature birth*.

*Abortion*

*Premature birth*

*Immature delivery*

*Premature delivery*

Expulsion of the conceptus after the 16th week and before the 28th week is called *immature delivery*, and giving birth to a child after the 28th week and before the 38th week is *premature delivery* (premature birth). Fetal death is often associated with chromosomal aberrations and congenital malformations. Serious malformations lead to fetal death. Spontaneous abortion is one way of selectively ending abnormal pregnancies. The products of abortion are hardly ever examined. Where such examinations have been carried out, they have shown that a large percentage of the products of abortion display genetic and chromosomal aberrations as well as pathological changes and malformations. While the percentage of malformations is about 2% in neonates, it is about 50% in early abortions. Frequently observed abnormalities include neural tube defects, cleft palate and cleft lip, polydactyly and cardiac defects.

*Causes of intrauterine death*

Intrauterine death may have many different *causes*, of which the best known are infections, chemicals, dietary factors and chromosomal aberrations. Death may be caused by a direct effect of a chemical compound or indirectly via a toxic effect on the mother. It is often difficult to distinguish between direct and indirect effects. In experimental animals, intrauterine death often depends on the dose of the compound. Losses may occur both before and after implantation. If the embryo dies early in gestation, it is resorbed. In that case, only the resorption site is visible. If death occurs at a later stage, resorption is no longer possible. The result is a dead fetus *in utero* or the expulsion of a dead fetus.

### 3.6 OTHER EFFECTS

*Pharmacological effects*

In addition to the above-mentioned effects, there may also be *pharmacological* effects in the neonate. These are usually the result of administration of drugs to the mother during the last trimester of pregnancy or during delivery. Although such effects may be serious, they are often *reversible*. Examples include the withdrawal symptoms in the neonate caused by the mother's use of narcotics, psychopharmacological drugs or sleeping pills, and hypotension and hypoglycemia as a result of maternal use of antihypertensive drugs. Another example is hyperbilirubinemia (jaundice) as a result of sulfonamide administration to the mother. Pharmacological effects may occur during the fetal period. Barbiturates, alcohol, amphetamines and diazepam (Valium®) are thought to influence the REM sleep of the fetus.

### 3.7 TRANSPLACENTAL CARCINOGENESIS

> Why is it especially during the embryonic and fetal stages of development that carcinogens may induce their effects?

Embryonic and fetal tissues are very sensitive to carcinogens, because of the high proliferative activity of their cells. Transplacental carcinogenesis is the development of neoplasias in the offspring of women who have been exposed to compounds during pregnancy. Compounds that are known to have these effects in experimental animals include nitroso compounds, polycyclic aromatic hydrocarbons and mycotoxins. In man, only one compound is known to cause transplacental carcinogenesis, namely *diethylstilbestrol* (DES). Adenocarcinomas of the vagina have been observed in young women whose mothers were treated with this compound because of threatened abortion.

*Sensitive period*

In general, the *sensitive period* for transplacental carcinogenesis coincides with late organogenesis. With a few exceptions, the tumors do not manifest themselves until adulthood. Some compounds have both carcinogenic and teratogenic properties. This does not imply, however, that all carcinogens also have teratogenic properties.

DES is the only compound known to cause abnormalities (adenomas) and malignant tumors (adenocarcinomas) in the same target organs, namely the cervix and vagina.

### 3.8 DIRECT AND INDIRECT EFFECTS

The injury to the developing embryo or fetus may be direct or indirect. The main causes of indirect injury are changes in the yolk sac and the placenta, and changes in the blood circulation between mother and embryo or fetus.

*Placental insufficiency*

In only a few cases are diseases of the placenta itself the cause of fetal abnormalities. Changes in the placenta are more often the result of maternal diseases or chromosomal aberrations in the fetus. In women suffering from *toxemia*, the weight of the placenta and that of the fetus are reduced. *Placental insufficiency* occurs as a result of changes in the maternal blood supply caused by placental infarctions. The reduced birth weight of children of mothers who smoke during pregnancy has also been associated with reduced placental function.

The compound trypan blue induces teratogenic effects in rat embryos. These effects have been shown not to be caused by a direct interaction with the embryo, but by a disturbance of the transport function of the yolk sac, resulting in an insufficient supply of nutrients to the embryo.

The placenta may also be the *target organ* of chemicals including pharmaceuticals, which may ultimately lead to teratogenic or other effects on reproduction. An example of such a compound is cadmium. Such compounds may cause reduced placental function by interfering with placental transport, uteroplacental circulation, endocrine function and metabolism of the placenta, for instance through bioactivation. Sudden changes in the blood circulation between mother and fetus may also cause developmental defects. Spasms in the maternal arteries, for example, give rise to hypoxia (lack of oxygen) in the fetus. Ergotamine derivatives (ergot extracts) cause fetal death as a result of severe vasoconstriction.

## 4    Summary

Reproduction is a complex process, involving many organ systems and functions. The influence of chemicals on this process may lead to infertility and developmental defects. In general, embryo/fetotoxic, including teratogenic compounds may induce four types of effects: death, growth retardation, malformations and functional disorders. These effects may become manifest immediately at the moment of exposure to a compound or much later in development. Fundamental knowledge of normal reproduction and prenatal development is lacking. This is one of the reasons why only general characteristics of reproductive toxicology can be described.

## SELF ASSESSMENT QUESTIONS

1    What interpretation of teratology was used in the past, and what is the current view?

2    Before the 20th century, what were considered to be the main causes of congenital abnormalities?

3    How may teratological insights contribute to the prevention of the birth of children with congenital abnormalities?

4    Which drug has caused a world-wide change of attitude to research on the teratogenicity and reproductive toxicity of compounds?

5    How was it discovered that this compound causes congenital abnormalities?

6    What is meant by secondary prevention of congenital abnormalities?

7    Name two microorganisms that may cause congenital abnormalities.

8    When does spermatogenesis start?

9    When does the last phase of the reduction division (meiosis) of female germ cells start? When does it end?

10   What may be the causes of congenital infertility in men and women?

11   During which period are externally visible defects more frequently induced, the embryonic or the fetal period?

12   At birth, the oxygen supply via the placenta is cut off. What adaptations take place in the blood circulation of the neonate?

13   When may use of the sedative thalidomide lead to abnormalities of the extremities?

14   What safety procedures need to be observed if man turns out to be more sensitive to the teratogenic effect of a compound than experimental animals?

15   The higher the dose of a teratogenic compound, the more serious the developmental defects induced by this compound may be. Put the following effects in order of seriousness: death, growth retardation, cleft palate, spina bifida, delayed bone growth.

16   Why are functional defects not always immediately visible at birth?

17   What is the assumed frequency (prevalence) of spontaneous congenital abnormalities visible at birth?

18   How could smoking or exposure to carbon monoxide during pregnancy cause fetal growth retardation?

19   What are the possible causes of the large-scale natural selection of fertilized ova?

20   Describe the effects of taking DES during pregnancy. When do these effects manifest themselves?

FEEDBACK

1    **Answers to the assignments**

31.1  Examples of subject areas closely related to teratology are: gynecology, obstetrics, pediatrics, (clinical) genetics, embryology, anatomy, pathology, internal medicine, microbiology, toxicology/pharmacology, biology, physiology and epidemiology.

31.2 Developmental toxicology is an integral part of reproductive toxicology (see Figure 32.13, shaded area).

31.3 About 23.5 years.

31.4 About 3 months (counting from the spermatogonium stage). See also Table 32.5.

31.5 Between day 34 and day 44 after the first day of the last menstruation.

31.6 The ratios between experimental animals and humans for the threshold doses in Table 31.2 are: thalidomide 5 – 2.5 (rabbit); polychlorinated biphenyls 1.8 (rhesus monkey) and 14.3 (dog); alcohol 3.8–7.6 (rat); aminopterin 2 (rat); methotrexate 4.8 (rat); methylmercury 50 (cat and rat); DES 10 – 2.5 (rhesus monkey); diphenylhydantoin 25 (mouse). From these ratios it can be concluded that man is more sensitive to these compounds than the experimental animals used.

## 2    Answers to the self assessment questions

1    Teratology used to be interpreted as the study of 'monsters' and birth defects. It was mainly a descriptive branch of science. Nowadays, teratology is interpreted as the science which deals with the recognition, detection of causes of birth defects. This branch of science seeks to accumulate fundamental knowledge in order to contribute to the prevention of congenital abnormalities.

2    Congenital abnormalities were often attributed to natural causes (e.g. hybridization) or regarded as a punishment from God. Sometimes they were attributed to the influence of emotional experiences on pregnant women.

3    For example, by preventing pregnant women from being exposed to teratogenic compounds.

4    Thalidomide.

5    The congenital abnormalities induced by this compound were highly characteristic and clearly visible at birth.

6    In secondary prevention, it is not the effect, i.e. the congenital abnormality, that is prevented but the birth of an individual with a congenital abnormality by means of induced abortion.

7    *Toxoplasma* and rubella virus.

8    During puberty.

9    Shortly before ovulation. Shortly after fertilization.

10    Infertility may arise in many different ways. It may be the result of, for example, abnormal or incomplete development of the male or female repro-

ductive organs, of hormonal disorders or of genetic abnormalities. It may also result from the interference of chemicals or other toxic agents with the processes of spermatogenesis and oogenesis.

11    Externally visible abnormalities that are induced during intrauterine life more frequently result from the interference of a teratogen with organogenesis, i.e. during the embryonic period, than from exposure during fetal development.

12    When the umbilical cord is ligated, the neonate is no longer supplied with oxygen and can no longer eliminate $CO_2$. The accumulation of $CO_2$ in the blood stimulates the respiratory centres in the central nervous system, resulting in a first attempt to breath. As the lungs expand, blood flows into them and the pressure in the right side of the heart falls. More blood reaches the left half of the heart via the pulmonary vein. As a result of the changes in pressure, the foramen ovale between the left and the right atrium closes functionally. The ductus arteriosus (Botalli's duct) closes by muscular contraction of its wall and the ductus venosus becomes obliterated.

13    If the embryo is exposed to thalidomide between the 24th day and the 33rd day of gestation (see Figure 31.4).

14    In that case, an extra high safety factor will have to be used. The best solution remains, of course, complete prevention of exposure.

15    The order is:

    1  growth retardation
    2  delayed bone growth
    3  cleft palate
    4  spina bifida
    5  death

16    Functional defects are not always immediately visible at birth, as some functions are not performed until a later stage of life. Examples of these are the functions related to reproduction or walking.

17    About 2%.

18    Smoking increases the nicotine level in the blood of the mother, leading to narrowing of the placental blood vessels. As a consequence, the blood supply to the embryo and fetus is disturbed. Carbon monoxide in the blood of the mother and/or embryo constitutes a hazard to the embryo's oxygen supply. Both factors may indirectly lead to growth retardation in the embryo or fetus.

19    Possible causes are:

    • chromosomal aberrations
    • genetic abnormalities
    • endocrine disorders
    • immunological disorders
    • infectious agents

- metabolic disorders
- psychogenic factors
- embryo/fetotoxic factors
- mutagenic factors
- traumata
- uterine abnormalities

20    The answer is given in section 3.7.

# Contents Study unit 32
# Methods in reproductive toxicology

0-8493-9232-2/96/$0.00 + $.50

# Study unit 32

# Methods in reproductive toxicology

*P. W. J. Peters and J. M. Garbis-Berkvens*

INTRODUCTION

Study unit 31 gave a brief introduction to reproductive toxicology, including teratology. It showed that little is known about the mechanisms of adverse reproductive and teratogenic effects. The present study unit deals with methods for the detection of the teratogenic and/or adverse reproductive effects of substances. These methods may be experimental, i.e. based on animal experiments, but they may also involve epidemiological research.

LEARNING OBJECTIVES

After studying this unit, you should be able to

— describe the various research methods used in reproductive toxicology

— compare the various types of epidemiological research used in reproductive toxicology, give examples of their application and indicate the limitations of each method

— deduce from a case study which type of epidemiological method has been used

— describe experimental research techniques used in teratogenicity and reproductive toxicity studies

— describe the different test systems used in the various types of preliminary study, and explain their limitations

— compare the various types of segment study, indicate the specific exposure times and the changes that are assessed

— explain the importance of several specific tests, other than segment or generation tests

— indicate the relationships between preliminary studies, segment and generation studies, and specific tests, and highlight the differences and similarities

— describe the relationships between research, risk evaluation and risk management in relation to reproductive toxicity

— explain what is meant by: risk assessment, risk characterization, risk evaluation and risk management

— know the applications of reproductive toxicology in preventive medicine and compare the various types of prenatal diagnosis

— give examples of primary and secondary prevention and point out the differences between the two.

949

*Study hints*

The present study unit is a sequel of unit 31. You should therefore study that unit first and make sure that you have mastered the relevant terminology. The study load for this unit is estimated at 4 hours, but largely depends on your prior knowledge of biology and embryology.

STUDY CORE

## 1 Epidemiological research

Epidemiology is the study of the occurrence and the determinants of illness in man. In this context the illnesses and their determinants are: reproductive disorders (libido, gametogenesis), intrauterine death, abnormal growth, morphological abnormalities and functional disorders. Epidemiological research constitutes the only means of determining whether a substance has an adverse effect on reproduction or a teratogenic effect in man. Most studies carried out so far in this field have concentrated on birth defects, and not on abnormalities in reproduction. Epidemiological research enables identification of the teratogenicity of drugs and other exogenous factors, and provides insight into the outcome of pregnancy in populations exposed to chemicals. It also allows the effectiveness of preventive measures to be evaluated.

*Methods of epidemiological research*

Various *methods of epidemiological research* can be used to determine the effects of chemicals.

1 *Descriptive studies*, that characterize the abnormalities according to frequency, race, sex and other variables.
2 *Analytical studies*, that determine the association between possible environmental factors and malformations .

### 1.1 DESCRIPTIVE STUDIES

*Descriptive studies*

*Retrospective studies*

*Descriptive studies* are particularly useful in formulating a hypothesis on a possible relationship between exposure to substances and the occurrence of developmental defects. They are always *retrospective* in nature. Examples are case studies and surveillance studies.

*Case studies*

*a Case studies*

*Case studies* describe one or more cases of a developmental defect which have given rise to the suspicion that there might be a relationship between known exposure to a drug or other chemical and the defect. In many cases the connection cannot be established with certainty, but case studies may provide a first indication that a substance has an adverse effect on development. Valproic acid, retinoic acid and warfarin, for example, were later proven to be teratogenic as a result of case studies. Teratogenic effects are sometimes also ascribed to a drug unjustly, as happened in the case of Bendectin®. This drug, used to treat morning sickness during pregnancy, was considered teratogenic on the basis of case studies, but extensive and well-controlled studies later showed that it was not.

*Surveillance studies*

*b Surveillance studies*

In *surveillance studies*, the information is routinely collected and analyzed. The reports are published regularly. These studies are always performed on large groups of subjects.

950

The two most notorious teratogens, rubella virus and thalidomide, were discovered by alert physicians who noticed clusters of similar cases of developmental defects.

It often takes a long time, however, before a positive relationship can be established. Surveillance studies should therefore rather be regarded as an aid in further epidemiological research.

## 1.2   ANALYTICAL STUDIES

*Retrospective and prospective*

Analytical studies may be either *retrospective* or *prospective*. Their purpose is to find a relationship between a substance and a particular abnormality and to trace any changes that may occur.

*Cross-sectional or prevalence studies*

### a   Cross-sectional studies

*Cross-sectional studies* or *prevalence studies* aim at establishing *how often an abnormality occurs in a given representative population* and whether there is any relationship to a *causal factor*. They are retrospective, and are usually a prelude to a prospective study. Studies registering all cases of exposure to, for example, a particular drug are also included in this type of research.

*Overreporting*

One disadvantage of this method is that memory plays an important part; *overreporting* often takes place. This entails that abnormalities are reported more frequently than normal cases. For retinoic acid, for example, an incidence of developmental defects of 84 was reported, while in a prospective study the incidence appeared to be only 38.

*Case-control studies*

### b   Case-control (patient control) studies

This type of study compares the frequency of developmental disturbances and the extent of exposure to a potentially teratogenic substance in a group with those in a control group that does not show the developmental defects. The starting point is always the individual with a developmental defect, while the control group consists of individuals with a different defect or without any developmental defect at all. These studies are usually retrospective. An example is provided by studies on the use of drugs in mothers of children that show a specific developmental defect. The percentage of drug users among these mothers is compared to the percentage of users among a control group of mothers who have a child without or with a different defect. Here too, there is the disadvantage of the mother's playing an important role. The selection of the control group may also cause problems. An advantage of this type of study is that it is relatively rapid and reasonably efficient, and that it is a common research method for physicians.

*Cohort studies*
*Relationship exposure/abnormalities*

### c   Cohort studies

*Cohort studies* are usually prospective. They register the use of drugs or the *exposure* to a substance during pregnancy and the developmental defects at birth. The frequency of developmental defects is subsequently compared with that in mothers who did not use these drugs or were not exposed. An advantage of this method is that a clear relationship can be demonstrated between exposure and effect, that the measurements can be of high quality and that possible interactions can be assessed. A disadvantage is that it often takes years before there are any results, because the use of certain drugs or exposure to certain substances is uncommon, or because certain abnormalities are very rare. In such cases, large numbers of subjects are required for reliable statistical evaluation of the data.

What abnormalities can be found in children of women who smoked during pregnancy?

Smoking during pregnancy can cause a low birth weight in children. A relationship has also been suggested between smoking and complications during pregnancy (See Table 32.1).

Epidemiological research as described above also has many weak points. In the case of *drugs*, the survey is fairly simple. One must always be aware, however, that the disease for which the drug is prescribed may also play a role in the development of the defect.

In the case of *occupational exposure*, research becomes much more difficult because the extent and duration of exposure are often unknown. This is even more so in cases of *environmental exposure*.

*Combined action*

Another difficulty in determining which substance is the causal factor is that the exposure is often to more than one substance. In agriculture, for instance, several pesticides may be used, and laboratory workers often handle many different chemicals. Interaction between substances may occur and give rise to new effects. So far, there is little epidemiological evidence in the literature to indicate that occupational exposure is harmful to the development of the embryo/fetus. Risks usually occur only in the case of exposure to levels that are toxic to the mother.

*Value of epidemiological research*

The *value of epidemiological research* is also limited by a large number of additional factors which need to be taken into account, such as lifestyle and dietary habits, age, race, paternal exposure and incorrect diagnosis. External examination of a newborn baby may easily overlook important internal abnormalities, which may lead to an incomplete or incorrect diagnosis. It is often difficult to determine what causes an increased risk if there is only a slight increase in frequency.

Epidemiological studies of the teratogenicity of substances should also include developmental defects in abortion products.

*Registration of birth defects*

Another important source of epidemiological data is the routine *registration of birth defects*, which establishes the frequency of developmental defects. This allows any increase in the frequency of defects to be detected, causes to be determined and preventive measures to be taken. At the international level, this registration is carried out by the International Clearinghouse for Birth Defects Monitoring Systems with its International Centre for Birth Defects in Rome. The

TABLE 32.1

Association between smoking and complications during pregnancy

| | Non-smokers | <20 cigarettes per day | ≥20 cigarettes per day |
|---|---|---|---|
| number of births | 28358 | 15328 | 6581 |
| perinatal mortality | 23.3* | 28.0 | 33.4 |
| premature detachment of placenta | 16.1 | 20.6 | 28.9 |
| placenta obstructs cervix | 6.4 | 8.2 | 13.1 |
| hemorrhages | 116.5 | 141.6 | 180.1 |
| premature rupture of membranes | 13.8 | 23.3 | 35.8 |

*Number per 1000 births.

European Union has the registration system EUROCAT (European Registration of Congenital Anomalies and Twins).

Table 32.2 lists several epidemiological methods which are preferred in various types of exposure, taking into account the frequency with which a developmental disturbance takes place.

## 2 Experimental studies of reproductive toxicity and teratogenicity

*Definition*

In general, studies of reproductive toxicity can be defined as studies that identify substances which have an effect on the normal course of reproduction. Such substances may exert their harmful effects during the various stages: formation of germ cells, conception, embryonic development, fetal stages, the process of birth and further postnatal development. Since abnormalities in reproduction (infertility) and development (embryonic or fetal death, growth retardation, structural and functional defects) may also occur spontaneously, it would be more accurate to say that these studies seek to identify substances that may either induce or increase the spontaneous incidence of such abnormalities. This section describes the selection of which test to use and the manner in which the various tests are performed. They are mainly tests carried out in animals, the aim of which is primarily to allow risk assessment in man.

*Animal models*

*Guidelines*

It is important to be aware of the fact that this information is derived from *animal models* and thus can only be an indication of the harmfulness of a substance to man. As in other areas of toxicity research, there are *guidelines* for the design and execution of reproductive toxicity tests and teratogenicity tests. These guidelines have been drawn up by the various national and international authorities and may show slight variations, depending on differences with regard to opinions, type of compound and application of the substances. It should be emphasized that these are GUIDELINES and not binding regulations. In certain cases, studies may therefore deviate from the guidelines. In general, such tests will be accepted by a registration authority if the researchers are able to demonstrate on scientific grounds that their studies are at least equivalent to the tests outlined in the guidelines and that their validity is such that they allow extrapolation to man.

*Modify your test choice!*

TABLE 32.2
Epidemiological methods applied in teratology and reproductive toxicology under specific conditions

| | Type of exposure | | |
|---|---|---|---|
| | *drug* | *environmental exposure* | *occupational exposure* |
| *low-frequency developmental defect* | *case control study* within a population to whom the drug has been prescribed | *correlation study* comparing the frequency of developmental defects in various areas (e.g. pesticides and neural tube defects) *case control study* in areas where specific exposure occurs | *retrospective cohort study, case-control study* in or near an industrial plant |
| *high-frequency developmental defect* | *prospective case control study* comparing drug users to non-users | *cross-sectional study* in the relevant area | *cross sectional study* in an industry, *prospective study* of exposed and non-exposed persons |

## 2.1 PROPERTIES OF THE SUBSTANCE

*Properties and uses of a substance*

Before choosing a test system the *properties and uses* of the substance should be known. Drugs, food additives and, to a lesser degree, cosmetics are used deliberately. In the case of drugs, the indications, dosages, pharmacological and kinetic properties, and possible side effects on development must be known. Exposure to food additives, and food contaminations such as insecticide residues, usually differs from exposure to environmental toxicants and chemicals in the work situation, with regard to the degree and duration of the exposure. This is why different guidelines have been drawn up for the various categories of substances. The tests listed in Table 32.3 will be discussed in other sections of this unit.

ASSIGNMENT  32.1

What is meant by a preliminary study or test?

## 2.2 CHOICE OF EXPERIMENTAL ANIMALS AND PERFORMANCE OF THE TEST

*Animal species*

The choice of the *animal species* to be used for the tests is pragmatic rather than based on a balanced comparison with, for example, the physiology of man. This approach implies that animal species are chosen that have a relatively short life span, large litter size and well-known characteristics. It also implies that the species opted for has already been used in other (general) toxicity tests and that it is relatively cheap. Usually, a non-inbred strain of rats is chosen as rodent species and the rabbit as a non-rodent.

*Rabbits are often classified as rodents, but this is incorrect.*

TABLE  32.3
Recommended reproductive toxicity and teratogenicity tests for new substances to be put on the market, depending on the results (+/−) of the preliminary study

| Compound | Result of preliminary study | Definitive study |
|---|---|---|
| food additives (such as coloring agents and antioxidants) | − + | segment II study on two animal species two-generation study with teratogenicity test |
| pharmaceutical products (drugs) | − | segment II study on two animal species combination segment I, II and III |
| | + | segment I study segment II study on two animal species segment III study specific research |
| crop protection agents (such as pesticides and herbicides) | − + | segment II study segment II study on two animal species two-generation study |
| industrial products (occupational exposure) | − | if limited number of exposed subjects: end of test if considerable number of exposed subjects: further specific research |
| | + | further specific research |
| cosmetics | − | end of test |
| | + | further specific research |

The various regulations and GLP are discussed in Study unit 14.

Research involving animal experiments has to be carried out in accordance with current legislation and regulations, such as occupational health and safety acts, the animal experiments acts and the rules of "Good Laboratory Practice" (GLP).

## 2.3 CHOICE OF DOSAGE

*Dose-response relationship*

Since it is assumed in reproductive toxicology that a *relationship exists between the dose of a toxicant and the toxic response*, it is common practice to study the effect of various dosages. In teratogenicity tests the choice of dosage may be especially complex, since in addition to the specific embryotoxicity or teratogenicity maternal toxicity may occur, which may cause indirect embryotoxic or teratogenic effects. Broadly speaking, there are two ways of determining the dosage levels to be used. With clearly teratogenic substances a definitive choice of the dosages is made after the substances have been tested in a preliminary test on pregnant test animals. If the data obtained from kinetic or general toxicity studies do not suggest specific teratogenicity, the preliminary studies are often conducted in non-pregnant experimental animals. In general it can be stated that the toxicity of a substance is likely to be higher in pregnant animals than in non-pregnant animals.

## 2.4 STATISTICAL PROCESSING OF DATA

*Litter as statistical unit*

In the past, the fetus was often used as the statistical unit in reproductive and teratogenicity studies. However, this is incorrect and increases the likelihood of false-negative results, since fetuses from the same mother animal are biologically and statistically non-independent units. Genetically as well as physiologically, they are dependent on the mother. In other words, litter mates are more alike than fetuses of different litters. The *litter* should therefore be regarded as the *statistical unit* and consequently statistical methods should be applied to mean values per litter (modified Wilcoxon tests, analysis of variance etc.). These statistical methods compare the groups treated with control groups within the same generation. When evaluating a test, it is important to compare the spontaneous frequencies of developmental defects in the control and treatment groups with those determined on the basis of the cumulative values of control groups in the past (so-called historical control; see Table 32.4).

## 2.5 PRELIMINARY TESTS AND *IN VITRO* SCREENING TESTS

Because of the high costs of reproductive toxicity and teratogenicity tests, short-term and *in vitro* tests have been developed and partially validated. Their significance lies in the fact that they allow a distinction to be made between substances that are likely to affect reproduction and development and those that do not. In addition, preliminary tests or pilot tests may be used for the choice of dosage, as was indicated in section 2.3. These preliminary and *in vitro* tests must be quick and cheap, and should be reproducible with a minimum of false-negative results.

TABLE 32.4
Examples of spontaneous prenatal mortality in rats and rabbits, determined on the basis of cumulative control values in relation to the number of ovulated oocytes

| | Prenatal loss (%) | | | |
|---|---|---|---|---|
| | Pre-implantation | Embryonic | Fetal | Total |
| rat | 6 | 6 | 1 | 13 |
| rabbit | 12 | 7 | 5 | 24 |

### 2.5.1 Preliminary tests on mammals (in vivo)

*Period of exposure*

*Choice of the preliminary test*

Preliminary tests are usually performed on the same animal species and under the same experimental conditions as the definitive experiments. The number of experimental animals used is, however, much smaller and the examination of the fetuses and newborn animals is less extensive. Some researchers also reduce the *exposure time* to those days during which the complex processes of organ formation occur, e.g. the closure of the neural tube (on days 10 and 11 of gestation in rats). The *choice of the preliminary test* depends greatly on the laboratory concerned. The preliminary test not only serves to determine the doses to be used, but also sets priorities with regard to the substances to be studied. Finally, possible variations in husbandry conditions, such as diet, care and accommodation, may be checked during the preliminary test.

### 2.5.2 Preliminary tests in non-mammals and in vitro tests

*Limb bud culture system*

Over the past few years, researchers have sought to use relatively simple biological systems instead of intact experimental animals. In general, this is only possible if the toxic mechanism of the substance is reasonably clear. Even if this is not known, however, these tests can be performed to find out whether there is a specific moment during development at which the substance exerts its effects, or whether it interferes with a specific developmental pattern. In the definitive test this could then be taken into account. For example, the formation of muscle cells and cartilage and bone can be studied as embryonic forms of differentiation in a *limb bud culture system* to which the substance to be tested is added (see Figures 32.1 and 32.2). Disadvantages of these *in vitro* systems are, for instance, the absence of the metabolism and kinetics in the maternal system and the large difference between the functional cell systems of non-mammals (such as *Hydra attenuata*: a freshwater polyp) and those of mammals.

*Hydra assay*

The *Hydra assay* is sometimes recommended for the study of developmental toxicity. This system, however, does not really study development.

In the culture system using *Hydra attenuata*, two parameters are studied after addition of the test substance to the culture medium:

1   effects on the 'adult' stage, in which irreversible structural changes are observed (Figure 32.3);

2   effects on 'embryos', which are formed by dissociation and reassociation of cells of the adult stage (Figure 32.4).

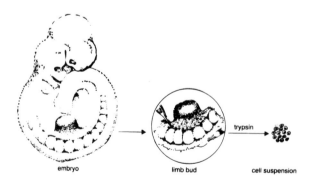

embryo                 limb bud                 cell suspension

FIGURE   32.1
The limb bud system
A specific part of an animal embryo is isolated and cultured in order to study the effects of a teratogen on the development of that part—in this case the lower limb bud. Trypsin is added to dissociate the cells from each other. By adding special substances, these cells may then be induced to develop into 'complete' limbs (Figure 32.2).

 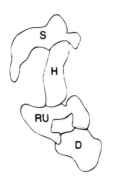

result of limb bud culture

S   = scapula
H   = humerus
RU = radius and ulna
D   = distal bone formation

FIGURE   32.2
Final result (control) of limb bud culture

| silhouette of an adult animal | stage |
| --- | --- |
| | normal |
| | club-shaped tentacles |
| | reduced tentacles |
| | tulip shape |
| | disaggregation |

FIGURE   32.3
Irreversible structural changes in the adult stage of *Hydra attenuata*

The ratio between the dose levels that affect the "adult" and the "embryonic" stages is thought to be a measure of the teratogenicity of the substance. This type of preliminary studies on the developmental effects of substances should, however, be validated first, before the definitive choice for a certain test system can be made.

### 2.5.2.1   Unicellular organisms

*Mutagenicity tests* make large-scale use of bacteria and unicellular organisms. Mutagenicity, however, involves only one mechanism, a permanent mutation in the structure and expression of the nucleotides in DNA.

Tests intended to determine whether a compound causes permanent damage to prenatal development involve a multitude of complex developmental sys-

*Mutagenicity tests*
See Study unit 11

957

| silhouette of the embryo | stage | development in hours |
|---|---|---|
|  | compact | 4 |
|  | with excavations and laminar | 18 |
|  | tentacle buds | 26 |
|  | extension of tentacle buds | 42 |
|  | mouth opening | 66 |
| 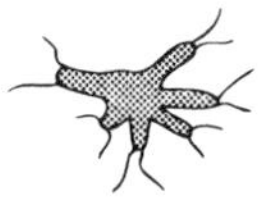 | polyps | 90 |

FIGURE 32.4
Embryonic changes in *Hydra attenuata*

tems and mechanisms. Microorganisms such as bacteria are obviously not suitable for such tests.

### 2.5.2.2  Pre-implantation embryo cultures

Fertilized ova of rodents and rabbits may be cultured from the unicellular stage to the blastula stage and beyond. It is even possible to treat fertilized ova *in vitro* and to re-implant them into the experimental animals. For preimplanted ova and their subsequent developmental stages the sensitivity to embryotoxic and teratogenic substances seems to depend mainly on the number of cells that are damaged or killed. This test system also requires validation.

*Validation research investigates the universal validity of a (new) test system.*

### 2.5.2.3  Organ cultures

*Morphogenesis*
*Study of morphogenetic aspects*

Cultures of embryonic and fetal organs allow certain aspects of *morphogenesis* to be studied, such as differentiation, cell adhesion, physiological cell death, metabolic processes and selective growth. The most widely applied organ cultures for studying the effects of substances on development are: limb bud system (see Figures 32.1 and 32.2), closure of the palate, and the initial formation of the teeth, formation of the thyroid gland, renal tissue, reproductive organs (primordial germ cells), pancreas, lens and bone. The advantage of organ culture over cell culture is that it enables not only the study of *cell differentiation* but also that of the complex *interactions* between the various tissues within an organ. The main disadvantage of organ culture is the virtually complete absence of metabolism. There is, however, a method for adding metabolizing enzyme systems to the culture medium. Another drawback of most *in vitro* systems is that developmental disturbances are hard to quantify.

*Study of cell differentiation and interaction*

### 2.5.2.4  Embryo cultures

Embryos of mammals are cultured in several laboratories. Mouse and rat embryos can be cultured from the neural plate stage to approximately the 25-somite stage (see Figure 32.5).

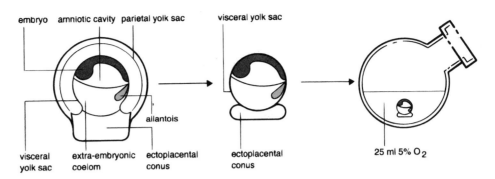

FIGURE   32.5
Culture systems of mammalian embryos up to the 25-somite stage

The culture medium consists either of rat serum to which the substances to be tested has been added or serum of rats that have been treated with the substance. In the latter case the normal metabolites of the substance are also present. Here too, it is possible to add metabolizing enzymes to the culture medium. An important development in this method is the possibility of culturing rodent embryos in human serum, for example from patients taking medicines. This allows study of the possible adverse effects of human metabolites.

*Morphological and functional characteristics*

*Histological assessment*

The developing embryos can be assessed on their *morphological* as well as on some of their *functional* properties (heart beat and blood circulation). A so-called morphological *scoring system* has been designed for the assessment of the structural development. This can be supplemented by a *histological assessment*.

Besides the rodent embryo culture, the chicken embryo test has a long history in studying the embryotoxicity and teratogenicity of substances, both *in ovo* and *in vitro*. Although this method has been applied for testing many substances, its predictive value has still not been satisfactorily established.

## 2.6   SEGMENT STUDIES

Segment studies were introduced in the 1960s to study the effect of substances on the various stages of the reproductive cycle in animal models. A distinction can be made between tests of fertility and reproduction (*segment I studies*), tests of embryotoxicity and teratogenicity (*segment II studies*), perinatal and postnatal tests (*segment III studies*) and *(multi-)generation* tests. All these experiments should be performed in accordance with national and international guidelines. Various combinations of tests are used to assess the risk of reproductive toxicity of substances, including embryotoxicity and teratogenicity (see Table 32.3).

*Segment I studies*
*Segment II studies*
*Segment III studies*
*(Multi-)generation tests*

Although little is known about dose-response relationships in this area, generally the dose-response curve for reproductive toxicants and teratogens in experimental animals seems to show a steep slope above the threshold level.

*No effect level*

This empirical generalization has been used to argue the existence of a *no effect level*. This does not necessarily mean, however, that this threshold level will always exist in man. The hypothesis should really be confirmed by accurate research in humans. This is one of the reasons why a safety factor is applied in extrapolations from test animals to man.

### 2.6.1 Segment I studies: fertility and reproduction tests

*Administration of exogenous compound before and during the mating period*

In segment I studies the test substance is *administered* to the experimental animals (both males and females) *prior to and during the period in which the animals mate*. In females, administration is continued up to mid-gestation and sometimes even up to the moment the young are weaned (see Figure 32.6).

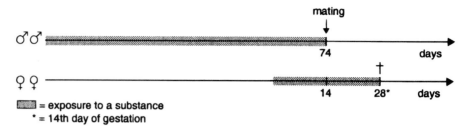

FIGURE 32.6
Study on fertility and reproduction: segment I study (rat)

*Information on gametogenesis up to and including implantation, as well as on maternal homeostasis*

This test can provide information on gametogenesis, mating, ovulation, fertilization, transport of the pre-embryo, implantation and maternal homeostasis. The exposure time depends on physiological parameters, such as the development of sperm and the estrus cycle. In male rats and mice, the exposure times can be 74 and 52 days, respectively (see Table 32.5 and Figure 32.7).

In the female rat the test substances are administered over several estrus cycles before mating. Prolongation of segment I studies may result in a partial overlap with perinatal and postnatal studies.

### 2.6.2 Segment II studies: embryotoxicity and teratogenicity tests

*During organogenesis*

*Information on structural developmental defects*

In segment II studies the test substances are administered to *pregnant test animals during organogenesis*, as this is the most sensitive period for the induction of *structural developmental defects* This period runs from the 6th up to and including the 15th day of gestation in rats, and from the 6th up to and including the 18th day in rabbits (see Figure 32.8).

*Maternal toxicity*

The mother animals are often killed just before the young are born to allow inspection *in utero* and to prevent malformed young from being eaten by the mother. The mother animals are examined for signs of toxicity during the entire period. Data on food intake, weight increase and general health allow signs of *toxicity in the mother animal* to be recognized. In this way, a distinction can be made between direct and indirect embryonic or fetal toxicity. Segment II studies are also used to determine losses before and after implantation.

The fetus is examined externally by means of a special bone stain or X-rays (Figure 32.9). The internal organs are also examined (Figure 32.10).

*Types of developmental disorders*

The developmental disorders can be classified into three main categories:

1 death
2 abnormalities in weight
3 morphological abnormalities

The morphological abnormalities can be further subdivided into malformations and 'variants'.

*Malformations* are structural abnormalities of the tissues, organs or skeleton which cause distortions of the body structure and/or interfere with body functions and/or are incompatible with life. In contrast, *variants* are structural abnormalities of the tissues, organs or skeleton which do not have any significant effect on body structure and/or body function and which deviate only slightly from what is considered normal.

TABLE 32.5
Minimal duration of spermatogenesis (days)

|  | pre-meiotic period | meiotic period | post-meiotic period | onset sperma-togenesis up to ejaculation |
|---|---|---|---|---|
| rat | 25 | 17 | 32 | 74 |
| mouse | 17 | 12 | 23 | 52 |

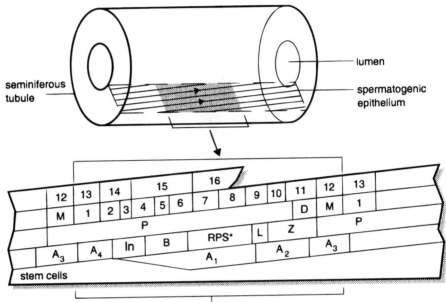

one cycle of the spermatogenic epithelium
duration in mice = 8.6 days (slightly different for each strain)

FIGURE 32.7
Schematic representation of spermatogenesis in the mouse up to spermiation
explanation:
$A_1$, $A_2$, $A_3$, $A_4$, In and B = generations of spermatogonia
RPS = resting primary spermatocytes
L, Z, P, D, M = succesive stages of meiosis
1 – 16 = stages in the development of spermatids up to ejaculation
* = S-phase of primary spermatocytes, the last phase of sermatogenesis during which incorporation of thymidine is possible

### 2.6.3 Segment III studies: perinatal and postnatal tests

*Perinatal and postnatal exposure*

Some time after the thalidomide tragedy, there was an increasing awareness that segment II studies cannot give a complete picture of all abnormalities, especially of functional developmental disorders. Therefore, segment II studies are now performed in combination with segment III studies, in which the mother animals are treated during the perinatal and postnatal period, i.e. starting from day 15 of gestation and during birth and lactation up to the moment the young are weaned (see Figure 32.11).

*The offspring are also examined for functional defects*

After this period, the young are killed and examined for abnormalities. These may have been induced during gestation and become manifest in the perinatal or neonatal period. They may, however, also have been induced and reached expression in the period of lactation. In addition to death, growth retardation and malformations, a number of functional disorders may also be detected by means of these studies.

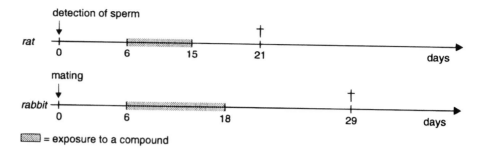

FIGURE   32.8
Study on embryotoxicity and teratogenicity. Segment II study

FIGURE   32.9
Skeleton of a rat fetus
After the fetus of a rat has been made transparent, the skeleton (bone and cartilage) is stained (dark elements in the picture), so that the circa 200 skeletal elements can be examined for defects (day 21 after mating).

### 2.6.4 Generation studies

*Continuous exposure of several generations*
*Assessment sometimes as in segment II studies*

*Histopathological examination*

*Basic study*

In these studies, *several generations* (mostly 2) of experimental animals are continuously exposed to the test substance, usually in their food. Several litters may be bred per generation, but the number is usually restricted to two. Some test designs require the mother animal to be killed just before the birth of the last litter, allowing the fetuses to be examined as in segment II studies. The third generation offspring may be subjected to a complete *histopathological examination*. In practice, generation studies appear to be performed in many different ways. The basic study may be defined as a two-generation study with two litters, involving three dosage groups and one control group. The parent animals should be treated with the substance for 2–10 weeks before mating (see Figure 32.12).

*Specific information*
*Multi-generation experiments*
*Parent animals*
*First generation*

*Indication of accumulation*

*Possible hereditary changes*
*Second generation*

The specific *information* obtained from these *multi-generation experiments* is to some extent dependent on the generation studied. The *parent animals* show whether the *data on fertility and gestation* deviate from the control data, while the *first generation* provides information on the *intrauterine environment, lactation* and *development*, as well as *growth* and further *maturation* of the offspring. The reproductive characteristics of the first generation may give an *indication of accumulation* of the harmful substance, since these animals have been exposed to the substance from the moment of conception. Information on accumulation and *possible hereditary changes* may also be derived from the *second generation*, which is the offspring of the test animals that were exposed to the substance from conception.

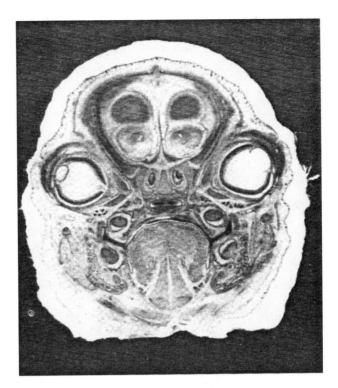

FIGURE 32.10
Cross-section of the head region of a rat fetus
The fixed fetus is sliced into 1 mm sections. After application of a surface stain, details of the organ structure become visible. Picture of a cross-section in the head region, showing the olfactory bulb (the olfactory organ), the eyes with the lenses, developing teeth and the tongue (day 21 after mating).

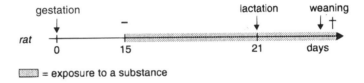

FIGURE 32.11
Perinatal and postnatal test. Segment III study

ASSIGNMENT 32.2

Indicate in Figure 32.12 which animals qualify for fertility and gestation tests, which for development, growth and maturation tests, and which for accumulation tests.

2.7 OTHER TERATOGENICITY AND REPRODUCTIVE TOXICITY TESTS

If the tests described above show that a substance has an effect on the reproductive function of male or female animals or both, it is important to determine the cause of infertility. Matings need to take place to show conclusively whether the infertility observed is due to the male or the female. In both sexes, infertility may be caused in two different ways: via adverse effects on the endocrine processes in reproduction (estrus cycle or mating behavior, gametogenesis) or via direct toxic effects on the reproductive organs.

*Specific tests*

Many different experiments can be used to obtain these data. *Specific tests* may be applied to study the migration and proliferation of primordial germ cells.

963

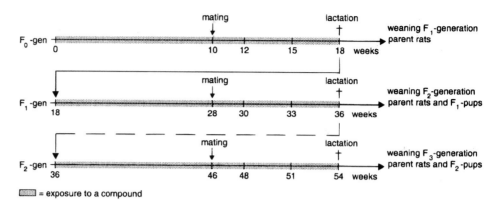

FIGURE 32.12
Example of a generation study, in which three generations (F$_0$, F$_1$, F$_2$) are continuously exposed.

*Detection of malformations*
*Function of organ systems*

There are also tests available for studying the function of the ovaries, the course of post-ovarian processes, the female reproductive organs and functions, the function of the testes, the post-testicular processes, the male reproductive organs, fertilization and implantation. In segment II studies the emphasis is on the detection of *malformations*. In addition, some substances may have permanent effects on the *functioning of organ systems*, such as behavioral changes, biochemical disturbances, and abnormal development and functioning of the immune system. These functional developmental disorders can only be detected when the functions concerned actually become effective. This implies that the effects are sometimes not detected until an advanced stage of development. A striking example of this is the so-called

*Transplacental carcinogenesis*

*transplacental carcinogenesis*, in which intrauterine exposure leads to the induction of carcinogenicity which is not expressed until after puberty. The best-known example of a substance having such an effect is DES. It will be clear that highly specific tests on experimental animals, especially designed for the purpose, are required to detect this type of effect. Much attention is being devoted to *behavioral tests*, which are used to determine whether intrauterine ex-

*Behavioral tests*

posure to a substance has caused permanent damage to the central nervous system. Various strategies are still being developed and only a few of these have been standardized and validated. In general, they are based on two different concepts. The first type of strategy is the idea that if an experimental animal that has been exposed to a substance *in utero* is able to perform various postnatal behavioral tests without any problems, the various functions of the central and peripheral nervous system are still intact. If one or more functions were disturbed, this would become manifest in the general behavior of the animal. This approach is no longer recommended, as little is known about the capacity of experimental animals to compensate for defects. Moreover, it is not known to what extent a function needs to be impaired before it causes a specific behavioral abnormality.

*Application of several test systems: the test battery*

This is one of the reasons for using a number of test systems that overlap with respect to both the stage of development of the experimental animal used and the part of the nervous system to be tested (second strategy). By doing so, several functions of the central nervous system are tested. Such a test system will provide information on early neurological and physical developmental defects, as well as on adult behavior.

964

### 3 Evaluation of the reproductive toxicity and teratogenicity of substances

The ultimate aim of toxicity research is to establish what adverse effects substances may have on human physiology.

This requires a qualitative assessment of the damage done on the one hand, and a quantitative determination (dose-response relationship) on the other. This is true for all aspects of toxicology. In this way, the so-called *reproductive toxicity profile of a substance* is established.

*Reproductive toxicity profile of a substance*

Whereas the qualitative assessment of the adverse effects of a reproductive toxicant is primarily descriptive (death, growth retardation, malformations and functional disorders), the quantitative assessment is mainly concerned with the circumstances under which the substance is used and the conditions of exposure.

*Risk characterization*

The data required for *risk characterization* are obtained from epidemiological studies, studies on experimental animals and knowledge of the methods for extrapolating animal data to the human situation. Accurate determination of the concentrations or doses to which individuals may be exposed, and which individuals are most sensitive to the effects of a substance under the circumstances, is also required. The combination of exposure assessment and risk characterization is referred to as *risk assessment*.

*Risk assessment*

*Risk management*

Subsequently, with the results of the risk assessment and the legal requirements, a *risk management strategy* can be implemented. This means that measures are taken to prevent or reduce the risk of damage from reproductive toxicants or teratogenic substances. A diagram of the various approaches to risk management is provided in Table 32.6.

ASSIGNMENT 32.3

Describe a number of measures which might lead to a reduction of a potential risk of teratogenicity or reproductive toxicity. Which data are used for the process of risk evaluation?

TABLE 32.6
Diagram of the relationship between the processes of research, risk evaluation and risk management

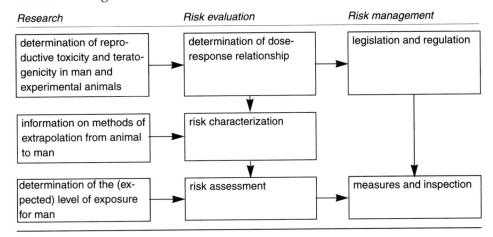

965

Evaluation of data on humans undoubtly provides the best results for establishing and characterizing the risk from a particular substance. These data are, however, rarely available, and are often difficult to interpret, particularly as regards the moment and extent of exposure. Sometimes a cluster of reports of a particular abnormality may be registered in a certain area. These figures, for example the number of birth defects, should be compared with the *spontaneous frequency* within a population, but this so-called normal frequency is often unknown. Furthermore, it is not always easy to give a good characterization of the population in a certain area.

*Spontaneous frequency*

Individual evaluation of the cases should also take place, emphasizing the specificity of the effect, the possible cause, the biological probability, the development in the course of time, and the existence of other risk factors. As was stated previously, correlation studies should establish whether there have been similar experiences with the same substance elsewhere.

*New substances*

Since the information referred to above is often not available, risks must be assessed on the basis of animal experiments alone. For *new substances*, this is the only method available.

The most reliable method of determining the reproductive toxicity of a substance in experimental animals is by performing repeated studies in various species displaying similar abnormalities. If only limited information from animal experiments is available, and provided it has been obtained from reliable studies, the data may give some indication of a potentially adverse effect of a substance. In addition, the data obtained from reproductive toxicity and teratogenicity tests, and in particular those on the nature and intensity of the biological effects, need to be assessed in relation to other data, such as those on pharmacokinetics and toxicokinetics, cytotoxicity, structure-activity relationships, maternal toxicity, and data derived from preliminary studies and *in vitro* test systems.

*Combination of qualitative data from animals and quantitative factors*

Qualitative information obtained from tests in experimental animals must subsequently be combined with quantitative factors. This means that the effects found at higher doses must be extrapolated to lower doses in order to be sure there is a *no observed-adverse-effect level* in animals. These data must then be extrapolated to the exposure level relevant to man.

See also Study unit 14

This practice of extrapolation, and in particular of determining the slope of the so-called dose-response curve, is the same as that applied in general toxicology. Several different mathematical models have been described in detail, particularly for carcinogenicity tests.

If no adequate extrapolation data are available, so-called safety factors are applied (for example a factor of 100). The final conclusions of reproductive toxicity studies are combined with those of other toxicity studies to determine the lowest dose which still produces an effect, in order to reach a final evaluation. This procedure is followed for all substances with the exception of drugs, that require a direct extrapolation for the category 'use of drug during pregnancy'. This is necessary because in the case of drugs, mostly no safety factor can be applied.

## 4    Prevention

Preventing developmental defects is obviously preferable to correcting them. Prevention can be either direct (primary) or indirect (secondary). *Primary prevention* is the most desirable form. It can be implemented, for example, by establishing the cause of a defect and eliminating it, or by taking measures to

*Primary prevention*

966

prevent or reduce exposure to the substance concerned. Some examples of such preventive measures are vaccination against rubella, withdrawal of thalidomide from the market and, to prevent *cretinism*, the administration of iodine in areas lacking natural iodine. Another method of primary prevention is to restrict the use of drugs during pregnancy to a minimum. Physicians should prescribe drugs to pregnant women only if strictly necessary, and even then should provide adequate guidance and perform regular check-ups. The same can be said with respect to women who wish to or are likely to become pregnant.

**Classification system for drugs used during pregnancy**

A number of countries have therefore introduced a classification system for the use of drugs during pregnancy. The information available to the physician includes a category 'use during pregnancy'.

Categories to be used for labelling of medicinal products for their use before and during pregnancy.

**Products for which human data are available**

*Medicinal products for which human data are available to evaluate the safety with respect to the course of pregnancy and the health of the unborn and the neonate:*

### Category A

This medicinal product has been assessed in pregnant women and no harmful effects are known with respect to the course of pregnancy and the health of the unborn and the neonate.

### Category C

This medicinal product does not increase the spontaneous incidence of birth defects, but it has potential hazardous pharmacological effects with respect to the course of pregnancy, to the unborn or the neonate (see further specific information).

### Category D

This medicinal product is known or suspected to cause birth defects and/or other irreversible adverse effects on pregnancy outcome. It may also have potential hazardous pharmacological effects with respect to the course of pregnancy, to the unborn or the neonate (see further specific information).

**Products for which insufficient human data are available**

*Medicinal products for which insufficient human data are available to evaluate the safety with respect to the course of pregnancy and the health of the unborn and the neonate:*

### Category B

B1: The safety of this medicinal product of use in human pregnancy has not been established. Evaluation of experimental animal studies does not indicate direct or indirect harmful effect with respect to the development of the embryo or fetus, the course of gestation and peri- and postnatal development. (See explanatory text for current experience in humans.)

B2: The safety of this medicinal product of use in human pregnancy has not been established. Experimental animal studies are insufficient to assess the safety with respect to the development of the embryo or fetus, the course of gestation and peri- and postnatal development. (See explanatory text for current experience in humans.)

B3: The safety of this medicinal product of use in human pregnancy has not been established. Evaluation of experimental animal studies has shown reproductive toxicity, e.g. birth defects or other effects on the development of the embryo or fetus, the course of gestation or peri- and postnatal development. (See explanatory text for current experience in humans.)

This classification is based on data available on humans, and, in the absence of such information, on data obtained from animal experiments. Primary prevention also includes regular screening for diseases which may have a harmful effect on the development of the embryo and/or fetus.

Providing information to physicians and the general public is another important form of prevention.

*Measures to prevent exposure*

It is also possible to take *measures to prevent exposure* to compounds at the workplace and in the environment. These concern substances that have a harmful effect on reproduction in general and on the course of pregnancy in particular.

*Genetic counselling*

Primary prevention also includes *genetic counselling*. The counsellor assesses the risk of a congenital abnormality, the chance of it being repeated, and what can be done to prevent it.

Genetic counselling is given for example to parents who already have a child with a congenital abnormality, or who have a familial history of congenital abnormalities. The aim of genetic counselling is to provide as much as possible information on the risk, the consequences and the options, in order to allow those involved to take a well-informed decision on the question of whether or not to have children, or to continue a pregnancy. It is ultimately up to the prospective parents to make a decision on the basis of the information provided.

*Secondary prevention*

*Prenatal diagnosis*

*Secondary prevention* can take the form of termination of a pregnancy after prenatal diagnosis has shown the presence of an abnormality in the embryo or fetus. In case of *prenatal diagnosis* it should be known what particular abnormalities one should be looking for. Not all abnormalities can be diagnosed prenatally. Prenatal examination can be carried out at certain stages of pregnancy. Table 32.7 lists the tests currently available.

*Chorionic villus sampling*

*a.    Chorionic villus sampling*

*8th to 10th week of pregnancy*
*Chromosomal aberrations and metabolic disorders*

This test can be performed in the *8th to 10th week of pregnancy*. Chorionic villus sampling enables the diagnosis of *chromosomal aberrations and metabolic disorders*. The cellular nuclei in the villi of the placenta contain the same chromosomes

TABLE   32.7
Various methods available for prenatal examination

| direct examination of the fetus | ultrasonography | |
| --- | --- | --- |
| biopsy of fetal skin and organs | | |
| amniocentesis | cells | chromosomal analysis biochemistry DNA analysis |
| | amniotic fluid | biochemistry |
| fetal blood sampling | cells plasma | |
| maternal blood sampling | blood typing biochemistry | |
| chorionic villus sampling | chromosomal analysis biochemistry DNA analysis | |

and genes as those in the embryo or fetus. The advantage of this test is that the result is available in only a few hours or days, and that it can be performed at an early stage of pregnancy. Discontinuation of a pregnancy, would then be less drastic and also less stressful.

*Ultrasonography*

### b.    Ultrasonography

High-frequency sound waves are used to visualize the *outline of the embryo or fetus as well as organs* such as the heart, kidneys and gastrointestinal tract.

*From the 7th week of pregnancy*

Abnormalities can be traced and the size and growth of the embryo or fetus can be determined. Ultrasonography can be performed *from the 7th week of pregnancy*.

Table 32.8 lists a number of developmental defects in the fetus which can be diagnosed by ultrasonography in the second trimester of pregnancy.

*Amniocentesis*

### c. Amniocentesis

*16th week of pregnancy*

From about the *16th week of pregnancy*, it is possible to take 15–20 ml of amniotic fluid from the uterus by means of a puncture through the abdominal and uterine walls. The vital cells present in the amniotic fluid, which originate from fetal skin and mucosae, can be cultured. After 10–14 days, enough cell divisions have usually taken place to allow reliable *chromosomal analysis*.

*Chromosomal analysis*

Prenatal diagnosis of hereditary metabolic disorders usually requires (micro-) biochemical analysis of cultured amniotic fluid cells. The results are then compared with similar analyses of control amniotic cells and skin fibroblasts from a patient suffering from the disease in question, as well as from the heterozygous parent (the carrier). Depending on the nature of the hereditary disorder and the method of analysis used, it takes 10–20 days before the result becomes available. Sometimes certain metabolic products in the amniotic fluid can provide information, which enables a faster result.

*Open neural tube defects*

To detect *open neural tube defects*, the level of a particular fetal protein (alpha fetoprotein or AFP) in the amniotic fluid is determined. Increased levels of this protein are found in anencephaly and in spina bifida in the fetus.

The test for AFP in the amniotic fluid is applied as a diagnostic method. In screening or population surveys involving determination of AFP in the maternal serum, a group of pregnant women may be identified who require further examination to establish the cause of the abnormal AFP values. This may be a defect of the neural tube in the fetus.

TABLE    32.8

Some developmental defects in the fetus which can be diagnosed by ultrasonography in the second trimester of pregnancy

Any unfamiliar terms can be found in the glossary.

| | |
|---|---|
| anencephaly | gastroschisis |
| microcephaly | duodenal atresia |
| hydrocephaly | cystic kidneys |
| meningomyelocele | hydronephrosis |
| spina bifida | thoracic dysplasia |
| encephalocele | achondrogenesis |
| omphalocele | hemimelia or amelia of the extremities |
| esophageal atresia | some congenital cardiac defects |

969

## 5  Summary

This study unit has elaborated on the various methods that are available to study adverse effects of substances with regard to reproduction and development. These are epidemiological studies, and animal experiments. The process of risk assessment based on the results of these studies can lead to measures to be taken by the authorities to prevent adverse effects. In addition, primary and secondary preventive measures can be taken to prevent the conception or birth of children with developmental defects. The latter type of prevention is of a clinical nature and is implemented through genetic counselling.

Figure 32.13 provides a schematic overview of the ways in which toxicological and/or pharmacological agents can induce adverse effects, and how these effects become manifest.

## SELF ASSESSMENT QUESTIONS

1  What are the characteristic determinants of disorders that can be measured by means of epidemiological research into disorders of reproduction and development?

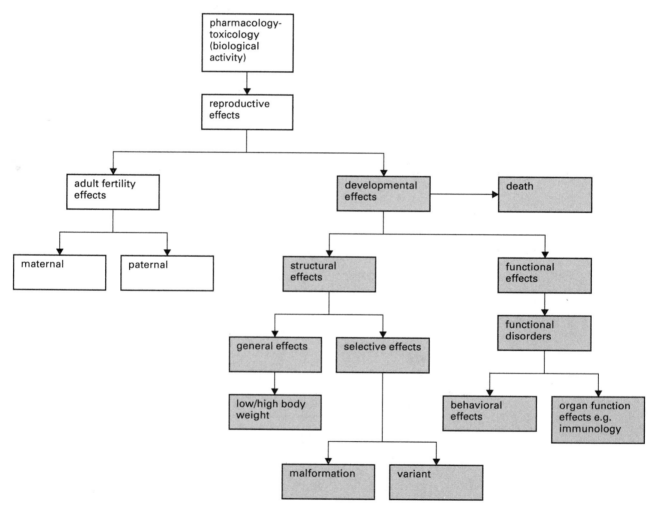

FIGURE   32.13
Possible manifestations of the effects of pharmacological and/or toxicological agents

2   Define the two methods used to study the effects of chemicals on development and reproduction in man.

3   Describe a cross-sectional study that is both prospective and retrospective in nature.

4   What is an important disadvantage of cross-sectional studies?

5   What term is used for a prospective study in which the frequency of developmental defects in women using a certain drug is compared with that in non-users?

6   What is the dose-effect relationship between smoking and complications during pregnancy?

7   What type of epidemiological study would you opt for in the case of occupational exposure that may pose a potential risk of a low-frequency developmental disorder?

8   What is the aim of experimental reproductive toxicity studies?

9   State the conditions under which researchers may deviate from the international guidelines for carrying out a test, for example for the embryo/fetotoxicity of a substance.

10   Which properties of a substance should be known when planning an experiment?

11   Which properties determine the choice of an experimental animal?

12   What is the statistical unit in a teratogenicity study (segment II study)?

13   What are the main differences between preliminary tests on mammals and definitive tests?

14   Describe some disadvantages of *in vitro* teratogenicity tests.

15   Why can unicellular organisms be used for mutagenicity tests, but not for teratogenicity tests?

16   Why are male experimental animals in a so-called segment I study treated with the substance to be tested for circa 10 weeks before mating?

17   Which parameters can be determined in a segment II study?

18   Which parameters can be determined in the $F_1$ generation of a generation test?

19   Describe the various steps in the process of risk assessment.

20   What is the difference between primary and secondary prevention of congenital disorders?

21   What prenatal analyses can the amniotic fluid be used for?

FEEDBACK

## 1  Answers to the assignments

32.1  A preliminary study or test consists of one or more experiments preceding the actual study or the actual experiment. It allows researchers to choose optimal experimental conditions for the definitive tests. See also section 2.5.

32.2  The $F_0$ generation (see Figure 32.12) is the parent generation and is therefore primarily used for research on fertility and gestation. The $F_1$ generation is used for research on abnormalities in development, growth and maturation. The reproductive characteristics of the $F_1$ generation, for example, the number of offspring in the $F_2$ litter, duration of gestation in $F_1$ animals etc., can be used to detect possible accumulation of the substance.

32.3  These include refusal of substances or withdrawal of substances already on the market, lowering of the acceptable level of substances in food or at the workplace, limiting the indications for which the drugs are prescribed or total exclusion of certain substances during pregnancy.

## 2  Answers to the self assessment questions

1  Characteristic determinants include: morphological abnormalities, functional disorders, abnormal growth, reproductive disorders and intrauterine death.

2  The methods for studying the effects of toxic agents on human reproduction are always epidemiological in nature. They may be either descriptive or analytical.

3  A cross-sectional study establishes whether there are certain abnormalities in a given population and whether any causal factors can be pointed out. Examples would be all cases of congenital abnormalities caused by drugs. The study may suggest an association. The following step then is to search in users of the drug how often the birth defect occurs. Or, in other words, by means of a prospective study findings are then verified.

4  A disadvantage of cross-sectional studies is that they are liable to overreporting.

5  A cohort study.

6  See Table 32.1.

7  See Table 32.2. A retrospective cohort study, or a case-control study in or around an industrial plant.

8  Experimental reproductive toxicity tests are used to detect adverse effects of toxic agents on the reproduction and development of organisms for the purpose of risk assessment.

9  Researchers must be able to demonstrate on scientific grounds that the method used is at least equivalent to the method outlined in the guidelines and that it allows extrapolation to man.

10    The administration of the substance (deliberate use, or as a contaminant), the likelihood of exposure to the substance (expected extent of exposure) and of course the general pharmacological and toxicological properties of the substance.

11    The choice will often be pragmatic rather than scientifically founded. An important practical consideration is the possibility of comparing the results of new tests with those obtained in general toxicological research. Other practical considerations, such as accommodation, life span and costs, also often play a decisive part.

12    The statistical unit in teratogenicity studies is the litter.

13    Preliminary studies and definitive studies differ mainly with respect to the number of animals, the number of different dosages and the duration of the experiments. Definitive studies allow conclusions and data for risk evaluation.

14    The absence of effects resulting from metabolism and kinetics. A variety of regulatory systems active in the intact organism are also usually absent in *in vitro* systems.

15    In mutagenesis, the genetic material of a single cell is affected. Teratogenic abnormalities usually involve interactions between cells, which implies that the intercellular communication mechanisms should be present in the test system. This is by definition not the case in single-cell test systems.

16    In order to determine whether the substance affects spermatogenesis or other processes directly involved in reproduction in which the male animal plays a part (for example mating).

17    Segment II studies are mainly used to study effects on structural development. See Section 2.6.2 for further information.

18    Parameters that can be measured are those related to the intrauterine environment, lactation, development, growth and further maturation. See section 2.6.4.

19    See section 3 and Table 32.6.

20    Primary prevention aims at preventing the induction or occurrence of teratogenic or adverse reproductive effects (for instance, by banning the use of certain chemicals, not using certain drugs during pregnancy etc.). Secondary prevention can take the form of aborting the abnormal embryo, or even intrauterine treatment of the abnormalities.

21    See section 4, part c.

# Contents Study unit 33
# Anatomy and toxicological pathology of the nervous system

0-8493-9232-2/96/$0.00 + $.50
© 1996 by CRC Press, Inc.

# Anatomy and toxicological pathology of the nervous system

*A. Bast*

## INTRODUCTION

Our knowledge of the harmful effects of substances on the nervous system is continuously increasing and the characterization of the effects is still improving. The neurotoxicity of xenobiotics sometimes comes into the limelight when environmental disasters occur. Many people will recall the case of *Minamata disease* in Japan in the 1950s and 60s and in Iraq in 1971–72. Minamata disease is caused by the consumption of fish and shellfish contaminated by methylmercury. Lesions of both the peripheral and central nervous systems, and the cerebral cortex have been reported. Neurotoxic symptoms of this disease are disruption of visual and sensory function, ataxia and impairment of hearing, speech and gait. Chronic poisoning also often causes general weakness of the extremities. The nervous system is a complicated structure. Nerve cells which die as a result of irreversible damage are not replaced.

*Minamata disease*

The nervous system may be divided *anatomically* into the central nervous system (brain and spinal cord) and peripheral nervous system, or *functionally* into the somatic and the autonomic (vegetative) nervous system. The *somatic system* is that part of the nervous system whose functioning one is aware of. The autonomic nervous system controls the functioning of the internal organs and for the most part we are not directly conscious of it. Based on their function the *somatic system* can be divided into the:

*Anatomical division*
*Functional division*

- somatomotor nervous system with efferent fibers;
- somatosensory nervous system with afferent fibers.

The *sensory* nervous system conducts stimuli from the senses to the central nervous system. In the *motor* nervous system impulses are transmitted from the central nervous system to the striated muscles which are responsible for movements.

Some neurotoxic substances influence the central nervous system, e.g. the insecticide dieldrin which causes epileptic symptoms, whilst others affect the peripheral nervous system. Of these neuropathies some influence only the sensory fibers and others only the motor fibers. There are also *polyneuropathies* (mixed neuropathies) in which several peripheral nerves are involved. Tri-*ortho*-cresyl phosphate, found in some lubricating oils, causes polyneuropathy.

*Neuropathies are disorders of the peripheral nervous system*

LEARNING OBJECTIVES

After completing this study unit you should be able to

— describe the anatomy of the nervous system and the different types of cells
— point out the differences in site, function and transmission between sympathetic, parasympathetic and motor nerves
— describe cholinergic and adrenergic transmission and ways in which they can be influenced
— name the routes along which acetylcholine and norepinephrine are synthesized and metabolized
— classify neurotoxic effects on the basis of their location and give examples of toxic substances in each of the different categories of neuropathies.

*Study hints*

The present understanding of the molecular and cellular mechanisms of neurotoxicity is still very incomplete. The neurotoxicity of substances is usually marked by a multiplicity of targets and symptoms. There is often also a difference between acute and chronic neurotoxicity. Symptoms of chronic poisoning may be diffuse and often manifest themselves gradually. All these considerations make it difficult to subdivide this study unit adequately according to, for example, categories of chemicals or targets. The following approach has been chosen. The study unit starts by looking at the anatomy of the nervous system. Then synaptic transmission is discussed, followed by a classification of neurotoxic effects according to their location. Both these will be illustrated by describing the neurotoxic mechanism of a number of substances. Lastly, polyneuropathies will be discussed by describing the molecular and cellular effects of various xenobiotics (drugs, pesticides and other chemicals). Excitation and nerve conduction are dealt with in Study unit 34. Behavioral toxicology is covered in Study unit 35. A combined set of self assessment questions covering units 33, 34 and 35 can be found at the end of Study unit 35. The study load for this unit is approximately 3 hours.

## STUDY CORE

### 1    Anatomy of the nervous system

#### 1.1    SUBDIVISIONS OF THE NERVOUS SYSTEM

The nervous system is divided into the *central nervous system (CNS)* comprising brain and spinal cord and the *peripheral nervous system (PNS)* which is largely made up of afferent and efferent nerve fibers (cranial or spinal fibers) whose function is sensory or motor, respectively. In addition to this anatomical subdivision, a functional subdivision is also made. Here a distinction is made between the *somatic* and *autonomic* nervous system. The *somatic* nervous system is that part of the nervous system whose function is consciously controlled. This contrasts with the autonomic nervous system (see also section 1.3), the functioning of which is not directly apparent to the individual.

*Autonomic nervous system*

The *autonomic nervous system* may be further divided into a *sympathetic* and a *parasympathetic* component. The peripheral nervous system also comprises the sympathetic nervous system (neurons arising from the thoracic and lumbar region of the spinal cord) and the parasympathetic system arising from the cranial and sacral divisions of the CNS.

## 1.2    CELL TYPES AND STRUCTURE

*Neurons*
*Glial cells*

In addition to nerve cells (*neurons*) the CNS also contains supporting cells in the form of glial or neuroglial cells which are more numerous than the neurons. The difference between *glial cells* and neurons lies in the fact that the former cannot conduct impulses and have retained their mitotic ability. There are three different types of glial cells:

*Astrocytes*

- *Astrocytes* establish the contact between neurons and the circulatory system. In this way they regulate the microenvironment of the neurons (transport and removal of material) and maintain the extracellular $K^+$ concentration.

*Oligodendrocytes*

- *Oligodendrocytes* enclose the axons (nerve fibers) of the CNS in a material rich in lipids, the myelin sheath, providing electrical insulation.

*Microglia*

- *Microglia* act as macrophages in the CNS and can thus remove components from the environment and break them down when necessary.

Neurons consist of a cell body (the soma or perikaryon), with a relatively large nucleus, and several processes (see Figure 33.1). There are two types of processes: dendrites and neurites or axons. *Dendrites* are mostly short and heavily branched; they receive impulses. Dendrites and also the soma often have many synapses, the sites at which information is transmitted from other nerve cells.

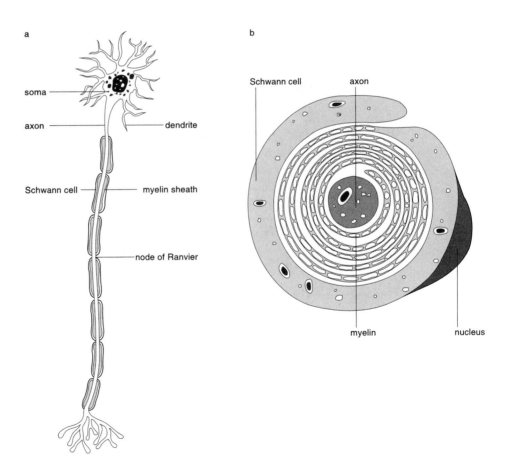

FIGURE    33.1
a. A neuron with its processes
The axon is myelinated.
b. Cross-section of a myelinated nerve fiber

A neuron has only one *axon* which conducts the nerve impulse from the soma (cell body) to the other nerve cells or to an effector organ such as a muscle or gland. At the end the axon is heavily branched, providing good contact with the receptor cells.

*Myelin sheath*

In the PNS, axons are enclosed by a *myelin sheath* interrupted only by the *nodes of Ranvier*. The insulated axon is enclosed by a second sheath, the *neurilemma*. This sheath is made up of *Schwann cells* (i.e. cells with the same function as oligodendrocytes in the CNS). A myelinated axon may contain anything from a few to several dozen myelin cells. Each lamella consists of two bimolecular lipid layers, about 35 Å thick, sandwiched between protein layers 20–30 Å thick. Damage to the myelin sheath, for example by organophosphates, may block the conduction of nerve impulses leading to paralysis and sensory impairment.

The *soma* naturally contains cytoplasm, mitochondria, the Golgi apparatus etc. Like the dendrites but unlike the axon, the soma also contains *Nissl bodies* (named after their discoverer) which are clusters of RNA and characteristic of nerve cells. Along the length of the axons and dendrites long chains of protein molecules (neurofilaments, together forming the neurofibrils) are found.

*Axonal transport*

These are thought to play a part in *axonal transport*. Enzymes and other proteins can migrate from the soma via (anterograde) axonal transport (through axoplasm) to the nerve endings. Transport in the opposite direction (retrograde transport) is also possible. Disruption of this axonal transport (e.g. by methyl n-butyl ketone or 2,5-hexanedione) impairs the functional integrity of the neuron.

## 1.3 SOMATIC VERSUS AUTONOMIC NERVOUS SYSTEM

*Somatic nervous system*

The *somatic nervous system* as part of the PNS consists of nerves originating from the motor anterior horn cells in the spinal cord and innervating the muscles of the somatic system. This system also includes some of the cranial nerves innervating the muscles of the face and eyes. In addition to these efferent motor nerve fibers the somatic nervous system also includes a large number of afferent sensory nerve fibers, which transmit information from the sense organs and nerve endings to the CNS.

*Autonomic nervous system*

The *autonomic (vegetative) nervous system* is part of the PNS and innervates organs such as the heart, lungs, blood vessels and kidneys.

The autonomic nervous system consists of parasympathetic and sympathetic divisions (see Figure 33.2).

The sympathetic nervous system activates organs involved in the processes needed to carry out physical work. The "three f's"—fight, fear and flight—may serve to help in memorizing the tasks of the sympathetic nervous system; together they represent situations of stress. Sympathetic nervous activity is reflected, for example, in stimulated cardiac function (chronotropy as well as inotropy), increased lung function (to increase oxygen uptake), increased blood circulation through the skeletal muscles (fight/flight), and so on. The sympathetic influence depresses digestive activity and activates the release of epinephrine from the adrenal glands. In this way the sympathetic tone is maintained, as the effect of the fast neurogenic response of the sympathetic nervous system can be prolonged by a slower hormonal response.

chronotropy = frequency
inotropy = force, energy

The parasympathetic nervous system acts mainly during rest when it stimulates the digestive organs, for example. Overstimulation of the parasympathetic nervous system (by neurotoxicants) may cause salivation, sweating or lowering of the blood pressure.

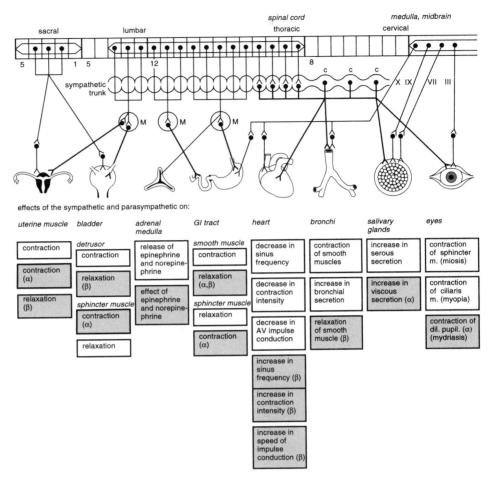

FIGURE 33.2

The autonomic nervous system

Note that the parasympathetic nerve pathways originate from the cranial and sacral divisions of the nervous system and that the ganglia are in or close to the organ innervated. Sympathetic neurons link up into ganglia of the sympathetic trunk and originate from the thoracic and lumbar parts of the spinal cord.

ASSIGNMENT 33.1

Why would it be a good thing to have a rest after meals?

1.4 PROTECTION OF THE NERVOUS SYSTEM

The CNS is very effectively protected against mechanical injury by the skull, backbone and certain membranes. Since the permeability of nerve membranes is low for polar and high molecular weight substances, the terms *blood-brain barrier* (CNS) and the *blood-nerve barrier* (PNS) have been introduced. The endothelial cells in the blood vessel walls together with the astrocytes form the *blood-brain barrier*. The cells are closely packed and thus impermeable to macromolecules. The endothelial cells have relatively few micropinocytotic vesicles, which in capillaries in other tissues are important for transport across the endothelial cellular layer. Lipophilic substances can cross the blood-brain barrier and penetrate the brain tissue.

*Blood-nerve barrier*

*Blood-brain barrier*

ASSIGNMENT 33.2

Plot the brain concentration of substances versus their lipophilicity.

An important function of the blood-brain barrier is its *selective permeability*, which allows glucose and other essential nutrients to be taken up and waste products to be eliminated. A continuous supply of oxygen and glucose is essential to the CNS.

The blood-brain barrier is not evident everywhere. Where cells produce hormones (hypophysis) or where they contain hormone- or chemoreceptors, the barrier effect is far less marked. Glutamate and a number of structurally related substances such as aspartate may affect regions of the brain which are not protected by the blood-brain barrier, such as certain parts of the hypothalamus. Although this phenomenon can only be demonstrated in experimental animals, it is still interesting because it may yield animal models which are potentially useful for human clinical situations, e.g. Huntington's chorea (a predominantly hereditary, chronic progressive and incurable form of chorea), xenobiotic-induced Parkinson's disease or tardive dyskinesia.

chorea = sudden uncoordinated movements
tardive = late
dyskinesia = motor impairment

The PNS is less well protected than the CNS. Thus neurotoxic effects become manifest much sooner in the PNS than in the CNS. The cytostatic adriamycin, for example, is toxic to the PNS but not to the CNS.

*Sensory cells*

*Sensory cells* are necessary to provide the nervous system with information from the internal and external environment. Some insecticides (pyrethroids and DDT) interfere with the sensory function. They cause a so-called repetitive activity in the afferent nerve fibers, i.e. a series of impulses is generated rather than a single impulse. This can lead to severe convulsions.

## 2    Synaptic transmission

Transmission of nerve impulses from an axon to an adjacent cell takes place in the synapse. Figure 33.3 shows a diagrammatic representation of a synapse.

*Neurotransmitter*

The bulbous presynaptic nerve ending contains vesicles in which the *neurotransmitter* is stored, often more than one neurotransmitter. The presynaptic and postsynaptic membranes are separated by the synaptic cleft.

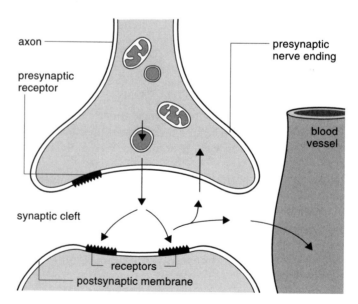

FIGURE    33.3
Diagrammatic representation of a synapse

An action potential can depolarize the presynaptic membrane so that $Ca^{2+}$ channels in the membrane open and $Ca^{2+}$ enters. The increased $Ca^{2+}$ concentration causes the synaptic vesicles to migrate to and merge with the membrane, and the neurotransmitter is then released by exocytosis into the synaptic cleft.

*Receptor*

Via diffusion the transmitter reaches the postsynaptic membrane and there interacts with specific binding proteins (*receptors*). Binding of a transmitter to a receptor can cause ion channels to open causing excitation (depolarization) or inhibition (hyperpolarization) (see next study unit, EPSP and IPSP).

Figure 33.4 illustrates the main transmitter systems for the parasympathetic, sympathetic and motor peripheral nervous systems.

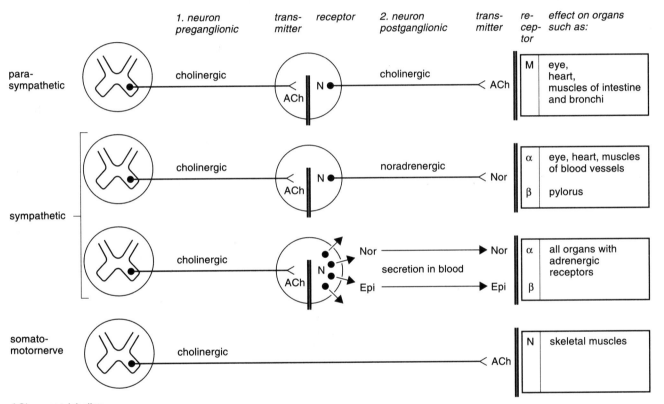

ACh = acetylcholine
Epi = epinephrine
Nor = norepinephrine
N = nicotinic receptors (n-cholinergic receptors)
M = muscarinic receptors (m-cholinergic receptors)
$\alpha, \beta$ = $\alpha$ and $\beta$ adrenergic receptors

FIGURE 33.4
Cholinergic and noradrenergic nerve pathways of the peripheral sympathetic, parasympathetic and motor systems
Cholinergic and noradrenergic effects can be differentiated by using antagonists.

- In cholinergic synapses of parasympathetic and sympathetic ganglia the effect of acetylcholine on nicotinic receptors (see subsequent text of this study unit) is antagonized by ganglion blockers.
- In cholinergic synapses of the postganglionic parasympathetic nerve endings the muscarinic receptors have an inhibitory effect (see subsequent text of this study unit).
- In the noradrenergic synapses of the postganglionic sympathetic nerve endings adrenergic receptor antagonists have an inhibitory effect (a distinction is made between $\alpha$ and $\beta$ receptors). The adrenergic receptor antagonists also inhibit the effects of epinephrine (and norepinephrine) released from the adrenal medulla.
- The motor nerves are cholinergic. The effect of acetylcholine on nicotinic receptors can be inhibited by muscle relaxants (e.g. curare).

The interaction between neurotransmitter and receptor on the postsynaptic membrane can be inhibited by so-called *antagonists*. Specific antagonists have enabled the distinction of many different types of interactions.

*Muscarinic receptor*

Some agonists have a certain degree of specificity, for example for the postsynaptic acetyl-choline receptors of the postganglionic fibers of the parasympathetic system. One such antagonist is muscarine which is found in the fly agaric mushroom (*Amanita muscaria*) (see Figure 33.7). Since the effects of muscarine resemble those of stimulation of the parasympathetic nervous system, this type of acetylcholine receptors in the parasympathetic "terminal synapses" are called *muscarinic receptors* and the effects of stimulation of these receptors are called muscarinic effects. By analogy, the effects induced by stimulating ACh receptors in the neuromuscular junctions are referred to as nicotinic and the

*Nicotinic receptor*

receptors *nicotinic receptors*. The parasympathetic and sympathetic *ganglia* appear to contain both muscarinic and nicotinic receptors. The nicotinic receptors are found in the synapses between the pre-and postganglionic fibers; the muscarinic receptors are situated postsynaptically on interneurons containing dopamine which modulate the ganglionic neurotransmission.

*Presynaptic receptors*

There are also receptors which are located *presynaptically* and affect the release of neurotransmitters. The various pre- and postsynaptic receptors constantly interact with each other. Figure 33.5 illustrates the post-and presynaptic interaction of acetylcholine and norepinephrine on the heart.

The acetylcholine released from the vagus nerve (see Figure 33.2) has a negative chronotropic effect on the heart (slows heart rate) by activating the postganglionic muscarinic receptors. In this way acetylcholine antagonizes the positive inotropic and chronotropic activity of norepinephrine released by the sympathetic nervous system. Norepinephrine works through the postsynaptic $\beta$-receptors. The interaction at the postsynaptic level is attributable to the fact that activation of postsynaptic muscarinic (M)-cholinergic receptors inhibits the biochemical reaction which follows stimulation of the cardiac $\beta$-receptors.

Activation of the presynaptic sympathetic M-receptors by acetylcholine inhibits the release of norepinephrine in the noradrenergic nerve endings. Acetylcholine also inhibits its own release (negative feedback).

Norepinephrine released by the noradrenergic nerve endings activates the $\beta$-adrenergic receptors on the cardiac tissue but also the presynaptic $\alpha_2$- adrenergic receptors on

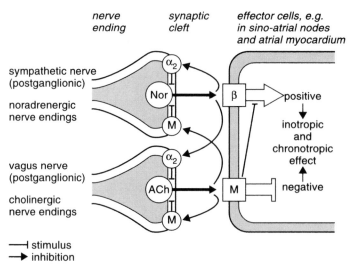

FIGURE 33.5
Post- and presynaptic interaction of acetylcholine and norepinephrine with the heart

noradrenergic and nearby cholinergic nerve paths. This may inhibit the release of nor-epinephrine itself and of acetylcholine.

ASSIGNMENT   33.3

Atropine is a muscarinic receptor blocker. What effect will atropine have on the heart? List all the possibilities, referring to Figure 33.5.

*Acetylcholine*

It is important that the neurotransmitter, after having been released into the synaptic cleft, is quickly inactivated again so that the nervous system can transmit fresh impulses. Figure 33.6 shows the synthesis and degradation of the neurotransmitter *acetylcholine*.

A distinction is made between the enzymes acetylcholinesterase and the non-specific cholinesterase (pseudocholinesterase). Acetylcholinesterase is found

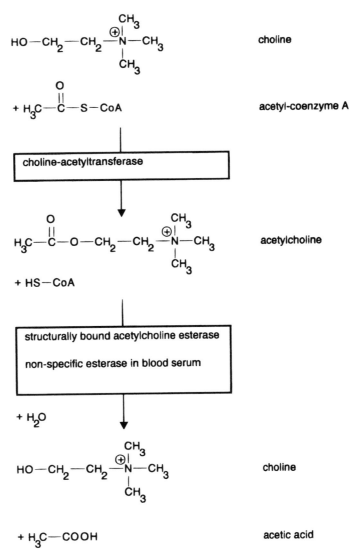

FIGURE   33.6
Synthesis and degradation of acetylcholine

primarily in pre- and postsynaptic membranes. Acetylcholine can be hydrolyzed within a few milliseconds. Acetic acid is removed in the blood whilst choline is again taken up into the neuron and used for acetylcholine synthesis. Pseudocholinesterase is found primarily in the serum and liver and prevents acetylcholine from passing from one organ to another.

There are many ways of influencing cholinergic neurotransmission. They are summarized in Table 33.1.

For acetylcholine to be *biologically active* (binding to receptors and activating receptors), a positively charged nitrogen atom, the relatively negatively charged carbonyl and ester linkage oxygen atoms are needed (see Figure 33.7). The antagonists which enable distinction in the autonomic nervous system between preganglionic nicotinic (N) receptors and postganglionic muscarinic (M) receptors are, as indicated earlier, nicotine and muscarine respectively (see Figure 33.7). Note that both muscarine and nicotine have a negatively and a positively charged center in their molecule.

Figure 33.7 shows two acetylcholinesterase inhibitors (antagonists), namely physostigmine and neostigmine.

ASSIGNMENT  33.4

The molecular structure of the acetylcholinesterase inhibitors shows both negatively and positively charged centers. Was this to be expected?

The drug hemicholinium-3 is a competitive antagonist. It inhibits the uptake of choline after acetylcholinesterase has hydrolyzed the acetylcholine into choline and acetic acid. This inhibits the synthesis of acetylcholine.

ASSIGNMENT  33.5

How might the effect of hemicholinium-3 be prevented?

Triethylcholine, diethylaminoethanol and other choline-related substances can also inhibit the synthesis of acetylcholine or cause the formation of false neurotransmitters.

TABLE  33.1
Influences on cholinergic neurotransmission

| Target | Inhibited by |
| --- | --- |
| synthesis of acetylcholine by choline-acetyltransferase | triethylcholine, diethylaminoethanol |
| storage of acetylcholine in vesicles of cholinergic nerve endings | false transmitters |
| release of acetylcholine into the synaptic cleft | botulin toxins, local anesthetics, $Ca^{++}$ deficiency, $Mg^{++}$ excess |
| binding of acetylcholine to postsynaptic receptors | curare (nicotinic receptor), hexamethonium (nicotinic receptor), atropine (muscarinic receptor) |
| hydrolysis of acetylcholine by acetylcholineesterase | physostigmine, neostigmine, alkylphosphate |
| transport across the membrane and reuptake of choline into the cholinergic neuron | hemicholinium-3 |

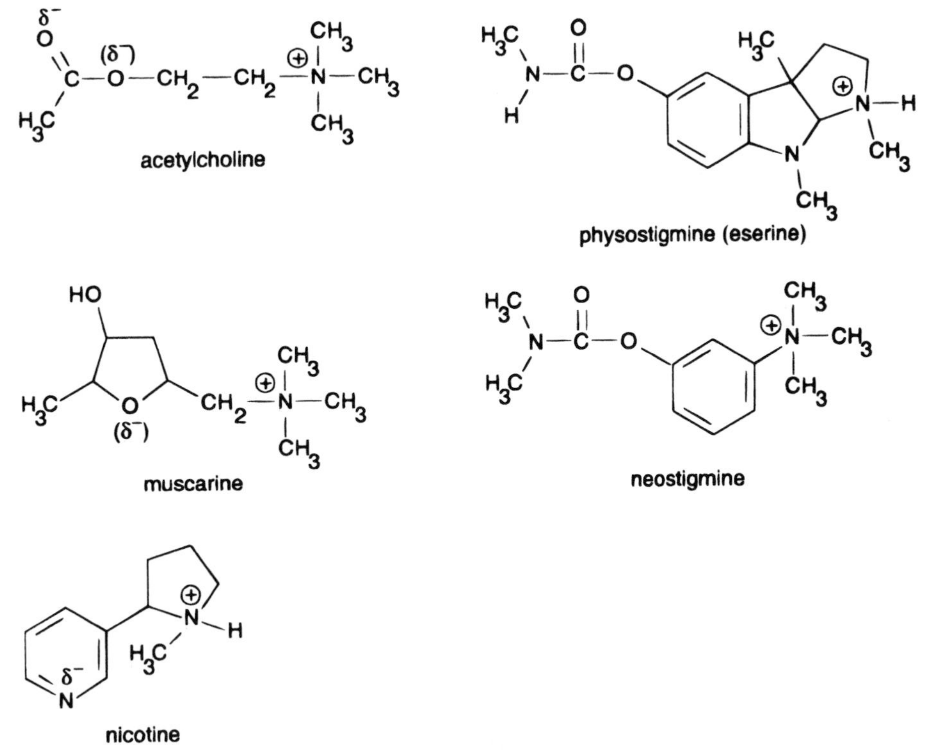

FIGURE 33.7
Structural formulae of the cholinergic agonists acetylcholine, muscarine and nicotine, and of the antagonists physostigmine and neostigmine

Cholinergic synapses are also present in the CNS, for example, in the respiratory center. In sympathetic nerve endings where norepinephrine is the neurotransmitter it is primarily the renewed uptake and metabolism of norepinephrine that terminate the transmitter effect (see Figure 33.8).

*Depolarization*

Postganglionic sympathetic nerve activity can cause *depolarization*. Norepinephrine is released by exocytosis. $Ca^{2+}$ ions and ATP play an essential part here. Norepinephrine diffuses to the effector cell where it can cause an effect by stimulating the $\alpha$- or $\beta$-adrenergic receptors. Only very little of the norepinephrine released appears in the bloodstream, while about 90% is absorbed into the varicosity (bulbous portion of the sympathetic nerve endings from where it is released). Intraneural norepinephrine not stored in the vesicles undergoes oxidative deamination in the mitochondria catalyzed by a monoamine oxidase (MAO).

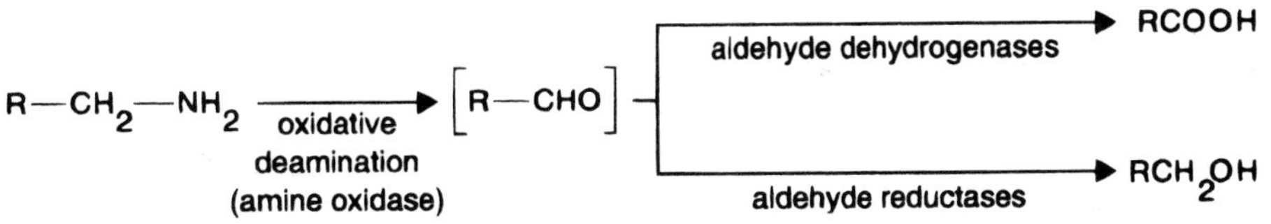

The aldehyde formed as an intermediate is reduced or oxidized in a subsequent reaction. The inactive metabolites diffuse into the bloodstream. In the effector organ norepinephrine is deaminated by oxidation and/or O-methylated by catechol-O-methyltransferase (COMT).

985

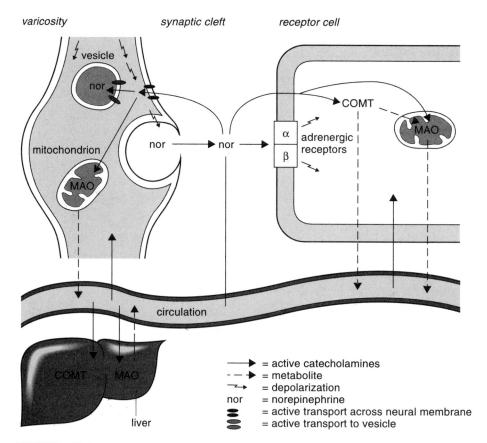

varicosity    synaptic cleft    receptor cell

FIGURE    33.8
Release and metabolic inactivation of norepinephrine

Catecholamines circulating in the bloodstream are metabolized in the liver by MAO and COMT.

The synthesis and storage of norepinephrine also form a target for toxic agents (see Figure 33.9).

The amino acid tyrosine is absorbed from the bloodstream intraneurally and hydroxylated by the enzyme tyrosine hydroxylase. In the cytosol, so-called dopa (3,4-dihydroxyphenylalanine) thus formed is then decarboxylated by dopa decarboxylase to dopamine (3,4-dihydroxyphenylethylamine).

A transport mechanism ensures the uptake of dopamine into the vesicles and this is where the synthesis in the dopaminergic neurons of the CNS ends and where dopamine acts as a neurotransmitter. In the vesicles of noradrenergic neurons dopamine is hydroxylated by dopamine $\beta$-hydroxylase into norepinephrine. In the adrenal medulla the hormone epinephrine can then be formed from norepinephrine by the enzyme phenylethanolamine N-methyltransferase.

Not only monoamines such as norepinephrine, dopamine or serotonin act as neurotransmitters in the CNS. Amino acids such as $\gamma$-aminobutyric acid (GABA) are also important as neurotransmitters.

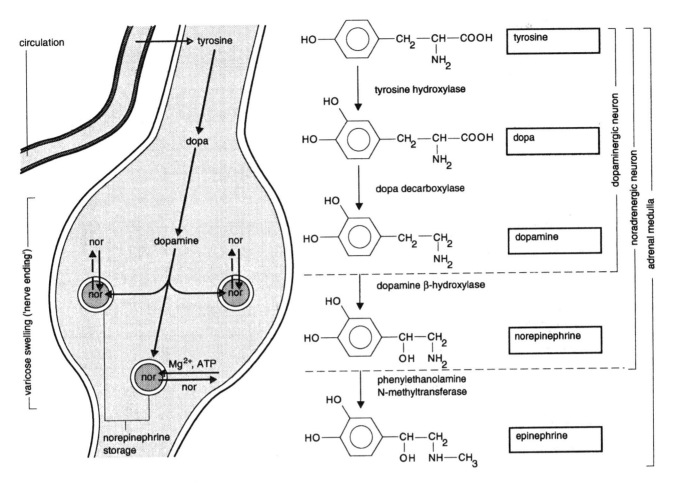

FIGURE   33.9
Synthesis and storage of norepinephrine

The discontinuity in nerve conduction caused by synaptic transmission, constitutes a useful opportunity for pharmacological agents to interfere. Neurotoxic effects also often occur here.

## 3   Classification of neurotoxic effects

Neurotoxic effects may be classified according to the site in the body where they occur. However, xenobiotics often show several neurotoxic effects. In addition, their effects often depend on dose, route of exposure or species. The following classification is based mainly on the results of experimental pathological research.

### 3.1   NOMENCLATURE

The *primary classification* of pathological responses is derived from the *site* of the toxic response followed by the suffix "-opathy" (see Table 33.2). Every lesion can be further classified by specifying the site more precisely. For example, an axonal lesion close to the cell body may be named a proximal axonopathy, or if it is close to the nerve ending a distal axonopathy. The location of the axons in the CNS and PNS are indicated by the terms "central" and "peripheral" respectively.

In the same way, the terms pre-and postsynaptopathy are used. In addition, the terms "motor" and "sensory" can be used to describe the function of the cell or process involved in the damage.

TABLE 33.2

Classification of neuropathological lesions according to cell type and location

| Cell type | Name | Further subdivision |
|-----------|------|---------------------|
| neuron | neuronopathy | sensory, motor |
| axon | axonopathy | proximal, distal |
| | | central, peripheral |
| synapse | synaptopathy | pre-, post- |
| oligodendrocyte | myelinopathy | |
| Schwann cell/astrocyte | astrocytic gliopathy | |
| vasculature | neurovasculopathy | |

ASSIGNMENT 33.6

How would you interpret the complex diagnosis "motor-sensory centriperipheral distal axonopathy"?

These terms of course say nothing about the nature of the lesion, only its site.

### 3.2 NEURONOPATHY

*Neuronopathy* refers to a lesion of the nerve cell body. It should not be confused with the earlier used term 'neuropathy' which is a general term for injury to peripheral nerves. Neurons are primarily dependent on glucose for their energy and are thus very sensitive to anoxic and hypoglycemic conditions.

Barbiturates induce anoxia in the brain, particularly in certain areas of the cerebral cortex such as the hippocampus and cerebellum. Permanent damage to the CNS by barbiturates however, is rare. Chronic exposure to carbon monoxide can cause lasting brain damage due to sclerosis of the white nerve tissue (leukoencephalopathy).

leukoencephalopathy; leuko = white, encephalon = brain.

Cyanide and azide inhibit cytochrome oxidase causing cytotoxic anoxia. Toxic substances can also affect the cell body of a neuron directly. For instance, methylmercury can initially cause a local loss of ribosomes and ultimately lead to disintegration of the Nissl bodies. Even the entire neuron may be destroyed. The cytostatic adriamycin affects neurons by intercalating with DNA. This inhibits RNA synthesis and ultimately neuron protein synthesis. Adriamycin hardly ever reaches the CNS.

ASSIGNMENT 33.7

What would you expect to see on comparison of the effects of adriamycin on the CNS with those of methylmercury?

The cytostatic action of the vinca alkaloid vincristine can cause accumulation of neurofibrils in the axons. This results in blockage of the axoplasmic transport via the neurofilaments. Aluminum can cause degranulation of neurofibrils, which has been believed to be the origin of Alzheimer's disease (senile dementia).

**Intermezzo**

Effects of cytotoxic substances on essential cell functions (energy metabolism, RNA- and protein synthesis, ionic homeostasis) may manifest themselves in the same way in all kinds of cell types: vacuolization, disintegration of the endoplasmic reticulum, cell death.

The space previously occupied by necrotizing nerve cells in the brain is filled by proliferating astrocytes. Glutamate administered to experimental animals in unphysiological quantities also causes neuropathy.

*Glutamate*

glutamate

*Glutamate* is a neurotransmitter that stimulates dendrites in the soma of certain nerve cells. Administration of glutamate can cause chronic depolarization of the soma membrane and ultimately disturb ionic homeostasis. Kainic acid (used as an anthelmintic in ascariasis) is even more potent than glutamate. Kainic acid is used to induce neuronal lesions in experimental animals.

### 3.3    AXONOPATHY

Toxic effects on the axon, especially in the peripheral nervous system, are the most common forms of neuropathy. The most extensively studied substances in this respect are acrylamide, carbon disulfide, n-hexane, methyl n-butyl ketone and organophosphates. These substances cause axonal degeneration in the *distal axons* of the central and peripheral nervous systems (centriperipheral *distal axonopathy*).

*Distal axonopathy*

The biochemical mechanisms underlying the toxic effects of these substances are not known. The ultimate effect is equivalent to cutting the nerve, resulting in Wallerian degeneration. Axonal degeneration distal to the lesion (chemical or physical) is observed.

### Intermezzo
*Wallerian degeneration*

When an axon is cut by chemical or physical means the same process is always observed microscopically. First, the ends on both sides of the lesion contract and swell. Next, the distal ends retract from their target cells and undergo degenerative changes known as Wallerian degeneration. The myelin retracts from the nodes and is ultimately destroyed together with the remains of the axon by phagocytosis. The soma of a neuron whose axon has been severed undergoes chromatolytic changes while the dendrites shrink.

The neuronal response to the lesion in the axon (Schwann cell clustering and demyelination) is prompted by the axon's attempts to repair itself by regeneration. There is increased synthesis activity in the cell body (together with swelling), dissolution of the Nissl bodies and movement of the nucleus towards the cell membrane.

*Chromatolysis*

This latter phenomenon is known as *chromatolysis* and indicates that new axoplasm is synthesized. The newly synthesized elements are transported along the axon and accumulate in the injured part.

Chemically induced distal axonopathy may be subdivided into two categories:

1.    axonopathy as caused by tri-*ortho*-cresyl phosphate, typically shows a focal or multifocal accumulation of smooth endoplasmic reticulum before the distal axon degenerates;

2.    substances such as carbon disulfide, acrylamide and n-hexane cause axonal swelling due to accumulation of filaments. It should be noted here that filaments are transported by slow axonal transport and smooth endoplasmic

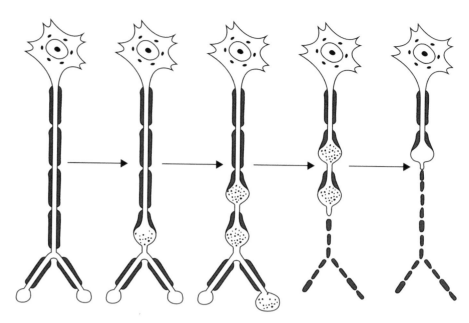

FIGURE 33.10
Degeneration of the axon, starting distally ('dying back')

reticulum by fast axonal transport. Degeneration that starts distally, known as "dying back", proceeds towards the cell body (see Figure 33.10).

For many axonal toxins, deregulation of intracellular energy production is the main cause of toxicity. Arsenic is a good example. Arsenic binds to lipoic acid, thus disrupting cocarboxylase function. In beri-beri-induced polyneuropathy, which is caused by thiamine (vitamin $B_1$) deficiency, interference with cocarboxylase activity is also involved. Thallium causes mitochondrial swelling and degeneration.

ASSIGNMENT 33.8

What will be the effect of thallium on the axon?

*Distal axonopathy*

The forms of axonopathy discussed so far belong to the category of *distal axonopathy*. There are two hypotheses for this kind of axonopathy:

- there is direct damage to neurofilaments, with those parts exposed for the longest time (mostly the distal parts of long axons) being affected first;
- the axonal transport of neurofilaments is delayed, so that the distal part of the axon is insufficiently supplied.

*Proximal axonopathy*

One form of *proximal axonopathy* is caused by $\beta,\beta$-imino diproprionitrile (IDPN). This substance is sometimes used in an animal model for motor neuron disease. The primary effect of IDPN is to delay the slow axonal transport of neurofilaments to the proximal axon, so that this part swells and the distal axon atrophies.

3.4 SYNAPTOPATHY

Neurotransmission may be affected by many substances. Notwithstanding, the integrity of the cells is by no means always threatened. The processes in the synapse on which xenobiotics may act are:

- biosynthesis and metabolism of the transmitter;
- axonal transport and release of the transmitter from storage granules;
- receptor-signal transmission;

- interaction of transmitter with the receptor;
- uptake and metabolism of the transmitter.

Interferences that cause no clear structural (irreversible) changes or which do not lead to toxic responses, belong to the field of neuropharmacology.

### Intermezzo

*Snake venom*

About one third of all 2500 known snake species are poisonous. Snake venom has two functions: it paralyzes the prey and starts the digestive process. The venoms of different snake species differ in composition. In view of its function, it is not surprising that snake venom contains enzymes. These may be enzymes that hydrolyze proteins and membrane components, leading to tissue necrosis and blood clotting. The paralytic effect of many snake venoms is caused by their attack on nerve membranes and/or skeletal muscles. The neuromuscular junction is often the target. Many snake venoms attack cholinergic neuromuscular transmission, albeit in various ways. Based on their mode of action, five main groups of snake venom toxins are currently distinguished:

1. non-competitive antagonists. These are paralytic toxins which bind (irreversibly) to the acetylcholine receptor without causing any biological activity. The prey usually dies, as its respiratory muscles no longer function;
2. the group of toxins that inhibit or merely increase the release of acetylcholine. The muscle cell is under- or overstimulated, so that it cannot react to nerve stimuli. The result is spasm or relaxation of the muscle;
3. the third type inhibits the enzyme acetylcholinesterase. This type of toxin is usually found in combination with the type described under 2;
4. the precise mode of action of the fourth group is still unknown. They are poisons responsible for damage to skin, connective tissue or skeletal muscles. They are known by some as myotoxins;
5. the last group is that of the cytotoxins and cardiotoxins. These toxins deregulate the membranes of numerous cells either by damaging them or by interfering with the transport of substances or the transduction of signals across the membrane.

*6-Hydroxydopamine*
sympathectomy = cutting of the sympathetic nerve

The toxicity of *6-hydroxydopamine* is significant. This amine is taken up in noradrenergic and dopaminergic axon endings and yields oxygen radicals through redox cycling. This causes a form of chemical sympathectomy which is commonly used as a model in experimental neurotoxicology.

> ASSIGNMENT   33.9
> What neurons are affected by 5,6–dihydroxytryptamine?

Postsynaptic destruction by kainic acid and glutamate has already been mentioned in section 3.2. The flavor enhancer monosodium glutamate has been much talked about following its use in baby foods and incrimination in the "Chinese restaurant syndrome" in adults.

Antagonists of the haloalkylamine type (such as phenoxybenzamine) can alkylate the $\alpha$-receptor. This causes a long-term inhibitory effect. Figure 33.11 indicates that alkylation of the receptor is preceded by a reversible interaction.

Another example is botulinum toxin produced by *Clostridium botulinum*. This toxin causes muscular paralysis by inhibiting the release of acetylcholine from the motor nerve endings.

The venom of the black widow spider prompts a very powerful release of acetylcholine from the storage granules, causing spasm and paralysis.

Other toxic substances affecting neurotransmission are boron hydride (decrease in norepinephrine and serotonin), carbon disulfide (decrease in norepinephrine and increase in dopamine), DDT and dieldrin (decrease in acetylcholine and norepinephrine), and manganese (decrease in serotonin, norepinephrine and dopamine).

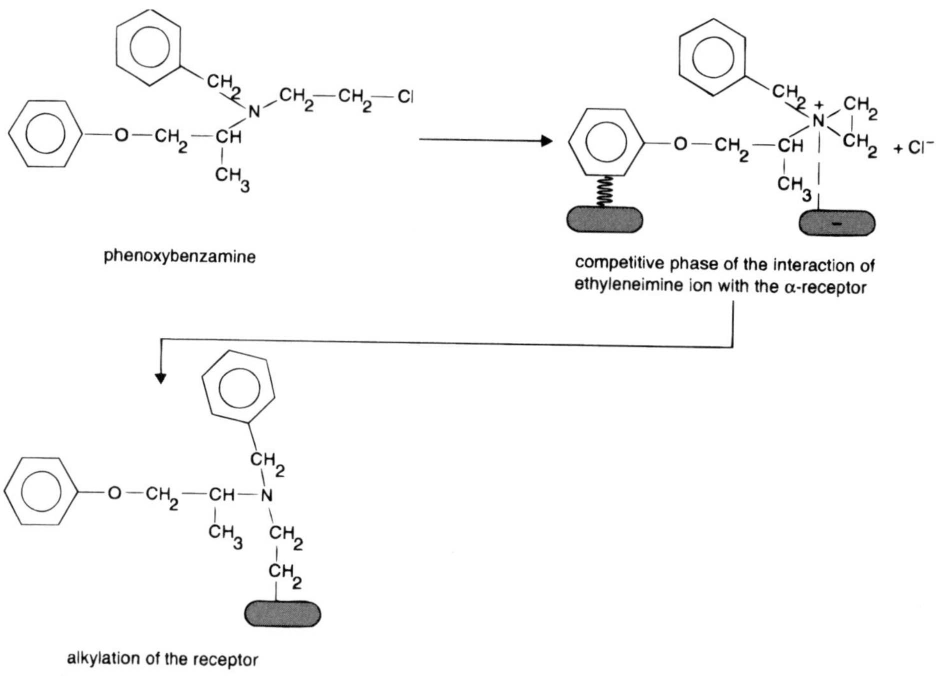

FIGURE 33.11
Interaction of phenoxybenzamine with the α-adrenergic receptor

3.5 MYELINOPATHY

*Causes of demyelination*

Loss of the myelin sheath, demyelination, can result from direct toxic action on the membrane structure. Other causes include inhibition of carbonic anhydrase or other enzymes involved in ionic and water transport, inhibition of enzymes involved in oxidative phosphorylation causing a reduction in the level of ATP (which is used for many transport functions) and chelation of metals.

> ASSIGNMENT 33.10
>
> In case of direct effects on the myelin sheath, fluid-filled vacuoles are often observed between the myelinic lamellae (intramyelinic edema). Explain this, on the basis of the information given above.

There are several examples of neurotoxins that have a direct effect on the myelin sheath. In the 1950s a number of very serious cases of *triethyltin* poisoning were reported in France (either fatal or causing permanent disability), following the use of Stalinon®, a diethyltin preparation for the treatment of acne, which was contaminated with triethyltin.

*Hexachlorophene*

The neurotoxic properties of the disinfectant *hexachlorophene* became apparent 30 years after its introduction. In 1972 a number of babies died in France because their baby talcum powder contained 6% hexachlorophene instead of the intended 3%. The cytotoxicity of hexachlorophene is caused by uncoupling of oxidative phosphorylation. Following those cases of poisoning, very strict guidelines were laid down for permitted levels of hexachlorophene in disinfectant soaps and dusting powders.

*Direct effects on oligodendrocytes and Schwann cells*

Demyelination may also be the result of direct action on oligodendrocytes and Schwann cells. Neurotoxins displaying this effect, include lead. (interfering with

Ca²⁺ transport in Schwann cells), and Triparanol®, used therapeutically as a cholesterol synthesis inhibitor. The latter, however, was found to be severely toxic among other reasons because it directly affects the fatty myelin sheath.

Demyelination, in which edema and blebs between the myelinic lamellae develop, is easily detected light microscopically because the blebs appear as vacuoles. Segmental demyelination as found on chronic exposure to perhexiline and diphtheria toxin is much more difficult to identify (see Figure 33.12).

*Summary*

Neurotoxins may be classified on the basis of the site of neurotoxic action. Several examples of neuronopathy, axonopathy, synaptopathy and myelinopathy have been discussed.

### 4 Test methods and some examples

Some years ago, an article reviewing the health risks from exposure to xenobiotics postulated the following:

*Cancer dominates nearly every discussion of health risks posed by chemical exposure and governs the premises of most of the statistical models devised to predict risk. No other health consequence enjoys such a status. But, if the entire gamut of toxicology is examined, systemic functional effects are more common, and probably more of a total health threat than cancer. For example, more than one fourth of the recommended workplace exposure standards (threshold limit values or TLVs) issued by the American Conference of Governmental Industrial Hygienists derived from effects on the nervous system. Since there is now so much ferment in risk modeling and analysis, it seems time to examine the novel and difficult issues posed by such effects.*

For more information on behavioral tests in toxicology, see Study unit 35

At the moment of writing no specific tests for neurotoxicity are required for routine toxicological research. The possible neurotoxicity of a substance can, however, have serious consequences for humans. Therefore, a variety of tests have been devised to be included in routine toxicological research. For example, behavioral tests and pharmacological methods are applied to examine clinically diagnosable changes in behavior.

If these tests identify changes in concentration, motor activity, posture, reflexes or autonomic functions, more specific tests will then be carried out. These

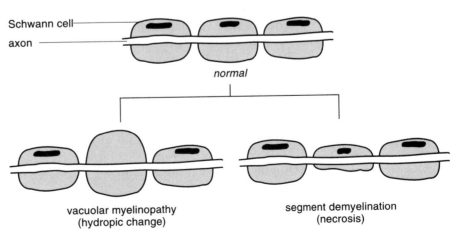

FIGURE   33.12
Myelinopathy

may be conditioning tests, or tests of spontaneous locomotor activity and coordination of balance.

For electrophysiological techniques in (neuro)toxicology, see Study unit 34

Very specific tests that are carried out for specific groups of substances, are the measurement of transmitter-stimulated adenylate cyclase and $Na^+/K^+$-ATPase (for substances affecting receptor function) and cholinesterase inhibition (for organophosphates and carbamates). Substances that affect impulse conduction such as DDT and pyrethroids can be studied using electrophysiological techniques.

Needless to say, in view of the complexity of the nervous system, routine pathological research is almost impossible. Recently, a large number of distal axonopathies, neuropathies and myelinopathies have been detected using a method that examines only two sites: the medulla oblongata and a nerve from the tibia. In this method, a particular technique of tissue fixation and staining is used.

Sometimes biochemical techniques can also be used, such as monitoring of cholesterol esters in plasma. An elevated plasma level of $\beta$-glucuronidase and $\beta$-galactosidase is characteristic of Wallerian degeneration. Measurement of cholinesterase in plasma, red blood cells and brain in order to test for cholinesterase inhibition is relatively simple and is routinely used for certain categories of pesticides. Although *in vitro* cultivation of nerve cells appears to pose no problems, in practice no *in vitro* tests are applied in routine neurotoxicity research yet.

The nervous system is an organ system that is often damaged during exposure at the work place. Since the nervous system has only a limited ability to repair itself, incipient injury as a result of exposure should be detected as soon as possible. Diagnosis of neuropathies is primarily a neurological speciality.

ASSIGNMENT 33.11

Although neurology has already concerned itself with the diagnosis of neuropathies for some time, diagnostic methods used in neurology are not necessarily applicable in neurotoxicology. Why is this so?

Unlike the neurologist, however, the neurotoxicologist nearly always deals with healthy subjects who had no reason to consult a doctor. In these individuals he has to look for abnormalities in the functioning of the nervous system which are usually still unnoticed and minor, but significant. The most sensitive method for doing this is to measure quantitative parameters in a group of exposed subjects and compare the values measured before exposure with those measured afterwards. Often such a *longitudinal* study is not possible because the exposure has already taken place. In that case a *cohort* study can be carried out. The values measured in a group of exposed workers can then be compared with those in a non-exposed but otherwise matched group of workers. The latter method is inevitably less sensitive, as comparison of two individuals for a particular parameter is always less exact than comparison of two values of a parameter within a single individual. The results may also be distorted by differences between the exposed and non-exposed group which are unrelated to exposure. One of the tasks of neurotoxicology is to find sensitive quantitative parameters for the functioning of the nervous system.

*Example of a parameter*

An example of such a parameter is the conduction speed in peripheral nerves. This parameter has long been successfully used in neurotoxicology.

Different substances with neurotoxic effects are known to affect different parts of the nervous system. Well-known examples are methanol, which attacks the optic nerve, lead, which initially affects peripheral motor nerves, and toluene, which in the case of chronic and extreme exposure (which applies to solvent abusers) causes cerebellar ataxia with atrophy of the cerebellum. Thus, if exposed subjects are to be examined for early neurological health effects it is not enough just to measure the conduction speeds of a few peripheral nerves.

*Broad range of methods*

It is therefore necessary to have a series of methods at hand which allow the measurement of a wide range of neurological functions. Since the methods have to be applied to healthy workers in an operational industrial situation, they have to meet other criteria as well.

Ideally this range of methods should have the following characteristics:

- the range is complete, that is to say every functional part of the nervous system is involved in at least one of the tests;
- the individual methods are specifically sensitive to neurological injury;
- the results are quantifiable;
- the findings are not easily manipulated by the subject tested and any attempts to do so are recognizable;
- the methods are not painful or unpleasant;
- the methods take little time;
- the equipment is mobile so that measurements can be taken at or close to the workplace.

The aim of this kind of study is to develop a range of methods which can check the proper functioning of parts of the peripheral nervous system as efficiently as possible.

The distal part of the peripheral nervous system is generally the most susceptible because of the length of the axons which extend from a cell body situated in or close to the spinal cord. Parameters which can be measured include sensitivity to vibration (e.g. whether or not the vibration of a tuning fork can be felt), the speed of nerve conduction, the refractory period, presence of tremors, ability of the test subject to stand still (stabilograph), auditory threshold and color perception.

*Neurotoxicity of pharmaceutical drugs, pesticides and other xenobiotics*

Exposure to pharmaceutical drugs occurs for the most part intentionally, certainly in the developmental phase of new drugs, under carefully controlled conditions. Drug-induced neurotoxic symptoms are therefore often clearly described. This is in contrast with environmental or dietary exposure.

*Solvents*

In toxicology, the term *solvents* usually means industrial solvents. These belong to various chemical categories, including aliphatic hydrocarbons (hexane), halogenated aliphatic hydrocarbons (methylene chloride), alcohols (methanol) and aromatic hydrocarbons (toluene).

Organic solvents are widely used in both industry and at home. The toxicity of n-hexane, methyl n-butyl ketone, methanol, ethanol and carbon disulfide has been described extensively. It is important to identify any symptoms of neurotoxicity at an early stage. It is therefore advisable also to assess the neurotoxicity of a substance.

In the majority of studies on the neurotoxicity of solvents, the solvents are treated as one group of substances, i.e. as if they have similar toxicological properties. It is true that the nervous system only has a limited number of ways at its disposal to react to toxic effects. The adverse effects may be found at various sites in the peripheral nervous system, although the most important neurotoxic solvents are known to cause distal neuropathies. It has not been possible to pinpoint specific sites in the CNS. Often the cerebellum is affected, but by no means always, and this is also not the only site that can be affected. The most common neurotoxic effects cannot easily be studied in experimental animals and no neuropathological data are available on workers chronically exposed to solvents. In cats, lesions in the optic tract were found after chronic exposure to n-hexane. In workers exposed for longer periods of time to n-hexane a deviation was found in the evoked potentials produced by a flashing light. A similar effect was seen in glue sniffers. Also effects on EEG and local changes in blood circulation (angiography) in the CNS have been observed following exposure to solvents.

*Combined exposure*

A great problem is *combined exposure*. Many industrial solvents are used in combination with other solvents or chemicals. Often very little is known about the toxic effects of such combinations.

The neurotoxic oxidation product of both hexane and methyl n-butyl ketone is 2,5-hexanedione. Probably also in the case of carbon disulfide, biotransformation products are the toxic agents. Carbon disulfide is converted to $CO_2$. The sulfur released may bind to functionally important thiol groups of proteins, resulting in inhibition of enzymes that are vital to the maintenance of cellular homeostasis. It might also be that carbon disulfide reacts with amino acids to form various neurotoxic dithiocarbamates or (like hexanedione) binds to neurofilaments during the latter's axonal transport.

*Heavy metals*

The toxicity of *heavy metals* is largely due to their reaction with sulfhydryl groups. Lipophilic organometallic compounds (such as methylmercury and triethyltin) easily pass the blood-brain barrier. Inorganic metallic compounds also reach the brain tissue. As an example, the neurotoxicity of lead will be discussed in the following.

Exposure to lead originates from its use in batteries, roofing materials, lead smelters, solder in food cans, poor glazing on crockery, old-fashioned lead water pipes and lead paints (flakes ingested by children). Emission is primarily from the use of alkyllead compounds as anti-knock agents in gasoline. Lead is then released into the environment as an oxide or chloride. The body burden of lead can be determined by measuring the lead level in the erythrocytes or by measuring the inhibition of hemoglobin synthesis, which is caused by lead. The latter phenomenon explains the porphyrinogenic effect of lead.

Children are particularly sensitive to lead. This may be expressed in the form of hyperkinesia, learning difficulties and even mental retardation. The pathological anatomical characteristics of lead neurotoxicity are listed in Table 33.3.

*Drugs*

Drugs designed to influence synaptic transmission are always suspected to be neurotoxic. There are many of them.

*Monoamine oxidase inhibitors*

*Monoamine oxidase inhibitors (MAO)*, for example, have been widely used as antidepressants or in the treatment of hypertension. Because of their side-effects this category of substances is now hardly applied anymore for such conditions.

*Methylphenyltetrahydropyridine (MPTP)*
MPTP is of interest in connection with basic research into Parkinson's disease

The selective neurotoxicity caused by 1-*methyl-4-phenyl-1,2,3,6-tetrahydropyridine (MPTP)* (see Figure 33.13), on the other hand, receives considerable attention. The strongly neurotoxic properties of this substance were first noticed in 1983 in a number of heroin addicts in the San Francisco Bay area. Their own attempts to synthesize a meperidine analog (a centrally acting opioid analgesic) yielded MPTP as a byproduct, which they unwittingly injected. Intravenous administration of MPTP causes akinesia and tremor, a picture similar to that of Parkinson's disease. Further research revealed that dopamine depletion in the

TABLE 33.3
Pathological anatomical characteristics of lead neurotoxicity

| Toxicity | Characteristics |
|---|---|
| encephalopathy | - preceded by fatigue, headache<br>- necrosis in cortex<br>- damage to blood vessels<br>- disturbance of amino acid balance<br>- edema |
| peripheral neuropathy | - in early stages, delayed stimulus conduction in motor nerves<br>- in humans: wrist drop and/or foot drop<br>- axonal degeneration in motor nerves<br>- in experimental animals: segmental demyelination |
| *in vitro* toxicity | - disturbance of transmitter function due to competition with $Ca^{2+}$ and $Na^+$ transport |

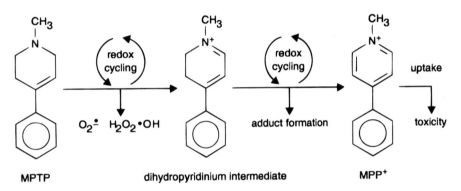

FIGURE 33.13
Conversion of methylphenyltetrahydropyridine (MTPT) to the methyl-phenylpyridinium ion (MPP⁺)

substantia nigra was the likely cause of toxicity. MPTP is now known to be oxidized by monoamine oxidase to $MPP^+$ via a dihydropyridinium intermediate (see Figure 33.13). $MPP^+$ appears to be selectively taken up into the substantia nigra via neuronal absorption mechanisms for dopamine. Redox cycling causes the formation of oxygen radicals and thus depletion of dopamine.

*Organophosphate insecticides* act by inhibiting acetylcholinesterase. The cholinergic transmission of motor nerves (nerve-muscle), the ganglia of the sympathetic nervous system, the parasympathetic nervous system and the CNS is first activated and subsequently blocked (depolarization followed by hyperpolarization). Also, the muscarinic receptor response (parasympathetic response) increases.

*Organophosphate insecticides*
For the mode of action of an organophosphate insecticide see Study unit 34

ASSIGNMENT 33.12
Which antidote would you suggest for the increased parasympathetic activity induced by organophosphates?

A well-known organophosphate insecticide is parathion.
*Parathion* is activated to paraoxon by biotransformation. Organophosphate acetylcholinesterase inhibitors have the following general structure:

$$X - \overset{\overset{\displaystyle O\ (0\%S)}{\|}}{\underset{\underset{\displaystyle Y'R'}{|}}{P}} - YR$$

where R and R' represent alkyl or aromatic groups or a hydrogen atom; Y and Y' generally are O but may also be S, N or C; X is an easily hydrolyzable group. The reaction of an organophosphate with the active site of acetylcholinesterase is represented in Figure 33.14.

Dephosphorylation of acetylcholinesterase via hydrolysis is a slow process. Reactivation of the enzyme can be accelerated by nucleophiles (see Figure 33.15).

Some organophosphates such as *malathion* and *dipterex* are more toxic to insects than to mammals because of the differences in biotransformation.

Finally, the many analogues should be mentioned that have been manufactured from the prototype of the organophosphate cholinesterase inhibitor group dyflos, *diisopropyfluorophosphate (DFP)*. These have been studied extensively as war gases during World War II

## 5    Summary

The nervous system is divided into the central nervous system (CNS) and peripheral nervous system (PNS). Apart from neurons the CNS also contains various types of glial cells. The PNS can be further subdivided into afferent and efferent nerve fibers, and the sympathetic and parasympathetic nervous systems. The nervous system is well protected both chemically and physically against injury.

The synapse contains various types of receptors. Their specificity for neurotransmitters such as acetylcholine and norepinephrine varies. The location of receptors also varies: there are pre- and postsynaptic receptors. The sites of biosynthesis and degradation routes of transmitters constitute important targets for toxic substances.

Neurotoxic effects can be classified on the basis of the sites at which they occur. They can be divided into neuronopathies, axonopathies, synaptopathies and myelinopathies. The screening of substances for neurotoxic properties is not (yet) part of the standard procedure in toxicity research. However, a variety of

dyphlos (DFP)

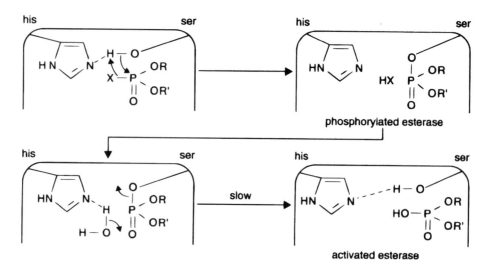

**FIGURE   33.14**
Reaction of an organophosphate with acetylcholinesterase
Hydrolysis of the phosphate from the esteratic site of the enzyme is slow; for some inhibitors this may take months.

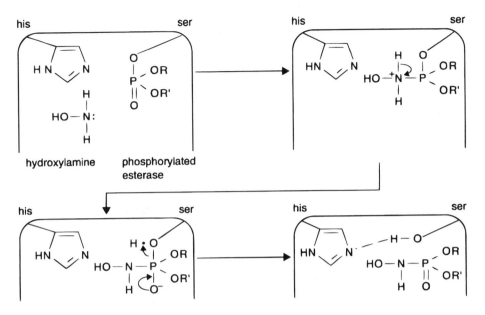

FIGURE  33.15
Reactivation of acetylcholinesterase by a hydroxylamine

*in vivo* and *in vitro* methods have been developed to screen for potential neuro-toxicity. Considerable attention is paid to the development of sensitive tests which can be used in the workplace. By way of illustration, a more detailed account is given of the neurotoxicity of solvents (hexane), lead, MAO inhibitors, MPTP and organophosphate insecticides.

## FEEDBACK

### Answers to the assignments

33.1  When the body is at rest the parasympathetic nervous system is still active, so that the digestive organs (intestinal peristalsis, release of digestive enzymes etc.) are still stimulated.

33.2  The lipophilicity of a substance is often determined by measuring its distribution between an octanol layer and a water layer.
    The distribution coefficient $P$ is the ratio of the concentration in the octanol layer to that in the water layer. For theoretical reasons log $P$ is usu-

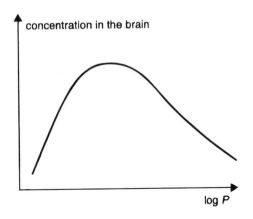

ally used. The relationship between the lipophilicity (log $P$) and the concentration found in brain tissue will be parabolic (or bilinear).

An increase in lipophilicity (log $P$) will lead to better penetration of the brain. A further increase in log $P$ will mean that passive diffusion through the membrane no longer acts effectively. The substance will, as it were, stick in the membrane.

33.3  The effects of atropine on the heart will be:
- negatively inotropic and chronotropic effects via postsynaptic M-receptors;
- inhibition of the release of acetylcholine via the presynaptic M-receptors on cholinergic neurons (and thus inhibition of the acetylcholine effects on postsynaptic M-receptors), but also inhibition of the release of norepinephrine via presynaptic M-receptors on adrenergic neurons (and thus inhibition of the norepinephrine effects on postsynaptic $\alpha$- and $\beta$ receptors).

33.4  Yes, because it is very likely that, again, especially the negative and positive charges of acetylcholine play a part in the binding of acetylcholine to the esterase. Thus, if inhibitors are to occupy the same binding site, they need to meet the same structural requirements.

33.5  Hemicholinium-3 acts by competitive inhibition of choline reuptake. By giving more choline the effect of hemicholinium-3 will be diminished.

33.6  This points to lesions of distal axons of both motor and sensory neurons in the central *and* peripheral nervous systems.

33.7  The cytostatic adriamycin does not enter the CNS, but methylmercury does. Adriamycin is known to cause cardiomyopathy; hence a maximum dose is prescribed for its application in humans.

33.8  Probably a distal axonopathy because energy metabolism is disturbed at that location.

33.9  Serotonin (5-hydroxytryptamine) is specifically taken up by serotoninergic neurons. 5,6-Dihydroxytryptamine is absorbed by serotoninergic neurons via the same mechanism. As in the case of 6-hydroxydopamine, oxidation (of 5,6-dihydroxytryptamine) leads to the formation of oxygen radicals. The result is specific degeneration of serotoninergic neurons.

33.10  Inhibition of ATP-dependent transport causes a change in intracellular osmolarity and hence disturbance of homeostasis.

33.11  The approach in neurology is not necessarily suited to solve the problem at issue here. The neurologist is approached by a "patient", that is to say someone with a problem and who wants to be cured. All being well, however, the neurotoxicologist is dealing with "healthy" subjects who had no reason to consult a doctor. In these healthy individuals he has to look for abnormalities in the nervous system which usually are minor but significant and unnoticed yet. He may find significant abnormalities in individual subjects. However, more often significant differences will be found between an exposed group taken as a whole and a carefully chosen control group. In order to identify such differences, sensitive methods are needed which produce quantifiable parameters.

33.12 A high dose of atropine, an inhibitor of the M(muscarinic) receptor response. Another non-specific treatment is activated charcoal (to bind the organophosphate in the gastro-intestinal tract) combined with gastric lavage. Finally, in some cases, depending on the organophosphate involved, the esterase can be reactivated (see Figure 33.15).

# Contents Study unit 34
# Functional neurotoxicology

0-8493-9232-2/96/$0.00 + $.50
© 1996 by CRC Press, Inc.

# Study unit 34

# Functional neurotoxicology

*T. A. de Vlieger*

INTRODUCTION

The nervous system is extremely sensitive to a number of substances, the chemical nature of which is very diverse. This sensitivity to chemicals has long been recognized, although at the time it was not realized that the effects of some substances resulted from contact with the nervous tissue. The fruit of the *Physostigma* plant, for example, has long been used in Africa as the "bean of judgment" because of the lethal effect it sometimes has when swallowed by suspects. The judges did not know that the bean was not lethal unless thoroughly chewed before being swallowed, so that a substance acting as an anticholinesterase would be released, which caused death. This substance subsequently served as a model in the development of nerve gases. It is not only man who applies the extreme sensitivity of the nervous system for aggressive or defensive purposes; animals and plants can do so as well. The inadvertent consumption of "fugu", for example, can be lethal, due to the neurotoxin present in this fish. Such defence mechanisms therefore tend to go hand in hand with a striking appearance. This is the fugu's defence against any hostile attacks, which, of course, only works if the attacking party actually recognizes the fish. In fact, victims are still claimed every year because this fish is considered to be a delicacy in Japan. Many snake and wasp poisons also contain neurotoxins, which enable these animals to catch prey larger than themselves (see Figure 34.1).

One could say that neurotoxicology has already been in existence for a long time as an "applied science" in nature. Many of the vegetable or animal substances which affect the nervous system have been used as the starting point for the development of drugs.

The function of the nervous system is to conduct and process information. Most of these activities take place by means of electrical phenomena. In this study unit, we shall try to provide an insight into the way in which toxins and other xenobiotics can disturb these electrical phenomena. The externally observable effects of poisoning can obviously vary widely, depending on the neurotoxin studied. This is because the nervous system is involved in virtually every activity of the animal organism, which means that neurotoxins may affect a wide range of functions. The external or behavioral effects will be discussed in Study unit 35. In the present unit, we will focus on the effects on the excitable neuronal membrane.

Researchers often make use of neurotoxins in studying the way in which the nervous system works. For a good understanding of the mechanism of action of toxins, some knowledge of the electrophysiology of the neuron is required.

*Indirect effects*
*Direct effects*

Neurotoxic effects leading to changes in the electrical properties of neurons can be subdivided into two major categories: *indirect effects*, resulting from structural changes induced by toxic substances, and *direct effects*.

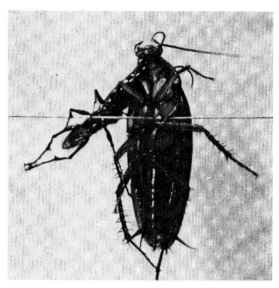

FIGURE 34.1
A wasp stinging a cockroach, injects a neurotoxin which paralyses it.

For details on structural changes within the nervous system in general, see also Study units 15 and 33.

In this study unit, we shall discuss the consequences of *swollen axons* and/or *demyelinization* on impulse conduction. In neurotoxicology, it is important to distinguish between the environments of the separate components of the nervous system. The peripheral parts are exposed to substances to a far greater extent than the central parts, which are shielded by the protective blood-brain barrier.

Next, the toxic effects on structures directly involved in electrical phenomena, namely the *ion channels*, are discussed. In order to throw more light on these phenomena, we shall also elaborate on the techniques used to study these channels. Finally, we shall touch on the effects of neurotoxins on neuromuscular and other *synapses*.

LEARNING OBJECTIVES

After having studied this unit, you should be able to:

— indicate how xenobiotics can disturb the electrophysiological properties of nerves
— describe the sites in the neuron and the nervous system at which xenobiotics act
— explain the main techniques by which electrophysiological changes *in vitro* and *in vivo* can be detected
— give some examples of substances which can cause electrophysiological changes and where possible indicate how these changes are brought about.

*Study hints*

In order to assess whether your prior knowledge is sufficient, a number of characteristics of neuronal electrical phenomena with which you are expected to be familiar are listed below. If you are not, we advise you to consult a book on neurophysiology.

a In the nervous system, a number of electrical phenomena are distinguished which differ in nature and shape. Some examples are action potentials, synaptic potentials and receptor potentials.

b  Sensory cells translate all kinds of physical and/or chemical processes into electrical activity. A receptor potential is produced in the process. Some sensory cells directly transform receptor potentials into a series of action potentials (e.g. all sensory cells in the skin) while in others, a synaptic connection is also established (rods and cones in the eye and the hair cells of the hearing and balance organs).

c  The physiological basis for these phenomena is formed by:

- the uneven distribution of ions over the inside and outside of the cell, which is maintained by energy-consuming processes;
- structural proteins in the membrane which allow ions to permeate selectively (the ion channels). These will be discussed in more detail in the section dealing with blockers of ion channels.

Whether ion channels are open or closed depends on various factors, such as the existing membrane potential or the binding of a transmitter molecule to a receptor. The *amplitude* and *direction* of any ionic current through the membrane depends upon the Nernst equilibrium potential for the ion concerned as well as on the ambient membrane potential. Action potentials are caused by a special category of ion channels, namely potential-dependent channels.

If you are familiar with the concepts above and know how to use them, the study load of this unit should not be more than 3 student learning hours.

## STUDY CORE

### 1  Changes in conductive properties caused by structural damage

Figure 34.2 shows a schematic representation of a motor neuron (a) the process (axon) of which is connected to a muscle, and of a sensory neuron (b) with the axon running from the skin or muscles to the central nervous system. Please note the names and location of the various parts. The long fibers (axons) of the neurons are sensitive to a great number of toxic substances which are active via many different biochemical routes, but whose common toxic characteristic is thought to be that eventually axonal transport is affected.

ASSIGNMENT  34.1

Why are motor and sensory neurons particularly sensitive to disturbances of the intracellular transport system?

### 1.1  STRUCTURAL DAMAGE TO AXONS

Damage to nerve fibers, whether of mechanical or chemical origin, is often accompanied by swelling and constrictions of the fiber. On the basis of physiological knowledge, one can hypothesize that such deformations may result in a number of *disturbances in the conduction of impulses*, such as a decrease in conduction rate, total blockage of action potential conduction or other abnormalities. Assuming that during the development of such axonal swellings no essential changes in the membrane composition occur, impulse blocking can be explained as follows.

*Disturbances in impulse conduction*

The left-hand side of Figure 34.3 shows the most important electrical phenomena occurring while the action potential is conducted. The axon shown has an action potential on the left. The opening in the membrane represents the opening of ion channels through which ions (mainly Na⁺ and K⁺) move.

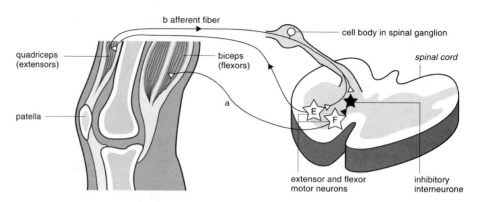

FIGURE   34.2

Diagram of two types of peripheral neurons: sensory neurons (b) which transport sensory information from skin and muscles, and motor neurons (a) which transmit information to the skeletal muscles.

Note the position of the cell bodies of both types of neurons, in the spinal ganglia and spinal cord, respectively. The locations where the action potential is produced are, in the first case, in the muscle (following sensory stimulation) and, in the second case, inside the spinal cord (following synaptic activity). The direction of transport within the long fibers (axons) of both cell types is thus opposite.

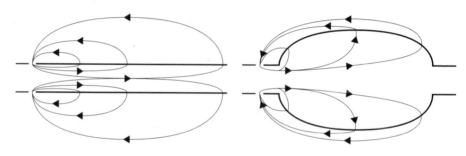

FIGURE   34.3

The action potential is conducted by local current circuits.

Sudden distention of a nervous fiber (the axon) causes the local circuit currents to spread over a much larger membrane surface, with the result that depolarization on the membrane which is not active will be much lower.

*Local circuit currents*

The movement of ions causes *local circuit currents* to develop around the active area. These currents will depolarize the membrane which is not yet activated, so that an action potential can arise there too. This is why the action potential is often referred to as a *self-propagating* phenomenon.

ASSIGNMENT   34.2

Why does the action potential in an axon move in one direction only?

The right-hand side of Figure 34.3 shows the situation occurring in a swollen axon. Needless to say, the local circuit currents will now have to cover a much greater membrane surface area. Consequently, the current density will decrease, as will the depolarization generated locally. The reduction in depolarization may be so considerable that the threshold is no longer surpassed. In such a case, the

*Blockage of conduction*
*Delay in conduction*

swelling has caused the conduction to be *blocked*. If no blockage occurs, a *delay in conduction* may be observed. This delay is established as follows.

As the membrane is very thin and separates two conductive fluids, its capacity is quite considerable (approximately 1 $\mu$F cm$^{-2}$). Any current which passes through the membrane has to charge or discharge this capacity, and this takes time.

ASSIGNMENT   34.3

Can you think of a reason for the favorable effect of the myelin sheath on the conduction rate of the action potential?

It will thus take longer to depolarize the membrane at a swelling than in an unswollen area. This is why at a swelling the action potential will, as it were, 'hesitate' for a moment.

*Repetitive firing*

Another phenomenon which may occur at a swelling is reflection or *repetitive firing*. This phenomenon is related to the one just described. After a stimulus, the neuron continues to produce action potentials for some time, but these run in the wrong direction. The delay caused by the swelling may be so great that the membrane, which had become refractory due to the passing action potential, has enough time to become excitable again and is then also brought to the threshold value again by the depolarizing current which is still present. Since the action potential will then go back in the direction from which it came, the term *reflection* is used.

*Reflection*

ASSIGNMENT   34.4

Try to analyze how repetitive firing can be caused by axonal swellings.

Within this context, it should be noted that the irregularities in conduction discussed so far bear a resemblance to similar phenomena in the heart (see Study unit 26). However, do bear in mind that the above involves only one cell, whereas the heart is a whole tissue. Local circuit currents, as mentioned before, are of major importance in the electrophysiological techniques discussed in section 4. Such techniques can be used to determine the presence of neurotoxic damage in intact animals and in humans.

It may well be possible that there are other ways in which deviations in the conductive system of neurons involving disturbances in transport may develop. After all, we have assumed that the composition of the membrane is not altered by neurotoxic substances. Ion channels, however, forming part of the membrane, need regular replacement. They are thought to be produced in the cellular nucleus and to find their way to the axon via the transport system.

*Changes in the composition of ion channels*
Doxorubicin is an anthracycline derivative, an antibiotic with an anti-tumor effect

*Changes in the composition of ion channels* in the membrane are also thought to cause disturbances in conduction. It is likely that both processes occur. More specific effects are believed to be exerted by substances affecting the sensory fibers first and damaging the motor fibers only at a later stage. Following doxorubicin intoxication, for example, the sensory ganglia may have lost their function entirely, while the motor cells are still intact. In this context, some toxicologists use the

TABLE   34.1
Substances which may cause conductive disorders through swelling

| Substance | Application |
|---|---|
| acrylamide | industrial raw material |
| isoniazid | antibacterial drug used in the treatment of tuberculosis |
| 2,5-hexanedione | metabolite of organic solvents such as n-hexane |
| $\beta,\beta'$-iminodipropionitril (IDPN) | raw material for plastic fibers |
| *Vinca* alkaloids, including vincristine, vinblastine | cytostatics |

term *toxicokinetic effect*. After all, the sensory ganglia are located outside the spinal cord, while the motor cells are located in the ventral horn, of the spinal cord. Sensory cells are therefore believed to be much more accessible.

*Delayed neuropathy*

This line of thought is challenged somewhat by our knowledge of substances which have exactly the opposite effect, i.e. they damage the motor cells first and then the sensory ones. An example of this phenomenon is *delayed neuropathy*, which is induced by organophosphates.

Secondary to the damage to the axon, the myelin sheath may also be affected. This effect is to be distinguished from the type of damage which will be discussed next.

## 1.2   SUBSTANCES WHICH PRIMARILY AFFECT THE MYELIN SHEATH

A group of substances which primarily affect the myelin sheath are known collectively as myelinotoxins (Table 34.2).

Myelinated axons run the risk of being damaged by substances which affect the cells responsible for the formation of myelin, the Schwann cells. In general, as long as demyelinization is not too advanced and has not been followed by degradation of the axon itself, conduction is not entirely blocked. The conduction rate, however, will be reduced because the action of the myelin sheath has been diminished.

ASSIGNMENT   34.5

Try to list the successive characteristics of conduction in a myelinated axon during progressive demyelinization.

*Crosstalk*

During continuous intoxication, swellings may develop, and it is possible that 'crosstalk' will occur. Crosstalk is the phenomenon of an active axon stimulating an adjacent axon. This is in itself the result of the local circuit currents. Under normal conditions, local circuit currents are also present, but the rigid arrangement of axons and the insulating effect of the myelin sheath prevent these currents from stimulating neighboring axons.

## 1.3   SUBSTANCES AFFECTING CELL BODIES

As a rule, cell bodies of neurons are injured when vital functions of a cell are affected, as may also occur in other types of cells. Basically, these effects are not much different from those leading to axon degeneration. They are mentioned

*Dying forward*

separately here since primary damage to the cell body is characterized by "*dying*

TABLE   34.2
Myelinotoxins

| |
|---|
| hexachlorophene |
| isoniazid |
| cyanate |
| triethyltin |
| salicyl anilides: fungicides |
| pyrithiamine: a thiamine antagonist |
| carbon monoxide |
| cyanide |
| lead |
| tellurium |
| diphtheria toxin |

*forward"*. This means that the process of degeneration starts at the cell body, after which the axon degenerates from the cell body towards its ending. The opposite phenomenon is termed *"dying backward"*, with the axons starting to degenerate at their ends and the process of degeneration progressing towards the cell body. An example of a substance which particularly affects the cell body is kainic acid. Its effect is explained in section 3b and in the previous study unit.

## 1.4   CELLULAR TRANSPORT MECHANISM FOR THE DISTRIBUTION OF SUBSTANCES

*Crossing the blood brain barrier via neuronal transport*

Special mention should be made of the phenomenon that certain organisms or substances use the neuronal transport mechanism in order to reach the central nervous system from peripheral areas. This is how the blood-brain barrier is crossed. To achieve this, however, the relevant substances first have to penetrate the nerve endings in the periphery. Tetanus toxin is able to do this. This toxin disturbs the inhibitory transmission in the spinal cord. Viruses can also use this penetration route. This system is used in research to trace the nervous pathways, for example by allowing fluorescent substances to be transported via axons. These substances are injected into the tissue near the endings of motor neurons and subsequently absorbed by the neuron. After some time, to allow transport of the substance to take place, the entire length of the relevant neuron will become marked.

## 1.5   SPECIAL SENSITIVITY OF NERVE ENDINGS

In nearly all cases of neuronopathy, whether it affects primarily the cell body, the axon or the myelin sheath, the nerve endings are observed to suffer *impaired function at an early stage*. As yet, the cause of this is unknown. In man, the subjective experience of malfunctioning of the senses is often one of the first symptoms of neuronopathy. In such cases it is not always easy to precisely localize the injury, since both peripheral and central interruption of sensory pathways will result in defective perception. Animal experiments, which allow examination of isolated sensory organs show that disorders of the Vater Pacini corpuscles (pressure corpuscles) and of muscle spindles do indeed occur. A well-known example of a toxic substance genuinely specific for sensory organs is the antibiotic streptomycin, which has toxic effects on the sensory cells in the auditory and balancing organ.

## 2   Direct effects on ion channels

The action potential is produced as a result of the presence of potential-excitable ion channels in the neuronal membrane.

Axons generally have only two types of ion channels (as opposed to cell bodies and nerve endings), namely $Na^+$ and $K^+$ channels. These are specialized membrane proteins which protrude through the membrane and, depending on the membrane potential, selectively allow ions to pass the membrane. In the past, the presence of these channels was demonstrated by means of the *voltage-clamp method*.

*Patch-clamp method*

Nowadays, however, another model, the so-called *patch-clamp method* is widely used. The principle is illustrated in Figure 34.4. The method is based on the phenomenon that, if specially treated, the point of a glass capillary can establish very tight contact with cell membranes. This contact is so tight that small dissolved particles, such as ions, cannot pass. The result is that the part of the membrane which is in contact with the pipette is completely isolated from the rest of the membrane and that through the pipette, only the current passing through

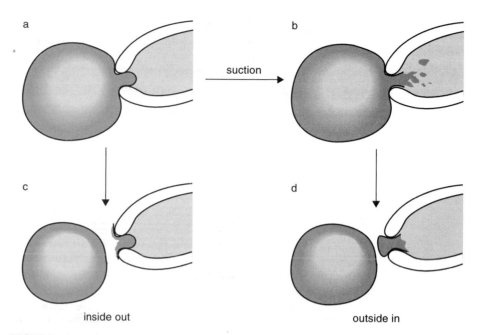

FIGURE   34.4

The patch-clamp method

In both cases, the method involved pressing a clean pipette against a cell, so that a "giga-seal" is formed between the glass wall and the cell membrane. (The term giga-seal originates from the resistance formed between the glass and the membrane, which has to be in the order of giga-ohms). In this cell-attached configuration (a), channels can be recorded. Underpressure can then be applied inside the pipette, which will break the patch. In this way, the "whole-cell" configuration (b) is obtained, which enables ionic currents through the cell to be measured.

By removing the pipette, starting from situations a and b, a membrane vesicle is first formed, followed by an isolated patch by breaking either the outside of the membrane vesicle or the part of the vesicle inside the pipette. The original inside of the membrane is thus facing either towards the pipette (d) or the other way (c).

that part of the membrane (the patch) is measured. It is also possible to separate the patch from the rest of the membrane. Ionic currents through a very tiny area of the membrane can then be studied, with full control of the composition of the fluids on either side of the membrane being possible.

The patch-clamp method has considerably increased our insight into the nature and function of ion channels. Figure 34.5 shows the result of a patch-clamp recording. The most striking feature is that the channel does not conduct continuously, but is either open or closed. This seems to apply to all other channels.

*Na+ –channel*

*Two closing mechanisms*

*Na activation*

*Na inactivation*

The *Na+ –channel*, which is responsible for quick depolarization during the action potential, can roughly be described as follows (see also Figure 34.6). It is a large protein with a pore through which Na+ ions pass selectively. This permeability, however, depends on the membrane potential in a particular way. This can be seen as follows. The Na ion channel has *two closing mechanisms*, one of which is closed during resting membrane potential and opens rapidly during depolarization (*the m-gate*). This is sometimes referred to as *Na activation*. The other closing mechanism (*the h-gate*) is open in the resting state and closes somewhat more slowly during depolarization than the m-gate opens. This mechanism is referred to as *Na–inactivation*. Thanks to these two mechanisms, the channel is well suited to performing its role in the process of the action potential. By opening at depolarization, the m-gate ensures a rapid (depolarizing) start to the action potential; in other words, the Na+ flow is started. By closing somewhat later, the h-gate initiates the repolarizing part of the action potential (needless to say, the K+ channel also contributes to repolarization). As may be concluded from the above, the Na+ channel protein is a very complex molecule. It is therefore not surprising that

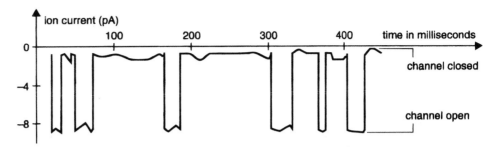

## FIGURE 34.5
### Patch-clamp recordings of ion channels

Ion channels are either open or closed. In patch-clamp recordings, whether an ion channel is open or closed can be deduced from whether or not a current can pass through. The recording in this figure shows an acetylcholine-influenced ion channel in a muscle cell.

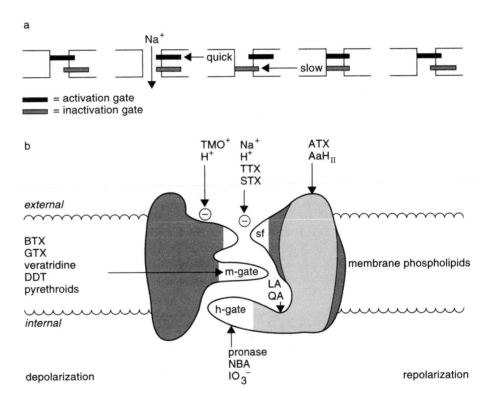

## FIGURE 34.6
### The functioning of the Na⁺ channel

a. Diagram of opening and closing of the Na⁺ channel (m-gate and h-gate respectively) during the action potential.

b. Diagram of the Na⁺ channel protein within the nervous membrane. The key functional components and pharmacological sites of action are indicated. Tetrodotoxin (TTX), saxitoxin (STX) and hydrogen ions ($H^+$) block the selectivity filter (sf) and bind to the same negatively charged site as the Na⁺ ions (Na⁺). Trimethyl oxonium ($TMO^+$) makes the ion channel unexcitable to TTX and reduces its permeability to Na⁺. $TMO^+$ and $H^+$ bind to a second negatively charged site on the external end of the ion channel. The enzyme pronase, N-bromoacetamide (NBA) and iodate ions ($IO_3^-$) prevent the closure of the h-gate on the inside of the membrane.

Sea anemone toxins (ATX) and a scorpion venom ($AaH_{II}$) cause the same effect but have their sites of action on the outside of the membrane. Batrachotoxin (BTX), grayanotoxin (GTX), veratridine, and the insecticide DDT and the pyrethroids stabilize the m-gate in the open position. Local anesthetics (LA) and quaternary ammonium compounds (QA) block the open Na⁺ channel and their bond is reinforced by the closure of the h-gate.

there is a variety of substances with a wide range of effects on this channel. Figure 34.6 gives an overview of these substances and their effects.

Figure 34.7 shows the structural formulae of some substances which activate the Na⁺ channels; Figure 34.8 shows those of some substances which, in contrast, inhibit the Na⁺ channels.

Depending on the manner in which a substance works, its effect on the action potential will vary. This can range from total blocking, in the case of "clogging" the pore, for example, to repetitive firing after a single stimulus if the m-gate is stabilized in the open position. Figure 34.9 shows an example of a neurotoxic effect on an action potential.

### ASSIGNMENT 34.6

On the basis of the information in Figure 34.6, indicate what effect low doses of TTX (tetrodotoxin) and DDT may have on the action potential?

We have dealt with the Na⁺ channel in such detail because this illustrates how an ion channel may be the site of action for a variety of substances.

*K ion channel*

In the *K ion channel*, the situation appears to be slightly different. First, recent studies have shown that there are several types of K⁺ channels, each with its own

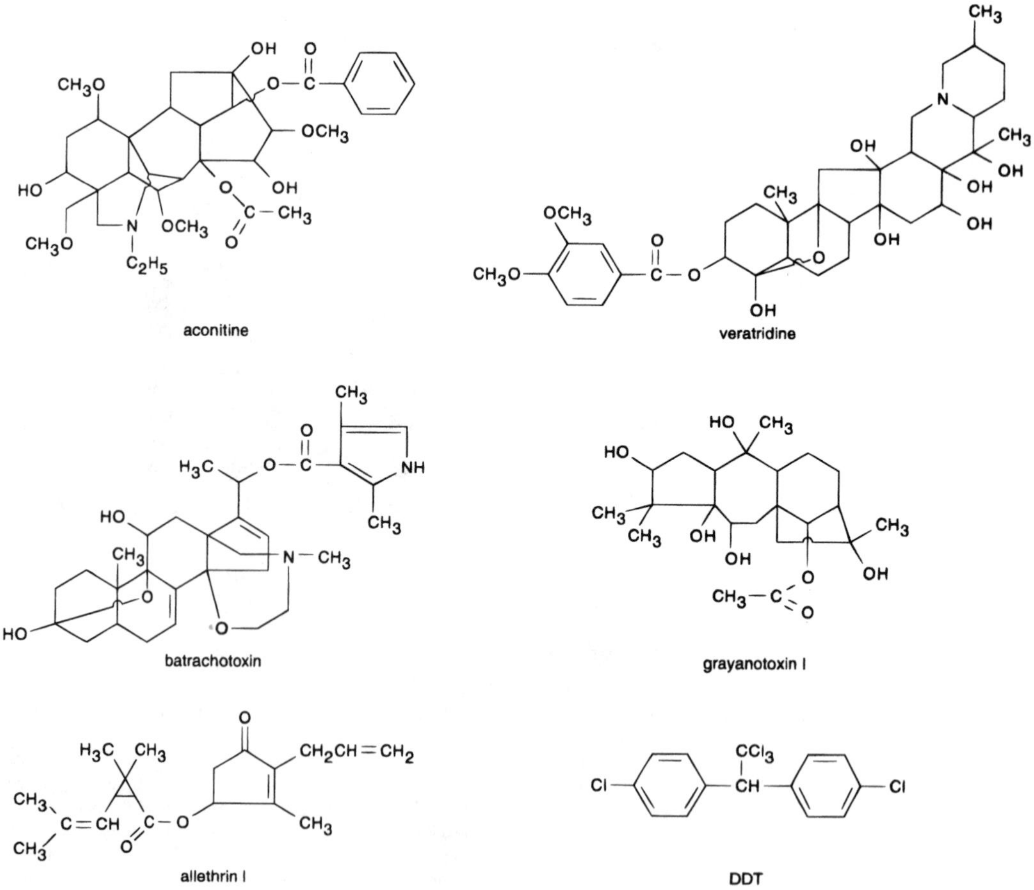

aconitine

veratridine

batrachotoxin

grayanotoxin I

allethrin I

DDT

### FIGURE 34.7
Substances which activate Na⁺ channels

These compounds react with open Na⁺ channels and increase the chance of the channel remaining open. This may lead to the formation of sequences of action potentials after one single stimulus and following a stronger stimulation, blockade of impulse conduction.

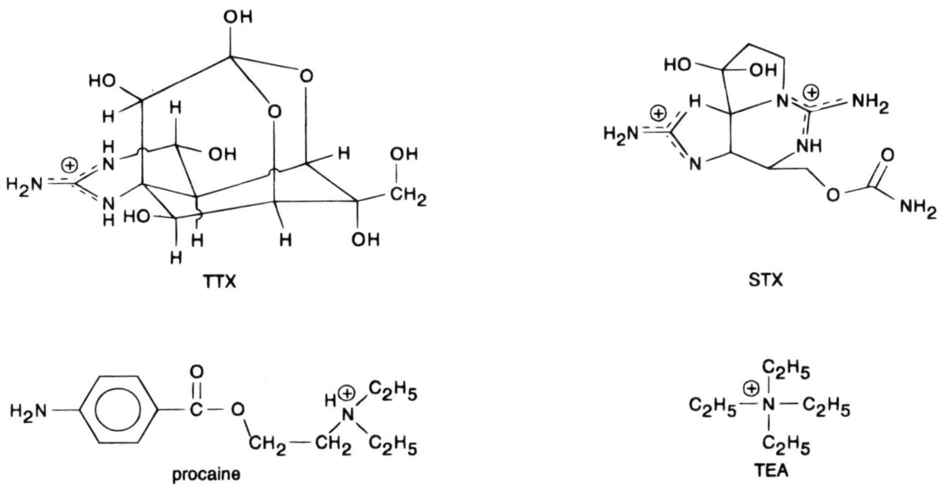

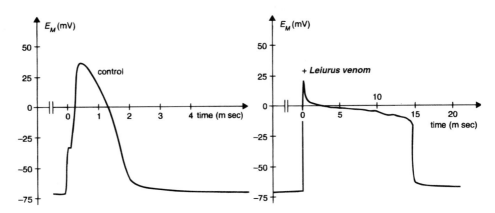

FIGURE   34.8

Na⁺ channel blockers

Tetrodotoxin (TTX) and saxitoxin (STX) are natural toxins with an extremely specific blocking effect on Na⁺ channels. Procaine is a Na⁺ channel blocker, which is clinically applied as a local anaesthetic. Tetraethylammonium (TEA) is used in experiments to block K⁺ channels. The effects of all these substances are reversible, i.e. after removal of the substance, the channel can revert to its normal functioning.

FIGURE   34.9

Effect of the administration of a Na⁺ channel toxin on the action potential

In this case, a peptide toxin originating from a scorpion (*Leiurus*) was applied. This toxin affects the h-gate, considerably delaying repolarization of the action potential. The action potential was recorded from a node of Ranvier taken from the nerve fiber of a frog before and after treatment with 1 µg ml⁻¹ *Leiurus* venom.

pharmacological characteristics. Certain K⁺ channels appear to be located mainly on nerve endings and perikaryon, rather than on axons. Virtually no neurotoxic substances are known to work selectively on K⁺ channels in axons. Many chemicals with an anesthetic effect, such as volatile organic solvents, block the functioning of both Na⁺ and K⁺ channels. An example of a different type of K⁺ channel is the *fast K⁺ –channel*, which reacts to the membrane potential in a totally different way. In addition, it appears to have a role which is totally different from that of the axonal K⁺ channel. The fast K⁺ channel can be blocked by 4-aminopyridine. In the future, more neurotoxicological information on various K⁺ channels will become available.

*Ca²⁺ ion channel*

Finally, special mention should be made of the *Ca²⁺ ion channel*, because this channel seems to have the special task of linking the electrical membrane phenomena with other processes. In muscle cells, for example, the $Ca^{2+}$ channel connects electrical membrane phenomena with contraction. In the neuron, the $Ca^{2+}$ channel is involved in connecting electrical membrane phenomena with secretory processes. Divalent ions such as Cd, Co, Mg, Ni (but also Pb) seem to be quite capable of blocking Ca ion channels. It is quite possible that part of the toxicity of these metals is based on this.

## 3 Synaptic transmission

ASSIGNMENT 34.7

List the various processes which occur during neuromuscular transmission

### 3.1 NEUROMUSCULAR TRANSMISSION

*Registration of miniature end-plate potentials*

It is possible to study the effects of neurotoxic substances on individual aspects of neuromuscular transmission. An important technique for this purpose is the *registration of miniature end-plate potentials* (MEPPs).

This technique has become available thanks to the discovery that even while a nerve is not being stimulated, depolarizations still occur (albeit of low amplitude, approximately 0.5 mV, whilst the end-plate potential is 20–30 mV). These miniature end-plate potentials have been demonstrated (the method will not be discussed here) to be the result of occasional exocytosis of a transmitter-filled vesicle. The process of exocytosis may be studied by examining the effects of various substances on the amplitude and frequency of these miniature end-plate potentials. In this way, secretion of the transmitter has been shown to be *blocked* by botulinum toxin, but, in contrast, is *stimulated* by the venom of the black widow spider to such an extent that the ending is emptied completely.

*Transmitter blockage, transmitter stimulation and binding to the acetylcholine receptor*
See previous study unit regarding the difference between the various cholinergic receptors.

Another way in which neuromuscular transmission may be affected is by the *binding* of substances to the *acetylcholine receptor*. Thus, the neurotoxins $\alpha$-bungarotoxin (a snake venom) and curare (a phytotoxin), bind to the acetylcholine receptor but do not imitate the effect of acetylcholine; they are therefore antagonists.

Figure 34.10 shows examples of substances acting on the neuromuscular synapse. In addition, there are a number of substances with an anticholinesterase effect. These include the nerve gases tabun, sarin, diisopropyl fluorophosphate and the organophosphorus insecticides, the prototype being parathion. The alkaloid physostigmine, a methyl carbamate, is another example.

Cholinergic transmission is disturbed by anticholinesterase drugs because acetylcholine is no longer broken down. Short-term effects are excitation of the neuromuscular synapse, followed by blockade. The transmitter production system may also be damaged. This effect is not necessarily restricted to the synthesizing enzymes, but may also involve concentrations of the transmitter in synaptic vesicles and transportation of these vesicles (see previous study unit).

So far, the discussion has been restricted to cholinergic transmission, because this is currently the best-studied transmission system. However, the pharmacology of noradrenergic transmission is also well-known. For instance, dibenzamine, phenoxybenzamine and halogenated alkylamine block adrenergic synapses, as they have an antagonist effect on $\alpha$-adrenergic receptors.

### 3.2 SYNAPTIC TRANSMISSION BETWEEN NEURONS

The effect of toxic substances on synaptic transmission is similar to that described for neuromuscular transmission. This implies that for each known transmitter, a number of substances are known which disturb the synaptic action of that transmitter.

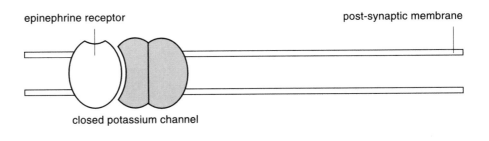

acetylcholine

suberyldicholine

carbachol

D-tubocurarine

FIGURE 34.10

Examples of substances acting on acetylcholine-controlled ion channels

These channels can, for instance, be found on muscular cells of skeletal muscles. Acetylcholine is the natural agonist for these channels, whilst carbachol and suberyldicholine are synthetic agonists. Curare alkaloids originating
from South American plants of the *Menispermaceae* family were used as arrow poison by Amazonian Indians. D-
tubocurarine is a cholinergic antagonist, which, in competition with acetylcholine, binds to the acetylcholine receptor. It has been used to induce muscle relaxation during surgical operations.

## Intermezzo

Bee poison consists of a large number of components, including enzymes such as phospholipidase
and hyaluronidase, physiologically active amines such as histamine, dopamine and norepinephrine, and a number of peptides. One of these peptides is the neurotoxin apamine. Apamine consists
of 18 amino acids, and its structure contains two sulfur bridges. Apamine specifically acts on certain postsynaptic membranes which are responsible for nerve impulse conduction in both the central and peripheral nervous system. It blocks the action of epinephrine in the transfer of nervous
impulses by obstructing $K^+$ ion channels in the neuronal membrane which are normally opened by
epinephrine (see Figure 34.11).

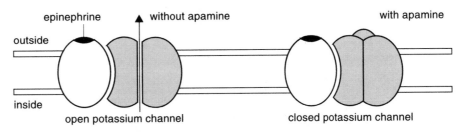

FIGURE 34.11

Neurotoxic action of apamine on the epinephrine receptor

Apamine selectively blocks epinephrine-dependent potassium channels. In the event of blocking, the normal effect of epinephrine, i.e. opening of $K^+$ channels, is suppressed.

Since epinephrine acts as a stress hormone, its blockade means that the organism will react less effectively to danger. Apamine also blocks the action of many other neurotransmitters in the neurons of vertebrate and invertebrate animals.

*Kainic acid and glutamate-related substances*
For the effect of kainic acid, 6-hydroxydopamine and 5, 6-dihydroxytryptamine, see previous study unit.

Kainic acid, 6-hydroxydopamine and 5,6-dihydroxytryptamine deserve special mention. Long-term administration of *kainic acid* and other *glutamate-related substances* in non-physiological quantities results in specific neuropathy. *Glutamate* is a transmitter for excitatory transmission to the dendrites of cell bodies. External administration causes long-term depolarization of a large part of the cell body. This long-term depolarization is thought to place too great a strain on the homeostatic mechanisms involved in the ion regulation of a cell.

This overload is followed by necrosis. External administration of these substances is thought specifically to affect cells with glutamate receptors. Interestingly, sodium glutamate is used as a food flavoring. Glutamate is suspected of being the cause of the "Chinese restaurant syndrome", characterized by a burning and tingling sensation in the face, neck and upper part of the body.

Peptides are proteins made up of a short amino acid chain (generally 10,000 daltons).

Apart from the "classic" transmitters, endogenous peptides can also act as transmitters and directly affect the CNS.

The category of neurogenic peptides, referred to as neuropeptides, can be defined as: endogenous peptides which are present in nerve cells or are involved in nervous system function.

The effect of pituitary hormones on behavior was first discovered in hypophysectomized animals that displayed behavioral disturbances which could in turn be reversed by hormonal treatment. Structure-activity studies showed a dissociation between the classic endocrine action and the central action of these hormones; small parts of the molecule, devoid of endocrine effects, appeared to have specific effects on central nervous system (CNS) functions. Such peptide molecules that specifically affect CNS functions were called neuropeptides.

Since the discovery in the brain of two pentapeptides with opiate-like activity in 1975, research on the function of peptides in the nervous system has markedly increased. Endogenous substances with opiate-like activity are called endorphins.

Many of the hypothalamic releasing factors and pituitary hormones appear to generate neuropeptides that are also present in brain areas other than the hypothalamus, and communicate with various transmitter systems. Hormones and their fragments can thus also function as neurohormones and, like neurotransmitters, can affect central synaptic transmission and subsequent behavior.

It can be expected that a number of xenobiotics will be discovered (in future) which have toxic effects on peptidergic systems.

This knowledge led to the hypothesis that hormonal systems present in the pituitary and brain play a crucial role in behavioral homeostasis and that disturbances in the (neuro)hormonal systems can lead to psychopathology.

## 4  Recording electrical signals in vivo

As shown in Figure 34.3, local circuit currents occur both intracellularly and extracellularly. Extracellular currents enable measurement of potential differences in the surrounding tissue resulting from the electrical activity of cells. These potential differences will increase as measurements are carried out nearer the place of activity, or as more cells contribute to the activity more or less synchronously.

*Electrocardiogram (ECG)*

An example of this is the *electrocardiogram (ECG)*. An ECG is obtained by applying electrodes to the skin which register the local circuit currents produced by the spread of the cardiac impulses originating from the heart. This electrical activity in the heart can be recorded at virtually any location on the skin. Deviations from the normal cardiogram are used to diagnose cardiac disorders.

*Electro-encephalogram (EEG)*

Similarly, an *electro-encephalogram (EEG)* provides a representation of electrical activity in the brain.

*Diagnosis using the EEG*

There are three ways in which an electro-encephalogram can be used to diagnose neurotoxic damage.

a   By applying electrodes to different areas of the skull, the activity in various areas of the brain can be recorded. (The normal pattern of such electrical phenomena is known.) This method is used to trace brain abnormalities, but abnormalities in the EEG pattern have also been demonstrated in workers who had been in contact with, for example, carbon disulfide, organic solvents or organic phosphates.

b   From long-term EEG abnormalities in the sleep-waking cycle can be demonstrated. The EEG in the sleeping state is clearly different from that in a state of wakefulness. Animal experiments have shown that the effects on the sleep-waking cycle of exposure to toluene or carbon monoxide can be measured in this way.

*Evoked Potentials*

c   Another possibility is to present external stimuli (sounds or light flashes) to the test subject while making an EEG. The effects of such stimuli are recorded on the EEG. This is referred to as the '*Evoked Potentials*' method (EPs).

EPs provide information regarding the arrival of the signals at the sensory system concerned (depending on the stimulus used). In this way, it has been possible to demonstrate abnormalities in EPs in female shoe factory workers who had been exposed to n-hexane and other solvents.

d   By using computers, the analysis of EEG recordings as applied in the three methods described above can be made considerably more expansive. For example, it is possible to analyze the frequency pattern of the EEG by applying Fourrier analysis. This makes it much easier to determine any abnormalities and also whether an abnormality is related to a particular frequency area. It is also possible, when using EPs, not to look at just one individual response but to give a large number of stimuli and take the computed average of the responses to these (the EEG). This gives a much clearer picture of the response to the stimulus concerned.

*Action potentials of muscles and nerves*

At suitable locations, the *action potentials of muscles and nerves* can also be recorded. This enables any deviations in amplitude, duration and conduction rate to be recorded. Studies of industrial workers have shown that substances such as acrylamide, carbon disulfide, n-hexane and lead may cause a decrease in conduction rate in nerves. In the case of lead poisoning, it seems that using this effect, damage can be measured even before any symptoms of disease occur.

*Electromyography (EMG)*

By applying needle-shaped electrodes to the muscles instead of the skin, the *electrical activity of muscles* can be recorded (*electromyography*). This is also possible in humans. Muscle activity can then be observed both at rest and during movement.

Electromyographic irregularities include extraordinary muscle activity even though no movements occur, deviations in shape, amplitude, duration, number or frequency of motor unit action potentials (a motor unit is a nervous fiber together with all the muscle fibers innervated by this nervous fiber; during contraction these will react as a unit). By means of EMG, motor unit deviations have been observed in workers exposed to n-hexane. This method also provides information on irregularities in neuromuscular transmission.

*Advantages of electrophysiological methods*

The *advantages of electrophysiological methods* in neurotoxicological research are firstly, that measurements can be carried out continuously (e.g. during exposure to a toxin) and secondly, that functional changes in the nervous system can be closely monitored without causing any damage to the subject under investigation. Backed by the electronic and computer techniques currently available, biopotentials can be analyzed and quantified very accurately. The disadvantages are that expensive equipment and highly-trained staff are required.

## 5    Summary

This study unit has looked at the way in which substances can disturb the electrophysiological mechanisms of a neuron and how this can be measured. The conductive characteristics of neurons can be affected by, among other things, structural damage to axons, the myelin sheath or the cell body. As many neurotropic drugs and neurotropic substances specifically act on the ion channels in the neuronal membrane, especially the Na ion channel, the opening and closing mechanism of this channel has been discussed in detail. The relevant sites of action of the various xenobiotics have been indicated. In addition to conduction disturbances within a single neuron, effects may occur due to disturbances in neuromuscular or neuro-neuronal synaptic transmission. In the final section, the major techniques used in the recording of electrical signals *in vivo* were described.

FEEDBACK

### Answers to the assignments

34.1  In general, its long, thin projections pose transport problems for the neuron. Structural proteins are produced near the cellular nucleus and must be transported to the areas where they are required. In addition, the nucleus must be informed about the situation in all processes (e.g. in the event of any damage). All this applies in particular to some sensory and motor cells since these may have projections measuring up to 1 m in length. The disparity between their great length and very small diameter (4–20 $\mu$m) makes clear that transport by diffusion will be totally inadequate. Interestingly, the transport system works in both directions, both from and towards the cell body. It is relatively easy to include substances in the transport process. They do not even have to be injected into the neurons; if they are injected in the near vicinity, the cell will absorb them. Certain viruses (for instance, the virus causing poliomyelitis) use this route to penetrate into the central nervous system, and are thus not hindered by the blood-brain barrier. Toxic substances may be transported in the same way.

34.2  The direction of conduction of the action potential is guaranteed by the phenomenon that the membrane, immediately after the active period, goes through a refractory period. During this period, it is initially impossible to evoke an action potential, and even shortly afterwards there is still an extremely high threshold, which is only gradually reduced.

34.3 Myelinization causes the distance between intra- and extracellular fluids to be increased. Since the capacity of a capacitor is, amongst other factors, inversely proportional to the distance between both conductors, this increase in distance between the two fluids entails a considerable reduction in membrane capacity. This decrease in capacity is the key factor in the accelerating effect of the myelin sheath. An active node of Ranvier can almost instantly depolarize another node in its vicinity to its threshold level.

34.4 Repetitive firing refers to the phenomenon of several action potentials in the axon following one stimulus. It can be explained through the decelerating effect of a swelling. The action potential may flow past the swollen part before activity has fully developed there. This means that a depolarizing current may still be present (in the swelling), while the rest of the axon has already ceased to be refractory. If this is the case, repetition may occur.

Please note that it is not possible to establish from the deformation observed in histological sections which deviations will occur.

34.5 In an undamaged axon, the action potential jumps rapidly from node to node (saltatory conduction). This means that only in the (uncovered) part of the membrane at the node of Ranvier the action potential ionic currents will occur. As the myelin gradually disappears, the membrane capacity will gradually increase. An increasingly longer time will thus be required to depolarize the inactive node. This will lead to a gradual reduction in conduction rate. At a certain moment, very little myelin will be left and the membrane will be virtually bare between the nodes. This membrane will now act as a leakage resistance for the local circuit currents, which will not be strong enough to stimulate the inactive node to the threshold level. Only then will the conduction be completely blocked.

34.6 TTX binds to the selectivity filter and this means that no Na ions can pass through the channel. A high dose of TTX will cause all channels to become blocked, thus making an action potential impossible. DDT, on the other hand, binds to the m-gate and stabilizes it in the open position, which will have a totally different effect. The Na channel will of course close after having been opened by depolarization, as the h-gate takes care of this. The original state is, however, not returned to, because the m-gate remains open. As soon as repolarization causes the h-gate to open again, the Na channel re-opens and a new action potential can begin. The result is that one single stimulus is followed by a long chain of action potentials.

34.7 The following processes are involved in neuromuscular transmission:
   a. The arrival of the action potential at the nerve ending of the motor neuron is accompanied by opening up of the Ca ion channels.
   The increase in the intracellular $Ca^{2+}$ concentration activates the secretory process in the ending.
   b. The transmitter released (acetylcholine in vertebrate animals) diffuses into the intracellular space and binds to receptors in the muscle cell.
   c. The ion channel attached to the acetylcholine receptor opens once acetylcholine has been bound.

d. A motor end-plate potential develops in the muscle cell, which in its turn leads to an action potential in the muscle cell. The action potential travels along the muscle cell membrane.

e. The $Ca^{2+}$ channels in the muscle cell membrane open up under the influence of the depolarization and $Ca^{2+}$ enters the muscle cell. An intracellular conductive system (the sarcoplasmic reticulum) ensures that $Ca^{2+}$ quickly reaches the contractile proteins.

f. Interaction of $Ca^{2+}$ with the muscle proteins initiates contraction.

g. Acetylcholine is removed by the acetylcholinesterase present in the synaptic cleft (primarily at the surface and infolding of the postjunctional membrane).

h. What is left of the transmitter (choline) is absorbed in the neuronal ending for re-use.

# Contents Study unit 35
# Neurobehavioral toxicology

0-8493-9232-2/96/$6.00 + $.50
© 1996 by CRC Press, Inc.

# Neurobehavioral toxicology

*R. J. M. Niesink*

INTRODUCTION

From the two preceding units, it has become clear that xenobiotics can have undesirable effects on the nervous system. Study unit 33 discussed the anatomic and biochemical effects, and Study unit 34 the electrophysiological aspects. The present unit focuses on the effects of neurotoxic substances at the highest level of integration, that of behavior.

CASE STUDY 1

*Lead exposure in children*

Various researchers have reported a relationship between exposure to lead (as demonstrated by its presence in blood, tooth enamel, dentin or hairs on the scalp) on the one hand, and intelligence quotient and hyperactive behavior on the other. Lead influences biochemical and physiological processes, particularly in the developing brain. This may lead to permanent cognitive and behavioral disturbances. Children showing a slightly increased concentration of lead in their blood at birth are assumed to run a higher risk of developing mental retardation.

In 1972, Pueschel and others examined about 700 children in Boston, all living in a high-risk area of the city (old working-class districts with many industries). A variety of data were collected, including the occurrence of the pica habit (frequently putting non-edible objects in the mouth and sometimes even swallowing them), intelligence, the lead content of the hairs on the scalp, lead in the blood etc. The mean lead content of the hairs on the scalp of the children was 118 $\mu$g per gram of hair, while the mean value for the whole city of Boston was 27 $\mu$g per gram of hair. In 44% (316 children) lead levels were found to be 37 $\mu$g per dl blood, on average; in 115 children, this figure exceeded 40 $\mu$g per dl (the World Health Organization's standard is 35 $\mu$g per dl). Nearly all of these children proved to have the pica habit; their average intelligence quotient was 86.

During a period of 18 months more attention was paid to their eating habit and their pica habits were discouraged. The IQ rose by an average of 8 points but the wooden movements of these children and their poor eye–hand coordination did not improve.

CASE STUDY 2

Ketjubung is the common name for *Datura fastuosa*, a common shrub in Indonesia. The seeds, roots, leaves and flowers of *Datura* species contain the belladonna alkaloids atropine and scopolamine. *Datura fastuosa* is used as a folk medicine in Indonesia, for instance as a remedy for rheumatic pains and asthma. Ketjubung poisoning can arise unintentionally if, through unfamiliarity with the plant, too many of its seeds or leaves are eaten. But the poisoning may also be the result of evil intent, for instance, to poison a person one intends to rob, or to take one's revenge or by way of a joke. The aim is easily achieved, for example by mixing in the seeds with the victim's food or drink.

The case histories of two Indonesian men who, because of their odd behavior, were brought to a missionary hospital in Jogyakarta illustrate some of the effects of ketjubung poisoning.

### Case histories

The two men had drunk a ketjubung seed infusion instead of tea. Shortly afterwards, they began to behave strangely. The police were notified, and they were brought to the hospital.

Patient A, 30 years of age, had drunk one glass of the "tea". Contact with him was impossible; he was pacing up and down the treatment room in an excited state. He squatted under a laboratory table for lengthy periods, purposefully reaching out in all directions trying to grasp something. This odd behavior evoked much laughter from the spectators. He was not aggressive, but did resist physical examination. His pulse rate was 132, his skin was red and hot and his tongue was dry. His pupils were fully dilated and unresponsive to light. Insertion of a stomach pump failed due to the patient's resistance. 100 mg phenobarbital were administered subcutaneously, after which he allowed himself to be escorted to a ward. His body temperature was 38.5°C, his leucocyte count was 12 400 mm$^{-3}$. Chloral hydrate 0.5 g was administered rectally.

Patient B., 32 years of age, was said to have drunk more than one glass. His behavior was similarly extraordinary, and he also resisted examination. Unlike patient A, he remained seated, gesticulating violently and continuously. His pulse rate was 108, his skin was red and hot, and his pupils were also dilated and unresponsive to light. His body temperature was 38.2°C, the leucocyte count 9600 mm$^{-3}$. An attempt to insert a stomach pump pipe was similarly unsuccessful. Treatment was the same as for patient A.

The following day, the physician on duty visited the patients at 7 a.m. To his surprise, he found two quiet, cooperative men, neither of whom remembered the incident. They no longer had fever, and both their pulse rates were both about 70; the pupils were still dilated but now showed some response to light. Physical examination did not reveal any abnormalities. Both men were discharged that same day.

The two examples described above, lead exposure and ketjubung poisoning, show that foreign substances can cause changes in behavior. Apart from the substances in these examples, there are also more common substances which influence behavior; think of the unwanted behavioral effects of alcohol. Although the effects shown above proved to be reversible, there are also effects which are found to be less reversible or, indeed, irreversible, leading to permanent behavioral changes.

In this study unit, it will be explained how (undesirable) effects of xenobiotics on behavior can be studied under experimental conditions in animal experiments, and some examples from different classes of substances will be examined. The importance of behavioral toxicology research for man will also be discussed.

LEARNING OBJECTIVES

After studying this unit, you will be expected to be able to

— describe which type of behavioral effects can be studied in behavioral toxicology research and how such studies are carried out
— describe the effects of some examples, such as lead, methylmercury and carbon monoxide, in animal experiments
— indicate what contribution behavioral toxicology can make to the toxicity research on a substance
— indicate which specific problems arise when extrapolating neurotoxicological data from animal experiments to human beings.

*Study hints*

This study unit is a sequel to the preceding two study units on neurotoxicology and, as such, should be studied only after those units. It is assumed that you are familiar with some basic principles of the biology of behavior. Provided your basic knowledge is sufficient, the study load for this unit is estimated to be no more than 3 hours. At the end of this unit, you will find a self assessment test which includes questions that refer to all three preceding study units.

STUDY CORE

## 1 The position of neurobehavioral toxicology within neurotoxicological research

### 1.1 THE POSITION OF BEHAVIORAL TOXICOLOGY WITHIN TOXICOLOGY

Definition.
In this study unit, the terms neurobehavioral toxicology, behavioral toxicology and neurotoxicology are used interchangeably. Some authors rank toxic effects on the CNS under behavioral toxicology and effects on the PNS under neurotoxicology.

Behavioral toxicology is the study of changes in the behavior of human beings and animals due to toxic substances. In this context, behavior is considered to constitute the ultimate integration of nervous functions at the level of the intact organism. The changes include effects on both the peripheral and the central nervous systems, and also effects mediated on the nervous system after an initial effect elsewhere, for instance on the endocrine system or, as happens more and more frequently these days, on the immune system.

Although the emphasis in toxicity research has long been focussed on the assessment of morphological changes, and particularly on changes relating to carcinogenic processes, recent interest has shifted towards a more fundamental evaluation of possible changes. An example of the latter is the growing interest in behavioral changes as a result of exposure to chemicals. In East European countries, such as the former Soviet Union, and in Finland, behavioral toxicology tests have been an integral part of the toxicological protocol for registration of substances for years, in contrast to Western Europe and the United States. It has been claimed that behavioral tests are more sensitive to changes than pathological tests, but such claims are often hard to substantiate. It should certainly be noted, however, that behavior is the functional integration of all activities of the nervous system, sometimes even including activities of other systems, such as the endocrine and immune systems. To study and completely understand the toxicity of a substance, behavioral toxicology research is a necessary complement to other toxicity tests.

One of the problems of behavioral toxicology is that there is often more than one toxic end point. The toxic end point is frequently determined by the duration, the moment and the dosage of exposure. Figure 35.1 clarifies this by showing

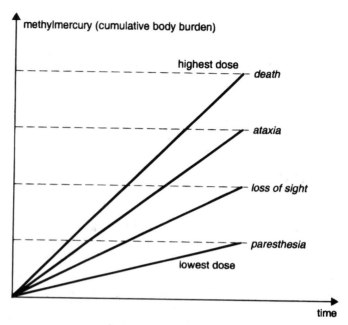

FIGURE   35.1

Schematic representation of the various toxic end points in a case of methylmercury poisoning in relation to exposure and time.

The dotted lines indicate the cumulative dose for which a certain effect is obtained.

schematically the relationship between exposure and toxic endpoint. The figure is based on data obtained from a case of methylmercury poisoning in Iraq. The original figure was a representation of the estimated exposure to methylmercury and various effects of methylmercury poisoning. From these data, paresthesias proved to be the first indication of toxic effects in adults. The figure reveals the probable relationship between the appearance of a particular toxic end point and the duration of exposure to various levels.

ASSIGNMENT   35.1

What can be concluded from the figure regarding the relationship between level of exposure, latency period and effect?

Paresthesia is an erroneous sensation, for example the feeling of ants crawling on one's skin.

At the lowest level of exposure, only paresthesias are found. Although there are dozens of behavioral tests, not one of them, nor any special sequence from them, is currently required for registration purposes. The various types of tests can be divided into two categories: tests studying stimulus-oriented behavior and tests studying internally generated behavior. The first category comprises two types of conditioned behavior: *operant behavior*, where animals are taught to carry out a certain task in order to receive a reward or avoid punishment; and *classical conditioning*, where the animal learns to show a specific response when a conditioned stimulus is presented. The stimulus-oriented tests also include the non-conditioned response, in which the activities (reactions) of the animal to a particular stimulus are registered. The study of internally generated behavior includes observing the behavior of animals in various experimental situations: exploratory behavior, biological rhythm and social behavior. The behavior of an animal which is exposed to, or treated with, a particular substance is compared with the behavior of an untreated animal. Of course, factors like age, sex, environment, diet and care are important as well. Several of these factors have an obvious influence on the behavior.

*operant behavior*

*classical conditioning*

1026

Over the last 20 years it has become clear that it will be impossible for behavioral toxicologists to develop one single test with which the various functions of the nervous system can be tested in one trial. Therefore, a battery of tests will have to be developed which will allow several behavioral variables that can be influenced by xenobiotics to be adequately examined. The question which method of toxicological investigation is the most suitable is still being debated. In a test which assesses many functions of the nervous system simultaneously (an "apical" assessment), a broad range of effects might be revealed. It may well be, however, that it is precisely in apical tests that anomalies remain unnoticed because of compensation. When developing a test battery, one should be aware that different tests assess different functions of the nervous system. These individual tests would have to be on motor function, sensory function and cognitive function.

An example of a proposed test battery is the following:

a.  *Passive avoidance test.* This test uses a shuttle box inside which an animal can move freely between a light and a dark compartment. By nature, rodents (rats, mice) prefer to sit in a dark spot. After a period of acclimatization, during which the animal can roam from one compartment to the other, it receives a mild electric shock while in the dark compartment. In a number of sessions the animal learns to move at the sound or sight of a signal, in order to avoid an electric shock. There are many variants of this test, in which, in essence, the following parameters may be used: learning time, expressed as the number of sessions required, or acquisition, i.e., the speed of response after the signal, and the extinction of the response learnt.

b.  *Auditory startle response.* In this test the reaction (movement) of the animal to an auditory signal is studied. Sometimes the auditory signal is preceded by a light stimulus.

c.  *Maze or open field.* The movements of an animal during its stay in a maze or open field (sometimes its own cage) are recorded automatically, during dark as well as light periods.

d.  *Movement patterns.* Various patterns in the way the animal moves are recorded, such as the length of its paces, the number of times it changes direction, and the length of straight stretches.

e.  *Operant-behavior test.* This assessment uses operant conditioning as developed by Skinner. The animal has to perform a certain action to obtain food or water, or to avoid receiving a shock, for example pushing a bar. Many modifications can be made in the stimulus, the duration of the interval between stimulus and reaction, the response required and the nature of the reward which functions as "reinforcement". In a "Skinner box", the performance of the entire program and registration of the responses is computerized.

In addition to the tests mentioned above, there are methods which concentrate on spontaneous behavior displayed in, for example, exploring a new environment or a maze, or the behavior with respect to an animal of the same species or a group of animals.

It will be understood that all these apical tests provide a non-specific answer following administration of the substance to be tested; the performance is either adequate or inadequate. More specific answers require further investigation.

ASSIGNMENT  35.2

Which of the nervous system functions are tested by tests a–d?

Functional reserve and adaptive possibilities of the nervous system are factors which can mask the effects in behavioral toxicology research. In many cases, there is no change in behavior, even though obvious structural changes may be observed. In addition, there are often complications in the statistical analysis of behavioral toxicology research, caused by, for example the large variations in behavior or because of the repeated use of the same experimental animals.

## 1.2    FUNCTIONAL TERATOLOGY

Functional teratology is the field of science which tries to identify and explain changes in behavior in individuals who have been exposed to toxic substances before birth (*in utero*). It is supposed that prenatal exposure to toxic substances does not always result in visible morphological or detectable biochemical changes, but that it may often result in subtle (biochemical) functional adaptations which can manifest themselves as behavioral changes in the developing individual. It is reasonable to assume that the developing nervous system, with its high mitotic and cell migration rate, is particularly sensitive to disturbances by foreign substances. Moreover, the absence of a blood-brain barrier and the as yet incompletely developed biotransformation system make the developing individual particularly vulnerable.

The development of the central nervous system stretches over a relatively long period of time and continues after birth. In studies of behavioral effects resulting from prenatal exposure, both teratological and behavioral toxicological aspects have to be recognized. In most functional teratology experiments, the exposure levels are so low that no teratological effects will be observed. Other factors which have to be considered are the latent effects, i.e., effects which cannot be detected directly after birth but which manifest themselves only at adolescence (puberty) or at maturity. Several of the substances which are teratogenic to the CNS are known to be responsible for abnormalities in motor function development and learning disorders after birth, even when applied in (prenatal) dosages which do not evoke structural pathological effects. Well-known examples are alcohol and methylmercury. Alcohol causes retarded development, hyperactivity, subtle motor function abnormalities and mental retardation, even at very low levels of exposure. Cases of women who, through eating contaminated fish, exposed their children to high doses of mercury have shown that this prenatal exposure can cause cerebral paralysis phenomena.

Since the introduction of the term "behavioral teratology" this branch of toxicology has developed along three lines:

- screening of drugs, environmental pollutants and substances in food for behavioral teratological effects;
- searching for biochemical correlations in cases of prolonged behavioral effects;
- searching for new tests capable of demonstrating subtle changes in the CNS.

## 1.3    LATENT DAMAGE

It is generally agreed that the developing nervous system is extremely sensitive to the action of neurotoxic substances. On the other hand, it should also be noted that, in some respects, the developing CNS is also much more resilient than that of the mature individual. The age at which the effects of neurotoxic substances are studied or observed is very important. Behavioral teratologists have demonstrated that mice prenatally exposed to methylmercury displayed behavioral effects only much later, at maturity or even senescence. One theoretical explanation for this could be the reserve capacity of the brain. According to this theory, the damage caused by early exposure can only become manifest when the brain, because of increased age, has sufficiently decreased in capacity. One way or another, this hidden (latent) damage needs to be taken into account in the risk assessment of neurotoxic substances. There are many indications supporting the idea of a decline in functional capacity with increasing age. Examples include the reduced numbers of neuronal cells in certain areas of the brain, lowered oxygen demand and neurotransmitter synthesis.

The bold line in Figure 35.2 shows schematically the hypothetical decline in brain capacity with increasing age, if this is not accelerated by functional external factors. A more rapid decline in functional capacity might be the result of a multitude of external factors, including exposure to neurotoxic substances. The finer lines in the figure indicate possible accelerations (0.1, 0.5 or 1%) in the ageing process, which could, for example, be caused by exposure to neurotoxic substances. Supposing a certain effect only becomes visible when functional brain capacity has fallen to less than 70%. The figure shows that, for a person whose functional capacity has declined at the highest rate (1% acceleration), this effect would already become visible at the age of 45. For a person whose functional capacity has declined at a normal rate, the effect would only become visible at a point far beyond the age of 95. Because of additivity, even the slightest acceleration of the ageing process causes a dramatic increase in the possible effect.

Although the figure is merely part of a much wider hypothesis, it shows that longitudinal studies and methods which are capable of detecting hidden brain damage at an early stage, can be highly important in the risk assessment of neurotoxic substances.

## 2    Animal research

This section will deal with behavioral toxicological research using animal models. Of these, tests for motor, sensory and cognitive functions will be discussed. Some findings of animal experiments will be discussed, focussing on CO, methylmercury and lead.

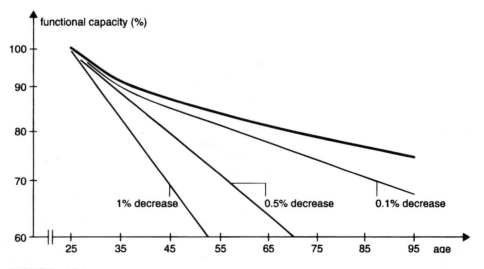

FIGURE   35.2

Hypothetical decrease of functional brain capacity as a result of exposure to neurotoxic substances

## 2.1    TESTING MOTOR FUNCTION

The development of the motor system in an animal is one of the first forms of behavior that can be measured with relative ease. Measuring the motor function is not only important in judging whether the development of the motor system in an animal is normal or abnormal, it also yields a considerable amount of information regarding the general physical state of a (mature) animal. The pattern of motor development in rodents, particularly rats and mice, is well characterized. After birth, an increase in motor activity is observed, which reaches a maximum at about 15 days after birth. This form of activity then slowly declines until it reaches the level of the mature animal. Most of the differences in development reported in the literature can be traced back to differences in methods of measurement. All experiments clearly show that a relationship exists between the development of specific neurochemical systems and the development of motor activity. It has been postulated that the catecholaminergic systems, which are associated with arousal, develop at an earlier stage than those systems which are assumed to have a more inhibitory function, such as serotonergic, GABA-ergic and cholinergic systems.

In this way, the increase in motor activity might be caused by the initial dominance of excitatory transmitter systems, and the gradual decrease in motor activity might be caused by the development of the inhibitory transmitter systems. It should, however, also be borne in mind that the motor system itself is not one uniform behavioral variable, since what is generally measured is usually a combination of various motor activities. Differences can often be traced back to the fact that some authors fail to discriminate between different forms of motor activity. In neurotoxicology it is especially crucial to indicate clearly what has been measured, in what way, and under what circumstances. The substances in question often produce irreversible changes in the functioning of the nervous system and toxicologists are particularly interested in knowing where and, possibly, how these substances act.

*Toxicity of lead*

In the first half of the 1970s, a number of articles were published showing that mice exposed to lead through their mother's milk were hyperactive throughout their development, compared to control mice. This hyperactivity persisted until maturity. The researchers assumed that the increased motor activity observed in lead-exposed mice would provide a good animal model for lead toxicity in human beings and possibly even for the hyperkinetic syndrome in man. One of the reasons for this line of thought was that the mice were only exposed to lead during the neonatal phase, which corresponded to the characteristic neonatal exposure of children suffering from lead poisoning. In addition, the mice in question showed the same paradoxical response to certain psychotropic drugs, such as amphetamine, as the children did. Moreover, some neurochemical abnormalities could be demonstrated that were identical to the neurochemical abnormalities found in the children. At the same time, there were also arguments against a direct effect of lead. For example, mice which were given drinking water containing lead drank less, and hence produced considerably less milk than the control group. Also, the paradoxical reaction of the mice to substances like amphetamine could be explained as a shift in the dose-effect curve rather than an altered response to the drug. Follow-up studies did show that both phenomena could also be the result of malnutrition alone. Experimental findings published in the following years were inconclusive, some showing increased motor activity, others no effect and still others decreased motor activity following neonatal exposure to lead. The interpretation of these results became more and more problematic. Each researcher used a different test method and different doses, and tissue measurements were lacking, which meant a lack of data on internal exposure. Supplementary pathological examination was hardly ever carried out.

Even if identical behavioral tests had been used, there would still be no reason to assume that different dosages or different exposure times would necessarily lead to the same results. Lead can affect the developing nervous tissue or the myelinization process of the neonate in various places. Changes in motor activity can thus be the result of selective destruction of certain parts of the nervous system and can therefore lead to an increase or decrease in motor activity, depending on the affected part.

ASSIGNMENT   35.3

Why would lead be especially able to cause persistent damage?

*Carbon monoxide*

In order to study the effects of hypoxia on motor activity, rats were exposed to carbon monoxide. A group of 5-day-old rats and a group of mature rats were exposed to a lethal concentration of carbon monoxide. The exposure was terminated when respiratory arrest was observed. The animals that survived the exposure were subsequently tested as a group in a maze. Exposure to CO caused hyperactivity in the young animals which persisted for 5 months. In a follow-up experiment, rats aged 5 days, 16–20 weeks and 18 months (mature) were exposed to a lethal dose of 0.42% CO until respiratory arrest set in. The animals surviving the exposure were tested individually in a maze. Hyperactivity was observed in female subjects exposed at age 16–20 weeks, but not in the males. The motor activity was found to correlate with the exposure time. The female animals proved to be significantly more resistant to the lethal effect of CO than the males.

ASSIGNMENT   35.4

What can be deduced from these results?

Unlike postnatal exposure, prenatal exposure to CO causes a decrease in motor activity. A decline in protein content was observed in the brains of animals prenatally exposed to CO, together with changes in enzyme activity. These experiments show that tests which measure motor activity can sometimes be used as an early measure of the (neuro)toxicity of a substance.

*Methylmercury*

Prenatal exposure to methylmercury has been found to cause increased motor activity and a shift in the peak of motor activity (normally at 15 days) in rats. The shift proved to be dependent on the moment of exposure. The literature shows that activity parameters can be used to detect subtle functional changes in the nervous system. It is, however, not (yet) possible to correlate such changes in activity with neuropathological or other biological measures of toxicity. Nor can it be claimed that the direction in which a motor function changes, that is, increase or decrease, reveals anything about the nature of the neural injury. Postnatally observed behavioral changes are often only of a transitory nature; differences in motor activity often cease to be detectable at maturity. At best, these data can be seen as a measure of the disturbed development of the nervous system and should only be used with the utmost caution. Since complex behavioral changes during the postnatal period are hard to quantify, techniques for measuring motor activity remain valuable. Changes in motor activity can also be used as an early indication of injury to the (peripheral) motor nervous system in mature animals.

EXAMPLE

In an experiment, rats were placed in a treadmill and exposed to low doses of acrylamide. In a different group of animals, who were also exposed to acrylamide, intracranial electrodes were installed to measure evoked potentials. The group in the treadmill showed activity changes (a decline in activity), before changes in the brain potentials became visible in the other group. Other types of experiments, in which other parameters (biochemical, pathological) were used apart from activity, also showed that changes in motor activity could often be observed before changes in the other parameters could be measured. Motor activity thus proves to be a good parameter for detecting early injury to the (peripheral) motor nervous system.

*Grip test*

Besides the activity measurements described above (maze, open field), other tests have been reported in the literature. Examples include the grip test and recording the structure of movement. The *grip test* uses a transducer to measure the force with which an experimental animal (usually a rat) holds on to a ring while a researcher tries to pull the animal away from it. In a second type of test, changes in an experimental animal's walking pattern are determined after exposure to a particular substance. This can be done, for example, by painting the rat's paws with ink and letting it walk along a straight line over a sheet of paper.

ASSIGNMENT   35.5

Describe the disadvantages of these methods.

Nowadays, additional factors are often measured besides the activity, such as rearing (standing on the hind legs) or the movement pattern of the animal in an open field. Whether measuring these extra factors increases the sensitivity of the methods is not yet clear.

2.2   TESTING SENSORY FUNCTION

If one wants to find out whether the functioning of sensory systems changes because of exposure to neurotoxic substances, then psychophysical and psychophysiological techniques will have to be used. It has to be taken into account, however, that the perception of a stimulus at threshold level not only depends on the intensity of the stimulus and the sensory sensitivity, but also on subjective preferences and processes involved in the carrying out of the response. As was shown above, it is possible to circumvent these factors by means of electrophysiological methods (for example, EEG). The EEG can be used to measure evoked potentials which arise in reaction to a stimulus. The early components of these brain potentials (in the first 100 ms) can provide information on the functioning of the sensory pathways. The later components provide information on the way in which the stimulus is integrated into the rest of the brain processes. Using simple experiments like this, it has been found that even the simplest stimulus, such as a pure tone, is perceived differently in the brains of different individuals.

Subjects may differ in:

• their reaction to a new stimulus (orientation reaction)

• their habituation to a repeated stimulus and

• the information value they attach to a stimulus with respect to their own situation.

Research into the functioning of sensory perception is closely related to psychology and behavioral analysis. Classic pavlovian conditioning has proved to be one of the best techniques for establishing the effects of harmful substances on the somatosensory part of the nervous system. One problem that arises here, however, is that the very first signs of sensory dysfunction often lie within the standard error of experimental measurement.

*Methylmercury*

In the outbreak of *methylmercury* poisoning in Minamata, Japan, it was soon discovered that one of the targets of the substance was the visual cortex. As in investigations into motor function abnormalities caused by chemicals, many techniques have been developed to detect sensory abnormalities. In the case of methylmercury, the effect of exposure of monkeys to this substance was examined with a *visual discrimination test*. Monkeys were taught to give a specific response when receiving a particular visual stimulus, in this case pressing a button. The mercury-exposed animals were found to perform significantly worse at low intensity or high frequency of the light stimulus. This type of tests is difficult to carry out in large groups of subjects because the learning component is very labor-intensive. The use of computerized equipment may facilitate the use of these tests in the future.

*Visual discrimination test*

*Electrophysiological techniques*

Another method for measuring sensory functions is the application of electrophysiological techniques. In these, electrodes are installed in or on the brain of an experimental animal. A visual or auditory stimulus is then given and the brain potentials are measured.

*Reflex test*

In addition to the discrimination test and the measurement of electrophysiological potentials, there are also tests which simply study *reflexes* resulting from visual or auditory (auditory startle reflex) stimuli. This test is based on the decrease in the reflex movement resulting from exposure to toxic substances which specifically affect the auditory nerves or the auditory cortex. The advantage of this test over, for instance, the visual discrimination test, is that hardly any training is required.

## 2.3 TESTING COGNITIVE FUNCTION

Most research on behavioral toxicology is concerned with processes such as attention, habituation, discrimination, learning, decision-making and the like. In studying the effects of harmful substances on the functioning of the CNS in these processes, behavioral toxicology elaborates on insights that have emerged from behavioral pharmacology. One such insight is that although behavior is the result of the functioning of the nervous system, the nervous system in turn depends on stimuli that reach it and have reached it in the past. The relationship between stimulus (S) and behavior (R for response) is not simply one in which one stimulus always precedes only one response, responses cause further effects which in turn can act as stimuli. There are effects that reinforce behavior as well as effects which reduce it. The first type is known as reward, the second as punishment.

In the following, carbon monoxide, lead and methylmercury will be used as examples. For the sake of brevity, the following effects will be discussed: the effect of carbon monoxide on schedule-controlled behavior in mature animals, lead on learning behavior and schedule-controlled behavior in postnatally exposed animals, and methylmercury on prenatally (*in utero*) exposed animals. Naturally, many substances have been tested over the years, but to discuss them all here is outside the scope of this unit.

*Carbon monoxide*

In experiments studying the effect of *carbon monoxide*, rats were exposed to CO before or before as well as during the experiment. Since the carboxyhemoglobin level in the plasma rises only slowly—the maximal concentration is usually only reached after 90 minutes—, this means that the majority of animals were tested under circumstances in which the plasma concentrations slowly increase. The most important effect observed in the schedule-controlled experiments was the increased interval time between stimulus and response and the cessation of the response in groups with high exposure levels ($\geqslant$700 ppm for 90 minutes). The effects of CO exposure in schedule-controlled behavioral tests were also studied in pigeons. The pigeons proved to be highly insensitive to the effect of carbon monoxide; only when exposed to $\geqslant$ 1700 ppm for 90 minutes could slight effects be observed.

The experiments show that the effect of CO on schedule-controlled behavior is a decrease in the speed of reaction, caused, in most cases, by an increase in interval periods or increased delays after the reward. The exposure levels were not very toxic to the animals, which was apparent from the fact that no structural changes could be observed at these exposure levels. A further indication that the dosages were not particularly toxic came from the fact that the effect of carbon monoxide was reversible: after the period of exposure, the animals' performance returned to normal levels. Recent findings in the literature show that primates, or even better, human beings themselves, constitute better models than rats or pigeons for the study of behavioral effects of CO in human beings.

*Lead*

Various groups of researchers have investigated the effect of postnatal exposure to lead (through mother's milk, for example) on cognitive functions. Exposure during the first 10 days of life proved to have a clear negative effect on the learning performance in a T-maze, while exposure between day 10 and day 20 scarcely had any influence. This suggests that the effect of lead shortly after birth might be stronger than later on. In a schedule-controlled behavioral test it was also found that postnatal exposure to lead resulted in an obvious effect. These tests show that the brain of a newly born rat is still sensitive to lead exposure. Such behavioral effects from exposure to lead have also been found in similar experiments with monkeys. By using learning tests and operant techniques, subtle differences in behavior as a consequence of exposure to neurotoxic substances can thus be measured. As far as the effects of lead on motor activity are concerned, there are still many questions to be answered regarding the interpretation of the effects found.

Exposure of animals to neurotoxic substances during gestation may have various consequences for the gestation or for the offspring.

ASSIGNMENT   35.6

Indicate the most important consequences of exposure to neurotoxic substances during gestation.

Naturally, behavioral toxicology or teratology tests are performed only when first indications show no abnormalities in the descendants. This type of test is informative regarding the development of the offspring: is development proceeding normally or are there any developmental disturbances as a result of prenatal exposure? In the case of exposure to *methylmercury*, the experimental design for such studies is nearly always the same. During the first, second or third week of gestation, the animals receive a certain oral dose of methylmercury, once or repeatedly. Following birth, the young animals are tested for their motor development, while at a later age they may be subjected to, for instance, a learning test.

*Methylmercury*

ASSIGNMENT 35.7

What are the methodological problems directly after birth with regard to the mother-pup relationship, and how can these be avoided?

It was found in the experiments with methylmercury that the learning performance of prenatally exposed mice (exposure of the mother 3 and 5 mg kg$^{-1}$) was poorer than that of control animals. Higher doses were found to reduce the size of the litter; for this reason the offspring in the highest exposure group were not tested. Cross-fostering experiments showed that the effect was ascribable entirely to the prenatal exposure to methylmercury.

Similar experiments in rats showed that not only the high level of the dosage but also the moment of exposure during the prenatal period was important for the behavioral effect after birth. Exposure to methylmercury in the last stages of gestation proved to entail much higher risks for the rats than in the earlier stages.

It has been shown in various test situations that even very low exposure levels can give rise to measurable behavioral changes in cognitive tests.

## 3 Applications in human beings

As was shown in the previous section, neurotoxicity tests are usually performed on various animals. Finding suitable animals, so that the effects of a substance can be extrapolated to human beings, has proved to be exceptionally difficult. Human beings show types of neurotoxicity which are difficult to determine in animal experiments, such as disturbances of sleep, memory, motivation and mood. However, well the dysfunctions of the nervous system can be measured, the results pose at least two problems. Firstly, we do not know how to interpret the (abnormal) animal behavior in terms of psychological processes, and even less how to interpret behavior in relation to the action of the nervous system. Secondly, we do not know whether behavioral abnormalities found in animals have any predictive value for man. If we wish to determine this value, it is necessary to be able to measure properly the dysfunctions in man resulting from exposure to substances that show a harmful effect in animal tests. If not, it will never be possible to establish any correlations between what is observed in man and what is measured in animals in laboratory tests. Since people are regularly exposed to (neuro)toxic substances, and regularly have complaints of reduced functioning, there is a good reason for wanting to have methods at hand which directly measure toxic effects on human behavior. The question is then whether the dysfunction can be objectively determined and whether the dysfunction is caused by a suspected substance to which the individual has been exposed. In answering this question, psychological measurements are just as important as the chemical analyses necessary to determine how much of the substance has entered the body and what its fate is. Every year a vast number of new chemicals are synthesized. Fortunately, only a few of them have neurotoxic properties that constitute a health risk. Moreover, the population at large will only encounter a few of these substances, since most of them are only used in industry. Unfortunately, neurotoxic chemicals continue to be found in the environment, for instance in foodstuffs intended for human consumption. Sometimes the latter occurs through *direct contact* with industrial waste products, as in the severe methylmercury poisoning in Japan, the so-called Minamata disease. In other cases, the cause may be carelessness and ignorance, such as in the consumption of seed-corn contaminated with methylmercury in Iraq. In contrast, the risk of *long-term exposure* to neurochemical substances is much greater in industry and agriculture (cropdusters). On the other hand, people in such situations are now more aware of the risks associated with the use of certain substances, and various preventive measures are being taken to minimize the exposure.

*Screening*

*Screening* in the context of neurotoxicology can have an epidemiological character. The causes of some mass poisonings, such as that with triaryl phosphates in Morocco, have been elucidated in this way. For some substances, like clioquinol, neurotoxic properties have come to light through epidemiological surveys.

There may also be situations, as in a factory for example, where people exposed to a well-known substance show more or less clear signs of neurotoxic effects. An investigation of such a group may provide a definitive answer, but it is extremely important also to make good use of such situations to determine the dose-response relationships in man. These quantitative relationships are very important in establishing MAC values and standards for the maximum allowable concentrations of a substance in water, soil, air and foodstuffs.

*Dose-response relationships*

There are a few conditions for obtaining usable data on *dose-response relationships*. It should be possible to determine the dose, or better still the exposure to the substance in subgroups of the total population to be surveyed. This exposure should be sufficiently homogeneous to serve as a mean value for the subgroup. The exposure then corresponds to the relevant concentrations in the air, in drinking water or in foodstuffs. A second condition is that one should be able to determine the effect. In practice, these are minimal effects. This condition can be fulfilled if the effect can be graded for each individual. Examples include measuring the rate of nerve impulse conduction after lead exposure, or establishing for each individual whether there is an effect or not. The percentage of people showing the effect is then the quantal measuring outcome or 'response', and can be used in determining the dose-response relationship. Even a relatively small deviation in the outcome for a subgroup, from that of the whole population under normal conditions, can be statistically significant. However, it should be kept in mind that the same outcome for a single individual does not allow any conclusions about his or her condition.

For many substances, only very little is known about their general toxicological profile. This obviously implies that it is also unknown at what concentrations they start to present a danger to the functioning of the nervous system. Behavioral toxicology research is also very important in the determination of MAC values, for instance for solvents such as toluene. In principle, there is little difference between industrial and home environments as regards the need for investigations by neurotoxicologists. Such situations, in which exposure to neurotoxic substances has taken place and behavioral toxicology research is desirable, can be roughly classified as follows:

a   A group of people has been or is exposed to a known neurotoxic substance. The neurotoxicologist is expected to provide insight into the incidence of neurotoxic damage and the severity of the consequences.

b   Exposure has occurred to substances whose possible neurotoxicity is unknown, but there are symptoms which indicate that the nervous system has been affected. Information is required about the etiology of the symptoms.

c   Exposure has occurred to substances whose possible neurotoxicity is unknown, and no clear symptoms are found in the exposed population. The neurotoxicologist is asked to determine whether there could be harmful consequences now or later.

Employees in certain industries are usually exposed for longer periods and are consequently more at risk at work than in the outside environment. Under well-controlled working conditions, a regular screening at the workplace is easily achieved. The results of repeated tests and systematic observation of certain abnormalities in an exposed person, such as headache, loss of memory and the like—so-called longitudinal studies—can be compared with results obtained earlier. In this way, even slight abnormalities can be detected at an early stage. Such research should be carried out especially when the risks due to working with a certain substance are unknown. This of course requires tests that can still register neurotoxic effects even when taken repeatedly. At the initiative of the WHO an international effort is currently being made to create a test battery with which toxic effects can be reliably established at the level of human behavior. Various diagnostic methods, including some neuropsychological methods, can be employed in human studies, depending on the effect of the substance under investigation. Examples are neurological inspection (explorative studies of the level of consciousness of subjects), clinical-neurological examination (motor function, coordination, sensibility and reflex measurements) and neurophysiological research (EEG, EMG, nerve conductivity, evoked potentials).

## 4    Neurotropic and psychotropic drugs

Most behavioral toxicology tests, especially animal experiments, are based on and derived from psychopharmacology.

It is obvious that the problem of behavioral effects deserves special attention for those drugs which are intended as neurotropic or psychotropic drugs to influence the brain and nerve functions. A large selection of these drugs are available and their effect is mainly achieved through their influence on the various forms of synaptic impulse transmission.

Neurons with widely different functions in the nervous system can make use of the same transmitter. This makes the task of finding drugs which are sufficiently specific for certain abnormalities in the central nervous system, extraordinarily difficult. Nonetheless, the last decades have seen important advances. Broad spectrum drugs, such as neuroleptics of the *chlorpromazine* type and *MAO inhibitors*, have in many applications been replaced by compounds with a more specific effect. Unfortunately, these new drugs show side effects as well. Apart from acute poisoning through overdose, many of the undesirable effects occur as extensions of the intended action of the drug. This also includes side effects which are observed following prolonged use of *minor tranquilizers*, *benzodiazepine derivatives* and *barbiturates*. These side effects can assume the character of chronic poisoning accompanied by fatigue, nystagmus and light cerebellar ataxia. Sometimes, correction is possible by means of a reduced dosage or by interrupting the treatment. In other cases the side effect will have to be accepted as secondary to the therapeutic effect. This can be said, for example, of the symptom of a dry mouth as a side effect of the numerous anti-cholinergic drugs. The compromise can also be more far-reaching, such as delayed reactions caused by tranquilizers, which may force the user to refrain from driving a car. Side effects of this nature are usually listed in the patient information sheet accompanying prepacked drugs.

Another point to be taken into account is that prolonged suppression of the functional activity of certain neurons can lead to loss of function or to a state comparable with denervation hypersensitivity. There are indications that this can happen after long-term use of some anti-epileptic agents, major tranquilizers and neuroleptic drugs.

For many substances affecting the CNS, discontinuing a prolonged continuous treatment may lead to unpleasant and occasionally severe withdrawal

*Tolerance*

symptoms. In this complex process a number of aspects can be distinguished: habituation (*tolerance*), psychological dependence, physiological dependence and the withdrawal syndrome. These facets can all be observed to a greater or lesser degree in addiction to *opiates* and, as far as their action is concerned, related pain killers (such as *meperidine* and *methadone*), *barbiturates* and some other sedatives and narcotics, as well as alcohol.

## Intermezzo
*Addiction and tolerance*

The addiction process is far more complicated and more difficult to fathom than the mechanisms by which opiates affect the patient's emotional state. Pharmacologists usually distinguish three stages of addiction: tolerance, drug-dependence and compulsive drug-seeking behavior. Upon repeated administration of certain drugs or medicines, the first effect is *tolerance*. Higher and higher doses are needed to achieve the same effect. Tolerance is also observed for many drugs that are not otherwise addictive. There are two types of tolerance. Firstly, there is *metabolic tolerance*, whereby a change occurs in the liver processes responsible for the degradation of all kinds of substances. Long-term exposure to certain compounds can induce the metabolizing liver enzymes. In other words, the drug will be active for a shorter period of time, since it is metabolized more rapidly. Metabolic tolerance of aspirin and penicillin is quite common and also occurs in opiate users. In the case of opiates and other addictive drugs, however, *cellular tolerance* is much more often found. In cellular tolerance, the subject shows a much weaker reaction to a compound than an individual who encounters it for the first time, even if both subjects have the same concentrations in the blood and brain. In this type of tolerance, the brain cells show a much weaker reaction than before.

*Physical dependence*

When a user stops taking a certain drug, after having used it for a long time, and then experiences severe physical withdrawal symptoms, this is known as *physical dependence*. The symptoms are usually the reverse of the normal acute effects. Thus, morphine has a euphoric, anesthetic and analgesic effect. If the addict discontinues it after chronic usage, he or she becomes depressive, experiences nervous breakdown and becomes hypersensitive to pain stimuli.

*Psychological dependence*

The first two components of the addiction process, cellular tolerance and physical dependence, are also observed in animals treated with opiates, but the third factor, compulsive drug-seeking behavior (*psychological dependence*) can scarcely be detected in animals.

Various theories on compulsive drug seeking behavior have been proposed, in which both biological and sociological mechanisms are assumed.

Psychotropic drugs can influence the brain in remarkable ways: they cause changes in the mental state of the user, so that some drugs are sought merely for recreational purposes, while others are useful in treating mental disorders. Knowledge of the action of these substances at the molecular level has been exceptionally important for the development of new, stronger, more selective and safer drugs. The cause of this progress has been two-fold. First, pharmacologists have acquired a better understanding of the specific interaction of a compound with certain receptor sites. Secondly, research into psychoactive substances has produced many new neurotransmitters, which in turn can be used in therapeutic applications, or which provide new 'targets' for the pharmaceutical industry.

Behavioral pharmacology research has made a significant contribution to the development of behavioral toxicology. This not only concerns the development of animal models but also leads to an improved understanding of the mechanisms underlying behavioral toxicological effects.

## 5    Summary

Behavioral toxicology is the branch of toxicology that attempts to measure and describe neurotoxic effects, to elucidate neurotoxic modes of action, and to predict neurotoxic effects. By doing so, it uses techniques developed in the behavioral sciences. Behavioral changes are established by means of observation methods, operant techniques, learning and memory tests etc., or by a combination of these techniques. The focus in prevention is on the timely recognition of neurotoxic properties of substances. In addition, the application of this knowledge in registration procedures and setting of standards is of prime importance. The recognition of possible neurotoxic properties of new substances stems from preventive toxicity research. Behavioral toxicology research plays an important part in determining the MAC values of, for example, solvents. The examples discussed in this study unit, lead, methylmercury and CO, show that it is possible to detect minor changes in the functioning of the (central) nervous system arising from exposure to neurotoxic substances. This is achieved by studying changes in reflexes, schedule-controlled behavior, learning and memory tests, motor activity and other behavioral parameters. Although behavioral tests have not (yet) been standardized, there is general agreement that several tests will have to be applied with which various parameters are measured, in order to demonstrate or rule out potential neurotoxicity for a compound.

This study unit has briefly discussed behavioral pharmacology research on psychotropic drugs. Behavioral pharmacology has, as it were, served as a model for the development of behavioral toxicology. On the other hand, behavioral toxicology research constitutes an important component in the research on new (psychotropic) drugs.

Cooperation between psychologists and (neuro)toxicologists should lead to the development of methods allowing damage to CNS functions to be determined adequately and at the earliest possible stage.

SELF ASSESSMENT QUESTIONS

These self assessment questions include references to the preceding three study units.

1    Why is it that in many cases neurotoxicity is first observed in the PNS rather than the CNS?

2    What is central distal axonopathy?

3    How do organophosphate insecticides work, what are the symptoms of intoxication by these substances, and for which effects can atropine be used as an antidote in such cases?

4    At which sites in the process of synaptic transmission can (theoretically) xenobiotics act?

5    For the following substances, indicate which type of neurotoxic effect they have been associated with.

    1    carbon monoxide
    2    aluminum
    3    hexachlorophene
    4    sodium glutamate

6    Knowing that the increase in age (newly born → adolescent) is accompanied by an increase in nerve fiber diameter, can you predict the consequences of this and explain them?

7    The excitotoxin alanosine acts as a false transmitter on the secondary neu-
     ron of a sensory nerve pathway. Clioquinol causes central distal axonopa-
     thy. Describe these two neuropathies by means of a figure.

8    Studies of the effects of prenatal exposure to neurotoxic substances on
     motor activity often use a substance with a short half-life, 5-azacytidine.
     This substance specifically destroys proliferating cells in the fetal brain
     but not in the brain of the mother. What is the advantage of prenatal ex-
     posure to this substance, over exposure to methylmercury or carbon
     monoxide?

9    Behavioral toxicologists used to claim that behavioral toxicity tests are often
     more sensitive than classical toxicology methods. What is the basis of this
     claim of greater sensitivity and what are the arguments raised by oppo-
     nents of this claim?

## FEEDBACK

### 1    Answers to the assignments

35.1 It can be concluded from the figure that: a higher level of exposure causes
     a shorter latency time, an intensified toxic effect and a wide spectrum of
     symptoms.

35.2 The shuttle box is partly used for cognitive function tests, although sen-
     sory (reaction to light) and motor function (the escape reaction itself) as-
     pects are not excluded.
         The auditory startle response is used to test sensory functions, although
     the motor functions cannot be excluded here either.
         The maze can be used to test cognitive functions and (in an open field)
     motor functions, depending on the protocol.
         The test mentioned under d assesses motor functions only.

35.3 Since lead is not easily removed from the central nervous system during
     development, it will remain there for a long time once it has entered.
     Consequently, it can continue its harmful action for protracted periods.

35.4 From the results, it can be deduced that severe forms of hypoxia can lead
     to an increase in motor activity. Interpretation of the results is made more
     difficult by the fact that there appear to be sex differences in sensitivity
     which result in unequal exposure times.

35.5 The disadvantage of the grip test lies in the fact that the force with which
     the technician pulls against the animal is subjective and can vary between
     researchers as well as between experiments. The disadvantage of the se-
     cond method is of course that the patterns are very difficult to quantify
     objectively.

35.6 The most striking consequences are: interruption of the gestation (resorp-
     tion of the fetus), pronounced teratogenic effects and apparently no struc-
     tural abnormalities. In addition, the offspring may show specific neurotoxic
     effects, such as behavioral abnormalities and motor disorders.

35.7 Prenatal exposure to the toxic substance does not necessarily affect only the offspring; it can also influence the nervous system of the mother and thus her behavior. A change in the mother's behavior can interfere with the behavior of the offspring. One possible solution may be to remove the litter from the mother immediately after birth, and to let the young be reared by a female animal that has also just given birth but that has not been in contact with the toxic substance during gestation. This swapping of mothers is called cross-fostering.

## 2    Answers to the self assessment questions

1    The protection afforded by the PNS is less effective than that of the CNS, although there are exceptions. Many distal axonopathies result from damage to the cell bodies in the spinal cord.

2    Central distal axonopathy refers to lesions of the axon endings in the CNS.

3    Organophosphate insecticides decrease the action of acetylcholinesterase. As a result the acetylcholine released in the synaptic transmission can not be metabolized. The transfer system from the motor nerve to the striated muscle and the transmission in the ganglia of the sympathetic nervous system (nicotine-like action of acetylcholine) and in the CNS become blocked after first having been excited. At the same time, the parasympathetic innervation of the glands, smooth muscle and heart (muscarine-like action of acetylcholine) is intensified. Only in the latter process is atropine an effective and selective antidote.

4    Sites of action for drugs and other xenobiotic in the process of synaptic transmission:

    1    synthesis of the neurotransmitter

    2    release of the neurotransmitter

    3    postsynaptic receptors

    4    intrasynaptic metabolic inactivation

    5    active reuptake of neurotransmitter molecules or their precursors/metabolites by the presynaptic membrane

    6    intracellular metabolic inactivation

    7    active reuptake of precursor (7′) and neurotransmitter (7″) by the granule membrane

    8    conduction of presynaptic action potential

    9    supply of mitochondria, granules and enzymes

    10    active uptake of precursors by the cell membrane

    11    removal of transmitter molecules or metabolites

    12    presynaptic receptors

    13    receptor/effector systems.

5    1    carbon monoxide—neuronopathy (CNS)

    2    aluminum—neuronopathy (CNS)

    3    hexachlorophene—myelinopathy

    4    sodium glutamate—synaptopathy

6     The increasing fiber diameter causes a decreasing longitudinal resistance of the axon and an increasing spatial distribution of the local circuit current. Consequently, the conduction rate of the impulse increases.

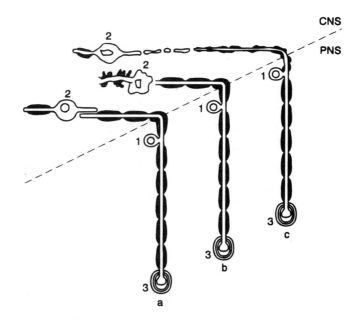

7     The figure shows (1) the ganglion cells in the dorsal horn, (2) the secondary sensory neurons in the CNS and by way of examples of sensory organs (3) some Vater-Pacini corpuscles. The transition between CNS and PNS is indicated by the broken line.

     a.   Normal sensory pathway.

     b.   Neuronopathy caused by alanosine; the prolonged depolarization of this false transmitter damages the secondary nerve cell.

     c.   Centrally, clioquinol causes a central retrograde degeneration in the ganglion cell of the dorsal root. This is an example of central distal axonopathy.

8     The short half-life of this compound makes it easier to determine the exact moment of exposure and the duration of exposure in the fetus, compared to a mercury compound or carbon monoxide. It is thus easier to establish a relationship between (subsequent) effect(s) and the moment at which anatomical injury occurs during development.

9     Using behavioral toxicology tests, effects of (neuro)toxic substances are often found at exposure levels where other toxicity tests (pathology, biochemistry) fail to show demonstrable effects (alcohol is a good example). One problem with such behavioral changes is that the effects found are often reversible. Even more problematic, however, is the fact that it is usually not possible to give a mechanistic explanation for the changes found.

# Contents Study unit 36
# Introduction to nutritional toxicology

0-8493-9232-2/96/$6.00 + $.50

# Introduction to nutritional toxicology

*J. H. Koeman*

INTRODUCTION

*Nutritional toxicology*

*Nutritional toxicology* is the branch of toxicology that studies the possible adverse effects of dietary substances on health, and the modulating influence of food components on these effects. It is a broad multidisciplinary field of study, encompassing toxicology, nutrition and food science (see Figure 36.1).

*Toxicology* may be defined as the science that studies the adverse effects of chemical compounds in organisms and the interaction of such compounds with organisms.

*Nutrition*
See Study unit 1

*Nutrition* studies the relationship between the quality of the diet and dietary habits on the one hand and the consumer's health on the other. In practice, nutrition draws on the same basic disciplines as toxicology. The only difference is that nutrition is mainly concerned with the nutritive properties of foodstuffs, whereas toxicology concentrates on the aspects which are hazardous to health.

*Food science*

*Food science* is concerned with the properties and condition of foodstuffs, e.g. their chemical composition (nutrients, artificial odors and flavorings, toxins, contaminants, etc.), their texture (physical condition) and microbiological features (e.g. presence of pathogenic microorganisms). The basis of food science is formed mainly by chemistry, physics and microbiology.

The principal objectives of nutritional toxicology are:

1. to record any toxic and toxicity modulating properties of foodstuffs;
2. to increase knowledge and understanding of the toxic and toxicity modulating properties of foodstuffs by means of epidemiological and experimental research;

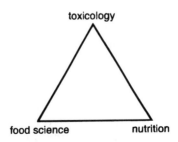

FIGURE 36.1
Nutritional toxicology as part of a broad multidisciplinary field of study

3. to assess the dangers (risks) due to toxic properties of foodstuffs on the basis (*inter alia*) of the levels in which they occur in foodstuffs and the dietary habits and lifestyles of consumers;

4. to keep society informed of measures aimed at limiting or preventing toxicological risk (policy on the use of substances, standards, information, etc.).

This study unit aims in the first place to provide a broad overview of potential toxicants in our food. Secondly, it shows that the type of nutrition influences the extent to which toxic effects may become apparent and thirdly, it describes how standards are established for potential toxicants in foodstuffs. The next study unit will give an application of nutritional toxicology. It gives a review of the history of the toxicological research of aspartame.

LEARNING OBJECTIVES

After studying this unit you should be able to:

— name the main objectives of nutritional toxicology
— understand the multidisciplinary nature of nutritional toxicology
— know the main sources of potential toxicants in food
— understand how the composition of food and dietary habits can modulate the toxicity of compounds
— know the principles which govern the setting of standards for potential toxicants in food.

*Study hints*

The study material in this unit is intended primarily to help the student to form a frame of reference so that, when assessing or advising on matters concerning nutritional toxicology, he or she can manage data in an orderly fashion (presenting it logically, checking on completeness of information, or on insight into modes of action).

The study unit is thus intended merely as an introduction, and the study load should not be more than 1.5 hours.

## STUDY CORE

### 1 Sources of potentially toxic substances in food

Figure 36.2 gives an overview of the sources of potential toxicants found in food.

There are three broad categories of compounds:

1. natural compounds;

2. compounds that may enter food as a result of industrial processes, either directly, (as part of the processing itself) or indirectly (via emissions into the environment);

3. so-called additives, i.e. compounds that are deliberately used in food production.

Figure 36.2 demonstrates that compounds may also originate from the various stages in the food production process. These stages and the examples of compounds and categories of compounds shown in the figure will be briefly discussed in the following sections.

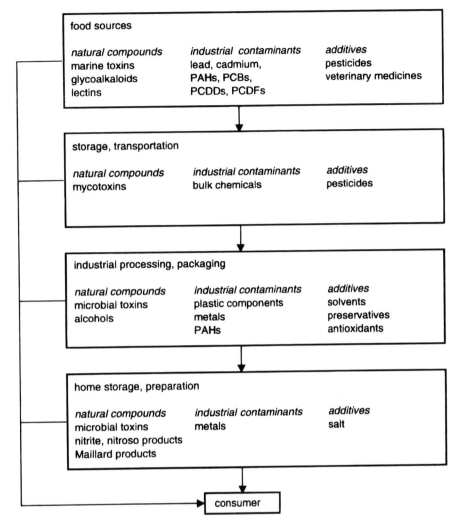

FIGURE 36.2
Sources of potential toxicants in food

The formation of brown pigments and flavor compounds from reducing sugars, heated in the presence of amines is called the Maillard reaction. The formed products are mutagenic organic compounds; they are responsible for the taste of grilled meat, for example. Maillard reactions have been implicated in the formation of imidazoquinolines and imidazoquinoxalines, heterocyclic amines which were first isolated from fried and boiled proteinaceous foods.

## 1.1   FOOD SOURCES

An important point is that a relatively large number of compounds may occur in foods of both vegetable and animal origin.

*Natural toxic compounds*

Many food sources, especially vegetable ones, *naturally* contain compounds that are *toxic* to man. The frequently voiced idea that whatever is natural is safe is by no means true. Marine toxins, glycoalkaloids and lectins are examples of natural toxins in food.

*Marine toxins*

There is a wide variety of *marine toxins*. Most are produced by single-cell organisms (dinoflagellates, for example) and occur secondarily in animals eaten by man (e.g. molluscs such as mussels). In Europe and North America cases of *paralytic shellfish poisoning* (after blooms of dinoflagellates of the genus *Gonyaulax*, which produce gonyautoxins and saxitoxins) and *diarrhetic shellfish poisoning* (after blooms of dinoflagellates of the genus *Dinophysis*, which produce dinophysis toxins) occur regularly. The latter type of poisoning is regularly found in North-Western Europe.

*Glycoalkaloids*

*Glycoalkaloids* are found, for example, in potatoes and tomatoes. Consumption of varieties with a high content of these compounds may cause poisoning. In potatoes, solanine and chaconine constitute 95% of the total glycoalkaloid content. These so-called industrial varieties in particular are unsuitable for human consumption. More attention needs to be paid to possible chronic toxicity, notably since some glycoalkaloids are teratogenic.

*Lectins*

*Lectins* (or hemagglutinins) are toxic proteins found in the seeds of certain plants. They are rendered harmless by heating (detoxication). Inadequate heating of certain bean varieties can cause severe poisoning.

Industrial contaminants, pesticides and veterinary medicines are examples of toxic compounds not naturally occurring in our food.

*Industrial contaminants*

*Industrial contaminants* finding their way into food sources are a well recognized problem because of their widespread presence in the environment. The most familiar compounds in this category are shown in Figure 36.2. There is increasing concern over polychlorinated dibenzodioxins (PCDDs) and polychlorinated dibenzofurans (PCDFs) because relatively high concentrations have been identified in breast milk.

*Pesticides and veterinary medicines*

*Pesticides and veterinary medicines* are widely used to combat disease and pests which may adversely affect the production of vegetable and animal foodstuffs. Residues of these compounds can sometimes find their way to the human consumer.

## 1.2    STORAGE AND TRANSPORTATION

During storage and transportation also, certain potentially toxic substances can enter foodstuffs (or raw materials used in food manufacture). Examples include mycotoxins and pesticides.

*Mycotoxins*

*Mycotoxins* are compounds formed by fungi. Many fungi are now known to produce mycotoxins (mainly of the genera *Aspergillus* and *Penicillium*).

*Contamination during bulk transport*

If certain raw materials used in the food industry (e.g. vegetable oils) are transported in bulk, the products may incidentally be *contaminated* by compounds previously transported in the same containers (e.g. mineral oils).

*Pesticides*

*Pesticides* (e.g. fumigants) are also sometimes used during storage and transportation to control vermin and other organisms which might otherwise damage the stock.

## 1.3    INDUSTRIAL PROCESSING AND PACKAGING

Processing and packaging is the next stage in which undesirable compounds may be introduced.

*Microbial toxins*

*Microbial toxins*, for example endotoxins produced by *Staphylococcus*, *Salmonoella* and *Shigella* species and exotoxins such as botulinum toxin (*Clostridium botulinum*) may be food contaminants introduced during the stage of packaging or food processing.

*Fermentation*

The manufacture of *fermented products* may, in addition to the desired products, give rise to products with less desirable properties such as higher alcohols in alcoholic ('ethanolic') beverages. Pentanols, in particular, are toxic, causing damage to the nervous system, insomnia and headache.

*Processing*

*Processing* methods such as mechanical treatment, heating, smoking, are often accompanied by changes in chemical composition due to the addition of compounds (traces of metals) or the formation of new products such as polycyclic aromatic hydrocarbons (PAH). Compounds may migrate from packaging materials into packaged foods (e.g. lead from the solder in certain metal cans, and plastic monomers and additives).

*Additives*

*Additives* are used, above all, in the processing and packaging stage. They are designed to improve or at least influence flavor, texture and storage life (e.g. emulsifiers, antioxidants, preservatives).

Solvent residues may also be found as a result of their use in extraction processes, e.g. trichloroethylene and methylene chloride used in the decaffeination of coffee.

### 1.4 HOME STORAGE AND PREPARATION

This stage comprises the actions performed (or neglected) by the consumer himself or herself.

*Microbiological contamination*

Here too, there is a risk of *microbiological contamination* (poor hygiene, products stored for too long or incorrectly).

*Nitrite*

In products rich in nitrates (certain green vegetables), *nitrite* may be formed after preparation and storage, by microbiological reduction. Nitrite is a toxicological hazard in itself but it may also react with a number of nitrogenous compounds (e.g. amines, indoles) to form nitroso compounds (in the product, but also in the consumer's stomach).

*Lead and cadmium*

*Pb* and *Cd* may reach food or drink via pottery (pigments, glazes), especially as a result of interaction with acid products such as fruit juices.

Finally, it should be noted that even an everyday ingredient such as cooking salt is potentially toxic.

The above review of potentially toxic compounds is of course in no way exhaustive. The 16th century Swiss physician Paracelsus remarked that "All things are poisonous", and added that "It is only the dose that makes a thing not poisonous". The job of the toxicologist is to determine whether the presence of compounds with potentially toxic properties does in fact constitute a real risk.

### 2 Modulating influence of nutrition on the toxicity of compounds

In a broad sense, it can be stated that a healthy person is less susceptible to adverse influences from the environment, including exposure to potentially toxic compounds, than someone in a poor state of health.

*Increased susceptibility through dietary deficiency*

Both experimental and epidemiological research have, for instance, shown that certain dietary deficiencies increase sensitivity to toxicants.

> ASSIGNMENT 36.1
>
> Which examples can you give that have a bearing on cytotoxicology?

antithyroid = toxic to the thyroid gland

Deficiency in the essential micronutrient iodine renders the thyroid more sensitive to antithyroid compounds.

Poor physical condition and thiamine deficiency increase the cardiotoxic effects of cobalt and arsenic compounds.

For cirrhosis of the liver see Study units 22 and 23

Another example is the higher risk of cirrhosis of the liver following chronic alcohol abuse combined with choline, protein or vitamin $B_{12}$ deficiencies.

*Biotransformation enzymes*

The constitution of the biochemical processes in the body, and thence also its physiology, are influenced in a complex way by diet. A good example is the influence on the enzyme systems in the liver, which are involved in the biochemical conversion of foreign compounds, the so-called *biotransformation enzymes*.

These enzymes play a dual role. On the one hand they can activate certain compounds into toxic products, and on the other hand they have a detoxicating action. The common environmental pollutant benzo[a]pyrene, for example, is converted by enzymes of the cytochrome P-450 complex into a carcinogenic metabolite (see Study unit 10). This metabolite is then detoxicated by other biotransformation enzymes including glutathione transferases.

Macronutrients such as proteins and lipids affect the activity of biotransformation enzymes. A similar modulating influence is exerted by various non-essential compounds which are also commonly found in foodstuffs, such as indole compounds and isothiocyanates. The balance between the activating and detoxicating functions of biotransformation enzymes ultimately determines the availability of any toxic (and/or carcinogenic) metabolite. Some food components and dietary habits stimulate the formation of toxic metabolites (e.g. a relatively high carbohydrate or protein intake). Others have the opposite effect. The anticarcinogenic effect of indoles is thought to derive from their inducing effect on the biotransformation enzyme glutathione transferase, which plays a major role in detoxicating reactive metabolites.

*Multifactorial processes*

Chronic illness involving toxic compounds is rarely the result of a single-cause relationship between the presence of the compound on the one hand and the development of the illness on the other. The illness is always the result of *multifactorial processes*, and its manifestation may be determined not only by the individual's hereditary characteristics but also by dietary habits and lifestyle. Physical functions and underlying biochemical constitution vary from one individual to another, in accordance with the variables mentioned above. The individual becomes ill when there is a shift in the physiological balance to the extent that a critical threshold is exceeded (see Figure 36.3).

The fact that not all chain smokers die of lung cancer is probably due to a combination of a favorable genetic constitution and a protective effect provided by the survivors' dietary habits and lifestyle.

## 3   Standards

NEL = no effect level

In evaluating the toxicologically acceptable level of additives in food the starting point is usually considered to be the "no-observed-(adverse) effect level" (NOEL or NOAEL) as determined in toxicity studies. This is the maximum dietary level at which no effects are observed in experimental animals after long-term exposure.

ADI = acceptable daily intake (in mg per kg body weight per day)

The *acceptable daily intake* (ADI) for humans is calculated from the NOEL. Both NOEL and ADI are usually expressed in mg per kg body weight per day. Extrapolation from NOEL to ADI is carried out by applying arbitrary safety factors, usually the factor 100. The ADI is converted to the maximum permissible level in the product, using an average human body weight (60 kg) and the so-called *food factor*.

For example, it may be assumed that the average intake of fruit and vegetables is 400 g a day. The maximum permissible levels will thus be 60 × ADI × 1000/400 g per kg of product. Normally, when setting maximum permissible levels (such as residue tolerances), the levels which may occur in practice during proper use in industrial manufacturing (e.g. preservatives) are also taken into account.

The diagram in Figure 36.4 shows the procedure that is usually followed in standard setting .

*Pesticides Act*

Under the *Pesticides Act*, rules may also be laid down for compliance with safety terms when harvesting plants or animals which have been treated with pesticides. The maximum permissible levels allowed are nearly always lower than the toxicologically permissible levels.

*Practical residue limits*

Sometimes, maximum permissible levels are also set for compounds which occur in foods as inadvertent contaminants. These levels are known as *practical residue limits*. Also important to the consumer are the quality requirements relating to the presence of contaminants and additives. These are laid down, for example,

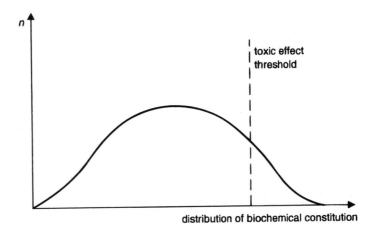

FIGURE  36.3
If the distribution of the biochemical constitution in a population is more or less normal, chronic disorders such as cardiovascular disease and cancer can be expected to occur in individuals in whom a critical threshold of biochemical balance is exceeded. Any change in external circumstances, e.g. in food composition or dietary habits, may lead to a shift of the curve and exceeding the threshold in both directions.

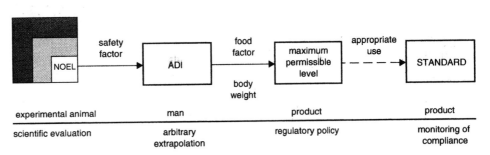

FIGURE  36.4
Conventional procedure for setting standards (schematic)

in government product regulations and orders on agricultural product quality. Acceptability of a residue in public health terms is, for most compounds, based on the assumption that a minimum quantity of the substance is needed to induce a harmful effect. In concentrations below that level the consumer's body can cope with the compound by means of biochemical degradation and excretion processes. This hypothesis is supported by a large body of toxicological research.

*Carcinogens*

Exceptions are, however, those chemicals that *initiate carcinogenic effects*. For these one has to assume that there is effectively no threshold dose below which the compound will not be carcinogenic. For this reason, compounds which induce or are suspected of inducing, this kind of effect are not permitted for general use in the environment.

*Uncertainties in the setting of standards*

There are a number of uncertainties surrounding the regulatory system outlined above:

1. the validity of the NOEL as determined in toxicity studies can not be proved;
2. in setting an ADI it is assumed that animal data are a good basis from which to derive limits of human hazard;
3. metabolites of additives formed by either the plant or the consumer may also be toxic;
4. toxic impurities may be present, in changing quantities and may not be taken into account in toxicity research, and
5. at the time of consumption, more than one compound may be present as a residue in foodstuffs.

To compensate for the uncertainties mentioned under (1) and (2) as much as possible, safety factors are applied when extrapolating from NOEL to ADI. In addition, techniques for recording the test animal's state of health are constantly being refined. The less the toxic action of the compound is understood, the greater the safety factors that are applied. In the last 20 years especially, there has been a sharp increase in the contribution of biochemistry and analytical chemistry to toxicity research. This means that there is usually adequate information on the biotransformation and possible presence of toxic impurities at hand. As a result, the uncertainties indicated in (3) and (4) are significantly reduced. It should be noted, however, that *chronic* toxicity data on the major metabolites of additives and pesticides are still lacking. Where residues and various compounds occur together in the same foodstuff (5), possible synergism or cumulative effects should be considered.

---

EXAMPLE

Based on toxicity research (usually chronic experiments in rats) the NOEL for an insecticide is set at 1 mg per kg body weight per day.

Application of the commonly used safety factor of 100 gives an ADI for humans of 0.01 mg per kg body weight per day.

The maximum permissible intake for any human individual is thus $60 \times 0.01$ mg per day, or 0.6 mg.

The compound is mainly used on fruit and/or vegetables, for which the food factor is 400 g (of fruit and vegetables per day).

So, the maximum permissible daily level in fruit and vegetables (mg kg$^{-1}$) is

$(1.0 \text{ kg} / 0.4 \text{ kg}) \times 0.6 \text{ mg} = 1.5$ mg per kg (fruit and vegetables).

If in practice it is then found that, given proper agricultural use, the residue levels on fruit and vegetables are never higher than, for example, 0.5 mg per kg of the product, it is to be expected that the authorities will adopt this level as the legal standard.

## SELF ASSESSMENT QUESTIONS

1   With the page outlining the learning objectives in front of you, describe the objectives and concepts mentioned.

2   Without referring to the text, draw the figures illustrating
    a. the origins of potentially toxic substances in food
    b. the conventional procedure for setting standards.

3   How can food have a modulating effect on the toxicity of compounds?

## FEEDBACK

Check your answers against the text and Figures in this study unit.

**Answer to the assignment**

36.1 Examples of increased susceptibility as a result of dietary components in which a link can be made with cytotoxic protection mechanisms are: vitamin A, C and E deficiency and selenium deficiency. See Study unit 10.

# Contents Study unit 37
# Food toxicity: the toxicological history of aspartame

# Food toxicity: the toxicological history of aspartame

*J. C. S. Kleinjans*

INTRODUCTION

A characteristic aspect of the cultural evolution of man is his manipulation of food. This includes boiling, frying and roasting, but also improving the taste of food. The world economy was founded on the ancient trade in herbs and spices, which were considered necessary to make the consumption of common food-stuffs more pleasant. Similarly, the sweet taste of certain food components was and is highly valued, and honey and fruit were popular. As early as the Middle Ages, a technique was developed that made it possible to purify the substance responsible for this sweet taste, which could then be added to food according to need and taste. Although sugar refining dates from the fourteenth century, nevertheless it remained scarce until the twentieth century. The ever-increasing demand for sweeteners could only be met by technological advances in the large-scale extraction of sucrose from sugar cane and sugar beets.

By then, artificial sweeteners had been discovered. In 1879, Constantine Fahlberg had accidentally synthesized saccharin. The possibility of replacing sucrose by artificial sugar substitutes goes back more than a century. The most important synthetic sweeteners besides saccharin are cyclamate and, since its discovery in 1965, aspartame.

> Try to imagine the consequences of substitution of sugar for the health of the average population.

The nutritional pattern of (Western) man has developed as a function of, among

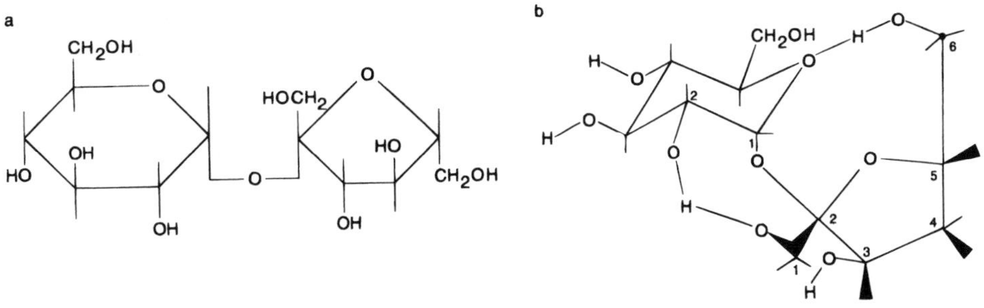

FIGURE   37.1
Structural formula of sucrose
a. representation in a flat plane
b. steric representation

other factors, agroindustrial relations. The rise of technology has contributed to this expansion, diversity and quality. For the greater part of this century, food has been regarded as beneficial to health. Since the mid-1970s, however, this perception of food has changed as a result of our growing awareness of environmental pollution and the threat it poses to our health. The current trend is to distrust foodstuffs because of possible chemical contamination and processing procedure. As a reaction to this, products labelled "natural" are in demand.

Many chemicals that are deliberately added to food improve its quality or enhance its smell, flavor or color. Some of these were introduced before toxicological testing was required. These additives have since been tested for toxicity. Those that showed any harmful effects were eliminated from the food production process to be replaced by food additives, which were tested and approved. These regulations were applied for the sugar substitutes saccharin and cyclamate.

Aspartame, in contrast, was brought on the market after guidelines for the admission of substances as food additives had been introduced. Toxicological research into its properties has consequently not been retrospective. The research has served to evaluate in advance any negative health effects, both in general and in each of its various areas of use. The history of aspartame research provides a unique panorama of the possibilities that the science of toxicology has at its disposal to analyze the mechanisms by which foreign chemicals induce their harmful effects. Such knowledge enables us to determine the possible risks involved in human use.

LEARNING OBJECTIVES

Having studied this unit, you will be able to:

— indicate how and to what extent the toxicological profile of aspartame differs from that of previous synthetic sweeteners
— indicate why the various studies described in this unit were carried out and what conclusions have been drawn regarding the toxicity of aspartame
— describe how aspartame is metabolized in the body and indicate to what extent its metabolites are toxic
— estimate the exposure to aspartame and identify high-risk groups
— give an impression of the background of aspartame research.

*Study hints*

This study unit integrates several aspects from the previous units. You are expected to be familiar with the concepts, methods of calculation, etc. that have come up in these units. If you are not, you may need to refer to them.

This unit focuses on a subject from nutritional toxicology, namely the toxicology of aspartame. As a result, your knowledge of physiology, in particular of nutritional physiology, will frequently be called upon. It is therefore advisable to have a textbook on (human) physiology to consult.

This study unit poses many questions to which no immediate answers are to be found in the feedback section. Their objective is to indicate controversial areas. These questions are not numbered.

STUDY CORE

1    Sugar substitutes as food additives

Artificial sweeteners are used to replace sucrose in foodstuffs. Society's demand for these synthetic products can be explained from their properties and uses. Not only can they contribute to better health, but they also have technological uses. Sugar substitutes increase the range of choice available to those who do not want to or are not able to use sucrose as a sweetener. In addition, they are also used in cosmetics and pharmaceuticals. The ideal sweetener, however, does not exist. Even sucrose does not meet the technological requirements of the ideal sweetener; for example, too much of it is needed to mask the bitter taste of certain drugs. The ideal sugar substitute is at least as sweet as sucrose, does not smell or impart color and has a clear taste that is immediately perceptible and does not linger. In addition, its consumption should obviously be safe.

ASSIGNMENT 37.1

Specify the physico-chemical properties of the ideal sweetener.

The craving for sweetness is perhaps innate to man. Taste organs can be found in the 4-month-old fetus. An injection of a sweet stimulus directly into the amniotic fluid increases the swallowing frequency.

ASSIGNMENT 37.2

Give a brief description of the sensory physiology of taste and the taste organs.

The perception of sweetness does vary between individuals. The taste and sweetening power of sucrose are taken as a standard, since sucrose has been generally accepted by man. Table 37.1 indicates the relative sweetness of some important alternatives to that of sucrose.

Research has obviously been carried out into the relationship between the chemical structure of these sweeteners and their sweetening power or sweet taste. The most plausible theory to date that explains sweet taste is that of Shallenberger and Acree (1971). This theory postulates that the principle property causing the perception of sweetness is the formation of two hydrogen bonds, at an interval of approximately 3 Å. The stimulus molecule would have to possess an AH-B configuration, with A and B representing electronegative atoms and H being a hydrogen atom that is part of the polar AH system. The AH-B complex is thought to react with a complementary AH-B site of the the receptor, in the taste bud, as a result of which the two hydrogen bonds are formed. It has been suggested that a third lipophilic site may be necessary for intense sweetness.

The relatively high sweetening power of aspartame (see Table 37.1) can be explained using this model. The molecule possesses a lipophilic group in the phenylalanine side chain (the aromatic ring structure) that is thought to engage a third functional unit of the receptor in the response. Experiments with volun-

TABLE 37.1
Relative sweetness to sucrose of some sugar alternatives

| Name of compound | Sweetness (sucrose = 1) |
|---|---|
| acesulphame K | 200 |
| aspartame | 180 |
| cyclamate | 30 |
| fructose (crystalline) | 1.2–1.7 |
| fructose (90%, syrup) | 1.5 |
| L-sugars | 1 |
| mannitol | 0.7 |
| saccharin | 300 |
| sorbitol | 0.5–0.7 |
| xylitol | 1 |

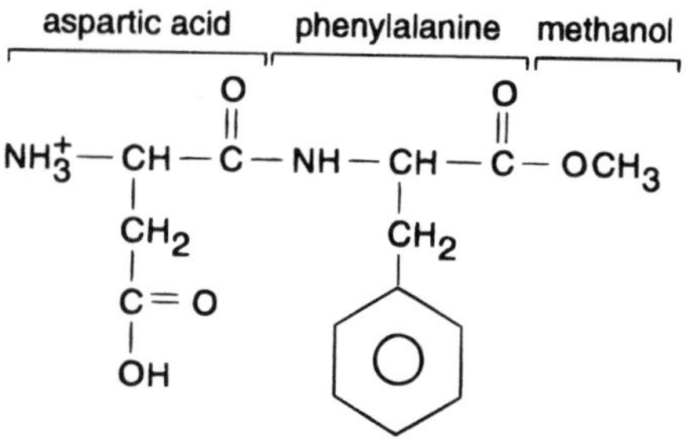

FIGURE 37.2

Structural formula of aspartame, and its components (aspartic acid, phenylalanine and methanol) after hydrolysis in the intestine. The figure itself shows the unhydrolyzed aspartame molecule.

teers, using the various components of the aspartame molecule, have shown that the AH-X configuration leads to a sensation of bitterness, which turns into a sensation of sweetness when the B component is subsequently applied to the tongue. A possible conclusion from these findings is that the same receptor discriminates between sweet and bitter tastes.

The differences in chemical structure between the alternative sweeteners seem to make it unlikely that only one type of receptor is involved in the sensation of sweetness.

## 1.1 LOW-CALORIE SUGAR SUBSTITUTES

The most frequently used low-calorie sugar substitutes are the sugar fructose and the polyalcohols sorbitol, mannitol and xylitol. The sweetening power of this category of compounds is equal to or less than that of sucrose (see Table 37.1). Their use is desirable because:

- they do not induce dental caries
- they offer diabetics an alternative to glucose.

In a normal Western diet, sucrose accounts for 15% of the total energy intake. Substituting sucrose by polyalcohols may be efficient. Xylitol, in particular, can play a role in preventing dental decay, since it is not fermented by bacteria in the mouth, and even inhibits the growth of a strain of streptococci thought to be responsible for caries. Polyalcohols also find application as sweeteners for diabetic patients, since they lead to smaller fluctuations in the blood sugar level.

The consumption of polyalcohols is probably not accompanied by toxic effects. Sorbitol and xylitol are normal products of intracellular carbohydrate metabolism in man. Oral intake of more than 20 g may cause diarrhea. However, little is known about the long-term effects of the use of polyalcohols.

> ASSIGNMENT 37.3
>
> Explain why an acute oral dose of sorbitol may cause diarrhea.

## 1.2 NON-CALORIC SUGAR SUBSTITUTES

The main substances included in this category are saccharin, cyclamate and aspartame. Only saccharin and cyclamate are non-calorific. The advantage of aspartame is that it has only a very low calorific value in comparison to sucrose, namely 12.5 kJ (= 3 kcal) per gram, but also (like saccharin) great sweetening power. A total of 867 mg of aspartame per person per day would suffice to replace the average total daily intake of sucrose in the diet. This would imply a daily reduction in energy intake of approximately 2500 kJ (600 kcal).

These compounds have considerable sweetening power (see Table 37.1). They are added to products that do not need bulk and whose energy content should be as low as possible. They are used by diabetics and people on diets as 'table top sweeteners' to replace sugar in coffee and tea. They are also added to soft drinks and desserts for diabetic patients. The registration of these sweeteners for various applications varies from one country to another. The toxicological literature on saccharin, cyclamate and aspartame is very extensive. The conclusions as to whether or not they constitute a health hazard are ambiguous and, as a result, governmental policies differ between countries. The manufacturing costs of these alternative sweeteners are generally low, and small quantities are enough to produce considerable sweetening power. This makes their use more cost-effective than that of sugar. Governments are thus faced with economic facts, combined with the unpredictability of the health effects of using synthetic sugar substitutes as food additives.

An additional aspect is that food manufacturers sometimes combine various sugar substitutes in one product to compensate for an unpleasant aftertaste or the poor stability of individual compounds. In several European countries, saccharin–cyclamate combinations are commonly used. In the future, products containing fructose syrup combinations will also be available.

ASSIGNMENT 37.4
Describe the potential toxicological consequence of using combinations of sweeteners in foodstuffs.

The following sections will discuss the current state of toxicological research into the various non-calorific sugar substitutes.

## 2    Brief history and toxicology of saccharin

Alternative sweeteners were discovered by careless chemists. In 1878, the German researcher Constantine Fahlberg was working in Ira Remmen's laboratory in Baltimore on the oxidative derivatization of *o*-toluenesulfonamide. A trace of the heterocyclic compound produced remained on Fahlberg's hands, and he discovered its sweet taste when eating bread in the evening. "Sie schmeckt angenehm süss, sogar süsser als der Rohrzucker" ("It tastes pleasantly sweet, even sweeter than cane sugar"), he observed.

Fahlberg took out a patent on the new compound, which he named saccharin. After some unpleasant disputes about the rights, Fahlberg started the industrial production of saccharin in Germany, and by 1900 he was producing as much as

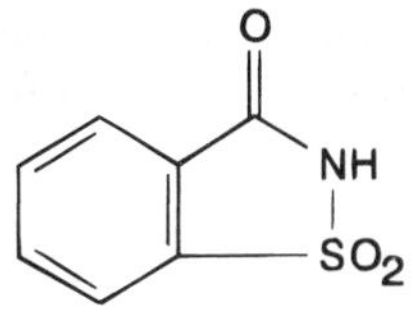

saccharum (Lat.) = sugar

saccharin

FIGURE   37.3
Structural formula of saccharin

190 000 kg per year. The turn of the century also saw the start of the discussion about the toxic effects of consuming saccharin, a discussion that continues unresolved to this day.

One of the first toxicological studies of saccharin was carried out in France. Diabetics ingested 5 g of saccharin per day for 5 months. No harmful effects were found. Nevertheless, France prohibited saccharin production and importation. Germany followed in 1902, partly under pressure from the sugar beet industry. Saccharin was still available, but only on prescription. Opposition to saccharin in the United States arose within the framework of the Food and Drug Act (1906), but President Roosevelt publicly declared himself in favor of the use of this sweetener. It was not until 1912 that saccharin was forbidden in the US, on the grounds that saccharin, unlike sugar, did not have any nutritional or calorific value, and should therefore be classified under the law as an "adulterant".

The shortage of sugar during the first World War, followed by the rationing of sugar in the US and Europe during the years between the wars and its shortage during the Second World War, put the use of saccharin in a different perspective. As a result, its production rose steadily.

In 1959, the FDA in the United States (see section 5) declared saccharin 'generally recognized as safe'. The effect was striking. In 1953, only 10 000 kg of saccharin per year had been consumed; by 1962 the annual consumption had risen to 1.2 million kg and by 1970, after cyclamate had been banned (see section 3), as much as 2 million kg of saccharin were consumed annually. The consumption pattern has hardly changed since.

Carcinogenicity is discussed in Study unit 12

After the Second World War, however, questions began to be asked as to the possible carcinogenic properties of saccharin. Investigation of carcinogenicity of a chemical compound for man is difficult because the substance cannot be tested in man. From a biological point of view, non-human primates are the best alternatives, but in view of the long latency period of the carcinogenic response, an experiment using primates would take some 10–20 years. Therefore, carcinogenicity tests are carried out using rodents, which live for only 2–3 years. Unfortunately, effects found in rodents have to be extrapolated to man.

Since the 1950s, several carcinogenicity studies of saccharin have been carried out on various species of test animals. Male rats that were exposed to saccharin for their entire lives developed a statistically significant number of urinary bladder tumors.

No apparent carcinogenic effect of saccharin has been demonstrated in rhesus monkeys. The carcinogenic effect of saccharin on the rat urinary bladder has been studied in more detail. The effect of saccharin on growth of urinary bladder tumors, induced by known carcinogens, such as nitrosamines and polycyclic aromatic hydrocarbons, has been studied. This has shown that urinary bladder carcinogenesis induced in rats is promoted by saccharin.

Both in man and in rats, the absorption from the gastro-intestinal tract of saccharin is slow and incomplete, while its elimination via the kidneys is rapid ($t_{1/2}$ in man is 70 minutes, in rats 30 minutes). Saccharin is not significantly metabolized either in man or in rats.

ASSIGNMENT 37.5

Give a schematic representation of the plasma concentration/time curve of a compound with slow absorption and high clearance.

Higher concentrations of saccharin than in plasma are only found in the intestinal wall, kidney and urinary bladder in rats when given saccharin up to 10% of their total daily food intake. The concentration gradient between the bladder wall and the contents of the urinary bladder is 1:100. Two-generation studies have provided an indication of bioaccumulation of saccharin, although the concentrations of saccharin found in the tissues were somewhat lower than in one-generation studies, using the same doses.

The accumulation of saccharin in the bladder would not seem to be a cause for great concern, because bladder contents form part of the central compartment (see Study unit 6), which has a high clearance rate.

ASSIGNMENT   37.6

Does the urinary bladder wall also form part of the central compartment with a high clearance rate?

*Summary*

Some toxicity studies have demonstrated that saccharin increases the incidence of urinary bladder cancer in male rats. The mode of action of saccharin in the development of bladder cancer in rats is unknown. The carcinogenic action of saccharin is assumed to be indirect. This suggests the existence of a threshold dose, which implies that such an effect can not take place below a certain dose. The quantity of saccharin given daily to the rats in the experiments was excessive, well beyond the daily intake of man.

## 3   Brief history and toxicology of cyclamate

GRAS = generally recognized as safe

Cyclamate was discovered in 1937 by Andrieth and Sveda at the University of Illinois. The patent later passed on to Abbott Laboratories, who carried out the necessary toxicity tests that allowed them to put the new sweetener on the market in 1949. The sodium and calcium salts of cyclamate were placed on the *GRAS* list in the US in 1958. It remained there until 1969, when alarming data suggested that cyclamate combined with saccharin had induced urinary bladder tumors in rats. Canada immediately prohibited the use of cyclamate as a food additive, and the product was subsequently removed from the GRAS list. At that time, cyclamate consumption in Canada and the US amounted to millions of kilograms per year.

The original study that reported the carcinogenicity of cyclamate has been repeated, but no bladder tumors were shown. Since then, at least 30 carcinogenicity studies with cyclamate have been carried out on rats, mice, hamsters, dogs and monkeys. No urinary bladder tumors were found, even after lifetime studies with cyclamate. In one study, 3 out of 24 rats fed cyclamate developed bladder carcinomas, while no tumors were found in the control group.

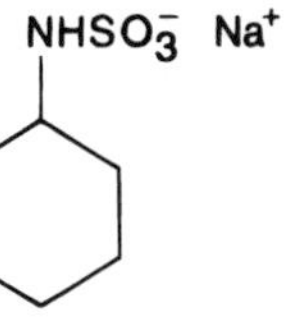

(sodium) cyclamate

FIGURE   37.4
Structural formula of (sodium)cyclamate

There is very slight evidence that cyclamate enhances the potency of other carcinogens to induce urinary bladder cancer. Implantation of cholesterol pellets containing 20% sodium cyclamate directly into the bladders of mice produced a higher incidence of bladder carcinomas than implantation of cholesterol alone. More than 50% of rats, after a single dose of N-methyl-N-nitrosourea directly into the bladder, developed bladder tumors, if they subsequently received 1 or 2 g of sodium cyclamate per kg body weight per day for the rest of their lives. Again, this finding has never been reproduced.

Cyclamate has been shown unequivocally to produce a toxic effect directly related to its metabolism *in vivo*. Originally, cyclamate was thought not to be biotransformed in man, but to be excreted in the urine unmodified. Most people metabolize no more than 1% of cyclamate, but there is a subpopulation that can transform up to 60% of the ingested dose into cyclohexylamine.

For more information about atrophy, see Study unit 15

Cyclohexylamine, 200 mg per kg body weight daily, to young male rats for 90 days causes the testes to be reduced in weight (testicular atrophy). On the other hand, 100–500 mg of cyclohexylamine per kg body weight for 12 years had no adverse effects on the testicles in three different species of monkey, but it is unknown whether these particular monkeys metabolize cyclamate to cyclohexylamine. It should be noted that this cyclamate metabolite is not carcinogenic.

*Summary*

Cyclamate, like saccharin, was suspected for a short period to induce urinary bladder cancer. Further studies, however, were unable to confirm such an effect and have concluded that other, unknown factors must be responsible for the carcinogenic effect. Some people metabolize cyclamate to cyclohexylamine, which in male rats damages the testes.

## 4    Brief history of aspartame

In 1965, James M. Schlatter was working with Robert H. Matuur at Searle Laboratories to develop an inhibitor of the gastrointestinal hormone gastrin. Schlatter synthesized aspartame as a building block for gastrin.

Figure 37.2 gives the chemical structure of aspartame

A small amount of the compound attached to his fingers, and he discovered its intensely sweet taste when he licked his fingers to pick up a piece of weighing paper. The sweetening power of the peptide can not be predicted by the properties of its components. Phenylalanine has a bitter taste and aspartic acid is tasteless to slightly sour. Moreover, only the ester of the L-stereoisomers of the two amino acids has a sweet taste; other combinations taste bitter. Finally, the methyl group is also essential: aspartylphenylalanine is a tasteless compound. Since the sweetening power of aspartame was discovered, all kinds of homologs have been synthesized by derivatization of one of the three components of the dipeptide methyl ester. In this way, a whole series of more or less sweet compounds was created. Derivatives of L-aspartic acid, in particular, proved to have amazing sweetening capacities.

The technological application of aspartame is complicated by its relatively low stability. Depending on acidity and temperature, aspartame may decompose into various components (see Figure 37.5).

A separate problem is the formation of the heterocyclic compound diketopiperazine. During the process of registration of aspartame, diketopiperazine has also been subjected to extensive toxicity testing. At the time aspartame was introduced as a food additive, national and international legislators registered new food additives on the basis of sophisticated toxicological criteria. This is in

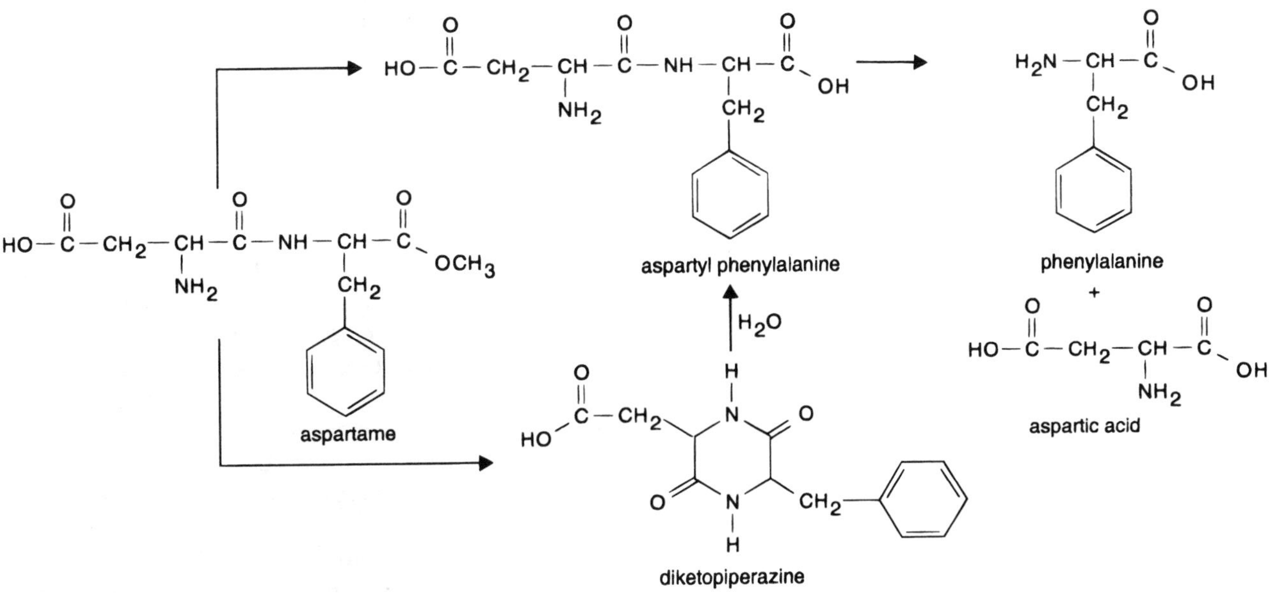

FIGURE 37.5
Metabolism of aspartame
Aspartame decomposes into non-sweet compounds.

contrast to research into other food additives, which had sometimes been in use for decades before a toxicological perspective developed (e.g., saccharin). The result is that research into the safety of aspartame consumption has been extensive and rationally designed.

Research into aspartame has focused on both the parent compound and on its constituent parts, since the latter also become available in the organism as a result of biotransformation.

In the US, aspartame was admitted by the FDA in 1974 to be used as a 'table-top sweetener' as well as a powder in certain foodstuffs.

At the same time, the first reports appeared on toxic effects of high doses of amino acids in animals. This led to aspartame being viewed with suspicion.

ASSIGNMENT 37.7

Amino acids are essential food components. At high doses they may show toxicity. What are the targets in which these amino acids affect physiological processes?

ASSIGNMENT 37.8

Mention some toxic effects of the most important natural food components.

In the United States, the safety of aspartame was re-evaluated on these critical points and re-established by the FDA in 1981. In 1983, permission was granted to use aspartame as a sweetener in carbonated beverages and in syrups used to sweeten soft drinks. The use of aspartame as a table-top sweetener is permitted in many Western countries, though government policies regarding its use in foodstuffs and soft drinks are much more diverse. Each registration procedure is characterized by a re-evaluation of the very extensive toxicological literature on aspartame. The original manufacturer, Searle and Co., is also forced to make major investments in toxicological studies to be able to counter each new wave of criticism.

## 5 Regulations concerning sugar substitutes

JEFCA = Joint Expert Committee on Food Additives

At an international level, various organizations are involved in setting standards and regulations concerning food additives, including synthetic sugar substitutes. First, the *Joint Expert Committee on Food Additives* (JEFCA) stands under the combined auspices of the FAO and the WHO. JEFCA consists of many experts who have been selected as national representatives based upon their personal expertise. This committee advises annually on technical and scientific matters, it specifies quality standards, and evaluates the toxicological status of various food additives. One of the important tasks of the committee is to determine the maximum safe daily intake of a substance, called the acceptable daily intake or ADI. Their advice may differ from political points of view held by the FAO or the WHO.

ADI = acceptable daily intake

The *Codex Alimentaris Committee*, which concentrates on standardization, also operates at the FAO/WHO level. The European Union (EU) is advised on food additives by the *Scientific Committee for Food*. This committee also consists of recognized experts who provide independent advice. The EU implements its advice in the form of recommendations to its member states. In the end, each national government determines its own policy concerning food additives.

The policies of many Western countries are based on the organization in the US. The use of food additives has been regulated since 1906 by means of the *Food and Drug Act*. The original Food and Drug Act prohibited the presence of any unnatural substance in foodstuffs and thus in fact banned all food additives. Safety on the basis of 'presence' has been regulated since 1938 in the Federal Food, Drug and Cosmetic Act. Since 1958, substances that are 'generally recognized as safe' (i.e. that are on the GRAS list) have also been admitted for technological uses in food, even though these substances do not, or not yet, possess the legal status of food additives. The year 1958 also saw the incorporation of the *Delaney Clause* into food legislation in the United States.

The Delaney clause in the US Food, Drug and Cosmetic Act, states that food additives that cause cancer in humans or animals at any level shall not be considered safe and are, therefore, prohibited from such use.

Food legislation in the US is enforced by the Food and Drug Administration (FDA) in cooperation with the Department of Agriculture. In 1982, the FDA published a handbook that explicitly describes the safety tests to which food additives have to be subjected (Toxicological Principles for the Safety Assessment of Direct Food Additives and Color Additives Used in Food). Since then, the American food additives policy has set the tone, although, as was stated before, each national government has its own policy.

## 6 Developments in the toxicology of aspartame

### 6.1 COMPLAINTS AND SYMPTOMS AFTER USE OF ASPARTAME

After the registration of aspartame for use in soft drinks in the United States, an increase in the number of health complaints was registered among aspartame consumers. Sixty-seven percent of these complaints, of a total of 231 complaints investigated, involved neurological/psychological symptoms such as headache (45% of the total), changes of mood, e.g. depression, (43%), insomnia (22%), vertigo (21%), fatigue (20%), reduced vision (9%) and hyperactivity (5%). Twenty-four percent of those complaining suffered from gastrointestinal symptoms: abdominal pain (46%), nausea (43%), diarrhea (32%), vomiting (23%). Fifteen percent reported allergic symptoms, in particular rashes (30% of those reporting). A number of women (6% of the total) reported changes in their menstrual pattern.

EXAMPLES

A number of individual cases are described below.

- A 30-year-old woman developed a red rash on the skin of her face and chest, approximately 8 hours after consumption of a soft drink containing aspartame. The rash persisted for approximately 3 days. The symptom recurred a month later after consumption of ice tea sweetened with aspartame.

- A man, aged 28, suffered from recurrent insomnia after using a sweetener containing aspartame in his coffee and a diet drink sweetened with aspartame.

- A 62-year-old male reported an acute depression, with suicidal feelings, after he had used aspartame as a table-top sweetener for 10 days. The depression lasted for 3 days after ceasing to use the product. It has not recurred. The man has not used aspartame again.

- A 2-year-old girl had an epileptic attack 21 days after consuming aspartame-containing products. Over a period of 7 months she had three more attacks, which did not necessarily follow consumption of aspartame.

In 15% of the complaints, it was possible to establish beyond doubt that the symptoms recurred on renewed use of aspartame.

> On the basis of the complaints reported, suggest which are the main target organs after aspartame intake.

Many of the complaints concerned neurological/psychological symptoms suggesting the central nervous system (CNS) to be the target organ.


6.2   METABOLISM OF ASPARTAME

It is possible to link the metabolism of aspartame and the symptoms reported. As we have seen, aspartame is a methyl ester of a dipeptide that in turn consists of an ester of L-aspartic acid and L-phenylalanine. Both these components of the aspartame molecule are found in the normal diet. A hypothesis for aspartame metabolism has been developed based on our knowledge of how the animal metabolizes the individual components. A schematic representation of aspartame metabolism is provided in Figure 37.6.

This hypothesis has been tested by comparing the metabolism of aspartame with that of its individual components. Both aspartame and its components were labelled with $^{14}C$ and given orally to laboratory animals and human volunteers. Blood, urine, feces and expired air were sampled. The radioactivity of the samples was measured.

The following observations were made about the various aspartame metabolites:


a.   *Methanol*

In rats, no difference was observed between the metabolism of $^{14}C$-methanol and ($^{14}C$-methyl) aspartame. Sixty percent of the dose of the radioactive label was found in the expired air; 0.45% of the dose was measured as the maximum plasma concentration 3 hours after administration. In the early stage, monkeys excreted more $^{14}C$ in the expired air after oral administration of $^{14}C$-methanol, but the cumulative values over 8 hours were the same (70% of the dose). Peak plasma va-

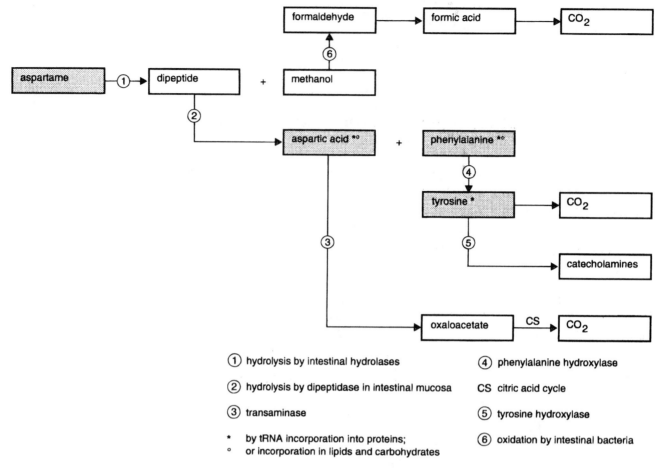

FIGURE 37.6
Transformation of aspartame in the intestinal lumen, mucosal cells and other parts of the organism

lues were also identical (0.25% per ml), although the timings were different, 3 hours after $^{14}$C-methanol, but 6 hours after ($^{14}$C-methyl) aspartame. Both rats and monkeys excreted only 5–7% of the oral dose of $^{14}$C in the urine and feces. This study was not carried out in man.

### b. Aspartic acid

A similar experimental set-up was used to compare the metabolic routes of $^{14}$C-aspartic acid and ($^{14}$C-aspartyl) aspartame in rats and monkeys (see Table 37.2).

In monkeys, plasma concentrations of $^{14}$C ranged from 52.5 to 120.3% of the dose per liter of plasma after oral administration of ($^{14}$C-aspartyl) aspartame, and from 71.5 to 167.0% per liter after administration of $^{14}$C-aspartic acid. The time required to reach the peak plasma concentration varied from 20 minutes to 5 hours.

After approximately 7 hours, the plasma levels of radioactivity and the elimination rates were the same.

### c. Phenylalanine

Table 37.3 shows the data on the metabolism of $^{14}$C-phenylalanine and ($^{14}$C-phenylalanyl) aspartame in rats and monkeys. Administration of ($^{14}$C-phenylalanyl) aspartame and $^{14}$C-phenylalanine in monkeys resulted in comparable plasma characteristics.

TABLE 37.2
Recovery of radioactivity (% of dose) after oral administration of 20 mg kg$^{-1}$ ($^{14}$C-aspartyl) aspartame and $^{14}$C-aspartic acid

|  | Urine | Feces | Expired air |
|---|---|---|---|
| A. rat |  |  |  |
| $^{14}$C-aspartyl aspartame | 3.7 | 1.1 | 68.3 |
| $^{14}$C-aspartic acid | 3.5 | 0.3 | 58.5 |
| B. monkey |  |  |  |
| $^{14}$C-aspartyl aspartame | 2.1 | 1.6 | 77.0 |
| $^{14}$C-aspartic acid | 3.8 | 1.6 | 67.3 |

TABLE 37.3
Recovery of radioactivity (% of dose) after oral administration of 20 mg kg$^{-1}$ of ($^{14}$C-phenylalanyl) aspartame and $^{14}$C-phenylalanine in rats and monkeys

|  | Urine | Feces | Expired air |
|---|---|---|---|
| A. rat |  |  |  |
| $^{14}$C-phenylalanyl aspartame | 1.6 | 0.3 | 10.4 |
| $^{14}$C-phenylalanine | 3.9 | 0.4 | 17.0 |
| B. monkey |  |  |  |
| $^{14}$C-phenylalanyl aspartame | 2.8 | 1.5 | 17.5 |
| $^{14}$C-phenylalanine | 3.1 | 4.7 | 18.0 |

Three human volunteers were given ($^{14}$C-phenylalanyl) aspartame orally. Approximately 0.42% of the dose of $^{14}$C was found in the urine, while the maximum plasma concentration was 0.004% per ml, compared to 0.015% in monkeys.

It has also been demonstrated that the plasma of rats, dogs, monkeys and humans was free of the parent compound, ($^{14}$C-phenylalanyl) aspartame (data not shown).

*Conclusion*

Aspartame is hydrolysed completely in the gastrointestinal tract and decomposes to methanol, aspartic acid and phenylalanine. These are absorbed and follow their normal metabolic routes.

ASSIGNMENT 37.9

Explain why monkeys exhale $^{14}$C-CO$_2$ more rapidly after ingestion of $^{14}$C-methanol than after ($^{14}$C-methyl) aspartame.

In a separate experiment in rats, the distribution of labelled aspartame in the various tissues was compared with that of aspartic acid and phenylalanine. The rats were killed at 0.5, 2, 6 and 24 hours and 7 days after oral administration.

The distribution of phenylalanine and aspartame was very similar. After half an hour, the highest levels were measured in the stomach lumen and in the upper part of the small intestine. Radioactivity was also found in the pancreas, the mucosal layer of the gastrointestinal epithelium, the hair follicles, the salivary glands and the liver. Low levels were measured in the kidneys, adrenal glands, bone marrow, spleen and eyes. Traces of radioactivity were found in the brain and spinal cord, the heart, lungs and testes.

After 2 hours, radioactivity in the stomach decreased, while that in the lumen of the small intestine had risen considerably. After 6 hours, high levels of radioactivity were found in the cecum and also detected in the feces. The radioactivity in the body as a whole had decreased relative to earlier stages.

After 24 hours the gastrointestinal tract showed no radioactivity. The radioactivity in the rest of the body remained, although at lower concentrations. After 7 days only low levels of radioactivity could still be traced.

An equivalent experiment using ($^{14}$C-aspartyl) aspartame and aspartic acid showed similar distributions over the various tissues.

## 6.3 CARCINOGENICITY STUDIES ON ASPARTAME

The possibility of aspartame exerting carcinogenic effects was investigated by its manufacturer in the context of the US registration procedure. The data from this study showed a potential carcinogenic effect on the brain after oral ingestion of high doses of aspartame. Following this study, three further carcinogenicity studies were performed. In the first study, rats had received aspartame (0, 1, 2 and 4 g per kg body weight per day) for 2 years. The group treated with 4 g of aspartame showed a slightly higher incidence of brain tumors (6.3%) than the control group (0.8%). No dose-dependence was observed, however. In the second study, aspartame was also administered for 2 years, and no difference was found between the control group and the group receiving aspartame. In the third study, aspartame was given over the rat's lifetime. The result was that the group that had 4 g of aspartame per kg body weight per day, had fewer brain tumors than the controls (1.3% vs 3.5%).

Aspartame does not seem to be carcinogenic in experimental animals, nor does it induce urinary bladder tumors in rats like saccharin (section 2 of this unit).

## 6.4 OTHER TOXICITY OF ASPARTAME

Acute toxicity

To be able to determine an LD$_{50}$, an acute toxicity experiment was carried out in mice, rats and rabbits. No acutely lethal dose of orally administered aspartame was found (highest dose tested was 5 g per kg body weight).

Subchronic toxicity

In mice, rats and dogs, subchronic experiments, 39–90 days, the highest dose, 10 g per kg per day, caused loss of weight in rodents. Toxic effects were not reported.

Aspartame was also given for 52–110 weeks to mice, rats, hamsters, dogs and monkeys. In mice, sporadic effects were observed on clinical, chemical and hematological parameters, which could not be positively linked to aspartame or to the dose administered.

Chronic toxicity

Long-term administration of aspartame to rats at doses of 2–8 g per kg per day causes weight loss. This chronic administration of aspartame also caused weight increase of the spleen and kidney. There were minor shifts in the clinico-chemical picture of the urine (specific gravity, pH, Ca$^{2+}$ excretion). In the liver, the activity of phenylalanine hydroxylase was shown to increase considerably with the amount of aspartame administered. Shifts in mortality rate were observed, which were independent of the dose of aspartame. Long-term administration of aspartame to dogs at doses of 1–4 g per kg per day did not cause any major changes in body weight, food intake, clinical chemico-physical factors, or anatomical and morphological properties.

A separate problem is the effect of aspartame on the central nervous system. High doses of the amino acids aspartic acid and glutamic acid have been known for sometime to cause neuronal damage in the brain of experimental animals. Since aspartame is hydrolyzed completely in the gastrointestinal tract, there is a risk of brain damage due to the increased supply of aspartic acid. The metabolism of aspartic acid is closely related to that of glutamic acid. In fact, these two amino acids are converted into each other in the liver. Moreover, both competitively use the same metabolic pathway. Metabolism of one leads to accumulation of the other. Ingestion of a high dose of aspartic acid, for example, causes an increase in the plasma concentrations of both aspartic acid and glutamic acid.

> ASSIGNMENT   37.10
> Give a brief description of the metabolism of amino acids with two carboxyl groups.

Glutamic acid is found in the normal diet and may be consumed in combination with aspartame.

Mechanisms of necrosis and cell death are described in Study units 15 and 16

In studies using young mice, a single dose of 250 mg of aspartic acid per kg plus 250 mg of glutamic acid per kg has been shown to cause cell death in the hypothalamus of 30% of the animals. On its own, 500 mg per kg of glutamic acid caused hypothalamic necrosis in 17% of the animals.

One other report is available of an oral dose of glutamic acid causing hypothalamic cell death in newborn monkeys. As a follow-up to this finding, an experiment has been carried out in which a single, very high dose of aspartame (2 g per kg) was administered to primates. At this dose of aspartame, no histopathological effect could be established in the hypothalamus of the animals. A second group of primates was given the same dose of aspartame plus 1 g of glutamic acid per kg. Again, no neuronal necrosis was observed after administration of this dose.

The potential effects of changes in the concentration ratios of the amino acids aspartic acid, glutamic acid, phenylalanine and tyrosine after consumption of aspartame, however, still remain the subject of debate.

## 7    Toxicokinetics of aspartame

The previous sections have introduced the association between the metabolism of aspartame, particularly the hydrolysis of the dipeptide into the amino acids, aspartic acid and phenylalanine, and its potential toxic effects such as brain damage in animals, and neurological complaints in humans.

The acute effects of aspartame on the plasma concentrations of amino acids, and consequently on the concentrations reached in the central nervous system, have been investigated in animal experiments and human studies.

### 7.1   PLASMA CONCENTRATIONS OF ASPARTIC ACID AND PHENYLALANINE AFTER INGESTION OF A SINGLE ORAL DOSE OF ASPARTAME

An equal number of male and female volunteers was used. They had been subjected to general health and clinico-chemical tests to ensure the absence of any liver dysfunction. Prior to the experiment, they had fasted for 10 hours and had not consumed any alcohol for 24 hours. Aspartame was administered dissolved in 300 or 500 ml of orange juice. Blood was sampled from a vein in the arm at $t$ = 0, 0.25, 0.5, 0.75, 1, 1.5, 2, 3, 4, 5, 6, 7, 8 and 24 hours after ingestion of aspartame and the concentrations of the various amino acids were measured (see Table 37.4).

In the same study, the plasma concentration profiles of the branched-chain amino acids valine, leucine and isoleucine were determined after 34 mg of aspartame per kg. The concentrations of these amino acids appeared to decrease simultaneously with an increase in the plasma concentrations of phenylalanine and tyrosine.

Since combinations of high plasma concentrations of aspartame and glutamic acid may have neurotoxic effects, six volunteers were given a meal of a hamburger and a milk shake plus aspartame (34 mg per kg) and sodium glutamic acid (also 34 mg per kg).

Measured 4 hours after the meal, glutamic acid plasma concentrations had risen from 4 to 11 $\mu$mol per 100 ml; meanwhile the plasma concentration of aspartic acid increased from 0.3 to 1 $\mu$mol per 100 ml. The plasma phenylalanine concentration rose from 4.7 to 9.0 $\mu$mol per 100 ml and the concentration of tyrosine rose from 5.0 to 11.5 $\mu$mol per 100 ml. In the control group, 4 h after a meal, just orange juice without aspartame, these amino acid concentrations were 10, 0.8, 7.1 and 9.3 $\mu$mol per 100 ml, respectively. These values were not significantly different from those in the group who had the meal plus aspartame and sodium glutamate.

Since, in practice, aspartame may be taken repeatedly over time, a separate experiment was carried out to study the effect on the phenylalanine plasma concentrations of three oral doses of aspartame (30 mg per kg), one administered 2 hours after the other (see Figure 37.7). For this purpose, eight volunteers drank

TABLE 37.4

Maximum plasma concentrations (average ± S.D.) of aspartic acid (ASP), glutamic acid (GLU), phenylalanine (PHE) and tyrosine (TYR) after oral administration of various doses of aspartame in man.

The plasma concentrations of the amino acids returned to normal in the course of 6 hours.

| Dose of aspartame mg kg$^{-1}$ | Number of volunteers | Pl ASP $\mu$ mol dl$^{-1}$ | T hr | Pl GLU $\mu$mol dl$^{-1}$ | T hr | Pl PHE $\mu$mol dl$^{-1}$ | T hr | Pl TYR $\mu$mol dl$^{-1}$ | T hr |
|---|---|---|---|---|---|---|---|---|---|
| 0 | 12 | 0.15±0.50 | | 4±6 | | 5±6 | | 5±6 | |
| 34 | 6 | 0.6 ± 0.4 | 1 | 6 ± 3 | 1 | 11 ± 3 | 1 | 6 ± 2 | 0.5 |
| 50 | 18 | 0.6 ± 0.4 | 0.5 | 5 ± 3 | 1–3 | 16 ± 5 | 1 | 8 ± 3 | 0.5–2 |
| 100 | 18 | 0.4 ± 0.2 | 0.5 | 5 ± 1.5 | 0.5 | 20 ± 5 | 0.5–1.5 | 10 ± 3 | 1.5–2 |
| 150 | 18 | 1.0 ± 0.7 | 0.5 | 7 ± 3 | 0.75–1.5 | 35 ± 9 | 1.5 | 11 ± 3 | 2 |
| 200 | 18 | 0.8 ± 0.6 | 0.5 | 6 ± 2 | 1.5 | 49 ± 16 | 1.5–2 | 14 ± 4 | 3 |

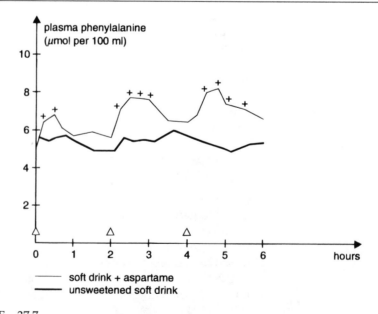

FIGURE 37.7

Mean phenylalanine plasma concentrations in healthy adults, after repeated intake of an unsweetened soft drink or a (sweet) soft drink containing aspartame, 10 mg kg$^{-1}$ body weight, at time = $\Delta$. Values marked with + differ significantly (p < 0.05) from control group values

a soft drink sweetened with aspartame; the same experiment was repeated with an unsweetened soft drink. Phenylalanine concentrations in the blood were measured at 15 minute intervals.

ASSIGNMENT 37.11

The mean phenylalanine plasma concentration slowly rose over the 6 hours that the blood concentrations were measured. What does this indicate?

## 7.2 PLASMA METHANOL CONCENTRATIONS AFTER CONSUMPTION OF ASPARTAME

Ingestion of aspartame not only causes changes in the plasma concentrations of amino acids, but the plasma concentration of methanol, the third metabolite of aspartame, also rises.

Figure 37.8 shows the increase in the plasma concentration of methanol (8a) and the fluctuations in the concentration of formic acid (8b) after oral administration of 200 mg of aspartame per kg body weight to six volunteers. Table 37.5 shows the urinary excretion of formic acid during 24 hours after ingestion of 200 mg of aspartame per kg.

ASSIGNMENT 37.12

Why is the excretion of formic acid in the urine expressed per mg of creatinine?

The plasma values of formic acid were observed to oscillate about a particular level. This suggested that the rate of formation of formic acid from methanol, the aspartame metabolite, was not greater than the excretion rate in the urine. Excretion of formic acid is thus efficient. Formic acid is therefore not considered to be a health hazard.

## 7.3 KINETICS OF ASPARTAME IN CHILDREN

When evaluating the potential health hazards of xenobiotics, one should always be aware of the fact that a normal population may include subpopulations, which run a higher risk than the average population, due to genetic predisposition, illness or lifestyle. This is also true for aspartame.

Diabetics may consume large quantities of aspartame, in addition to having an amino acid metabolism that deviates from the norm. As a result of an inborn error of metabolism, patients suffering from phenylketonuria are unable to convert phenylalanine into tyrosine, since they lack the enzyme phenylalanine hydroxylase. The resulting accumulation of phenylalanine may lead to brain damage. Children constitute a separate risk group, since their basal levels of the amino acids are higher than in adults. Moreover, many children consume large amounts of soft drinks, ice cream, etc., which may be sweetened with aspartame. In an experiment, 24 children aged 8–14 months received doses of aspartame of 34 mg per kg ($n = 10$), 50 mg per kg ($n = 6$) or 100 mg per kg ($n = 8$) in a soft drink. Four blood samples were taken per child, but taken so that the test group as a whole provided 6 points. Table 37.6 compares the effects of these doses of aspartame on the plasma concentrations of the amino acids in children and in adults.

There was only a slight increase in the plasma concentrations of phenylalanine in children after consuming aspartame. This seems to rule out the risk of brain damage. Furthermore, the clearance of the increased plasma amino acid concentrations seemed as efficient in children as in adults.

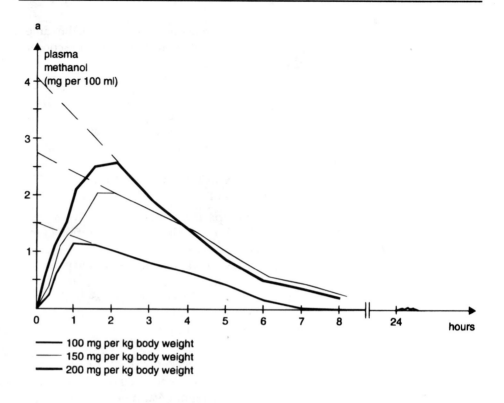

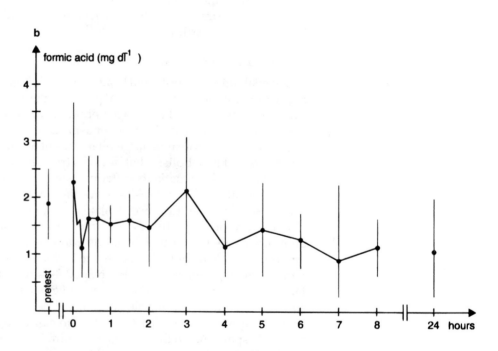

FIGURE   37.8
a. Mean methanol plasma concentrations in normal adults after administration of 100, 150 or 200 mg aspartame per kg body weight
b. Mean (± S.D.) plasma concentrations of formic acid in normal adults after administration of 200 mg aspartame per kg body weight

TABLE 37.5
Urinary excretion of formic acid after an oral dose of 200 mg aspartame per kg in volunteers.

| Urine sample | Amount of formic acid ($\mu g\ mg^{-1}$ creatinine) |
|---|---|
| control | $34 \pm 22$ |
| 0–4 hours | $101 \pm 30$ |
| 4–8 hours | $81 \pm 22$ |
| 8–24 hours | $38 \pm 12$ |

TABLE 37.6
Maximum plasma concentrations ($\pm$ S.D.) of aspartic acid (ASP), glutamic acid (GLU), phenylalanine (PHE) and tyrosine (TYR) in children and adults after consumption of aspartame

| Dose of aspartame mg $kg^{-1}$ | ASP ($\mu mol\ 100\ ml^{-1}$) | | GLU ($\mu mol\ 100\ ml^{-1}$) | | PHE ($\mu mol\ 100\ ml^{-1}$) | | TYR ($\mu mol\ 100\ ml^{-1}$) | |
|---|---|---|---|---|---|---|---|---|
| | Children | Adults | Children | Adults | Children | Adults | Children | Adults |
| 0 | $2.2 \pm 1.1$ | $0.3 \pm 0.1$ | $6.3 \pm 1.9$ | $4.8 \pm 1.6$ | $4.8 \pm 0.8$ | $5.7 \pm 1.2$ | $6.3 \pm 2.3$ | $5.4 \pm 1.5$ |
| 34 | $2.2 \pm 1.4$ | $0.3 \pm 0.2$ | $8.2 \pm 2.3$ | $6.2 \pm 3.0$ | $9.4 \pm 1.4$ | $11.1 \pm 4.0$ | $7.5 \pm 1.1$ | $6.6 \pm 1.8$ |
| 0 | $1.5 \pm 1.0$ | $0.4 \pm 0.3$ | $6.9 \pm 1.7$ | $3.2 \pm 2.2$ | $5.7 \pm 0.5$ | $4.6 \pm 1.7$ | $6.9 \pm 1.4$ | $5.2 \pm 1.6$ |
| 50 | $2.0 \pm 0.3$ | $0.5 \pm 0.6$ | $8.4 \pm 1.5$ | $4.7 \pm 2.6$ | $11.6 \pm 4.4$ | $16.2 \pm 4.9$ | $9.9 \pm 2.1$ | $8.1 \pm 1.5$ |
| 0 | $1.1 \pm 0.6$ | $0.2 \pm 0.1$ | $6.7 \pm 2.3$ | $3.9 \pm 2.7$ | $4.6 \pm 0.8$ | $5.4 \pm 1.1$ | $6.2 \pm 0.1$ | $5.6 \pm 1.2$ |
| 100 | $2.0 \pm 1.0$ | $0.4 \pm 0.2$ | $9.2 \pm 2.9$ | $5.1 \pm 1.5$ | $22.3 \pm 11.5$ | $20.6 \pm 6.8$ | $13.7 \pm 3.4$ | $9.5 \pm 3.1$ |

## 7.4 PASSAGE OF THE BLOOD–BRAIN BARRIER BY ASPARTAME METABOLITES

If consumption of aspartame induces a rise in amino acid concentrations in the central nervous system, this could, in theory, lead to various toxic effects. High concentrations of phenylalanine and aspartic acid, possibly combined with high concentrations of glutamic acid, could cause neuronal cell death. Increases in the concentrations of phenylalanine and tyrosine also involve a certain risk. They are precursors in catecholamine synthesis. Catecholamines are important neurotransmitters, particularly in the brain. Moreover, increased concentrations of phenylalanine may have a negative effect on the brain levels of tryptophane. Tryptophane is required for the synthesis of indoleamines, in particular serotonin, another important neurotransmitter. The consumption of aspartame may thus hypothetically cause a shift in the concentrations of these amino acids in the brain, thus altering the functioning of the central nervous system. This hypothesis can be tested in laboratory animals (Table 37.7). These shifts may be related to the neurological complaints reported after consumption of aspartame.

In a follow-up study using oral doses of aspartame from 0 to 200 mg per kg body weight, dose–response relationships were found for phenylalanine and tyrosine in the brain. The concentrations of the relevant amino acids in the CNS were observed to change as a function of their plasma levels.

Passage through the blood–brain barrier of large neutral amino acids, such as phenylalanine and tyrosine, occurs via a common carrier. The various amino acids of these groups compete with each other for transport by this carrier.

For catecholamines see Study unit 33

### ASSIGNMENT 37.13

Describe the characteristics of competitive receptor binding. (This has been dealt with in Study unit 7).

TABLE 37.7

Effects on amino acid levels in blood and CNS 1 hour after oral administration of 200 mg aspartame per kg to rats

| | Tyrosine | Phenylalanine | Leucine | Isoleucine | Valine |
|---|---|---|---|---|---|
| A. CNS levels (nmol g$^{-1}$) | | | | | |
| control | $41 \pm 2$ | $32 \pm 2$ | $55 \pm 3$ | $26 \pm 3$ | $61 \pm 3$ |
| aspartame | $117 \pm 6$ | $77 \pm 5$ | $56 \pm 2$ | $27 \pm 2$ | $63 \pm 4$ |
| B. blood levels (nmol g$^{-1}$) | | | | | |
| control | $73 \pm 6$ | $70 \pm 3$ | $167 \pm 6$ | $110 \pm 8$ | $198 \pm 12$ |
| aspartame | $171 \pm 6$ | $120 \pm 8$ | $145 \pm 9$ | $106 \pm 3$ | $187 \pm 12$ |

Tryptophane and the branched-chain amino acids valine, leucine and isoleucine are amino acids that compete for a common carrier. Their transport across the blood–brain barrier may thus be inhibited by competitive receptor binding due to the high plasma levels of phenylalanine and tyrosine obtained from aspartame. This might result in deficiencies of those amino acids in the central nervous system.

Anesthetized rats received an intra-arterial injection of $^{14}$C-tryptophane. Increasing concentrations of neutral amino acids were also added to the injection fluid, after which the influx of radioactivity into the CNS was measured (Table 37.8).

There is a decrease in the levels of tryptophane as the concentrations of neutral amino acids increase. No dramatic changes in the CNS concentrations of tryptophane or branched-chain amino acids, however, were found after oral administration of aspartame to rats. Decreasing plasma concentrations of the branched-chain amino acids occur as plasma concentrations of phenylalanine and tyrosine increase following aspartame consumption. This has been established in man more clearly than in rats (see section 7.1).

Decreased plasma levels of branched-chain amino acids may be the result of increased insulin secretion, which in turn is initiated by the consumption of carbohydrates (in the kinetic studies in man, aspartame was administered in orange juice). If the concentrations of branched-chain amino acids are reduced, the competition for the common carrier in the blood–brain barrier is decreased. Relatively more phenylalanine and tyrosine can be transported to the central nervous system. To test this hypothesis, aspartame was administered to rats with and without glucose (Table 37.9).

In rats, the combined administration of glucose and aspartame causes a dramatic rise of phenylalanine in the CNS. This seems to confirm the above hypothesis. A biological effect of these changes in the CNS amino acid levels might be concentration shifts of the neurotransmitters synthesized from them (Table 37.10).

This table shows that in the central nervous system as a whole, no significant changes in neurotransmitter concentrations are found 1 hour after ingestion of aspartame. In a separate experiment, 200 mg aspartame per kg intraperitoneally increased norepinephrine in the locus ceruleus (the origin of noradrenergic neurons) and the amygdala, a part of the limbic system, compared with the control rats.

## 8    Risk evaluation of human use of aspartame

Risk evaluation of human use of aspartame may serve to answer the following two questions:

TABLE 37.8

Competitive inhibition of tryptophane transport by amino acids across the blood–brain barrier in rats by amino acids.

| Amino acid | Competing with tryptophane uptake in CNS (% of dose) | | | |
|---|---|---|---|---|
| | dose 0.1 mmol | dose 0.5 mmol | dose 1mmol | dose 4 mmol |
| phenylalanine | 16.8 ± 0.5 | 7.9 ± 1.0 | 0.5 ± 1.6 | 3.6 ± 0.5 |
| α-methyltyrosine | 25.7 ± 0.5 | 20.7 ± 0.4 | 14.8 ± 2.6 | 8.7 ± 0.3 |
| leucine | 20.2 ± 0.5 | 10.3 ± 0.1 | 8.7 ± 0.4 | 3.8 ± 0.1 |
| valine | 28.4 ± 1.0 | 21.5 ± 0.1 | 18.6 ± 0.7 | 10.8 ± 0.6 |

TABLE 37.9

Effects of aspartame (200 mg per kg) and glucose (3 g per kg) on plasma and CNS levels of amino acids in rats.

| | Water | Water and glucose | Aspartame and glucose | Water and aspartame |
|---|---|---|---|---|
| A plasma (nmol ml$^{-1}$) | | | | |
| phenylalanine | 59.9 ± 1.2 | 53.5 ± 1.3 | 100.3 ± 4.6 | 97.3 ± 3.9 |
| tyrosine | 64.9 ± 2.8 | 58.9 ± 2.6 | 152.9 ± 4.9 | 157.2 ± 11.3 |
| valine | 148.7 ± 4.5 | 83.7 ± 3.6 | 76.2 ± 2.4 | 126.0 ± 3.1 |
| isoleucine | 90.4 ± 2.8 | 47.4 ± 2.4 | 41.4 ± 1.5 | 74.6 ± 1.9 |
| leucine | 132.6 ± 4.4 | 78.7 ± 3.7 | 65.6 ± 2.7 | 104.4 ± 3.4 |
| tryptophane | 71.1 ± 4.7 | 81.1 ± 4.5 | 67.8 ± 2.6 | 69.3 ± 2.7 |
| B brain (nmol g$^{-1}$) | | | | |
| phenylalanine | 39.3 ± 0.9 | 56.4 ± 1.4 | 108.3 ± 2.4 | 75.5 ± 2.3 |
| tyrosine | 54.4 ± 2.7 | 73.1 ± 3.3 | 187.1 ± 9.5 | 139.7 ± 8.4 |
| valine | 79.1 ± 1.1 | 59.8 ± 1.7 | 51.6 ± 1.3 | 65.8 ± 1.5 |
| isoleucine | 33.3 ± 0.8 | 23.1 ± 0.8 | 18.2 ± 0.5 | 26.5 ± 0.6 |
| leucine | 62.0 ± 0.7 | 49.9 ± 1.0 | 41.9 ± 1.0 | 51.2 ± 1.3 |
| tryptophane | 20.8 ± 0 | 30.2 ± 0.5 | 25.5 ± 0.7 | 20.3 ± 0.6 |

TABLE 37.10

Effects of aspartame (200 mg per kg) on neurotransmitter concentrations in the CNS of rats

| Neurotransmitters ng g$^{-1}$ | Control | Aspartame |
|---|---|---|
| dopamine | 920 ± 27 | 976 ± 21 |
| norepinephrine | 393 ± 28 | 349 ± 17 |
| serotonin | 514 ± 22 | 536 ± 24 |

a Are any toxic consequences to be expected from consumption of aspartame, despite the dose?

b If so, do these toxic consequences occur when aspartame is used on a large scale as a sugar substitute?

*Following on from a:*

The most specific toxic effect of aspartame so far reported is the development of neuronal necrosis in the hypothalamus. This necrosis is caused by high concentrations of both aspartic acid and glutamic acid in the body. In the mouse, the threshold value of the combined plasma levels of aspartic acid and glutamic acid above which hypothalamic lesions occur, has been reported to be 50–70 $\mu$mol per 100 ml. In monkeys, combined plasma concentrations of 200–500 $\mu$mol per 100 ml have not shown neuronal injury in the brain. In man, an oral dose of 200 mg of aspartame per kg produced an average of 6.9 ± 3.7 $\mu$mol per 100 ml combined plasma concentration of aspartic acid and glutamic acid. In one particular individual, this rose to 11 $\mu$mol per 100 ml. A dose of 100 mg aspartame per kg in 1-year-olds gave a mean maximum 104% higher than adults for the plasma concentration of aspartic acid plus glutamic acid. Extrapolating from the mouse studies, the safety margin becomes very small compared with the threshold above which neuronal necrosis may develop. In children, the higher basal blood levels of these amino acids must be considered. One may reasonably expect the child's brain to be more similar to those of primates than to rodents. In primates, no threshold value for the development of hypothalamic lesions has been established.

The above data were obtained from studies of acute doses of aspartame. In ordinary life, aspartame users, particularly children, will tend to consume aspartame daily and for a long time, albeit at lower doses.

In another study, volunteers, aged 2–21 years, had aspartame daily for 13 weeks as an additive to a variety of foodstuffs. The doses of aspartame ranged from 27.5 to 72 mg per kg per 24 hours. The effects of aspartame on a series of clinico-chemical parameters were analyzed and compared with those of control groups consuming sucrose instead of aspartame.

No differences were seen between the age groups taking aspartame or sucrose as regards general state of health, eye functions, occurrence of acne, or serum phenylalanine and tyrosine concentrations. Methanol could not be demonstrated in the serum. There were no differences in various clinico-chemical parameters. Reported complaints from the volunteers were non-specific. Again, therefore, no indications were found for a toxic effect of aspartame.

APT = aspartate amino transferase
ALT = alanine aminotransferase
APT and ALT are both liver enzymes that occur in plasma following (liver)cell damage. See also Study unit 23.

Within the framework of the acute dose studies, a case was reported in which aspartame, 200 mg per kg, caused hepatic dysfunction, measured as increased serum levels of *APT* and *ALT*.

In conclusion, only very high oral doses of aspartame, for example consumed by children, may result in toxic effects, such as disturbance of hepatic and brain function.

*Following on from b:*

The question at issue is whether 'normal' use of aspartame, as a sugar substitute, may result in a sufficiently high dosage to cause toxic effects. Ten years ago, aspartame was used exclusively as a table-top sweetener. Consumption of aspartame in this form is easily controllable, although the possibility of a child eating a whole box of sweeteners at once can never be ruled out. Now, the addition (up to a certain maximum) of aspartame to lemonades and soft drinks and other products has been permitted.

In this respect, it is useful to look at data on consumption in, for example, the US. In view of the sweetening power of aspartame, a liter of soft drink could contain up to 750 mg of the sweetener. The FDA has estimated the maximum daily intake at 1.7 g. Other estimates range from 867 mg to 1056 mg per day. It is imaginable that a child, with a sweet tooth, might exceed this dose. The plasma level of phenylalanine reached under such circumstances could be cause for concern, particularly if the enhancing effect of glucose, usually also present in sweet foodstuffs, is considered.

On the other hand, the component amino acids of aspartame are also found in the normal diet. As we have seen, consumption of a meal consisting of a hamburger and a milk shake makes the total plasma concentration of aspartic acid and glutamic acid rise from 50 to 130 $\mu$mol per 100 ml. The phenylalanine concentration increases from 5 to 7 $\mu$mol per 100 ml. A diet containing 18% protein increases the tryptophane in the brain by 27%, that of phenylalanine by 24% and that of tyrosine by 80%, relative to plasma levels.

It is in the light of these findings that the effects of aspartame consumption on the plasma concentrations of amino acids should be evaluated.

## FEEDBACK

### Answers to assignments

37.1 Such a substance should have physico-chemical qualities that produce no problems during food-processing. In other words, it should be stable. Factors such as its behavior in dry or dissolved form, temperature, acidity, ionic strength all have to be considered. Other important physico-chemical properties are its volatility, its solubility in hydrophobic and hydrophilic solvents, and its degree of crystallization.

37.2 For the exact physiology, please refer to a textbook on human physiology (See also Figure 37.9).

37.3 Sorbitol is absorbed only slightly from the gastrointestinal tract. Thus a high oral dose causes an osmotic imbalance in the intestinal lumen. This results in less water being absorbed and even the possibility of water being withdrawn from the intestinal epithelium. The feces become more liquid.

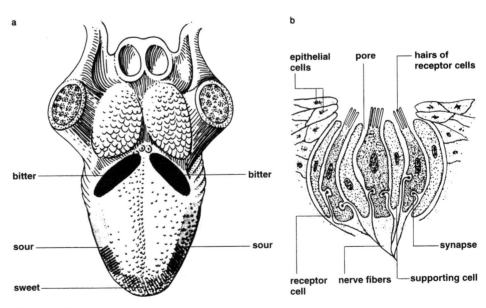

Figure 37.9

a. shows the location of the main zones of taste (sweet, sour and bitter) on the tongue. There is considerable overlap between the various areas.

b. is a cross section of a taste bud on the tongue. Dissolved substances depolarize the hair cells, which cause a receptor potential. The subsequent release of a transmitter stimulates the afferent nerves.

37.4 As with any combinations of xenobiotics, mixtures of sweeteners in food-stuffs, could pose a potential toxicological problem. It would depend on the bioavailability of the individual compounds, and their biological effect. The combined use of compounds A and B might have three effects: inhibition, simple addition, or synergy (disproportionate enhancement). More detailed information regarding combination toxicity is provided in Study units 7 and 9.

37.5 Information can be found in general textbooks on pharmacology. In this example there will be a plasma concentration–time curve with a very low maximum concentration because the substance absorbed is immediately eliminated.

37.6 The bladder lumen forms part of the central compartment, while the bladder wall (epithelium) does not. The metabolism and rate of release from the bladder wall differs from that from the lumen. Therefore, concentrations of foreign agents may be higher or lower in the epithelial tissue than in the urine.

37.7 Amino acids serve as energy substrates, as building blocks for proteins, enzymes and peptide hormones, and, sometimes after considerable chemical changes, as substrates for a variety of endogenous substances such as neurotransmitters. Physiologically, their function is not specific. Nevertheless, toxic effects of an excessive dose of a particular amino acid will affect tissues that have a high turnover of that amino acid. This occurs in the liver and the brain. The toxic effect may thus be very diverse. This is true under normal conditions, but pathological disturbances of amino acid metabolism may cause further alterations.

37.8 "Natural" is a concept that in everyday language has the connotation of "harmless". As a principle, this is of course incorrect. Any substance is toxic, provided sufficiently high doses of it are administered. The natural diet (i.e. food not modified by technological processes) contains a whole range of substances that are in this sense potentially toxic:

- lipids are associated with the development of various types of cancer;
- heating of proteins altered by heat, may result in the formation of toxic compounds;
- as with lipids, increased ingestion of sugars causes obesity, and in that way cause various illnesses. Sugars also form the substrate for the development of caries;
- plants contain numerous substances that may be toxic;
- food may contain allergenic components for individuals with an allergic predisposition;
- high doses of vitamins may cause serious toxicological problems, and may sometimes even cause death (e.g., vitamin A).

37.9 After methanol, $CO_2$ is exhaled more rapidly than after aspartame. This may imply that:

- methanol is absorbed from the stomach, unlike aspartame
- methanol passes through the stomach to the intestine more rapidly than aspartame

- the methyl group of aspartame first needs to be removed by intestinal esterases.

37.10 Aspartic acid and phenylalanine are transported to tissues with a high amino acid conversion rate, such as the liver and the pancreas. Aspartic acid is oxidized in the citric acid cycle. It is also converted into glutamic acid in the liver. Phenylalanine cannot be produced in the body itself. Like aspartic acid, it can be incorporated into the mitochondrial citric acid cycle, but can also be converted into tyrosine.
Tyrosine acts as a substrate in the synthesis of catecholaminergic neurotransmitters. Both amino acids can be used in protein synthesis.

Detailed information on the metabolism of amino acids can be found in basic books on biochemistry.

37.11 Accumulation will occur if repeated administration of an agent occurs within the half-life of that agent. This causes an increase in plasma levels. See also Study unit 6.

37.12 Creatinine is a product of general metabolism and is constantly present in the blood (in steady state). Renal clearance of creatinine is almost complete and takes place by glomerular filtration. The amount of creatinine that passes the kidney per unit of time is therefore a measure of total glomerular filtration. If a substance is present in the urine at a particular concentration ($\mu$g per ml), the quotient of its urine concentration and the urine concentration of creatinine is a measure for its clearance. See creatinine clearance in Study unit 6.

37.13 Please refer to Study unit 7 for an explanation of the principle of competitive inhibition.

# Contents Study unit 38
# Medical and clinical toxicology

0-8493-9232-2/96/$6.00 + $.50

# Medical and clinical toxicology

*B. Sangster*

## INTRODUCTION

This study unit intends to make the reader acquainted with the field of medical toxicology. Considering the space available this can only be in the form of a first introduction.

## CASE 1 PATIENT 1

A 36-year-old man was admitted to a local hospital with nausea, vomiting, severe abdominal cramps, explosive defecation, heavy sweating and excessive salivation. These symptoms had appeared within 1 hour of eating chicken soup. He was somnolent. His heart rate was 10–15 bpm, his blood pressure 100/35 mm Hg and his body temperature 35.0°C.

The ECG showed sinus bradycardia with a frequency of 30 bpm. An AV conduction disturbance was causing a ventricular frequency of 10–15 bpm. He was immediately given isoproterenol intravenously, upon which his ventricular frequency rose to 40 bpm. Subsequently, the patient was transferred to a university hospital for further treatment.

On admission there he was conscious. According to his medical record he had been healthy all his life, except that he suffered from epilepsy for which he took carbamazepine. The medication was adequate to prevent fits. The family history revealed that a son of 10 years old had died shortly before. This son had suffered regular fits for a year which closely resembled the attack for which the father was now admitted.

Heart rate was 40 bpm, blood pressure 80/50 mm Hg and temperature 32.2°C. Body weight was later established as 70 kg and height as 183 cm. The patient's clothing was soaked. His pupils were very constricted (pin-points) and did not react to light. Peristalsis was abnormally energetic. Physical examination revealed no other abnormalities.

Laboratory tests showed no abnormalities other than an elevated concentration of leukocytes in the blood: 14,400 cm$^{-3}$. The distribution was as follows: granulocytes 24%, segmented granulocytes 47%, lymphocytes 26%, monocytes 3%. Blood glucose was 18 mmol l$^{-1}$.

The ECG showed a regular sinus rhythm with a second degree AV block, normal intraventricular conduction and normal repolarization with a ventricular frequency of 40 bpm.

Toxicological analysis revealed that blood cholinesterase and serum pseudocholinesterase activity were normal. Extensive tests for the presence of sub-

*Maprotiline*
*Orphenadrine*

stances such as acetaldehyde, acetone, barbiturates, ethanol, glutethimide, meprobamate, methanol, methaqualone, paraldehyde, chlorinated hydrocarbons, *maprotiline, orphenadrine, para*-nitrophenol, phenothiazines and tricyclic antidepressants were negative. Treatment with isoproterenol was continued. The patient recovered to such an extent that treatment could be discontinued after 4 hours. The next day he was transferred to the Department of Internal Medicine.

During his stay there the fits recurred. The combination of his symptoms with the fact that his blood cholinesterase activity was normal prompted the conclusion that he must have been poisoned by a substance with a cholinomimetic effect which affects the muscarinic receptors only.

The correctness of this assumption was supported by the fact that, during another fit, the symptoms disappeared immediately after intravenous administration of 0.25 mg atropine sulfate. All subsequent fits were also successfully treated in this way. Further observation revealed a relationship between the fits and visits by his wife, and showed that they began about 30 minutes after she had left. Enquiries from the family's general practitioner revealed that the wife took carbachol to stimulate bladder function. She apparently took fairly large quantities of the drug.

Because of its physical properties (strongly hydrophilic due to its quaternary structure), there is no method for detecting carbachol in biological materials. The diagnosis of carbachol poisoning could therefore not be established by chemical analysis of blood, serum, urine or stomach contents.

The Forensic Medical Laboratory (Department of Justice) prepared carbachol tablets containing known proportions of indium and bismuth. These were given to the wife on a normal prescription. The same proportions of both substances, indium and bismuth, were identified in the patient's stomach content when he next had a fit.

After her arrest, the wife admitted that she had deliberately and repeatedly given her husband (and deceased son) 15–20 tablets, each containing 2 mg carbachol. She had dissolved the carbachol in soup, coffee etc. After she had been taken into preventive custody, the patient suffered no more fits.

The above case shows a number of aspects from the field of medical toxicology. This study unit describes the field of medical toxicology and explains the distinction between clinical and medical toxicology. It introduces the basic principles for patient diagnosis and treatment in cases of acute and chronic intoxication. The study material is illustrated by means of a number of case histories and situations requiring solutions to problems of medical toxicology. Although occupational toxicology also comes under the heading of medical toxicology, it will be treated in a separate study unit (Study unit 40).

LEARNING OBJECTIVES

After studying this unit you should be able to:

— define the term medical toxicology
— indicate how some medical disciplines relate to medical toxicology
— describe how medical toxicology relates to a number of the natural sciences
— explain the role of clinical toxicology within the field of medical toxicology
— give examples of some common cases of acute intoxication
— describe the diagnosis and treatment of some common cases of acute intoxication

— give examples of some common cases of chronic intoxication
— describe differences and similarities between acute and chronic intoxication as far as diagnosis and treatment are concerned
— indicate the disciplines of toxicology and the duties of the clinician involved in a given case study.

*Study hints*

This study unit is largely descriptive. Read it through, and write down any terms you do not know and look them up in a medical dictionary. Read through the case histories, then decide what are the duties of the physician and what are those of other practitioners of toxicology. Take notes from the sections on diagnosis and treatment. The study load for this study unit is estimated at 4 student learning hours.

## STUDY CORE

### 1 Medical toxicology

*Clinical toxicology*

Medical toxicology comprises the entire field of interest covered by physicians concerned with toxicology. It includes activities aimed at the protection of health, the assessment of risks to health, and experimental research. *Clinical toxicology* is a subdivision of *medical toxicology* and encompasses the direct diagnosis and treatment of patients who have been the victims of poisoning. Clinical toxicology is also that branch of *medicine* which deals with the diagnostics and treatment of intoxicated patients. Interest in this specialism has increased sharply in recent years. This is partly because, regrettably, physicians are now faced more often than in the past with patients who have suffered intoxication. It is also due to the fact that society has become increasingly aware of the potential hazards from the many substances with which it is in daily contact. As a result, patients are asking more frequently whether their symptoms or ailments are caused by intoxication, and doctors are sooner, when examining patients, thinking of the possibility of intoxication. Medical toxicology is no independent medical specialism recognized as such. It is very much a multidisciplinary field and is practiced in close cooperation with many other medical and also non-medical disciplines.

#### 1.1 RELATIONSHIP WITH MEDICAL DISCIPLINES

Victims of intoxication or toxicological problems may be found in virtually all medical disciplines. A patient who has suffered poisoning or is suspected of having suffered poisoning is treated in the first instance by his *family doctor*. If his/her condition is serious, the patient will be referred to a hospital for further treatment. If intoxication occurs at work, he/she will first be treated by the *company doctor* or the company nurse acting under the direction of the former. This applies of course only to companies or plants which have their own company medical staff or have access to a regional occupational health service.

*Internist*

Internal medicine forms an excellent basis for clinical toxicology. Basically, depending on the type of intoxication, any organ system may be affected. Assistance will thus be needed from consultants specialized in the organ system affected by a given type of intoxication. If an intoxicated patient dies, in most countries the attending physician does not sign the death certificate, since

*Family doctor*

*Company doctor*

the law requires the physician to declare him or herself convinced that death was from natural causes.

Once a patient's unnatural death has been reported, the *Public Prosecutor* institutes an inquiry. The prime concern of that inquiry is to ascertain whether a criminal act was involved, or whether the poisoning was the result of gross negligence i.e. the fault of a third party. In this context the patient is examined by the *local coroner*. The latter is usually a physician employed by a department of the general health service such as the Local Department of Medicine and Health or the District Health Authority. Sometimes the Public Prosecutor may request an autopsy. This is usually carried out by a *pathologist* employed by the Department of Justice's Forensic Laboratory.

*Local Department of Medicine and Health, District Health Department*

*Pathologist*

The *state information and assistance officers* associated with workmans compensation should be notified of all serious cases of intoxication occurring at places of work so that the district medical officer can look into the problem. There will then be an investigation into whether, for example, the safety regulations were complied with, or whether preventative measures should be taken or regulations to be drafted for the handling of the substances concerned. Minor cases of poisoning have to be recorded by the company itself. Whatever the outcome of an intoxication, medical insurance experts may also be involved in the consequences of poisoning. Cases occurring at schools will be dealt with initially by *school or youth doctors*, or by the appropriate department of the *municipal health service*. Individual patients may, however, consult their own family doctor and be referred or not as the case may be.

*School doctor*
*General health service*

In cases of *environmental pollution*, patients will go to their family doctor for examination and treatment of their symptoms. Sometimes doctors from the municipal health service will hold office hours in the area concerned. When screening of the general public is necessary, this is in the first instance the responsibility of the municipal health service. Environmental medical officers are experts in social medicine and are employed by a regional municipal health service. They advise and assist the services based in a region larger than the municipality. Depending on the patients treated or the problems met, the medical toxicologist will work alongside the various medical experts and bodies.

*Environmental pollution*

## 1.2    RELATIONSHIP WITH OTHER DISCIPLINE

Toxicology is the science that studies the harmful effects of exogenous substances on living organisms. The clinical toxicologist applies the acquired knowledge to the diagnosis and treatment of patients. An integral part of this science is the study of the individual who is exposed for whatever reason to substances of this kind and who manifests symptoms of disease. The multidisciplinary nature of clinical toxicology is apparent from the close cooperation practiced with those doing toxicological work in disciplines other than medicine.

Diagnosing a poisoned patient entails intensive cooperation with trained analytical chemists (analytical toxicologists). These are usually (hospital) pharmacists or chemists.

*Analytical chemistry*

The clinical toxicologist is sometimes required to conduct animal experiments in order to be able to offer his patients adequate treatment. The knowledge and experience of research performed in other disciplines such as pharmacology and biological toxicology, are invaluable to these experiments. They are therefore carried out in close cooperation.

*Pharmacology*

General toxicology

Analogous to pharmacological data, data from (general) toxicological research form the basis of patient diagnosis and treatment. Clinical questions may thus prompt research of interest to all areas of toxicology.

## 1.3 MEDICAL TOXICOLOGY RESEARCH

The effects observed in pharmacological and toxicological research on animals indicate the symptoms which may be expected in the human victim of intoxication. Animal experiments also provide an opportunity for studying the pathophysiological mechanisms underlying the symptoms of disease. The previous section described how a clinical question can lead to experimental research on animals if there is insufficient insight into the mechanisms of the intoxication involved. In this way, the practicability of new methods of treatment can also be tested before they are used on patients. It should be pointed out though, that the effects of compounds may vary from one species to another. This means that animal data are not always valid for man. Extrapolation from animals to man is therefore not without risks. Clinical toxicology research, i.e. observations of victims of intoxication, can answer the question to what extent expectations based on animal observations are in fact applicable to man. Clinical toxicology research thus offers a chance of checking to what extent data from animal experiments are relevant to man.

Clinical toxicology research

*Clinical toxicology research* studies the relationship between dose and effect in man, the type of effects and the pathophysiology of cases of human poisoning. As such research is performed not only by clinicians but also by, for example, physicians working in industrial medicine, the preferred term is medical toxicology.

Another important subdivision of medical toxicology research is concerned with the assessment and improvement of methods of treatment. As was described above, health protection measures are taken on the basis of animal experiments. The effectiveness of these measures has to be tested by research. This can sometimes be very difficult or even impossible. In such situations it may be necessary to conduct a study using human volunteers. The ethical acceptability of such studies must be thoroughly checked beforehand; the volunteers' health must not be endangered. In practice, they are primarily studies designed to form the basis of standards, for example on food, to protect public health. They can be carried out with doses far lower than those leading to manifest intoxication. Such studies are carried out under direct medical supervision and hence often by medical toxicologists.

## 2 Intoxication as a cause of disease

Exogenous factors

There are many causes of illness and disease. The cause may for example be changes in genetic material, hereditary or otherwise, degeneration in one or more organs, or neoplasms. Anatomical or functional changes in organs may be the result of factors operated by the organism itself or of exogenous factors. Microorganisms, such as viruses, bacteria, and parasites are *exogenous factors*. Exogenous pathogenic factors may also be of a chemical or physical nature. A bruise or cut, for example, is the result of absorption of kinetic energy, and a burn is the result of absorption of thermal energy. Intoxication is also caused by an exogenous factor. The following sections look at the potential causes of intoxication, for both local and systemic effects.

## 2.1 LOCAL VERSUS SYSTEMIC EFFECTS

Reaction at the site of contact

Intoxication may be the result of a physico-chemical *reaction at the site of contact* between the substance and the body. Such processes are sometimes described as *intoxication* and sometimes as *injuries* or *burns*. In general, marked changes in pH and oxidation-reduction processes are involved.

See, for example, Study unit 10

The integrity of the cell membrane is essential for the cell to function properly. Marked changes in pH alter the structure of proteins. This destroys the integrity of the cell membrane, and the cell dies. This kind of process comes into play when acids or bases come into contact with the skin or mucosa of, for example, the eyes, mouth and throat or esophagus.

Similarly, contact with oxidizing agents such as hydrogen peroxide, fluorine and chlorine or with reducing agents such as ferrous sulfate or ferrous fumarate can alter the structure of the cell membrane and cause the cell to die.

When a group of cells has become nonviable they turn necrotic. Around the area of necrosis, an inflammatory reaction develops which is accompanied by swelling. If the necrotic tissue has been rejected and the lesion has extended under the basement membrane of the skin or mucosa, an *ulcer* has formed. The ulcer contains granulation tissue consisting of fibroblasts and capillaries. From this, scar tissue is formed, which is covered by epithelium and grows from the epithelial border surrounding the ulcer over the granulation tissue. In subsequent months, the scar tissue will decrease in volume and shrivel up. This may, for example, restrict the mobility of a joint.

There may also be secondary atrophy of the muscles controlling the joint. Passage through an organ like the esophagus may be hampered if a shriveled circular lesion, such as one caused by a corrosive substance, has developed. Depending on the site of the process, pathological symptoms may thus appear either immediately or not until much later as a result of this type of intoxication.

*Systemic effects*

In the case of *systemic effects*, the substance is first absorbed by the body and then transported. Changes at the site of uptake are rare. Once the substance reaches the various organs, it may affect the function of those organs or parts of them, and cause it to change. The resulting phenomena are the symptoms of systemic intoxication.

## 2.2   TREATMENT, SIDE-EFFECTS, OVERDOSAGE, INTOXICATION

The harmful effect of a foreign substance is sometimes the result of the body reacting differently. The ultimate effect is determined not just by the substance itself but also the way in which the body reacts to it (interaction of compound and organism).

*Intoxication*

In order to avoid semantic confusion, it is important to define the term *intoxication* accurately, especially in the case of xenobiotics to which humans are exposed for a specific purpose, such as medicines. A medicine is administered in a specified dose to induce a specific therapeutic effect. This effect will be achieved if the concentration of the drug in the effector organ or near the receptor is within a given range. Pathological symptoms appearing at these specified concentrations are called *side-effects*. If the concentration is higher than the quantity required for a therapeutic effect, however, and the patient shows no pathological symptoms, this is known as an *overdose*. If, on the other hand, pathological symptoms are indeed apparent, the term *intoxication* is used (see Table 38.1).

*Side-effects*

*Overdoses*
*Intoxication*

ASSIGNMENT   38.1

Indicate whether the following examples, a, b and c, involve intoxication, side-effects, overdoses or neither of these three.

*Example a*

Repeated administration of chloramphenicol to patients with infections (e.g. meningitis) causes inhibition of neutrophil granulocyte formation in some patients.

*Example b*

Consumption of large quantities of low-calorie soft drinks (containing polyalcohols) sometimes causes diarrhea.

*Example c*

Repeated use of morphine sometimes leads to physical dependence on this drug.

## 2.3 ACUTE VERSUS CHRONIC

Two types of intoxication can be distinguished: acute and chronic intoxication. There is a practical need for this distinction, since the clinical picture of acute intoxication by a certain substance is not necessarily the same as that of chronic intoxication by the same substance. In addition, the circumstances in which the clinical toxicologist performs his work are very different according to whether he/she is dealing with acute or chronic cases.

*Acute intoxication*

A patient suffers *acute intoxication* when he or she becomes ill after a single, brief exposure to a relatively large quantity of a substance. This may for example occur after taking an excessive quantity of drugs, household products or pesticides, and after accidents such as leakage from tanks, or fires. The symptoms generally appear soon after exposure and are usually severe. In such cases, the patient requires immediate medical attention and usually has to be admitted to a hospital.

*Chronic intoxication*

A patient suffers *chronic intoxication* when he becomes ill after repeated exposure to a far smaller quantity of a substance than in the case of acute intoxication. The duration of exposure may vary from a few days to many years. The symptoms usually develop gradually. This happens, for instance, in the course of one's occupation or when one spends much time on certain hobbies. The symptoms may indeed be very severe, but they seldom require immediate medical intervention. This kind of patient will generally be examined and treated initially by his family doctor. Some patients will be referred to a hospital outpatients' department and, depending on the problem, may then have to be hospitalized.

Large groups of individuals or even substantial proportions of the general public may be exposed over long periods of time to quantities of substances considerably lower than those in the above-mentioned cases of chronic intoxication. This may happen as a result of air pollution, soil contamination or contaminated food, containing pesticide residues or toxins naturally present in foodstuffs.

TABLE 38.1
Terminology of effects induced by medical drugs

| | Concentration at receptor | |
|---|---|---|
| | Intended | Higher than intended |
| "ill" | side-effect | intoxication |
| "healthy" | treatment | overdose |

When pathological symptoms occur as a result, these are also cases of chronic intoxication. However, such problems generally present themselves to the clinical toxicologist in a very different way from other types of chronic intoxication. This is because of the considerably lower levels of exposure and the circumstances in which exposure takes place.

*Environmental incidents*

In addition to general environmental pollution as a possible source of chronic intoxication, the last few decades have seen an increasing number of so-called environmental incidents as a potential source of health problems. *Environmental incidents* are defined as localized pollution episodes in which the level of pollution is far higher than in most cases of environmental pollution. The majority of cases involve soil contamination and contamination of homes by, for example, pesticides.

*Disaster*

Cases of acute intoxication usually involve just one patient or a few patients. If large groups of people suffer acute intoxication, this is known as a *disaster*. Chronic intoxication usually involves larger groups of victims than acute intoxication, while cases of soil contamination usually involve groups of a few hundred people (see Figure 38.1). It is easier to establish a link between exposure and effect, i.e. symptoms, for acute intoxication than it is for chronic intoxication. The present knowledge of and experience in diagnosing and treating cases of acute intoxication go back much further than those of chronic intoxications associated with environmental pollution.

## 3    Acute intoxication

The previous section defined acute intoxication as a pathological state which is caused by a single, brief exposure to a relatively large quantity of a substance. Usually, the symptoms appear soon after exposure and are often such that medical intervention is needed. If possible, action is taken before the patient develops symptoms. Further treatment and observation are usually carried out in the hospital, ideally in an intensive care unit.

Human beings may be poisoned by a very large number of substances. The number of physicians and paramedical personnel who have a broad ready knowledge of the symptoms and treatment of acute intoxication is, however,

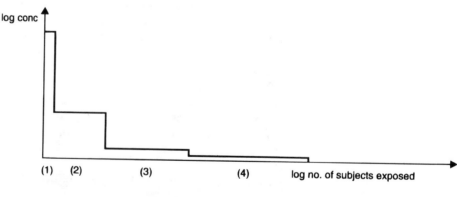

1  acute intoxication (accident, autointoxication)
2  chronic intoxication (occupational)
3  chronic intoxication (environmental incident)
4  chronic intoxication (environmental pollution)

FIGURE    38.1

Relationship between the number of individuals exposed and the level of exposure in various types of intoxication

relative small. The term acute intoxication implies that action is required *immediately*. This combination of factors may give medical personnel the feeling that every second counts. In the tense situation which sometimes results, mistakes are easily made. It is therefore important to remember that the number of intoxications in which every second really does count is actually very small (see Table 38.2).

It goes without saying that adequate treatment should not be unnecessarily delayed. The circumstances in which acute intoxication occurs may vary widely (see Table 38.3).

*Types of acute intoxication*

This is of great practical significance. A distinction is made between *accidental intoxication* and *deliberate autointoxication homicide* and *Polle's syndrome*. Strictly speaking, homicide is also deliberate intoxication, but the person intending to cause illness or death is not the patient himself. Another important practical consideration is whether the victims are children or adults and whether the intoxication concerns one individual or a group of people.

## 3.1 ACCIDENTAL INTOXICATION

*Unintentional*

As the name suggests, accidental intoxication occurs *unintentionally*. Most such cases involve children eating or drinking a product not meant to be consumed. Accidental intoxication due to mishaps with 'chemicals' occur in all age groups.

### 3.1.1 Children

*Cleaning products*

Of all household products, *cleaning products* are the most important toxicants. Depending on the product's composition, potential harmful effects are burning of the lips, mouth and throat, the esophagus and, rarely, the stomach. Table 38.4 summarizes some important groups of these products.

*Mineral oils*

A second important group is that of products containing fractions of *mineral oils* as solvents. Apart from aliphatic hydrocarbons, also aromatic substances such as toluene and xylene are regularly added to these products. Ingestion of aliphatic and aromatic hydrocarbons can cause chemical pneumonitis. Large quantities may also cause symptoms which reflect the effects of these substances on the central nervous system.

TABLE 38.2
Examples of intoxication requiring rapid response

| *Urgent action is required following ingestion of/exposure to relatively large doses of:* |
| --- |
| cholinesterase inhibitors |
| cyanide |
| carbon monoxide |
| opiates |
| orphenadrine |
| paraquat |

TABLE 38.3
Broad categories of acute intoxication

| Accidental intoxications | Intentional intoxications |
| --- | --- |
| children | autointoxications |
| all ages (accidents) | attempted homicides |
| | Polle's syndrome |

TABLE 38.4

Substances most frequently involved in human exposure in the United States

| Substance | No. | %* |
|---|---|---|
| cleaning substances | 191,830 | 10.4 |
| analgesics | 183,013 | 10.0 |
| cosmetics | 153,424 | 8.3 |
| plants | 112,564 | 6.1 |
| cough and cold preparations | 105,185 | 5.7 |
| bites/envenomations | 76,941 | 4.2 |
| pesticides (includes rodenticides) | 70,523 | 3.8 |
| topicals | 69,096 | 3.8 |
| antimicrobials | 64,805 | 3.5 |
| foreign bodies | 64,472 | 3.5 |
| hydrocarbons | 63,536 | 3.5 |
| sedatives/hypnotics/antipsychotics | 58,450 | 3.2 |
| chemicals | 53,666 | 2.9 |
| alcohols | 50,296 | 2.7 |
| food poisoning | 46,482 | 2.5 |
| vitamins | 40,883 | 2.2 |

Note: Despite a high frequency of involvement, these substances are not necessarily the most toxic, but rather often represent only ready availability.

*Percentages are based on the total number of human exposures rather than the total number of substances.

Reprinted from Litovitz, T. *et al.*, 1991 AAPCC Annual Report. AJEM 1992; 10(5): 452–505.

*Drugs*

*Drugs* are mostly kept in medicine cabinets which, surprisingly, rarely have locks. Often, though, they are left lying around the house. Oral contraceptives are commonly to be found on the bedside table. Medicines which need to be taken several times a day, as most of them do, are carried round in a handbag or pocket. All these places are easily accessible to children. This is important when it comes to preventive measures.

*Imitating adults*

Children at play imitate adult behavior. This includes obvious actions like ta-king tablets or alcoholic drinks. But children may also imitate adult actions using the wrong products. In one instance, a child trying to make sandwiches used dishwasher powder. The result was corrosive burns to the lips and mouth. Children in the age groups concerned are not very good at telling what they have done. When asked exactly what they have eaten or drunk and how much, they rarely give an adequate answer. Because the parent, who is often very frightened, communicates his or her fear to the child, the information given by the child may be even less reliable. Nor should the reliability of the information supplied by bystanders, including parents, be overestimated. They may under- or overestimate the quantity possibly ingested because they feel guilty for not ha-ving kept a proper eye on the child.

To play it safe, in practice the substance in question will be assumed to have been ingested at the highest dose possible from what was found in the child's immediate vicinity. Although this is often a traumatic experience for such children, the circumstances in which children are exposed to toxic substances force those providing medical treatment at all times to follow this procedure, which best safeguards the health of the child.

ASSIGNMENT   38.2
What will be the implications of this approach for the number
of hospital admissions?

### 3.1.2 Accidents

In accidents involving chemicals, people may be poisoned by many different
types of substances, depending on where and how the accident occurs. It is not
possible to distinguish special categories of accidents. For example, substances
such as turpentine, hydrochloric acid or paraquat solutions may be drunk by
mistake out of lemonade bottles. Likewise, leakage from road tankers after a
traffic accident may cause accidental intoxication of passengers, rescue workers
and onlookers. In the case of a fire, products of pyrolysis may be released by the
burning item while leaks may also be caused by the fire itself. Every year, many
people are admitted to a hospital after inhaling chlorine gas. Toilet cleaners, for
example, first put bleach (sodium hypochlorite) and then hydrochloric acid into
the toilet bowl. The result is that chlorine gas is released in this relatively small
space. The gas reacts with the cells of the mucous membranes of the person who
is cleaning. The clinical effect of this is pain in the eyes, nose and large bronchial
tubes, and in serious cases conjunctivitis and bronchial spasm. The ensuing acute
shortage of breath usually means an emergency admission.

*CNSLD patients*

People with *chronic non-specific lung disease* (CNSLD) such as asthmatic bronchitis, bronchitis or asthma react more violently than people with healthy lungs.

*Chlorine gas cloud*

When a *cloud of chlorine gas* drifts over a population center, as happened in Ypres,
Belgium, during World War I, the reported symptoms are more acute; the mucous lining of the bronchi is totally destroyed causing severe bronchial spasm
and the coughing up of considerable quantities of sputum and blood. Some of
those affected died of asphyxia.

Chlorine may accidentally escape during its *manufacturing*. This may also
cause a cloud of chlorine gas to drift over a center of population. Random factors, in addition to the quantity that has escaped and atmospheric conditions
at the time, may determine the number of individuals who suffer harmful effects.

Another kind of accidental intoxication is fairly common in fires.

*Categories of individuals potentially
exposed in fires*

Three *categories of potentially exposed individuals* may be distinguished: *people inside the burning object* when the fire breaks out (occupants of houses, department
store customers, aircraft passengers), *rescue workers* (firemen, policemen and am-
bulancemen), and *bystanders* (especially large numbers of onlookers). At the
heart of the fire and close by, the following pathogenic factors apply: inhalation
of hot air, inhalation of smoke, oxygen deficiency and the presence of carbon
monoxide (CO) and other pyrolytic products.

*Pulmonary edema by damage to
alveolar cells*

*Nitrogen*

Heat trauma can cause *pulmonary edema* as a result of *damage to the alveolar cells*,
the so-called adult respiratory distress syndrome, or ARDS. Inhalation of large
quantities of *smoke* causes bronchial spasm. Inhalation of CO can cause *carbon
monoxide intoxication*. If the burning material contains *nitrogen*, which is virtually always the case, hydrocyanic acid (HCN) and oxides of nitrogen (NO, $NO_2$)
may be released. Inhalation of *hydrocyanic acid* leads very rapidly to death.
Cyanide has been found in victims who have died in fires. As opposed to our
knowledge of carbon monoxide, however, it is not yet known to what extent
cyanide constitutes a significant threat to the patient and, in the event of death,

to what extent it has contributed to it. Nitrous fumes, following a latency period of some 6 hours during which the patient may be symptom-free, cause ARDS necessitating ventilation with a positive end-expiratory pressure (PEEP). This form of ventilation maintains a pressure in the chest which is higher than that of the outside air both during and after expiration. The nitrous fumes may be a potential hazard to bystanders in particular, especially in cases of fire involving products containing a relatively high percentage of nitrogen, such as fertilizers, polyurethane, polyacrylonitrile and celluloid.

*Chlorinated products*
*Fluorinated substances*

When *chlorinated products* such as polyvinyl chloride burn, hydrochloric acid fumes and phosgene may be given off. Burning of *fluorinated substances* such as Teflon (polytetrafluoroethylene), may cause the release of highly toxic fumes containing fluorine. Fires are thus a significant source of potential poisoning.

*Inert gases*

Every year cases of accidental intoxication as a result of exposure to *inert gases* are reported. These accidents mostly occur inside ships (tankers, grain transporter vessels), silos and storage tanks. These inert gases are introduced into the spaces concerned in order to prevent explosion or overheating by displacing the oxygen. A major practical problem here is that often these substances are not biologically inert. Gases used for this purpose are, for example, combustion gases, which contain little or no oxygen but do contain a small percentage of carbon monoxide in addition to carbon dioxide and nitrogen. If someone becomes unconscious in an environment of this kind it is due not only to oxygen deficiency but also to carbon monoxide intoxication which requires a completely different treatment.

Over and above these examples of regularly occurring, accidental intoxications, however, there are cases of *poisoning of a more incidental nature*.

---

EXAMPLES

Two women died after eating frozen food which had become contaminated with nitrite during transportation due to a leaking freezer system.

Another example is that of an epidemic in a hospital department where neonates were nursed in incubators. One infant after the other developed serious methemoglobinemia. Several of them died. After an intensive search throughout the hospital, during which new cases of illness appeared, resorcinol was found to have been added to the babies' food instead of glucose by mistake.

---

Unfortunately this kind of poisoning will occur again and again. In detecting the cause, there will be a high demand on those involved, in the race against time, not only to treat the patients but also to identify and eliminate the cause in order to keep the total number of patients—and sometimes of deaths too—to a minimum.

3.2    DELIBERATE INTOXICATION

*3.2.1 Deliberate autointoxication*

Deliberate autointoxication is intoxication in which the patient *administers the toxic substance intentionally to himself*. If the substance is administered intentionally by a third party this is known as attempted homicide. Deliberate autointoxication was previously described as *suicide* or *attempted suicide*. This term is

*Suicide or attempted suicide*

inappropriate, however, since it appeared that self-poisoning was rarely intended to actually end the patient's life. In general, the patients have psychiatric, mental or social problems they cannot solve. In a last cry for help or attention from those close to them they take an overdose of drugs or other preparations such as a household products or pesticides. Usually this is done on the spur of the moment and often the natural reluctance to poison oneself is suppressed by the use of alcohol. The intoxication is in fact part of a completely different process, which has already gone on for a long time and which continues after the intoxication.

*Combined intoxication*

As stated above, in many cases the patient has taken not only an overdose of medical drugs or household products, pesticides or other substances, but alcohol too. In practice, the problem is therefore often one of *combined intoxication*. It can be very difficult to ascertain what has been taken. Even if communication with the patient is possible, what he or she says can not automatically be believed. The poison may have been administered on impulse in a highly emotional state. Early effects of the substances ingested may further affect the person's thinking. Sometimes downright misleading information is given. Just as for children, several groups of drugs and other products can be distinguished which account for a relatively large number of deliberate autointoxications.

### 3.2.2 Homicide

Homicide or attempted homicide is rare compared to other forms of murder and manslaughter. When an attempt succeeds death is from unnatural causes and the clinical toxicologist will not be involved with the patient. If the patient does not die but does become ill, he/she will consult his/her family doctor and, depending on how ill he/she is, will or will not be urgently admitted to the hospital. If no poisoning is suspected, the patient's symptoms will determine the unit to which he/she is admitted. If poisoning is recognized as a possible cause of the patient's illness, it is most important that the attending physicians are aware of certain points and do not immediately tell the patient the cause of his illness, which is usually the case with other patients. In practice, after all, homicide by toxic substances usually involves administration by a very close member of the patient's family—a spouse, child or parent. The relationship with the offender often seems to be good.

*Thallium sulfate*

In the case of homicide, the offender's options are limited in that the substance to be administered has to be tasteless and odorless. A commonly used substance is *thallium sulfate*. This rodenticide is still in use in some countries, and relatively easy to obtain. If a large quantity is administered, within a few hours or days the patient dies from cardiovascular complications. At lower doses or if small quantities are given repeatedly over a longer period of time, paresthesia sets in with pain in the sole of the foot as a very characteristic symptom. Paralysis of the extremities (paresis) and paresthesia in the extremities subsequently develop.

Paresthesia is abnormal sensation.

*Polyneuropathy* is not confined to the peripheral motor and sensory nerves but is also present in the abdominal nerves. This is reflected in impaired peristalsis and, in cases of serious intoxication, in a paralytic ileus. Neurotransmission in the central nervous system may also be disturbed, the symptoms being confusion, hallucination and in severe cases coma. After a week or so the hair falls out, leaving the patient totally bald. If the diagnosis has not been made previously, this is usually the moment when thallium intoxication is suspected. Cases of (attempted)

*Homicide using other toxic compounds*

*homicide using other toxic substances* are more incidental in nature. Examples are warfarin, digoxin, carbachol and N-nitrosodimethylamine.

### 3.2.3 Polle's syndrome

*Poisoning of children by parents*

A special category of poisoning is that in which *parents poison children* with the aim of attracting attention to themselves. The individual concerned may be seeking to draw attention to himself through pretended or self-inflicted ailments (the Von Münchausen syndrome). If such a patient poisons one or more children,

*Polle's syndrome*

this is known as *"Polle syndrome"*. It is said by some that Polle was Baron Von Münchausen's daughter by his second wife, who died young. According to others, Polle was the birthplace of Von Münchausen's daughter by his second marriage, who died of convulsions soon afterwards in Bad Münster. Bizarre poisonings by common salt, barbiturates, methaqualone and opiates are on record in this connection.

In cases of homicide and Polle's syndrome, much depends on the toxicological expertise of the physicians concerned and above all on their resourcefulness. Just as much depends on their insight into psychology, as the problem is seldom one of criminality in the customary sense of the word. The reason for the poisoning usually lies in complex psychological and/or psychiatric problems in the offenders and between offender and victim.

## 4    Chronic intoxication

Chronic intoxication is defined as a pathological condition occurring after repeated exposure to a potentially toxic substance, in which the concentration of that substance at the receptor or in the effector organ is higher than intended. The level of exposure is generally lower than and on a different scale from that in acute intoxication. For practical reasons, a further distinction is made between chronic intoxication associated largely with *occupational exposure* and chronic intoxication associated with *environmental pollution*. In essence, the pathophysiological mechanisms underlying these two types of intoxication are not different. Given the differences in exposure level, they only represent different points on the same dose (i.e. exposure)–response curve. After all, the level of occupational exposure to a particular substance is generally higher than the exposure level in cases of environmental pollution.

### 4.1    OCCUPATIONAL TOXICOLOGY

Occupation-related illness is as old as the human race. The principal objective of occupational toxicology is to collect data needed to determine health hazards at work, and eliminate these hazards as quickly as possible or keep them to a minimum. Since the whole of Study unit 40 is devoted to the discipline of occupational toxicology, this section of medical toxicology will not be considered any further here.

### 4.2    ENVIRONMENTAL POLLUTION

The primary responsibility for the health aspects of environmental pollution lies not with occupational physicians but with physicians concerned with public health. Other differences between occupational toxicology and the toxicological aspects of environmental pollution are more matters of content.

> ASSIGNMENT   38.3
>
> If the circumstances of exposures encountered in occupational toxicology are compared with those in environmental toxicology, what conclusions can be drawn regarding their similarities and differences?

Occupational medicine deals with a limited number of age groups of (usually) men, preselected on the basis of medical criteria concerning their health status. In cases of environmental pollution, all age categories are exposed, from infants to the elderly, and these may include pregnant women and individuals with pre-existing pathological conditions. At work, to conclude, there is a degree of "voluntary" exposure or degree of occupational risk which a worker accepts by virtue of seeking a career in a certain field. Environmental pollution, however, is an involuntary exposure, and there is less inclination to regard certain risks as acceptable. This important difference is reflected in the terminology of standards designed to safeguard health. Occupational health speaks of MACs, or maximun allowable concentrations, while for foodstuffs available to the general public, for example, a criterion is ADI or acceptable daily intake.

## 4.3    PHARMACOTOXICOLOGY

Environmental and occupational situations entail exposure to substances to which ideally nobody would be exposed at all. The situation pertaining to drugs is essentially different. If the prescribed treatment is correct, it is in the patient's interest to be exposed to the substance(s) concerned. A concentration in the effector organ or at the receptor higher than intended may be the result of too high a dose or of changes in the patient's homeostasis (kinetics/biotransformation).

*Very close therapeutic and toxic concentrations*

Particularly with medical drugs whose *therapeutic* and *toxic concentrations* are very close (small therapeutic index, narrow therapeutic range), it may be necessary to check regularly that the concentration has not become too high. This applies especially to patients in whom the disorder for which the drug is prescribed tends to cause deterioration of, for example, kidney function. Another example are substances which have the property that they themselves can damage the kidney function, such as aminoglucoside antibiotics or lithium salts. Antiepileptic drugs such as phenobarbital can accelerate their own biotransformation and that of other anti-epileptics or other drugs so that the concentration will in fact drop. Since an optimum concentration of these substances is most important for an optimum therapeutic effect, their concentration in the effector organ needs regular checking. A form of toxicity which is less easy to identify by analysis may be the result of competition for protein binding where two drugs high in protein binding are administered simultaneously. Well known examples are combinations of coumarins, blood sugar level lowering drugs taken orally, some sulfonamides, phenylbutazone and salicylates.

ASSIGNMENT    38.4

What is the result of protein competition at protein binding sites?

*Side-effects of medical drugs*

A problem related to chronic toxicity induced by medical drugs is that of *drug side-effects*. Side-effects *per se* are very precisely defined, but particularly in the case of drugs with a low therapeutic index it may be difficult to determine whether the case in question is one of intoxication or a side-effect.

Those with expert knowledge of chronic intoxication by medical drugs are physicians working in the various specialist areas of medicine, and the hospital pharmacist. In this respect, the latter is the prime counterpart for the family doctor.

## 4.4    DETECTION OF EARLY EFFECTS

*Prevention of toxicity*

Both at work and in the administration of medical drugs, the aim is to *prevent manifest toxicity*. To that end, there are various methods for examining and

*Determination of exposure*

*Identification of effects*
For the position in occupational medicine, see Study unit 40

*Drug monitoring*

studying the individuals exposed. These methods are applied at different locations and under widely differing conditions but have many points in common. The central aim is to determine the *exposure* of the individuals concerned to the potentially toxic substance in such a way that action can be taken if this exposure level rises, before it has become so high that illness ensues. Another method, used to complement this method, or when measurement of exposure is cumbersome, is the *identification of effects* which precede manifest clinical disease.

Occupational medicine uses the periodic medical check-up.

The counterpart to occupational medicine's biological monitoring in curative health care is *drug monitoring*. Depending on the clinical state of the patient, his plasma levels of the above-mentioned antiepileptic drugs, aminoglucoside antibiotics, digitalis glucosides and lithium salts will be measured in order to prevent toxicity.

## 5 Examination of the patient

*Diagnosis*
*Treatment*

*Prognosis*

A patient generally goes to see a doctor when he has complaints. He expects the doctor to examine him and identify the cause of his symptoms (*diagnosis*). Even more importantly, the patient expects to be relieved of his symptoms (*treatment*). Especially if this will take a long time or, still worse, if it is not possible, he will want to know how his symptoms will develop and what his life expectancy is (*prognosis*). Patients also visit the doctor when they do not have symptoms. They often have questions concerning health. People who come (or may come) into contact with potentially toxic substances at work, in the course of their hobbies or elsewhere will ask questions about possible symptoms and any shortening of their life expectancy. By analogy with the practice in genetics it is called 'toxicological counselling'.

The questions which patients put to a clinical toxicologist are not essentially different from those people generally put to their family doctor. This means that the basic principles applicable to medicine as a whole also fully apply to clinical toxicology.

Departure from this "Medical ABC" (see Table 38.5) increases the chances of failing to reach a diagnosis or of making the wrong diagnosis, with all the implications this has for treatment and prognosis. The basic principles are defined in greater detail for every area of medicine, according to the problems specific to that discipline. This section discusses these basic principles as defined for the field of clinical toxicology.

*Patient history*

Examination starts with the *patient history*. After the patient has described his complaints, a series of further questions is asked to obtain as full a picture as possible of the symptoms (case history). Then questions of a more routine nature are asked to complete the picture of the patient's medical condition (gene-ral medical history). If the patient is unconscious or confused, a child or a person with limited mental powers, the required information is obtained from parents, relatives, friends or acquaintances (reported medical history).

*Physical examination*

After taking the patient's history the *physical examination* follows. First of all, the part of the body or the site of the reported complaints is examined (status localis). Then the entire body is examined following a fixed schedule (status praesens). In this examination, which constitutes the physical diagnosis, the following methods are used: visual examination (inspection), feeling (palpation), tapping (percussion) and listening (auscultation).

TABLE 38.5
The ABC of medicine

| |
| --- |
| *patient history* |
| *physical examination* |
| epicrisis |
| differential diagnosis |
| *supplementary tests* |
| blood tests |
| biochemical tests |
| X-ray |
| electrophysiological tests |
| nuclear analysis |
| toxicological analysis |
| *diagnosis* |
| *therapy* |
| *patient history/physical examination/supplementary tests* |
| *confirmation of diagnosis/evaluation of therapy* |

*Epicrisis*
*Differential diagnosis*

After the patient history has been taken and the physical examination made, a first inventory is drawn up, the *epicrisis*. This is used to decide which pathological conditions may be responsible for the patient's complaints, i.e. a *differential diagnosis* is made.

On the basis of the differential diagnosis a further examination program is drawn up. A selection is made from the many available methods for supplementary examination so that a diagnosis can be reached as quickly as possible and with minimal inconvenience to the patient.

After the diagnosis is made, a plan of treatment can be drawn up. During the treatment the patient is regularly examined using the tests described above in order to check that his reaction to the treatment is as expected. The aim of this is to keep checking that the diagnosis was correct and that there are no side effects to the treatment given.

5.1 PATIENT HISTORY

Whenever a general medical history is taken, in any discipline of medicine, questions must be asked about intoxication. In practice, this means inquiring about the patient's use of tobacco, alcohol, drugs and medicines. In clinical toxicology, it is vital to ask about exposure to potentially toxic substances. Consequently, this is always an important section of the case history. In cases of acute intoxication, the patient is rarely capable of providing a detailed history, which is often quite strenuous. Moreover, the time is often lacking to compile a detailed patient history because treatment has to be started promptly. The following therefore considers patient histories in acute and chronic intoxication separately.

*Acute intoxication*

In the case of *acute intoxication*, the first need is to obtain a quick detailed insight into the nature and severity of the patient's complaints. Questions will then be asked about the nature of (possible) intoxication. Once the doctor knows along which route the patient has been exposed to which substance(s), the patient history is further determined by the effects to be expected from the type of intoxication in question. Lastly, the doctor inquires after preexisting illnesses and any medicines used, since those may influence the further course of the intoxication episode and the treatment. Often patients are scared (accidental intoxication) or emotional (deliberate intoxication) and feel ill. The information needed for treatment is best obtained by asking brief, specific questions which can preferably be answered by a simple yes or no.

A time-consuming and expensive method of checking whether the patient history is correct as regards the quantity ingested is the performance of additional toxicological analysis. In practice, this will only be considered when the patient's clinical state requires it. Given the fact that patient histories are by definition unreliable as far as type and severity of the intoxication are concerned, an attempt will always be made to obtain or confirm the relevant data by taking a history from other members of the patient's household. Questions must then be asked not just about medicines used by the patient but also about those used by the rest of the household, including pets. If there is the slightest doubt, the doctor will ask for the house to be searched for (empty) packaging. Not only prescription drugs should be searched for but also over-the-counter medicines obtainable from the pharmacy such as analgesics (salicylates, acetaminophen) and sedatives. Another way of finding out about the patient's use of medicines is to ask his family doctor or local pharmacist. Despite such measures, it is often very difficult to find out from patient history data which substances have caused the intoxication. A case in point is when the patient has deliberately or involuntarily misled the doctor.

When the patient is unconscious, it is not possible to draw on medical information he has supplied himself, and the information supplied by others, as described above, will then have to suffice. In such circumstances the symptoms may also provide a strong indication of the type of intoxication involved.

In cases of acute intoxication in children, the reliability of the patient history is also a great problem. Often it is not known what the child has taken and how much. Sometimes it is not even known whether the child has actually taken anything at all.

After establishing what the patient's complaints are, the full facts of the accident need to be known. Again, this poses a great problem since an accident is typically an unforeseen event and what exactly happened is unknown: what was in the wrongly-labelled bottle, what chemical reaction occurred during the laboratory accident, what was in the road tanker which crashed and started to leak?

The main practical conclusion in all acute intoxications is that the patient history is by definition unreliable and that most patients have ingested less than they claim! Acute intoxication rarely offers the chance of taking a general medical history. This should thus be done once the patient has been detoxified!

*Chronic intoxication*

There are two major differences between patient histories in acute intoxication and in non-acute (*chronic*) intoxication.

ASSIGNMENT  38.5

Consider what these two differences are.

As usual, the physician starts with taking the case history and trying to gain detailed insight into the nature and development of the complaints. Next, the patient history focuses on any possible exposure in past and present, to potentially toxic substances (see Table 38.6).

*Intoxication from environmental pollution*

In cases of *chronic intoxication from environmental pollution* the questions asked will concern the nature of the pollution in order to determine the severity of any

TABLE 38.6
Principal points to be considered when compiling an occupational patient history (based on Brooks, 1981)

1 chronological list of all jobs held, starting from the first, with exact dates if possible
2 details of what the jobs entailed and how the work was performed
3 list of substances and materials handled by the patient
4 list of substances handled by other workers on the same premises
5 estimate of exposure to the various substances, based on 1 and 3
6 rough estimate of the degree of exposure to the various substances (low, moderate or high)
7 personal protection used: masks, clothing, etc.
8 details of the working conditions: ventilation, etc.
9 details of additional jobs (moonlighting) and hobbies
10 time of first symptoms, in relation to 1
11 relationships between presence at or absence from work and symptoms
12 any other workers with similar symptoms
13 results of tests, periodic medical check-ups, etc

possible exposure. In cases of local *air pollution*, the patient is asked about the position of his house in relation to the source of pollution. How long has the individual lived in that house and where did he/she live before, and how long has the source of pollution been present and how have (possible) emissions changed in recent years? The questioner will try to establish any link between the symptoms and climatic conditions such as temperature, wind direction, wind-force, fog, and how absence from work and for example holidays affect the symptoms. In cases of *soil contamination*, the places where the patient has lived in the past will be recorded in detail. The patient will be asked about the kind of area the house is in, e.g. beside a river or the sea, or on a higher sandy area. Detailed questions will then be asked about the layout of the house and where the bedrooms are, since a sizable number of hours are spent in these every day. It is also informative to know how the house is ventilated and heated. The patient will also be asked about the possibility of direct contact between the contaminants and the occupants during work in the garden. A separate aspect is the consumption of vegetables grown in their own gardens or in contaminated allotments. If the house is fitted with insulating material or treated with pesticides etc., some of the questions mentioned above will be asked. In this case, it is important to record exactly when the house was fitted or treated and whether instructions on occupancy after treatment and on ventilation were followed properly.

The patient must always be asked whether the whole day is spent at the same address or works elsewhere, and if so, where. Because whole families are often examined for the same problem in such cases, these data must be recorded separately for each family member. Once the above data have been collected, the development of symptoms will be related to whether or not the person stays in the house or in a specific part of it (bedroom). In the case of air pollution, a relationship between climatic conditions and symptoms is investigated. With soil contamination, a possible link between the season (heating, ventilation, water table) and symptoms is sought. Often the patient does not know what kind of contamination is involved. When the case history is complete, the general medical history is taken. After that the patient is examined.

*Vital functions*

## 5.2 PHYSICAL EXAMINATION

As with the general medical history, every physician must follow a fixed series of procedures in a physical examination, so that afterwards there does not need to be any doubts as to what was examined and what was not. In a case of acute intoxication he must first check a number of *vital functions*. These are consciousness, breathing and circulation. Depending on his findings, treatment will sometimes be started immediately. If this is not necessary he will first examine the organ or part of the body in the patient complaints in which abnormalities may be expected. The remainder of the body is then examined systematically.

*Consciousness*

If the state of *consciousness* is lowered, the degree of reduction is investigated. The distinction here is between sopor (deep sleep) and coma (unconsciousness). If the patient cannot be woken up and does not react when spoken to, he/she is comatose (or hard of hearing!). Next, different levels of coma can then be distinguished, according to the degree of impairment of the CNS function: does the patient react to pain stimuli (intoxication with analgesics), are there tendon reflexes? In very deep coma, the patient no longer breathes and his body temperature may have dropped. To compare the coma levels of different patients so-called "coma scales" have been devised. The best-known of these is the Glasgow Coma Grade Scale. In clinical practice, however, the use of scales can easily lead to misunderstandings, and so it is better to describe the patient's clinical state and reserve this type of classification for scientific research. Coma is a potential danger to the patient. Because he has lain in the same position for a long time and the normal reflexes such as coughing are absent, there is a risk of inhaling secretions and collapsing of a lung, both of which can cause hypoxia and later infection (bronchial pneumonia). Unconscious patients are thus intubated endotracheally to prevent aspiration and cleanse the bronchi.

*Respiration*

*Respiration* is judged by observing the movement of the chest, feeling the breath in front of the mouth or listening with the stethoscope to the breathing murmur in the chest or in front of the mouth.

*Impaired gas transport*

Even though the respiratory function may be adequate, *gas transport* to the alveoli may be *impaired* if there is *obstruction* of the upper or lower respiratory tract. This occurs in the case of glottal edema. Ingestion of corrosive fluids or inhalation of highly irritant gases or fumes causes swelling of the larynx and the entrance to the trachea. Narrowing of the passage causes an audible inhalation, an inspiratory stridor. In that case, an airway must be created as quickly as possible by intubation or, if this is not possible, by an (emergency) tracheotomy. Adequate respiration is important because of the damage caused by oxygen deficiency.

*Damage at alveolar level*

*Obstruction of the lower respiratory tract*

*Damage at alveolar level* will cause the arterial blood to be undersaturated with oxygen. Such damage may be the result of inhalation of gases causing pulmonary edema (ARDS) and of *obstruction of the lower respiratory tract* due to spasm or accumulated secretions and/or blood. Here too the patient is restless when compos mentis. His lips, face, nose, hands and feet are bluish in color. There is central cyanosis. In such circumstances the doctor will immediately listen to the lungs and try to differentiate. If a whistling respiratory sound is heard, with the whistling most pronounced during expiration (wheezing rhonchi), and the expiration time is protracted, i.e. longer than normal, the bronchi are most likely in spasm. In that case bronchospasmolytic drugs and oxygen will be given. If a coarse bubbling sound is heard during both inspiration and expiration (coarse rhonchi), secretions or blood are present in the bronchial tree and the patient is asked to cough the sputum into a dish so that it can be assessed. Oxygen is then given and the physiotherapist will try to help the patient expel the secretions. Sometimes it is necessary to intubate in order to 'empty' the bronchi. The air passages are then cleaned through the tube using a flexible catheter. This is, however, a last resort, because of the danger of secondary bacterial infection. If on inspiration a fine crackling noise is heard (crepitation), this is caused by air penetrating the alveoli containing fluid. These patients often groan, which is an important symptom indicative of pulmonary edema. By groaning the patient creates a resistance against which he exhales. He gives himself a positive end-expiratory pressure (PEEP), as it were. In such patients the most important and urgent question is whether or not to apply artificial respiration immediately.

The common factor in all these conditions is that oxygen undersaturation very quickly brings the percentage of non-oxygenated hemoglobin to more than 5%. This manifests itself in central cyanosis. If the patient is anemic, cyanosis is not seen until there is a more serious oxygen deficiency. This can give a misleading impression of the gravity of the situation because the picture in regard to cyanosis appears less acute.

*Methemoglobinemia*
Methemoglobinemia is dealt with in Study unit 27.

At this point *methemoglobinemia* needs to be discussed, not so much because this is always a life-threatening pathological condition, but because the initial reaction on first seeing the striking cyanosis is to intervene immediately. This is because patients with this degree of cyanosis usually have very serious respiratory insufficiency or are on the point of dying. The second impression is great surprise at the relatively good condition of the patient despite his deep blue color. This is because a methemoglobin level of, for example, 25% under normal conditions matches a $pO_2$ of less than 40 mm Hg.

*Circulation*

The third vital function is *circulation*. A first impression is obtained from feeling the pulse, when pulse *rate* and *regularity* are measured. Especially if the pulse is irregular, the heart rate and rhythm are checked by listening with the stethoscope to the heart itself and counting. There may be a discrepancy between heart rate and pulse rate if insufficient filling of the heart causes some of the beats not to be felt at the pulse. The pulse also provides, albeit roughly, an *idea of blood pressure*. If the pulse does not feel strong and 'full', blood pressure will be taken immediately using the sphygmomanometer cuff and stethoscope. If the blood pressure is low, this may cause insufficient blood supply to the tissues. This causes a discrepancy between the oxygen demand of the various organs and the oxygen supply. The result is an increased extraction of oxygen in the tissues and thus a higher percentage of non-saturated hemoglobin in the capillaries.

*Cyanosis*

Clinically, this too appears as *cyanosis*. But here, the cyanosis is seen primarily at the ends of the extremities because that is where the circulation is poorest and because oxygenation of the arterial blood as such is unimpaired. For this reason, it is referred to as peripheral cyanosis. If the circulation is inadequate, an infusion will be given immediately to provide plasma, plasma substitutes or drugs. The patient will also be connected to a monitor for continuous observation and monitoring of the electrical activity of the heart. Depending on the cause, treatment of the circulatory disorder will also be started.

In addition to the above-mentioned three vital functions measured in the case of acute intoxication to find out whether immediate action is necessary, there is another clinical condition in which treatment must be started before any other diagnostic measures are taken. This is the case for patients showing *generalized spontaneous, involuntary motor activity*. In a toxicological context, this is *status epilepticus*, as may be observed in acute intoxication by various drugs, and, for example, by *chlorinated hydrocarbons* such as γ-hexachlorocyclohexane (lindane) and substances like endrin, dieldrin, aldrin and endosulfan. Generalized cramps may also occur in the case of *strychnine* and *crimidine* intoxications. These are

*Spontaneous motor activity*
*Status epilepticus*

probably largely central in origin. Lastly, there may be muscle spasms in intoxications with *cholinesterase inhibitors* which are the result of protracted depolarization of the striated muscles. This situation is serious because respiratory muscles are involved in the process of uncoordinated, involuntary motor activity in the same way as the other muscles. The result is hampered respiration causing *hypoxia* and *hypercapnia*. The latter leads to respiratory acidosis. The generalized activity of all muscles also causes a sharp increase in oxygen demand, so that cyanosis usually develops, as well as lactic acidosis because the muscles switch from aerobic to anaerobic metabolism. A serious state of *combined metabolic and respiratory acidosis* is thus created.

There are other clinical conditions that involve spontaneous motor activity. These include the *extrapyramidal syndrome*, which rarely requires immediate treatment.

*Hypocapnia is the state in which carbon dioxide pressure in the arterial blood is lower than normal.*

### 5.3    SUPPLEMENTARY TESTS

*Supplementary tests in the past*

Supplementary tests follow on from the patient history and the physical examination. In the past, possible supplementary tests were restricted largely to *morphological* tests of blood and bone marrow, morphological and *chemical* analysis of urine, measurement of the erythrocyte sedimentation rate and *bacteriological* tests.

The developments in chemistry and physics have enormously increased the range of diagnostic aids. Developments in automation have lead to increases in scale and greater capacity, and have enabled the clinician to make practical use of these diagnostic possibilities. This has been of great benefit to patient diagnosis and treatment. Unfortunately, it has also meant a considerable increase in the cost of medical care for the population.

> ASSIGNMENT    38.6
>
> Some clinicians prefer chemical tests and physical measurements to patient history and physical examination. Explain why.

The patient history would seem to provide the most important information required for diagnosis. The physical examination comes second in this respect and supplementary tests, despite the many possibilities, come third.

Optimum use is made of these possibilities by applying them in the most specific way possible.

The ideal test would be the one that gives a positive result in the case of illness and a negative one if there is no illness. Such a test, however, will rarely, if ever, be available. The task of the clinical toxicologist is to make the best possible choice of supplementary tests, to be carried out in the right order, on the basis of patient history and physical examination. When this is carried out properly, it is an efficient way of arriving at a diagnosis. If it is done without taking account of the aspects described above, it is likely that after a while the significance of false-positive and false-negative test results are being evaluated. The net result of such a procedure would be that the chance of a correct diagnosis is considerably reduced and that the patient will face increasing and unnecessary worries about his health.

### 5.4    TREATMENT OF INTOXICATION

The treatment of intoxicated patients is based on five aspects:

1    knowledge of the properties of the substance concerned;
2    prevention of absorption;

3    speeding up elimination;

4    treatment of symptoms;

5    administration of specific antagonists (antidotes).

*Knowledge of the properties of the substance concerned*

It goes without saying that a good knowledge of the pharmacological and toxicological properties and of the pharmacokinetics and biotransformation of the substance in question is needed in order to give appropriate help to the poisoned patient. Unfortunately, in some instances useless or even harmful treatment is given or, equally seriously, treatment is not given because those in charge do not have this specific knowledge. It stands to reason that a general practitioner cannot be abreast of all the latest data.

*Prevention of absorption*

Everything must be done to prevent any further absorption of the substance. If successful, treatment is then generally simpler than the treatment of the intoxication after absorption has taken place. A number of methods are available.

*Emesis or vomiting*

The patient is induced to *vomit (emesis)*. The best way is to induce reflex vomiting by tickling the back of the throat.

> ASSIGNMENT  38.7
>
> Why is it dangerous to induce vomiting when *corrosive substances* have been swallowed?

Vomiting after *petroleum products* have been taken carries the risk of aspiration. If, however, a patient has swallowed *parathion* dissolved in an organic solvent such as petroleum, the patient should be made to vomit. The reason lies in the fact that parathion intoxication is more life-threatening than the pulmonary edema which may result from aspiration of the petroleum.

Another way of inducing vomiting is to administering *apomorphine*. This substance works quickly and effectively but also has a number of drawbacks. It does not work if the stomach is not sufficiently full and may potentiate the toxic effect of certain medicines on the CNS. It can also cause persistent vomiting, a drop in blood pressure and sometimes a state of excitement and convulsions. Apomorphine is contraindicated in infants and young children.

*Gastric lavage*

In *gastric lavage*, a tube with as wide a diameter as possible and a number of large holes at the end is inserted via the mouth into the stomach. Through it, tepid water is lead into the stomach and subsequently syphoned back. The rinsing is continued until the returning water is clear. In cases of *intoxication with medicines* which adhere to the stomach wall and are highly toxic, such as carbromal, washing will be carefully directed with the aid of a gastroscope. *Comatose patients* must be intubated prior to lavage. Gastric lavage is contraindicated if corrosive substances or petroleum products have been ingested. With corrosive substances, there is a danger of their passing through the esophagus again and exerting their corrosive effect a second time. There is also the risk of the esophagus being perforated by the catheter through the lesion. This risk is increased by the fact that gastric lavage is quite often accompanied by vomiting, which may lead to aspiration.

*Adsorbents*

Medicines and various other substances may be adsorbed on to certain substances. An effective *adsorbent* is *medicinal activated charcoal* (carbo adsorbents), which is administered orally as an aqueous suspension. It is given to prevent absorption in that area of the gastrointestinal tract which cannot be reached by gastric lavage. If, however, medicines are given orally to treat the intoxication, for example acetylcysteine for acetaminophen poisoning, adsorbent charcoal should, of course, not be given because the drug given as treatment will then be adsorbed as well. The herbicides *paraquat* and *diquat* bind very strongly to certain mineral adsorbents. The first measure to be taken if these substances have been ingested is to administer a special kind of mineral preparation, known as *Fuller's earth*. After ingestion of thallium salts, absorption can be prevented by giving Prussian blue (also known as Berlin blue, $KFe[Fe(CN)_6]$).

*Laxatives*

*Laxatives* are intended to accelerate the transit of the substance ingested to prevent that portion of it which is in the lumen of the intestine, from being absorbed. In this way the adsorbent is transported to its site of action, and subsequently eliminated. A commonly used and effective laxative is *sodium sulfate*. Following ingestion of lead compounds, sodium sulfate not only prevents absorption by accelerating transit but also by forming insoluble lead sulfate. In such situations, administration of the laxative will continue until no more lead can be detected in the bowel by X-ray. In comatose patients and in intoxication by medicines which have anticholinergic effects, peristalsis is sluggish and a laxative will have to be given again a few hours later. Sometimes an enema is needed to induce defecation.

### Acceleration of elimination

If the substance has already been absorbed, treatment will be started with a view to limiting the degree of intoxication and keeping its duration as short as possible. This may be achieved by applying a strategy that causes accelerated elimination of the drug from the body. There are various methods to achieve this effect, and the method chosen will depend on the properties of the substance to be eliminated and the severity of the intoxication.

*Forced diuresis*

*Forced diuresis* increases renal clearance of the substance present in an elevated concentration by increasing urine production to about 12 liters per 24 hours. By forced diuresis, the elimination of some substances may be increased tenfold. A favorable result can be expected if all or a large part of the substance or its pharmacologically/toxicologically significant metabolites are eliminated unchanged in the urine. The effect of forced diuresis is greater the smaller the distribution volume of the substance in question.

*Altering urinary pH*

Renal tubules reabsorb ionized drugs from the glomerular filtrate with less efficiency than when these are in the non-ionized form or not at all. By *altering the pH of the urine*, the percentage of some substances dissolved in the filtrate which is ionized can, depending on their $pK_a$, be increased, thus enhancing their excretion. Application of this method is restricted by the limits within which the pH can be altered. Intravenous administration of *sodium bicarbonate* can increase urinary pH to about 7.5.

ASSIGNMENT 38.8

For which types of substance can a favorable effect be expected from increasing the alkalinity with sodium bicarbonate?

Urinary pH must be checked regularly and, if necessary, more sodium bicarbonate is given. If much bicarbonate is given, the pH of the blood must be determined also because the blood alkalinity may become too high. Intravenous administration of *ammonium chloride* can lower urinary pH to about 5.0. For medicines which are weak bases, with $pK_a = 6.0$ and more, acidifying the urine can thus be expected to have a favorable effect. In cases of amphetamine ($pK_a = 9.9$) intoxication, elimination of this substance is increased by artificially lowering urinary pH. Acidification of the urine is applied only sporadically because ammonium chloride is poorly tolerated. Also *vitamin C* can lower urinary pH quite considerably.

*Hyperventilation*

Substances absorbed through the lungs and eliminated mainly through the lungs, may be eliminated more rapidly by *hyperventilation*. The best-known example is carbon monoxide (CO) intoxication. Hyperventilation can be induced by causing the patient to inhale *carbogen* (95% $O_2$ and 5% $CO_2$) through a face mask. The artificially increased $pCO_2$ of the blood provides the stimulus to hyperventilate. In cases of severe carbon monoxide intoxication there is metabolic acidosis. Carbogen is then contraindicated because the artificially raised $pCO_2$ causes a further lowering of the pH of the blood. In such cases, the patient is artificially ventilated, using a high respiratory minute volume and 100% oxygen.

*Hemodialysis*

Many substances can be eliminated from the plasma using *hemodialysis*. The dialysis apparatus has a concentration gradient for the substance between plasma on one side of the membrane and the rinsing fluid on the other. This concentration gradient causes the substance to diffuse across the membrane into the rinsing solution. The quantity of the substance that diffuses per unit of time is directly proportional to the concentration gradient of the free form of the substance on both sides of the membrane. For effective hemodialysis, the substance should be hydrophilic and of low molecular mass, so that it can cross the membrane easily. The plasma concentration must be of a sufficiently high level; if this gradient is not steep enough, the quantity of the substance diffusing from plasma to rinsing solution is too small. As in forced diuresis, the efficiency is greater the smaller the distribution volume of the substance. Hemodialysis eliminates substances many times faster than forced diuresis. Hemodialysis can only be carried out for a few hours, whereas forced diuresis can be continued 24 hours a day. Hemodialysis is a very stressful and rigorous measure, so that forceful indications are required to apply this treatment. These are determined by the severity of the intoxication and by the plasma concentration.

If a patient with pre-existing renal insufficiency is intoxicated by a substance that is eliminated mainly by the kidney, hemodialysis is considered even if the intoxication is less severe. In such patients immediate efforts will be made to eliminate toxic substances likely to damage the kidney tissue, including hemodialysis.

*Hemoperfusion*

From a technical point of view, *hemoperfusion* is similar to hemodialysis. Here, the blood is led not over a membrane but through a column containing adsorbing particles. To this end, thinly coated adsorbent charcoal particles are mostly used. The coating is needed to prevent damage to the cellular components of the blood. It is 100 times thinner than the dialysis membrane. Apart from adsorbent charcoal, uncoated synthetic resins can be used. While hemodialysis has been used to treat intoxications since the 1950s, hemoperfusion only became clinically applicable at the end of the 1970s. Hemoperfusion differs significantly from hemodialysis in that it can also eliminate *lipophilic compounds*. Moreover, the clearance of many substances is higher, for some substances even 100%. Clinically, this is, for instance, apparent in patients who have gone into a deep coma as a result of barbiturate intoxication, and who are wide awake only one or two hours after hemoperfusion. When treated with other methods, they would certainly have remained in a coma for several days. Hemoperfusion appears to be replacing hemodialysis in the treatment of intoxication more and more.

*Exchange transfusion and plasmapheresis*

In *exchange transfusion and plasmapheresis*, fractionated blood is taken. In the former case donorblood is given in return. In plasmapheresis, donor plasma and the patient's own cellular blood components are returned.

Cases in which this procedure is indicated are few. Exchange transfusions are, for example, applied in young children for whom hemodialysis or hemofiltration are technically impossible. They are also used in cases of severe intoxication in which the plasma concentrations are low and the distribution volumes small, by substances which have a small volume of distribution or substances which have a small real distribution volume and are a strongly bound to plasma proteins (e.g. thyroxine). A completely different indication for exchange transfusion are cases of intoxication in which the oxygen transport to the tissues is severely hampered, as in methemoglobinemia resulting, for example, from nitrate and nitrite intoxication.

*Chelators*

*Chelators* are organic substances which can form stable complexes with heavy metals. They can thus either break or prevent the binding of metallic ions to tissues. The complexes formed are called *chelates*. The chelate consists of the metallic ion and the organic substance, which has two or more ligands. The ligands contain O, S or N atoms which can donate a pair of electrons to form a stable covalent bond with the metallic ion. Because the chelator has two or more ligands, either a ring structure is formed with one metallic ion, or a larger complex comprising several metallic ions and several chelator molecules. To be clinically applicable, a chelating agent should meet several conditions. The substance should be water-soluble and non-degradable. It should have access to the site in the body where the metal ion is bound, and be easily eliminated by the kidneys. The complex must be stable at the body's pH. Lastly, the complex must be less toxic than the free metal ion.

The oldest and best known chelator is *dimercaprol* (see Table 38.7). This was originally developed to counteract the effects of lewisite, the arsenic-based war gas (hence the name British antilewisite). It is used in the treatment of intoxication by arsenic, mercury and gold.

A sharply defined indication is required for the administration of dimercaprol, such as reliable blood and urinary levels of the toxic agent and a clinical picture that confirms the severity of the intoxication. The reason is that dimercaprol itself is rather toxic and poorly tolerated. Roughly half the patients treated with it show symptoms such as nausea, vomiting, soreness of the throat, mouth and eyes, paresthesia, muscle cramps, hypertension and tachycardia. Fever is also common.

Table 38.7 lists a number of chelators, their applications and possible side-effects.

*Removal from the enterohepatic or entero-enteral cycle*

In some types of intoxication the toxic substance and/or its harmful metabolites circulate in an enterohepatic or entero-enteral cycle. Elimination of these substances can be promoted by adsorbing them in the lumen so that they are no longer available for reabsorption. The best-known example of *removal from the enterohepatic or entero-enteral cycle* is shown by cases of thallium intoxication, in which *Prussian Blue* is given daily. This latter substance is not absorbed in the intestine. At its surface it exchanges potassium for thallium, and this speeds up thallium elimination. The cyanide contained in the Prussian Blue molecule cannot be released in ionic form, so there is no danger of cyanide intoxication.

TABLE 38.7
Some important chelators

| Chelator | Application(s) | Possible side-effects |
|---|---|---|
| \ndimercaprol | arsenic-based war gas\nlewisite\narsenic, mercury and gold intoxication | nausea\nvomiting\nmuscle cramps\nhypertension |
| \npenicillamine | lead and copper intoxication | nephrotoxic syndrome\nfever\nlymphadenopathy |
| \ncalcium disodium acetate | lead and copper intoxication | (sporadic)\ntubular damage |
| \ndeteroxamine | iron intoxication\nexcessive accumulation of iron | aggravation of existing\nurinary tract infections |

Another example is the use of adsorbent charcoal in cases of imipramine intoxication, since the latter substance and its active metabolites circulate in an enterohepatic cycle.

There are various methods for inducing liver enzymes so that the capacity for the biotransformation of certain substances is increased. The best-known example is the use of barbiturates. However, it takes a few days for the biotransformation capacity to be increased so *induction of biotransformation* is of no practical significance. One method of *promoting biotransformation* is to counteract the depletion of certain conjugation systems, as applied in, for example, acetaminophen intoxication. Very little of the substance is excreted in the urine unchanged; most of it is conjugated in the liver by glucuronidation and sulfation, and a very small proportion is oxidized and converted to a reactive intermediate that damage liver cells unless they are conjugated in turn by glutathione. If an overdose of acetaminophen is taken, the liver's conjugation capacity (glucuronation and sulfation) may be exceeded. In that case a more toxic reactive intermediate is formed. The amount of glutathione in the liver will then be insufficient to conjugate the increased quantity of metabolites. If, because of this, the concentration of unconjugated metabolite increases, it binds to liver cells resulting in necrosis of the liver cells, and this ultimately causes the patient to die in a hepatic coma. One of the aims of treatment is to prevent glutathione depletion. This can be achieved by administering *acetylcysteine* orally or parenterally within 12–24 hours of acetaminophen ingestion. Acetylcysteine contains an SH group and is thought to act as a precursor in glutathione synthesis.

*Symptomatic treatment*

Every victim of intoxication needs to be monitored closely. The aim of symptomatic treatment is to maintain the vital functions, enabling the body to elimi-

*Induction of biotransformation*
*Promoting biotransformation*

Toxicology: Principles and Applications

nate the toxic substance itself. The normal principles of medical treatment apply here, backed up by knowledge of the pathophysiology of the type of intoxication involved.

### Antagonists (antidotes)

It is often assumed that many intoxications can be treated by using antidotes, but nothing is farther from the truth. The number of specific antidotes is quite small. The definition of an "antidote" varies from author to author and as a result there is confusion over which substances do and which do not fall within this group. Ideally, the word 'antidote' should be banished from the medical vocabulary and replaced by a classification of these substances according to their effect. Also, the word 'antidote' suggests that once it has been given, all is well, and the patient will need less attention. The false feeling of security that the term antidote evokes is inappropriate, certainly bearing in mind that such substances are by no means always easy to apply because of their own powerful pharmacological effect, their limited effective time, or because they themselves are potentially toxic. All substances classified as antidotes exert their effect via one form of antagonism or another. The biological activity of substances can, for example, be altered by *chemical antagonism*, as discussed in connection with chelators. The present section, will take a closer look at other forms of antagonism which make use of pharmacological, physiological or biochemical mechanisms.

An example of specific *pharmacological antagonism* is the use of *atropine* to treat intoxication by cholinesterase inhibitors such as organophosphorus compounds (e.g. parathion) and carbamates. Since the breakdown of acetylcholine in the synapse is inhibited, its concentration rises. The muscarinic and central effects of acetylcholine can be counteracted by atropine. In cases of intoxication by organophosphorus compounds, oximes must also be given after ingestion; these may reactivate phosphorylated acetylcholinesterase.

*Atropine intoxication*

In cases of *atropine intoxication*, all symptoms can be stopped by increasing the amount of acetylcholine in the synapse. This is achieved by administering *physostigmine*, a reversible cholinesterase inhibitor.

*Neostigmine* is given in cases of intoxication by anticholinergic drugs with a quaternary ammonium structure when virtually all symptoms are peripheral. It is also given to suppress the muscle-paralyzing effect of non-depolarizing muscle relaxants such as curare.

*Opiates*

Opiate antagonists can counteract the effect of *opiates*, methadone and pentazocine by competition for their receptors in the CNS. The most important indication in these types of intoxication is depression of the respiratory center. The drug of choice is *naloxone*, which has a virtually complete antagonistic effect.

*Methemoglobin*

In intoxications where *methemoglobin* is formed (e.g. acetanilide, aniline, chlorates and nitrates), substances can be administered to reduce the methemoglobin to hemoglobin. The most effective in this respect is *methylthionine* (methylene blue) which is reduced to a colorless substance. In fact, the process involved is a reversible oxidation-reduction system. At high concentrations, methylene blue oxidizes the iron atom in hemoglobin from ferrous to ferric so that methemoglobin is formed. At low concentrations, methylene blue accelerates the reduction of methemoglobin to hemoglobin. This only happens *in vivo*. The reduction of methemoglobin is catalyzed by methemoglobin reductases which are dependent on pyridine nucleotides. In the transfer of electrons from reduced pyridine nucleotides to methemoglobin, methylene blue acts as an electron acceptor, becomes colorless, donates the electrons to methemoglobin and returns to its colored form.

Another reductant, which acts more slowly and less effectively, is *ascorbic acid*. This is given in less serious cases of methemoglobinemia in which the danger of an overdose of methylene blue is greater because the less methemoglobin is present, the more prominent the oxidizing properties of methylene blue are.

Sometimes *ethanol* is given in cases of intoxication by methanol or ethylene glycol (antifreeze). Methanol poisoning causes the formation of toxic formic acid, while ethylene glycol intoxication leads to the production of oxalic acid. The enzyme system that catalyzes these conversions is almost totally saturated in the event of an overdose. The production of formic or oxalic acid is then more or less constant (zero-order kinetics). If ethanol is introduced into this enzyme system, the production of the toxic degradation product will decrease as the proportion of ethanol to methanol or ethylene glycol increases. Ethanol is converted to acetic acid which can be further metabolized via the Krebs cycle. Administration of ethanol, either orally or intravenously, is part of the treatment for the types of intoxication mentioned above.

## 6    Case history

The following section describes the case history of a victim of intoxication. This case history is meant to illustrate the study material contained in the preceding sections. It is not intended to give a full account of all aspects of the intoxications from which the patient described suffered.

CASE 1 PATIENT 2

It appears from the case history of the patient mentioned in the introduction, that his 10-year-old son (weight 35 kg) had been hospitalized several times elsewhere with the same symptoms as shown by the father. After a period of clinical observation during which no diagnosis could be arrived at, the boy was discharged in good health. After that he had a few minor attacks at home. Even though the possibility of intoxication was considered, albeit with no specific substance or group of substances in mind, it was assumed that the attacks were the result of a disturbed psychosocial relationship with the mother. He was taken into a children's home for treatment of this and had several attacks there too. They only occurred shortly after the mother had been to visit him. This appeared to confirm the conclusion reached earlier. After the boy had been at the children's home for a year, he had a serious attack during a weekend visit at home. He was quickly taken to hospital. Despite intensive efforts to resuscitate him he died. As there was no clear cause of death the doctors treating him reported a death from unnatural causes. An official inquiry and autopsy also failed to give an adequate explanation of the patient's death. On their request, the parents were informed about the findings of the official inquiry. A week after the parents were notified that no explanation of their son's death had been found, the father had his first attack.

*Discussion*

The diagnosis of carbachol intoxication was made on the basis of the typical combination of symptoms. The possibility of intoxication by a cholinesterase inhibitor could be excluded because there were no nicotinic symptoms and the activities of the enzymes cholinesterase and pseudocholinesterase were normal. Other possible substances were bethanechol, methacholine, muscarine and pilocarpine. Of these, pilocarpine is the commonest because it is used in ophthalmology. Muscarine is a constituent of the fungus *Amanita muscara*.

The leucocytosis and hyperglycemia were caused by the release of endogenous catecholamines in the patient's very precarious hemodynamic state, and of the exogenously administered catecholamine isoproterenol.

> ASSIGNMENT 38.9
>
> A diagnosis of carbachol intoxication was made in the above case. Why is this diagnosis so hard to establish and on what grounds will it have been made? What type of intoxication is (presumably) involved here, and also in the case of the father (see introduction)?

## 7 Summary

This study unit dealing with medical toxicology, gives an overview of the fields of interest encountered whenever medical science engages in toxicological work. It discusses various aspects relating to both curative and preventive medicine as well as applied and fundamental research. The diagnosis and treatment of intoxication victims are emphasized. The aim of this study unit is to familiarize anyone concerned with toxicology with the issues and problems intoxicated human beings meet with.

## SELF ASSESSMENT QUESTIONS

1  Why is it difficult to establish the cause(s) of possible intoxication in fire victims?

2  The term "autointoxication" was used in the past as a synonym for attempted suicide. Why is that a misnomer?

3  If medicines to treat intoxication are given orally, adsorbent charcoal is not given to absorb the poison ingested. Why not?

4  The $pK_a$ of phenobarbital is 7.2. How can the renal clearance of this substance be accelerated?

## FEEDBACK

### 1 Answers to the assignments

38.1  a  Side effect;
    b  Intoxication;
    c  Side effect.

38.2  In retrospect, the result is that every year more children are treated and admitted to the hospital than is necessary.

38.3  In occupational toxicology, exposure is primarily through inhalation and through the skin whereas in environmental pollution exposure is more often oral and to a lesser extent dermal, although inhalational exposure is also very important in relation to air pollution.

38.4 The result of this competition is that the concentration of the free, unbound fraction of one or both drugs increases, causing the concentration in the effector organ to be increased too, and hence the effect.

38.5 Firstly, in cases of non-acute intoxication there is far more time to record the patient history. Secondly, this time is badly needed to compile the usually much more complex history about the substances to which the patient may have been exposed.

38.6 The results of chemical tests and physical measurements are in general very objective. The findings of patient histories and physical examinations are less easy to quantify and process. This has led to a disproportionate increase in the confidence placed in the significance of supplementary tests when it comes to making a diagnosis. Some doctors have thus neglected patient history and physical examination in favor of a broad screening of the patient.

38.7 It is dangerous to induce vomiting after ingestion of corrosive substances because they then passes through the esophagus twice and can cause further damage.

38.8 For drugs that are weak acids ($pK_a \leq 7$), a favorable effect may result from making the urine more alkaline. The $pK_a$ of phenobarbital is 7.2. In cases of intoxication by this drug forced diuresis will be performed together with alkalinizing of the urine.

38.9 The degree of complexity of the intoxication was enhanced because the possibility of *analytical-toxicological support* was lacking, so that the diagnosis could only be reached on the basis of *clinical findings*. This case was probably a variant of *Polle's syndrome*.

## 2 Answers to the self assessment questions

1 It is sometimes very difficult to predict what the harmful effects in onlookers will be. This is partly because there is still little known about the formation of pyrolysis products and because the pathophysiology of these intoxications is very complex due to the many processes that may be involved.

2 The aim of autointoxication is not always death. It is most often a cry for attention.

3 Administration of the adsorbent may also cause the therapeutic agent to be adsorbed, thus reducing the latter's bioavailability.

4 In practice, a case of phenobarbital intoxication may be "treated" by forced diuresis and by alkalizing the urine, for example by an infusion of sodium bicarbonate.

# Contents Study unit 39
## Ecotoxicology

# Study unit 39

# Ecotoxicology

*N. M. van Straalen*

### INTRODUCTION

Ecotoxicology is concerned with the study of potentially harmful substances in the environment. Although environmental sciences as a whole have a relatively long tradition, the field of ecotoxicology was introduced only recently. It has become evident that any reliable assessment of the environmental risks of a substance must involve the following three disciplines: environmental chemistry, toxicology and ecology. Ecotoxicology could therefore be presented as a triangle composed of these three disciplines (see Figure 39.1).

*Environmental chemistry*

*Environmental chemistry* deals with the occurrence of chemicals in the environment, their distribution over the various environmental compartments and the effects of physicochemical factors on the behavior of substances (binding, mobility). It is also concerned with tracing distribution routes and studying processes such as deposition and degradation. Analysis based on the principles of environmental chemistry describes the concentrations of harmful substances to which plants and animals may be exposed. However, the actual exposure is determined not only by these concentrations, but also by the plants or animals themselves. Fish, for instance, are able to avoid the polluted water around a discharge pipe, so that they are not exposed to substances which sediment close to the pipe.

*Toxicology*

*Toxicology* concentrates on the effects of substances at the level of the individual organism. As appears from the other study units in this textbook, particular attention is paid to target organs and to the analysis of specific (biochemical) changes caused in the organism by the substance. Toxicology also deals with the transformation of toxicants in the organism, the formation of metabolites and the analysis of protective mechanisms. The contribution made by (general) toxicology to ecotoxicology is important because it can offer a mechanistic explanation of effects observed in the field.

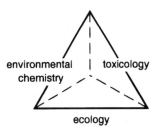

FIGURE 39.1
Diagram of the subdisciplines making up ecotoxicology

1113

EXAMPLE

The decline in population size of the common seal (*Phoca vitulina*) in the tidal flat ecosystem of the Netherlands, Germany and Denmark is associated with serious reproductive failure. Toxicological research revealed vitamin A and thyroid hormone deficiencies in seals fed with polychlorobiphenyl (PCB) contaminated fish. Certain PCB compounds appeared to be metabolized to reactive products that interfered with a transport protein for retinol and thyroid hormone in the blood. This provided evidence for the assumption that the reduction in the number of seals was primarily due to diffuse contamination by PCBs.

*Ecology*

*Ecology*, finally, forms the basis for ecotoxicology. After all, ecotoxicology is mainly concerned with the effects of substances on the ecosystem, specialized knowledge is required on the life cycles of organisms, the "natural" environmental factors which regulate or restrict populations, the genetic variability within a population, etc. Ecology can provide a framework for the formulation of ecotoxicological theory. This approach to ecotoxicology forms the basis for the present study unit.

The aim of ecotoxicological research is to recognize, predict and analyze the effects of potentially toxic substances in the environment. Ecotoxicological knowledge may be used, for instance, to give advice on the seriousness of a particular case of pollution, on the maximum allowable concentration of a substance in the environment, or on the decision as to whether new chemicals are permitted or not.

It is not easy to make a well-founded analysis of an environmental problem; the results or recommendations are often more complicated than the outside world expects. This is inherent to the complexity of ecosystems. After a lively discussion on this subject, someone once sighed: "Just give me a freeze-dried talking fish on a stick" ("which I can simply put into the water and which will tell me everything about the quality of the water)." Ecotoxicology does not provide such simple "measuring sticks". It is possible, however, to apply a number of theories from modern ecology to the analysis of environmental problems, so that a differentiated and well-founded opinion can be formulated. Inevitably, this study unit can deal only briefly with these matters.

LEARNING OBJECTIVES

After studying this unit, you should be able to:

— give a description of the major concepts and terms
— indicate the subjects studied by ecotoxicology and the contribution made by various subdisciplines
— formulate in general terms what factors play a role in the accumulation of a substance in an organism and in the effects of substances on populations and ecosystems
— indicate the relative importance of these factors when applied to a specific example.

*Study hints*

If you are not familiar with certain concepts in this study unit, please consult an introductory book on environmental science and/or a book on biology (population biology/genetics). You are advised to use a calculator to work out the assignments in this study unit.

The study load is estimated at 4 hours.

STUDY CORE

## 1    Dispersal of substances in the environment

Many types of human activity cause the release of harmful substances or the alteration of the properties or quantities of normally harmless substances in such a way that they do become harmful. These substances need not always be manmade. Aluminum, for instance, is an integral component of the earth's crust and as such totally harmless. However, as soon as the aluminum in the soil dissolves due to continuous deposition of acidifying substances of anthropogenic origin, it may cause damage to plant roots.

*Xenobiotic*

Contaminants of the environment are often called *xenobiotic* (foreign to the body), although this term is frequently used incorrectly. Many metals, for instance, may be toxic in certain concentrations, but are required in small quantities for metabolism. It should also be pointed out that not all ecotoxic substances are intrinsically toxic. So-called *macrocontaminants* (e.g. phosphate, ammonia) create environmental problems because they greatly favor certain organisms, which means that other organisms are excluded and the ecosystem is disturbed.

*Macrocontaminants*

*Primary versus secondary pollutants*

A distinction is made between *primary pollutants* (substances as they are emitted) and *secondary pollutants* (substances formed in the environment under the influence of primary pollutants).

---

EXAMPLE

A well-known example is ozone, a substance which normally occurs in the atmosphere in low concentrations (20 $\mu$g m$^{-3}$). However, when the air is polluted by nitrogen oxides and hydrocarbons (released from motor traffic exhaust gases), ozone is formed in the air via photochemical reactions between these substances and oxygen. Its concentration may amount to 100 $\mu$g m$^{-3}$ and sometimes even to 350 $\mu$g m$^{-3}$, which is harmful to plants.

---

Table 39.1 lists a number of well-known substances and their main anthropogenic sources.

The concentration of a substance in the environment can be determined by means of chemical analyses. This is not as simple as is often thought, in particular in the case of microcontaminants. For many substances, appropriate methods of analysis are not even available. For instance, it was not until a reliable analytical method had been developed that the presence of the pesticide bentazon in the drinking water was discovered. For accurate analyses, the methods of various laboratories are calibrated by means of a so-called *round robin study*. This means that a well-mixed sample is divided into several portions, which are analyzed independently from each other in various laboratories.

*Round robin studies*

The concentration of a substance can be expressed in various units, depending on the medium. Table 39.2 shows some units together with the method of

TABLE 39.1

Examples of some categories of pollutants and their anthropogenic sources

| Category | Example | Major source |
|---|---|---|
| heavy metals | cadmium | metal processing industry |
| eutrophying substances | phosphate | domestic waste water |
| polycyclic aromatic hydrocarbons | benzo[a]pyrene | waste incineration |
| organic solvents | benzene | motor traffic |
| chlorinated organic compounds | polychlorinated biphenyls | large electrical installations |
| pesticides | acetylcholinesterase inhibitors | agriculture |
| air pollutants | sulfur dioxide | oil refining |
| climate-affecting substances | chlorofluorohydrocarbons | cooling systems |
| radioactive substances | cesium-137 | nuclear industry |

TABLE 39.2

Overview of units used to express the concentration of a substance

| Compartment | Units | Abbreviation | Conversion |
|---|---|---|---|
| air (gases) | $\mu g \ m^{-3}$ | | $1 \mu g \ m^{-3} = V/A \ \mu l \ m^{-3}$ |
| | $\mu mol \ m^{-3}$ | | $1 \ \mu mol \ m^{-3} = V \ \mu l \ m^{-3}$ |
| | $\mu l \ m^{-3}$ | ppbv | |
| | $\mu l \ l^{-1}$ | ppmv | |
| water | $\mu g \ l^{-1}$ | ppb | |
| | $mg \ l^{-1}$ | ppm | |
| | $\mu mol \ l^{-1}$ | $\mu M$ | $1 \ \mu mol \ l^{-1} = A \ \mu g \ l^{-1}$ |
| soil | $\mu g \ kg^{-1}$ | ppb | |
| | $mg \ kg^{-1}$ | ppm | |
| | $\mu g \ g^{-1}$ | ppm | |
| | $\mu mol \ g^{-1}$ | | $1 \ \mu mol \ g^{-1} = A \ \mu g \ g^{-1}$ |

A = molecular weight of the substance
V = molar volume at current pressure and temperature

conversion. The abbreviations ppm (parts per million, e.g. $\mu g \ g^{-1}$, $\mu l \ l^{-1}$) and ppb (parts per billion) should be avoided as they are rather confusing.

Concentrations should preferably be expressed in molar units, because the effect of a substance does not depend on the mass, but on the number of molecules. In practice, however, the molar unit system is still little used.

ASSIGNMENT 39.1

Table 39.3 gives some reference values for the concentrations of a number of substances in air, water and soil. Convert these values to molar units. Which of the two substances given for each compartment has the highest reference value?

The behavior of a substance in the environment (its fate) depends on many different factors. Between *emission* (discharge) and *immission* (exposure), a number of transport processes (also called *transmission*) take place, that can be grouped together as follows:

*Transmission*

*Distribution*

—*Distribution.* Due to physical factors (e.g. movement of water and air) or biological factors (e.g. fish and bird migration), immission and emission of a substance may occur at totally different locations. Air in particular allows substances to be distributed over very long distances (for example, the acidification of Swedish lakes as a result of sulfur dioxide discharge in Germany). Distribution

TABLE 39.3
Reference values for some substances in soil, water and air

| | |
|---|---|
| *soil (mg kg⁻¹)* | |
| cadmium (Cd) | 0.8 |
| cyanide (CN) | |
| 1.0 | |
| *water (µg l⁻¹)* | |
| arsenic (As) | 50 |
| lead (Pb) | 50 |
| *air (µg m⁻³)* | |
| ozone (O₃) | 100 |
| ammonia (NH₃) | 80 |

often means *dilution*, although this does not necessarily lead to the 'disappearance' of the substance. Many substances tend to spread very heterogeneously throughout the environment and may, after dilution, accumulate again elsewhere.

*Adsorption*

—*Adsorption.* Depending on its properties the substance will be distributed over the various compartments of the environment (soil, water, air). This distribution is primarily determined by substance properties such as *volatility, water solubility* and *lipophilicity* (affinity for lipids and dead organic material). These properties are expressed in partition coefficients such as the *Henry coefficient* for partitioning of a substance over water and gas, and the *octanol–water partition coefficient* for partitioning over an organic solvent and water. Adsorption may lead to both increase and reduction in exposure; the strong adhesion of some substances to the sediment on a river bed decreases the exposure of pelagic (free swimming) organisms, but increases that of the benthos (organisms that live in or on the bottom of a river).

*Transformation*

—*Transformation.* The chemical form in which a substance is emitted may change during transport due to physicochemical factors (e.g. sunlight) or biological factors (e.g. microorganisms). Such alterations are called *degradation* (also called decomposition), *biodegradation* (caused by biological factors), *photodegradation* (caused by light), etcetera. Substances which do not degrade or degrade very slowly in the environment are called *persistent.*

In addition to its toxicity, the persistence of a substance is one of the most important factors determining its harmfulness to the environment: a highly toxic substance which can easily be degraded may be less harmful to the environment than a much less toxic but very persistent substance. Transformation processes may cause a substance to lose its activity, but may also make it more toxic. A well-known example is the formation of methylmercury (a highly neurotoxic compound) from mercuric sulfide (a relatively harmless substance) by methane bacteria in the sediment of rivers and lakes.

*Bioavailability*

Ultimately, the transport processes lead to exposure of organisms and uptake of the substance. At that point *bioavailability* plays an important role. The *bioavailable fraction* of a substance is that part of the total concentration which can actually be taken up by an organism. The bioavailable concentration is often estimated on the basis of a series of extraction techniques, e.g. determination of the fractions which are soluble in water, in diluted acid, etc. This is called *fractional analysis*, or *sequential extraction*. In the case of heavy metals it is termed *speciation*: the distribution of a metal over the various chemical species (e.g. carbonate, hydroxide, chloride, etc.). Pesticides sometimes form a *soil-bound residue*; this is a fraction which adheres so strongly to the soil that it cannot be removed by extraction.

---

EXAMPLE

Binding of heavy metals in the soil roughly increases in the order Cd, Zn, Pb, Cu. This explains, for instance, why an element like Cd penetrates into biological tissues to a much greater extent than Pb. In addition, the extractability of most metals decreases with an increase in the clay content fraction of the soil particles < 2 $\mu$m or in the organic matter content (humus). The effect of the clay content can be explained by the fact that divalent cations bind to the negatively charged ends of aluminum-silicon crystals in clay particles. Humic substances (humic acids and fulvic acids) bind heavy metals because of the presence of many hydroxyl and carboxyl groups on the aromatic molecular structure. The different behavior of metals in the soil is also reflected in background concentrations in uncontaminated soils. In very humous, clayey soils higher concentrations are present than in sandy soils which are poor in humus. This is illustrated in Figure 39.2. It shows that at higher clay content background concentrations for both Cd and Cu increase; with Cu the effect is stronger than with Cd. This reflects the difference in these metals' affinity for the clay fraction of the soil material.

---

Even if the total amount of a substance remains constant, the bioavailable fraction may change due to a shift in the balance between the bound and soluble fractions. Acidification of the soil, for instance, causes the binding of heavy metals to clay particles to become weaker, resulting in an increase in the concentration in the water compartment. The source of a substance also plays a role in this respect: in general, heavy metals which are deposited onto the soil from the air are bioavailable to a much higher degree than metals originating from metal mining wastes. The total content of a substance is therefore only relatively significant unless other circumstances (type of soil, pH, source) are also speci-

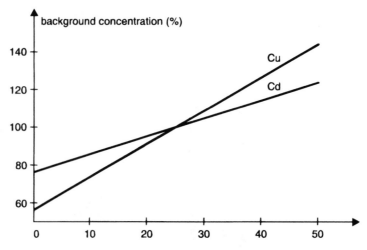

FIGURE 39.2
Background concentrations for copper and cadmium in a soil with an organic matter content of 10% in relation to the clay content of the soil.
The background concentrations are expressed as a percentage of the values applying to a soil with a 25% clay content. These values are 0.8 mg kg$^{-1}$ for Cd and 36 mg kg$^{-1}$ for copper.

fied. Nevertheless, government policies are almost exclusively based on total amounts.

ASSIGNMENT 39.2

Table 39.4 shows toxicity data of two chlorophenols for the earthworm *Lumbricus rubellus* in soils with different percentages of clay and humus. Explain the differences in toxicity between the two substances and between the soils in terms of environmental chemistry.

*Summary*

The behavior of a substance in the environment has a strong impact on the way in which organisms are exposed. The more strongly a substance adheres to solid components, the smaller—in general—its bioavailability. The balance between the available and the bound fractions may shift as environmental conditions change.

## 2 Accumulation of substances by organisms

The concentration of a substance present in an organism is determined by the balance between uptake, conversion and excretion. The residue depends both on the nature of the substance and on the organism. Some substances tend to accumulate strongly in the biota, while others do not; some organisms always contain many substances while others do not. One of the tasks of ecotoxicology is to formulate general rules on the basis of which it is possible to predict what type of substance tends to accumulate in what type of organism. Before discussing the relevant theory, however, it is necessary to define a number of concepts.

*Predicting accumulation*

—*Accumulation* is the process by which the amount of a substance present in an organism (the *body burden*) is increased during its lifetime because the uptake is greater than the sum of excretion and degradation. To distinguish it from the following type, this type of accumulation is also referred to as *accumulation sensu lato*.

*Accumulation*

*Accumulation sensu lato*

—*Accumulation sensu stricto* is the process by which, during the lifetime of an organism, not only the total body burden but also the concentration (burden per unit of weight) is increased. Because organisms change their body size, accumulation sensu lato does not necessarily lead to accumulation sensu stricto. It is even possible that the concentration decreases during life because a dose taken up at an early age is "diluted" due to increasing body weight.

*Accumulation sensu stricto*

—*Bioconcentration* is the phenomenon that the equilibrium concentration or average concentration of a substance in an organism is higher than that in the

*Bioconcentration*

TABLE 39.4

Toxicity of two chlorophenols for the earthworm *Lumbricus rubellus*, determined in two different soils.

|  | soil 1 | soil 2 |
|---|---|---|
| $LC_{50}$ 2,4,5-trichlorophenol (mg kg$^{-1}$) | 201 | 290 |
| $LC_{50}$ 2,3,4,5-tetrachlorophenol (mg kg$^{-1}$) | 514 | 828 |
| clay content of the soil (%) | 1.4 | 2.4 |
| humus content of the soil (%) | 3.7 | 6.1 |

*Bioconcentration factor*

surrounding environment. In the case of bioconcentration, it is always necessary to specify with what compartment of the environment the organism is compared (water, sediment, soil). The *bioconcentration factor (BCF)* indicates the ratio of the relevant concentrations (expressed in identical units).

*Biomagnification*

—*Biomagnification* is the phenomenon whereby the equilibrium concentration in an organism is higher than that in its food. In this case, one should always consider the whole organism. The observation that the concentration of a substance in the liver of a mole is higher than that in a whole earthworm does not necessarily indicate biomagnification. If expressed on the basis of the total body weight, the concentrations might be the same.

*Bioaccumulation*

—The term *bioaccumulation* is used to refer to a high concentration in an organism after absorption from both the medium (e.g. water) and food. The term is also used as a synonym of accumulation, biomagnification and bioconcentration; as a result, the term has become rather confusing and should be avoided.

---

EXAMPLE

The necessity of making a clear distinction between the concepts defined above can be proven by an example. The amount of lead in primitive soil organisms such as springtails increases continuously during their lives. In laboratory experiments, an equilibrium level is not reached until after a period of time which exceeds the average lifespan of the animals in the field. Even so, the highest level, which is reached in old animals, is still lower than the concentration in the surrounding environment (soil). This means that there is accumulation without bioconcentration.

---

ASSIGNMENT 39.3

If the concentration of a substance in an organism does not change with time, is it valid to say that the substance is *regulated* by the organism?

We will now concentrate on three factors which influence the extent to which an organism accumulates substances. These three factors are: position in the food chain, body size and physiological variables.

### 2.1 FOOD CHAINS

The organisms in a community can roughly be classified into various trophic levels, in which level i organisms feed on level i − 1 and are eaten by level i + 1.

Usually (but not always) the number of organisms and their collective biomass decrease towards the higher levels in the food chain. This ecological pyramid has been used to explain how the concentrations of persistent substances change. If, at the transition between levels of the food chain, there is loss of biomass (in the form of respiration), but not of a persistent substance, the substance will concentrate more and more and will reach high levels in top predators such as birds of prey (see Figure 39.3). This is the classic conception of biomagnification.

Data from various sources are in accordance with this theory. A classic example is the distribution of DDT residues over various organisms in a salt marsh habitat in the United States in the 1960s. The concentrations ranged from 0.00005 $\mu$g ml$^{-1}$ in the water, to 0.3 $\mu$g g$^{-1}$ in fish and 25 $\mu$g g$^{-1}$ in cormorants.

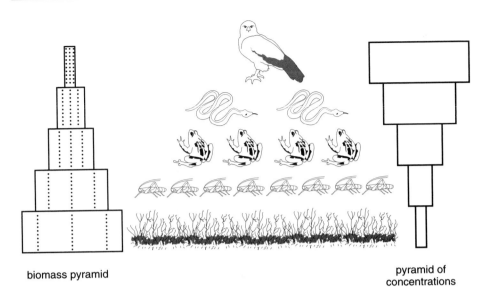

biomass pyramid

pyramid of
concentrations

FIGURE   39.3

Schematic representation of the way in which the concentration of persistent substances such as DDT might increase in a food chain (biomagnification)

Biomass pyramid on the left; inverted pyramid of concentrations on the right. According to theory, the same amount of DDT is concentrated in ever smaller amounts of biomass, as a result of which its concentration rises.

*Food webs*

The general validity of the principle of biomagnification has been strongly criticized in modern ecotoxicology. Firstly, organisms can virtually never be subdivided into clearly separate trophic groups; the term *food webs* is preferred to food pyramids. Secondly, the theory is unable to explain why there are great differences between species of one and the same trophic level. In the abovementioned study into the occurrence of DDT in salt marsh organisms, for example, a concentration of 5.43 $\mu$g g$^{-1}$ was found in the herring gull (*Larus argentatus*), while the concentration in a related gull species, *Larus delawarensis*, was 75.5$\mu$g g$^{-1}$.

Thirdly, various cases have been found where the concentration did not rise at higher levels of the food chain but in fact decreased. The concentrations of heavy metals in insects feeding on leaves or plant sap are nearly always lower than that in the plant itself.

*Critical transfer routes*

Food chain relationships may play a role in the so-called *critical transfer routes*. These are links in the food chain at which a predator depends upon a relatively limited choice of prey, which puts a heavy burden on the prey. This is most obvious in interactions with *saprophagous organisms* (organisms which feed on dead organic material). Examples are woodlice, feeding on dead leaves, moles, feeding on earthworms, and otters, feeding on eels.

### 2.2   BODY SIZE

Many ecological variables are related to the size of an organism. This is largely due to the fact that large organisms consume less per unit of body weight, produce less and have a lower metabolism than small organisms. If the metabolic rate (expressed as the calorific equivalent of the oxygen consumption per individual per day) of a large number of different animals is plotted against their body weights, the result is something similar to what is shown in Figure 39.4.

This shows that the oxygen consumption is not directly proportional to the size of an animal. The relationship is often described by a so-called power curve

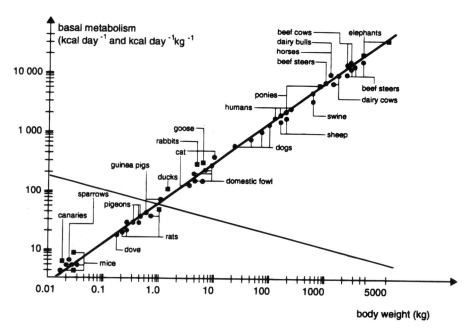

FIGURE   39.4

The basic metabolism of warm-blooded animals, in relation to their body weight

Metabolism is expressed in kcal per day (rising line) and in kcal per day per kg body weight (declining line).

which is expressed as:

$$y = aw^b$$

where

$y$ = oxygen uptake
$w$ = weight
$a$ = constant
$b$ = constant.

If the two variables are plotted logarithmically, the result is a straight line: log $y$ = log $a$ + $b$ log $w$, of which the slope $b$ is approximately 0.75 (see Figure 39.4). The oxygen uptake per unit of weight ($z$) equals $z = y/w = aw^{b-1}$. Since b < 1, $z$ decreases with increasing $w$. These relationships are called *allometric relationships* (relationships between the weight and another variable that is not directly proportional to the weight). The cause of the allometry lies in the changing ratio between surface area and volume in animals of different sizes. The volume of an animal is directly proportional to its weight, whereas its surface area increases with its weight to the power of 2/3. Since the uptake of energy takes place via a surface, and the energy consumption is determined by the volume, the metabolism is increased as a weighted sum of these two effects, which is in practice indistinguishable from an increase with the power of 0.75. Allometric relationships are also of importance in ecotoxicology because the uptake of a substance always takes place via a surface, and processing is proportional to metabolism.

*Generalizations*

On the basis of what has been stated above, the following *generalizations* can be made:

- When exposed to substances, *small organisms* will take up these substances rapidly as a result of their relatively large body surface area/body weight ratio. Small organisms, however, also have a relatively high metabolism; if this is relevant for the metabolism or excretion of the substance, its concentrations can also fall again quite rapidly.

- Large organisms will take up a relatively smaller amount of a substance, but by their relatively slow metabolism the substance will be eliminated slowly too. Persistent substances which are difficult to process will therefore eventually accumulate in large animals.

The effects of body size are in a way parallel to those of food chains, since animals in higher trophic levels are usually also larger. It is therefore difficult to distinguish between these two factors.

In practice, the importance of body size becomes apparent when substance levels in animals of the same species but from different areas are compared, if the animals from one area are larger than those from the other area. Figure 39.5 gives an imaginary example. It shows a clear difference in average concentration between the animals from different areas, but one should not conclude that animals are exposed to higher levels in area 2, since the difference can be attributed entirely to the difference in body weight.

## 2.3   PHYSIOLOGICAL VARIABLES

Modern ecotoxicology is more and more coming to the conclusion that the uptake and the residue of a substance in an organism are determined primarily by physiological variables. Physiological effects are superimposed upon any differences resulting from food chains and body weights, and may even completely undo or reverse the effects of those differences. The variables involved are mainly factors related to the uptake of a substance, the possibilities of internal storage, the presence of processing mechanisms and excretion routes. In the following, a number of examples will be presented of which there is relatively firm evidence that physiological differences between organisms are important for the differences in levels of xenobiotics found in them.

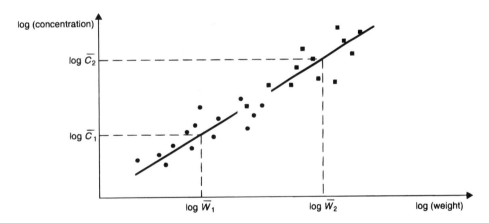

FIGURE   39.5
Fictitious example of a relationship between the body weight of an organism and the concentration of a substance
If the same organism is found in two different areas, but has a smaller body size in area 1 than in area 2, there is a seeming difference in burden.
$\bar{c}$ = mean concentration
$\bar{w}$ = mean weight

1123

*Specific mechanisms of uptake*

*Specific mechanisms of uptake* are of particular importance for substances which are taken up via a pathway which is really intended for another substance. Woodlice, for example, contain extremely high levels of copper; they build up a large copper reserve in certain cells of the hepatopancreas. This is probably related to the role played by copper in the oxygen-transporting blood pigment of these animals, hemocyanin. Because of their high copper demand, woodlice also take up large amounts of other heavy metals which are not necessary for their metabolism (Pb, Cd). Fungi (mushrooms) may also contain very high levels of heavy metals, which are related to their specific mineral requirements. The fly agaric (*Amanita muscaria*), for example, contains high levels of vanadium because it produces a specific vanadium-containing substance called amavadin.

*Storage capacity*

*Storage capacity.* The fat content of an animal is of importance for substances which have a high affinity for lipids, such as the well known organochlorine compounds PCBs, PCDDs and PCDFs. The more body fat an animal has the higher the body burden of these substances. For this reason, the level of highly lipophilic substances is often expressed not on the basis of the total body weight, but on the basis of the lipid weight. The term lipid, however, includes a heterogeneous collection of components; whether some lipids have a higher affinity for lipophilic substances than for others is unknown. For heavy metals, the presence of storage organs is of importance.

Cadmium, for example, accumulates in the liver in all higher animals, because that is where a specific protein, metallothionein, which binds the metal, is synthesized. In earthworms, heavy metals accumulate in the chloragogen tissue around the intestine, where they are bound inorganically in lysosomal structures which develop into intracellular granules.

*Processing mechanisms*

*Processing mechanisms.* Many aromatic compounds are converted within an organism to metabolites which are more water-soluble and which can be excreted after conjugation with an endogenous substance. The first step in these processes is often an oxidation reaction, for example hydroxylation. The enzyme system responsible for this (known as mixed-function oxidase or MFO) is not equally well developed in all animals. In general, the activity of the MFO system increases in the order fish, birds, mammals. In birds, there is a striking difference between fish-eating species and other species. It has been made plausible, for example, that the high levels of organochlorine compounds in the cormorant and other fish-eating birds are related to the poor metabolizing capacity of these animals.

*Excretion mechanisms*

*Excretion mechanisms.* The extent to which substances can be excreted varies greatly from one species to another. The adult stages of holometabolic insects (flies, butterflies, wasps), for example, generally contain low levels of heavy metals even if the larvae have been exposed to high levels of these. This is caused by the fact that shortly after pupation, the animal secretes *the meconium*, in which the waste products which have accumulated during the larval stage are concentrated. In springtails, a similar type of excretion takes place even at each ecdysis, by rejection of the intestinal epithelium. Other animals, such as mites and spiders, do not have such mechanisms at their disposal and therefore contain much higher levels.

EXAMPLE

As an example of the interrelation of the variables mentioned above (food chains, body size, physiology) the results are presented of a study into the PCB levels in various groups of organisms in a lake. The study examined sediment, water, plankton (mostly blue-green algae and water fleas), crustacea (mostly freshwater isopods and cladocera), mollusks (zebra mussels) and eels. A number of individual PCB congeners with varying degrees of chlorination were determined (indicated by the numbers 28, 52, 101, 138, 153 and 180)(Tables 39.5 and 39.6). The PCB levels were expressed on the basis of fresh weight and on the basis of lipid weight; for the sediment they were expressed on the basis of dry weight and the content of organic carbon, respectively.

ASSIGNMENT 39.4

How may the factors mentioned above have influenced the results shown in Tables 39.5 and 39.6? Which factor is decisive?

*Summary*

Xenobiotics have a tendency to distribute quite heterogeneously over various organisms. Factors influencing accumulation of substances in an organism include the following: position in the food chain, body weight, and the availability of certain physiological processing mechanisms.

## 3 Effects on populations and ecosystems

The greatest challenge to the science of ecotoxicology lies in predicting effects of substances on populations, communities and ecosystems. According to many, little progress has been made in this area, especially so because a great deal of basic knowledge on the structure and functioning of unstressed ecosystems is still lacking.

TABLE 39.5
PCB concentrations in sediment (ng PCB per g dry weight) and in organisms (ng PCB per g fresh weight) in a lake

| PCB number | 28 | 52 | 101 | 138 | 153 | 180 |
| chlorination | 2,4,4′ | 2,2′,5,5′ | 2,2′,4,5,5′ | 2,2′,3,4,4′5′ | 2,2′,4,4′,5,5′ | 2,2′,3,4,4′,5,5′ |
| --- | --- | --- | --- | --- | --- | --- |
| sediment | 1.35 | 2.34 | 4.09 | 13.74 | 7.21 | 3.37 |
| plankton | 0.23 | 0.30 | 0.53 | 0.69 | 0.54 | 0.22 |
| molluscs | 0.52 | 0.89 | 3.85 | 4.52 | 5.77 | 1.25 |
| crustacea | 2.93 | 3.15 | 4.31 | 4.18 | 3.97 | 0.80 |
| eel | 3.98 | 14.75 | 28.42 | 97.35 | 89.02 | 40.92 |

TABLE 39.6
PCB concentrations in sediment (ng PCB per g organic carbon) and in organisms (ng PCB per g lipid weight) in a lake.
Cf. legend of table 39.5.

| PCB number | 28 | 52 | 101 | 138 | 153 | 180 |
| --- | --- | --- | --- | --- | --- | --- |
| sediment | 17 | 25 | 42 | 129 | 65 | 33 |
| plankton | 68 | 102 | 206 | 259 | 209 | 60 |
| molluscs | 36 | 57 | 220 | 258 | 322 | 75 |
| crustacea | 362 | 400 | 532 | 529 | 505 | 107 |
| eel | 21 | 83 | 186 | 966 | 932 | 436 |

*Functional redundancy*

Ecosystems generally display a high degree of *functional redundancy*, which means that organisms can take over each other's function because food chains run parallel to each other and are linked to form food webs in various ways. In this way, all organisms contribute to the *diffuse stability* of an ecosystem. This is also expressed by the concept of *connectivity*, a measure for the "interlinkedness" of the food web. It is often suggested, however, that homeostasis of ecosystems also depends on mutualistic interactions between specialized organisms which have developed in co-evolution. Such relationships might be referred to as "*critical interactions*", i.e. interactions whose disturbance would have major consequences for the ecosystem as a whole. Examples are the mycorrhizal symbiosis between fungi and plant roots, the interaction between a predator and its prey, the competition for nutrients between various species of algae, etc.

*Connectivity*

*Resilience of a system*

The vulnerability of populations and ecosystems is also determined by the degree to which recovery is possible after a disturbance. This is referred to as the *resilience of a system*. It has proved extremely difficult to draw up general rules for this resilience. In the following sections, a number of aspects of effects on populations and ecosystems will be briefly discussed. First, the influence of substances on the structure of a population, in particular its genetic composition, will be discussed. After this, it will be explained how one can attempt to quantify and validate the effects on populations and ecosystems by means of ecotoxicological research.

## 3.1 SELECTION AND RESISTANCE

*Differences in sensitivity within a population*

The individuals within a population may display great *differences in sensitivity* to a substance, for instance because of differences in age, nutritional state, sex etc. These differences are largely physiologically determined. There are however also *genetically determined* (inheritable) *differences in sensitivity* between individuals. In the latter case, selection for resistant individuals will eventually lead to a locally adapted population, which is genetically different from other populations of the same species. Ultimately, toxic pollution can change a complete community by extreme selection.

*Consequences of genetically determined resistance*

Development of *genetically determined resistance* in a population may have a number of important consequences:

- resistance to pesticides may mean that higher dosages need to be used and that the burden on the environment is increased;

- development of resistance may require a certain metabolic effort ("the cost of resistance"). As a result, a population also changes in other respects, usually considered disadvantageous (e.g. reduced growth yield).

- it is often difficult for a genetically changed population to return to the original situation. After sanitation of a polluted area, recovery will take a shorter or longer period of time or not take place at all, depending on how the adaptation was brought about.

*Rate of resistance development*

The rate with which resistance may develop in a population is determined by the *genetic variation* in the original population (including the frequency of resistant types) and the *heritability* of the resistance. The latter parameters indicate how similar relatives (e.g. mothers and daughters) are to each other with respect to resistance, in comparison with non-related individuals. Also of importance are the relative *dominance* of the resistance as a genetic characteristic and the *selection pressure*. Often, resistance by selection initially develops only slowly. It gradually builds up ever more rapidly until, after many generations, a whole population has become resistant.

*Multiple resistance*

*Cross resistance*

Resistance to more than one substance may be classified as multiple resistance and cross resistance. In the case of *multiple resistance*, the resistances to various substances develop independently from each other, by simultaneous or successive exposure to each of the substances separately. The term *cross resistance* (also called co-tolerance) is used when a population not only becomes resistant to the substance to which it is exposed, but at the same time also to other substances to which it is not exposed. Cross resistance is an indication that substances have the same mode of action. Houseflies, for example, easily develop resistance to a whole group of insecticides at once, such as the cyclodienes (aldrin, dieldrin, endrin etc.).

The most complete information on development of resistance is available on plants (to heavy metals) and arthropods (to pesticides).

*Metal vegetation*

In the vicinity of metal ore mines, one always finds a specific vegetation, conpisting of metal-resistant ecotypes of plant species which form sensitive populations elsewhere. The number of species in which this phenomenon occurs is limited. Some examples are *Silene vulgaris* (bladder silene), *Agrostis capillaris* (common bent), *Thlaspi calaminare* (calamine pennycress) and *Armeria maritima* (common thrift). In the case of the calamine violet (*Viola calaminaria*), a separate species has even developed, which is found only on zinc-containing soils.

Metal-resistant vegetations are not only found near ore mines, but also in the vicinity of metal smelters.

*Resistance to insecticides*

The large-scale use of pesticides has led to the development of resistance in over 400 species of arthropods. It is remarkable that these species include only few parasites and predators. Phytophagous insects (which feed on plant leaves and sap), which are often pest insects, develop insecticide resistance much more rapidly and on a much larger scale. This has been associated with the fact that phytophagous insects, much more so than their natural enemies, are continuously confronted with toxic insect-repellant substances in the plant. It is conceivable that this is why these animals have developed a more flexible detoxication system, which also protects them from exposure to insecticides. The difficulty with which the natural enemies of pest insects develop resistance makes integrated control (by both biological and chemical means) a very complicated matter.

## 3.2 EFFECTS AT THE POPULATION LEVEL

A question often asked is whether a population of a certain organism will be more sensitive to a given concentration of a substance than the individual members of that population. From the following it would appear that this question cannot be answered in a general sense. Populations may show both sensitive and less sensitive reactions, depending on the circumstances. What is relevant here is the question of what factors make a population sensitive or not sensitive.

*Life-cycle toxicity tests*

*Intrinsic population growth rate*

For a sound estimate of population effects, the toxicity of a substance needs to be studied in all life stages of the organism. Such research is referred to as *life-cycle toxicity tests*. This can be done, for example, by rearing a number of newly-hatched young as a cohort at different concentrations of exposure, and monitoring any differences in survival, growth and reproduction. From the observations, one can calculate the so-called *intrinsic population growth rate* (often presented as *r*) from the following formulae:

$$R_0 = \sum_{i=0}^{i=n} l_i \cdot m_i$$

$$T = \frac{\sum_{i=1}^{i=n} i \cdot l_i \cdot m_i}{R_0}$$

$$r = \frac{\ln R_0}{T}$$

where

$l_i$ = survival up to age group $i$

$m_i$ = offspring produced in age group $i$

$n$ = number of age groups

$R_0$ = net replacement factor, also called net reproductive rate

$T$ = regeneration time, average age at which offspring is reproduced

$r$ = intrinsic population growth rate (increase per number present per time unit).

The intrinsic population growth rate is the increase in size of a population if survival and fertility were to remain time-invariant. This means that survival and fertility are age-dependent but not time-dependent. The net replacement factor is the factor by which the size of a population is multiplied after each generation time.

By calculating the value of $r$ for each exposure level, one gets an impression of the way in which the substance influences the population as a whole through its effects on the individual values of $l_i$ and $m_i$. Parameter $r$ gives, as it were, an integrated picture of the effects on survival and reproduction. Since the balance between mortality and reproduction is different for each individual organism, $r$ will react differently for each organism.

In addition to the population growth rate, other parameters have been developed by which the effects of substances on a population can be analyzed. The following parameters have proved important:

*Carrying capacity*

*Carrying capacity*, i.e. the maximum number of organisms which can live in a certain area

*Intrinsic biomass turnover*

*Intrinsic biomass turnover*, i.e. the ratio between the rate of production (growth + reproduction) of the organisms in a population (expressed in, for example, g m$^{-2}$ yr$^{-1}$) and the total biomass (expressed in, for example, g m$^{-2}$)

*Oscillation frequency*

*Oscillation frequency*, i.e. the frequency with which period fluctuations occur in a population. These fluctuations occur when a population reaches its maximum density and are caused by a delay in its regulatory mechanism. This oscillation frequency can be used as a measure for the effect of a substance. Another parameter used is the so-called "*pregnancy*" of the oscillations, a measure for the regularity of the fluctuation pattern.

As an example of the use of these parameters, Figure 39.6 shows the effect of pentachlorophenol (PCP) in reproduction experiments in the rotifer *Brachionus rubens*. The four parameters analyzed are found to react differently, with $r$ being the least sensitive and $p$ the most. The conclusion which can be drawn is that PCP has little influence on the growth rate of a population under optimum circum-

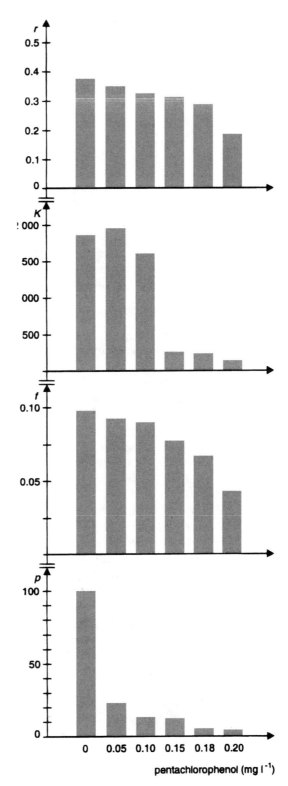

FIGURE 39.6
Effects of pentachlorophenol on the population growth rate (r), the carrying capacity (K), the oscillation frequency (f) and the pregnancy of the oscillation pattern (p) in reproduction experiments in the rotifer *Brachionus rubens*

stances, but that it does influence the average density reached after a certain length of time ($K$). PCP moreover has a very subtle effect on the development time of these animals, so that the population oscillates less regularly (effect on $p$).

This is an example of the 'magnifying glass effect' of population parameters: effects which are hardly discernible at the level of the individual organism are amplified to such an extent by the large number of organisms that they become clearly recognizable at population level.

ASSIGNMENT   39.5

Table 39.7 gives the life cycles of two hypothetical species. Suppose that both species are exposed to a toxic substance in the third year of their lives ($i = 2$). As a result, reproduction fails completely, without their chances of survival being affected. The organisms can compensate for this by having twice as many descendants as normal in the fourth year ($i = 3$). Which species is most affected by the substance, judging by the population growth rate $r$?

### 3.3   REGULATION MECHANISMS

*Effect of the substance*

As was stated above, not every population will react with equal sensitivity. The reaction appears to depend on the way in which a population is regulated and on the effect of the substance. As far as the substances are concerned, two different types of effect can be distinguished: effects on *reproduction* and effects on *survival*. Populations, can be classified as *food-regulated populations* and *predator-regulated populations*.

*Food-regulated population*

The individuals in a *food-regulated population* are well equipped to cope with temporary food shortages; they are able to postpone their reproduction if the food supply is insufficient for a certain period of time.

*Predator-regulated population*

Individuals in a *predator-regulated population* have a relative surplus of food. For the persistence of their population they depend primarily on continuous high reproduction. As a result, food-regulated populations are susceptible mainly to substances which influence survival, whereas predator-regulated populations are especially sensitive to substances which affect reproduction.

This manner of thinking leads to a balanced picture of the effects of substances in a community. In the case of organisms at the base of the food web, one tends to be very alert to effects of substances on reproduction, because this is of great importance to the persistence of such populations. Carnivores at the top of a food web, on the other hand, are by definition food-regulated. This means that they are very vulnerable, in particular to substances which shorten their life-

TABLE   39.7
Hypothetical life cycles of two species (A and B)

| $i$ | A | | B | |
|---|---|---|---|---|
| | $l_i$ | $m_i$ | $l_i$ | $m_i$ |
| 0 | 1 | 0 | 1 | 0 |
| 1 | 0.5 | 0 | 0.8 | 0 |
| 2 | 0.05 | 16 | 0.6 | 1 |
| 3 | 0.01 | 20 | 0.4 | 1 |

$l_i$ = survival up to age class $i$ (age in years)
$m_i$ = fertility in age class $i$

time. The extent to which populations are regulated by food will vary in time. A substance which affects survival is expected to be particularly effective in times of food shortage.

The development of a theory on population regulation has only recently taken a start within the field of ecotoxicology. There is little information with which to test such theories. Figure 39.7 gives one of the few examples. The population growth rate of the rotifer *Brachionus rubens* was measured at different food densities and at different concentrations of vanadate (a substance which particularly influences survival) and 3,4-dichloroaniline (a substance which primarily inhibits reproduction). For vanadate, a clear interaction has been found between food and exposure, whereas this is not so for 3,4-dichloroaniline. This is in accordance with the theory.

### 3.4 EFFECTS AT THE COMMUNITY LEVEL

*Species diversity*

As with effects at the population level, effects in communities are generally also measured using summarizing parameters which relate to the structure of the community. A commonly used structural characteristic is *species diversity*. Species diversity can be expressed in various indices, such as the number of species, the distribution of numbers of organisms among species, and the similarity to a reference situation as regards the species present. A common indice is the *Shannon and Weaver index of diversity*. The Shannon and Weaver index (denoted by *H*) measures the species diversity of a community by the proportions $P_i$ of each species *i* in the total number of individuals, making up *s* species together. The index is calculated from the formula:

$$H = -\sum_{i=1}^{i=s} P_i \cdot \log P_i$$

and is expressed in "bits" if the base of the logarithm is taken as 2, and in "decits" if the base of the logarithm is 10. *H* increases with increasing number of species and with increasing evenness of the distribution of individuals over species: a community of 100 individuals with 5 species, each counting 20 individuals is considered more diverse than a community of 100 individuals in which one species is represented by 96 individuals while the other four have only one. (Check this by calculating *H* for both cases.)

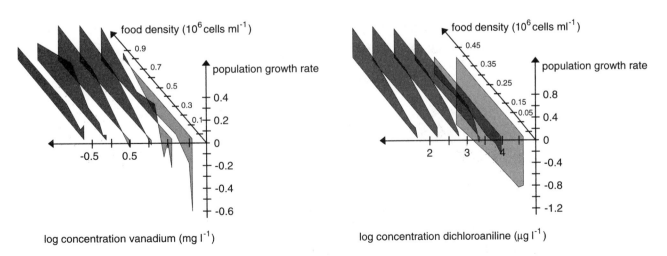

FIGURE 39.7
Effects of vanadate (left) and 3,4-dichloroaniline (right) on the population growth rate of the rotifer *Brachionus rubens*, at various food densities (expressed in the number of algae cells per ml of culture medium)

*Functional groups*

Many researchers are skeptical about the possibilities of applying structural characteristics of communities such as species diversity to estimate the gravity of a case of pollution. The assessment can be improved by classifying the organisms in a community into *functional groups* rather than counting them for each species. In a soil community, for example, the earthworms, mites and springtails can be distinguished into epigeal (living on the surface of the ground), hemiedaphic (living in the top soil) and euedaphic (living deep in the ground) groups. Effects of heavy metals are manifest in a reduction in the size of the hemiedaphic group to the advantage of the euedaphic group. In surface water, the ratio of zooplankton to phytoplankton is utilized. Eutrophication (enrichment with nutrients such as nitrate and phosphate) leads to dominance of phytoplankton and to reduced efficiency of the food web.

*Abundance biomass comparison (ABC) method*

A recently developed method of analyzing the effects of substances on communities is the so-called *ABC method (abundance biomass comparison)*. It involves constructing curves of a community, with the various species plotted on the x-axis in order of density, and the contribution made by each species to the total number and to the total biomass plotted cumulatively on the y-axis (see Figure 39.8). According to theory, in non-polluted systems the abundance curve lies

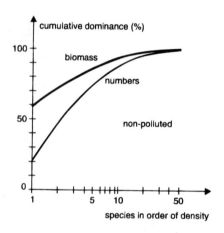

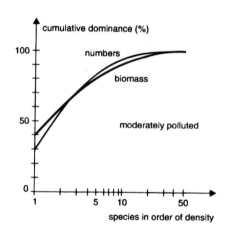

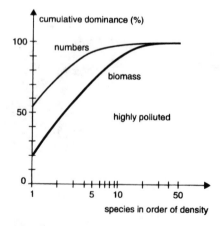

FIGURE 39.8

Dominance curves of the communities of unstressed (non-polluted), moderately polluted and highly polluted ecosystems

The x-axis shows the species in order of density, while on the y-axis, the contributions of each species to the total numbers and the total biomass have been plotted cumulatively.

beneath the biomass curve, while in highly polluted systems, the abundance curve lies above that for biomass. In other words, pollution leads to a shift of the community towards large numbers of small, opportunistic, species.

When applied to the benthic (i.e. living on the bottom) macrofauna of the Wadden Sea, the ABC method was found to be quite suitable for biological quality assessment. A weak point of the theory is that it is difficult to distinguish moderately polluted systems from non-polluted systems in an early stage of ecological succession. The reason is that in the course of community development (from the pioneer stage to a climax situation) shifts take place that correspond to a pollution gradient from moderately to non-polluted in the ABC method. In other words, because of pollution, a community is inhibited from normal development and continues to consist of small, rapidly growing species with a good capacity for colonization and recovery. This situation is very recognizable in polluted surface waters such as the river Rhine. Ecotoxicological effects at the level of communities are more difficult to predict than effects at the population level. A consistent theory has yet to be developed. Analysis of the functional groups in a community seems to offer a better perspective than analysis of the species present.

---

EXAMPLE

Under the influence of acidification, many communities are presently undergoing drastic changes, with alkalophilic species making way for acid-tolerant species. In freshwater pools affected by acid deposition, for example, the water flea *Bosmina longispina* is common, while undisturbed waters are characterized by the presence of *Bosmina longirorostris*. Among the water plants, the shoreweed *Littorella uniflora* gives way to a peat moss, *Sphagnum cuspidatum*. Such shifts in species have direct consequences for the ecological functioning of a pool if the new species belong to a different functional group than the old ones. This is probably not the case for the water fleas, but it is so for the aquatic plants.

---

### 3.5 EFFECTS AT THE ECOSYSTEM LEVEL

*Model ecosystems*

Because effects at the ecosystem level can be predicted only in very general terms, so-called *model ecosystems* are used extensively. These are also known as *micro-ecosystems*, *microcosms* or *mesocosms*.

Designing a model ecosystem is a matter of balancing between two extremes. On the one hand, the system should function as a model of the real ecosystem, and should therefore display a certain degree of complexity. On the other hand, it should be simple enough to experiment with and obtain reproducible results. According to some researchers, it is impossible to combine these two extremes in one system. The great variety of different approaches is apparent from the following enumeration.

*Large-scale model systems*

*Large-scale model systems.* In rare cases, experiments are carried out with virtually complete ecosystems. An example is the Little Rock Lake Acidification Experiment. A lake in the north of the United States was divided in two by a screen, after which one half of the lake was artificially acidified. The sprinkling experiments carried out within the framework of Swedish and Norwegian acidification research program also fall into this category. In general, this type of experiment suffers from lack of replication, and the results are difficult to interpret.

*Enclosures*

*Enclosures* are systems which are closed off in some way or other, but which are otherwise exposed to the same conditions as the real ecosystem. Examples are marine model plankton ecosystems consisting of large plastic bags with a volume of several cubic meters, which are filled with natural sea water, and suspended outside in the water. In the terrestrial environment, enclosures take the form of fenced experimental fields or plots divided into compartments by steel plates.

*Ponds, streams and ditches*

*Ponds, streams and ditches* are frequently used systems in analyzing the fate and effects of pesticides in an aquatic environment. In principle, limited replication is possible, while the relatively small scale renders the systems reasonably manageable. The larger systems tend to be situated outdoors where they enjoy the advantage of natural environmental conditions (light, temperature). The size of the facilities varies greatly from one study to another; large scale setups are present in only a few institutes because of the large investments in equipment and personnel necessary to maintain the facility.

*Microecosystems*

*Microecosystems* are systems which are set up and studied in a laboratory, which is greatly to the advantage of the reproducibility and manipulability of the experiments as compared with field work. A microecosystem for soil, for example may consist of a relatively small column of soil (5 to 10 centimeter in diameter) in which microbial activity can be studied in relation to the activity of soil animals. These systems are also used to analyze the behavior of the substances in the soil profile, specifically their leaching out of the column.

The results of tests with model ecosystems do not allow general conclusions concerning effects of substances on ecosystems yet. In general, model ecosystems have been found not to be more sensitive, and in fact usually to be less sensitive to toxic substances than the individual species. The following points should be taken into account in this connection:

- The *burden* in complicated systems disappears rapidly after administration, because the substance is degraded or is somehow rendered biologically unavailable (attachment to suspended silt, conversion into insoluble products). In laboratory experiments, the burden is usually maintained as constant as possible.
- Because of the labor intensiveness of keeping track of all the species in complex *communities*, sum parameters are often used. By doing so, *effects on individual, susceptible species* may be overlooked.
- The design of the experiments (limited possibilities for replication) often makes it difficult to distinguish statistically between the effects found and *normal biological variation*.
- Depending on the circumstances, a *population* may be less sensitive than the *individuals* of which it is composed (see above).

*Summary*

With rising levels of integration (population—community—ecosystem) the effects of toxic substances become more difficult to predict. The best-developed theory is that based on age-structured populations; it can be used to account for effects observed in chronic toxicity experiments in population parameters.

## 4    Ecotoxicological risk assessment

The results of ecotoxicological research find application in a variety of decisions and procedures in environmental policy, such as admission of pesticides, setting standards for maximum acceptable concentrations, support of emission-restricting measures, testing of activities with major consequences for the environment, spotting of new environmental problems, etc. Much attention is currently being paid to risk assessment.

See also Study unit 14

Governmental policy in Western Europe and the US is based on the assumption that compounds hazardous to the environment may carry certain risks for both man and the environment; as a next stage, the policy aims to quantify these risks and to restrict them to a minimum, i.e. render them controllable. Risk assessment is an area which is still very much in the development stage. We will restrict ourselves to a general outline.

In ecotoxicological risk assessment, the probability is calculated of a certain undesired event taking place. For example, the chance is calculated that a person will die as a result of an explosion in a factory at a certain distance. Another example is calculation of the chance that an arbitrary species in a community is exposed to a concentration which is higher than its NOEC (no-observed-effect concentration). This example will be discussed in the following sections.

The *probability* that one of the species in a community is exposed to an *unacceptable concentration* can be divided into two components:

- the probability that the concentration in the environment exceeds a certain value
- the probability that the NOEC of a species is lower than that certain value.

The first component can be estimated by using environmental chemical models. These models take into account the most important physicochemical processes, such as volatilization, adsorption, degradation, water movement, etc. They make it possible, for example, to predict the course of the concentration of a substance in a river after discharge as a result of an accident. It is also possible to calculate the deposition of acidifying substances at a certain distance from a source of air pollution. Such calculations are called *exposure assessment*.

*Exposure assessment*

The second component of risk assessment is much more difficult to estimate. One has to rely solely on the results of laboratory experiments in which only a very limited number of organisms have been tested. Recently, models have become available with which the variation in sensitivity can be estimated within a community on the basis of the mean and standard deviation of a body of toxicity data (NOEC, $LC_{50}$).

An example of ecotoxicological risk assessment which was carried out more or less according to this procedure is provided in Figure 39.9. On the basis of toxicity data for cadmium for a number (7) of invertebrate soil animals, a calculation was carried out of the percentage of species that were not affected by a certain concentration of cadmium in the soil. If this concentration is very low, all species are protected against effects (left in Figure 39.9). If it equals the average NOEC (9.4 $\mu$g g$^{-1}$), 50% are protected (right). The $HC_5$ (*hazardous concentration for 5% of the species*) is the concentration corresponding with a protection level of 95%. The curve shows that $HC_5 = 0.16$ $\mu$g g$^{-1}$; this is lower than the reference value for clean soil used by the authorities (0.8 $\mu$g g$^{-1}$). It can be concluded from this that even a minor increase of the present background levels for cadmium will threaten the functioning of some susceptible soil organisms.

*$HC_5$ (hazardous concentration for 5% of the species)*

### ASSIGNMENT 39.6

If the risk assessment procedure described above is used to calculate the $HC_5$ value for the concentration of a pesticide in

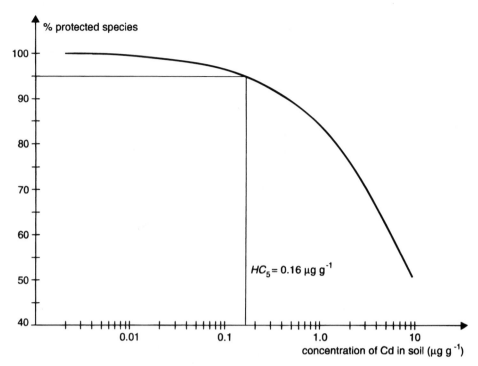

FIGURE   39.9

The estimated percentage of species in a soil community which are not affected by a certain concentration of cadmium in the soil

The curve was calculated from toxicity data for soil invertebrates (earthworms, springtails, etc.) according to a model described in N.M. van Straalen and C.A.J. Denneman (1988), 1st European Conference on Ecotoxicology, Copenhagen.

the soil, very low values are found for some compounds, which in the actual use of the pesticides are exceeded by far. What other criteria should be included in ecotoxicological evaluation of pesticides?

*Summary*

By means of ecotoxicological risk assessment, it is possible to calculate the chance that certain undesired effects on the environment will occur. The environmental risk is determined on the basis of the predicted concentration of a substance in the environment and the distribution of sensitivity in a community.

SELF ASSESSMENT QUESTIONS

1   Which disciplines form part of ecotoxicology and what is the contribution of each of them?

2   Express the following concentrations in molar units: 1 ppm methane in air, 1 ppm cadmium in soil, 1 ppm phosphate in water.

3   Which three transmission processes determine the fate of a substance between emission and immission?

4   What is the difference between bioconcentration and biomagnification?

5   What characteristics of an organism are of importance for the accumulation of lipophilic substances?

6   What factors determine the rate at which a population develops resistance to toxic substances?

7   From the example provided in Table 39.7, calculate how the population growth rate will be affected by a substance which halves the chance of survival from the third to the fourth year for both species.

8   What is the difference between protection aimed at the structure and protection aimed at the function of ecosystems? What would be the best approach in ecotoxicological risk assessment of substances in the environment?


FEEDBACK

1   **Answers to the assignments**

39.1 Using Table 39.2 and the atomic weights which can be found in a handbook of tables, the values can be converted as follows:

cadmium: $0.8$ mg kg$^{-1}$ = $7.1$ $\mu$mol kg$^{-1}$

cyanide: $1.0$ mg kg$^{-1}$ = $38.5$ $\mu$mol kg$^{-1}$

arsenic: $50$ $\mu$g l$^{-1}$ = $0.67$ $\mu$mol l$^{-1}$

lead: $50$ $\mu$g l$^{-1}$ = $0.24$ $\mu$mol l$^{-1}$

ozone: $100$ $\mu$g m$^{-3}$ = $2.1$ $\mu$mol m$^{-3}$

ammonia: $80$ $\mu$g m$^{-3}$ = $4.7$ $\mu$mol m$^{-3}$

Whether one substance has a higher reference value than the other thus depends on the units in which the concentrations are expressed.

39.2 As the degree of chlorination of chlorophenol increases, its lipophilicity also increases. For this reason, high-chlorinated phenols adhere more firmly to dead organic material in the soil than low-chlorinated congeners. Since the earthworm takes up substances from the soil pore water via the skin, the more water-soluble compounds are more toxic than those with low water solubility. It is also for this reason that the same chlorophenol is less toxic in a soil rich in humus (soil 2) than in one poor in humus (soil 1). For this type of substance, the clay content is not of such importance.

39.3 No. Regulation is a term which is only used if the internal concentration is, within certain limits, independent of the external concentration. For xenobiotics, this is usually not the case; if the concentration in the environment increases, the internal concentration is also increased (up to a new steady state level).

39.4 The data show that the concentrations expressed in weight units of lipid are higher than those expressed in total fresh weight. This reflects the fact that the PCBs are primarily associated with the adipose tissue of organisms. There is no univocal connection between the lipophilicity of the PCB (which increases with rising chlorination) and the ratio between the sediment concentration and the concentration in the organisms. Biological factors apparently dominate over the behavior which is expected on the basis of substance properties. For plankton, the small size and rapid turnover of the organisms are probably important factors. PCBs do not get the opportunity to accumulate in organisms with such a short life-span. The difference between molluscs and crustacea indicates a physio-logical difference in metabolic processing capacity (possibly MFO activity). The striking difference in behavior between the individual PCBs is even more difficult to explain. The eel concentrates mainly the highly chlorinated congeners, while the low-chlorinated forms tend to accumu-late in crustaceans. The results show that both body size and physiology are important, but at the same time demonstrate that our knowledge is still insufficiently developed to predict the precise behavior of an indi-vidual substance.

39.5 In the unburdened situation, $R_0 = 1$ and $r = 0$ for both species, as may be expected under field conditions. After failure of reproduction in the third year and compensation by doubling of the reproduction in the fourth year, $R_0 = 0.01 \times 40 = 0.4$, $T = 3$ years, $r = -0.305$ per year for species A, and $R_0 = 0.4 \times 2 = 0.8$, $T = 3$ years, $r = -0.074$ per year for species B.

Species A thus suffers much more from the substance, despite its great effort in the fourth year. This example illustrates that species which are highly dependent on a continuous high reproduction for the maintenance of their population are affected in particular by substances which have a direct effect on reproduction.

39.6 The situation described is caused by the fact that pesticides are never en-tirely selective and therefore always have side effects, especially on sus-ceptible species. An additional criterion in the assessment of pesticides is the question whether the undesired side effects will have been recovered within a reasonable period of time.

## 2 Answers to the self assessment questions

1 Environmental chemistry: analysis of substances in the environment and their fate
Toxicology: analysis of internal distribution and modes of action
Ecology: evaluation of effects at the level of populations, communities and ecosystems.

2 1 ppm methane in air = 45 $\mu$mol m$^{-3}$ at 0°C and 1 atm (molar volume = 22.4 l); 1 ppm Cd in soil = 8.9 $\mu$mol kg$^{-1}$ (atomic weight of Cd is 112.4); 1 ppm phosphate in water = 10.5 $\mu$mol l$^{-1}$ (molecular weight of phos-phate is 95).

3 Distribution, adsorption and transformation.

4 In the case of bioconcentration, an organism is compared with its envi-ronment (water, soil); in the case of biomagnification, an organism is com-pared with its food.

5 The fat content of an organism (and possibly the type of lipid) and the pres-ence of physiological processing mechanisms such as the mixed function oxidase system. In addition, body size (the body surface area in relation to body weight) may influence uptake, while the position in a food chain is of importance for exposure.

6    The genetic variation in the original population, the heritability of the re-
     sistance, the relative dominance and the selection pressure.

7    For species A: $R_0 = 0.05 \times 16 + 0.005 \times 20 = 0.9$, $T = 2.1$ year, $r = -0.050$ per
     year, and for species B: $R_0 = 0.6 \times 1 + 0.2 \times 1 = 0.8$, $T = 2.3$ year, $r = -0.097$
     per year. This means that the substance concerned has a greater effect on
     species B than on species A (cf. assignment 39.5).

8    A protection strategy aimed at the structure primarily attempts to main-
     tain the species composition of a community, while a strategy aimed at the
     function attempts to maintain such processes as photosynthesis, decom-
     position, etc. Protection of the structure of an ecosystem is probably suffi-
     cient guarantee for protection of functions, where the reverse is certainly
     not true.

# Contents Study unit 40
# Occupational toxicology

# Occupational toxicology

*P. J. A. Borm and P. Th. Henderson*

INTRODUCTION

*Industrial toxicology*

*Industrial toxicology* is a subdiscipline of toxicology concerned primarily with the health hazards caused by industrial chemicals. It covers all substances which have any kind of industrial application. Its field of application is not restricted to the chemical industry, where millions of tons of chemicals are synthesized every year, but also includes processing and treatment of materials in many other types of industrial plants, including natural substances and minerals.

It was pointed out centuries ago that workers in the mining industry who came into contact with a variety of metals and other elements tended to develop specific diseases. The symptoms regularly observed as a result of contact with arsenic and mercury in the mining industry were described in detail by Paracelsus in his 1567 treatise "Von der Bergsucht und anderen Bergkrankheiten" (miner's sickness and other diseases of mining). A work from the same period, "De Re Metallica" by Georgius Agricola (Georg Bauer, 1556), deals with the health aspects of working with metals. Agricola even considered the preventive aspects, such as wearing protective clothing (masks) and using ventilation.

One result of industrial progress in the last century was the increased use of chemicals not occurring in nature. The first ones to assume a significant share of the market were synthetic dyestuffs.

It soon became apparent that some of the chemical intermediates used in the synthesis of dyestuffs, especially aniline derivatives, could cause bladder cancer in the workers concerned. This occupational disease was properly called "aniline cancer". It was later found that the bladder tumors were probably caused by other aromatic amino compounds such as benzidine and 2-naphthylamine.

Occupational exposure to PAH (polycyclic aromatic hydrocarbons, the main constituents of coal tar products) is a subject of continuing interest to (industrial) toxicologists.

At virtually every workplace substances can be found that carry a toxicological risk. Even office staff are not exempt from exposure to chemicals, considering the frequent use of correction fluids containing trichloroethane in the typing pool, and the exposure to ozone emitted by photocopiers. Hence, the term increasingly used is *"occupational"* toxicology rather than *industrial* toxicology. In this study unit the two terms will be used interchangeably. Because chemicals are so widely used, does this mean that the very fact of having a job will lead to poisoning or ultimately to an occupational disease? Fortunately not; *chemical* does not necessarily mean *toxic*, and "toxic" does not have to be synonymous

*Occupational toxicology*

with *dangerous*. One of the tasks of occupational toxicology is to make fine distinctions of this kind and put any risks into perspective. The main objectives of occupational toxicology may be described as follows:

- to collect and interpret all the data needed to identify toxic hazards at work. This may be achieved by studying the literature, by laboratory or field research or by examination of the workers concerned;
- to eliminate established hazards or minimize them as far as possible.

From the above it will be apparent that occupational toxicology is very much a practical field and relies on multidisciplinary cooperation.

LEARNING OBJECTIVES

After completing this study unit you should be able to

— describe the field covered by occupational toxicology
— describe its relationship to other disciplines of toxicology and medicine
— describe the various types of investigation in occupational toxicology, the areas to which each method of investigation is best suited and the possibilities and limitations of each method
— state the objectives of environmental and biological monitoring
— give examples of environmental and biological monitoring, stating what the two forms of monitoring have in common and how they differ
— illustrate, by means of examples, the following terms commonly used in occupational toxicology:

  plant survey

  exposure test

  categorial data

  intervention study

  cohort study

  case control study

  MAC

— describe how health monitoring is carried out in practice
— describe the role of epidemiological research in occupational toxicology and illustrate, by means of examples, the different approaches it uses in occupational toxicology
— name the risk factors on exposure in occupational toxicology
— explain the sex-linked risks due to occupational exposure from differences in physiology
— explain why carcinogens are particularly important in occupational toxicology.

*Study hints*

This study unit explains many concepts and methods commonly used in occupational toxicology. Try to understand what the terms mean and work out for yourself the context of the methods used. Because occupational toxicology is a field geared primarily to practical applications, you will meet with many terms which have already been discussed before. The subject matter is related in particular to that of Study units 2 and 13. There is a large body of text to be read in this study unit, and the estimated study load for it is 4 1/2 learning hours.

STUDY CORE

## 1  The role of the industrial toxicologist in occupational health care

In the light of the objectives described above, occupational toxicology may be regarded as an important element in occupational health care.

*System-linked and non-system-linked stimuli*

The healthy functioning of human beings at work depends at all times on a variety of influences, both positive and negative. These influences may be divided into *system-linked and non-system-linked stimuli*. Examples of system-linked stimuli are light, noise, humidity, ambient temperature, but also physiological factors such as physical movement and muscle loads. These are continuously needed factors, and both an upper and a lower limit can be set for the load which can be tolerated by the worker. The aim here must always be an optimum level (the ergonomic approach). Non-system-linked stimuli, by contrast, are in no way necessary. Examples of these are ionizing radiation, mechanical vibrations and (toxic) foreign chemicals. These effects can never be beneficial and may even be harmful, especially if a certain exposure limit of intensity or duration is exceeded. For these stimuli, then, there is no lower limit, but only an upper limit. The ideal must always be no exposure at all (zero exposure).

The search for solutions to problems concerning chemical health hazards at the work place necessitates close cooperation between toxicologists, hygienists and clinicians. The division of responsibilities amongst the disciplines in question may be summarized as follows (see also Figure 40.1):

*Occupational toxicology*

*Occupational toxicology*—assessing risks in specific situations on the basis of data from literature or the results of the toxicologists' own investigations; determining *exposure levels* for toxic substances on the basis of health criteria; carries out relevant *research*.

*Occupational hygiene*

*Occupational hygiene*—is concerned with *exposure monitoring* and thus more with the occupational environment (ambient factors) and the work process; records levels of toxic substances at the workplace in order to prevent limit values being exceeded; prevents exposure or keeps it at a minimum.

*Occupational medicine*

*Occupational medicine*—monitors the health and promotes the well-being of workers as individuals and as a group, using medical knowledge of disease and health and toxicological and occupational health data.

Lastly, it should be noted that employers and employees too have a major part to play in all this, e.g. highlight any possible problems, and one which is laid down by law (Occupational Safety and Health Act, Health and Safety at Work

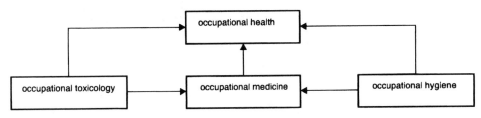

FIGURE   40.1
Disciplines involved in occupational health

Act, Control Of Substances Hazardous to Health Regulations). This will be looked at more closely in the section on legislation (4.6).

## 1.1   INDUSTRIAL TOXICOLOGY RESEARCH

Industrial toxicology is primarily a preventive science. All its activities are always aimed at the question: how can we handle industrial chemicals in such a way that there is no risk to the workers' health? To answer this question a series of data is needed which may be listed as follows:

- data pertaining to the *substance*(s) handled
- data pertaining to the work situation, particularly to *exposure*
- data pertaining to the *individuals* who come into contact with the substance(s).

These points are elaborated on below in a number of questions with the corresponding answers.

*What substance*

1. *What substance* is involved?
   Experience shows that it is often very difficult to identify the toxic agent.

ASSIGNMENT   40.1

Why might it not be easy to identify a toxic agent within a company or plant?

*Inventory*

If chemical risks within a company are to be manageable, the first thing needed is a reliable *inventory* of all foreign chemicals present. This list has to be constantly updated (in cooperation with the purchasing department), but is not conclusive. There may also be, for example, intermediate products manufactured by the company itself.

*Physico-chemical properties*

2. What are the *physicochemical properties*?
   Once substances have been identified, their properties can usually be found in manuals of chemistry and physics. In many cases it will be important to know not only their volatility, vapor pressure and solubility (in water, oil, etc.) but also their particle size and stability.

*Toxic properties*

3. What are the *toxic properties*?
   Where toxicity data are known, these generally relate to research on experimental animals. They have to be extrapolated to man. Other important data are those on the mode of action. Are effects observed after short-term exposure or after chronic exposure? Where do the substances act (respiratory tract, liver, offspring)? What is the relationship between exposure and the probability of an effect? In other words, what is known about a dose-response relationship? These questions frequently necessitate further experimental research.

*Contact with the substance*

4. How do workers come into *contact with the substance* in question?
   What are the routes of exposure and uptake? Depending on their physico-chemical properties and processing practices within the plant, substances may be absorbed by inhalation or via the skin. In a few cases both routes are important, for example in exposure to hydrogen cyanide gas, which is very lipophilic. Whether exposure takes place via the oral route often depends on personal hygiene, conditions of hygiene at work and a variety of behavioral factors (washing the hands, smoking, eating whilst working, etc.). The answers to the above questions are usually based on thorough observation and analysis of the work situation.

It is also possible for larger inhaled particles to enter the mouth and throat via mucociliary transport and subsequently be swallowed (secondary ingestion).

*Identifying chemical exposure*

5. How can *chemical exposure* be identified?

The presence of a chemical substance within work premises does not necessarily mean there is exposure to it, and exposure does not in itself imply uptake by the organism. Both of these can be ascertained by measurements. The various methods available are referred to collectively as *exposure monitoring*. A distinction is drawn between *environmental monitoring* (measurements in the area in which a person works) and *biological monitoring* (measurements on the person himself).

*Early detection*

6. How can effects be detected at an early stage?

This question can be answered on the basis of data obtained from research on exposed individuals. How the study findings are interpreted will depend very much on the effect measured. Methods include biological effect monitoring, function tests (liver, kidney, lung), complaint patterns, morbidity data (e.g. absenteeism) and mortality data.

These questions will be discussed in more detail below. Section 2.1 deals with the methods of investigation used in a so-called "plant survey".

## 2 Exposure monitoring

### 2.1 ENVIRONMENTAL STUDIES

Efficient exposure monitoring usually begins with a study of the environment, with special emphasis on the presence of any chemical contaminant. It is becoming increasingly important to measure the levels of (potentially) toxic substances in the atmosphere in which people live and work.

Environmental studies to identify toxicological risks at the workplace or in the environment are usually carried out by monitoring levels of the components deemed the most significant. Whether certain exposures should be deemed relevant is determined by a "plant survey" which investigates every stage of the production process and exposure conditions. From this survey and the chemical characteristics of the substance in question a measurement strategy can then be devised. This strategy will of course depend on the objective of the measurement (epidemiology, prevention of lethal concentration peaks, compliance with standards).

Toxic substances in the atmosphere around us and at the workplace may present themselves in a number of physical forms.

> ASSIGNMENT 40.2
>
> Which are the physical forms in which toxic substances may present themselves in our working environment?

Because our senses are unable to detect many toxic substances (e.g. CO) or are not sufficiently sensitive (odor threshold), monitoring of the workplace and the environment generally employs a sixth sense: instrumentation (see Table 40.1).

*Environmental monitoring*

In studies at the workplace, *environmental monitoring* usually entails measurement of the ambient *air*. This type of monitoring may be used for a number of different purposes, and these purposes will implicitly determine the content and

TABLE 40.1
Substances with a high odor threshold in relation to their toxicity

|  | MAC (ppm) | Odor threshold (ppm) | Odor safety factor |
|---|---|---|---|
| carbon monoxide | 50 | 100 000 | 0.0005 |
| vinyl chloride | 3 | 3 000 | 0.001 |
| methyl isocyanate | 0.02 | 2.1 | 0.009 |
| hydrogen arsenide | 0.05 | 0.5 | 0.10 |
| phosgene | 0.1 | 0.9 | 0.11 |
| chloroform | 10 | 85 | 0.12 |
| toluene 2,4-diisocyanate | 0.02 | 0.17 | 0.12 |
| ethylene oxide | 50 | 430 | 0.12 |
| methylacrylonitrile | 1 | 7 | 0.14 |
| hydrogen selenide | 0.05 | 0.3 | 0.17 |

designation of the monitoring program employed. In the following, a number of purposes are listed which are frequently combined:

1. protection of the worker against acute or chronic effects of exposure
2. monitoring of compliance with standards (TLV-TWA, TLV-C, MAC-TWA; MAC-C) or other mandatory regulations
3. acquiring information on employee exposures
4. record-keeping to enable later epidemiological follow-up and to establish correlations with medical abnormalities or complaints.

*Stationary and personal monitoring*

Depending on the monitoring objective, the sophistication of current technology, the properties of the substance and the characteristics of the workplace, one can choose between two types of monitoring: *stationary* and *personal*.

### 2.1.1 Plant survey

A plant survey aimed at exposure to potentially toxic substances is an absolute must when it comes to assessing health risks to exposed workers. This type of survey may be conducted from a number of viewpoints. The ultimate design will also depend very much on the kind of company or plant concerned. In the following, only the detection of exposure and possible health risks from toxic agents in the chemical industry is discussed. Roughly, the following successive steps may be distinguished:

*Screening*

1. Screening of all the chemicals used in a given plant, to be broken down by:
   - plant, location
   - production process
   - type of technological process (open or closed, granulator)
   - quantity used or produced.

*Collecting data*

2. Collecting data on material safety data sheets, containing:
   - toxicological information
   - risks from chronic or acute exposure
   - standards for exposure.

*Priorities*

3. Prioritization on the basis of the information collected under 1 and 2. In simple cases this may be a matter of pure common sense (e.g. where there is exposure to just one or two substances). Usually, hundreds of substances are used in a chemical plant. In that case a model scoring system is used,

*Walk-through survey*

in which a high score indicates a high priority. The chemical giant Du Pont, for example, uses a scale of priorities which is represented as Table 40.2.

4.   A walk-through survey is an on-the-spot review of the situation and discussion with technical and production personnel who are fully conversant with all aspects of the production process. This also provides a picture of the plant's dimensions, distances and secondary working conditions.

A scale of priorities like this, naturally depends on a large number of factors and hence is rather specific to the plant concerned. It must therefore be realized that this kind of protocol is a method to structure the assessment of health hazards. Priority scores must not be an end in themselves and one must always be on the look-out for pitfalls inherent in the system.

---

EXAMPLE

Nancy Wilkinson has recently been appointed occupational hygienist in the occupational health department at International Chemicals, Inc. After having been shown round the affiliated plants by the occupational physicians in charge, Nancy decides to get to know her area of responsibility as effectively as possible, starting where the situation is worst. She thus compiles an inventory of the chemical substances and related problems in 'her' plants. She plans to use these records to establish her own order of priorities. As it happens, she has an excellent method for doing this, which was explained in detail by a Du Pont official during her training as an occupational hygienist.

Nancy draws up the inventory of 20 plants and (six months later) decides on the following categories of priority:

>100:   immediate measurement and recommendations for action (2 plants)

80–100: as above, but with priority 2

50–80:   measurements at a later stage, in consultation with the plant management

25–50:   further consultation with plant management during periodic visits

< 25:   no action.

---

2.1.2 *Personal environmental monitoring*

To monitor the air breathed in by an individual an air sample is taken in the worker's breathing zone (<30 cm from nose and mouth). Collecting the air and capturing the components to be measured is usually done actively with a pump, but it may also be achieved by passive diffusion of the components to diffuse through a membrane filter. There are many techniques for trapping the components to be studied; Table 40.3 lists some of them.

In all the techniques listed in the table, the amount of the toxic substance in the sample still needs to be analyzed afterwards.

ASSIGNMENT   40.3

Why are the above techniques and apparatus not appropriate for monitoring toxic peaks?

A number of highly toxic chemicals, which are not perceived by the senses when they reach toxic levels (e.g. CO), can be detected by electronic dosimeters, with

TABLE 40.2

Commonly used approach to setting priorities for further study of chemical exposure factors

| | | | | score |
|---|---|---|---|---|
| 1. *uptake routes:* | | | | |
| lung and skin | | | | 8 |
| lung | | | | 4 |
| skin | | | | 2 |
| eye or mouth | | | | 1 |

2. *acute toxicity data from animal studies:*

| oral $LD_{50}$ (mg kg$^{-1}$) | inhalation (ppm) | skin $LD_{50}$ (mg kg$^{-1}$) | toxicity | |
|---|---|---|---|---|
| <5 | <10 | <10 | extreme | 8 |
| 5–50 | 50–100 | 10–200 | high | 4 |
| 50–500 | 100–1000 | 200–5000 | slight | 2 |
| >500 | >1000 | >5000 | low | 1 |

| 3. *chronic toxicity data:* | |
|---|---|
| lethal, carcinogenic, embryotoxic | 8 |
| significant damage to lungs, liver, kidney and nervous system; reproductive effects | 4 |
| minor effects (largely local), such as cholinesterase inhibition, skin sensitization | 2 |
| no chronic toxic effects known | 1 |

| 4. *warning properties of substance (odor or irritation threshold):* | |
|---|---|
| >3× the exposure limit | 8 |
| >1× but <3× this limit | 4 |
| >0.1× and <1× the limit | 2 |
| <0.1× the exposure limit | 1 |

| 5. *physical factors:* | |
|---|---|
| gas, respirable aerosol, liquids with a vapor tension higher than 300 mm Hg | 8 |
| highly volatile substances with vapor tension between 100 and 300 mm Hg at 25°C | 4 |
| non-volatile liquids with vapor tension <100 mm Hg at 25°C | 2 |
| non-dusty solids | 1 |

| 6. *quantity used per unit time (kg/year):* | |
|---|---|
| >50 000 | 8 |
| 5 000–50 000 | 4 |
| 500–5 000 | 2 |
| <500 | 1 |

| 7. *number of workers potentially exposed to the toxic substance:* | |
|---|---|
| >125 | 8 |
| 25–124 | 4 |
| 5–24 | 2 |
| 1–4 | 1 |

| 8. *degree and manner of exposure:* | |
|---|---|
| open process, manually operated, frequent intervention in the process during service or maintenance, regular leaks and spillages, absence of ventilation, etc. | 16 |
| 'controlled release', some manual operation, ventilation and shielding present but inadequate | 8 |
| closed process, fully remote-controlled, no manual operation, little leakage or spillage, good shielding and ventilation | 1 |

A high score (righthand column) = a high risk

TABLE 40.3
Some techniques and apparatus used in personal air monitoring

| Technique | Packing | Used in particular for |
|---|---|---|
| sampling tube | activated charcoal silica gel etc. | organic gases/vapours |
| cellulose ester filter | PVC etc. | toxic components in fumes |
| cyclones | | respirable fraction of dust |
| impingers | liquid absorption medium | |
| gas bags | | gases/vapours where condensation or absorption is not important |
| badges | | as for sampling tube |

or without an alarm. However, these are only available for a limited number of substances. Personal monitoring provides an *estimate* of an *individual's mean exposure* over a previously determined period of time (e.g. an 8-hour working day). Depending on the sampling and analysis method this estimate can be made for several components at once.

### 2.1.3 Stationary monitoring

Stationary monitoring is designed to measure levels of a potentially toxic substance continuously or at fixed intervals, and is usually meant to:

1 monitor the process for leaks
2 provide evidence that legal requirements are being complied with (MAC)
3 give an alarm whenever a predetermined level is exceeded.

The stationary method is less suitable for determining personal risks or relationships between exposure and absorbed dose. It can, however, estimate a *mean exposure for groups of workers*. Such data are often used in epidemiological studies which are concerned with exposure categories rather than the exact dose per individual. The great majority of instruments used for stationary monitoring provide a direct readout, which is an advantage when monitoring short-term high exposures. Using a mobile system enables recording of the maximum levels at a number of workplaces in a plant, the so-called emission points. Emission points can then be continuously monitored using a stationary system. Such systems must meet exact criteria. They must, for example:

1 be able to function unattended 24 hours a day, 7 days a week
2 be very sensitive, as most of the substances requiring continuous monitoring because of their toxicity can cause damage to man at very low levels (ppm and even ppb)
3 have a stable base line (minimal drift) and a reproducible action (no interim changes in sensitivity)
4 be highly selective and specific vis à vis the agent being monitored.

These requirements implicitly determine the detection method and the type of sensing or sampling system which will be chosen for a particular application. The analytical methods used for the continuous monitoring of MAC compliance range from the classic basic laboratory techniques to optical and mass spectrometry. Only the four main principles on which many systems are based are listed here:

- *electrochemical cells*: the toxic component being monitored diffuses through a membrane in a sealed system in which the substance produces a current as a result of an electrochemical reaction and this is then measured.
- *infrared spectrophotometry*: the chemical component absorbs IR radiation of a specific wavelength whilst background gases do not.
- *semiconductor sensors*
- *flame ionization detectors.*

Stationary monitoring systems appear to be developed largely by industry itself. That makes sense because companies know a good deal about their own products. Still, there is clearly a considerable difference between checking that toluene remains between 30 and 32% during the process and ensuring that the ambient workplace level of 100 ppm for toluene is not exceeded.

### 2.1.4 Measurement strategies for environmental monitoring

Environmental monitoring for toxic substances at the work place requires knowledge of analytical procedures and a protocol which describes when, where, how, how often and for how long measurements should be taken in order to provide a reliable estimate of the exposure. Such protocols are devised using a measurement strategy.

A measurement strategy is based on a large number of considerations, the main ones being:

1  The *measurement objective*—the aim may be to define an overall classification of exposures, to determine the chemical exposure of persons performing a specific task or, for example, the mean exposure of a group of operators on night duty.

2  Degree of *reliability* required—do the results need to be 90% reliable, for example, or 99% reliable?

3  Knowledge of *sources of error* and the size of the error introduced—a variance of unknown size creeps into measurements, made up of analytical, strategic and associated factors.

4  *Cost aspect*—primarily important as regards the number of samples to be taken and the manpower required.

A first step towards a good measurement strategy is to use knowledge gained in an earlier plant survey or from another source. Every process comprises a more or less fixed sequence of steps and actions. This makes using knowledge of the process one way of reducing both cost and strategic variance. Elements of this foreknowledge include the type of process, its rate, ventilation, special operations such as filling, cleaning and emptying, how long the installations have been in use, and so on. A major difficulty with this basic knowledge is that it can be very hard to quantify and ideally needs to be combined with information which is quantitative (earlier measurements, ambient temperature, process temperature). This is illustrated by the diagram in Figure 40.2.

Assumptions are unavoidable, partly because knowledge of the substance in question is limited, and partly in order to keep the measurement protocol practicable and affordable. Verification of all assumptions is impossible and if it were, this would make a study in itself.

Some assumptions are so common as to have become conventions. Typical conventions are the assumption, for example, that the work process is stationary, that the distribution of concentration levels is log normal and that stationary and personal monitoring are equivalent. The first assumption implies that measurements obtained at different times all belong to the same statistical distribution. In fact this stationary nature of the process is a prime requisite for further statistical processing. Yet there are many conditions in which serious question marks have to be placed against the correctness of this convention. Take for example the ageing of installations, differing production rates and seasonal effects.

### 2.2 MONITORING OF INTERNAL AND EXTERNAL EXPOSURE

*Chemical exposure*

A toxicological risk is determined not only by the toxic properties of a substance but also by the extent and duration of exposure to it, usually expressed in terms of *chemical exposure*. A distinction is usually made here between internal and external exposure (Figure 40.3). This is done to distinguish between the mere presence of substances in the working environment (e.g. in the air) and the actual functional exposure of the organism based on the quantities taken up.

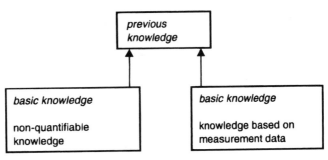

FIGURE    40.2
Quantifiable and non-quantifiable data from which the previous knowledge required for a plant survey is derived

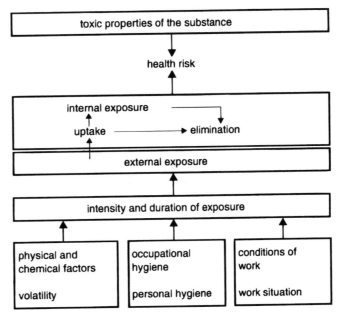

FIGURE    40.3
Factors and processes which may contribute to the health risk of a substance in a work situation

*Toxicokinetic parameters*

In a work situation, exposure to chemical substances usually takes place continuously or repeatedly (e.g. 8 hours a day, 5 days a week).

The degree of a worker's internal exposure over time not only depends on the concentration of the substance in question, e.g. in the air which is inhaled daily, but also on physical exertion (maximal breathing capacity) and the way a substance behaves within the body. The latter aspect can be characterized by a variety of *toxicokinetic parameters*. One of these is the *half-life* ($t_{1/2}$), which is a measure of the time during which a substance is present in the body. Hardly degradable lipophilic substances (such as PCBs and some chlorinated hydrocarbon pesticides) have long half-lives and show a tendency to *accumulate* in the organism after repeated exposure. The same applies to some non-system-linked metals for which there is no physiological method of elimination (lead, mercury, cadmium, etc.). Accumulation will thus occur primarily where there is frequent exposure to substances which have a relatively long ($t_{1/2}$).

EXAMPLES

Figure 40.4 illustrates two (theoretical) situations reflecting the concentrations of two substances over four successive working weeks. Every day, 5 days a week, a worker takes up a certain constant quantity of substance A or substance B. The ($t_{1/2}$) values of A and B are 24 and 96 hours, respectively.

It will be clear from the example that with occupational exposure to industrial toxicants the degree of internal exposure is determined not only by levels in the ambient air but also by the duration of time worked and time away from

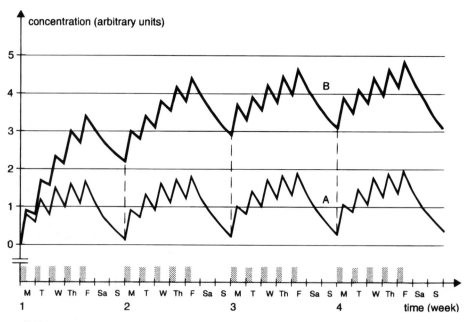

FIGURE 40.4

Internal exposure of two workers A and B as a result of exposure to two different industrial chemicals

Worker A is exposed to a substance with a $t_{1/2}$ of 24 hours; worker B to a substance with a $t_{1/2}$ of 96 hours. The shaded columns indicate the periods of working time.

work (breaks, weekends, days off, holidays). If the exposure pattern changes, for example because of overtime, the plateau concentration may well increase, even though the ambient concentration remains the same. On the other hand, as a result of *multiple exposure* or *changes in a worker's health* (particularly impairment of liver or kidney function) the $t_{1/2}$ of a substance may unexpectedly increase. In that case, if his pattern of work (exposure pattern) remains unchanged, the ratio of $(t_{1/2})/\Delta t$ will change so that a plateau concentration is reached which exceeds a certain threshold.

Many substances are converted by enzymatic processes (biotransformation). This may create metabolites which are more toxic than the parent substance. Where this is the case, the toxicokinetic properties of the metabolite(s) must also be taken into account. Degree and duration of chemical exposure at work are determined by an interplay of different factors, such as the type of activity and the production process. The way in which a substance is processed or treated also determines the chance of exposure. For instance, working with volatile substances at a high ambient temperature will result in a high vapor concentration. Some substances are absorbed through the skin. In a warm or humid climate this can lead to increased uptake. One example is working in horticulture in greenhouses with a variety of lipophilic pesticides. Some treatments of solid substances (grinding, sanding, metal drilling, paints, etc.) causes small particles to be released into the air. The smaller the particles, the deeper they can penetrate into the lungs when inhaled. In such cases exposure can be reduced by using ventilation, extraction and personal protection aids. Extra exposure may occur as a result of poor work hygiene or inadequate personal hygiene. Workers do not always wash their hands before eating. Both these are often linked to an absence of washing facilities and/or eating, drinking and smoking whilst working; hence the importance of a walk-through survey. Sometimes tobacco smoke itself contains the same toxic substances to which a person is exposed at work (cadmium). Lastly, it must always be borne in mind that exposure to a given substance may also occur away from work, for example during a leisure activity (hobbies) or as part of the general environment, including nutrition.

*Exposure in work situations*

*Health surveillance*

In work situations exposure is usually to low concentrations over a long period of time, causing an insidious risk to health. It is precisely here that we need to maintain surveillance. The methods available are often collectively known as *health surveillance* or monitoring. Investigation techniques in this field are divided into measurements which record the presence of substances in the environment (external exposure) and measuring substances in individuals (internal exposure). Some monitoring methods are listed in Table 40.4.

### 2.2.1 Environmental monitoring

*Environmental monitoring*

The first of these approaches, *environmental monitoring* (EM), can in a given work situation provide us with an estimate of the dose based on concentrations in the

TABLE 40.4
Methods used to monitor exposure and health effects in the work situation

environmental monitoring (EM)
personal air sampling
biological monitoring (BM)
biological effect monitoring (BEM)
health effect monitoring (HEM)

air. In practice it is also used to establish compliance with the standards set by the authorities (see also section 2.1, Environmental studies). Despite refinements to measurement strategies and techniques, EM still presents a disadvantage in that it can not take sufficient account of total exposure from several sources and a number of personal factors, so that different workers may show different internal exposures even if the concentration in the air at the workplace is the same.

If exposure is exclusively at the workplace and only takes place via inhalation, EM can provide a fairly reliable estimate of *body burden*, but only a rough estimate of the *body burden level* which in fact determines the health risk. EM measurements do not take account of respiratory minute volume (the measure of effort), or of actual uptake and metabolism, which can vary widely from one person to another. Nevertheless, EM does provide a good idea of industrial hygiene, which is of course most important from the point of view of technical prevention.

### 2.2.2 Biological monitoring

*Biological monitoring*

For a better direct estimate of the quantity of a toxic substance in body organs it will be necessary to use *biological monitoring* (BM). This takes measurements from the individual concerned, by determining concentrations of the substance itself or in many cases its metabolites in biological samples. The prime objective of this method is to establish the total quantity of the substance taken up over a given period or ideally the quantity present in the organ or tissue where the effect is first expressed (target dose). Although in principle any biological material could be used for BM, in practice those generally used are blood (whole, plasma, serum), urine, exhaled air or (in a few cases) saliva. The choice of sample and sampling interval is determined by the fate of the substance in the body (its toxicokinetics). To develop an effective measurement strategy and technique for BM, comprehensive study of the biotransformation and toxicokinetics of every toxic agent is therefore necessary. BM has considerable advantages, in that it also takes account of uptake of a toxic substance occurring outside work, in addition to personal hygiene (at work), the degree of exertion and all kinds of biological mechanisms. BM is not suitable for substances which produce a contact effect, such as highly irritant chemicals. These already produce their effects before they are absorbed. BM and EM are thus clearly complementary methods. Both are essential tools in monitoring exposure.

It should be noted that data on internal exposure to a toxic substance in a given situation (however reliable) give no indication as to the health risk. To assess the risk we need to know the *relationship* between *internal exposure* and *response* (particularly the no-observed-adverse-effect level or threshold dose) (see figure 40.5).

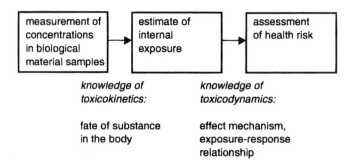

FIGURE 40.5
Relationship between monitoring and health risk assessment

For most toxic substances, however, this relationship is not (yet) known, especially for man. Unfortunately we do not yet know enough to use BM for more than about 50 substances in practice, but these are substances that are widely used. This even prompts the question of whether it is really practicable to develop a BM method for each of the nearly 700 substances on the MAC list, let alone the thousands of industrial chemicals currently in use.

In many situations workers are exposed to complex mixtures of substances which are hard to identify. Work in a waste incineration plant is a case in point. In such cases methods specific to one substance are usually of little help and one has to resort to non-specific methods. These are not geared to one specific substance but seek to show exposure to a large group of compounds.

*General exposure test*

An example of a *general exposure test* is the determination of thioether compounds in urine. These compounds can be regarded as detoxication products of chemically reactive substances. After these substances have been taken up (or produced by the body itself via biotransformation), they are biochemically detoxified by binding to nucleophilic sulfur in a sulfhydryl group. The main detoxication route here is glutathione conjugation which leads to excretion of mercapturic acid (thioethers).

---

EXAMPLE

Figure 40.6a shows how this test is used. Workers at a waste incinerator were exposed to a combination of chemicals, including ethylbenzene, benzene, styrene, various polymers and their combustion products. The thioether level of one of the workers (a non-smoker) was monitored for several days. Elevated levels of thio compounds were found in his midday urine. This increase was not attributable to a *diurnal rhythm*.

As can be seen from Figure 40.6b a technician working in a randomly chosen laboratory (also a non-smoker) was found to have an irregular excretion pattern which was *unrelated to his hours of work*.

In such cases one can draw only a qualitative conclusion on the internal exposure of the worker concerned, since the background thioether level is rather high, possibly due to exposure to cigarette smoke, certain foods, etc. In cases like this the method used to identify the suspect compound needs to be made more sensitive or specific.

This was done for the development of a BM method for measuring exposure to carbon disulfide, to which spinners in the viscose-rayon industry are subjected. $CS_2$ uptake leads to an increased urinary excretion of thioethers (Figure 40.7).

Because of the relatively high background exposure (smoking, etc.) there was a high reference value, so that this test is rather non-specific. More detailed research resulted in the isolation and identification of the thioether metabolite responsible: 2-thiothiazolidine-4-carbonic acid (TTCA). A selective method of measuring TTCA was then developed using HPLC. This led to a more *specific* method of BM for exposure to carbon disulfide. Given that TTCA is not normally found in urine, in this situation the reference value is virtually nil. As a result this exposure test is extremely sensitive. The TTCA test can also be used to trace exposure to other chemicals such as dithiocarbamates (insecticides) which form $CS_2$ when metabolized (Figure 40.8).

---

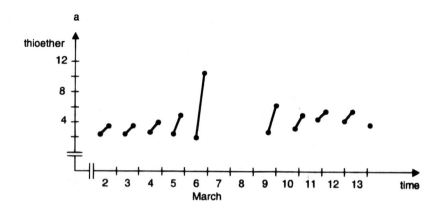

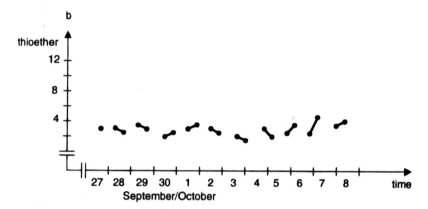

FIGURE 40.6

Thioether excretion over time in urine samples from workers in a chemical plant

a urine samples from a waste incineration worker (non-smoker)

b urine samples from a technician (non-smoker) The thioether concentrations were expressed in mmoles SH per mol creatinine

### 2.2.3 Measurement strategy in biological monitoring

The main choices to be made when developing a measurement strategy for biological monitoring are concerned with:

- *which substance or substances* are to be analyzed (parent substance or metabolites);
- the *biological material* to be examined (blood, saliva, urine, exhaled air, etc.);
- the *time of sampling.*

These choices are largely determined by the biotransformation and toxicokinetics of the agent concerned. The example below illustrates this.

---

EXAMPLE

Styrene is a volatile compound used in the plastics industry, not just as a monomer in the manufacture of polystyrene but also as a hardener in a variety of polyester products (boat building). Although in experimental animals (rat) styrene is largely metabolized to a mercapturic acid (in a sequence of steps), exposure of humans to styrene hardly lead to an increase in excretion of mercapturic acid.

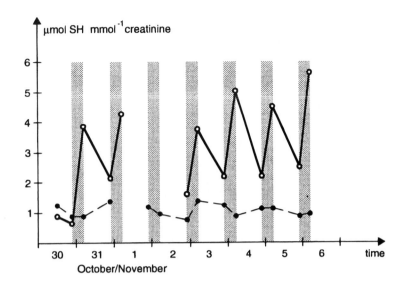

FIGURE 40.7
Urinary excretion of thio compounds by a spinner in the viscose-rayon industry, exposed to a carbon disulfide level of about 20 mg m$^{-3}$ air (7 ppm)
Thio compounds were determined by thioether measurement.

Humans metabolize styrene almost entirely to mandelic acid and phenyl glyoxylic acid which are excreted in the urine (Figure 40.9).

Using the values of a number of toxicokinetic parameters on clearance, half-life and distribution volumes, BM data can be interpreted in terms of internal exposure.

More information can sometimes be obtained by measurements in various media such as exhaled air, blood and/or urine (see Figure 40.10).

A number of practical preconditions constantly have to be taken into consideration. One of them is that an exposure test must cause as little risk or inconvenience as possible to the individuals being tested. In addition, the production process at the plant must not be disrupted.

The cost aspect (apparatus, level of training of the occupational medical service personnel) is also a factor in the final choice.

For instance, the collection of 24-hour urine is found not to be feasible in practice. As a rule, urine is collected throughout the working day (8 hours) or in the last hours of the exposure period. Early morning urine is also often taken on the day of exposure (beforehand) or on the morning afterwards.

Exhaled air or blood is often tested using spot samples. If these are taken at successive times, a total picture of the fate of a substance in the body can be reconstructed.

### 2.2.4 Advantages and limitations of biological monitoring

*Advantages of biological monitoring*

BM has considerable *advantages* over EM as it is aimed at recording the total internal exposure. It includes measuring the uptake of foreign substances away from the work environment and also takes into account personal differences in

1157

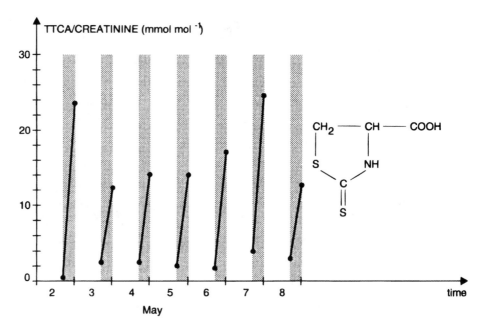

FIGURE   40.8
Urinary excretion of TTCA by a spinner exposed to a carbon disulfide level of approximately 8 mg m⁻³ (2.5 ppm)

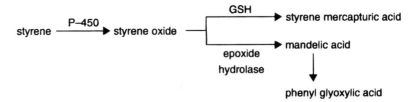

FIGURE   40.9
Biotransformation of styrene to styrene mercapturic acid and phenyl glyoxylic acid
Biotransformation in man is almost totally via conversion to mandelic acid and phenyl glyoxylic acid.

hygiene at work, rate of uptake, biochemical metabolism and elimination from the body.

> ASSIGNMENT   40.4
>
> With inhalatory exposure to a given concentration of an airborne substance, the more strenuous the work being done, the more of the substance will be taken up and, conversely, volatile substances will be eliminated more quickly during physical exertion. Give the reasons.

*Limitations*

BM is not very useful for substances which cause a contact effect. This group of compounds includes all kinds of irritants and chemically reactive compounds (HCl, ammonia vapor, etc.) which have an irritant or harmful effect on the skin and mucosa (i.e. of the respiratory tract and eyes).

These local effects occur irrespective of whether the substance in question is taken up by the body.

Another limitation of BM as an aid to health monitoring is that sampling and measurement are always performed after the event, when the harm has already been done.

To obtain a reliable picture of the total chemical exposure of individuals in a particular work situation, both BM and EM must be used to complement each other.

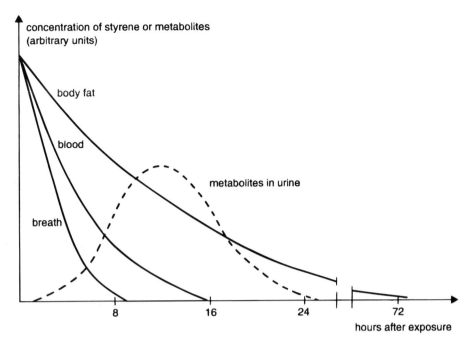

FIGURE 40.10
Biological monitoring of styrene and metabolites
In this example the measurements were performed on a number of different biological samples.

## 3 Health monitoring

### 3.1 FROM OCCUPATIONAL POISONING TO EARLY EFFECTS ON HEALTH

Occupational disease was already recognized in ancient times, notably poisoning in connection with the extraction and processing of metals. A classic example is mercury poisoning as a consequence of working in silver mines. Pliny described the symptoms typically observed in slaves working in the Spanish mines. Abnormalities in the nervous system accompanied by tremor and ataxia were particularly noted.

Even today metal poisoning is still sometimes seen. It occurs primarily as a result of the impurities present in certain ores. Thus, cadmium is always present in lead, copper and zinc ores. This means, for example, that work in the zinc industry entails not just exposure to zinc, but to the toxic cadmium as well.

The rise of the chemical industry from the beginning of the last century caused a large fraction of the working population to be brought into contact with a new type of foreign compound: the organic synthetic compounds. In the first half of the 19th century these were largely coal tar derivatives, nitroglycerin and nitrocellulose. The second half saw the introduction of synthetic dyes. Further advances in chemistry in the 20th century gave rise to the concept of bulk chemicals. Millions of tons of halogenated hydrocarbons, countless pesticides and polymers (plastics and rubber) are now manufactured every year. Developments like this all bring with them their own specific problems.

Formerly, poisoning incurred during work usually ended in clearly recognizable illness, and often in death. Nowadays, the focus has clearly shifted. Occupational poisoning has become less readily identifiable. Lameness (arsenic) and paralysis (mercury) are no longer seen. They have given way to less specific symptoms such as general malaise and ill health, fatigue, loss of appetite, headache, dizziness and nausea. Yet, these more subjective symptoms may also be clear indications of occupational poisoning. Over the years exposure levels have generally been sharply reduced. This is the result both of better provision for occupational hygiene and greater worker awareness. As a consequence, there has been a shift in emphasis from evident poisoning accompanied by symptoms of disease towards early symptoms. Table 40.5 illustrates this for exposure to lead and mercury.

The progression from exposure to the ultimate consequences of occupational poisoning is a gradual one. There are a number of clear steps, each with its own characteristics. The chance of damage to health or the degree to which there is already impairment can be determined using a variety of parameters. In cases of *insidious poisoning*, for instance in situations where workers are exposed to relatively low concentrations over long periods of time, these parameters can be used to monitor exposure and subsequently health.

*Definition*

| | |
|---|---|
| death/permanent disability ↑ | morbidity and mortality studies |
| disease ↑ | medical examination |
| harmful effect ↑ | function tests |
| internal exposure ↑ | biological monitoring |
| external exposure ↑ | environmental monitoring |
| presence of a substance | inventory, workplace studies |

It is one of the tasks of occupational toxicology to use the acquired insight into the action of toxic agents in order to expand and improve diagnostic methods. Better knowledge of the primary target sites through which cell physiology is affected can lead to increasingly sophisticated methods of investigation.

Progress in this area has meant that the occupational medical study of workers has seen a shift in emphasis away from clinically oriented research (to detect manifest cases of poisoning or occupational disease) towards early diagnosis. In recent years occupational medicine focusses more and more on monitoring. Prevention is the main concern.

## 3.2 BIOLOGICAL EFFECT MONITORING (BEM)

Biological effect monitoring also forms part of the pattern of developments outlined above. It comprises the measuring, and assessment of the presence, of early effects in workers, of which the implications for health are not relevant and/or not yet established, in order to compare the exposure and/or health risk with

TABLE 40.5
Symptoms caused by exposure to lead and mercury

| | High exposure | Low exposure |
|---|---|---|
| lead | colic<br>constipation | changes in stimulus conduction by the nervous system |
| | anemia<br>lead line | impaired kidney function |
| mercury | stomatitis<br>tremor<br>ataxia | impaired kidney function |

The table shows that symptoms may vary according to the degree of exposure.

an appropriate standard. With BEM a primary reaction of the body to the presence of the foreign substance is usually measured. Such a primary effect can be biochemical, physiological or structural. However, in principle it does not need to be harmful (no adverse effect).

A variety of tests currently being developed are based on these *"early" effects*. The twofold meaning of the word "early" is essential in this context. In a test of this type the effect to be measured should appear early, i.e. at relatively low, non-toxic concentrations. It should also appear early in the sense that it manifests itself before the *really harmful effects* become apparent.

A well-known example of BEM is the cholinesterase test to detect exposure to organophosphorus compounds, the group to which many insecticides belong. As far known, there are no implications for health of the biological effect measured in this test, namely the inhibition of cholinesterase enzymes in the blood. This is the case, however, when muscle function is measured using an electroneuromyogram (ENMG), with which a reduction in impulse conduction can be demonstrated. This reaction can be seen as a sensitive signal indicative of subclinical damage to the peripheral nervous system (harmful effect).

### 3.3 MEDICAL HEALTH CHECKS

*Health status*

The ENMG is designed not so much to establish exposure, but to detect an (incipient) adverse effect. The test therefore forms part of medical health checks, because based on its results, one can judge the *health status* of the worker examined. In this way, for instance, a developing disease can be detected in an otherwise healthy person. Preventive measures may stop the disease from reaching the clinical stage. This is not possible with the results of BEM, which merely indicate that the substance with which the worker has been in contact has been taken up and has reacted somewhere in the body, although without adverse effects on health.

As in BEM, the determinations made at the health check are not agent specific. For instance, an increase in a certain enzyme activity, such as $\gamma$-glutamyl transpeptidase in serum, does not in itself indicate toxic damage to the liver; as this may also occur on infection of the liver.

Many of the tests used in the health check are laboratory tests also used in clinical research. The results of such determinations must be interpreted on the basis of comparison with the corresponding values found in an optimally chosen reference group (called reference or normal values). Preference is often given to using personal reference values, i.e. measured values taken from the subject himself, but before exposure.

Table 40.6 gives examples of well-known types of occupational poisoning. The list does not attempt to be exhaustive.

TABLE 40.6
Disorders resulting from chemical exposure at work

| Pathology | Toxic agent | Diagnosis/effect parameter |
|---|---|---|
| *respiratory disease* | | |
| asthma | diisocyanates | various lung function tests: |
| pulmonary edema | irritant gases: | spirometry |
| | chlorine, phosgene, metal oxides | diffusion capacity |
| 'acute pneumonia' (high fever) | metal vapor, polymer fumes | |
| fibrosis | silica, asbestos, paraquat | |
| chronic bronchitis | irritant gases, | |
| | Cd compounds | |
| *kidney damage* | metals: | creatinine clearance |
| | chromium, cadmium and mercury compounds | proteinuria |

TABLE 40.6 (Continued)

| Pathology | Toxic agent | Diagnosis/effect parameter |
|---|---|---|
| | solvents, halogenated hydrocarbons, ethyl glycol | $\beta_2$-microglobulin<br>lysosomal enzyme activity in urine |
| liver damage | halogenated hydrocarbons (aliphatic and aromatic) | bilirubin |
| | aromatic nitro compounds<br>paraquat | elevated enzyme activity in serum:<br>aspartate aminotransferase (APT)<br>alanine aminotransferase (ALT)<br>glutamyltransferase |
| blood abnormalities | | |
| impairment of cell formation (anemia, etc.) | lead | blood picture |
| hemolysis | benzene<br>arsine<br>hydrazine | |
| methemoglobinemia | nitrite<br>nitro compounds<br>aromatic amines | $Fe^{+++}$ Hb-concentration |
| carboxyhemoglobinemia | carbon monoxide<br>methylene chloride | CoHb-concentration |
| impairment of blood coagulation | warfarin (rodenticide) | prothrombin test |
| cardiovascular disease | | |
| ventricular fibrillation (sometimes acute cardiac arrest) | trichloroethene | ECG, HR, BP<br>circulatory effort tests |
| cardiomyopathy | cobalt compounds | (bicycle ergometer) |
| bradycardia, vascular abnormalities | carbon disulfide | |
| vasodilatation, hypotension | nitroglycerin | |
| neurotoxic effects | | |
| narcosis | solvents | test for reaction and coordination skills |
| excitation (tremor, muscle contractions) | organophosphorus compounds<br>methyl bromide<br>pentachlorophenol | |
| neuropathy (paralysis, reduced sensibility) | n-hexane<br>acrylamide<br>trichloroethene | various neurophysiological tests:<br>coordination test |
| | lead<br>mercury | EEG<br>ENMG |
| encephalopathy, ataxia | biphenyl, styrene, methyl bromide, lead, mercury, manganese, carbon disulfide, acrylamide | behavioral tests |
| dermatotoxic effects | | |
| primary irritation: | chemical, reactive substances | skin irritation |
| blistering, ulceration, contact dermatitis, ortho-ergic eczema | solvents<br>detergents<br>methyl bromide | standard exposure tests |
| contact eczema | bichromate salts<br>epoxy resins<br>halogenated aromatic hydrocarbons<br>formaldehyde<br>nickel | allergy testing |
| scleroderma | vinyl chloride | |
| alopecia | chloroprene | |
| porphyria | chlorinated hydrocarbons (PCBs, TCDD) | |
| depigmentation | hydroquinones | |

The first column gives the type of pathology, the last column the effect parameter.

### 3.4  EPIDEMIOLOGICAL RESEARCH

To improve working conditions it is necessary first to find out which factors were responsible for adversely affecting workers' health. Epidemiological research provides the basis for this and is still the ultimate judge of a given risk. Medical epidemiology studies often cover groups of workers in specific plants or branches of the (chemical) industry. Epidemiology makes use of both quan-

*Quantitative data*

*Categorial data*

titative and categorial data. *Quantitative data* refer to measurable variables such as height, weight, blood pressure and concentrations of substances in blood or urine (obtained e.g. by BM). In contrast, *categorial data* refer to variables such as mortality (dead/not dead) or morbidity (ill/not ill). However, categorial data may be subdivided into categories when looking at specific mortality (e.g. total cancer morbidity subdivided according to specific carcinomas), specific morbidity or seriousness of the illness. Another characteristic of epidemiology is that it often uses *ratios* (relative risk, odds ratio) and rates, such as standardized mortality rate (SMR) per 100 000 per year.

*Objective of epidemiological research*

The objective of epidemiological research in occupational toxicology may be:

- to describe the distribution and extent of diseases in a particular company or branch of industry;
- to study and/or establish the relationship between any exposure to risk factors (chemicals) and disorders;
- to determine both qualitatively and quantitatively the true risk to humans in a (non-experimental) lifelike work situation;
- to study exposure-response relationships;
- to identify the etiological factors in the pathogenesis of occupational diseases (which chemicals cause specific disorders in which people and by which type of exposure).

The data obtained from such research can be useful in the prevention, control and treatment of work-related disorders. Epidemiology may use various approaches in meeting these objectives, such as:

- descriptive research,
- analytical research,
- experimental or intervention research.

*Descriptive research*

*Descriptive research*, comprising prevalence and incidence studies, in a way forms the basis for the second type of research, namely analytical studies. An example of a prevalence study is comparison of the prevalence of silicosis in two different regions where there are ceramics industries. Table 40.7 shows the results of a study of this kind carried out in the 1970s.

It can clearly be seen that in both regions the prevalence is higher in those individuals with the longest exposure. Total prevalence in the two regions is clearly different, however. Although a relationship to the size of the companies was suspected, firm conclusions can only be drawn after further analytical research.

*Analytical research*

*Analytical research* aims at tracing factors which cause an increase in certain disorders and at establishing the size of the source(s) concerned. Here too several approaches are possible, which can be divided roughly into two:

1  case-control studies
2  cohort studies, which may be retrospective or prospective.

TABLE 40.7

Prevalence of silicosis in 520 workers in small fine ceramics factories in Gouda and 1975 workers in two larger mechanized plants in the Maastricht area

*Duration of exposure*

| | Gouda | | | Maastricht | | |
|---|---|---|---|---|---|---|
| | Number of workers | Number of silicosis cases | Prevalence (%) | Number of workers | Number of silicosis cases | Prevalence (%) |
| ≤3 year | 103 | 1 | 1.0 | 552 | 0 | 0.0 |
| 4–9 | 118 | 2 | 1.7 | 484 | 0 | 0.0 |
| 10–19 | 82 | 11 | 13.4 | 426 | 2 | 0.5 |
| 20–24 | 58 | 9 | 15.5 | 197 | 4 | 2.0 |
| 25–29 | 66 | 18 | 27.3 | 178 | 9 | 5.1 |
| ≥30 year | 93 | 28 | 30.1 | 138 | 18 | 13.0 |
| total | 520 | 69 | 13.3 | 1975 | 33 | 1.7 |

*Case-control study*

*Cohort study*
Latin: cohors—a defined area or group

These two approaches are totally different. A *case-control study* describes the factors which occur in a *selected* group of patients compared with a selected control group. This approach makes sense and saves time when studying disorders which are rare in a normal (and occupational) population, e.g. bladder cancer, pancreatic carcinoma. In a *cohort study*, mortality (death) and morbidity (disease) are studied in a certain group for a predetermined period of time and compared with those of a control cohort. This control group is different in that it is not subjected to the exposure(s) whose relative risk is to be determined.

Industrial toxicology regularly uses both techniques. Case-control studies are mostly conducted to test a specific hypothesis.

EXAMPLE

Suppose the literature reports that certain pesticides produce neurotoxic effects in experimental animals which are very similar to Parkinson's disease. To test this, a group of patients with Parkinson's disease could be selected together with an (optimum) control group, to see if the Parkinson's group contains a relatively larger number of individuals who have worked with pesticides or whether that group as a whole has absorbed a higher dose.

Cohort studies often establish and evaluate, making it possible to assess causes and their quantitative significance (the relative risk of lung cancer is higher in asbestos workers who smoke than in those who do not).

An exposure–response relationship may be used as an *indicator* of a cause-effect relationship, while in theory the third type of study, the experimental study, could serve as *proof*. An intervention study is an epidemiological investigation that is sometimes carried out to study the effect of measures taken to change exposure conditions. In *intervention studies* the variable supposed to be the cause is removed from (a portion of) the population. For obvious reasons, it is unfortunately almost impossible to perform this type of study in the industrial situation. That is why it is so important for epidemiological studies to have accurate exposure data (from EM or BM) available in order to determine a dose-response relationship in cohort studies.

Intervention studies

## 4 Risks and risk factors

### 4.1 MULTIPLE EXPOSURE

It is exceptional in industrial toxicological practice to encounter exposure to just one substance. Workers are generally exposed to a variety of substances, either simultaneously or at intervals. Other factors in addition to chemical factors play a part in this complex problem.

The question is whether such combinations increase or decrease the risk of damage to health.

In this textbook the emphasis will primarily be on the consequences of combined exposure to chemicals. There are several possibilities in the case of multiple exposure. The least complicated situation is of course when the effects of the various substances do not influence each other. In such cases, MAC values based on single exposure can usually be applied, unchanged and independently of each other. In all other cases, however, there is the possibility of combined action, either mutually or not. This effect is termed "interaction".

### 4.2 INTERACTIONS

An interaction may in principle result in one of the following effects:

*Synergism*

1 *Synergism*: The term synergism describes the situation in which the effect of a substance is enhanced by combination with one or more other substances. There are several possibilities here:

- *addition*: the combined effect is equal to the sum of the individual effects
- *superaddition*: the combined effect is greater than the sum of the individual effects. If in such cases one of the substances is not itself bioactive, the term used is potentiation.

*Antagonism*

2 *Antagonism*: This is the situation where the effect of a toxic substance is reduced or inhibited by the presence of another substance; the combined effect is less than the sum of the individual effects.

> ASSIGNMENT 40.5
>
> When in toxicology can the antagonistic effect of chemicals be used for specific purposes?

*Interaction mechanisms*

The ultimate effect of a bioactive substance is usually the result of a sequence of events. To understand how a toxic effect is induced, it helps to divide the total process into a number of constituent processes. Three phases can be distinguished: the exposure phase, the toxicokinetic phase and the toxicodynamic phase (see Figure 40.11).

TABLE 40.8
Factors contributing to multiple exposure

| Multiple exposure | |
| --- | --- |
| chemical factors | variety of chemicals in the environment (workplace, diet, hobbies, etc.) |
| physical factors | heat, noise, vibration, radiation, humidity |
| biological factors | risk of infection, microorganisms |
| psychosocial factors | stress |

dose
|

| exposure phase | behavior of substance in the environment, changes in route of uptake |
| toxicokinetic phase | uptake, distribution, biotransformation (bioactivation, detoxication), excretion |
| toxicodynamic phase | interaction with receptors or other (macro)molecules at the site of toxic action |

↓
effect

FIGURE 40.11
Different phases in the induction of a toxic effect

In each of these three phases combinations of substances may cause interactions. Metabolic interactions, for example, may inhibit or delay biotransformation. The result of this in terms of the toxic effect will depend, *inter alia*, on whether toxification or detoxication is involved.

Combined exposure to a metabolizable substance A and a substance B which modifies the metabolism of A can in principle lead to one of the following scenarios:

TABLE 40.9
Result of interaction between two substances A and B

Substance A undergoes biotransformation, substance B influences the biotransformation of substance A.

| substance A undergoes | substance B causes | |
| --- | --- | --- |
| | inhibition | induction |
| bioactivation | antagonism | synergism |
| detoxication | synergism | antagonism |

If the initial substance is toxic, induction of the (detoxicating) metabolism will reduce possible systemic toxicity, whereas inhibition will increase its toxicity at the same exposure.

EXAMPLE

An example of this kind of interaction is exposure to *m*-xylene and aspirin. Co-exposure to substances which induce cytochrome P-450 (other solvents such as styrene or medication such as phenobarbital) result in increased conversion of *m*-xylene to *m*-methyl benzyl alcohol (see Figure 40.12). Substances which inhibit P-450, however, cause decreased biotransformation of *m*-xylene. Interaction may also occur during the phase 2 reaction. As the figure shows, aspirin is converted to a glycine conjugate. The same happens to methylbenzoic acid. If the quantity of glycine is limited, simultaneous exposure to *m*-xylene (inhaled) and aspirin (ingested) creates the possibility of mutualinhibition of elimination. It has indeed been shown that a dose of 1500 mg aspirin causes 50% inhibition in the level of m-xylene eliminated in methyl hippuric acid (100 ppm). The converse is also true.

1166

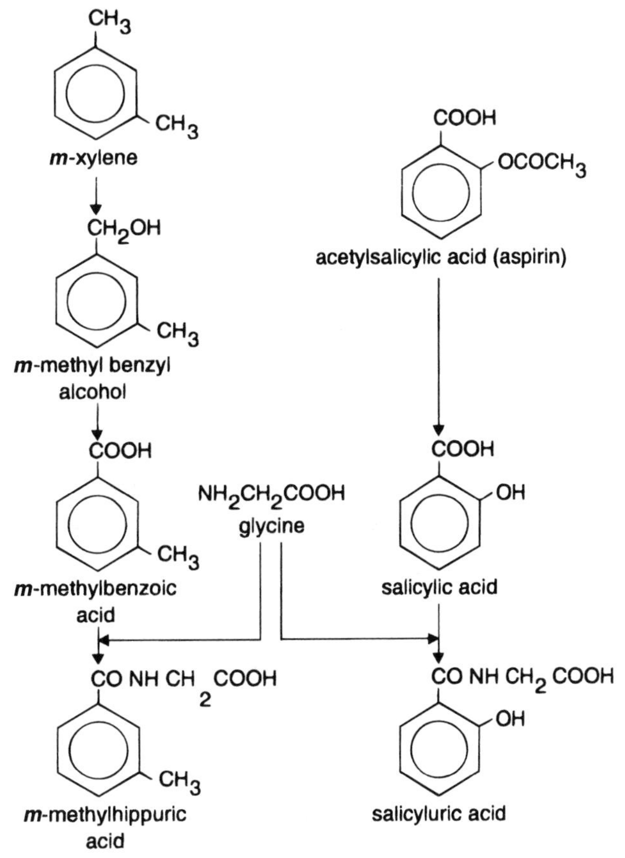

FIGURE 40.12
Biotransformation of *m*-xylene to *m*-methylhippuric acid
The figure shows that glycine can be a limiting factor in biotransformation and that the biotransformation of aspirin can indirectly influence the biotransformation of m-xylene.

If the parent substance is relatively harmless, but its metabolism entails bioactivation (vinyl chloride, carbon tetrachloride, benzene, dichloromethane), the converse is true. Induction of metabolism may mean an increased risk in the event of simultaneous exposure. In the case of a number of carcinogens, multiple exposure with effects on biotransformation may require a different risk evaluation.

Knowledge of multiple exposure, relevant to occupational toxicology, is very fragmentary and contains several contradictory results.

ASSIGNMENT 40.6

Explain why it is difficult to predict metabolic interactions with toxicological implications using animal experiments.

*Practical situations*

As has been stated before, it is more often the exception than the rule for workers in the chemical industry to be exposed to just one chemical substance at one given point in time. Usually several chemicals are present at the workplace at the same time. For instance, paints, varnishes and reaction mixtures often contain a mixture of different solvents. Ethanol is a widely used industrial solvent, but even when an individual is exposed for 8 hours to an inhalation level of 1900 mg m$^{-3}$, such an exposure is equivalent only to a single glass of wine or beer. This means that exposure or coexposure to ethanol by inhalation is thus negli-

TABLE 40.10
Some drugs which must be regarded as capable of altering the metabolism of workplace substances, when taken simultaneously (chronically)

| Category | Example |
| --- | --- |
| analgesics, antipyretics | antipyrine, phenylbutazone |
| antibiotics | rifampicin |
| anticonvulsants | phenytoin |
| antimycotics | griseofulvin |
| antimalarial drugs | quinine |
| psychoactive drugs | imipramine |
| hypnotics | phenobarbital |
| steroids | testosterone |
| vitamins | vitamin C |
| stimulants | alcohol |
| dietary components: | |
| indoles | indole-3-carbinol |
| safrole derivatives | safrole |
| PAHs | benzo[a]pyrene |

gible compared to the amounts ingested by the oral route. What is not negligible, however, is the increase in oral consumption of alcohol at work. Workers in the building trade and other heavy industries may drink 4 to 5 bottles of beer each per day. A significant number of employees are also taking medicines, including antihypertensive drugs (β blockers), antihistamines (e.g. chlorpheniramine, cimetidine) against hay fever or stomach upsets, anti-epileptic drugs (carbamazepine, phenytoin) and drugs for Parkinson's disease (orphenadrine). If to this are added substances absorbed with food and smoking, people can almost be regarded as walking test tubes!

Workers in the chemical industry are exposed to a large number of compounds and the interaction of these substances may lead to changes in their kinetics and/or toxicity at the workplace. This type of interaction may have implications for biological monitoring, but also for the acceptable level of exposure in relation to the MAC value.

Everyday practice involves a multitude of factors that may influence toxicity and risk. A rise in ambient temperature, for example, may cause:

- an increase in perfusion through the skin, which accelerates the absorption of substances;
- an increase in sweat secretion, that leads to increased epidermal hydration which in turn facilitates the uptake of polar compounds;
- disinclination to wear protective clothing such as masks, etc.

The complexity of risk assessment in situations where interactions may occur as a result of both chemical and physical factors is best illustrated by the example of multiple exposure during welding (see Figure 40.13).

4.3 SEX-LINKED OCCUPATIONAL RISKS

Limit values for exposure at the workplace are set in such a way that they (more or less) guarantee that the relevant uptake levels will cause no harmful effects in the individual and in his or her offspring.

*Individual sensitivity*

The possibility of a harmful effect following exposure to toxic chemicals is determined not only by the exposure characteristics (concentration, duration, frequency, route of exposure) but also by the characteristics of the exposed person

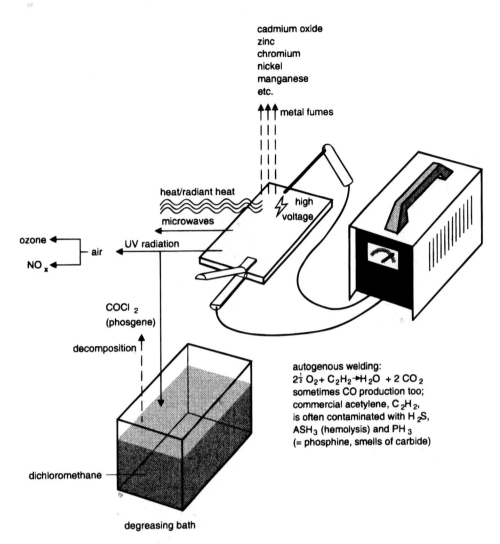

cadmium oxide
zinc
chromium
nickel
manganese
etc.

metal fumes

heat/radiant heat

microwaves

high voltage

ozone

air

NO$_x$

UV radiation

COCl$_2$
(phosgene)

decomposition

autogenous welding:
$2\frac{1}{2}$ O$_2$+ C$_2$H$_2$→H$_2$O + 2 CO$_2$
sometimes CO production too;
commercial acetylene, C$_2$H$_2$,
is often contaminated with H$_2$S,
ASH$_3$ (hemolysis) and PH$_3$
(= phosphine, smells of carbide)

dichloromethane

degreasing bath

FIGURE   40.13
Multiple exposure in welding

(age, genetis, body weight, any diseases, sex). These personal factors partly determine *individual sensitivity*, which varies from one person to another. An example is the increase in sex-linked sensitivity which is gaining in importance as more and more women are going out to work.

In theory the other or additional health risks to women as compared with men may be divided into:

1   non-reproductive differences,
2   differences linked to the reproductive system and childbearing.

These latter differences may be further subdivided into extra risks affecting conception, the period of pregnancy and the postnatal period.

*Non-reproductive effects*
For sex differences, see also
Study unit 4

It is known that the risk of exposure to certain substances is different for the two sexes. This seems obvious with respect to teratogenicity (fetotoxicity, embryotoxicity), but apart from these effects, there are other differences. Some substances are more readily *taken up* by the (thinner) skin of women than the (thicker) skin of men. The difference in body fat mass between women and men can also influence the distribution and hence the elimination rate of substances. Differences in toxicokinetics may occur not only because distribution within the body is different; differences in *biotransformation* may also cause a different kinetics and alter bioactivation. For instance, for phase 1 reactions it has long been known that there are sometimes sex differences in the metabolism of xenobiotics between experimental animals. Often, these differences are so specific that extrapolation of this kind of data to man is a risky exercise. It can only be attempted when the molecular mechanism in experimental animals (and man) is known and is the same.

---

EXAMPLE

An example is the renal toxicity of hexachloro-1,3-butadiene. Female rats are 4 times as sensitive to renal damage from this substance than males. The compound in question undergoes bioactivation by conjugation with GSH. This difference is not observed in mice. Only when we know more about the bioactivation mechanism of butadiene in man shall we be able to reach a well-founded conclusion.

---

The *availability of co-substrates* for conjugation (phase 2) reactions can also differ between the sexes. Male hepatocytes contain larger amounts of inorganic sulfate than the equivalent female cells. In conjugation reactions where there is binding to a sulfate group (e.g. phenols) the sulfate reserve in women will thus be exhausted sooner than in men.

*Reproduction-related differences*

Clearly the most important extra risks to female workers concern the female reproductive system and offspring. It should be understood here that the same effects can be caused by different mechanisms and that it is also the stage of fetal development which determines the risk and ultimate effect of chemical exposure. It is also important to realize that a woman runs a great risk during the period when she is not yet aware that she is pregnant. A classification according to mechanism as discussed in units 12 and 32 (teratogenicity, embryotoxicity and fetotoxicity) is purely academic in occupational toxicology, because in practice such a difference can never be made and the outcome of the effect is often the same, for instance spontaneous abortion and congenital malformation.

Some chemical substances or occupations where women come into contact with several substances are known to carry a higher degree of risk, for example the heavy metals, PCBs, dioxins and solvents (through mother's milk), work in hospitals (operating rooms) and the rubber industry.

4.4 CARCINOGENS IN THE WORKING ENVIRONMENT

Carcinogens are a group of industrial substances which require separate approaches. Although diet and smoking are the main factors that can be held responsible for cancer deaths in the population as a whole, the part played by occupational exposure to carcinogens cannot be ignored. Estimates vary greatly. The most reliable would seem to be an estimate of 4% (2% minimum, 8% maximum) by Doll and Peto. At first sight this percentage appears to be on the low side. However, it should be realized that occupational exposure is often an extra risk over and above the cancer risk caused by other factors such as lifestyle. So, in relation to the total number of cases of cancer the number of occupational cancers is low in absolute terms, but the *relative risk*, on the other hand, is extremely high. Relative risk is understood as the chance of someone developing a certain disorder as a result of occupational exposure compared with the risk for the population as a whole.

TABLE 40.11
Effects of chemical substances on reproduction

*before pregnancy*
menstrual irregularities
depression of libido
reduced potency
fertility impairment
germ cell mutation

*during pregnancy*
mother:
increased sensitivity to chemicals
toxemia
abortion

offspring:
abortion
prematurity
malformation
growth retardation
mutation
tumor growth

*after pregnancy*
toxic effects in the child from:
mother's milk (PCBs)
father's work clothing (asbestos)

(Sullivan, 1979)

The classic example of occupational cancer is the frequent occurrence of scrotal cancer in chimney sweeps. This phenomenon was described as early as 1775 by the London physician Percival Pott. He established that this form of skin cancer was the result of chronic exposure to soot. A hundred years later the German physician Volkmann reported that workers in daily contact with coal tar products developed skin growths on their forearms and hands. This carcinogenicity was later found to be caused by the polycyclic aromatic hydrocarbons (PAHs) present in tar products.

Aromatic amino compounds are also industrial chemicals that can cause cancer. The first chemical plants appeared in Western Europe in the second half of the last century. These initially manufactured synthetic dyes, mostly aniline and azo dyes. It was soon discovered that the incidence of cancer among the workers in these factories increased. A particularly notorious form was bladder cancer, which soon acquired the popular name of 'aniline cancer'. In fact, aniline itself was found not to be hazardous, but a group of other aromatic amines was put on the black list. The best-known of these are 2-naphthylamine and *p*-dimethylaminoazobenzene. Important examples of substances recently classified as occupational carcinogens are asbestos and vinyl chloride. Both substances induce a rare form of cancer. Asbestos can cause mesothelioma, a malignant disorder of the pleura and/or peritoneum with a very poor survival rate. Smoking has no effect on the development of mesothelioma. This is in contrast of the synergistic effect of smoking on the development of lung cancer, of which asbestos workers also run a higher risk.

In 1974 a vigilant company doctor in the American plastics industry noted that three workers previously engaged in cleaning (high exposure!) in a PVC plant had died of angiocarcinoma, a rather rare form of liver cancer. This confirmed the suspicion that vinyl chloride was also carcinogenic in man, as results of animal experiments in the sixties had already suggested. Epidemiological studies in the years thereafter helped to identify an increased cancer mortality in individuals who had undergone long-term occupational exposure to vinyl chloride. The sites affected were not just the liver, but also the brain and lymphatic system.

A large number of chemicals are known to cause cancer in experimental animals. Some of these compounds are (or used to be) present in our diet and/or in the air we breath. However, only very few of the substances found to be carcinogenic in animal experiments have been proved to be carcinogenic in man too.

> ASSIGNMENT   40.7
>
> What is the value of the statement that only a few of the substances found to be carcinogenic in animal experiments are shown to be carcinogenic in man too?

Nevertheless, it is assumed that all substances carcinogenic to experimental animals are potentially carcinogenic in man.

The most reliable information on the possible carcinogenicity of a substance can be obtained from the IARC (International Agency for Research on Cancer) in Lyon. This department of the World Health Organization, had by 1985 studied 585 substances suspected of being human carcinogens. Of these 147 proved to be carcinogenic in experimental animals and for only 44 of these was there any evidence that they might also be carcinogenic in man. In making these surveys, much attention was paid to the study of health statistics for factory workers.

In IARC Monographs particular emphasis is put on the amount of evidence for carcinogenicity based on data in the available literature. Four grades are distinguished in this respect, relating, on the one hand, to carcinogenicity in experimental animals (long-term animal experiments) and, on the other, to carcinogenicity in man (epidemiological studies):

- sufficient evidence
- limited evidence
- inadequate evidence
- no evidence

It should be noted that a high degree of evidence is not the same as high potency. The potency of aflatoxin B in inducing cancer in experimental animals is greater by a factor of $10^6$ than that of trichloroethylene. The evidence, however, is the same in both cases.

Table 40.12 shows a list of carcinogens and their industrial uses. In some cases no relationship could be established between exposure to a certain substance and the development of cancer. Only certain industrial activities could be categorized as carrying any risk:

| activity | target organ |
|---|---|
| furniture industry | nasal cavity |
| rubber manufacture | bladder, lungs, stomach, hemopoietic system |
| footwear industry | nasal cavity |
| hematite extraction | lungs |

TABLE 40.12
Examples of human carcinogens and their industrial uses

| Name of substance | Found in | IARC classification |
|---|---|---|
| acrylonitrile | plastics industry | 2A |
| 4-aminobiphenyl | antioxidant, rubber industry | 1 |
| aminotriazole | herbicide | 2B |
| asbestos | insulation material | 1 |
| auramine | dyestuffs industry | 2B |
| benzene | solvent, chemical industry | 1 |
| benzidine | dyestuffs industry | 1 |
| benzidine dyes | dyestuffs industry | 2B |
| benzo[a]pyrene | coal tar products, exhaust gases | 2A |
| beryllium | electrotechnical, metals inudstriy | 2A |
| bis(chloromethyl)ether | plastics | 1 |
| cadmium | metal goods, batteries, dyes | 2B |
| chlorophenols | chemical industry | 2B |
| chloroform | solvent | 2B |
| chromium (CrVI) | metal goods, paints | 1 |
| dianisidine | dyestuffs industry | 2B |
| 1,2-dibromoethane | soil decontamination | 2B |
| DDT | insecticide | 2B |
| 3,3-dichlorobenzidine | dyestuffs industry | 2B |
| diethylsulfate | chemistry (ethylating agent) | 2A |
| 1,4-dioxane | solvent | 2B |
| epichlorohydrin | epoxy resins | 2B |
| ethylene oxide | chemical industry | 2B |
| ethylene thiourea | rubber vulcanization | 2B |
| formaldehyde | desinfectant, UF foams, glues | 2B |
| dimethyl sulfate | chemistry (methylating agent) | 2A |
| hydrazine | fuel, chemical industry | 2B |
| mustard gas | chemical industry (alkylating agent) | 1 |
| 2-naphthylamine | rubber, dyestuffs industry | 1 |
| nickel | steel, electrotechnical industry | 2A |
| nickel refining | | 1 |
| PCBs | transformers and condensers insulating liquid, plasticizers | 2B |
| mineral oils, soot and tar | incineration and waste products | 1 |
| TCDD | byproduct of waste incineration | 2B |
| carbon tetrachloride | solvent and degreasing agent | 2B |
| o-toluidine | inks, textile dyestuffs | 2A |
| vinyl chloride | PVC industry | 1 |

*IARC classification:
Group 1: carcinogenic to man (evidence from epidemiological studies)
Group 2A: probably carcinogenic to man
Group 2B: possibly carcinogenic to man
(IARC Monographs, Supplement 4, WHO, Lyon 1982)

EXAMPLE

An example taken from the IARC concerns a study in workers exposed to benzene. Of those exposed to airborne benzene in the factory for the whole of their working life (100 ppm), 14–17% appeared to have died of leukemia. The use of benzene as a solvent in, e.g. the rubber industry, is now universally banned. Unfortunately, benzene is an irreplaceable component of many essential products. Currently the manufacture and use of this substance is only admitted with careful monitoring.

*Standards for exposure to workplace carcinogens*
Chemical carcinogens include substances for which, because of their mode of action, no safe dose or exposure threshold can be set.

This is the case for those compounds whose carcinogenic effect is ultimately the result of an irreversible modification of DNA. It will be clear that no concentration can be given for these substances which satisfies the definition of a MAC value. In other words, the MAC for such compounds should in principle be zero. In practice this is not feasible, since the use of some genotoxic carcinogens is still regarded as of great social importance. In such cases when setting threshold values, it is necessary to refer to the highest cancer risk which is still deemed acceptable, for example $10^{-6}$ or 1 in 1 000 000 individuals. Taking this as the starting point one can extrapolate the corresponding concentration from the dose-response curve or exposure-response curve. Unfortunately for most substances there are hardly any data available on the course of these curves at low concentrations. The most commonly used model here is the one-hit model. In this model, it is assumed that the extrapolated concentration will lead to a lower risk than that assumed by the calculation. The uncertainty due to the fact that extrapolation is based on animal data, however, remains.

## 4.5   RISK ASSESSMENT AND EVALUATION

From the previous sections it has become obvious that occupational exposure to chemicals can constitute a risk.

Identification of risk factors has been discussed in sections 2.1.1 and 2.1.4. The process of estimation and assessment of health risks is one step up from that. At both mesolevel (company, occupational medical service) and macrolevel (government, research institutes) one should constantly consider the possible health risks of certain chemical exposures. These considerations culminate in regulations for the handling of certain substances or in *maximum allowable concentrations* for specific substances (MACs).

*Maximum allowable concentrations (MAC)*

The first step in setting a MAC is the assessment and evaluation of the health risks by an expert working group. This stage uses all relevant toxicity data on the substance in question, which may come from *in vitro* and *in vivo* studies. Human *in vivo* data are particularly valuable here.

ASSIGNMENT   40.8

Why are human *in vivo* data so important when setting MACs?

*Human in vivo studies*

*Human in vivo studies* may be classified into three types:

- studies using *volunteers*
- *industrial field survey studies* which vary in size according to the number of workers
- *epidemiological studies*, mostly retrospective

The first type of study usually yields relevant data on the biotransformation and kinetics of the substance. The second often provides information on the nature and manner of exposure and is sometimes associated with (early) health effects, while epidemiological studies mostly measure morbidity or mortality and seek to establish a link with a certain exposure.

*Risk group*

There is no strict, conventional definition of the term *high risk group*, but it is understood as a group which has a greater chance of adverse effects as a result of exposure to a certain environmental factor (e.g. a toxic substance) than the rest of the workforce. Workers may be placed in a high risk group on the basis of one or more of the following characteristics:

*Risk situation*

- persons in a higher *risk situation*; for example exposures arising from the workplace or the particular job or from other sources (hobbies, smoking, etc.). This group also includes workers in situations that may lead to potential high exposures (e.g. workers in nuclear power stations, operators in plants with closed manufacturing systems, transporters of chemical waste);

(The following parameters are specific to the individual:)

*Higher uptake/potential uptake*

- individuals performing strenuous work involving a higher respiratory rate may have a higher uptake or potential uptake; persons who have a lot of skin contact with substances and ingest substances orally (e.g. due to poor hygiene);

*Increased sensitivity*

- *increased sensitivity*, caused by abnormal kinetics or dynamics of the substance. Often this kind of risk factor cannot be altered, because it is linked to genetic factors (slow and fast acetylators), to age, sex, acquired abnormalities or interaction with other substances. Examples are allergic reactions leading to eczema or asthma;

*Low reserve capacity*

- individuals with a *low reserve capacity* may, at the same (chronic) exposure and even under "normal" working conditions, show relatively more health effects or demonstrate them sooner.

### 4.6 LEGISLATION AND STANDARDS IN OCCUPATIONAL TOXICOLOGY

The improvement of working conditions is supported by experts in safety and health, and in the social sciences.

*United States*

In the US, the Occupation Safety and Health Act is administered by the Occupational Safety and Health Administration (OSHA). The Occupation Safety and Health Act concerns health and safety in the workplace. The Occupational Safety and Health Administration sets standards for worker exposure to specific chemicals, for air concentration values, and for monitoring procedures. Construction and environmental controls also come under this act. It also provides for research, information, education, and training in occupational safety and health. By establishing NIOSH (National Institute for Occupational Safety and Health) the act provided for appropriate studies to be carried out so that regulatory decisions could be based on the best available information. The Occupational Safety and Health Administration and the National Institute for Occupational Safety and Health periodically compile a list of potential hazards, along with recommendations for limits of exposure.

*Europe*

In Europe, the Control Of Substances Hazardous to Health Regulations (COSHH) sets out the measures which must be taken by employers, the self employed and employees to comply with their general duties under the Health And Safety Etc.

Act with regard to Substances Hazardous to Health. These regulations implement an European Community Council Directive. They have been brought in under the Health and Safety at Work Act 1974 (HSW Act). This Act regards the prevention of adverse health effects due to exposure at work to toxic substances primarily as the responsibility of employers and employees alike. The COSHH regulations contain a definition of what is to be regarded as a substance hazardous to health. It is stated that a substance hazardous to health is any substance (or preparation) which falls into one of five classes:

*Class a*: Substances listed in Part 1A of the Approved List as dangerous to supply within the meaning of the Classification, Packaging and Labelling Regulations 1984.

*Class b*: Substances for which an Occupational Exposure Standard (OES) (originally Maximum Exposure Limits, MELs) is specified in Schedule 1 of the COSHH Regulations or for which the Health and Safety Commission has approved an occupational exposure standard in the latest Guidance Note EH 40 which is revised annually.

*Class c*: Micro-organisms which create a hazard to the health of any person.

*Class d*: Dust of any kind, when present at a substantial concentration in air.

*Class e*: Substances which while not covered in classes *a—d* create a hazard to health comparable with that created by substances in the first four categories.

The main objective of occupational toxicology can only be reached if exposure conditions at the work place are defined that do not induce an unacceptable health risk. In practice, permissible levels of exposure to industrial chemicals have been defined. These levels are expressed in terms of allowable atmospheric concentrations or as permissible biological levels.

*Allowable atmospheric concentrations*

Allowable atmospheric concentrations are: MACs, MELs, OES, TLVs, TLV-C, TWAE, TWAC and STELs.

*Maximum allowable concentrations*

Maximum allowable concentrations (MACs) are the upper limit of concentrations of certain atmospheric contaminants allowed in the ambient air of the workplace. Maximum exposure limits (MELs) in COSHH regulations sets average exposure limits which should not be exceeded. If a maximum exposure limit has been set for a substance, it is laid down that so far as inhalation exposure is concerned, adequate control means reducing exposure so far as is reasonably particable and to below the maximum exposure limit. The MEL may currently take two forms:

- a long term maximum exposure limit with an 8 hour time weighted average (TWA) exposure period,
- a short term 10 minute reference period maximum exposure limit.

*Occupational exposure standard*

The *occupational exposure standard* (OES; COSHH-regulations) is the concentration, averaged over a reference period, of an airborne substance which is believed is unlikely to be injurious to employees exposed daily to the material. Exposure by inhalation should be reduced to the OES but it is recognized that this may take some time in some cases.

*Threshold Limit Values*

*Threshold limit values* (TLVs) are occupational exposure limits recommended by the American Conference of Governmental Industrial Hygienists (ACGIH). TLVs are the upper permissive limits of airborne concentrations of substances. They represent conditions under which it is believed that nearly all employees may be repeatedly exposed day after day without adverse effect. Threshold limit value, ceiling (TLV-C) represents the concentration that should not be exceeded even momentarily. TWAC or TWAE is the time-weighted average concentration (or exposure) for a normal 40-hour working week to which nearly all workers may be repeatedly exposed, without adverse effect. Short-term exposure limits (STELs) are the maximal concentrations to which a worker can be exposed for up to 15 consecutive minutes.

MACs, TLVs etc. aimed at safeguarding health, are managerial values. Although the starting point in setting up them is health as far as possible, some of these values do not comply, for a variety of reasons. Take for example substances for which a no-observed-adverse-effect levels can not be given. This is the case for substances to which no 'no-observed-adverse-effect-levels' can be attributed. Examples are many of the carcinogens. To meet the starting criterion, the standards would in such cases have to be set at zero, which in practice means a total ban. If the use of the substance has to be regarded as socially unavoidable, a value will be set which, although low, still carries a certain risk. The diagram in Figure 40.14 summarizes the various stages in the process of evaluating a toxicological risk.

## 5    Summary

Occupational toxicology is primarily concerned with assessment of the toxicological risk involved in handling chemicals. Therefore, it is an important part of occupational health care. Cases of serious occupational poisoning, which once frequently led to manifest disease and invalidity, are hardly seen any more. The accent has shifted to the insidious types of poisoning, especially in situations where workers are exposed over long periods of time to relatively low concentrations of chemical substances. This means that the practical approach is directed more towards health surveillance, the main concern being prevention. An important instrument in this respect is exposure monitoring, which consists mainly of recording levels of toxic substances in the work environment (environmental monitoring) and measuring the internal exposures to which workers are subjected (biological monitoring). On the basis of such measurements steps may be taken to minimize exposure and ensure that safe limit values (thresholds above which there is a risk to health) are not exceeded. The setting of such exposure limits, which form the basis of health surveillance, is one of the responsibilities of occupational toxicology. Use is made of data from predictive experimental research on animals and from epidemiological studies on groups of workers to examine chemical exposure in certain companies or branches of industry. The importance of epidemiology lies above all in the fact that genuine risks can be determined in real-life, non-experimental work situations. Epidemiological studies can also confirm a suspected risk.

In practical risk assessment the occupational toxicologist constantly has to deal with a variety of complicating factors. Examples are multiple exposures and individual risk factors. The latter include hereditary or acquired abnormalities in toxicokinetics and/or dynamics which may often cause increased sensitivity to certain substances.

SELF ASSESSMENT QUESTIONS

1    How is it apparent from Table 40.2 that the firm Du Pont attaches great importance to the work situation and the way in which substances are handled?

2    Despite the 1972 OSHA and NIOSH recommendations on asbestos, mesothelioma as a result of exposure to asbestos is still quite common. Why?

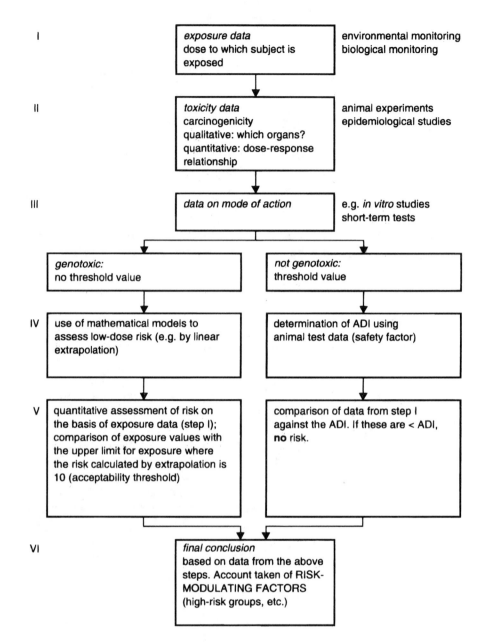

FIGURE 40.14

Processes of assessing and evaluating toxicological risks.

3    A retrospective cohort study of insulation workers ($n = 340$) who had worked with asbestos in the period 1940 to 1960, monitored the number of asbestosis cases up to 1980. This group included 60 workers who no longer worked with asbestos after 1950 but did insulation work using polymer foams (PUR). All the subjects were still alive on 1 January 1980; 5 of the 60 PUR workers had asbestosis and 35 subjects in the other group had this form of pulmonary fibrosis. Calculate the prevalence of asbestosis in the two groups and in the group as a whole. Explain the difference. Can this be described as an intervention study?

4    What are the possibilities and limitations of biological monitoring (BM) as compared with environmental monitoring (EM)?

5    Even at very low concentrations (< 1 ppm) exposure to toluene diisocyanate (TDI; MW = 174) can induce asthmatic reactions in some individuals. The reactions usually occur 2 to 6 hours after exposure. The MAC for the substance is 0.14 mg m$^{-3}$. Express the MAC in terms of ppm.
How should workers handling this substance be monitored?

## FEEDBACK

### 1    Answers to the assignments

40.1  As a rule, the substances used in industry are not known by their chemical name but by a trade name or code. One reason for this is commercial secrecy. Chemical products are also often made up of mixtures of different substances. Depending on their industrial use, many substances handled have a varying degree of purity, and this means that in many cases the chemical products contain impurities. Sometimes these impurities are far more dangerous than the actual substance being investigated.

40.2  Substances may manifest themselves in the atmosphere of the workplace in various physical forms: (pure or diluted) gas, vapor, aerosol (adsorbed on to water droplets), fumes (welding fumes, cigarette smoke) or adsorbed on to "inert" solid particles (e.g. heavy metals in fly ash).

40.3  These techniques can only be used for measuring toxic peak concentrations, because the result is not available till much later, and because they provide a time-weighted average.

40.4  Uptake is greater when strenuous physical work is being done because respiratory minute volume will increase. Volatile substances will be eliminated more quickly because of the increased exhalation rate.

40.5  As a rule, protection against or treatment of poisoning (antidote therapy) purposely uses antagonistic effects. See also Study unit 38.

40.6  Because of the great species differences in metabolism, especially reflected in interaction effects.

40.7  The significance of this statement is of course very small. Human carcinogenicity can only really be determined by epidemiological research. It may be that some of these substances are not carcinogenic to man, perhaps due to a different metabolism or some other (more specific?) repair mechanism. It may also be that the latency period in man is longer. Conversely, it has been established that all substances proved to be carcinogenic in man are also carcinogenic in test animals.

40.8  Human *in vivo* data are important in the process of setting MACs or TLVs because they do not require extrapolation from animal to man and already reflect an important determining factor of toxicity, namely the kinetics of the substance.

### 2    Answers to the self assessment questions

1    This is shown by the high score of the items under heading 8 (highest 16 points) in contrast to acute or chronic toxicity data (highest 8 points).

2　The reason why mesothelioma as a result of exposure to asbestos is still seen is that the latency period is long, and it thus occurs in individuals who were exposed many years previously. Exposure to asbestos is still possible now, e.g. in demolition work (asbestos cement) or in garages (asbestos in brake linings).

3　For information: roughly speaking, asbestos can cause three types of lung disease:

1. asbestosis—diffuse pulmonary fibrosis, observed only after lengthy exposure to high concentrations; clear dose-response relationship
2. mesothelioma—malignant disorder of the pleura; may be observed even after brief exposure to low concentrations
3. bronchogenic carcinoma, enhanced by smoking.

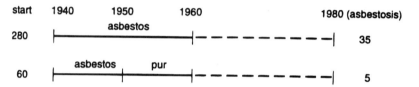

The prevalences are 35/280 and 5/60, which means 12.5 and 8.3% respectively. The prevalence in the asbestos/PUR insulation workers is thus lower than in those working only with asbestos. This makes sense since the latter group had received a higher dose and had been exposed for twice as long. But exposures to asbestos may have been higher between 1940 and 1950 than they were between 1950 and 1960.

One can indeed describe this as an intervention study, though in this case it did not set out to be, but was prompted by technological considerations. These data do not allow conclusions to be drawn on

1. the effect of PUR on its own, and
2. any interaction between PUR and asbestos.

4　BM measures internal exposure whilst EM only estimates it; BM also takes individual characteristics and habits into account.

Limitations of BM are that there is no point in sampling substances which have a contact effect and that at the time of sampling and/or analysis of the results the individual in question is already exposed.

5　1 ppm is one part per million, thus for example 1 ml m$^{-3}$

$$0.14 \text{ mg TDI} = \frac{0.14}{\text{MW}} \text{ mmol TDI, MW} = 174 \rightarrow \frac{0.14}{174} \text{ mmol} = 0.8 \text{ μmol}$$

1 mol = 22.4 liters = 22 400 ml
1 μmol = 22.4 · 10$^{-3}$ ml → 0.8 μmol = 18 · 10$^{-3}$ ml

In other words:
0.14 mg m$^{-3}$ = 18 · 10$^{-3}$ ml m$^{-3}$ = 18 ppb = 0.018 ppm

Environmental monitoring is the method of choice, because the effects in question here are acute effects, and may appear at very low ambient concentrations.

# Content of Achievement test

# Achievement test

### INTRODUCTION

You have now finished studying the textbook. The following examination allows you to check for yourself whether you have a thorough command of the subject matter. You should try to spend no longer than 2–3 hours on the test.

The achievement test consists of 50 multiple-choice questions. There usually are four options of which, in most cases, only one is correct. In addition to the multiple-choice questions, the test also includes 7 essay questions. You should try to give brief, but unambiguous answers to these questions.

Some helpful recommendations to bear in mind while carrying out the achievement test are the following:

- read each question carefully
- attempt to formulate a correct answer before looking at the options provided
- check whether your answer corresponds with one (or sometimes more than one) of the options
- if so, indicate that option (or those options)
- if not, read the options carefully; they might put you on the right track.

*Checking*

After you have checked your answers against those given in the feedback section, you are advised to study again those units specified for each of the questions which you have answered incorrectly.

To do this achievement test, find a quiet environment where you can work for 4 hours solidly, without being interrupted and make sure to be well rested before you start.
Good luck!

## ACHIEVEMENT TEST

### 1   Multiple-choice questions

1   Which of the following statements is *incorrect*?

   a.   Chronic toxicity studies lasting more than 24 months are not useful in rats because, after 24 months, mortality will exceed the incidence of substance-induced tumors.

   b.   Chronic toxicity tests take longer in rabbits than in rats.

   c.   If a chronic toxicity test is not aimed at detecting carcinogenic effects, a shorter exposure time will suffice.

   d.   The highest dosage used in chronic toxicity tests is always a mildly toxic dosage.

2   Which of the following statements is correct/incorrect?
   I. The term '$LD_{50}$ test' or '$LC_{50}$ test' is a synonym for acute toxicity test.
   II. During chronic toxicity studies, a number of animals will usually die. The eventual aim of such a study, however, is to establish the sublethal toxic effects of a substance.

   a.   I is correct, II is incorrect

   b.   I is incorrect, II is correct

   c.   I and II are both correct

   d.   I and II are both incorrect

3   Which of the following statements is correct/incorrect?
   I. Within the field of toxicology, bioactivation is a synonym of toxification.
   II. The cytochrome P-450 enzyme system is able to catalyze both bioactivation and bioinactivation reactions.

   a.   I is correct, II is incorrect

   b.   I is incorrect, II is correct

   c.   I and II are both correct

   d.   I and II are both incorrect

4   Which of the following statements is correct/incorrect?
   I. In the Ames test, both initiating and promoting effects of carcinogens can be detected.
   II. In the Ames test with *Salmonella typhimurium* is based on the property of (some) mutagenic substances to mutate a mutant back to its original form.

   a.   I is correct, II is incorrect

   b.   I is incorrect, II is correct

   c.   I and II are both correct

   d.   I and II are both incorrect

5   Studies of toxicity mechanisms sometimes make use of enzyme induction. In a study on the mechanism by which bromobenzene brings about hepatic necrosis in rats, pretreatment of the animals with phenobarbital appeared to cause an intensification of the toxic effect, whereas preliminary treatment with 3-methylcholanthrene (3-MC) was found to offer protection against hepatic necrosis. Analysis of the effects of pretreatment with 3-MC on the metabolites of bromobenzene present in the urine of rats provided the following results:

*Pretreatment*    Percentage of the total quantity of metabolites in the urine

| | bromophenol | | bromobenzene dihydradiol | | 4-bromophenyl mercapturic acid | various |
|---|---|---|---|---|---|---|
| | 2-isomer | 4-isomer | 2,3-isomer | 3,4-isomer | | |
| no 3-MC | 4 | 37 | ≤1 | 4 | 48 | 6 à 7 |
| 3-MC | 21 | 20 | 10 | 7 | 31 | 11 |

Question:

Induction of which two metabolic processes by 3-MC will have contributed to the protection against bromobenzene-induced necrosis?

   a.    2,3-epoxidation and dihydrodiol formation

   b.    2,3-epoxidation and 3,4-epoxidation

   c.    3,4-epoxidation and dihydrodiol formation

   d.    3,4-epoxidation and GSH conjugation

6    Oxidation of hydroquinone,

can lead to lipid peroxidation by:

   a.    semiquinone radical formation

   b.    superoxide anion radical formation

   c.    semiquinone radical formation and superoxide anion radical formation

   d.    quinone formation

7    A patient is treated with two different compounds (A and B) for a period of 6 weeks, according to the table provided below.

*dosing scheme**

| time** | substance/dose (mg) |
|---|---|
| 1 | A/40 |
| 2 | A/60 |
| 3 | A/80 |
| 4 | B/40 |
| 5 | B/60 |
| 6 | B/80 |

*the compounds are administered intravenously
**the time between two doses is 1 week

After each dose, the elimination half-life ($t_{1/2}$) is determined:

| dose (mg) | $t_{1/2}$ for A (hours) | $t_{1/2}$ for B (hours) |
|---|---|---|
| 40 | 10 | 3.47 |
| 60 | 15 | 3.47 |
| 80 | 80 | 3.47 |

Of what order is the elimination process in case A and case B, respectively?

| Compound A | Compound B |
|---|---|
| a. first-order process | first-order process |
| b. zero-order process | first-order process |
| c. first-order process | zero-order process |
| d. zero-order process | zero-order process. |

8 First read the data provided for Question 7.

What are the values of the elimination rate constants ($k$) of the compounds A and B from the example in Question 7 at an initial dose ($D_0$) of 100 mg?

At an initial dose of 100 mg, the elimination rate constants are:

| Compound A | Compound B |
|---|---|
| a. 0.173 mg per hour | 0.200 mg per hour |
| b. 4.000 mg per hour | 14.408 mg per hour |
| c. 4.000 mg per hour | 0.200 mg per hour |
| d. 0.173 mg per hour | 14.408 mg per hour |

9 Which of the following statements is correct/incorrect?
I. An isochromatid gap is not a chromosome aberration because, in the case of an isochromatid gap, the parts of the chromosome are still connected with each other.
II. An isochromatid gap is not a chromosome aberration because chromosome aberrations always involve more than one gene.
a. I is correct, II is incorrect
b. I is incorrect, II is correct
c. I and II are both correct
d. I and II are both incorrect.

10 Which of the following reactive oxygen species can act both as reducing and as oxidizing agents?
a. superoxide anion radicals
b. hydrogen peroxide
c. singlet oxygen
d. hydroxyl radicals.

11 Amalgam, which is commonly used in dentistry to fill cavities in teeth, contains mercury.

Which of the following statements is correct/incorrect?
I. Exposure to mercury due to 'leaking' of mercury from amalgam fillings in a patient's teeth is an example of a risk.
II. Exposure to mercury due to the use of amalgam by a dentist in his practice while treating patients is an example of a hazard.
a. I is correct, II is incorrect
b. I is incorrect, II is correct
c. I and II are both correct
d. I and II are both incorrect.

12    Examples of xenobiotics that are absorbed by means of specific endoge-nous transfer systems include: 5-fluorouracil (which is absorbed via the pyrimidine transport system), thallium (absorbed via the iron uptake sys-tem) and lead (probably absorbed via the calcium uptake system). With ref-erence to the absorption processes of 5-fluorouracil, thallium and lead, one may therefore state that:
I. they are based on facilitated diffusion and/or active transport;
II. the absorption takes place via a zero-order process.
    a.    I is correct, II is incorrect
    b.    I is incorrect, II is correct
    c.    I and II are both correct
    d.    I and II are both incorrect

13    What would the plot look like if, in the case of a quantal response, the re-sults of an experiment are shown with the log dose plotted on the $x$-axis and the percentage of responders on the $y$-axis?
    a.    a straight line
    b.    an S-shaped curve
    c.    a so-called Gaussian curve (such as the normal distribution)
    d.    none of the above options is correct

14    Combination of methyl alcohol and ethyl alcohol causes a reduction in the acute toxicity of methyl alcohol due to competition for metabolic oxida-tion. This is an example of:
    a.    synergism
    b.    chemical antagonism
    c.    functional antagonism
    d.    receptor antagonism

15    Which of the following statements is correct/incorrect?
I. Because phenobarbital is capable of inducing cancer of the liver in mice, it is classified as an initiator.
II. The increased incidence of lung cancer among workers in the asbestos industry who smoke, in relation to the incidence in their non-smoking col-leagues is due to a synergistic carcinogenic effect of cigarette smoke.
    a.    I is correct, II is incorrect
    b.    I is incorrect, II is correct
    c.    I and II are both correct
    d.    I and II are both incorrect

16    Various chemicals induce disturbances of the mitochondrial processes di-rectly, while others do so indirectly. On what is this distinction based?
    a.    On whether the damage is done to mitochondrial membranes or cy-toplasmic structures
    b.    On whether the disturbed process takes place in the cytoplasm or in a mitochondrion.
    c.    On whether or not there is a disturbance of the mitochondrial process of ATP synthesis.
    d.    On whether or not the electron transfer to oxygen in the mitochon-drion is disturbed

17 Which of the following compounds have no no-effect level?
    a.   hexachlorocyclohexane and ethylmethane sulfonicacid (EMS)
    b.   ethylmethanesulfonic acid (EMS) and diethyl nitrosamine
    c.   diethylnitrosamine and tetrachlorodibenzo-*p*-dioxin (TCDD)
    d.   hexachlorocyclohexane and tetrachlorodibenzo-*p*-dioxin (TCDD)

18 Which of the following statements is correct/incorrect?
I. Highly lipophilic substances have a low oil/water partition coefficient.
II. Highly lipophilic compounds are easily excreted without first being metabolized.
    a.   I is correct, II is incorrect
    b.   I is incorrect, II is correct
    c.   I and II are both correct
    d.   I and II are both incorrect

19

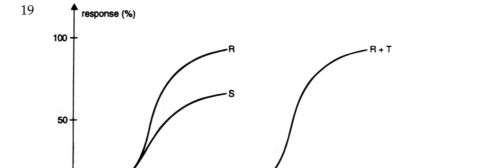

The above figure shows log dose–response curves for a substance R, for a substance S, and for substance R combined with substance T. All of the substances act via the same receptor.

Which of the following statements concerning the data in the figure is correct/incorrect?
I. R and S are equally toxic
II. T is a competitive antagonist of R.
    a.   I is correct, II is incorrect
    b.   I is incorrect, II is correct
    c.   I and II are both correct
    d.   I and II are both incorrect

20 In the following two unspecified pigments $X_1$ and $X_2$ are described. '... $X_1$ ...' is the iron-free degradation product of the heme component of hemoglobin and is usually excreted as a yellow-green-brown pigment in the bile. In severe conditions, this compound may accumulate in the hepatocytes and intercellular canaliculi, in which case it is microscopically visible as green-brown to black globular depositions.
'... $X_2$ ...' is the pigment which is often associated with lipid peroxidation. This compound is probably the end product of the free radical-initiated peroxidation of polyunsaturated membrane lipids by free radicals.

Which pigments are meant by $X_1$ and $X_2$?

| | $X_1$ | $X_2$ |
|---|---|---|
| a. | hemosiderin | bilirubin |
| b. | lipofuscin | hemosiderin |
| c. | bilirubin | hemosiderin |
| d. | bilirubin | lipofuscin |

21 Thalidomide causes selective anatomical changes during development. Methylmercury causes mental abnormalities during the (fetal) development, but does not cause any structural changes.
Which of the following statements is correct/incorrect?

I. Thalidomide is teratogenic
II. Methylmercury is teratogenic.

a. I is correct, II is incorrect
b. I is incorrect, II is correct
c. I and II are both correct
d. I and II are both incorrect

22 Which of the following statements is correct/incorrect?
I. In contrast to most other organs of the body, the human placenta is not able to bioactivate substances.
II. Perinatal carcinogenic substances are also embryotoxic.

a. I is correct, II is incorrect
b. I is incorrect, II is correct
c. I and II are both correct
d. I and II are both incorrect

23 Which of the following statements is correct/incorrect?
I. The fact that the sugar substitute saccharin is not metabolized in the body means that saccharin is biologically inactive.
II. The bladder wall seems to be the main target organ of the carcinogenic effect of saccharin, at least in rats. In this connection, a 1:100 ratio for the saccharin concentrations in the bladder wall and bladder contents, respectively, after a single oral dose administered to rats might be harmful.

a. I is correct, II is incorrect
b. I is incorrect, II is correct
c. I and II are both correct
d. I and II are both incorrect

24 In somebody who is occupationally exposed to a constant source of Hg for a long period of time, a steady-state level of the Hg plasma concentration may be expected to be reached only after a number of months (up to 1 year). In toxicological jargon, the _____ is then said to have reached a stable level.
The word which should be filled in is:

a. emission
b. exposure
c. organ concentration
d. body burden

25 Oncogenes are involved in:

a. the bioactivation of procarcinogens to ultimate carcinogens
b. the induction of point mutations in the DNA
c. the promotion of growth of neoplastic transformations
d. both the initiation and the promotion of tumors

26   The illustration below (b) shows the result of an immunoperoxidase reaction for TSH in the pituitary of adult rats (× 190). Figure a is a control section; the immunoreactive TSH cells show clear differences in the intensity of the staining reaction, which reflect differences in the quantities of hormone present. Figure b shows the pituitary of an adult rat after exposure for a number of weeks to a high dose of compound X.

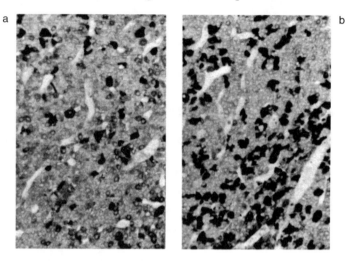

To what compound was the rat in figure b exposed?
a. TBTO (Tributyltin oxide)
b. a bromide
c. TBTO or a bromide
d. neither TBTO nor a bromide

27   24 hours after intracerebral administration of compound Q, a specific degeneration of serotonergic neurons in the brain is observed.

Exposure to what compound has taken place?
a. 6-hydroxydopamine
b. 5,6-dihydroxytryptamine
c. 6-hydroxydopamine or 5,6-dihydroxytryptamine
d. neither 6-hydroxydopamine nor 5,6-dihydroxytryptamine

28   Ischemia may cause damage to cells in the central nervous system (CNS). Which cells in the CNS will be the most sensitive to ischemia?
a. astrocytes
b. microglial cells
c. oligodendroglial cells
d. neuronal cells

29   Phototoxicity tests have been developed to study damage caused by the combined action of light and chemicals. A distinction can be made between phototoxicity in a strict sense and photoallergies.

Which of the following statements is correct/incorrect?

I. In both photoallergy and phototoxicity, light energy is suspected to cause the formation of reactive intermediates from the foreign compound.

II. In phototoxicity, free radicals react with body cells, whereas in photoallergy, free radicals interact with body proteins which subsequently act as allergens.

   a.   I is correct, II is incorrect

   b.   I is incorrect, II is correct

   c.   I and II are both correct

   d.   I and II are both incorrect

30    Which of the sections shown below (b, c, d or e) was taken from an experimental animal exposed to an overdose of acetaminophen? Section a is a control section.

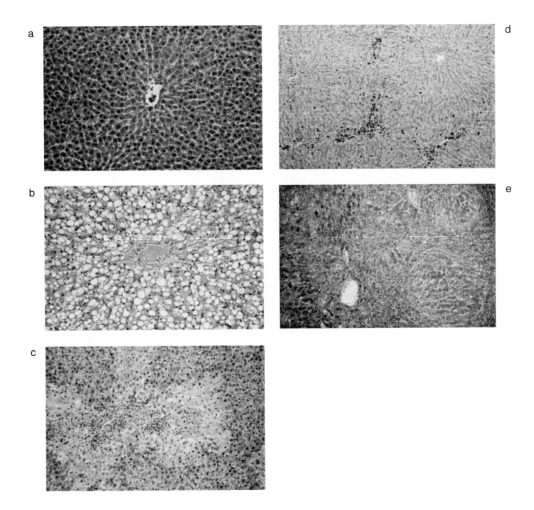

31    Nephrotoxic xenobiotics may cause proteinuria in various ways. Which of the following mechanisms does *not* play a role in this process?

   a.   increased glomerular permeability

   b.   damage to the parenchymal tissue of the proximal tubules

   c.   increased tubular secretion

   d.   reduced tubular reabsorption

32    Under normal physiological circumstances, large proteins such as albumin cannot enter the glomerular filtrate through the walls of the glomerular capillaries.

Which of the following factor(s) is/are responsible for these proteins not being able to pass across the walls of the glomerular capillaries?
I. The size of the endothelial fenestrations
II. The electrical charge of the protein

a.    only factor I
b.    only factor II
c.    both factor I and factor II
d.    neither factor I nor factor II

33    The particle size distribution of an aerosol has been measured. The contribution of the particles to the weight was plotted against their aerodynamic diameter, ranging from 1 to 10 $\mu$m. The result was a straight line showing a 100-fold increase.

Which of the following conclusions about the distribution of the number of particles as the diameter increases is correct?

a.    it decreases continuously
b.    it remains constant
c.    it increases continuously
d.    it shows a peak

34    Ecotoxicological effects of a certain compound at the population level are determined largely by:

a.    that component in the life cycle which is affected most by the toxic compound concerned
b.    the factors which most restrict a population in its natural environment
c.    a combination of the type of effect and the type of population regulation
d.    none of the above

35    Which of the following statements is correct/incorrect?
I. Lead causes disturbance of heme biosynthesis by inhibition of the enzyme $\delta$-aminolevulinic acid dehydratase.

II. Exposure to lead can be established by measuring the activity of $\delta$-aminolevulinic acid dehydratase in the blood.

a.    I is correct, II is incorrect
b.    I is incorrect, II is correct
c.    I and II are both correct
d.    I and II are both incorrect

36    Hexachlorobutadiene (HCBD) is a by-product formed during the synthesis of a number of chlorinated hydrocarbons. Oral administration of a single dose of HCBD causes necrosis of the proximal tubules in the rat kidney. The weight of the liver of rats treated with HCBD is somewhat, increased, and the concentration of glutathione is reduced. Inhibitors or inducers of the MFO system do not affect the nephrotoxicity of HCBD. However,

drainage of the bile from the body via a cannula prevents necrosis in the renal tubules.

Which of the following conclusions concerning HCBD-induced nephrotoxicity, based on the data provided above, is correct?

HCBD-induced nephrotoxicity is caused:

a. by a reactive intermediate of HCBD formed in the tubular cells by intervention of the cytochrome P-450 enzyme system

b. by a metabolite which is reabsorbed via the enterohepatic circulation, reaches the tubular cells and exerts its toxic effect there either directly or after bioactivation

c. by the fact that HCBD is reabsorbed via the enterohepatic circulation and subsequently undergoes bioactivation in the renal tubular cells

d. by the fact that HCBD glucuronide is excreted into the bile, is subsequently hydrolyzed in the intestine into glucuronic acid and HCBD under the influence of the intestinal bacteria, after which HCBD is reabsorbed via the enterohepatic circulation and activated in the tubular cells by means of the MFO enzyme system

37 Which of the following factors increases the risk of the development of a carcinoma of the stomach?

a. chronic alcoholism

b. the consumption of large quantities of meat

c. a high acidity (low pH) of the stomach

d. a diet rich in nitrate

38 "Standards" such as TLVs values and ADIs are used in the evaluation of health risks.

Which problem is encountered when these standards are applied in risk evaluation in the case of environmental incidents?

a. these standards are all based on animal experiments

b. these standards are all based on data on acute intoxication in man

c. these standards have all been set for the purpose of health protection (prevention)

d. these standards do not take sufficient account of differences between individuals

39 In what intoxication can Berlin blue ($KFe[Fe(CN)_6]$) be administered to interrupt enteroenteral or enterohepatic circulation?

a. lead intoxication

b. cyanide intoxication

c. thallium intoxication

d. mercury intoxication

40 The protective effect of dietary fiber against colonic cancer is due to:

a. increased intestinal motility

b. encapsulation of carcinogenic compounds

c. preservation of the intestinal flora

d. inhibition of the absorption of procarcinogens

41  Xenobiotic X is administered to an isolated rat liver (perfusion flow 40 ml min⁻¹) The concentrations of X flowing into and out of the organ are 38 and 18 $\mu$M respectively.

How will the elimination rate and clearance change if the metabolism of X is increased?

a.  the elimination rate is increased; clearance is increased

b.  the elimination rate remains more or less constant; clearance is increased

c.  the elimination rate is decreased; clearance is increased

d.  the elimination rate is increased; clearance is decreased.

42  Dioxin (TCDD) gives the most pronounced immunotoxic effects in experimental animals if administered perinatally.

Which of the following statements concerning the cause of this perinatal hypersensitivity is correct?

a.  Sensitivity to the immunotoxicity of dioxin is genetically determined.

b.  Dioxin binds to the Ah receptor of epithelial cells in the thymus, causing the production of T-lymphocytes to be decelerated.

c.  Perinatal exposure to dioxin results in increased differentiation of thymic epithelial cells at an early age.

d.  Immediately after birth, the organism has not yet formed many memory cells.

43  The figure below shows the effects of compound X and compound Y on the electrocardiogram (ECG). Figure a is a control ECG, figure b shows the effect of compound X and figure c that of compound Y.
What compounds are most likely to correspond to compounds X and Y?

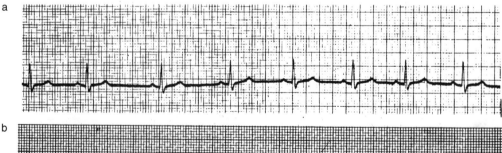

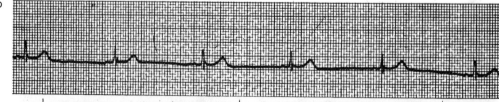

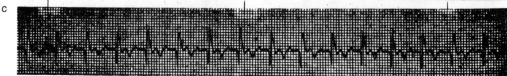

| | compound X | compound Y |
|---|---|---|
| a. | digoxin | amphetamine |
| b. | amphetamine | digoxin |
| c. | cobalt | digoxin |
| d. | amphetamine | cobalt |

44 Interim evaluation (after one week) of a biomonitoring program on dimethylacetamide (DMAC) shows 2 out of 20 exposed employees to display increasing concentrations of monomethylacetamide (MMAC) in the urine. During that week, their inhalatory exposure had not been any different from that of the other 18 employees. The conversion of DMAC to MMAC proceeds via an N-demethylation reaction catalyzed by the cytochrome P-450 enzyme system in the liver.

On what factor is this difference *not* based?
a. The bioavailability of DMAC is lower for these two employees.
b. The two employees concerned are slow metabolizers of DMAC, something which might be genetically determined.
c. In these two employees, induction of cytochrome P-450 has taken place, for example because they used certain medicines.
d. Metabolism was saturated in the two persons concerned, so that the percentage of metabolite out of the total dose is smaller.

45 A $CO_2$ provocation test is carried out in a healthy human test subject. Before adding inhalatory $CO_2$, the $CO_2$ pressure of the arterial blood is 5 kPa (normal atmospheric pressure is 100 kPa). After addition of $CO_2$, the respiratory minute volume is found to have increased by a factor five, without the test subject appearing to have any difficulty in breathing.

What was the percentage of $CO_2$ in the air supplied?
a. 2%
b. 4%
c. 5%
d. 20%

46 Hypoxia caused by intoxication does *not* occur as a result of:
a. carbon monoxide intoxication
b. methemoglobinemia
c. exposure to benzene
d. cyanide intoxication

47 Which of the following statements is correct?
I. Ethyl alcohol metabolism follows zero-order kinetics.
II. Ethyl alcohol can be administered therapeutically in the treatment of intoxication with methyl alcohol.
a. I is correct, II is incorrect
b. I is incorrect, II is correct
c. I and II are both correct
d. I and II are both incorrect

48 Which US agency is mainly responsible for the formulation of regulations under the Toxic Substances Control Act (TSCA)?
   a. Food and Drug Administration
   b. Labor Department
   c. Consumer Products Safety Commission
   d. Environmental Protection Agency

49 Given the temperature is 25°C, pressure is 760 mm mercury and the concentration of carbon monoxide is 22 ppm, convert this to mg m$^{-3}$.
   a. 19.2 mg m$^{-3}$
   b. 25.2 mg m$^{-3}$
   c. 23.5 mg m$^{-3}$
   d. 20.6 mg m$^{-3}$

50 Which of the following statements is true?

   Methemoglobinemia:
   a. develops when the heme part of hemoglobin is oxidized to hematin
   b. is usually due to an inherited deficiency of NADH methemoglobin reductase
   c. can be treated by means of reducing agents such as ascorbic acid
   d. if sufficiently severe causes the blood to become cyanosed in color

## 2  Essay questions

I   A 5-year-old girl with a body weight of 15 kg ingests an unknown quantity of Pepto Bismol, which contains salicylic acid. After ingestion, the plasma salicylic acid concentration is 1080 mg ml$^{-1}$. In this case, the volume of distribution for the salicylic acid is 0.3l per kg.
    How much salicylic acid did the girl ingest?

II  Calculate the log $K_{ow}$ values for 3,4-dinitrochlorobenzene and 2,3-dichlorotoluene, both from the $\pi$ constants and by Rekker's method.

III Pyrethroids are insecticides that are applied for their neurotoxic properties. In a study by Miyamoto (1976), pyrethroids (10 mg per plate) were dissolved in dimethyl sulfoxide. No revertants were found in relation to control plates nor in relation to nitrosoguanidine. Describe briefly (maximum 150 words) what type of test is used here, what the underlying mechanism is of the test used, and what the result is. Also explain the function of nitrosoguanidine.

IV  Describe the bioactivation reactions (with chemical structural formulas) which are or may be involved in the induction of the hepatotoxic effect of carbon tetrachloride. Also describe the cytotoxic mechanism of the effect.

V   Cephaloridine, an antibiotic belonging to the cephalosporins, is nephrotoxic in man and in experimental animals. Administration of, for example, 150 mg per kg body weight causes severe necrosis of tubular cells in rabbits, without there being simultaneous hepatic damage. Cephaloridine is an organic anion and is excreted actively into the tubular cells by the renal tubular anion transport system. Unlike the other cephalosporins, cephaloridine is not excreted actively from the tubular cells into the lumen. The table provided below shows the effect of exposure of guinea pigs to cephaloridine, and the effect of pretreatment with probenecid.

### DOSE-RESPONSIVENESS OF THE GUINEA PIG TO THE EFFECTS OF PROBENECID ON CEPHALORIDINE TRANSPORT AND TOXICITY[25]

| Probenecid dose[a] (mg/kg) | Cortical cephaloridine[b] (μg/g) | | Proximal tubular necrosis[c] (no. of animals) | | | |
|---|---|---|---|---|---|---|
| | 0.5 hr[a] | 3 hr[a] | None | Mild | Moderate | Severe |
| 0 | 3123 ± 63 (6) | 3576 ± 148 (6) | 1 | 0 | 4 | 7 |
| 5 | 2068 ± 73 (6) | 1940 ± 91 (6) | 0 | 2 | 4 | 6 |
| 10 | 1403 ± 134 (6) | 1263 ± 132 (6) | 6 | 5 | 1 | 0 |
| 20 | 882 ± 64 (6) | 589 ± 44 (6) | 11 | 1 | 0 | 0 |
| 40 | — | 478 ± 26 (6) | 12 | 0 | 0 | 0 |

[a] Cephaloridine, 400 mg/kg, s.c., was given 0.5 hr after s.c. probenecid. Sacrifice was at 0.5 and 3 hr after injection of cephaloridine.

[b] Results are the means ± SEM, with the numbers of animals given in parentheses.

[c] Scored with randomly assorted coded slides.

a. What conclusions can be drawn from this with respect to the toxicity of cephaloridine?

b. What effect does treatment with probenecid have on the toxicity of cephaloridine? Explain your answer.

VI Some toxic compounds display selective toxicity for one particular organ or organ system.

Give three examples of organ-selective compounds, specifying the target organ, the toxic effect and the mechanism underlying the selectivity.

VII Read the abstract printed below, of a study on the toxicity of butylated hydroxytoluene.

#### Characteristics of the Acute Hepatic Damage Induced by High Doses of BHT
C. J. Powell & P. Grasso
The Robens Institute, University of Surrey, Guildford, GU2 5XH, Surrey, UK

Butylated hydroxytoluene (BHT) an efficient and widely used antioxidant, has recently been implicated as a hepatocarcinogen in the rat. As the mechanism by which these lesions arise is of critical importance in assessing the relevance for man, interest is presently focussed upon the early effects of this compound on the liver.

We have previously demonstrated that a single high dose of 1000 mg BHT/kg caused centrilobular hepatic lesions[1], while a lower dose (500 mg BHT/kg), given repeatedly, induces periportal damage. We therefore investigated the acute effects of an intermediate dose level in order to define the primary target cells for liver damage.

Male Wistar rats weighing 250 g, were given 1 or 2 doses of 800 mg BHT/kg, 24 h apart and examined 24 h after administration.

Liver weights increased 20% within the first 24 h and up to 33% by 48 h. Hepatocyte proliferation was high, with mitotic indices of up to 2.4%; a level comparable to that occurring after a 60% partial hepatectomy.

Twenty-four hours after a single dose of BHT/kg there was cytoplasmic disorganization of centrilobular hepatocytes. The first frankly degenerative lesions were in cells around terminal central veins. These consisted of vacuolated or necrotic hepatocytes, often forming an annulus which was separated from the blood vessel by 2 or 3 layers of normal hepatocytes. These lesions were usually accompanied by a profuse macrophage infiltrate. In more severely affected animals, the damage extended to involve the entire centrilobular and midzonal regions, producing confluent centrilobular necrosis.

These results demonstrate that very high levels of cell proliferation characterize the initial response of the liver to high doses of BHT. We propose that when high doses of BHT are administered repeatedly hepatocyte hyperplasia may persist beyond the initial phase of compensatory regeneration, and that this is directly related to the increased incidence of liver tumours in BHT exposed animals.

#### Reference
Powell CJ, Connelly JC, Jones SM, Grasso P & Bridges JW. Hepatic responses to the administration of high doses of BHT to the rat: Their relevance to hepatocarcinogenicity. *Food Chemical Toxicology* 1986; 24 1131–43.

a. Is this an *in vitro*, an *in vivo* or an *in vitro ex vivo* study? Explain your answer.

b. Indicate in a schematic drawing of the liver lobule where the effects occur of the various dosages (1000 mg kg⁻¹ BHT, repeated administration of 500 mg; two doses of 800 mg kg⁻¹, examined after 24 and 48 hours).

c. Is it possible to conclude on the basis of this study whether BHT is a carcinogenic or a mutagenic compound? Explain your answer.

## FEEDBACK

### 1 Answers to the multiple-choice questions

The numbers in brackets indicate the study unit(s) dealing with the relevant subject matter.

1 Option a is incorrect (1 and 14)

2 Option b is correct (1 and 14)

3 Option c is correct (3)

4 Option b is correct (11)

5 Option a is correct (3, 4, 10)

6 Option c is correct (10)

7 Option b is correct (6)

8 Option c is correct (6)

9 Option a is correct (11)

10 Option a is correct (10)

11 Option d is correct (2)

12 Option a is correct (5)

13 Option b is correct (7)

14 Option d is correct (7, 9)

15 Option b is correct (12, 13)

16 Option b is correct (16)

17 Option b is correct (7, 11, 13)

18 Option d is correct (5, 8)

19 Option b is correct (7)

20 Option d is correct (15)

21 Option c is correct (31, 32)

22 Option d is correct (31)

23 Option b is correct (37)

24 Option d is correct (2)

25 Option c is correct (12)

26 Option b is correct (Study unit 29).
The sections clearly show that the number of cells with high immunoreactivity for TSH is increased in figure b. TBTO decreases the immunoreactivity of the TSH cells in the pituitary (see section 29.5), while bromide, e.g. NaBr, increases their immunoreactivity (see section 29.5).

27 Option b is correct (Study units 33 to 35).
Exposure of nervous tissue to 6-hydroxydopamine gives rise to lesion of dopaminergic and noradrenergic nerve terminals (see section 33.3.4). 5,6-dihydroxytryptamine is taken up by serotonergic neurons in the same way as serotonin, and gives rise to the formation of reactive oxygen species after oxidation. Selective serotonergic neuropathy will therefore be the result. See also assignment 33.9 and the answer provided.

28 Option d is correct (Study units 33 to 35).
The neuronal cells will be the most sensitive to ischemia because they lack reserve energy depots and any appropriate protective mechanisms.

29 Option c is correct (Study unit 17).
Light energy is suspected to be responsible for the formation of free radicals from the foreign compound in both phototoxicity and photoallergy. In phototoxicity, these radicals directly attack body cells, while in photoallergy, they combine with or change body proteins, which consequently start to act as allergens and to evoke an antibody reaction.

30 Option c is correct (Study units 22/23).
Section c shows a case of centrilobular hepatic necrosis, a histopathological abnormality most frequently encountered after an overdose of acetaminophen. The other sections show different pathological phenomena; b shows total hepatic steatosis, d accumulation of pigment and e cirrhosis.

31 Option c is correct (Study unit 24).
Active secretion of proteins does not take place in the kidney.

32 Option b is correct (Study unit 24).
The size, shape, molecular mass and electrical charge determine whether a protein can pass across the wall of the glomerular capillary.

33 Option d is correct (Study unit 21).
An increase in weight slightly more than 10-fold is found for an increase in the diameter from 1 to 2 $\mu$m, while an 8-fold increase would be expected if the distribution were to remain constant.
An increase from 1 to 10 $\mu$m leads to a 100-fold increase in the contribution, while a 1000-fold increase would be expected if the distribution were to remain constant.

34 Option c is correct (Study unit 38).

35 Option b is correct (Study unit 27).
The induction of $\delta$-aminolevulinic acid dehydratase resulting from the presence of lead in the blood is only of diagnostic significance.

36 Option b is correct (Study units 22/23).
Inhibition or induction does not influence the nephrotoxicity of HCBD, which suggests that the MFO system is not involved in its toxic effect. When the bile is diverted via a cannula, the nephrotoxic effect is absent. This indicates that it is a product in the bile that is responsible for the nephrotoxic effect, presumably a metabolite formed via a phase II reaction. Because in this latter case, no nephrotoxic effect is observed, it cannot be HCBD itself which causes the effect.

37 Option d is correct (Study units 20/21).
The conversion of nitrate to nitrite and nitrosamines is a predisposing factor for the development of carcinomas of the stomach.

38 Option c is correct (Study unit 39).

39 Option c is correct (Study units 20/21 and 39).

40 Option a is correct (Study unit 21).

41 Option a is correct (Study unit 25).

42 Option c is correct (Study units 28/29).
Dioxin accelerates differentiation from thymic epithelial cell to T-lymphocyte.

43 Option a is correct (Study unit 26).

Figure b shows a case of sinus bradycardia, figure c one of sinus tachycardia. Digitalis glycosides (such as digoxin) cause bradycardia, while stimulating compounds such as amphetamine give rise to tachycardia.

44 Option c is correct (Study unit 40).
Enzyme induction would have led to an increase in the quantity of MMAC in the urine.

45 Option b (4%) is correct (Study unit 19).
The alveolar air contains 5% $CO_2$. This percentage is maintained by efficient ventilatory adaptation. In the case of a five-fold increase in the ventilation, with unchanged $CO_2$ production, the $CO_2$ transport capacity of the ventilation air is found to be reduced by a factor 5. This corresponds with an inhalational concentration of 4% ($(5-4)/5 = 1/5$).

46 Option c is correct (Study unit 28).
Options a, b and d all cause a change (reduction) in oxygen supply to the tissues as a result of a decrease in oxygen transport capacity of the blood. Benzene causes leukemia by directly affecting the stem cells.

47 Option c is correct (Study unit 23 and others).

48 Option c (EPA) is correct (Study unit 14).

49 Concentration in $mg\ m^{-3}$ = (ppm · molecular wt)/24.45 = ($22 \cdot 28.01$) / 24.45 = 25.2 Option b is correct (Study unit 40).

50 Option d is correct (Study unit 27)

## 2 Answers to the open questions

I $V_D = 15\ kg \cdot 0.31\ l\ kg^{-1} = 4.5l$
$V_D$ = total absorbed $(A)/C_p$
$0.3l\ kg^{-1} = A/(1.080\ mg\ ml^{-1})$
$4.5l = A/(1.080\ mg\ ml^{-1})$
A = 4824 mg or 4.8 g

II *π constants*:

| | |
|---|---|
| for 3,4-dinitrochlorobenzene: | log Kow ($C_6H_6$) + π-(Cl) + 2 · ($\pi NO_2$) = 2.13 + 0.71 −0.56 = 2.28 |
| for 2,3-dichlorotoluene: | 2.69 + 2 · (0.71) = 4.11 |
| *by Rekker's method*: | |
| for 3,4-dinitrochlorobenzene: | $fC_6H_3$ + 2 · $fNO_2$ + fCl = 1.431 − 0.156 + 0.37 = 1.645 |
| for 2,3-dichlorotoluene: | $fC_6H_3$ + $fCH_3$ + 2 · fCl = 1.688 + 0.702 + 1.844 = 4.234 |

III The test used is a reverse mutation test, comparable to the Ames test. It makes use of bacteria strains that are sensitive to mutagenic properties. The bacteria used have also been cultured in such a way that a mutation has caused them to lose their ability to synthesize a particular amino acid. Using mutagenic substances, a reverse mutation can be brought about, so that the bacteria regain their ability to synthesize the amino acid. If the bacteria strains are cultured in the presence of the substance to be tested on a medium not containing the amino acid concerned, and are able to reproduce, one may conclude that the tested substance has a mutagenic effect.

In the study described, the substances to be studied are pyrethroids. The nitrosoguanidine serves as a positive control, i.e. it is a substance known to cause reverse mutation in the test used.

IV Cytochrome P-450 can also catalyze reductions. This is the case, for example, for the metabolic activation of halogenated alkanes. Carbon tetrachloride undergoes both one-electron and two-electron reduction:

**fig. answer question IV 30**

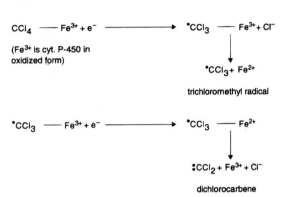

Both reactive intermediates (trichloromethyl radical and dichlorocarbene) can induce hepatotoxic effects. The trichloromethyl radical can initiate lipid peroxidation, while carbenes can inactivate heme proteins by complex formation:

$$\begin{matrix} \diagdown \\ \diagup \end{matrix} C : \!\!-\!\!-\!\!-\! Fe^{2+}$$

V a. The table shows that cephaloridine (without preliminary treatment) *accumulates in the cortex* (tubular cells) of the kidney. It shows moreover that the toxicity of cephaloridine is *dose-dependent* (the more cephaloridine has accumulated, the more extensive and/or severe the necrosis of the tubular cells).

b. Pretreatment with probenecid *prevents accumulation* of cephaloridine in the renal cortex (the higher the dosage of probenecid, the lower the concentration of cephaloridine). This is a *kinetic effect*; probenecid inhibits the active excretion of cephaloridine from the blood into the tubular cells. Probenecid probably *blocks* the *active anion transport* system.

VI Organ selectivity means that an organ or organ system is damaged by a particular compound at dosages or exposure levels which are so low that other organs or organ systems are not affected. When dealing with individual organs or organ systems, the textbook in fact discusses the compounds selective for that organ or organ system.

Mechanisms of selectivity may be based on the accessibility of the organ, kinetic properties (accumulation), blood perfusion, biotransformation, specific receptors, etc.

VII  a. This is an *in vivo* study. The compound is administered to living animals and causes the effect in the animal while it is still alive.

b. Repeated administration of 500 mg kg$^{-1}$ causes periportal lesions (area a in the figure below; CV = central vein, PT = portal triad).
1000 mg kg$^{-1}$ causes centrilobular lesions (area b in the figure).
800 mg kg$^{-1}$ initially causes disorganization of the centrilobular hepatocytes (b in the figure), which spreads to the midzonal area (c in the figure).

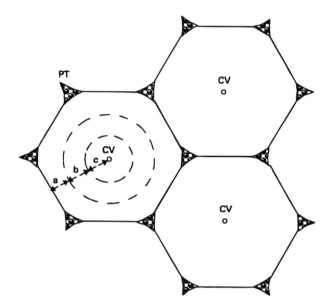

c. It is not possible to conclude from the results whether BHT is a mutagen or a carcinogen. Whether a compound is mutagenic can only be established by tests in which mutations can be detected, such as the Ames test. Whether a compound is carcinogenic (in experimental animals) can in fact only be determined by means of chronic toxicity research.

Exposure to BHT gives rise to increased cell proliferation, which is not in itself a carcinogenic reaction. The authors postulate that repeated exposure to BHT might lead to a degree of cell proliferation that would make repair mechanisms inadequate. This might be the cause of an increased incidence of tumors.

# Abbreviations and symbols commonly used in toxicology

| | |
|---|---|
| AA | allyl alcohol; ascorbic acid |
| AAF | N-acetyl-2-aminofluorene |
| AAS | atomic absorption spectroscopy |
| ABC (method) | abundance biomass comparison (method) |
| ACGIH | American Conference of Governmental Industrial Hygienists, |
| ACh | acetylcholine |
| ACTH | adrenocorticotropic hormone |
| ADH | alcohol dehydrogenase; antidiuretic hormone |
| ADI | acceptable daily intake |
| AF-2 | furylfuramide |
| AFC | antibody forming cells |
| AFP | alpha fetoprotein |
| AH | aniline 4-hydroxylation |
| AIDS | acquired immunodeficiency syndrome |
| $\delta$ALA (-synthetase) | delta aminolevulinic acid (synthetase) |
| ALDH | acetaldehyde dehydrogenase |
| AIDH | aldehyde dehydrogenase |
| ALT | alanine-aminotransaminase; alanine aminotransferase |
| AMP | adenosine 5'-monophosphate |
| ANCOVA | analysis of covariance |
| ANOVA | analysis of variance |
| AOA | aminooxyacetic acid |
| AP | acid phosphatase; antipyrine |
| ARDS | adult respiratory distress syndrome |
| ASP | aspartate aminotransferase |
| AST | aspartate-aminotransaminase |
| AT | amitryptyline |
| ATP | adenosine 5'-triphosphate |
| AUC | area under the plasma concentration vs time curve |
| AV | atrioventricular |
| B(a)P | benzo[a]pyrene |
| B(e)P | benzo[e]pyrene |
| BA | benzo[a]anthracene; benzoic acid |
| BAC | blood alcohol concentration |
| BAL | bronchoalveolar lavage; British Anti Lewisite, see dimercaprol |
| BAM (test) | Bovine Alveolar Macrophage (test) |
| BCF | bioconcentration factor |
| BEM | biological effect monitoring |
| BHA | 3-tert. butyl-4-hydroxyanisole |
| BHT | 3,5-ditert. butyl-4-hydroxytoluene |
| bis-BP | bis-(2,3-dibromopropyl)phosphate |

| | |
|---|---|
| BM | biological monitoring |
| BN | Brown Norway |
| BNF | $\beta$-naphthoflavone |
| BOD | biological oxygen demand |
| BP | benzopyrene |
| BrB | bromobenzene |
| BrdU | bromodeoxyuridine |
| BrP | bromophenol |
| BSA | bovine serum albumin |
| BSP | bromosulfophthalein |
| BSP -GSH | bromosulfophthalein-glutathione conjugate |
| BTA | batrachotoxin |
| BUN | blood urea nitrogen |
| C | central compartment |
| C | compliance |
| $C_0$ | the theoretical plasma concentration at time $t_0$ |
| $C_c$ | plasma concentration |
| CDNB | 1-chloro-2,4-dinitrobenzene |
| CFU | colony-forming units |
| Chol | cholesterol |
| CI | Chou's Combination Index |
| Cl | clearance |
| $Cl_h$ | hepatic clearance |
| $Cl_m$ | metabolic clearance |
| ClOF | clofibrate |
| $Cl_r$ | renal clearance |
| $Cl_s$ | systemic clearance |
| CNS | central nervous system |
| CNSLD | Chronic Non-Specific Lung Disease |
| CO | carbon monoxide |
| COD | chemical oxygen demand |
| COMT | catechol-O-methyltransferase |
| Con A | concanavalin A |
| COSHH | Control Of Substances Hazardous to Health Regulations |
| CPK | creatine phosphokinase |
| CPMP | Committee for Proprietary Medicinal Products |
| CRH | corticotropin-releasing hormone |
| CSF | cerebrospinal fluid; colony-stimulating factor |
| CT | coal tar |
| CTL | cytotoxic T-lymphocytes |
| Cyt P-450 | cytochrome P-450 |
| DA | dopamine |

| | | | | |
|---|---|---|---|---|
| Da | Dalton | FEV$_1$ | amount of air expelled during the first second of expiration, expressed as percentage of the total amount expelled |
| DBH | dopamine-beta-hydroxylase | | |
| DBSP | dibromosulfophthalein | | |
| DCDFE | 1,1-dichloro-2,2-difluoroethene | FITC | fluorescein isothiocyanate |
| DCNB | 2,4-dichloronitrobenzene | FMO | flavin-containing monooxygenase |
| DDC | diethyl dithiocarbamate | fmol | fentomol ($10^{-15}$ moles) |
| DDT | 1,1,1-trichloro-2, 2-bis(4-chlorophenyl)ethane | FP | fecapentaene |
| | | FRC | Functional Residual Capacity |
| DEM | diethyl maleate | FSH | follicle-stimulating hormone |
| DES | diethylstilbesterol | FSIS | Food Safety and Inspection Service |
| DEX | dexamethasone | FVC | forced vital capacity |
| DFP | diisopropylfluorophosphate | G6PD | glucose-6-phosphate dehydrogenase |
| $D_{GI}$ | the amount of a substance still present in the gastrointestinal tract | GABA | $\gamma$-aminobutyric acid |
| | | GC/MS | gas chromatography/mass spectroscopy |
| DMI | desipramine | GFR | glomerular filtration rate |
| DMSO | dimethyl sulfoxide | GH | growth hormone |
| DNA | deoxyribonucleic acid | GIH | growth hormone-inhibiting hormone |
| DNCB | 2,4-dinitrochlorobenzene | GLP | Good Laboratory Practice |
| DNOC | dinitro-*ortho*-cresol | GMP | guanosine monophosphate; Good Manufacturing Practice; glucose monophosphate |
| DOPA | dioleoylphosphatidic acid; 3,4-dihydroxyphenylalanine | | |
| DPH | 5,5-diphenylhydantoin | GOT | glutamic oxaloacetic transaminase (obsolete term for alanine aminotransferase) |
| ds | double stranded | | |
| dsDNA | double stranded [native] DNA | | |
| DSF | disulfiram, tetraethylthiuram disulfide | GPT | glutamic pyruvic transaminase, (obsolete term for aspartate aminotransferase) |
| DSM-III R | Diagnostic and Statistical Manual of Mental Disorders version 3 revised | | |
| | | GRAS | generally recognized as safe |
| DST | dexamethasone suppression test | GRH | growth hormone-releasing hormone |
| DTP | 2,2'-dithiopyridine | GSH | glutathione (reduced) |
| DTT | dithiothreitol | GSSG | glutathione (oxidized) |
| DXR | doxorubicin | GST | glutathione S-transferase |
| E | extraction ratio; relative effect | GT | (UDP-)glucuronyl transferase |
| EBV | Epstein Barr virus | GTA | grayanotoxin |
| EC Directive | European Community Directive | GVH | graft versus host |
| ECD | electrochemical detection | H | hydantoin |
| ECG | electrocardiogram | h or hr | hour |
| EDTA | ethylenediamine-*N,N,N',N'*-tetraacetic acid | H$_2$O$_2$ | hydrogen peroxide |
| | | HbCO | carboxyhemoglobin |
| EEG | electro-encephalogram | HbF | fetal hemoglobin |
| EGF | epidermal growth factor | HBSS | Hank's balanced salt solution |
| EH | epoxide hydrolase | HBV | hepatitis B virus |
| EHC | enterohepatic circulation | HC | 7-hydroxycoumarin |
| ELISA | enzyme-linked immunosorbent assay | HC5 | hazardous concentration for 5% of the species |
| EM | environmental monitoring; electron microscopy | | |
| | | HCB | hexachlorobenzene |
| EP | evoked potentials | HCBD | hexachloro-1,3,-butadiene |
| EPA | Environmental Protection Agency (US) | HCN | hydrocyanic acid |
| ESR | electron spin resonance (spectroscopy) | HDL | High Density Lipoproteins |
| EtOH | ethanol | HE (stain) | hematoxylin–eosin (stain) |
| ETU | ethylene thiourea | HLA | human leukocyte antigens |
| EUROCAT | European Registration of Congenital Anomalies and Twins | HMA | 3-hydroxymethylantipyrine |
| | | HMP | hexose monophosphate |
| FAD | flavin-adenine dinucleotide | HMW | high molecular weight |
| FANFT | 2-formamido-4-(5-nitro-2-furyl)thiazole | HPA | hypothalamic-pituitary-adrenocortical |
| FAS | fetal alcohol syndrome | HPLC | high performance liquid chromatography |
| FCS | fetal calf serum | HPV | human papilloma virus |
| FDA | Food and Drug Administration (US); fluorescein diacetate | HSA | human serum albumin |
| | | HSW Act | Health and Safety at Work Act (EU) |
| FDCA | Food, Drug and Cosmetic Act (US) | 5-HT | 5-hydroxytryptamine, serotonin |

| | | | |
|---|---|---|---|
| HVA | homovanillic acid | MRL | maximum residue levels; maximum residue limit |
| i.m. | intramuscular(ly) | | |
| i.p. | intraperitoneal(ly) | MS | mass spectroscopy |
| i.v. | intravenous(ly) | MSH | melanocyte-stimulating hormone |
| IARC | International Agency for Research on Cancer | MT | metallothionein |
| | | MTBA | 4-methylthiobenzoic acid |
| ICG | indocyanine green | MTI | Mixture Toxicity Index |
| ICSH | interstitial-cell-stimulating hormone | MTX | methotrexate |
| IDPN | $\beta,\beta$-iminodiproprionitrile | 1-MU | 1-methyluric acid |
| IFN | interferon | N | 1-naphthol |
| Ig | immunoglobulin | NA | noradrenaline, (the European name for norepinephrine) |
| IgA | immunoglobulin A | | |
| IgG | immunoglobulin G | NABQI | N-acetylbenzoquinone imine |
| IL | interleukin | NAD | nicotinamide adenine dinucleotide |
| INDO | indometacin | NADP | nicotinamide-adenine dinucleotide phosphate |
| INH | isoniazid | | |
| IU | international unit | NBA | N-bromoacetamide |
| JECFA | Joint Expert Committee on Food Additives | NE | norepinephrine |
| JMPRH | Joint FAO/WHO Meeting on Pesticide Residues | NEFA | non-esterified fatty acids |
| | | NF | nitrofurantoin |
| $k$ | elimination rate constant | NHEL | no-hormonal effect level |
| $K_A$ or $K_a$ | association constant | NIOSH | National Institute for Occupational Safety and Health |
| $k_A$ | absorption rate constant | | |
| $K_D$ or $K_d$ | dissociation constant | NK | natural killer cell |
| $k_E$ | excretion rate constant | NMB | 2-nitro-5-mercaptobenzoic acid |
| $K_M$ | Michaelis-Menten constant for a metabolic process | NMN | N-methylnicotinamide |
| | | NMR | nuclear magnetic resonance |
| $k_M$ | metabolic rate constant | NMU | N-methyl-N-nitrosourea |
| $k_{ME}$ | rate constant for the excretion of the metabolite | NO | nitrogen oxide |
| | | NO(A)EL | no-observed-(adverse)-effect level |
| LATS | long-acting thyroid stimulator | NORA | norantipyrine |
| LC/MS | liquid chromatography/mass spectroscopy | NRP | National Residue Program (US) |
| | | ns | not significant |
| LDH | lactate dehydrogenase | 1-NS | 1-naphthol sulfate |
| LDL | Low Density Lipoproteins | NSAIDs | non-steroidal antiinflammatory drugs |
| LH | luteinizing hormone | NT | nortriptyline |
| LM | light microscopy | $^1O_2$ | singlet oxygen |
| LMW | low molecular weight | $O_2{}^{\bullet}$ | superoxide anion radical |
| LPS | lipopolysaccharide | OC | oral contraceptives |
| LSD | lysergic acid diethylamide | ODC | ornithine decarboxylase |
| LT | leukotriene | OES | occupational exposure standard |
| MAB | N-methyl-4-aminoazobenzene | HO$^{\bullet}$ | hydroxyl radical |
| Mab | monoclonal antibody | OHA | 4-hydroxyantipyrine |
| MAC | Maximum Allowable Concentration | OHT | hydroxytestosterone |
| MAO | monoamine oxidase | OSHA | Occupational Safety and Health Administration |
| 3-MC | 3-methylcholanthrene | | |
| MDA | malondialdehyde | $p$-AH | para-aminohippuric acid |
| 1,3-MDU | 1,3-dimethyluric acid | p.o. | oral (per os) |
| MEPP | miniature end-plate potentials | p/s ratio | polyunsaturated-to-saturated fatty acid ratio |
| $MEV_1$ | maximum exhaled volume in 1 s | | |
| MFO | mixed-function oxidase | P-450 | cytochrome P-450 |
| MHC | major histocompatibility complex | PA | phosphatidic acid |
| min | minute(s) | PAF | platelet activating factor |
| MLV | multilamellar vesicle(s) | PAH | polycyclic aromatic hydrocarbon; para-aminohippuric acid |
| MMC | mucosal mast cell | | |
| MMTB | methyl 4-(methylthio)benzoate | PAP | p-aminophenol |
| MPS | mononuclear phagocyte system | PAS | Periodic Acid–Schiff |
| MPTP | 1-methyl-4-phenyl-1,2,3,6-tetrahydro-pyridine | PB | phenobarbital |
| | | PBBs | polybrominated biphenyls |

| | | | |
|---|---|---|---|
| PBL | peripheral blood lymphocytes | STOX | styrene-7,8-oxide |
| PBS | phosphate buffered saline | STX | saxitoxin |
| PC | phosphatidylcholine | $T$ | interval time |
| PCBs | polychlorinated biphenyls | T | peripheral compartment (Tissue) |
| PCDFs | polychlorinated dibenzofurans | $t$ | time |
| PCMB | p-chloromercuribenzoate | $t_{1/2}$ | elimination half-life |
| PCP | pentachlorophenol | $T_3$ | triiodothyronine |
| PCT | proximal convoluted tubule | $T_4$ | tetraiodothyronine |
| PEEP | positive end-expiratory pressure | TBA | tetrabutylammoniumhydroxide |
| PEG | polyethyleneglycol | TBG | thyroxine-binding globulin |
| PEPCK | phosphoenolpyruvate carboxykinase | TBTO | bis(tri-n-butyltin)oxide |
| PG | prostaglandin | TCA | trichloroacetic acid; tricyclic antidepressant |
| PHA | phytohemagglutinin | | |
| PK | pyruvate kinase | TCDD | 2,3,7,8-tetrachlorodibenzo-$p$-dioxin |
| PL | phospholipid(s) | TCDF | 2,3,7,8-tetrachlorodibenzofuran |
| PLN | popliteal lymph node | TDI | toluene diisocyanate |
| PMN | polymorphonuclear leukocytes | TDM | therapeutic drug monitoring |
| PNH | paroxysmal nocturnal hemoglobinuria | TEA | tetraethylammonium; tetraethylammoniumhydroxide; triethylamine |
| PNS | peripheral nervous system | | |
| $P_{oct}$ | octanol–water partition coefficient | | |
| ppb | parts per billion | TFE | tetrafluoroethylene |
| ppm | parts per million | TG | triglycerides |
| PR | pars recta | TH | theophylline |
| PRL | prolactin | THV | terminal hepatic vein |
| PTC | proximal tubular cell(s) | TLC | thin layer chromatography |
| R | resistance | TLV | Threshold Limit Value |
| RBCs | red blood cells | TLV-C | threshold limit value, ceiling |
| RDC | research diagnostic criteria | TMA | tetramethylammonium chloride |
| REM sleep | Rapid Eye Movement sleep | TNF | tumor necrosis factor |
| RER | rough endoplasmic reticulum | TPA | 12-O-tetradecanoyl-phorbol-13-acetic acid |
| RES | reticulo-endothelial system | TRH | thyrotropin (TSH) releasing hormone |
| RIA | radio-immunoassay | TRIS | tris(hydroxymethyl)aminomethane |
| ROS | reactive oxygen species | Tris | 2-amino-2-hydroxymethylpropane-1,3-diol |
| RV | Residual Volume | TSCA | Toxic Substances Control Act (US) |
| s.d. | standard deviation | TSH | thyroid-stimulating hormone |
| SA node | sinoatrial node | TST | testosterone |
| SAP | serum alkaline phosphatase | TTCA | 2-thio-thiazolidine-4-carbonic acid |
| SARs | structure–activity relationships | TTX | tetrodotoxin |
| s.c. | subcutaneous(ly) | TWAC | time-weighted average concentration |
| SCE(-test) | sister chromatid exchange (test) | TWAE | time-weighted average exposure |
| SEM | standard error of the mean | Tx | thromboxane |
| SER | smooth endoplasmic reticulum | UDPG | uridine 5′-diphosphoglucose |
| SGOT | serum glutamic oxaloacetic transaminase | UDPGT | UDP-glucuronyl transferase (=GT) |
| SGPT | serum glutamic pyruvic transaminase | UV | ultraviolet |
| SKF-525A | diethylaminoethyl-2,2-diphenylvalerate | VATER association | vertebral, anal, tracheal, esophageal, renal association |
| SLE | systemic lupus erythematosus | | |
| SOD | superoxide dismutase | $V_d$ | volume of distribution |
| SRBC | sheep red blood cells | VIP | vasoactive intestinal peptide |
| SRS-A | slow-reacting substance of anaphylaxis | Vit. E | vitamin E (alpha-tocopherol) |
| ss | single stranded | VLDL | Very Low Density Lipoproteins |
| SSB | single strand breaks | VT | Tidal Volume |
| ST | sulfotransferase | WHO | World Health Organization |
| STELs | short-term exposure limits | | |

# Formula Index

# Glossary

**Abdominal** concerning the portion of the body between the diaphragm and the pelvis

**Abiotic** non-living

**Abortion** end of pregnancy before the embryo or fetus is viable outside the uterus.

**Acanthosis** type of skin irritation (dermatitis) which is characterized by thickening of the epidermis due to the proliferation of cells of the stratum spinosum.

**Acetaldehyde** organic compound used for manufacturing paraldehyde, acetic acid, butanol, anilin dyes and synthetic rubber, and for silver-plating mirrors. Very small quantities are used in artificial flavorings. Is the primary metabolite of ethanol, formed by enzymatic oxidation (alcohol dehydrogenase). The primary toxic effect is irritation of the skin and lungs.

**Acetaminophen** (Paracetamol; 4-hydrophenylacetamide) the active ingredient of various analgesics, such as Tylenol®. It is an analgesic and antipyretic; it is also used to manufacture azo dyes and chemicals used in photography. In larger doses, acetaminophen is hepatotoxic. Following an overdose, the detoxication mechanism is saturated due to glutathione depletion, causing an increase in the concentration of the active metabolite, which in turn binds to several hepatocellular structures. Histopathologically, paracetamol causes cell edema and hydropic degeneration, leading to centrilobular necrosis.

**Acetylaminofluorene** chemical originally developed as an insecticide. Because it is strongly carcinogenic (it especially causes bladder cancer) it is frequently used in toxicology as a model chemical for studying the different processes occurring in carcinogenesis and for hepatotoxic effects. The primary metabolite is formed by oxygenation, catalyzed by cytochrome P-450. Some of the reactions occurring here are aromatic hydroxylation (a detoxication reaction) or N-hydroxylation (an activation reaction). Species differences in cytochrome P-450 are thought to be responsible for the difference in carcinogenic susceptibility. In subsequent phase 2 reactions (sulfate ester formation, acetylation and glucuronidation), reactive metabolites are formed, which can react with nucleophilic substituents of nucleic acids and proteins.

**Acetylcholine** chemical transmitter released by nerve endings.

**Achondroplasia** condition influenced by genetic factors as well as hormonal levels, that produces a small person with short arms and legs, but normal trunk and head.

**Acidosis** condition in which the blood has a higher hydrogen ion concentration than normal, with a decreased pH.

**Acromegaly** abnormal pattern of bone and connective-tissue growth characterized by enlarged hands, face, and feet, and associated with excessive pituitary growth hormone that is secreted after the epiphyseal cartilages have been replaced.

**Ad libitum food** free access to food.

**Addiction** physical or psychological dependence upon one or more drugs. Once addicted to a particular drug, individuals cannot function normally in its absence.

**Adenocarcinoma** malignant epithelial tumor forming tubular structures. In the United States, adenocarcinoma of the large intestine is the second most common cause of death by cancer. It is assumed that diets low in roughage play an important role, in view of the slow passage of such food and the longer contact of potential carcinogens with the intestinal wall. This might possibly allow certain intestinal bacteria to activate bile acids into carcinogenic substances. The adenocarcinomas of the large intestine are generally tumors which grow rather slowly. Metastasis is mostly to the regional lymph glands, the liver and the lungs.

**Adenoma** benign tumor derived from glandular tissue. Adenomas in the liver consist almost entirely of hepatocytes and no longer display any lobular or portal structure. Fibrotic cords, consisting of connective-tissue structures, may occasionally be found. Adenomas are usually solitary. Pressure exerted by the tumor on the biliary passages may lead to jaundice (icterus). Hemorrhages in the tumor may cause pain. Liver cell adenomas are associated with the use of oral contraceptives. The risk is minimal, but increases with the duration of use (more than 5 years) and the dosage. It is not clear whether the contraceptives act as an initiator or as a promotor.

**Adrenal cortex** the outer covering of the adrenal gland.

**Adrenal glands** hormone-producing glands located superior to the kidneys; each consists of medulla and cortex areas.

**Adrenal medulla** the central part of the adrenal gland.

**Adrenalectomy** the removal of the adrenal glands.

**Adrenalin** European name for epinephrine.

**Adrenergic** norepinephrine-sensitive. Also nerve fibres that release norepinephrine as a neurotransmitter.

*α*-**Adrenergic receptor** one of several types of norepinephrine-sensitive binding sites.

*β*-**Adrenergic receptors** one of several types of norepinephrine-sensitive binding sites.

**Adrenoceptor** adrenergic receptor.

**Adrenocorticotropic hormone** a hormone that influences the activity of the adrenal cortex and is released by the anterior portion of the pituitary.

**Adrenodemedullation** surgical removal of the adrenal medulla.

**Afferent** transporting or conducting toward a central region.

**Aflatoxins** group of mycotoxins, produced by *Aspergillus flavus* and related moulds, some with carcinogenic and others with hepatotoxic properties. In birds, aflatoxin affects male reproduction and growth. Aflatoxin B-1 is hepatotoxic and one of the most potent carcinogenic agents known. Aflatoxins occur as contaminants in human and animal foodstuffs, particularly in cereals and peanuts. Although they are mostly carcinogenic to the liver, there are distinct differences between species. Aflatoxin B-1 is converted by the cytochrome P-450 dependent monooxygenase system into a very reactive epoxide. The carcinogenicity is thought to be caused by interaction of the reactive epoxide with DNA, and the hepatotoxicity by interaction with liver proteins, causing steatosis or necrosis. Epidemiological studies indicate that the presence of the hepatitis B virus potentiates the carcinogenic action of aflatoxin.

**Agonist** substance reacting with a receptor leading to physiological and biochemical changes and ultimately resulting in a biological effect.

**Alcoholism** type of behavioral disorder involving heavy drinking that interferes with the individual's ability to function at home and at work.

**Alloxan** compound which can cause selective degeneration of the *β*-cells of the Langerhans' islets in experimental animals, resulting in diabetes with insulin deficiency. The alloxan concentrations which damage the *β* cells do not affect the *α*-2 cells and their ability to secrete glucagon. Apart from its toxic effect on the pancreas, alloxan causes cataract and is a teratogenic agent.

**Allyl alcohol** colorless liquid, smelling like mustard and causing irritation of the eyes. It can be manufactured by heating glycerol with formic acid. Used to manufacture war gases, allyl compounds, resins and plasticizers.

**Alpha fetoprotein (= fetoprotein; AFP)** protein normally occurring in the blood of a fetus; in minimal amounts it is present in the amniotic fluid. An increased amount of AFP in the amniotic fluid suggests that the fetus loses abnormal amounts of AFP. Often this is the case in spina bifida, but also in some other deviations it occurs.

**Alveolar bronchiolization** common response of the alveolar epithelium to many xenobiotics. It involves replacement of the squamous epithelium of the alveoli by cuboidal basophilic epithelium, which resembles that of the bronchioli. Alveolar bronchiolization takes place in the peribronchiolar areas, which show some infiltration by inflammatory cells. Occasionally the condition leads to the development of tumors.

**Alveolitis** inflammatory process affecting the alveoli. It is characterized by desquamation of Type I pneumocytes, proliferation of Type II pneumocytes, metaplasia and hyaline membrane formation. Alveolitis may result from exposure to phosgene, high oxygen concentrations (as in artificial respiration), ozone, paraquat and various cytostatics.

**Amelia** limb reduction deformity, in which limbs are completely missing. Especially due to the effects of thalidomide.

**Amenorrhea (primary/secondary)** absence of menstruation; when menstruation has not been established at the time when it should have been, it is primary amenorrhea; absence of menstruation after it has once commenced is referred to as secondary amenorrhea.

**Aminonicotinamide** (6-Aminonicotinamide; 6-ANA) an antimetabolite of nicotinamide. It inhibits glucose-6-phosphate dehydrogenase as well as the folic acid antagonists, which in turn inhibit dihydrofolic acid reductase. In dogs, small doses of 6-ANA cause practically selective damage to neuroglial cells in the grey matter of the brain, and the satellite cells in the ganglia. Apart from having neurotoxic effects, it is also teratogenic.

**Amnesia** failure of memory often due to some traumatic injury.

**Amniocentesis** procedure for obtaining amniotic fluid. Amniotic fluid is removed by inserting a needle through a pregnant woman's abdomen into the sac containing the fetus. Fetal cells in the fluid can be grown in a laboratory and subjected to chromosomal and/or biochemical analysis.

**Anabolism** the energy-requiring building-up phase of metabolism in which simpler substances are synthesized to more complex substances.

**Analgesic** drug that relieves pain.

**Anemia** deficiency in circulating hemoglobin. An abnormality in the hemoglobin synthesis may be caused by defective heme synthesis or by an irregularity in the *α* or *β* chain.

**Anencephaly** congenital absence of the whole or part of the brain and coverings.

**Angioma** tumor of vessels. Angiomas may consist of new vessels but also of deformed vessels. A distinction is made between hemeangiomas, which originate in blood vessels, and lymphangiomas which originate in lymphatic vessels.

**Anomaly**   deviation from the regular arrangement.

**Anorexia nervosa**   eating disorder characterized by intentional starvation, distorted body image, excessive amounts of energy, and an intense fear of gaining weight.

**Antabuse (Disulfiram)**   a substance which blocks the metabolism of acetaldehyde. If disulfiram is combined with alcohol, there is a buildup of acetaldehyde and the person will feel ill. The drug is sometimes used to aid in the treatment of alcoholics to encourage them to abstain from drinking.

**Antagonist**   substance reacting with a receptor resulting in a blockade of the functioning of the agonist.

**Anthracosis**   accumulation of coal dust in alveolar macrophages, efferent lymphatic vessels and lymph nodes. Unlike silicosis and asbestosis, anthracosis usually does not lead to severe fibrosis of the alveolar septa. The accumulation of coal dust colors the lungs and the regional lymph glands grey to black.

**Antidiuretic hormone (vasopressin)**   pituitary gland hormone that controls the reabsorption of water by the kidney.

**Antidepressant**   drug used to improve mood and treat depression. Most antidepressants increase levels of monoamines in the brain.

**Antipsychotics**   class of drugs also called 'major tranquillizers' that relieve the symptoms of psychosis. Most common antipsychotics are the phenothiazines.

**Anxiolytics**   class of drugs that relieve anxiety. It includes the barbiturates and the benzodiazepines.

**Aphagia**   inability to swallow.

**Aphrodisiac**   drug that improves sexual performance and/or desire.

**Aplasia**   absence of the organ coupled with persistence of a rudiment that never developed completely. Thus, aplasia of the lung refers to a condition in which the main bronchus ends blindly in non-descriptive tissue composed of rudimentary ducts and connective tissue.

**Apoptosis**   in fact the physiological disintegration of cells, accompanied by the formation of acidophilic bodies, called Councilman bodies. Apoptosis is a form of (natural) necrosis of individual cells, recognizable by the presence of rounded formations the size of or smaller than a liver cell, highly eosinophilic and with a homogeneous structure. Islets of acidophilic bodies are seen, sometimes in particular around the central vein.

**Arsenic**   metalloid (Arsenic, As) used in the production of metal and glass, and in agriculture. Human exposure occurs through food, tobacco, smoke, air and water. Biologically, three groups of compounds are of importance; inorganic arsenic compounds, organic compounds and gases. Arsenic is readily ingested through the gastrointestinal and the respiratory tract; it accumulates in skin, hair and nails. Its cellular toxicity is caused by reactions with SH-containing mitochondrial enzymes, resulting in decreased cell respiration. In oxidative phosphorylation, arsenic can also compete with phosphate. Some degree of detoxication can take place through reductive methylation. Acute symptoms include fever, enlargement of the liver, reversible brain damage and irritations of the gastrointestinal tract. Additional symptoms are disorders of the upper respiratory tract and peripheral neuropathies. Chronical symptoms consist of desquamation and pigmentation of the skin, symmetrical distal neurophaties, altered hematopoiesis and degenerative changes of liver and kidneys. Epidemiological data indicate carcinogenic properties. In man, a dose of between 1 and 2.5 mg per kg body weight may be fatal. Biological indicators are the presence of arsenic in urine, blood and hair. In cases of acute poisoning, dimercaptopropanol can be administered; this is not effective in case of chronic poisoning.

**Asbestos**   is the collective name of two groups of fibrous minerals: chrysotile, belonging to the serpentines, and amphiboles, which include, for instance, crocidolite, amosite and tremolite. The health risks of asbestos are caused only by breathing in asbestos dust; touching it is not dangerous in itself. Inhaling asbestos dust can cause three types of health problems: asbestosis, brown lung disease caused by asbestos, which, like silicosis, is a pneumoconiosis, lung cancer, and mesothelioma, a malignant tumor arising from the pleural membrane or the peritoneum (= mesothelium). 85% of the cases of mesothelioma, a rather rare form of cancer are caused by exposure to amphibolic asbestos (crocidolite and amosite). Chrysotile probably does not cause mesothelioma.

**Asbestosis**   occupational disease, occurring mainly in people who handle asbestos, like workers in asbestos mines and the asbestos processing industry. Asbestosis can be caused by all kinds of asbestos; it occurs only after years of exposure to high concentrations of asbestos dust. There is a clear relation between the amount of asbestos dust inhaled and the gravity of the asbestosis. The histopathological picture is radically different from that in silicosis. At microscopic level, the pleura is thickened and shows fibrotic areas with needle-shaped particles, surrounded by cells. Lung cancer is also frequently observed in persons who are at risk of developing asbestosis, but only if they smoke. In this case, the carcinogen, asbestos and cigarette smoke clearly have a synergistic effect.

**Association (epidemiology)**   this means that the things that are associated are linked in some way that make them turn up together more often than they would by change ('positive association'). It is helpful to recognize existing associations so that in attempting to measure one factor, one does not inadvertently measure another factor too, that is associated with it.

**Atherosclerosis**   disease characterized by thickening of the intima (which in turn is a result of the proliferation of smooth muscle cells of the media), by degeneration of smooth muscle cells of the intima and media including excessive formation of connective tissue. The disease is often accompanied by infiltration of various blood components and calcification. These changes can occur in various proportions. Atherosclerosis can be distinguished from arteriosclerosis because of the presence of large amounts of lipids in the former. The main effects of arteriosclerosis and atherosclerosis can be found in loss of elasticity, constriction of the arteries and increased risk for thrombosis.

**Atresia**  defect caused by incomplete formation of a lumen. Many hollow organs originate as strands and cords of cells, the centres of which are programmed to die, thus forming a central cavity or lumen. Atresia of the esophagus is characteristic by partial occlusion of the lumen, which was not fully established in embryogenesis.

**Atrophy**  decrease in the size and mass of an organ or tissue, caused by a decrease in the total amount of cytoplasm. In a simple atrophy, the individual cells decrease in size. In numerical atrophy, there is a decrease in the number of cells. Microscopically, there may be: shrinkage of individual cells (simple atrophy) and reduction of the number of cells (numerical atrophy)

**Atropine**  alkaloid of belladonna; parasympatholyticum. It is a drug capable of neutralizing the effect of parasympathetic stimulation.

**Autolysis**  (Gr. lysein = to loosen) refers to the digestion of proteins by the body's own enzymes: it is a form of self-digestion.

**Autonomic nervous system**  the part of the nervous system that functions involuntarily and is responsible for innervating cardiac muscle, smooth muscle, and glands. The part of the peripheral nervous system that controls the automatic or vegetative functions of the body. It is made up of the sympathetic nervous system and the parasympathetic nervous system.

**Aversive conditioning**  type of counterconditioning in which punishment is used in order to associate negative feeling with an undesirable response.

**Avitaminosis**  deficiency disease resulting from a lack of one or more vitamins. It is often caused by an imbalanced diet. Examples of such deficiency diseases are rachitis (rickets; vitamin D deficiency), beriberi (vitamin B deficiency) and scorbutus or scurvy (vitamin C or ascorbic acid deficiency).

**Avoidance conditioning**  process through which organisms learn to avoid unpleasant consequences by engaging in preventative actions. Often, external stimuli signal the necessity for such responses, but in some cases such warning signals are internally generated by the passage of time.

**Axon**  the process of a nerve cell by which impulses are carried away from the cell.

**Axonopathy**  toxic effects to the axon, in particular in the peripheral nervous system; these are the most common form of neuropathy. Axonopathies are characterized by a structural change in the axon, without there being any visible changes to the cell body. It is not clear whether or not a change in the cell body is the cause for the axonopathy. In most cases, the first degenerative changes in axonopathies occur distally from the cell body, i.e. away from it. In exceptional cases the first changes may also occur proximally, i.e. near the cell body.

**Basal-cell carcinoma**  (= basalioma) carcinoma, characterized by cords and groups of epithelial cells, separated by strands of collagenous connective tissue. The histological picture is malignant. It is a tumor derived from the cells of the stratum basale. The skin overlying the tumor has a normal appearance, sometimes there are ulcerations. In man this tumor is well circumscribed and benign, but may infiltrate later.

**Basophilic**  (Gr. philein = to love) refers to the characteristic of staining (blue) in reaction to alkaline stains, as opposed to eosinophilic or acidophilic.

**Benedectin®**  see doxylamine.

**Benzo[a]pyrene**  polycyclic aromatic hydrocarbon, formed for instance as a by-product in waste incinerators. It was first isolated in 1932 from coal tar and has proved to be very carcinogenic. Exposure occurs mainly through air pollution, cigarette smoke and food. Benzopyrene (Bp) is converted by cytochrome P-450, via a series of intermediary products, to a mutagenic and carcinogenic epoxide. Bp is both a local and a systemic carcinogen. The ultimate carcinogenic and mutagenic metabolite is 7.8-diol-9.10-epoxide.

**β-HCH (β-hexachlorocyclohexane)**  compound which occurs as a contaminant in the insecticide lindane. The effects of β-HCH are mainly acutely neurotoxic, whereas γ-HCH has a chronic effect in man. The insecticidal effect of the γ-isomer was discovered shortly before the Second World War

**Bilirubin**  the breakdown product of the porphyrin ring of hemoglobin, does not contain iron. It is a golden yellow pigment, excreted in bile. If bilirubin is not sufficiently excreted, the bilirubin levels in blood and lymph increase. A yellow discoloration occurs in the skin and sclera, called jaundice or icterus. Bilirubin may also occur locally in a tissue, for instance together with hemosiderin, as remnants of a hemorrhage.

**Bleomycin**  collective name for a number of antibiotics derived from *Streptomyces verticillus*. These chemicals are used as immunosuppressants. They depress the bone marrow activity only slightly and are particularly active against squamous-cell carcinomas; combined with platinum, they are also active against testis tumors. Labelled with radioactive cobalt or thorium, they are used as diagnostics for the detection of metastases. Although they do not depress bone marrow activity, they are rather toxic. Shortly after administration shivering may occur, accompanied by severe nausea and vomiting. Chronic administration, especially in doses of over 300 mg per square meter body surface, often causes interstitial fibrosis of the lung ('bleomycin lung'), which can be fatal. Skin problems also occur frequently.

**Blister** (or vesicle) fluid-containing, elevated lesion of the skin. A distinction is made between intraepithelial and subepidermal types of blisters. The fluid emanates from intercellular (spongiosis) and/or intracellular edema.

**Blood-brain barrier** covering on the capillaries in the brain and spinal cord that blocks many xenobiotics that are not lipid soluble from getting into the brain.

**Blotting** following electrophoresis, the transfer of nucleic acids and/or proteins from a gel strip to a specialized, chemically reactive paper (or other matrix) on which the nucleic acids etc. may become covalently bound in a pattern similar to that present in the original gel.

**Bolus** an area of high concentration of a substance in the body just after it has been administered and before it has had time to diffuse throughout the body.

**Bradycardia** reduction in heart rate from the normal level.

**Brainstem** the portion of the brain consisting of the medulla, pons and midbrain.

**Bronchial adenocarcinoma** adenocarcinoma that derives from transformed epithelial cells of the bronchi or the trachea.

**Broncho-alveolar carcinoma** also called alveolar cell carcinoma, is a mucus-producing tumor consisting of columnar cells. Originally they are Type II or Clara-cells growing along the alveolar wall. This type of tumor gives the alveolar wall a carpet-like structure.

**Bronchiolization** see alveolar bronchiolization.

**Butylated hydroxyanisole (BHA)** widely used food additive, used as an antioxidant to prevent fats, oils and fat-containing foodstuffs from turning rancid. The acute toxicity of BHA is relatively small. However, in animal experiments, BHA has proved carcinogenic. It causes hyperplasias, papillomas and carcinomas in the forestomach of rats, hamsters and probably mice. In non-rodents, such as pigs and monkeys, proliferative pathological changes in the esophagus following exposure to BHA have been described. Because BHA does not produce positive effects in short-term tests for genotoxic activity, it is regarded as a non-genotoxic epigenetic carcinogen. For this class of chemical carcinogens, a threshold value for tumor induction is assumed to exist.

**Cadmium** metal used for electroplating and in batteries, as a color pigment for paints and as a stabilizer in plastics. Cadmium is a nephrotoxicant and hepatotoxicant, probably acting by displacement and substitution of essential metals in proteins and enzymes.

**Cannula** a tube implanted into an organism, usually a vein, through which material may be injected.

**Carbon tetrachloride** carcinogen and environmental pollutant. It is a colorless liquid with a characteristic smell. It was formerly used as a solvent for oils, fats, waxes and resins, and also as a stain remover in laundries. It has also been used as a disinfectant and as an intermediate product in the synthesis of fluorinated hydrocarbons. Although it was frequently used in the past, less harmful substances are nowadays employed. Repeated skin contact with carbon tetrachloride can cause dermatitis. Acute systemic effects of carbon tetrachloride include depression of the central nervous system, gastrointestinal effects and kidney and liver damage, accompanied by nausea, stomach-ache and jaundice. The effects are stronger when alcohol is consumed simultaneously; in serious cases, coma may occur, followed by death due to severe deterioration of the kidney function. The hepatotoxicity is caused by the formation of the trichloromethyl radical by the action of cytochrome P-450. The trichloromethyl radical initiates peroxidation. Further, it is strongly electrophilic and binds to the nucleophilic substituents of proteins.

**Carboxyhemoglobin** hemoglobin combined with carbon monoxide. Once this has happened, the hemoglobin is no longer capable of carrying oxygen.

**Carcinoma** cancer, a malignant tumor of squamous, glandular or sensory epithelium with a tendency to infiltrate and metastasize (= form daughter tumors). The most common carcinomas are those of the stomach, the intestine, the breast, the esophagus, the uterus, the lungs, the tongue and the bladder. A carcinoma always has an epithelial origin. Hepatocellular carcinomas are primary malignant neoplasms derived from liver cells. This type of carcinoma is 10 to 20 times more common in Africa than it is in Europe. Of all hepatocellular carcinomas sixty to seventy percent are found in combination with cirrhosis of the liver. Macroscopically, these tumors are often large, multinucleated (metastases!), soft, yellowish, sometimes green (bile production!). The occurrence of these carcinomas is often accompanied by hemorrhages and they are often highly vascularized. Microscopically, eosinophilic granules can be observed in the cytoplasm. There are vesicular nuclei with clearly visible nucleoli; giant cells are often found. The structure of the cells is often trabecular or tubular; the tubules contain an accumulation of bile. The plates of parenchymal cells often include more than one layer of cells. Occasionally, tubule-like structures may be found. Examples of hepatocarcinogens which may cause carcinomas are mycotoxins (such as aflatoxin), thoracic contrast media and possibly oral contraceptives.

**Cardiomyopathy** pathological change in the heart muscle causing inadequate functioning. A distinction is made between: hypertrophic, congestive (or ventricle dilatating), and restrictive and/or obliterative cardiomyopathies. The term congestive or ventricle dila-ting cardiomyopathy is used to describe a heterogeneous group of heart muscle diseases. It is characterized by abnormal ventricular blood congestion with failure of the systolic pumping function and by abnormal dilation of the ventricular cavities. The toxicological type is associated mainly with chronic alcoholism or chronic administration of certain drugs (antineoplastic drugs). Obliterative cardiomyopathy is characterized by endocardial fibrous thickening and mural thrombosis, resulting in a partial congestion or constriction of the ventricular cavities. Restrictive cardiomyopathy is characterized by infiltration processes which, for example in the event of amyloidosis or ventricular fibrosis, have a negative influence on the normal contraction of the heart muscle and cause changes in the filling of the ventricles.

**Case control study**   an epidemiologic study in which one collects a group of people with a certain disease (cases) to compare with another group of people without that disease (controls) to see if some factor (suspect of being a cause) is more common in the disease group. Most important is the fact that people must already have the disease to be chosen as cases.

**Case study**   the study of one example or occurrence.

**Catabolism**   process in which living cells break down more complex substances into simpler substances.

**Catecholamines**   any of a group of amines which are secreted in the human body to act as neurotransmitters; examples are epinephrine, norepinephrine and dopamine.

**Causal factor (epidemiology)**   that which produces an effect or result: that from which anything proceeds, and without which it would not exist. It is a substance exerting its power into act, to make a thing begin to be.

**Cell debris**   is used to refer to waste products or remains of dead cells.

**Cellular edema**   histopathological process involving a moderate, reversible cell damage. The increased amount of intracellular water has made the cell increase in size, without the cytoplasm being turbid or vacuolated. Although cellular edema is not always easily distinguishable under a microscope, it has the following characteristics: cytoplasm is lighter in color, cytoplasm has a foamy structure, and nuclei are (sometimes) lighter in color. At ultrastructural level, dilation of the endoplasmic reticulum and swelling of mitochondria occur. Macroscopically, the weight and size of the organ increase, and its color fades. Cellular edema can be caused by many types of cell damage. In particular, factors which interfere with the $Na^+/K^+$-pump, such as ouabain, hypoxia and mitochondrial poisons frequently cause cellular edema.

**Cellular hypertrophy**   (numerical hypertrophy = hyperplasia), pathological process in which the cells and nuclei increase in size and the amount of DNA increases. The nucleus often becomes more irregular in shape, while the nucleoli increase in number and size. The same happens to cell organelles in the cytoplasm. Mitochondria increase in size and number. Thus the number of cell components increases, whereas the cell itself increases in size.

**Central nervous system (CNS)**   the brain and the spinal cord.

**Centrilobular area**   that part of the anatomical liver lobule which is located in its centre (around the central vein).

**Centrilobular necrosis**   (periacinal necrosis) necrosis around the central vein of the liver lobule. This type of necrosis is often associated with: hydropic degeneration and steatosis, glycogen depletion, loss of liver-specific enzyme activity in the relevant area, and increase of alkaline phosphatase activity.

**Cerebellum**   part of the hindbrain; controls movement coordination.

**Cerebral cortex**   outer surface layer of the cerebrum.

**Cerebrospinal fluid**   fluid produced in the cerebral ventricles; fills the ventricles and surrounds the CNS.

**Cerebrum**   largest part of the brain.

**Cervix**   the cylindrical, inferior portion of the uterus leading to the vagina.

**Chemoreceptors**   receptors sensitive to various chemical stimulations and changes.

**Chloracne**   1. serious type of acne caused by exposure to chlorinated hydrocarbons; 2. acne is a lesion of the hair follicle, caused by hyperproliferation of keratinized cells in the follicle, leading to the formation of keratin plugs, retention of the fatty secretion of the sebaceous glands and distension of the follicle lumen.

**Chloroquine**   substance used as antimalarial drug against rheumatoid arthritis and lupus erythematosis. It accumulates in different organs and may cause stomach complaints and visual disturbances.

**Chlorphentermine**   clinically applied chemical with sympathomimetic properties; it is also an anorectic. One of its side effects is sleeplessness; the development of tolerance can also form a problem. Other symptoms that may occur are nervousness and irritability, while peripheral side effects typical of sympathicomimetics are rarely completely absent.

**Chlorpromazine**   the prototype of a particular type of antipsychotic (phenotiazine type). Derivatives of this compound were used as dyes in the 19th century. Although chlorpromazine is relatively safe, it may cause neurological disorders (extrapyramidal side effects); like other antipsychotic medicines, it can increase the risk of tardive dyskinesias (movement disturbances, involving grotesque movements, which sometimes occur in elderly people).

**Cholecystokinin (CCK)**   hormone which contracts the gallbladder; secreted by the upper intestinal mucosa.

**Cholestasis**   term used to refer to reduced transport of bile. This disorder may result from interference with bilirubin transport (reduced secretion of bile by the hepatocytes, for example as a result of impaired conjugation) or from a physical obstruction of the biliary passages. Histopathologically, two types of cholestasis are distinguished: canalicular or hepatocellular cholestasis and cholangiolitic cholestasis. Canalicular cholestasis, which may be caused by oral contraceptives and anabolic steroids, does not show signs of cytotoxicity. The histopathological picture involves the presence of centrilobular bile plugs in an otherwise normal-looking liver. Cholangiolitic cholestasis also presents other histological changes, such as swollen or hydropically degenerated liver cells and periportal inflammatory reactions (= cholangiolitis).

**Cholinergic**  acetylcholine-sensitive.

**Circadian rhythm**  rhythm with a periodicity of 24 h.

**Cirrhosis**  of the liver is a diffuse process, and may be regarded as following the process of fibrosis. Histologically, cirrhosis always shows signs of fibrosis (connective tissue formation), in addition to the parenchyma being affected and the normal trabecular structure being disturbed. Hyperplastic nodules are also often found.

**Coagulative necrosis**  form of necrosis. Macroscopically, several forms of necrosis can be distinguished. In coagulative necrosis, the necrotic focus is dry, with a solid consistency and is usually greyish to greyish-yellow in color. Microscopically, the general structure of the tissue usually remains intact for longer periods (days or weeks), whereas the intracellular structures are no longer discernible. The nuclear membrane and the nuclear contents stain less clearly and the cytoplasm is condensed as a result of protein denaturation. Sometimes lysis of specific cell structures occurs. A frequent cause of coagulative necrosis is anoxia. If the anoxia is caused by an insufficient supply of arterial blood, this is called ischemic necrosis. Important causes of coagulative necrosis are physical influences, corrosive agents and various poisons. Immunological processes may also cause coagulative necrosis. Coagulative necrosis is characterized by the recognizability of the tissue structure and the cell outlines, and the greatly increased eosinophility of the cytoplasm.

**Cocaine**  stimulant drug that also has anesthetic properties. It is a naturally occurring substance, isolated from the South American coca plant, *Erythroxylon coca*. Administration of cocaine produces a feeling of euphoria and is stimulating; larger doses, however, cause irritability and depression. It can cause raised blood pressure, tachycardia (increased heart rate) and palpitations. It has various effects on the central nervous system and may cause psychosis. Chronic use, especially of large doses, may cause conditions difficult to discern from schizophrenic syndromes. Several biochemical processes are involved in the action of cocaine on the central nervous system, particularly inhibition of the reabsorption of monoamines. The resultant increase in the supply of dopamine, norepinephrine and serotonin is responsible for the effects on the central nervous system, whereas especially epinephrine is responsible for the peripheral sympathomimetic effects. Both the free base and the hydrochloride salt are used clinically; drug users employ mainly the free base. Many of the effects of cocaine can be blocked by means of dopamine, norepinephrine and serotonin antagonists.

**Cohort study**  so called because a group of individuals is designated as a cohort and their characteristics are recorded. Then they are watched to see what diseases occur among them. Most important is the fact that people with specific characteristics and people without those same characteristics are identified first and their subsequent disease rates are compared.

**Cohort**  this refers to an entire group of people who are identified as starting some experience together. It has to be specified what experience the group is starting and include all of the group.

**Colitis**  diffuse inflammatory reaction of the mucosa and submucosa of the large intestine and may be caused by NSAIDs (nonsteroidal antiinflammatory drugs). Colitis is accompanied by the formation of ulcers. It is restricted to the mucosa and submucosa. Infiltration takes place only into the submucosa, not the muscularis mucosa or serosa. There may sometimes be slight hyperplasia of the mucosa.

**Collagenous connective tissue**  connective tissue in which there is a predominant presence of collagen. Collagen (Gr. kolla = glue; gencin = to produce) is a protein-like substance in connective tissue which is often present in the form of fibres. When tissues containing collagen are boiled gelatin is formed.

**Compliance**  the elasticity, the stretch or stiffness of the lung, in other words the extent to which for example the volume of the lungs may be increased. It is expressed as a quotient:

$$\frac{\text{increase in (lung) volume}}{\text{increase in (intrapulmonic) pressure}}$$

**Computed tomography**  computer-constructed imaging technique of a thin slice through the body, derived from X-ray absorption data.

**Conditioned response**  response evoked by a conditioned stimulus.

**Conditioned stimulus**  stimulus which acquires the capacity to evoke particular responses through repeated pairing with another stimulus capable of eliciting such reactions.

**Contact urticaria**  a type of contact dermatitis which is marked by the appearance of elevated wheals on the skin. This skin condition may occur in two forms: an immunological form and a non-immunological form. Characteristic are hyperemia and edema of the dermis. Contact urticaria can be a result of (skin) contact with foodstuffs, cosmetics or drugs, but it can also be caused by animal toxins (jellyfish, bees). On microscopic examination, mast cells, chromatophores (= pigment cells) and some eosinophilic leukocytes can be seen.

**Control group**  group in an experiment which is not exposed to the independent variable under investigation.

The behavior of subjects in this condition is used as a base-line against which to evaluate the effects of experimental treatments.

**Corpus luteum**   yellow ovarian glandular body that arises from a major follicle that has released its ovum; it secretes progesterone; if the ovum released has been fertilized, the corpus luteum grows and secretes during gestation; if not, it atrophies and disappears.

**Correlation coefficient**   statistic which indicates the degree of relationship between two or more variables. The larger the correlation (the more it departs from 0.00), the stronger the observed relationship.

**Correlation studies**   studies designed to yield information concerning the degree of relationship between two variables.

**Correlational method of research**   method of research in which variables of interest are observed in a careful and systematic manner in order to determine whether changes in one are associated with changes in the other.

**Corrosive sublimate**   trivial name of mercuric chloride.

**Corrosives**   (corrosive agents), caustics or escharotics, are substances which, like heat, denature proteins, thus damaging the cell protoplasm. Devitalization occurs in the form of coagulative (solidifying) or liquefactive necrosis, depending on the end product. Examples are the strong acids, the strong bases and corrosive sublimate. It corrodes the mucous membranes of the digestive tract, and concentrations in the tubular epithelium of the kidneys reach necrotizing levels. If the patient survives and the area damaged by the corrosive is not too large, the tissue damage is followed by an inflammatory process, which leads to recovery of the tissues.

**Corticosteroids**   steroid hormones released by the adrenal cortex.

**Corticosterone**   steroid hormone, released by the adrenal cortex.

**Corticotropin-releasing factor (CRF)**   hormone released by the hypothalamus that activates the anterior portion of the pituitary to release adrenocorticotropic hormone.

**Cortisol**   glucocorticoid produced by the adrenal cortex.

**Cotransmitters**   factors that are colocalized and coreleased with the classical neurotransmitters in the autonomic nerve endings; they are released during stimulation of the autonomic nerves; vaso-inhibitory peptide and galanin are parasympathetic cotransmitters; neuropeptide-Y, galanin, adenosine triphosphate and epinephrine are sympathetic cotransmitters.

**Cranial**   pertaining to the skull.

**Cranial nerves**   12 pairs of nerves arising from the brain and the brain stem, connecting the outlying parts of the body and their receptors with the CNS.

**Craving**   extremely strong selective appetite.

**Creatinine**   substance which is formed in the body and is found in the blood. It is produced from creatine in the process of muscle metabolism. Creatine is a substance found in muscular tissue which plays an important role in the chemical aspects of muscle contraction. Creatinine clearance is used to measure the glomerular filtration rate as a test of renal function.

**Cretinism**   arrested physical and mental development resulting from failure of the fetal thyroid to secrete hormone in utero; congenital hypothyroidism.

**Cross-sectional study**   type of research design in which subjects of different ages are studied at one point in time.

**Croton oil**   vegetable product, pressed from the seeds of *Croton tiglium*. In the past it was used as very active laxative; however, it is also a drastic vesicant, causing severe irritation, bloody stools and pain. In research on carcinogenesis it is used as a promoting agent.

**Cystic kidney (cystic renal dysplasia)**   abnormality of differentiation in the kidney, or a part of the kidney, that results in the persistence of abnormal structures such as cartilage and undifferentiated mesenchyme. This sporadic lesion, which does not exhibit a familial tendency, is usually unilateral, but on occasion is bilateral.

**Degenerative changes**   When the action of a noxe causes a cell to die within minutes or hours, this is called acute lethal cell damage. The concomitant morphological changes in the cell are called degenerative changes. Initially these are reversible, provided the action of the noxa, for instance anoxia, stops.

**Dermatitis**   1. most common response of the skin to a toxic effect, accompanied by hyperplasia (cell proliferation), degeneration and/or inflammation. 2. A distinction is made between acute and chronic types of dermatitis; it may be accompanied by the formation of blisters, pustules, red patches, scales, etc. It often involves hyperemia and exudation of inflammatory products in the dermis. At times, blisters and vesicles are formed in the epidermis as well. 3. Dermatitis may lead to necrosis of skin tissue. In the event that parts of the epidermis disappear, one speaks of an ulcer.

**DES**   see diethylstilbestrol.

**Dexamethasone**   drug acting on glucocorticoid receptors.

**Diabetes mellitus**   disease caused by deficient insulin release, leading to failure of the body tissue to oxidize carbohydrates at a normal rate. Although diabetes mellitus is not normally the result of exposure to chemicals, xenobiotics may cause hyperglycemia, presumably through an effect on the $\beta$ cells of the Langerhans' islets. Thus alloxan has been shown to cause diabetes in test animals by destroying the $\beta$ cells. In cases of diabetes mellitus the exocrine tissue of the pancreas is usually normal; sometimes degenerations of the secretory duct epithelium and in severe cases acinar degeneration might be found. The Langerhans' islets sometimes show reduced numbers of beta cells, as well as the presence of a tissue type with myeloid-like characteristics.

**Diazepam (Valium®)** benzodiazepine derivative used extensively in clinical practice as an anxiolytic, muscle relaxant, sedative/hypnotic and anticonvulsant. There is evidence of physical and psychological dependence. This substance can cause neonatal withdrawal effects and in case of prolonged use also 'floppy infant syndrome'.

**Dibenzofurans** abbreviation of polychlorinated dibenzofurans (PCDF). Structurally, PCDFs are closely related to polychlorodibenzo-*p*-dioxins (for instance (TCDD); they may be formed during the manufacturing of PCBs, or when PCBs are heated. PCDF mixtures consist of a large number of related compounds; theoretically, 135 different chlorodibenzofurans are possible. Animal experiments investigating the harmfulness of PCDFs have shown a wide range of effects. It should be kept in mind that the toxicity of the different isomers differs greatly. 2,3,7,8-tetrachlorodibenzofuran is almost as poisonous, and has nearly the same effects, as 2,3,7,8-tetrachlorodibenzo-*p*-dioxin.

**Diethylnitrosamine** like dimethylnitrosamine, one of the very potent carcinogenic nitrosamines. It occurs in tobacco and tobacco smoke. Nitrites, used as preservatives in food, can also give rise to the formation of nitrosamines. The presence of vitamin C or E or other antioxidants can prevent the formation of nitrosamines from nitrite. The target organs are liver, lungs, kidneys, bladder, esophagus and pancreas. Nitrosamines are activated to form reactive electrophilic agents by oxidation.

**Diethylstilbestrol (DES)** synthetic, non-steroidal, orally active estrogenic compound with greater biological activity than endogenous estrogens. It is used in the treatment of carcinomas having specific estrogen-binding capacity and as a 'morning after' contraceptive. It was formerly used in pregnancy when estrogen therapy was thought to be necessary, but was associated with increased incidence of vaginal and cervical adenocarcinoma and malformations of the genital tract in daughters of exposed mothers. It is a transplacental carcinogen.

**Disulfiram** see antabuse.

**Diuresis** increased secretion of urine.

**Dopamine** intermediate in norepinephrine synthesis; a CNS transmitter.

**Double blind** experimental design in which neither the subjects nor those who dispense the treatment condition know who receives the treatment and who receives the placebo.

**Doxylamine (Benedictin®)** an antihistamine that formerly was used in pregnant women for antihistaminic and sedative properties. Although it has excellent sedative properties, it has been falsely implicated in teratogenesis and in causing neurobehavioral toxicity, and is therefore no longer used.

**Dysmorphogenesis** teratogenesis.

**Dysplasia** proportional abnormality in shape and size of tissues. It involves an abnormal development, deviating from the normal pattern. The abnormal development of individual cells, for instance epithelial cells, is also called dysplasia. In such cases large, small and polymorphic nuclei and cells are seen. In this type of dysplasia the mitotic count is usually increased, while the normal position of the cells with respect to each other is also affected. This form of dysplasia can be a precursor of neoplasia. Incomplete or aberrant development of a part, system, or region of the body.

**Dystrophic calcification** calcareous deposit in regressively changed, often necrotic tissue or connective tissue which has undergone hyalinization. Necrosis generally produces an alkaline environment. Usually the serum calcium level is normal. If it is raised, a combined dystrophic/metastatic calcification occurs. Dystrophic calcification occurs in many disorders. In atherosclerosis, this calcification is found in the atheroma or the hyalinized fibrous connective tissue of the thickened tunica intima. An example of dystrophic calcification is the calcification of necrotized parts of kidney epithelium following poisoning with corrosive sublimate (mercuric chloride).

**Dystrophy** special form of atrophy, a growth disturbance or degeneration of an organ or tissue caused by a nutritional disorder.

**Edema** excessive accumulation of intercellular and/or intracellular fluid as a result of transudation from capillaries due to increased hydrostatic pressure, increased permeability of the capillary wall and/or decreased colloid osmotic pressure of the plasma.

**Efferent** carrying away from a center.

**Elastase** enzyme which occurs for instance in some snake poisons. It is occasionally used to induce experimental lung emphysema in experimental animals.

**Embryo** organism in its early stages of development; in humans the first two months after conception.

**Embryogenesis** development of the embryo.

**Encephalocele** herniation of the brain and meninges usually through a developmental defect in the skull and usually at one of the major sutures of the cranium, but not limited to these sites. A covering skin or mucous membrane is initially present but may be ruptured as the herniation enlarges.

**Encephalopathy** degenerative change within the central nervous system. Intravenous administration of atropine and histamine in dogs causes very diverse symptoms: dyspnea, asphyxia, tachycardia, secretion of mucus, diarrhea, tremors or cramp in the skeletal muscles, disturbances of muscle coordination and abnormal enlargement of the pupil (mydriasis). In some animals, histopathological examination reveals selective necrotic changes in the hippocampus, some other cortical areas, in the basal ganglia and in the cortex of the cerebellum.

**Endocrine glands** ductless glands that empty their secretions directly into the blood.

**Endogenous** arising within the body.

**Endorphins** naturally occurring neurochemicals whose effects resemble the opiates.

**β-Endorphin** one of several types of neuropeptides that exhibit morphine-like actions.

**Enteritis** diffuse inflammation of the mucosal epithelium of the intestine, with infiltration of inflammatory cells. Enteritis may on occasion develop after exposure of the small intestine to caustic substances or metals such as mercury or arsenic.

**Eosin** red stain which combines mainly with alkaline elements of the cell, i.e. with the alkaline groups of cytoplasmic proteins. It is for this reason that such groups or proteins are called eosinophilic.

**Eosinophilia** term used to refer to increased staining intensity by eosin, due to the presence of a greater number of eosinophilic components.

**Epichlorohydrin** carcinogenic agent in test animals. It is used for manufacturing epoxy resins. cellulose esters, ethers, paints, varnishes and laquers. It can enter the body through the gastrointestinal tract, the respiratory tract or the skin. It causes acute irritation of the skin and eyes, usually in the form of desquamation and sometimes dermatitis. Systemic symptoms of epichlorohydrin poisoning are usually gastrointestinal in nature; cyanosis (a bluish discoloration of the skin, caused by lack of hemoglobin) and pneumonia may also occur. Chronic exposure in test animals leads to lung, kidney and liver disorders.

**Epidemiology** the scientific study of the pattern of disease in a population. Often epidemiologists seek to determine the cause of disease by looking for pattern of overlap between those who get a particular disease and those who are exposed to some particular factor, such as an air pollutant, in their environment. The study of how and why diseases and other conditions are distributed within the population the way they are.

**Epinephrine** generic name for the catecholamine released from the adrenal cortex: also known by the trade name Adrenalin.

**Epithelioma** benign proliferation of the epidermis. Epitheliomas can be subdivided into keratinizing, calcifying and tricho-epitheliomas. Keratinizing epithelioma: subcutaneous space, wall of proliferating, well-differentiated squamous epithelium. Calcifying epithelioma (= necrotizing): intradermal or subcutaneous spaces, wall of basal cells; in the lumen keratinizing cells without nuclei (shadow cells). Tricho-epithelioma, is a tumor of the hair follicle simulating abortive pilar structures and containing hair cysts.

**Erosion** erosive change; superficial loss of epithelium. It may be found in various types of surface epithelium such as that of the skin, the gastrointestinal tract (gastric ulcer = hemorrhagic erosion) and the cervix. In the skin it is a superficial injury to the epidermis exposing the cutis.

**Estradiol** see estrogens.

**Estriol** estrogen metabolite present in the urine of pregnant women.

**Estrogens** ovarian hormones: estrone, estriol, estradiol; responsible for the female secondary sex characteristics; also prepares the reproductive system for fertilization and implantation of the ovum.

**Estrone** hormone similar to estradiol.

**Estrus cycle** periodic episodes of estrus, marked by sexual receptivity in mature females of most mammalian species.

**Ethanol (alcohol)** liquid which occurs in certain beverages and is also used as a solvent, dehydrating agent and antiseptic. The TLV value (threshold limit value) is 1000 ppm. Ethanol inhibits the central nervous system and has anesthetic properties. Even small doses cause disturbances in the motor and cognitive functions. Larger doses cause anesthesia, loss of sensory perception, decreased coordination, nausea, vomiting, etc. Chronic use results in pharmacokinetic and pharmacodynamic tolerance and dependence. Alcohol has teratogenic effects and causes the fetal alcohol syndrome. Apart from the effects on the CNS, alcohol influences many other organs and organ systems, including the liver. Although the effect on the liver (steatosis, hepatitis, cirrhosis) can be partly attributed to nutritional deficiencies, ethanol also influences the liver directly. If it is used in combination with medication, the potentiating effect of alcohol must be kept in mind.

**Eumenorrhea** normal menstruation pattern.

**Exocrine glands** glands that have ducts through which their secretions are carried to a particular site.

**Exocytosis** fusion of the vesicle membrane to the surface membrane and subsequent expulsion of the vesicle content to the cell exterior.

**Exudation** Hyperemia and vascular leakage often develop simultaneously in a case of inflammation. An inflammatory stimulus is soon followed by dilation of the arterioles, dilation of the venules and increased blood flow through the capillary network. The dilation of arterioles may be preceded by an initial arteriolar constriction. The acceleration of the blood flow is followed by a period in which capillaries and venules becoming overfilled with erythrocytes. There is local stasis of the flow of blood and fluid escapes through the vascular walls. This process is called exudation; the fluid which escapes is called the exudate (L. exsudare = to sweat out).

**Fenfluramine** prescription diet drug: an appetite suppressant.

**Fetal alcohol syndrome (FAS)** refers to a pattern of defects in children born to alcoholic mothers. Three criteria for FAS are: prenatal or postnatal growth retardation; characteristic facial anomalies such as microcephaly, small eye opening, and thinner upper lip; central nervous system dysfunction such as mental retardation and developmental delays.

**Fetotoxicity**   the deleterious effects exhibited by a fetus as a result of exposure to a toxic agent. Fetotoxicity manifestations include: lethality, growth impairment, physiological dysfunctions.

**Fibroma**   benign tumor, derived from connective tissue cells; it is rounded, well circumscribed and firm. A distinction is made between a soft (fibroma molle) and a hard (fibroma durum) type. Characteristics: presence of a fibrous capsule, bundles of interwoven collagenous fibres and connective tissue cells, and fusiform cells, with large, round, hypochromatic nuclei.

**Fibrosarcoma**   malignant tumor arising from connective tissue cells. Characteristics: resembles a fibroma, but unlike the latter it is not surrounded by a fibrous capsule and it is ill-defined.

**Fibrosis**   refers to the presence of an increased amount of reticulin and collagenous fibres on the basis of neoplasia. The new connective tissue is the result of fibroblast activity, but other cells, lipocytes (= fat cells) in particular, are also suspected to play a role. Although direct stimulation of the connective tissue forming cells is possible, connective tissue formation will practically always be preceded by a more or less extensive form of parenchymal necrosis.

Fibrosis is a regenerative reaction to a chronic (inflammatory) process. Fibrosis results in increased rigidity (decreased elasticity).

**First order process**   any process in which the rate of that process is dependent of the substrate concentration.

**Fistula**   abnormal passage between organs or between a body cavity and the outside.

**Focal necrosis**   form of lytic necrosis in which foci of necrosis, including one or more cells, are distributed in a random pattern. This form of necrosis is frequently found as a result of hepatotoxic xenobiotics and infectuous diseases. The secondary inflammatory reaction with histiocytes, lymphocytes, plasma cells and activated Kupffer cells plays an important role. This form of necrosis is not a common toxicological phenomenon.

**Follicle stimulating hormone (FSH)**   hormone produced by the anterior pituitary that stimulates ovarian follicle production in females and sperm production in males.

**Forestomach**   as found in the rat and other rodents is a continuation of the esophagus. Its very function is not known, but it probably serves as a type of storage organ for food before this enters the glandular stomach. In particular in ruminants the forestomach has evolved into three separate parts, the rumen, the reticulum and the omasum. In this last group of animals the glandular stomach, with its three different types of epithelium, is formed by the abomasum.

**Ganglion**   group of nerve cell bodies, usually located in the peripheral nervous system.

**Gap junction**   intercellular specialization with the cell membranes of adjacent cells only 20 Å apart.

**Gastrin**   hormone released by mucous cells in the stomach wall as a response to local reflexes caused by the presence of food; it reaches the gastric glands through the general circulation. Gastrin has a strongly stimulating effect on the release of gastric acid; it also stimulates the secretion of pepsin.

**Gastrointestinal**   pertaining to the stomach and intestine.

**Gastroschisis**   failure of closure of the embryonic anterior abdominal wall at the midventral line. The viscera may protrude with or without a complete or partial covering of a membrane, variably comprised of modified skin, peritoneum and muscle aponeuroses.

**Genotype**   the genetic composition of an individual.

**Gigantism**   excessive growth due to hypersecretion of pituitary growth hormone from birth.

**Glands of Brunner**   exocrine glands that are located in the intestinal mucosa and secrete an alkaline mucoid fluid.

**Glands of Lieberkühn**   exocrine glands located in the intestinal mucosa.

**Glucagon**   protein hormone formed by the $\alpha$ cells of the pancreatic islets; raises the glucose level of blood.

**Glucocorticoids**   adrenal cortex hormones that affect metabolism of fats and carbohydrates.

**Glutamate**   see monosodiumglutamate.

**Gonadotropin-releasing factor (GRF)**   hormone released by the hypothalamus that activates the anterior portion of the pituitary to release gonadotropic hormones.

**Gonadotropic hormones**   the gonad-stimulating hormones produced by the anterior pituitary.

**Gonads**   glands or organs producing gametes; an ovary or testis.

**Good Laboratory Practice (GLP)**   the organizational systems and procedures which are required in laboratories to ensure that high quality investigations are carried out. In the US and the EU this is a code of laboratory procedures laid down under the law and to be followed by laboratories undertaking toxicity tests, the results of which will be used for regulatory or legal purposes.

**Granuloma**   lesion consisting of granulation tissue, usually of inflammatory origin. The tumor eventually shrivels up, leaving scars. Granulomas may be found both in the centrilobular and in the portal area. They consist of small accumulations of cells of the mononuclear phagocyte system.

**Growth hormone (somatotropic hormone)**   hormone that is secreted by the anterior pituitary and stimulates growth; directly influences protein, fat, and carbohydrate metabolism and regulates growth rate.

**Growth hormone releasing factor** hormone released by the hypothalamus that activates the anterior portion of the pituitary to release growth hormone.

**Habituation** progressive loss of behavioral response probability with repetition of a stimulus.

**Hemangioma** neoplasm derived from a blood vessel. This distinguishes it from a tumor which arises from a lymph vessel. Hemangiomas are usually benign. However, malignant vascular tumors are also occasionally found (hemangiosarcoma). When cavities are predominantly large in an angioma, the tumor is called a cavernous hemangioma; when they are relatively small, it is called a capillary hemangioma. Both types are usually found in one and the same lesion. Long-term exposure to vinyl chloride, arsenic and thorotrast (a radiologic contrast medium which is no longer used) may lead to hemangiosarcomas in man. In the case of vinyl chloride, the hemangiosarcoma is often combined with peliosis hepatis.

**Hemochromatosis** (Gr. chroma = color; haima = blood) in man is a pathological condition resulting from an increased resorption of iron from the gastrointestinal tract, accompanied by deposition of a bronze-colored, iron-containing pigment (hemosiderin) in the body, in particular in parenchymatous organs.

**Hemolytic anemia** accelerated peripheral breakdown of erythrocytes. It can be a result of toxic injury, infectious agents or immune-mediated processes. Peroxidative processes play an important role in the toxicology of red cells. This is due to the fact that all three elements which play a part in these processes (oxygen, a transition metal ion and unsaturated lipids) are present in the red cell. Oxidative stress may cause structural changes in the hemoglobin, producing denaturation and precipitation inside the red cell. The precipitates, irregularly shaped, acidophilic inclusion bodies known as Heinz bodies, may attach themselves to the cell membrane and cause changes in its permeability, lysis or deformation of the cell membrane. Such deformation may cause the cells to be trapped and broken down in the spleen.

**Hemorrhage** means bleeding; hemorrhagic means accompanied by, characterized by, or resulting from bleeding.

**Heinz bodies** dark staining refractile granules, consisting of denatured hemoglobin, in erythrocytes. Familiar examples of poisoning accompanied by hemolysis and the formation of Heinz bodies are phenothiazine intoxication and chronic copper intoxication (the latter particularly in sheep).

**Heterolysis** the destruction of cells by external enzymes.

**Hemimelia** limb reduction deformity, involving major reduction in the distal portion of a limb.

**Hemosiderin accumulation** (Hemosiderosis) pathological accumulation of iron in organs and tissues, giving them a brown to yellowish brown coloration. The iron accumulates in the form of hemosiderin in macrophages or in the tissue itself. It may occur in one single organ or tissue, or throughout the body. Extensive iron accumulation may lead to cell death, frequently accompanied by reactive fibrosis. This is called hemochromatosis.

**Hepatoma** neoplasm originating in liver parenchymal cells. It may consist of adenomatous and carcinomatous elements.

**Hexanedione** (2,5-Hexanedione acetonylacetone; 2,5-HD) neurotoxic compound which forms protein adducts (pyrroles), which can form covalent bonds with neurofilaments. 2,5-HD is probably a metabolite of the hexane hydrocarbon solvents. It induces degenerative changes in long sensor and motor (spinal) fibres. The degeneration is of the 'giant-axonal' type, meaning that affected axons are markedly swollen by accumulation of convoluted neurofilament.

**High-density lipoproteins** plasma protein relatively high in protein, low in cholesterol; involved in transporting cholesterol and other lipids from plasma to the tissues.

**Hirsutism** excessive growth of hair at sites in which body hair is normally found.

**Histiocytoma** benign neoplasm arising from certain phagocytes which belong to the RES (= reticulo- endothelial system). It is an ill-defined tumor, composed of large, yellow (fat accumulation) or brown (hemosiderin infiltration) phagocytes. Sometimes a histiocytoma has a coiled appearance as a result of the concentric arrangement of spindle-shaped cells. In the centre of the whorl the endothelium of a capillary can often be discerned. The whole shows a tendency to sclerosis and is therefore also referred to as sclerosing hemangioma. This tumor is found particularly in the skin of the lower legs.

**Histopathology** the science of diseased tissues.

**Homeostasis** state of internal stability or equilibrium.

**Hormone** endogenous compound synthesized and secreted by an endocrine tissue into the blood stream; it influences the activity of a target tissue

**Hyaline** has been derived from Greek and means glassy, transparent. It is used to describe certain degenerations involving protein: hyaline degeneration.

**Hyaline droplet formation** excessive accumulation of proteins is quite uncommon. A well-known example is protein accumulation in the proximal tubule of the kidney, caused by excess protein in the glomerular filtrate. To prevent protein loss through urine, this protein is resorbed by the proximal tubular cells under physiological conditions. In the presence of an excessive supply of protein, the processing capacity of the epithelial cells falls short and proteins accumulate. Microscopically this condition is characterized by the presence of eosinophilic globules. Because of the transparent nature of the protein droplets, this is called hyaline droplet degeneration. Accumulation of protein globules in the proximal tubular epithelium is sometimes observed in acute erythrocyte hemolysis caused by toxic agents (certain heavy metals). Because hemoglobin can pass through the glomerular membrane, it will be present in the glomerular filtrate in cases of serious hemolysis; the proximal tubular cells then resorb as much of it as they can.

**Hydrocephalus**   any condition in which there is an abnormally large volume of the cerebrospinal fluid within the skull.

**Hydronephrosis**   distention of the renal pelvis and calices, and sometimes collecting ducts, secondary to obstruction of urine flow by calculi, tumors, neurological disorders, or any of various congenital anomalies.

**Hydropic degeneration**   (ballooning) irreversible follow-up stage of cellular edema, involving an irreversible disturbance in the cellular water balance. When vacuoles are clearly distinguishable, it is called vacuolar degeneration; when hardly any cytoplasm remains, the situation is called hydropic degeneration. Microscopically, cells and sometimes nuclei can be seen to be enlarged. It is often accompanied by karyopycnosis as a result of condensation of DNA.

**Hydroxydopamine**   (6-Hydroxydopamine;   6-OHDA) neurotoxic agent which is frequently used experimentally. It selectively destroys the catecholaminergic nerves. 6-OHDA is a structural analog of norepinephrine. Applied in small doses to experimental animals, it is transported to the sympathetic nerve ends, where it is oxidized to the corresponding quinone. The quinone is bound covalently to the nerve endings, thus blocking these permanently.

**5-Hydroxytryptamin (serotonin, 5-HT)**   neurotransmitter.

**Hyperbilirubinemia**   high plasma bilirubin.

**Hyperglycemia**   excessive blood glucose levels.

**Hyperinsulinemia**   excessive plasma insulin levels.

**Hyperkeratosis**   (proliferation of the stratum corneum) hyperplasia of the epidermis due to proliferation of the basal cells, for example as a result of dermal contact with PCB, TCDD or TCDF.

**Hyperthyroidism**   increased thyroid activity.

**Hypertrophy**   increase in size of certain cell organelles or whole cells. If the number of cells has increased as well, it is called hyperplasia. The macroscopic increase in the size and mass of tissues and/or organs is, therefore, caused by an increase in the size of the individual cells (more cytoplasm and cytoplasmic structures per cell). Such an adaptation reaction can be initiated under both physiological and toxic conditions and may in certain circumstances have pathological consequences. Hypertrophy of the myocardium, for instance, is observed in sportsmen, but also in chronic cases of slightly decreased blood oxygen levels.

**Hypoglycemia**   low blood glucose levels.

**Hypophysis (pituitary gland)**   complex endocrine organ situated at the base of the brain and connected to the hypothalamus by a stalk; it has a variety of functions including regulation of the gonads, thyroid, adrenal cortex, and other endocrine glands.

**Hypoproteinemia**   lack of proteins in the blood as a result of a congenital metabolic defect called nephrosis. It may also occur in disorders of the liver. The term hypoproteinemia is also used to refer to a deficiency disease as a result of a lack of protein in the diet.

**Hypothalamic-pituitary-adrenal axis**   the sequence of the following glands and hormones: the hypothalamus releasing corticotropin-releasing factor, the pituitary releasing adrenocorticotropic hormone and the adrenal cortex releasing corticosterone.

**Hypothalamus**   part of the diencephalon that forms the floor of the third ventricle of the brain; it is the highest centre of the autonomic nervous system and contains centres controlling various physiological functions such as emotion, hunger, thurst and circadian rhythms; it also has an important endocrine function, producing releasing and some inhibiting hormones that act on the anterior pituitary and regulate the release of its hormones.

**Hypothermia**   state of abnormally low body temperature.

**Hypothyroidism**   reduced thyroid activity.

**Hypoxia**   lack of oxygen in the tissues or in the inhaled air, anoxia refers to an insufficient level of oxygen in the tissues.

**Imipramine**   belongs to the so-called tricyclic antidepressants, a group of compounds used to treat depressed patients. The tricyclic antidepressants inhibit the reabsorption of norepinephrine and/or serotonin through the presynaptic membrane. Imipramine intoxication can express itself as central nervous system disorders (dizziness, extrapyramidal phenomena, coma), arrhythmias and respiratory problems.

**Implantation**   the attachment of the fertilized ovum to, or penetration into, an organ where it develops during gestation. Implantation almost always takes place in the uterus on the receptive mucous lining or endometrium.

**In vitro**   within a glass; in an artificial environment. In vitro experiments are those carried out in a 'test tube'.

**In vivo**   in the living body.

**Inflammation**   In a living organism, tissue damage leads to reactions from other cells and tissues. A distinction can be made between local and generalized reactions. In normal situations, local reactions will always occur. They consist of an inflammation reaction, accompanied by repair and sometimes regeneration of lost tissue. Therefore, an inflammation can be defined as a local reaction to tissue damage. Generalized reactions include fever, leukocytosis and generalized immunological reactions. Such generalized reactions do not always occur. The main clinical symptoms of inflammation are: pain (dolor), heat (calor), redness (rubor) and swelling (tumor). The redness is mainly caused by dilation of the blood vessels, increasing the blood flow in the tissues. The swelling is mainly caused by protein-rich fluid leaving the blood vessels and permeating the tissue; in addition, several types of cells can penetrate the tissue from the blood, and then start to multiply.

**Insulin**   protein hormone formed by the $\beta$ cells of the pancreatic islets; lowers the glucose level of blood; it also influences lipid and amino acid metabolism.

**Intravenous**   within or into a vein.

**Inulin**   substance which is not metabolized in the kidney, does not influence renal function, freely filtered and the amount once filtered is not resorbed. Some of it is also subject to secretion in the renal tubules. It is therefore frequently employed for measuring the glomerular filtration rate.

**Iprindole**   one of the tricyclic antidepressants, a group of drugs used to treat depressed patients. The main side effects of tricyclic antidepressants are related to their inhibition of the absorption of monoamines and their intrinsic anticholinergic properties. Even at therapeutical doses, cardiovascular disorders may occur, as well as anticholinergic side effects, such as dryness of the mouth, dizziness, urine retention, tachycardia and delirium.

**Ischemia**   (Gr. ischein = to hold back; haima = blood) lack of blood as a result of an impediment in its supply, for example a constriction or organic closure of an afferent vessel.

**Islets of Langerhans**   microscopic endocrine structures dispersed throughout the pancreas; they consist of three cell types: the $\alpha$ cells, which secrete glucagon; the $\beta$-cells, which secrete insulin; and the $\delta$-cells, which secrete gastrin.

**Isoniazid**   drug which, in combination with other drugs, is used for the treatment of tuberculosis. Isoniazid is frequently applied prophylactically. It is a bactericidal agent, although low concentrations are only bacteriostatic. Although side effects are rare, occasional allergic reactions have been reported. Some people acetylate isoniazid at a very low rate: for these patients, the chance of toxicity is somewhat smaller. Isoniazid is a neurotoxic agent, which can cause peripheral neuropathies. It should always be used in combination with pyridoxine, which can prevent the neurotoxic action. Liver damage, skin damage and effects on the central nervous system, such as psychoses, may also occur. The latter is caused by the inhibiting effect on the enzyme monoamine oxidase (MAO).

**Jaundice (icterus)**   yellow discoloration of the skin and eyes results, also called jaundice or icterus. When excretion of bilirubin in the bile is insufficient, the bilirubin level of the blood and tissue fluid rises. Bilirubin may also be found locally in tissues, often together with hemosiderin as the remains of a hemorrhage. Jaundice may have several causes: extrahepatic biliary obstruction, pathological processes in the liver, or increased production of bilirubin as a result of increased erythrocyte breakdown. The most common cause of extrahepatic biliary obstruction is a gallstone. Severe progressive jaundice may be caused by a tumor which is located inside the biliary passages or obstructs them from the outside, as a pancreatic carcinoma may do. Toxic injury caused by alcohol, drugs or poisons such as phosphorus and arsenic may also cause hepatic jaundice. Immune reactions may play a role. Primary or metastatic tumors in the liver may sometimes cause very serious jaundice by obstructing the intrahepatic bile ducts and may thus lead to injury of remaining hepatic tissue. The cause of prehepatic jaundice, also referred to as hemolytic jaundice, is increased disintegration of blood or hemolysis. Numerous factors may lead to hemolysis and anemia. Well-known causes are immune reactions, intoxication by snakebite, and parasitic diseases.

**Juxtaglomerular apparatus**   physiological complex in the kidney, consisting of macula densa cells at the beginning of the distal tubule, the parts of the afferent and efferent arterioles of the same nephron which are close to it, and the interstitial cells located in between. Its location makes it extremely suitable to receive signals about the composition of the urine at the beginning of the distal tubule (macula densa) and to regulate the glomerular filtration by controlling the blood flow through the glomerulus and the filtration pressure. The granule cells of the juxtaglomerular apparatus contain the proteolytic enzyme renin. Via the renin-angiotensin system, renin is involved in the excretion of water and salts from the kidney.

**Karyolysis**   light-microscopically visible irreversible change in the nuclei. In karyolysis, the nuclear membrane and the contents of the nucleus are hardly discernible with hematoxylin staining. As a result of degenerative enzymatic activity, the pycnotic nuclei liquefy completely. Thus, karyolysis involves a strikingly reduced staining of the nuclear membrane and the nuclear contents, and condensation of the cytoplasm due to protein denaturation.

**Karyopycnosis**   nuclear change in cell pathology. In the case of karyopycnosis, the nucleus has become a lump of chromatin, which stains dark in hematoxylin staining. This means that the nucleus is small and compact. Light-microscopic characteristics are the condensed nuclear chromatin, the shrivelled nucleus and the dark color in HE staining.

**Karyorrhexis**   light-microscopically visible irreversible change in the nuclei in necrosis. In karyorrhexis, the nuclei disintegrate into several pycnotic fragments.

**Kinetic volume of distribution**   hypothetical volume of body fluid that would be required to dissolve the total amount of a substance at the same concentration as that found in the blood or plasma. It is a proportionality constant relating the amount of drug in the body to the measured concentration in biological fluid (blood, plasma, plasma water).

**Kinetics** mathematical study of the changes of the concentration of a xenobiotic or its metabolites in the human or animal body after exposure.

**Lamina propria** the layer of connective tissue directly below a layer of epithelium.

**Large cell bronchial carcinoma** a combination of a squamous cell carcinoma and an adenoma, or of a squamous cell carcinoma and a small cell bronchial carcinoma. This tumor consists of large pleomorphic cells without any clear differentiation.

**Latency period** delay between exposure to a disease-causing agent and the appearance of manifestations of the disease; also defined as the period from disease initiation to disease detection.

**Lavage** the washing out, especially by irrigation, of a hollow organ or cavity.

**Laxative** substance causing evacuation of the intestinal contents.

**Lesion** a disturbance in the cell's homeostasis.

**Leukocytosis** refers to the presence of an excess of white blood cells in the blood. It would be more correct to use the term hyperleukocytosis.

**Leukemia** malignant disorder of cells occurring in the bloodstream and originating from the bone marrow. A distinction is made between myeloid and lymphatic leukemias. Leukemias behave clinically like a malignant tumor of abnormal lymphocytes or their precursors, originating in lymph nodes or the spleen. Myeloid leukemias affect granulocytes and their precursors in bone marrow.

**Leukopenia** reduced concentration of leukocytes in the blood.

**Limbic system** brain area playing a major role in emotional responses.

**Limit test** acute toxicity test in which, if no ill-effects occur at a preselected maximum dose, no further testing at greater exposure levels is required. This test involves only a single (usually high) dose and therefore greatly reduces the number of animals required for acute toxicity testing.

**Limit value (LV)** concentration at or below which Member States of the European Union must set their environmental quality standard and emission standard for a particular substance according to Union Directives.

**Lipid accumulation** fatty change in the enterocytes of the small intestine, as well as in hepatocytes. Some substances, e.g. tetracyclines, penetrate the cells of the mucosa and are phagocytosed by underlying macrophages. They interfere with the lysosomal enzyme system and accumulate in the macrophages. As a result of this, foam cells are formed in the lamina propria of the villus.

**Lipid peroxidation** enzymatic as well as nonenzymatic peroxidation of unsaturated cellular lipids. It involves initiation, propagation and termination reactions.

**Lipofuscin** also called age pigment, is an endogenous lipid pigment occurring in tissues where lipid peroxidation takes place. It is quite variable in composition, consisting mainly of degradation products of phospholipids, condensed with proteins and other cellular components, such as carbohydrates. Light-microscopically it is characterized by: formation within lysosomes (cytoplasmic granular deposition), yellow/golden brown deposits in HE sections and demonstrable with fluorescence microscopy

**Lipoma** a benign mesenchymal tumor composed of fat cells. It usually occurs as a single growth in the hypodermis and causes little discomfort. Macroscopic examination reveals a structure which resembles a patch-work quilt or a bunch of grapes. Lipomas often resemble normal adipose tissue; sometimes their color is slightly more yellowish. Because of their compactness and well-demarcated boundaries, they can easily be distinguished from the surrounding adipose tissue. Microscopic examination reveals various groups of cells separated from each other by connective tissue which contains capillaries. The fat cells in a lipoma are usually larger than ordinary fat cells.

**Lipophilic** having a high affinity for fat and high lipid solubility: a physicochemical property describing a partioning equilibrium of solute molecules between water and an immiscible organic solvent, favoring the latter.

**Lipoproteins** compounds made up of lipid (for example cholesterol, triglycerides) and plasma proteins. A distinction is made between high density lipoproteins (HDL), which have a protein content of 50%, low density lipoproteins (LDL), with a protein content of approximately 20% and very low density lipoproteins (VLDL) which contain only 10% proteins.

**Liquefactive necrosis** form of necrosis characterized by liquefaction of the damaged tissue. It occurs only in the brain and pancreas. In the brain it is called encephalomalacia. Corrosion by lyes, for instance in the digestive tract, also causes liquefactive necrosis. A coagulative necrosis coinciding with bacterial infection may also develop into a liquefactive necrosis. Characteristically, the original tissue structure is no longer recognizable, cell outlines fade away and the tissue is very pale in color.

**Liver function tests** number of diagnostic tests to determine the disturbance of different liver functions. Common tests are:
—determination of the albumin/globulin ratio,
—bilirubin concentration blood/urine.
—excretion of bromosulphthalein (BSP), and

—determination of serum enzymes: ALT (alanine aminotransferase); APT (asparatate aminotransferase), alkaline phosphatase, GGT (gamma-glutamyltranspeptidase).

**Local effect** effect of a chemical at the point of first contact or entry into the body.

**Logit transformation**  mathematical transformation relating the response to a stated dose or concentration of a toxicant to the response in the absence of the toxicant:

$$\text{logit} = \frac{\text{response to the stated dose}}{\text{response in absence of toxicant} - \text{response to the stated dose}}$$

**Long-term exposure**  continuous or repeated exposure to a substance over a long period of time, usually of several years in man, and of the greater part of the total life-span in animals or plants.

**Lowest-observed-adverse-effect level (LOAEL)**  lowest concentration or amount of a substance, found by experiment or observation, which causes an adverse alteration of morphology, functional capacity, growth, development, or life span of a target organism distinguishable from normal (control) organisms of the same species and strain under defined conditions of exposure.

**Lowest observed effect level (LOEL)**  lowest concentration or amount of a substance, found by experiment or observation, that causes any alteration in morphology, functional capacity, growth, development, or life span of target organisms distinguishable from normal (control) organisms of the same species and strain under defined conditions of exposure.

**LSD**  see lysergic acid diethylamide.

**Luteinizing hormone (LH)**  anterior pituitary hormone that stimulates maturation of cells in the ovary and acts on interstitial cells of the testis.

**Lymphoma**  malignant disorder of cells found in the lymph glands and thymus. It includes Hodgkin's disease (presence of giant cells and a heterogeneous population of benign inflammatory cells in lymph glands) and multiple myelomas (proliferation of plasma cells).

**Lysergic acid diethylamide (LSD)**  psychedelic and hallucinogenic drug.

**Macrovesicular steatosis**  intracellular accumulation of fat in large vacuoles; it may have a pathological or a physiological background. Macroscopically, the fat accumulation can result in swelling and yellow discoloration of the organ. Light-microscopically, the large fat vacuoles can be observed, sometimes apparently pushing aside all of the cytoplasm.

**Malformation**  ill or wrong formation; irregular or anomalous formation or structure of parts.

**Malignant**  tendency to become progressively worse and to result in death if not treated. In cancer, cells showing both uncontrolled growth and a tendency to invade and destroy other tissues.

**Mastocytoma**  dermal swelling, caused by infiltration of mast cells; it is a mesenchymal tumor.

**Maximum allowable concentration (MAC)**  regulatory value defining the concentration that if inhaled daily (in the case of work people for 8 hours with a working week of 40 hours, in the case of the general population 24 hours) does not, within the present state of knowledge, appear capable of causing appreciable harm, however long delayed during the working life or during subsequent life or in subsequent generations.

**Maximum residue limit (MRL) for pesticide residues**  maximum contents of a pesticide residue (expressed as mg per kg fresh weight) recommended by the Codex Alimentarius Commission to be legally permitted in or on food commodities and animal feeds. MRLs are based on data obtained following good agricultural practice and foods derived from commodities that comply with the respective MRLs are intended to be toxicologically acceptable.

**Mechanoreceptors**  receptors sensitive to mechanical pressures such as touch, sound or contractions.

**Meconium**  (1) first stools of a newborn baby; (2) the juice of the poppy.

**Median**  midpoint of a set of scores; 50 per cent of the scores fall above the median, 50 per cent below.

**Megakaryocyte**  (Gr. karyon = nucleus; kytos = cell) a large bone marrow cell with a large, lobed nucleus and responsible for the production of blood platelets.

**Megakaryocytosis**  the presence of megakaryocytes in the blood.

**Megaloblastic changes**  large, nucleated cells due to changes in the availability of folic acid which (indirectly) leads to a disturbance in the hematopoiesis (formation of blood cells). Megaloblasts are immature precursors of peripheral blood cells. The nuclei have matured insufficiently in relation to the cytoplasm. There is in fact inhibition of DNA synthesis, whilst the protein synthesis continues. The precursor cells are not only larger than normal, but also display a disproportion between nucleus and cytoplasm. Megaloblastic changes can be induced by methotrexate and various other cytotoxic drugs.

**Meiosis**  cell division resulting in production of haploid gametes.

**Melanin**  one of the endogenous pigments, occurring in the skin, the pigment layer of the retina and several other places. It is stored in strongly electron-scattering particles (melanosomes) in the cytoplasmic matrix. Skin pigmentation defects encompass both abnormally increased (hyperpigmentation) and abnormally decreased (hypopigmentation) pigment levels. These abnormalities may have endogenous or exogenous causes. In pigment abnormalities, the number of melanocytes is important as well as the phase in which the pigmentation process was arrested. A circumscribed hyperpigmentation may be caused by accumulation of melanophages.

**Melanoma**  malignant tumor arising from melanocytes; a distinction is made between black, brown and depigmented types. Characteristics: pigment cells in bundles of connective tissue, fusiform cells, cells with dendritic processes or cells resembling epithelial cells, the nuclei are round or oval and are hidden under the pigment and besides tumor cells, melanin-laden macrophages occur.

**Meningomyelocele**   protrussion of the spinal cord and associated meninges through a developmental defect in the spinal canal, resulting in exposure at the surface along the midline of the back.

**Mercuric chloride**   colorless crystalline compound, soluble in water, prepared by direct combination of mercury and cold dry chlorine. Upon heating, mercuric chloride sublimates (sublimate poisoning!), forming a white translucent mass. Dilutions are used as disinfectants. Mercuric chloride is extremely poisonous.

**Mesangium**   framework of the glomerulus, which arises from the vascular pole and extends into the intercapillary spaces, forming lobule centers.

**Mesenchyme**   the undifferentiated tissue of the early embryo that forms almost entirely from mesoderm.

**Mesothelioma**   tumor of the pleura, peritoneum or pericardium.

**Metamyelocyte**   an intermediary stage between the myelocyte with a round nucleus and the granulocyte with a rod shaped nucleus.

**Metaplasia**   reversible process, involving replacement of a well-differentiated tissue by another well-differentiated tissue. Metaplasia occurs in avitaminoses, in chronic inflammations and as a result of chemical stimuli. It is generally caused by chronic changes in the microenvironment of the cells.

**Metastasis**   the distant spread of malignant tumor from its site of origin, either via the bloodstream, the lymphatic system or across body cavities.

**Metastatic calcification**   formation of calcareous deposits due to hypercalcemia in tissue which does not display signs of preceding regressive changes. In tissues, calcium usually precipitates in the form of calcium phosphate. Metastatic calcification can occur in many tissues. It frequently begins in the kidneys, in the connective tissue surrounding the tubules, but it can also begin in the tubular epithelium or the tubule lumen. Furthermore, metastatic calcification can occur in the lungs, the gastric mucosa, the skin, the edge of the cornea and the vascular walls.

**Methotrexate**   an antineoplastic and immunosuppressive substance. It is a carcinogenic and mutagenic substance. As a folic acid analog, it inhibits the enzyme dihydrofolic acid reductase, thus inhibiting the synthesis of the substrates of nucleic acid synthesis and protein synthesis. Methotrexate causes bone marrow depression, kidney damage and ulcerative stomatitis (stomach ulcers) and it is hepatotoxic.

**Methyl bromide**   a gas which is poisonous to many organisms. It is used as an agricultural soil disinfectant and in shipping as a stock protector, being highly poisonous to microorganisms and insects. It is therefore also a dangerous environmental pollutant. In mammals (and man) it acts especially on the nervous system and the genetic material, increasing the chances of contracting cancer or congenital abnormalities in the offspring. Methyl bromide can be taken up through respiration, orally and through the skin. The effects on the nervous system, as observed in market gardeners, involve irreversible changes, particularly paralysis. Methyl bromide is moderately biodegradable; on degradation inorganic bromides are formed.

**Methyl mercury**   toxicologically, the most important mercury compound. In nature, this can be formed by biomethylation in aquatic environments; it is also used as a fungicide. Some familiar epidemics of methylmercury poisoning have occurred in Japan (fish from polluted waters) and Iraq (seed for sowing). Because of the lipophilic character of the compound, the central nervous system forms the main target organ. Symptoms are visual disturbance, sensory distortion, coordination and speech disturbance, and deafness.

**Microcephaly**   abnormal smallness of the brain case specifically, or of the head as a whole.

**Micronucleus assay**   short-term test used to screen for the carcinogenicity and/or mutagenicity of chemicals. The ability of the chemical to induce micronuclei (a type of chromosome aberration) in bone marrow erythrocytes is examined.

**Microvesicular steatosis**   form of steatosis, in which the fat droplets are small in comparison with the cell itself and the nucleus is hardly dislocated. Microscopic characteristics are: small, clear cytoplasmic vacuoles and the nuclei are centrally located in the cytoplasm.

**Mitogen**   substance inducing mitosis and cell proliferation.

**Mitosis**   (Gr. mitos = thread) the ordinary process of cell division, as opposed to meiosis. Mitosis results in the formation of two diploid daughter cells with the same number of chromosomes as the parent cell. Mitoses are very common in tissue in the process of repair, during which cell division takes place. The characteristic structure of the nuclei immediately before or after mitosis is referred to as a mitose.

**Monoamine**   amine with one amino group; the neurotransmitters serotonin, norepinephrine and dopamine are monoamines.

**Monoclonal antibody**   antibody produced by cloned cells derived from a single lymphocyte.

**Monosodiumglutamate (MSG, glutamate)**   an excitatory neurotransmitter. Neonatal animals are particularly sensitive to large doses of MSG, which can result in permanent lesions of the hypothalamus, causing major neuroendocrinological abnormalities. This effect is suspected to be caused by the fact that in neonates the blood-brain barrier is still developed to prevent the glutamate from reaching the brain. This causes nerves to die because of overstimulation by glutamate. Some people are

**allergic** to the ingestion of large amounts of glutamate. Glutamate is added as a seasoning to food. The consequences of overdose are known as the "Chinese restaurant syndrome".

**Morphine**  active ingredient of opium; a drug used as analgesic and sedative.

**Motor neurons**  nerve cells that innervate muscle cells.

**Mucoid (mucous)**  pertaining to or containing mucus.

**Mucosa**  mucous membrane facing a cavity or the exterior of the body.

**Mucous (mucoid)**  pertaining to or containing mucus.

**Mucus**  sticky, thick fluid secreted by mucous glands.

**Multi stage model**  dose-response model for cancer death estimation. In this model it is assumed that cancer is initiated by cell mutations in finite series of steps.

**Muscarinic receptors**  one of several types of acetylcholine-sensitive binding sites: sensitive to muscarine but not to nicotine.

**Mustard gas**  see nitrogen mustard gas.

**Mutagen**  any substance that can induce mutations.

**Mutagenesis**  the process by which a change in genetic information either occurs in nature or is induced experimentally.

**Mutagenicity**  the ability of an agent to induce mutations, usually relative to other agents.

**Mutant**  individual in which a mutation has occurred especially when the mutation is visible.

**Mutation**  relatively stable change in genetic material that may be a chemical transformation of an individual gene (gene or point mutation), altering its function, or a rearrangement, gain or loss of part of a chromosome, that may be microscopically visible (chromosomal mutation). Mutations can be either germinal and inherited by subsequent generations, or somatic and passed through cell lineage by cell division.

**Mycotoxin**  toxin produced by a fungus.

**Myelinopathy**  pathological change restricted to the neuroglia or the Schwann cells. The nerve cells themselves are not directly affected, but they may occasionally display secondary changes. The loss of the myelin sheath, demyelinization, may be the result of a direct toxic effect on the membrane structure. Other causes may be: inhibition of the enzyme carboanhydrase or other enzymes involved in ion and water transport, inhibition of enzymes involved in the oxidative phosphorylation or the chelation of metals. Demyelinization may also result from direct effects on the oligodendrocytes and Schwann cells. Demyelinization with formation of edema and vesicles between the myelin lamellae is easily visible by light microscopy, as the vesicles can be seen as vacuoles.

**Myocarditis**  inflammation of the heart muscle tissue, caused by hypersensitivity reactions or directly result-ing from chemicals. Immunological myocarditis is characterized by infiltration of eosinophils and mononuclear cells (lymphocytes and plasma cells in particular) into the heart muscle. The infiltration can be focal or diffuse and is associated with local myocytolysis. The absence of extensive myocardial necrosis and fibrosis distinguishes immunological myocarditis from other types. Direct toxic myocarditis caused by chemicals results in extensive cell damage and cell death. Unlike the immunological type, this type is dose-related. Toxicological myocarditis is characterized by interstitial edema, multifocal necrosis and fibrosis, and infiltration of lymphocytes, plasma cells and neutrophils. Eosinophils are only rarely present.

**N-methyl-N'-nitro-N-nitrosoguanidine (MNNG)**  teratogenic agent, causing a multitude of effects in the mouse fetus. As an alkylating agent, it causes reproduction-related mutations and inhibition of DNA synthesis. On administration 7 to 12 days after conception, a wide range of malformations occur, for instance in the brain, palate, spinal column, ribs and extremities. In addition to its teratogenic and mutagenic effects, MNNG also acts as a carcinogen.

**Naloxone**  analog of morphine that acts as an opioid antagonist

**Naltiexone**  an opiate antagonist as naloxone.

**Narcosis**  state of diminished consciousness or complete unconsciousness caused by the use of narcotic drugs, which have a depressant action on the nervous system

**Natural killer cell (NK-cell)**  type of lymphocyte that is able to kill certain types of cancer cells. NK-cells are also able to affect virally infected cells.

**Necrosis**  the complex of morphological changes occurring after local intravital death of cells or tissue. It is visible because the dead cells have changed in appearance. In the case of acute lethal cell damage, cell death can be said to have occurred if the 'point of no return' has been passed. The subsequent changes in the cell are not only caused by autolysis due to lytic enzymes released from the lysosomes of the dead cells, but also by heterolysis caused by lytic enzymes from granulocytes. These have infiltrated the area with the dead cells from blood vessels in the adjacent tissues. This process occurs as part of the inflammation reaction. Microscopically, necrosis is easily distinguished from postmortal autolytic changes; often necrosis involves the presence of granulocytes or histiocytes. Several forms of necrosis are distinguished. In toxicology, coagulative necrosis and liquefactive necrosis are of particular importance.

**Neoplasia**  the process of forming neoplasms.

**Neoplasm**  a relatively autonomic growth of tissue. More precisely, it is a local autonomic progressive proliferation of the body's own cells, which have undergone a change, now proliferate without any form of coordination with the host organism and which do not perform any task beneficial to the host.

**Nephroblastomas (Wilms' tumors)** malignant tumors found mainly in children (below 5 years of age). They are often congenital and in fact "mixed" tumors. Microscopic examination reveals fetal glandular ducts with basophilic, high–columnar epithelium and mesenchyme with spindle cells; the nuclei are round, polymorphous or elongated ovals (smooth muscle cells) with large nucleoli. Cross-striated and longitudinally striated fibres may be present.

**Nephrotoxic** harmful to the cells of the kidney.

**Neurilemma** the sheath of the axon of a nerve fibre.

**Neurofibroma** benign mesenchymal tumor arising from the connective tissue cells of the endoneurium. The endoneurium is the layer of connective tissue surrounding the neurilemma. In man this is a tumor which seldom occurs on its own. Macroscopically, soft, well-circumscribed nodes can be seen, sometimes as large as a walnut. The cut surface shows a somewhat glassy appearance. Microscopically, very fine collagenous fibres and occasionally some Schwann cells and nerve fibres are visible.

**Neuroleptic drug** drug acting to prevent or alleviate mental disorders.

**Neuronopathy** lesion of the neurone with observable degenerative changes to the cell body. Characteristic of a neuronopathy is a primary involvement of the cell body with simultaneous or subsequent degeneration of the processes in which the cell body is involved. Since the neuronopathy is usually restricted to one neuronal system, the distribution pattern of this lesion within the nervous system is essentially different from that which is encountered in a central-peripheral distal axonopathy. An excess of vitamin $B_6$ causes damage to ganglion cells in the ganglia of the dorsal root. This damage is accompanied by degeneration of the central and peripheral activities carried out by the ganglion. Early changes consist of the formation of vacuoles in the cytoplasm of the ganglion cells.

**Neuropathy** term used to refer to a structural disorder of a part of the nervous system. A further classification is usually based on the structure affected. A structural disorder affecting the brain, for example, is called encephalopathy, one of the spinal cord is called myelopathy, one of a neurone is called neuronopathy, one affecting an axon is called axonopathy and one of the protective tissue (myelin sheath and oligodendrocytes) is called myelinopathy. A distinction is made between specific and nonspecific neuropathies. Specific neuropathies are caused by the direct effect of a substance on the nervous tissue. Since the effect is specific for the tissue concerned and often also dose-related, the predictability of such specific neuropathies is high. Nonspecific neuropathies are caused indirectly, for example by systemic effects such as respiratory or vascular accidents, or by immunological mechanisms. As the resulting effect is dependent on indirect factors and is frequently not related to the dose to which the organism has been exposed, the occurrence of such non-specific neuropathies cannot very reliably be predicted.

**Neuropeptide** peptide molecule directly affecting the nervous system, either as a neurotransmitter or as a neuromodulator.

**Neurotensin** hormone released by the gastro-intestinal tract.

**Neurotoxicity** the ability to produce an adverse effect on the nervous system

**Neurotransmitter** chemical mediator released by a presynaptic nerve ending that interacts with receptor molecules in the postsynaptic membrane; this process generally induces a permeability increase to an ion or ions and thereby influences the electrical activity of the postsynaptic cell.

**Nicotine** addictive stimulant ingredient in tobacco smoke.

**Nicotinic receptors** one of several types of acetylcholine-sensitive binding sites; sensitive to nicotine but not to muscarine.

**NIH-shift** the shift of a hydrogen atom during the rearrangement of an epoxide in(to) a phenol.

**Nitrogen mustard gas** a vesicant war gas. It causes superficial epidermal necrosis and damage of the alveolar epithelium. The permeability of the skin capillaries in the cutis is also increased, causing extravasation of liquid and development of edema as well as subepidermal blistering.

**Nitrosomorpholine** one of the nitrosamines known to be carcinogenic after metabolic activation. Nitrosamines are both naturally occurring and synthethic chemicals. Nitrosomorpholine occurs, for instance, in cigarette smoke. Nitrosamines must be bioactivated to manifest their carcinogenic properties. Oxidation converts the nitrosamines into active electrophilic reactive intermediates. The active species alkylate DNA in various places.

**No effect level** the dose level or concentration at which no significant toxic effects are observed.

**Norepinephrine (noradrenaline)** neurohumor secreted by the peripheral sympathetic nerve terminals, some cells of the CNS, and the adrenal medulla.

**Northern blotting** blotting of RNA.

**Noxa** a stimulus which disturbs the cellular homeostasis, causing a lesion which can lead to regressive changes in and even death of the cell. In toxicology, the noxa usually consists of a harmful substance, but it may also consist of the action of a physical agent, for instance radiation.

**Nucleus** group of nerve cell bodies, located in the central nervous system.

**Olfactory** pertaining to the sense of smell.

**Omphalocele** herniation of intraabdominal viscera into the umbilical cord. The herniated viscera are contained in a thin translucent sac of peritoneum and amnion.

**Oncogene** gene which can (potentially) induce neoplastic transformations in the cell in which it occurrs or into which it is introduced.

**Operant behavior** behavior that is voluntary and not elicited by a discrete, identifiable stimulus.

**Opiate** family of drugs that have properties similar to opium.

**Opioid** substance that exerts opiate-like effects

**Opium** the sap derived from the ripened seed pod of the opium poppy. It contains morphine and codeine.

**Opsonin** antibody that in combination with a particulate antigen increases the susceptibility of the latter to phagocytosis.

**Opsonization** the process in which a particular antigen becomes more susceptible to phagocytosis as a result of combination with an opsonin.

**Organogenesis** formation and development of the different organs of an animal or plant. Although the greater part occurs during the embryonic period, that of some organs, such as those of the special senses and the central nervous system, continue to be developed during the fetal period and in man even after birth.

**Organotin compounds** toxic metal compounds, involving a covalent bond between tin, and an organic group. Toxicologically most important are trimethyltin, triethyltin and tributyltin. Tin compounds with three organic side chains (trimethyltin, tributyltin and triphenyltin) are used as agricultural pesticides, the di- and monocompounds are also used as stabilizing agents in PVC. Tricompounds are also used in antifouling paints for ships. Triethyltin and trimethyltin are formed mainly as contaminants in the manufacturing of other alkyltin compounds. Both, are mainly neurotoxic; effects on both the central and the peripheral nervous system have been observed.

**Oropharyngeal** pertaining to the mouth and pharynx.

**Osmosis** passage (diffusion) of a solvent through a membrane from a dilute solution into a more concentrated one.

**Ouabain** obsolete glycoside that was used as cardiac stimulant and diuretic. It is obtained from the seed of *Stropharitus gratus, Acokanthera ouabaio* and related species. It acts as an inhibitor to $Na^+/K^+$-ATPase. The sensitivity of $Na^+/K^+$-ATPase to ouabain differs with the tissue.

**Oxidative stress** excessive consumption of reducing equivalents (in the form of e.g. NADPH, NADH, GSH, vitamins E and C) leading to a decrease in the reducing detoxication capacity with all its consequences such as lipid peroxidation.

**Pancreas** gland located behind the stomach, between the spleen and the duodenum

**Panlobular necrosis** necrosis that involves an entire liver lobule. If this change involves several adjacent lobules, the term massive necrosis is used.

**Papilloma** a benign epithelial tumor in which the stroma supporting the epithelium is thrown into branched finger-like projections. Sometimes the tumor is stalked. This type of tumor has a cauliflower-like appearance. Characteristics: narrow connective tissue core with papillary projections at various levels and sometimes the connective tissue constitutes a large part of the tumor (= fibropapilloma).

**Paralysis** loss of muscle function or sensation.

**Paraquat** a so-called contact herbicide, a dehydrant and defoliant used for harvesting cotton, potatoes and soybeans, and also used for destroying illegal marijuana fields. Paraquat causes mainly lung edema, hyperplasia of Type II pneumocytes and fibrosis. Paraquat is an oxidizing agent, which causes a single-electron oxidation/reduction reaction depleting cellular NADPH and producing superoxide radicals. Bioaccumulation in the lung overwhelms the detoxifying enzymes, causing lipid peroxidation of the alveolar membranes. Ingestion causes irritation, corrosion and ulceration of mouth and esophagus, stomach-ache and nausea.

**Parasympathetic nervous system** the part of the autonomic nervous system that controls the normal vegetative functioning of the body such as digestion of food and regulation of heart rate and blood pressure.

**Parenchyma** the essential, specifically functional tissue of an organ. It is surrounded by the interstitial tissue (= stroma or supporting tissue).

**Paresthesia** spontaneously occurring abnormal tingling sensations, sometimes described as 'pins and needles'.

**Pathogenesis** the manner in which a disease (Gr. pathos = disease) is produced (Gr. genesis = production).

**Pathology** the science of disease.

**Pelagic** organisms that swim or drift in the sea or other aqueous environment.

**Peliosis hepatis** a rare condition characterized by the presence of multiple microscopic pods of blood, often lined with endothelium, in the hepatic lobules. It is thought to stem from congestion of the liver and subsequent necrosis.

**Pentachlorophenol (PCP)** a fungicide and bactericide, used for preserving wood. It can enter the body through the skin, through inhalation or by accidental ingestion. Exposure to this chemical can cause a great many symptoms, such as irritation of the mucous membranes and the respiratory tract, anorexia, nausea, dizzy spells and raised body temperature. Pentachlorophenol is fetotoxic and teratogenic.

**Pentagastrin** a synthetically prepared analog of the endogenous hormone gastrin.

**Pericaryon** cell body of a neuron.

**Perinatal** currently used to describe the weeks before a birth, the birth and the succeeding few weeks. In man pertaining to the period extending from the 28th week of gestation to the 28th day after birth.

**Periportal (perivenular) coagulative necrosis** necrosis not located around the central vein but around the portal triad.

**Periportal area** the area of the anatomical liver lobule located around the portal vein. The periportal triad refers to the cord of hepatic tissue containing the portal vein, the bile ductules and the veins and arteries of the liver, including the surrounding connective tissue.

**Persistency** attribute of a substance describing the length of time that the substance remains in a particular environment before it is physically removed or chemically or biologically transformed.

**Pesticide** substance intended to kill pests; also used for any substance used for controlling, preventing, or destroying animal, microbial or plant pests.

**Petechiae** small round flat dark-red spots caused by bleeding into the skin or beneath the mucous membrane.

**Pharynx** cavity at the back of the mouth.

**Phenobarbital** barbiturate drug used to treat insomnia and anxiety and as an anticonvulsant in the treatment of epilepsy. Major side effects of phenobarbital used as antiepileptic are related to its hypnotic and sedative properties. Withdrawal effects, which are occasionally found, can also constitute an important side effect. Phenobarbital is one of the main metabolites of primidon, an obsolete used antiepileptic. Apart from the effects on the central nervous system, phenobarbital is the prototype of a substance causing induction of liver enzymes.

**Phenoclar** trade name of a PCB containing liquid. Like most applications of PCBs it consists of a mixture of different PCB congeners.

**Phenothiazines** group of structurally related compounds with various biological actions such as antipsychotic and anthelmintic. The first phenothiazine was synthesized as early as 1833. In the 1930s it was used as an anthelmintic, antiseptic and insecticide. Phenothiazine derivatives, including chlorpromazine, are now used as neuroleptics in psychiatry. The phenothiazine derivatives have a large number of side effects, some of which are directly related to the action on the central nervous system (hypotension, sedation, convulsions etc); a large number of peripheral side effects have also been reported.

**Phenylbutazone** one of the so-called pyrazolone derivatives. These are compounds whose antipyretic and analgetic properties are less pronounced than those of the salicylates, but which are more efficient antiinflammatory agents. The main disadvantage of these compounds is that they may have serious effects on the blood. Agranulocytosis (a sudden decrease in the number of white blood cells) is one of the possible side effects. Phenylbutazone may affect the plasma-protein binding properties of other drugs, particularly anticoagulants, sulfonamides and other antiinflammatory drugs. This may cause potentiation of the toxic effects of these compounds.

**Phocomelia** limb reduction defect in which all long bone segments are absent in one or more limbs so that the hands or feet attach directly to the trunk through their respective girdles.

**Phosgene or carbonyl chloride ($COCl_2$)** an odourless gas or volatile compound, used for the preparation of dyes, carbonyl esters, isocyanates, insecticides and pharmaceuticals. It has also been used as a war gas. Phosgene causes irritation of the eyes and the mucous membranes. The initial symptoms are generally mild, but 6 to 24 hours after the exposure, peribronchial edema, pulmonary hemorrhage and alveolar edema occur, leading to death from oxygen deficiency. The damage is caused by the conversion of phosgene into HCl and $CO_2$. Chronic exposure causes irreversible pathological changes in the lung, such as bronchitis, emphysema and fibrosis. Phosgene is the toxic agent produced from chloroform by cytochrome P-450.

**Phospholipidosis** condition in which there is intracellular accumulation of phospholipids from cellular components. It is observed in the form of layered, crystal-like inclusions. This type of change, which may also occur in organs other than the liver, is caused by, among other substances, the vasodilator 4,4'-diethylaminoethoxyhexestrol, used in the treatment of heart failure.

**Phosphorus** reactive nonmetallic element, common in nature in phosphate rock. Guano, a phosphorus-rich deposit consisting of fish bones and bird droppings, is an important source of phosphate. Most phosphorus compounds are manufactured as fertilizers and detergents. Phosphorus is an essential component of living tissue and bones, and plays an important part in metabolism in general, and muscle metabolism in particular. Toxicologically, phosphates play an important role because of their environmental effects.

**Photoallergic reaction** type of dermatotoxic reaction in which (sun) light brings about the formation of antigens in the skin. Conjugation of a hapten with a skin protein results in the formation of an antigen. The conjugation reaction is in fact a photochemical reaction. A toxic effect will only occur after subsequent exposure to light. Clinical features are (delayed) papules and eczema, and sometimes urticaria occurs. Histologically, there is a dense perivascular accumulation of inflammatory cells in the dermis.

**Phototoxic reactions** disorders caused by sunlight. Sunlight probably causes the formation of free radicals, which in turn give rise to lipid peroxidation. As a result, (skin) cells die and bring about local inflammatory reactions. A distinction is made between local phototoxicity, in which the reaction occurs at the site of contact with the toxic substance, and systemic phototoxicity. In the reaction the latter occurs in the skin under the influence of sunlight, but with the substance reaching the skin via a different route, usually the bloodstream.

**Pica habit** the habit of eating earth, especially in young children.

**Picryl chloride, 2-chloro-trinitrobenzene**  substance used experimental to induce local allergic reactions in experimental animals. Applied to the skin, it induces the characteristic symptoms of an allergic reaction. If it is previously administered orally, the allergic reaction after local application does not occur.

**Piecemeal necrosis**  form of necrosis of hepatocytes at the transition of parenchyma to connective tissue. It is accompanied by infiltration of lymphocytes, plasma cells, histiocytes and some polymorphonuclear leukocytes. In a normal liver it may be seen in the periportal area, and is related to the destruction of the plate of parenchymal cells at the periphery of Kiernan's lobule. In cirrhosis of the liver, piecemeal necrosis is found at the periphery of hyperplastic nodules. This form of necrosis is considered to be a cell-mediated immune reaction (T-cell and/or K-cell dependent), in which cells die through apoptosis.

**Pinocytosis**  the intake of small droplets of fluid by a cell by cytoplasmic engulfment.

**Placebo effect**  changes in behavior stemming from conditions or procedures which accompany, but are not directly related to, independent variables in an experiment. For example, changes in behavior following injections of a specific drug may result from the act of being injected, rather than from the drug itself.

**Pleomorphic and pleomorphism**  the occurrence of more than one form, in other words the capacity to appear in various forms. They may apply to the clinical picture of a disease or to certain organisms, such as bacteria.

**Plexus**  network of vessels or nerves.

**Plexus of Auerbach (plexus myentericus)**  important plexus in the coordination of the peristaltic contractions of the stomach.

**Plexus of Meissner (plexus submucosis)**  important plexus in the coordination of the peristaltic contractions of the stomach.

**Pneumoconiosis**  the general term for various forms of lung disease due to deposition of particulate matter in the lungs, a chronic–indurative fibrosis. Examples are aluminosis, anthracosis, asbestosis and silicosis. Pneumoconiosis siderotica or siderosis is the deposition of particles of iron in the lungs of miners and metal workers.

**Pollutant**  any undesirable solid, liquid or gaseous matter in a solid, liquid or gaseous environmental medium, although low concentrations of most substances being tolerable. A primary pollutant is one emitted into the atmosphere, water, sediments or soil from an identifiable source. A secondary pollutant is a pollutant formed by chemical reaction in the atmosphere.

**Polychlorinated dibenzodioxins (PCDDs)**  a group of about 75 structurally related compounds (dioxins). They have a skeleton of 3 linked rings with 1 to 8 chlorine atoms. In molecules with the same number of chlorine atoms, these can occur in different positions (isomers).

The central hexagon, with two oxygen atoms opposite one another, is called a dioxane ring. The full name of dioxins is polychlorinated dibenzo-*para*-dioxins, PCDDs for short. The Seveso dioxin contained 4 chlorine atoms in the positions 2,3,7,8; its official name is 2,3,7,8-tetrachlorodibenzo-*para*-dioxin, abbreviated 2,3,7,8-TCDD. The toxicity results from the presence of 4 chlorine atoms in a rectangle of 4 by 10 Angstroms. The related PCDF (polychlorodibenzofuran) compound 2,3,7,8-TCDF is only slightly less toxic. TCDD is mainly formed as undesirable contaminant in the production of trichlorophenols, and the pesticide 2,4,5-T or the bactericide hexachlorophene, which are manufactured from them. According to recent insights PCDDs and PCDFs can also be formed as contaminants in the synthesis of other chlorinated pesticides. Concentrations may be particularly high in the wood preservatives pentachlorophenol (PCP) and trichlorophenol. In incineration processes, particularly the burning of organic chlorine-containing household and industrial wastes, PCDDs and PCDFs are released. (Dioxin in milk near waste incinerators!) TCDD is highly toxic to guinea pigs (an $LD_{50}$ of 0.6–2 microgram per kg), but this dose varies greatly between different animal species. The following clinical effects of TCDD have been observed in farmers who have been working with 2,4,5-T for years, in employees of paper mills (contact with chlorophenols) and in Seveso victims: skin disorders (chloracne), damage to liver, pancreas, kidney and heart, effects on the immune system (T-lymphocytes), effects on hormone metabolism and reproductive functions. TCDD is probably a strong cancer-promoting agent and a weak cancer-initiating agent. The dioxin syndrome consists of a complex combination of symptoms. In addition to persistent chloracne, several other disorders are frequently seen. However, the dioxin syndrome is difficult to diagnose unequivocally.

**Polydactyly**  the presence of more than the normal number of digits or parts thereof on a hand or foot.

**Polyhalogenated biphenyls (PCBs and PBBs)**  Since 1930, polychlorobiphenyls (PCBs) and polybromobiphenyls (PBBs) have been widely used by mining industry as flameproof insulator. These substances have important ecotoxic properties, endangering particularly animals at the end of food chains (birds of prey, seals). PCB mixtures usually consist of a large number of related compounds. They are manufactured by substituting one or more hydrogen atoms in the biphenyl molecule by chlorine atoms; theoretically there are 209 different chlorobiphenyls. In man, the most important symptom is chloracne (in industrial workers). Fatal cases of liver damage have also been described. In chickens these compounds cause death; the most striking symptom is pulmonary edema. PCBs cause enzyme induction. Although this increases the ability to degrade foreign substances, it also increases the bioactivation of xenobiotics. In addition, the metabolism of substances produced by the body itself can also be increased. In the mink and the monkey, for instance, reproductive abnormalities have been observed, probably caused by the increased turnover of sex hormones. PCBs cause a major reduction in the weight of the thymus. This has consequences for the immune system; the immunological resistance against infectious diseases is decreased. In Taiwan, victims of PCB poisoning have been shown to suffer from immune suppression, chloracne and disturbance of the liver function.

**Polyp**  a stalked, benign mucosal tumor protruding into the lumen of a hollow organ. A distinction is made between tubular (adenomatous) and villous polyps. Adenomatous polyps are usually stalked polyps with hyperplastic mucosa and varying degrees of differentiation. The extent to which they occur in the population (=prevalence) is unknown. They are found in 10% of all autopsies. They are mostly without any symptoms but may bleed. They have a slight tendency to become malignant.

**Polyuria**  excretion of an excessive amount of urine.

**Postnatal**  relating to the period after birth.

**Postpartum**  after birth.

**Postsynaptic**  located distal to the synaptic cleft.

**Potassium cyanide (KCN)**  a white crystalline compound which smells strongly of bitter almonds. Both KCN and NaCN are used for extracting ores, for electrolytic silver-plating of metals and for various industrial manufacturing processes. It can be absorbed by inhalation, by swallowing and percutaneously. The cyanides are acutely toxic. The toxicity results from the inactivation of cytochrome oxidase activity, causing inhibition of the mitochondrial electron transport and oxidative phosphorylation. The symptoms of cyanide poisoning are: tiredness, headache, dizziness, nausea, vomiting, respiratory problems and death.

**Potentiation**  situation when one substance does not have a toxic effect on a certain organ or system, but when given together with another chemical it makes the latter much more toxic.

**Preganglionic**  preceding or in front of a ganglion.

**Prenatal**  pertaining to the period between the last menstrual period and birth of the child.

**Presynaptic**  located proximal to the synaptic cleft.

**Prevalence**  proportion of a population that has a disease or disorder at a specific point in time. Measurement of all cases of disease or other events prevailing at a given time (for example birth). It includes new cases and old cases that are still around.

**Procarcinogen**  substance that has to be metabolized before it can induce malignant tumors.

**Progesterone**  hormone of the corpus luteum responsible for preparing the uterus for the fertilized ovum.

**Prolactin**  hormone secreted by the anterior pituitary that stimulates milk production and lactation.

**Proliferative changes**  tissue changes involving a proliferation of the original tissue. A distinction is made between neoplastic and nonneoplastic proliferative changes. The first group is characterized by uncontrolled cell growth, whereas the latter group usually involves a reversible adaptation to a disturbed homeostasis.

**Promotor**  substance that is not carcinogenic itself, but when administered after an initiator of carcinogenesis, stimulates the clonal expansion of the initiated cell to produce a neoplasm.

**Prostaglandins**  family of products of the cyclo oxygenase-mediated peroxidation of the polyunsaturated fatty acid, arachidonic acid. They arise in a variety of tissues and are able to induce contraction in uterine and other smooth muscles, lower blood pressure, modify the actions of some hormones, and play an important role in the immune system.

**Proteinuria**  the excretion of protein in the urine. It is usually the result of increased permeability of the glomeruli in renal disease, but degeneration of renal tissue (tubular necrosis) may also lead to proteinuria.

**Protooncogene**  normal cellular structural gene that, when activated by mutations, amplifications, rearrangements, or viral transduction, functions as an oncogene and is associated with development of neoplasia. Protooncogenes regulate functions related to normal growth and differentiation of tissues.

**Pulmonary edema**  the passage of fluid with a high protein content into the alveolar spaces as a result of damage to the alveolar epithelium. It may result from toxic damage to the alveolar epithelium, but also from a disturbed cardiac function (right-sided decompensation).

**Pulmonary emphysema**  structural degeneration of the alveoli. It involves abnormal enlargement of the air spaces in the respiratory part of the lung. In many cases the alveolar walls are damaged, causing alveoli to fuse.

**Pylorus**  distal stomach opening, ringed by a sphincter, that releases the stomach contents into the duodenum.

**Pyridoxine (vitamin B$_{-6}$)**  a naturally occurring compound, which can cause damage to certain specific ganglia if administered in excess.

**Quantal effect**  effect that can be expressed only as 'occurring' or 'not-occurring', such as death or occurrence of a tumor.

**Quartz**  a cristalline form of silicon oxide. It is mainly found in slightly acidic rock, such as granite. Silicosis caused by quartz occurs especially where such rocks are processed, for instance in people who polish granite draining boards.

**Quinones**  3,6-diketone derivatives of 1,4-cyclohexadine (*para*-benzoquinones) or 5,6-diketone derivatives of 1,3-cyclohexadiene (*ortho*-benzoquinones). It is a series of aromatic compounds in whose molecules two hydrogen atoms in the same benzene nucleus are replaced by two oxygen atoms, forming carbonyl groups. The quinones are therefore diketones.

**Radioimmunoassay (RIA)** any assay procedure that employs an immune reaction, in which either the antigen or the antibody is labeled with a radionuclide to permit accurate quantification.

**Reflux esophagitis** inflammation of the esophagus due to the frequent regurgitation of acid and peptic juices from the stomach.

**Regeneration** recovery or healing (L. regeneratio = renewed production); the repair of tissue or of a part which has been damaged.

**Regressive changes** structural and functional disorders of cells, tissues or organs, caused by the action of a noxa, a harmful stimulus. Regressive changes are involved in many pathological processes. Regression, degeneration and devitalization of cells or tissues occur.

**REM-sleep (Rapid Eye Movement sleep)** period during sleep when the EEG shows rapid, low voltage activity (beta waves) which are normally only seen during waking. The eyes also move rapidly under closed lids. This phase is usually correlated with dreaming.

**Residual volume (RV)** the volume of air that remains in the lungs after the individual has breathed out as much as he can. This volume is increased in emphysema.

**Respiratory quotient (RQ)** ratio between inspired oxygen and expired carbon dioxide during a specified time.

**Reticulo-endothelial system (RES)** a community of cells-phagocytes-spread throughout the body. It includes macrophages and monocytes. The RES is concerned with the defence against microbial infection and with the removal of worn-out blood cells from the blood stream.

**Retinoic acid** formerly vitamin $A_1$ acid.

**RIA** see Radioimmunoassay.

**Risk assessment (risk analysis)** the process by which the potential adverse health effects from exposure to chemicals are characterized; it includes the development of both qualitative and quantitative expressions of risk. The process of risk assessment is divided into the following aspects: hazard identification, dose-response relationship assessment, exposure assessment and risk.

**Risk characterization** utilization of exposure and dose-response relationship assessments to estimate the probable incidence of adverse health effects under various conditions of human exposure.

**Risk management** the process of evaluating alternative regulatory options and selecting between them. This is not a scientific process, but involves consideration of the social, economic and political implications of a series of possible regulatory options. Risk assessment is one of the bases of risk management.

**Safety factor** a number by which the no-observed-adverse-effect level (NOAEL) is divided to obtain the acceptable daily intake (ADI) of a chemical for regulatory purposes. The factor is intended to account for the uncertainties inherent in estimating the potential effects of a chemical on humans from results obtained with experimental animals.

**Sarcoma** cancer of connective tissue.

**Sarcomere** one of the basic contractile units of which stratified muscle fibers are composed.

**Scatchard plot** graph that can be used to analyze molecular interactions in a mixed population of molecules in which molecules of different types bind reversibly to one another.

**Schedule of reinforcement** a programme determining relationships between the occurrence of reinforcing stimuli and responses.

**Sclerosis** the hardening of fibrous tissue. It is often a process secondary to hyaline change.

**Sensitization** the process which renders the body, more specifically the immune system, sensitive to foreign proteins or other xenobiotics. In such cases, a substance does not give rise to an immediate reaction upon first contact; only after subsequent exposure a more severe reaction will occur. This is referred to as a delayed hypersensitivity reaction (Type IV). The process consists of: (a) an induction phase during which a hapten conjugates with a skin protein, forming an allergen. Moreover, antigen recognition takes place in this phase; (b) a proliferation phase during which the differentiation of T-lymphocytes into effector cells and memory cells takes place; (c) a manifestation phase. The last phase is most evident after subsequent exposure to the substance concerned. It involves hapten conjugation, antigen recognition, cellular infiltration at the site of exposure and release of mediators.

**SER proliferation** frequent form of organelle proliferation (smooth endoplasmic reticulum). If the cell calls for increased functional activity, this may necessitate proliferation of one or more organelles. Therefore, organelle proliferation should be regarded as an adaptative process, rather than a pathological change. Many biotransformation enzymes, such as the monooxygenase cytochrome P-450, are linked to the smooth endoplasmic reticulum (SER). Hence, SER proliferation is a frequent form of organelle proliferation, particularly in the liver. It is a special form of hypertrophy, involving an increase in smooth endoplasmic reticulum, including induction of cytochrome P-450 enzymes. A well-known iinducer is phenobarbital. Ultrastructurally, SER proliferation can be observed most clearly as an accumulation of smooth membrane structures in the cytoplasm. This is often hardly observable by light microscopy, although enlarged cells, foamy cytoplasm, accentuated cell membranes and disappearance of other cytoplasmic structures can occasionally be seen.

**Serotonin (5-hydroxytryptamine, 5-HT)** neurotransmitter.

**Short-term exposure limit (STEL)** unless noted otherwise, the 15-minute time-weighted average exposure that should not be exceeded at any time during a work day (used by US NIOSH).

**Short-term** see acute.

**Sickle cell anemia** typical hereditary disease rather than a toxicological disorder. The change consists of modification of the structure of erythrocytes caused by amino acid substitutions in their polypeptide chain (valine substituted by glutamine). A distinction is made between homozygous and heterozygous types of sickle cell anemia. The disease is associated with an enlarged spleen, often accompanied by dilation of the heart and occasionally by congestion of the glomerular capillaries.

**Side effect** action of a drug other than the desired for a beneficial biological effect.

**Sideroblastic anemia** disturbed formation of erythrocytes in the bone marrow by chemicals through interfering with the iron metabolism and the heme synthesis. In this respect, vitamin $B_6$ (pyridoxine) is essential for the synthesis of delta aminolevulinic acid, a precursor of heme. When the incorporation of iron is disturbed, for example as a result of the antituberculous agent isoniazid, the iron will accumulate in the mitochondria. A stain for iron will show the iron as a ring around the nucleus of the normoblast. The cells are then called "ring" sideroblasts. They are formed in genetic diseases as side effects of hematogical inflammatory or neoplastic anomaly (e.g. leukemia).

**Significant difference** statistical concept of probability, specifically, that the chance of a large difference occurring in the behavior of subjects in various groups of an experiment by chance alone is quite low. When such a difference does occur, it is assumed to reflect some aspect of the experimental manipulation of conditions and therefore (since chance is ruled out) can be used as a reliable basis for further work.

**Silicosis** is a pneumoconiosis caused by inhalation of silica dust. The silica particles (quartz dust with particles of approx 1 micron in size) are phagocytized by macrophages and end up in lysosomes, which are then damaged by the silicic acid formed from the silica. The destruction of the macrophages that phagocytize the silica leads to the release of peroxidation products of polyunsaturated fatty acids, which, together with the process of phagocytosis itself, cause the fibrotic inflammation which characterizes silicosis.
Pathogenesis:
—quartz dust in pulmonary alveoli > phagocytosis > phagocytes destroyed > crystals and fibrogenic factors released > phagocytosis by new histiocytes > destruction of these histiocytes > chemical influence on surrounding cells.

**Single-cell necrosis** form of necrosis in which individual, nonadjacent cells have undergone necrotic change. It is often difficult to distinguish single-cell necrosis from apoptosis. Apoptosis is however usually not combined with an inflammatory reaction.

**Singlet oxygen** reactive oxygen species in which the two electrons that are unpaired in the ground state are paired, the result is an 'empty' molecular orbital, i.e. a free electron pair can be taken up.

**Sister chromatide exchange (SCE)** reciprocal exchange of chromatin between two replicated chromosomes that remain attached to each other until anaphase of mitosis. Used as a measure of mutagenicity of substances that produce this effect.

**Slow acetylators** individuals homozygous for a recessive gene. It is believed that this leads to a low activity of the hepatic acetyltransferase which acetylates e.g. isoniazid.

**Soma** (1) the entire body excluding the germ cells; (2) the main body of a nerve cell, from which other structures may project.

**Somatic nervous system** the part of the peripheral nervous system made up of the motor nerves that control voluntary muscles, and the sensory nerves carrying information from the conscious senses into the CNS.

**Somatostatin** growth hormone release-inhibiting factor.

**Somatotropic hormone** see growth hormone.

**Southern blotting** blotting of DNA.

**Speciation** the chemical form in which an element occurs.

**Sphincter** circular muscle surrounding and enclosing an orifice.

**Sphincter of Oddi** sphincter localized where the common duct of pancreas and liver enter the duodenum.

**Spina bifida** developmental abnormality involving defective closure of the bony encasement of the spinal cord. In case of the open form, no closure of the neural walls into a neural tube took place. At birth the neural tissue is degenerated without coverings.

**Squamous-cell carcinoma** malignant tumor of stratified squamous epithelium. It has an irregular surface and is often accompanied by hemorrhages and necrosis. Well-differentiated type: squamous epithelial cells, irregular keratinization and invasive growth. In the surrounding tissue inflammatory reactions occur. Poorly differentiated type: more cuboid cells, structure of the epidermis unrecognizable, shift in the nucleus/plasma ratio in favor of the nuclei, mitoses are frequent and infiltration.

**Startle response** behavioral response as a consequence of an unexpected frightening stimulus, e.g. an acoustic signal.

**Steady state** phase in which the rate of appearance of a drug in the circulation and its rate of elimination from the circulation are equal.

**Steatorrhea** passage of abnormal amounts of fat in the feces.

**Steatosis** infiltration of cells (e.g. hepatocytes) with fat.

**Stimulants** drugs such as caffeine, nicotine and amphetamines which increase the functioning of the nervous system and thereby facilitate physical and mental activity.

**Subacute** form of repeated exposure or administration usually occurring over about 21 days, not long enough to be called 'long-term' or 'chronic'.

**Subchronic** related to repeated dose exposure over a short period, usually about 10% of the life span. It is an imprecise term used to describe exposures of intermediate duration.

**Subcutaneous** an injection where the drug is left just under the skin.

**Sublimate** a solid obtained by sublimation, i.e. the conversion of a solid into a gas or vice versa, without melting.

**Submucosa** layer of connective tissue beneath a mucous membrane.

**Suicide substrate** any substrate whose uptake or metabolism by a cell is lethal for that cell or cell organelle.

**Sulfhemoglobin** abnormal form of hemoglobin that contains sulfur bounds to heme, with iron in either the Fe(II) or Fe(III) state. The latter may be designated sulfmethemoglobin.

**Sulfur dioxide** primary air pollutant generated by industries that burn fossil fuels. Commercial applications include use in fumigation of fruits and vegetables, bleaching, tanning, brewing, preserving and refrigeration. Sulfur dioxide is also present as a by-product of melting, paper manufacturing, and fabrication of rubber products. It is one of the main sources of acid rain. Sulfur dioxide affects particularly the upper respiratory tract and bronchi; however, it can also cause lung edema and respiratory paralysis. Exposure to sulfur dioxide can cause mucitis, coughing, external eye damage, bronchoconstriction, pneumonia, olfactory changes, thickening of the mucous layer of the upper respiratory tract and decreased ciliary transport. It is clear that particularly patients suffering from chronic non-specific lung disease will be troubled by increased levels of sulfur dioxide. Acute poisoning can cause asphyxia. It has been proved to increase the carcinogenicity of polycyclic aromatic hydrocarbons.

**Superoxide anion radical** reactive oxygen species that is formed when one electron is taken up by molecular oxygen. The formation of this species may involve endogenous substances and chemical-physiological processes as well as xenobiotics.

**Superoxide dismutase (SOD)** any of a range of metalloenzymes which catalyze the dismutation of superoxide. Superoxide dismutases occur widely in both prokaryotic and eukaryotic cells and are believed to have as their main or sole function the protection of aerobic or aerotolerant organisms from the toxic effects of superoxide.

**Surveillance** ongoing mechanism to collect information. If you do not have a surveillance system set up to report diseases, an epidemic could pass you by.

**Syndrome** the aggregate of signs, symptoms, or other manifestations considered to constitute the characteristics of a morbid entity.

**Synergism** toxicity greater than would be expected from the toxicities of two compounds when administered separately, one of the compounds has little or no intrinsic toxicity.

**Systemic** characterized by systemization, generalized, relating to the body as a whole. Systemic is often used in the sense of systemic administration, which tends to mean administration through the vascular system, as opposed to topical administration. Systemic administration means administration of a substance in such a way that it is distributed over the entire organism.

**Test battery** set of (behavioral) tests to measure more than one functional disturbance.

**Tetracyclines** group of antibiotics which are effective against gram-positive bacteria. In man, protracted use causes liver steatosis and kidney disorders. Photosensitivity may also occur. Tetracyclines tend to deposit at sites where active calcification occurs, for instance bone tissue and teeth.

**Thalidomide (Softenon®)** sedative hypnotic drug which in 1961 was discovered to be a highly potent human teratogen when ingested by pregnant women between the 20th and 38th days after conception. Subsequently, it was drawn from the market. The prevalent malformations were phocomelia and other reduction defects of the fetal limbs. Further, facial and internal malformations sometimes occurred.

**Thorax** portion of the trunk above the diaphragm and below the neck.

**Threshold limit value (TLV)** occupational exposure limit recommended by the American Conference of Governmental Industrial Hygienists (ACGIH). TLVs are the upper allowable limits of airborne concentrations of substances. They represent conditions under which it is believed that nearly all employees may be repeatedly exposed day after day without adverse effects.

**Threshold limit value, ceiling (TLV-c)** represents the concentration in an occupational situation that should not be exceeded even momentarily.

**Thyroid gland** one of the largest of the body's endocrine glands; it secretes thyroxine.

**Thyroid stimulating hormone** adenohypophysial hormone that stimulates the secretory activity of the thyroid gland.

**Thyroxine** iodinated, tyrosine-derived hormone that is synthesized and secreted by the thyroid gland; it raises cellular metabolic rate.

**Time-weighted average concentration (TWAC)** the concentration of a substance to which a person is exposed in the ambient air, averaged over a period of time, usually 8h.

**Time-weighted average exposure (TWAE)** TLV-value for a normal 40-hour working week to which nearly all workers may be repeatedly exposed, without adverse effect.

**Tissue hormones** There are a number of places in the body, such as the wall of the digestive tract, where individual, nonadjacent hormone-producing cells are found. The substances produced in such cells are called tissue hormones, local hormones or mediators. Angiotensin, bradykinin, histamine, serotonin and epinephrine are tissue hormones present in, for example, the vascular system. Gastrin, secretin and CCK (cholecystokinin) are found in the digestive tract. *Serotonin* is not only a tissue hormone but also a neurotransmitter. As a tissue hormone it causes local vascular constriction. *Histamine and heparin* are present in the granules of the basophilic granulocytes. Both substances play a role in the defence against parasites. They are also both responsible for the reactions in hypersensitivity and in an anaphylactic shock. *Heparin* has a negative effect on coagulation and is therefore also applied as an anticoagulant (=substance which inhibits clotting of blood, for example, in order to prevent the formation of a thrombus). *Histamine* causes capillaries to dilate, makes the musculature of the bronchi and intestinal tract contract, increases the permeability of the capillaries and stimulates the formation of gastric juice.

**Toxemia** a condition in which blood contains poisonous products.

**Toxic Substance Control Act (TSCA)** US law concerned with the regulation of new and existing chemicals.

**Toxicodynamics** relationship between toxicant concentration and effect, with specific emphasis on mechanisms of action.

**Toxicokinetics** study of the quantitative relationship between absorption, distribution, metabolism and excretion of toxicants and their metabolites. It involves the derivation of rate constants for each of these processes and their integration into mathematical models that can predict the distribution of the chemical throughout the body compartments on any time (point) after administration.

**Toxin** poison; usually an intensely poisonous substance produced by certain bacteria, fungi, algae and higher organisms.

**Toxoplasma** a genus of intestinal coccidia of cats and other felids with an extreme wide range of warm-blooded intermediate hosts, including man, in which asexual multiplication is found, ending with tissue cysts. It might cause birth defects mainly in the central nervous system.

**Transfection** the direct transfer of DNA sequences into a cell.

**Transition mutation** form of point mutation in which one purine nucleotide is replaced by another or one pyrimidine nucleotide is replaced by another.

**Transplacental carcinogens** a few carcinogens can cross the placenta and lead to neoplastic conversion in cells of certain tissues of the fetus. Usually, they affect those organs and tissues that are most sensitive in the last trimester of pregnancy. High doses of some hormones can affect the development of the endocrine system and lead to neoplasms in the offspring, often at puberty, in specific endocrine sensitive tissues. See diethylstilbestrol.

**Transversion mutation** type of point mutation in which a purine nucleotide is replaced by a pyrimidine nucleotide, or vice versa.

**Tributyltin oxide (TBTO)** alkyltin compound frequently employed as a fungicide and a molluscicide, and for that reason it is used in paints for ships. TBTO is an immunotoxic compound which also affects the central nervous system. Teratogenic effects have also been observed. The use in antifouling paints for ships causes serious environmental problems, because many of the tin compounds end up in the water, threatening the aquatic fauna such as murex snails and certain oyster species.

**Trichoepithelioma** benign skin tumor of the hair follicle simulating abortive pilar structures and containing horn cysts. It may be solitary or multiple, the latter being inherited.

**Trigeminus nervus (V)** one of the cranial nerves; the major sensory nerves of the face.

**Triiodothyronine** one of the two principal hormones secreted by the thyroid gland.

**Tri *ortho*-cresyl-phosphate (TOCP)** industrial compound, used as a plasticizer in laquers and varnishes, as an additive in lubricants and gas oil, and as a fire retardant. It has a low acute toxicity but causes serious neuropathies after bioactivation. It is a neurotoxic esterase and cholinesterase inhibitor. In the spinal cord of chickens, TOCP causes degeneration of the long sensor and motor fibres from the peripheral nerves.

**Trisomy** a state of aneuploidy in a diploid cell or organism in which one chromosome is present in three copies. Usually a result of nondisjunction.

**Trypan blue** a vital dye; a well-known experimental teratogen.

**Tryptophan** one of the essential amino acids necessary for growth; it is a precursor of serotonin.

**Turner's syndrome** genetic defect in women in which there is only one X chromosome instead of the usual two. Affected women are infertile, they have female external genitalia, but no ovaries and therefore no menstrual period.

**Ulcer or ulceration** a form of tissue loss at the surface of an epithelium or of the skin, which is only slowly compensated for (or not at all) by formation of new tissue and which therefore displays virtually no tendency to heal. An ulcer in the skin is deeper than an erosion and extends into the dermis.

**Ultrasonography**   imaging with ultrasound.

**Unconditioned response**   response elecited by an unconditioned stimulus.

**Unconditioned stimulus**   any stimulus possessing the capacity to elicit reactions from organisms in the absence of prior conditioning.

**Valium®**   see diazepam.

**Valproic acid**   an anticonvulsant.

**Vascular edema**   Chemical mediators such as histamine, serotonin and bradykinin cause a contraction of endothelial cells in the postcapillary venules. Due to this contraction, openings are formed between the endothelial cells, through which plasma and possibly other blood components penetrate into the surrounding tissue and thus cause the formation of edema. Because of capillary compression, this edema can disturb the blood flow through the tissue.

**Vasodilatation**   the relaxation of the smooth muscles of the vascular system producing dilated vessels.

**Vasopressin**   see antidiuretic hormone.

**Very low density lipoproteins (VLDL)**   plasma lipoproteins mainly involved in triglyceride transport.

**Villous atrophy**   atrophy of the intestinal villi.

**Villous stunting**   stunting (retarded growth) of intestinal villi.

**Visceral**   pertaining to the internal organs.

**Volume of distribution**   see kinetic volume of distribution.

**Von Gierke's disease**   glycogen storage disease.

**Wallerian degeneration**   fatty degeneration of a ruptured nerve fibre that occurs within the nerve sheath distal to the point of severance.

**War gases**   wide range of chemicals used for various military purposes. The term war gas is not quite accurate, because at normal temperatures and pressures, most of these compounds are liquids. The name is mainly applied to those compounds which have a direct effect on man. There are many ways of classifying chemical weapons; a frequent classification is that using three categories; irritants, incapacitants and lethal chemical weapons. The category of irritants includes compounds which at low concentrations immediately cause eye, respiratory tract and skin irritations. Upon termination of the exposure, the effects often disappear quickly; the ratio between lethal dose and active dose is high, so that no fatalities are to be expected when the compound is used in the open air and in normal quantities. The different kinds of tear gas used by police in many countries belong to the class of irritants. Some examples are chloroacetophenone, o-chlorobenzalmalonitrile and adamsite. The group of incapacitants includes compounds which temporarily incapacitate a person from performing tasks, without killing or causing permanent damage. In contrast to irritants, the effects do not occur immedately and frequently last longer. This category is often subdivided into physical and psychological incapacitants. The latter affect one's mental and/or psychological condition; a well-known example is LSD. Physical incapacitants can cause temporary blindness or muscular paralysis. This group includes the fluorinated ethers (which cause temporary convulsions) and curare (temporary paralysis). The lethal chemical weapons can be subdivided into asphyxiants, blistering poisons (vesicants) and general poisons, for instance nerve gases. The group of asphyxiants includes chlorine as well as phosgene, which is six times as toxic. The group of vesicants includes, for instance, the sulfur and nitrogen mustard gases and lewisite. Most nerve gases are organophosphate compounds, structurally related to well-known insecticides such as malathion. Of the hundreds of organophosphate compounds which inhibit cholinesterase, some have gained notoriety as chemical weapons, for instance tabun (used in the Iran-Iraq war), sarin (which affects mainly the respiratory tract), soman and VX. Most of these are extremely poisonous; a few drops of VX on the skin usually suffice to cause death.

**Warfarin**   an anticoagulant used as rodenticide.

**Welding fume exposure**   Inhalation of the particles in welding fumes leads to a type of pneumoconiosis which is obviously found most frequently in the lungs of welders. The microscopic picture is characterized by: fibrotic inflammation, epithelial hyperplasia, and accumulation of particles (from welding fumes) in macrophages.

**Xenobiotic**   any substance that is interacting with an organism and that is not a natural component of that organism.

**Xeroderma pigmentosa**   a group of rare inherited autosomal recessive disorders in which the skin is readily damaged by ultraviolet light. This condition produces atrophy, pigmentary changes, and tumors. Especially, it predisposes to cancer of the skin.

**Yohimbine**   $\alpha_2$-selective adrenergic antagonist.

**Zero order process**   the rate of the process is independent of the substrate concentration.

# Literature

*References*

Aaronson, S.A. 1994. Growth factors and cancer. *Science* 254:1146–1153.

Afshari, C.A. and J.C. Barrett. 1993. Cell cycle controls: Potential targets for chemical carcinogens? *Environ. Health Perspect.* Suppl. 5 101:9–14.

Anders, M.W. (ed.), 1985 *Bioactivation of foreign compounds*. Academic Press Inc., Orlando/Florida.

Arnold, D. 1990. EEC perspectives on relay toxicity and bioavailability studies. *Drug Met. Rev.*, 22:699–705.

Battershill, J.M. 1993. Guidelines for the safety assessment of microbial enzymes used in food. *Food Add. Contam.* 10:479–488.

Beckett, Geoffrey J. and John D. Hayes. 1993. Glutathione S-transferases: biomedical applications. *Adv. Clin. Chem.*, 30:281–380.

Beechinor, J.G. 1993. Quality, safety and efficacy criteria for product licensing. Part I. *Irish Vet. J.* 46;116–118.

Bernson, V., I. Bondesson, B. Ekwall, K. Sternberg and E. Walum. 1987. 'A multicentre evaluation study of in vitro cytotoxicity'. *ATLA*, 14;144.

Bigwood, E.J. 1973. The acceptable daily intake of food additives. *CRC Crit. Rev. Toxicol.* 2:41–93.

Bishop, J.M. 1982. 'Oncogenes', *Scientific American*, pp. 68–78.

Bishop, J.M., H.E. Varmus. 1988. Functions and origins of retroviral transforming genes. In: Weiss, R., N. Teich, H.E. Varmus and H. Harris, The analysis of malignancy by cell fusion: the position in 1988. *Cancer Res.* 48:3302–3306.

Bishop, J.M. 1991. Molecular themes in oncogenesis. *Cell* 64:235–248.

Bishop, J.M. 1987. The molecular genetics of cancer. *Science* 235:305–311.

Boisseau, J. 1990. Relay toxicity. *Drug Met. Rev.*, 22:685–697.

British Medical Association. 1987. *Living with Risk*. John Wiley and Sons, Chichester.

Butterworth, B.E. 1990. Consideration of both genotoxic and non-genotoxic mechanisms in predicting carcinogenic potential. *Mut. Res.* 239:117–132.

Cairns, J. 1978. Cancer: science and society. In: *A series of books in biology*, C.I. Davern (Editor) Freeman: San Francisco.

Caldwell, J. and W.B. Jakoby (eds.) 1983. *Biological basis of detoxification*. Academic Press Inc., New York-London.

Carr, C.J. 1987. Food additives: A benefit/risk dilemma. In: *Handbook of Toxicology*, Haley TJ and Berndt WO (Eds). Hemisphere, Washington, 426–438.

Chou, J. and T.C. Chou. 1985. *Dose-effect analysis with microcomputers*. Elsevier-Biosoft: Cambridge U.K.

Clay, D.R. 1985. The role of the EPA in evaluating and regulating chemicals. In: *Safety Evaluation and Regulation of Chemicals 2*. Homburger F. (Ed). Karger, Basel 5–10.

Cohen, S.M. and L.B. Ellwein. 1991. Genetic errors, cell proliferation, and carcinogenesis. *Cancer Res.* 51:6493–6505.

Cordle, M.K. 1988. USDA regulation of residues in meat and poultry products. *J. Anim. Sci.* 66:413–433.

Dayan, A.D. 1986. Interpretation of data. In: *Toxic Hazard Assessment of Chemicals*, Richardson, M.L. (Ed). Royal Society of Chemistry Press: London, 87–87.

Diggle, G.E. 1993. Overview of regulatory agencies. In: *General and Applied Toxicology, Volume 2*. Ballantyne, B., T. Marrs and P. Turner (Eds.). Macmillan Press Ltd. 107–1090.

Dobson, S. 1993. Why different regulatory decisions when the scientific information base is similar?—Environmental risk assessment. *Regulat. Toxicol. Pharmacol.*, 17:333–345.

Doll, R. and R. Peto. 1981. The causes of cancer: quantitative estimates of avoidable risks of cancer in the United States today. *J. Natl. Cancer Inst.*, 66:1191–1308.

Enslein, K. and P.N. 1978. Craig, A toxicity estimation model. *J. Environ. Pathol. Toxicol.* 2:115–121.

Fielder, R.J. and A.D. Martin. 1993. Regulation of industrial chemicals and pesticides in the EEC. In: *General and Applied Toxicology, Volume 2*. Ballantyne, B., T. Marrs and P. Turner (Eds.). Macmillan Press Ltd. 1133–1149.

Food and Drug Administration, USA. 1968. *Antibiotic residues in milk, dairy products and animal tissues: Methods, reports, and protocols*. Washington, D.C.: National Center for Antibiotic and Insulin Analysis.

Food and Drug Administration, USA. 1986. *General Principles for Evaluating the Safety of Compounds Used in Food-Producing Animals*. Rockville: Center for Veterinary Medicine.

Fujita, T., Iwasa, J., and C. Hansch. 1964. A new substituent constant, derived from partition coefficients. *J. Amer. Chem. Soc.*, 86:5175–5180.

Fukuto, T.R. and R.L. Metcalf. 1956. Structure and insecticidal activity of some diethyl substituted phenyl phosphates. *Agricultural and Food Chemistry* 4:930–935.

Gallo-Torres, H.E. 1977. Methodology for the determination of bioavailability of labelled residues. *J. Toxicol. Environ. Health* 2:827–845.

Gallo-Torres, H.E. 1990. The rat as a drug residue bioavailability model. *Drug Met. Rev.* 22:707–751.

Govi, G.B. 1992. Cancer risk assessment: The science that is not. *Regulat. Toxicol. Pharmacol.* 16:10–20.

Guest, I., H.S. Buttar, S. Smith and D.R. Varma. 1994. Evaluation of the rat embryo culture system as a predictive test for human teratogens. *Can. J. Physiol. Pharmacol.* 72/1:57–62.

Haenszel, W. et al. 1973. Large bowel cancer in Hawaiian Japanese. *J. Natl. Cancer Inst.* 51:1765–1779.

Handler, J.A., D.C. Kossor and R.S. Goldstein. 1994. Assessment of hepatobiliary function *in vivo* and *ex vivo* in the rat. *J. Pharmacol. Toxicol. Methods* 31/1:11–190.

Hankin, R.A. 1989. European harmonisation: A view from the Commission. *Brit. Inst. Regulat. Affairs I.* 8:1–4.

Hansch, C. 1973. Quantitative approaches to pharmacological structure-activity relationships. In: C.J. Cavallito ed. *Structure-activity Relationships*. Pergamon, Oxford, 75–165.

Hansch, C. 1972. Quantitative relationships between lipophilic character and drug metabolism. *Drug Metab. Rev.* 1:1–13.

Hermens, J., Könemann, H., Leeuwangh, P. and A. Musch. 1985. Quantitative structure-activity relationships in aquatic toxicity studies of chemicals and complex mixtures of chemicals. *Environ. Toxicol. Chem.* 4:273–279.

Hermens, J.H. 1983. *Quantitative structure toxicity relationships and mixture toxicity studies of aquatic pollutants*. University of Utrecht, Dissertation.

Herrman, J.L. 1993. The role of the World Health Organisation in the evaluation of pesticides. *Regulat. Toxicol. Pharmacol.* 17:282–286.

Hewlett, P.S. and R.L. Plackett. 1975. *Quantal Responses in Biology.* London, Edward Arnold, Hill, Rolla B., Mariano F. La Via. 1980 *Principles of pathobiology* (3rd ed.), Oxford University Press, New York.

Hodgson, E. and P.E. Levi (eds.). 1987. *Poisons in print.* Elsevier, New York-Amsterdam.

Hunter, T. 1984. 'The proteins of oncogenes'. *Scientific American,* 60–69.

Intropoulos, M.J. 1994. Endocrine considerations in toxicologic pathology. *Exp. Toxicol. Pathol.* 45/7:391–410.

Iersel, A.A.J. van, A.J. de Boer, C.W.M.L. van Holsteijn and B.J. Blaauboer. 1986. 'Hepatocyte culture as a model system for the study of hepatotoxicity. *Fd. Chem. Toxicol.,* 24:569.

Illing, H.P.A. 1989. Assessment of toxicology for major hazards: Some concepts and problems. *Human Toxicol.* 8:369–374.

Illing, H.P.A. 1991. Possible risk considerations for toxic risk assessment. *Human Exp. Toxicol.* 10:215–219.

Illing, H.P.A. 1993. Toxicology and disasters. In: Ballantyne, B., T. Marrs and P. Turner (Eds.). *General and Applied Toxicology. Volume 2.* Macmillan Press Ltd 1417–1448.

International Programme on Chemical Safety. 1987. *Principles for the Safety Assessment of Food Additives and Contaminants in Food.* Environmental Health Criteria 70, WHO, Geneva.

International Programme on Chemical Safety. 1990. *Principles for the Toxicological Assessment of Pesticide Residues in Food.* Environmental Health Criteria 104, WHO, Geneva.

International Programme on Chemical Safety. 1992. *Quality Management for Chemical Safety Testing.* Environmental Health Criteria 141, WHO, Geneva.

Ito, N. and M. Hirose 1987. The role of antioxidants in chemical carcinogenesis. *Japan J. Cancer Res.* 78:1011–1026.

Jadhav, S.J., R.P. Sharma and D.K. Salunkhe 1981. Naturally occurring toxic alkaloids in foods. *CRC Crit. Rev. in Toxicol.* 9:21–104.

Japanese Ministry of Agriculture. 1988. *Guidelines for Toxicity Studies of New Animal Drugs in Japan,* Japanese Ministry of Agriculture, Tokyo.

Johns, P.A. 1994. An examination of the drug review process within the United States. *J. Am. Coll. Toxicol.* 13/2:121–142.

Jones, G. 1985. The regulation of medicines in the UK. In: Burley DM and Binns (Eds). *Pharmaceutical Medicine.* Edward Arnold, London, 149–163.

Kidd, A.R.M., The working parties of the Committee for Veterinary Medicinal Products. *Brit. Inst. Regulat. Affairs J.* 189:8:13–15.

Klimisch, H.J., R. Bretz, J.E. Doe and D.A. Purser. 1987. Classification of dangerous substances and pesticides in the European Economic Community Directives: A proposed revision of criteria for inhalation toxicity. *Regulat. Toxicol. Pharmacol.* 7:21–34.

Knox, P., P.F. Uphill, J.R. Fry, J. Benford and M. Balls. 1986. 'The FRAME multicentre project on in vitro cytotoxicity'. *Fd. Chem. Toxicol.,* 24:457.

Kokoski, C.J. 1985. Regulatory food additive toxicology. In: Homburger F. and Marquis J.K. (Eds). *Chemical Safety Regulation and Compliance.* S. Karger, Basel, 24–33.

Könemann, H. and K. van Leeuwen. 1980. Toxicokinetics in fish: accumulation and elimination of six chlorobenzenes by guppies. *Chemosphere* 9:3–19.

Könemann, H. 1981. *Quantitative structure-activity relationships for kinetics and toxicity of aquatic pollutants and their mixtures in fish.* University of Utrecht, Dissertation.

Könemann, H. 1981. Quantitative structure-activity relationships in fish toxicity studies, 1, Relationship for 50 industrial pollutants. *Toxicology* 9:209–221.

Könemann, H. 1980. Structure-activity relationships and additivity in fish toxicities of environmental pollutants. Ecotoxicol. Environm. *Safety* 4:415–420.

Kroes, R., I. Munro and E. Poulsen. 1993. Workshop on the scientific evaluation of the safety factor for the acceptable daily intake (ADI): editorial summary. *Food Add. Contam.* 10:269–273.

Liener, F.J.E. 1966. 'Haemagglutinins in foods'. In: *Toxicants occurring naturally in foods*. Nat. Acad. of Sciences, Washington.

Lindner, E. 1974. *Toxikologie der Nahrungsmittel*. Georg Thieme Verlag, Stuttgart.

Lu, A.Y.H., P.G. Wislocki, S.-H.L. Chiu and G.T. Miwa. 1987. Tissue drug residues and their toxicological significance. *Drug Met. Rev.* 18:363–378.

Lu, F.C. 1990. *Basic toxicology: fundamentals, target organs and risk assessment 2nd ed.* London/Washington, Taylor & Francis.

MacMillan, D.E. 1987. Risk assessment for neurobehavioral toxicity. *Envir. Health Perspect.* 76:155–161.

Mann, R.D. 1993. Regulation of drugs in Europe and the United Kingdom. In: Ballantyne, B., T. Marrs and P. Turner (Eds.). *General and Applied Toxicology, Volume 2*. Macmillan Press Ltd 1091–1099.

McCann, J.E. Choie, H. Yamasaki and B.N. Ames, Detection of carcinogens as mutagens in the Salmonella/microsome test: assay of 300 chemicals. *Proc. Natl. Acacad. Sci.* 72:5135–5139.

Melnick, R.L., J. Huff, J.C. Barrett et al. 1993. Cell proliferation and chemical carcinogenesis: Symposium overview. *Environ. Health Perspect.* 101/Suppl. 5 (3–7).

Muir, W.R. 1980. Chemical selection and evaluation: Implementing and toxic substances control act. In: Haque R (Ed). Dynamics. *Exposure and Hazard Assessment of Toxic Chemicals*. Ann Arbor Science, Ann Arbor, Michigan, 15–19.

Nilsson, R., M. Tasheva and B. Jaeger. 1993. Why different regulatory decisions when the scientific information base is similar—human risk assessment? *Regulat. Toxicol. Pharmacol.* 17:292–333.

Parke, D.V. 1983. Biochemical mechanisms of chemical interactions. In: *Health aspects of chemical safety II*. Copenhagen, WHO Reg. Off. Europa.

Pearson, A.M. and T.R. Dutson (Eds). 1990. Meat and Health. *Adv. in Meat Res.*, Volume 6. Elsevier Applied Science, London.

Pilot, H.C. 1981. *Fundamentals of oncology*, 2nd edition, revised and expanded, Marcel Dekker, New York.

Plackett, R.L. and P.S. Hewlett. 1952. Quantal responses to mixtures of poisons. *J. Royal Stat. Soc. B.* 14:141–163.

Reiss, J. (ed.). 1981. *Mykotoxine in Lebensmitteln*. N.Y. Stuttgart, Fischer Verlag.

Rekker, R.F. 1980. $LD_{50}$ values: are they about to become predictable? *Trends in Pharmacol. Sci.*, 383–384.

Rekker, R.F. 1977. *The Hydrophobic Fragmental Constant*. Elsevier, Amsterdam.

Renwick, A.G. 1993. A data-derived safety (uncertainty) factor for the intense sweetener, saccharin. *Food Add. Contam.*, 10:337–350.

Renwick, A.G. 1993. Data-derived safety factors for the evaluation of food additives and environmental contaminants. *Food Add. Contam.* 10:275–305.

Renwick, A.G. 1991. Safety factors and establishment of acceptable daily intakes. *Food Add. Contam.* 8:135–150.

Richardson, M. (Ed). 1986. *Toxic Hazard Assessment of Chemicals*, Royal Society of Chemistry, London.

Rowland, M. and G. Tucker. 1986. 'Pharmacokinetics: Theory and Methodology'. In: *International Encyclopedia of Pharmacology and Therapeutics, Section 122*. Pergamon Press, Oxford.

Rubery, E.D., S.M. Barlow and J.H. Steadman. 1990. Criteria for setting quantitative estimates of acceptable intakes of chemicals in food in the UK. *Food Add. Contam.* 7:287–302.

Ruckpaul, K. & H.R. Hein (eds.). 1984. *Cytochrome P-450.* Berlin, Akademie Verlag.

Saarikoski, J. and M. Viluksela. 1982. Relation between physicochemical properties of phenols and their toxicity and accumulation in fish. *Ecotoxicol. Environ. Safety* 6:501–512.

Schmahl, D. 1976. Combination effects in chemical carcinogenesis (experimental research). *Oncology* 33:73–76.

Schmidt-Bleek, F. and M.M. Marchal. 1993. Comparing regulatory regimes for pesticide control in 22 countries: Towards a new generation of pesticide regulation. *Regulat. Toxicol. Pharmacol.* 17:262–281.

Schrap, S.M., P.J. De Vries and A. Opperhuizen, 1994. Experimental problems in determining sorption coefficients of organic chemicals; an example of chlorobenzenes. *Chemosphere* 28/5:931–945.

Simonson, L., H. Johnsen, S.P. Lund et al. 1994. Methodological approach to the evaluation of neurotoxicity data and the classification of neurotoxic chemicals. *J. Work Environm. Health* 20/1:1–12.

Sluyser, M. and J. Mester. 1985. 'Oncogenes homologous to steroid receptors?' *Nature,* 351:546.

Somogyi, A. 1979. Residues of carcinogenic animal drugs in food: Difficulties in evaluation of human safety. In: *Carcinogenic risks.* Strategies for Intervention. International Agency for Research on Cancer, Scientific Publication No. 25:123–127.

Speid, L.H., C.E. Lumley and S.R. Walker. 1990. Harmonisation of guidelines for toxicity testing of pharmaceuticals by 1992. *Regulat. Toxicol. Pharmacol.* 12:179–211.

Taft, R.W. 1956. Separation of polar, steric and resonance effects in reactivity. In: *Steric Effects in Organic Chemistry* (ed. M.S. Newman), Wiley, New York, 556–675.

Tallardi, R.J. and L.S. Jacob. 1979. *The Dose-response Relation in Pharmacology.* Frankfurt, Springer-Verlag.

Taylor, D.L. and H.H. Seliger (eds.). 1979. *Toxic dinoflagellate blooms.* N.Y. Amsterdam, Oxford, Elsevier/North Holland.

Teske, R.H. 1992. Chemical residues in food. *J. Am. Vet. Med. Assoc.* 201:253–256.

Valle-Rienstra, J.F. 1974. Food processing with chlorinated solvents'. *Food Technology* 28:25–32.

Ver Nooy, M.B., Regulation of drugs on the North American Continent. In: Ballantyne, B., T. Marrs and P. Turner, (Eds.) 1993. *General and Applied Toxicology,* Volume 2. Macmillan Press Ltd 1101–1103.

Ver Nooy, M.B. 1993. Regulation of food additives and food contact materials on the North American Continent. In: Ballantyne, B., T. Marrs and P. Turner (Eds.). *General and Applied Toxicology, Volume 2.* Macmillan Press Ltd 1551–1155.

Ward, J.M., H. Uno, Y. Kurata et al. 1993. Cell proliferation not associated with carcinogenesis in rodents and humans. *Environ. Health Perspect.* 101/Suppl. 5, 125–135.

Wartzen, G. 1993. Scientific assessment of the safety factor for the acceptable daily intake (ADI). Case study: butylated hydroxyanisole (BHA). *Food Add. Contam.* 10:307–314.

Wattenberg, L.W. 1979. 'Natural occurring inhibitors of chemical carcinogenesis'. In: *Naturally occurring carcinogen-mutagens and modulators of carcinogenesis.* Miller et al. (eds.), Japan Sci. Soc. Press, Tokyo.

Weinberg, R.A. 1983. 'A molecular basis of cancer'. *Sci. Am.* 102–116.

Weinberg, R.A. 1991. Tumor suppression genes. *Science* 254:1138–1146.

Weiss, S.M. and S. Lakshminarayan. 1994. Acute inhalation injury. *Clin. Chest Med.* 15/1:103–116.

Welling, P.G. 1986. Pharmacokinetics: processes and mathematics, ACS Monograph 185. Americ. Chem. Soc., Washington D.C.

WHO 1987, *Principles for the safety assessment of food additives and contaminants in food.* Environmental Health Criteria 70, Geneva.

Whysner, J., C.X. Wang, E. Zang et al. 1994. Dose response of promotion by butylated hydroxyanisole in chemically initiated tumours of the rat forestomach. *Food Chem. Toxicol.* 32/3:215–222.

Williams, D.R. 1993. *Feed Legislation.* HGM Publications, Bakewell, UK.

Wislocki, P.G. and A.Y.H. Lu. 1990. Formation and biological evaluation of ronidazole bound residues. *Drug Met. Rev.* 22:649–661.

Wodicka, V.O. 1980. Evaluating the safety of food constituents. *J. Environ. Pathol. Toxicol.* 3:139–147.

Wogan, G.N. 1992. Molecular epidemiology in cancer risk assessment and prevention: recent progress and avenues for future research. *Environm. Health Perspect.* 98:167–178.

Woodward, K.N., Maximum residue limits—the impact of UK and EC legislation. In: Garnsworthy, P.C. and D.J.A. Cole (Eds). 1993. *Recent Advances in Animal Nutrition.* Nottingham University Press, Nottingham, 165–172.

Woodward, K.N. 1993. Registration for marketing of veterinary medicines in the United States. In: Ballantyne, B., T. Marrs and P. Turner (Eds.). *General and Applied Toxicology, Volume 2.* Macmillan Press Ltd 1129–1132.

Woodward, K.N. 1993. Regulation of veterinary drugs in Europe, including the UK. In: Ballantyne, B., T. Marrs and P. Turner (Eds.). *General and Applied Toxicology, Volume 2.* Macmillan Press Ltd 1105–1128.

Woodward, K.N. 1991. The licensing of veterinary medicinal products in the United Kingdom—the work of the Veterinary Medicines Directorate. *Biologist,* 3:105–108.

Woodward, K.N., Use and regulatory control of veterinary drugs in food production. In: Creaser, C.S. and R. Purchase (Eds). 1991. *Food Contaminants: Sources and Surveillance.* Royal Society of Chemistry Press, London, 99–108.

Woodward, K.N., Uses and regulation of veterinary drugs. In: Hutson, D.H., D.R. Hawkins, G.D. Paulson and C.B. Struble (Eds). 1992. *Xenobiotics and Food-Producing Animals.* American Chemical Society Symposium Series 503, 2–16.

Wratton, S.D., M. Mead-Briggs, G. Gettinby, G. Ericson and D.G. Baggott. 1993. An evaluation of the potential effects of ivermectin on the decomposition of cattle dung pats. *Veterinary Record,* 133:365–371.

*General texts*

Albert, Adrien. 1985. *Selective toxicity.* Chapman and Hall, London New York, 750 pages.

Albert, Adrien. 1987. *Xenobiosis: foods, drugs and poisons in the human body.* Chapman Hall, New York, USA.

Amdur, Mary O. 1991. John Doull and Curtis D. Klaassen, *Casarett and Doull's Toxicology: The basic science of poisons, 4th Edition.* Pergamon Press, New York, xiii + 1033 pages.

Brown, Vernon K. 1988. *Acute and sub acute toxicology.* Edward Arnold, London, v + 125 pages.

Burck, K.B., E.T. Liu and J.W. Larrick. 1988. *Oncogenes, an introduction to the concept of cancer genes.* Springer-Verlag, Berlin, Heidelberg.

Calabrese, E.J. 1983. *Principles of Animal Extrapolation.* J. Wiley—Interscience Publications, Chichester.

Cartwright, A.C. and B.R. Matthews. 1991. *Pharmaceutical Product Licensing. Requirements for Europe.* Ellis Horwood, London.

Cohen, M.G. (ed.). 1986. *Target Organ Toxicity Vol. I and II.* CRC Press Inc., Boca Raton, Florida.

Commission of the European Communities. *The Rules Governing Medicinal Products in the European Community.* Office for Official Publications of the European Communities, Luxembourg, Volumes I-VII (note, various dates; the volumes cover human and veterinary medicines).

Cooper, C.S. and P.L. Grover (Eds). 1990. *Chemical Carcinogenesis and Mutagenesis (Vols I & II).* Springer-Verlag, Berlin, Heidelberg.

Crosby, N.T. 1991. *Determination of Veterinary Drug Residues in Food.* Ellis Horwood, London.

Curran, R.C. 1985. *Color Atlas of Histopathology.* Springer-Verlag, New York.

D'Arcy, P.F. and D.W.G. Harron (Eds). 1992. *Proceedings of the First International Conference on Harmonisation. Brussels 1991.* Queens University of Belfast Press, Belfast.

Doll, R. and R. Peto. 1981. *The causes of cancer.* Oxfor University Press, New York.

Gibson, G. Gordon and Paul Skett. 1986. *Introduction to drug metabolism.* Chapman and Hall, London New York, xii + 293 pages.

Glaister, J.R. 1986. *Principles of Toxicological Pathology.* Taylor and Francis, London/Philadelphia.

Gopinat, L. et al. 1987. *Atlas of experimental toxicological pathology.* Current Histopathology 13, MTP.

Haley, T.J. and W.O. Berndt (Eds). 1987. *Handbook of toxicology.* Hemisphere, Washington, D.C.

Hammett, L.P. 1970. *Physical Organic Chemistry,* McGraw-Hill, New York.

Hansch, C. and A. Leo. 1979. *Substituent Constants for Correlation Analysis in Chemistry and Biology.* Wiley, New York.

Harvey, Alan L. (Ed.). 1993. *Drugs from Natural Products.* Ellis Horwood Series in Pharmaceutical Technology, Ellis Horwood, vii + 171 pages'

International Programme on Chemical Safety. 1987. *Principles for the Safety Assessment of Food Additives and Contaminants in Food.* Environmental Health Criteria 70, WHO, Geneva.

International Programme on Chemical Safety. 1990. *Principles for the Toxicological Assessment of Pesticide Residues in Food.* Environmental Health Criteria 104, WHO, Geneva.

International Programme on Chemical Safety. 1992. *Quality Management for Chemical Safety Testing.* Environmental Health Criteria 141, WHO, Geneva.

James L. Schardein. 1993. *Chemically induced birth defects, 2nd edition.* Marcel Dekker, New York, USA, i-xiv + pp 1–902.

Kahn, P. and T. Graf (Eds). 1986. *Oncogenes and growth control.* Springer—Verlag, Berlin, Heidelberg.

Keith Snell and B. Mullock. 1987. *Biochemical toxicology: a practical approach.* IRL Press Limited, Oxford England, xv + 286 pages.

Koren, G. 1994. Maternal-Fetal Toxicology: *A clinician's guide, 2nd Edition.* Marcel Dekker New York, 824 pages.

Matteis, F. de and E.A. Lock (Eds.). 1987. *Selectivity and molecular mechanisms of toxicity.* The MacMillan Press Ltd, Hampshire and London.

Matthews, John C. 1993. *Fundamentals of receptor, enzyme and transport kinetics.* CRC Press, Boca Raton, 167 pages.

Moriarty, F. 1988. *Ecotoxicology: the study of pollutants in ecosystems, 2nd Edition.* Academic Press, London, 289 pages.

Ramade, F. translated by L.J.M. Hodgson. 1987. *Ecotoxicology*. John Wiley & Sons, London, x + 262 pages.

Richardson, M. (Ed). 1986. *Toxic Hazard Assessment of Chemicals*. Royal Society of Chemistry, London.

Salsburg, D.S. 1986. *Statistics for Toxicologists*. New York-Basel, Marcel Dekker Inc.

Sitkovsky, M.V. and P.V. Henkart. 1993. *Cytotoxic cells: Recognition, effector function, generation and methods*. Birkhäuser, xiv + 527 pages.

Smith, Roger P. 1992. *A primer of environmental toxicology*. Lea & Febiger, Philadelphia, ix + 300 pages.

Stegink, L.D. and L.J. Filer Jr. (eds.). 1984. *Aspartame: physiology and biochemistry*. Marcel Dekker Inc., New York-Basel.

Stern, C.D. and P.W.H. Holland (Eds.). 1993. *Essential developmental biology: a practical approach*. Oxford University Press-IRL Press, Oxford England, xxviii + 333 pages.

*The BMA guide to living with risk*. 1990. A report from the BMA professional and scientific division. Penguin Books, London.

Timbrel, J.A., *Introduction to toxicology*. 1989. Taylor & Francis, London/Washington.

Weiss, B. and J.L. O'Donoghue (Eds), *Neurobehavioral toxicity: Analysis and interpretation*. Raven Press, New York.

Welling, Peter G. and Felix de la Inglesia (Eds.). 1993. *Drug toxicokinetics*. Marcel Dekker, New York. xviii + 408 pages.

Wheater, P.R. et al. 1985. *Basic Histopathology*. Churchill Livingstone, Edinburgh/London.


*Series:*

Methods in Toxicology, Vol 1: In Vitro Biological System, C.A. Tyson and J.M. Frazier, Academic Press, London, 1993, xxi + 568 pages

Annual Review of Pharmacology and Toxicology, Vol. 1–33, Arthur K. Cho, Terrence F. Blaschke, Horace H. Loh and James L. Way (Eds.)

Drug and chemical toxicology, Vol. 1–8 DiCarlo, F.J. and F.W. Oehme (Eds), Vol 8: Animal models in toxicology, Shayne Cox Gad and Christopher P. Chengelis (Vol. Eds.), Marcel Dekker, New York, 1992, 904 pages

Handbook of natural toxins, Vol 1–7, Anthony T. Tu (series editor), Marcel Dekker, New York, 1990

# Credits

**Figure 2.3**
Modified from: National Institute of Public Health and Environmental Protection, Bilthoven, The Netherlands, 1993.

**Text in Self Assessment Questions Study unit 2. Question 2.1**
From: *Webster's New World Dictionary*, D.B. Guralnik, Ed., Simon & Schuster, N.York, 1980.

**Figure 4.1**
Modified from Figure 4.2 page 116, in, Gordon, G.G. and Skett, P., *Introduction to drug metabolism*, Chapman and Hall, London, New York, 1986.

**Figure 4.2**
Modified from Figure 4.3 page 116, in, Gordon, G.G. and Skett, P., *Introduction to drug metabolism*, Chapman and Hall, London, New York, 1986.

**Figure 4.7**
Modified from Figure 4.10 page 125, in, Gordon, G.G. and Skett, P., *Introduction to drug metabolism*, Chapman and Hall, London, New York, 1986.

**Figure 4.8**
Modified from: Figure 4.13 page 129, in, Gordon, G.G. and Skett, P., *Introduction to drug metabolism*, Chapman and Hall, London, New York, 1986.

**Figure answer 4.11 Self Assessment Questions**
Modified from Figure 5.8 page 166, in, Gordon, G.G. and Skett, P., *Introduction to drug metabolism*, Chapman and Hall, London, New York, 1986.

**Table 4.1**
Modified from Table 4.2 page 115, in, Gordon, G.G. and Skett, P., *Introduction to drug metabolism*, Chapman and Hall, London, New York, 1986.

**Figure 5.2**
Modified from Figure 19 page 17. Kurz, H., Neumann, H.G., Forth, W., Henschler, D., and Rummel, W., Allgemeine Pharmakologie, in, *Allgemeine und spezielle Pharmakologie und Toxikologie*, Forth, W., Henschler, D. and Rummel, W., Eds., B.I. Wissenschaftsverlag, Mannheim, Wien, Zürich, 1983, Chapter 1.

**Figure 5.4**
Modified from Figure 21 page 18. Kurz, H., Neumann, H.G., Forth, W., Henschler, D., and Rummel, W., Allgemeine Pharmakologie, in, *Allgemeine und spezielle Pharmakologie und Toxikologie*, Forth, W., Henschler, D. and Rummel, W., Eds., B.I. Wissenschaftsverlag, Mannheim, Wien, Zürich, 1983, Chapter 1.

**Figure 5.5**
Modified from Figure 22 page 19. Kurz, H., Neumann, H.G., Forth, W., Henschler, D., and Rummel, W., Allgemeine Pharmakologie, in, *Allgemeine und spezielle Pharmakologie und Toxikologie*, Forth, W., Henschler, D. and Rummel, W., Eds., B.I. Wissenschaftsverlag, Mannheim, Wien, Zürich, 1983, Chapter 1.

**Figure 5.6**
Modified from Figure 24 page 20. Kurz, H., Neumann, H.G., Forth, W., Henschler, D., and Rummel, W., Allgemeine Pharmakologie, in, *Allgemeine und spezielle Pharmakologie und Toxikologie*, Forth, W., Henschler, D. and Rummel, W., Eds., B.I. Wissenschaftsverlag, Mannheim, Wien, Zürich, 1983, Chapter 1.

**Table 5.1**
Modified from: Hogben et al., J. Pharmac. Exp. Ther., 126, 275, 1958.

**Figure 5.18**
Modified from: Witter, A.J. and J.M. Van Ree, *Algemene Farmacologie*, Wetenschappelijke Uitgeverij Bunge, Utrecht, 1984.

**Figure 5.19**
Modified from: Witter, A.J. and J.M. Van Ree, 1986, *Algemene Farmacologie*, Wetenschappelijke Uitgeverij Bunge, Utrecht, 1984.

**Table 5.2**
Modified from Table 13 page 24. Kurz, H., Neumann, H.G., Forth, W., Henschler, D., and Rummel, W., Allgemeine Pharmakologie, in, *Allgemeine und spezielle Pharmakologie und Toxikologie*, Forth, W., Henschler, D. and Rummel, W., Eds., B.I. Wissenschaftsverlag, Mannheim, Wien, Zürich, 1983, Chapter 1.

**Table 5.3**
Modified from Table 20 page 35. Kurz, H., Neumann, H.G., Forth, W., Henschler, D., and Rummel, W., Allgemeine

Pharmakologie, in, *Allgemeine und spezielle Pharmakologie und Toxikologie*, Forth, W., Henschler, D. and Rummel, W., Eds., B.I. Wissenschaftsverlag, Mannheim, Wien, Zürich, 1983, Chapter 1. With permission.

**Figure 7.13**
Modified from: Vos, J.G. et al., Toxicol. Applied Pharmacol., 18, 944–957, 1971.

**Figure 7.21**
Modified from Figure 3.3 page 13, in, *An introduction to the interpretation of quantal responses in biology*, Hewlett, P.S. and Plackett, R.L., Edward Arnold, London, 1979.

**Figure 7.26**
Modified from: Van Leeuwen C.J. et al., Ecotox. Environm. Safety 9, 26–39, 1985 and Aquatic Toxicol. 7, 165–175, 1985.

**Table 7.5a**
Modified from: Table 4.1 page 19, in, *An introduction to the interpretation of quantal responses in biology*, Hewlett, P.S. and Plackett, R.L., Edward Arnold, London, 1979.

**Table 7.5b**
Modified from: Table 3.1 page 14, in, *An introduction to the interpretation of quantal responses in biology*, Hewlett, P.S. and Plackett, R.L., Edward Arnold, London, 1979.

**Figure 8.7**
Modified from: Könemann H., Toxicology 9, 209–221, 1981 and Hermens, J. et al., Environm. Toxicol. Chem. 4, 273–279, 1985.

**Table 8.2**
Modified from: Könemann H., Toxicology 9, 209–221, 1981.

**Table 8.3**
Modified from: Fukuto, T.R. and Metcalf, R.L., Agricult. Food Chem. 4, 930–935, 1956.

**Table 8.4**
Modified from Table 3.1, in, Albert A., *Selective toxicity*, Chapman and Hall, London, New York, 1985, page 66.

**Table 8.5**
Modified from: Könemann, H. and Van Leeuwen, C.J., Chemosphere 9, 3–19, 1980.

**Table 8.6**
Modified from: Saarikoski, J. and Viluksela, M., Ecotoxicol. Environm. Safety 6, 383–383, 1982.

**Table 8.10a**
Modified from: Hansch, C., Drug Met. Rev., 1–13, 1972.

**Table 8.11**
Modified from: Hermens J. et al., Environm. Toxicol. Chem. 4, 273–279, 1985.

**Figure 10.18**
Orrenius, S., Biochemical mechanism of cytotoxicity, TIPS, November, 1985, FEST Supplement. With permission.

**Figure 11.16**
Röhrborn, G., Mutation in man, in, *Critical evaluation of mutagenicity tests*, R. Bab et al., Eds, Medizin Verlag, München. BGA Schriften 3/84, 19884, pages 21–35. With permission.

**Table 12.8**
Modified from: Wolfe, S.L., Genes regulating the cell cycle, cell cycle regulation and cancer, *Molecular and cellular biology*, Wadsworth Publishing Company, Belmont California, 1993, Chapter 22.

**Table 12.9**
Modified from: Wolfe, S.L., Genes regulating the cell cycle, cell cycle regulation and cancer, *Molecular and cellular biology*, Wadsworth Publishing Company, Belmont California, 1993, Chapter 22.

**Figure 12.7**
Modified from: Hunter, T., The proteins of oncogenes, Scientific American, 1984 (August), pages 60–68.

**Figure 12.8**
Modified from Figure 24–24, Cancer, in, Darnell, J.E., Lodish, H., and Baltimore, D., *Molecular Cell Biology*, 2nd edition, Scientific American Books, N. York, 1990.

**Figure 12.10**
Modified from: Southern, E.M., J.Mol. Biology, 98:508, 1975.

**Figure 12.11**
Modified from Fearon, E.R. and Vogelstein, B., A genetic model for colorectal tumorigenesis. Cell, 61, 759–767, 1990.

**Figure 12.12**
Modified from Boomsma, A.H., Cornelisse, C.J. and De Kleine, A., Oncogenen, tumorsuppressiegenen en de medische genetica van kanker, Ned. Tijdschr. Geneeskd, 136 (2), 1992.

**Figure 13.2**
Modified from: Wogan, G.N., Molecular epidemiology in cancer risk assessment and prevention: Recent progress and avenues for future research, Env. Health Persp., 98, 167–178, 1992.

**Figure 15.8**
Copyright, Dr. P.W. Wester, Department of Toxicology, National Institute of Public Health and Environmental Protection, Bilthoven, The Netherlands. With permission.

**Figure 15.9**
Copyright, Dr. L.H.I.C. Danze, Department of Toxicology, National Institute of Public Health and Environmental Protection, Bilthoven, The Netherlands. With permission.

**Figure 16.1**
Modified from: Thompson, R.G., *General Veterinary Pathology*, 2nd ed., W.B. Saunders & Company, 1984, page 18.

**Figure 16.4**
Modified from: Wyllie, A.H., Cell death: a new classification separating apoptosis from necrosis, in, *Cell death in biology and pathology*, Bowen, I.D. and Lockshin, R.A., Eds., Chapman and Hall, London, New York. 1981, pages 9–34.

**Figure 16.6**
Modified from: Trump, B.F. and Mergner, W.J., Cell injury, in, *The inflammatory process*, Vol. 1, 2nd ed., Zweifach, B.W., Grant, L, and McCluskey, R.T., Eds, Academic Press, New York, San Francisco, London, 1974, pages 115–257.

**Figure 16.7**
Modified from Figure 1., Carson, D.A. and J.M. Ribeiro, J.M., Apoptosis and disease, Lancet 341: 1251–1254, 1993.

**Figure 16.9**
Modified from: Farber, J.L., Biology of disease, Membrane injury and calcium homeostasis in the pathogenesis of coagulative necrosis, Lab. Invest., 47, 114–123, 1982.

**Figure 16.12**
Modified from: Piper, .M. et al., Energy metabolism and enzyme release of cultured adult rat heart muscle cells during anoxia, J. Mol. Cell. Cardiol., 16, 995–1007, 1984.

**Figure 16.14**
Modified from: Jennings, R.B. et al., Total ischemia in dog hearts, in vitro, 1 Comparison of high energy phosphate production, utilization and depletion, and of adenine nucleotide catabolism in total ischemia in vitro vs. severe ischemia in vivo, Circ. Res., 49. 892–900, 1981.

**Figure 16.16**
Copyright, Temmink, J.M.H., Agricultural University, Department of Toxicology, Wageningen. The Netherlands. With permission.

**Figures 16.17 and 16.18**
Trump, B.F. et al., Cell death and the disease process, The role of calcium, in, *Cell death in biology and pathology*, Bowen, I.D. and Lockshin, R.A., Eds., Chapman and Hall, London, New York. pages 209–242, 1981. With permission.

**Table 16.1**
Modified from: Borgers, M., et al., Changes in ultrastructrure and Ca²⁺ distribution in isolated working rabbit heart after ischemia, A time-related study, Am. J. Pathol., 126, 92–102, 1987.

**Figures 17.7, 17.8, 17.9, 17.10. 17.11, 17.12 and 17.13**
Mol, M.A.E., Twee nieuwe modellen in het huidtoxicologisch onderzoek, Tox-Post, July, 1988. With permission.

**Figures 18.10**
From the slide series: The effect of smoking. Griffin and George, Preston, West-Sussex, England, 1984. Copyright Fisons plc, Scientific Equipment Division 1984.

**Figures 21.2**
Modified from Figure 3.14: Glaister, J.R., *Principles of toxicological pathology*, Taylor & Francis Ltd., London, Philadelphia, Chapter 3, Target Organ Pathology, 1986.

**Figure 22.1**
Modified from Figure 2: Smith, R., The relation between consumption and damage, in, *Alcohol problems, ABC of alcohol, Articles from the British Medical Journal*, Leagrave Press LTD., Luton and London, 1982.

**Figures 22.3a and 22.3b**
Modified from Figures 1–9 and 1–12, Gerok, W., Funktion und Struktur der Leber, in, Gerok, W., et al., Eds., *Hepatologie*, Urban & Schwarzenberg, München, Wien, Baltimore, 1987, Chapter 1.

**Figure 22.6**
Modified from: Kessel, G.R. and Kardon, R.H., *Tissues and organs*, W.H. Freeman and Company, San Francisco, Oxford, 1979.

**Figure 22.8**
Modified from: Farber, E. and Fisher, M.M., *Toxic injury of the liver*, Marcel Dekker, New York, 1978.

**Figure 22.15**
Modified from figure 6–12, Buscher, H.P, in, Gerok, W., et al., Eds., *Hepatologie*, Urban & Schwarzenberg, München, Wien, Baltimore, 1987, Chapter 6, Cholestase.

**Figures 24.2a**
From: Bloom, W. & Fawcett, D.W., *A textbook of histology*, W.B. Saunders Company. Philadelphia, London, Toronto, 1968. With permission.

**Figures 24.3**
Modified from: Smith, E., *The kidney: Structure and Function in Health and Disease*, Oxford University Press.

**Figures 24.4, 24.6 and 24.10**
From: Junqueira, L.C., *Basic Histology* , Lange, Norwalk, Connecticut, 1986. With permission

**Figures 24.5, 24.17 and 24.18**
From: Olsen and Olsen, Renal Ultrastructure, in, Solez, K. and Whelton, A. Eds., *Acute renal failure*, Marcel Dekker, Inc. Basel, New York, 1984.

**Figure 24.11**
From: Bach, P.H. and Lock, E.A., Eds., Renal heterogeneity and target cell toxicity, *Proceedings of the second international symposium on nephrotoxicity*, University Surrey, U.K., John Wiley & Sons, Chicester, England.

**Figure 24.12**
Modified from Figure 3.29, Glaister, J.R., *Principles of toxicological pathology*, Taylor & Francis Ltd., London, Philadelphia, 1986, Chapter 3, Target Organ Pathology.

**Figures 24.13, 24.14, 24.15, 24.16, 24.17, and 24,18**
From: Solez, K., Human acute tubular necrosis, in, Solez, K. and Whelton, A., Eds., *Acute renal failure*, Marcel Dekker, Inc. Basel, New York, 1984. With permission.

**Figure 25.3**
Modified from: Goodman, M.N. et.al., Influence of fluorocarbon emulsions on hepatic metabolism in perfused rat liver, Am.J.Physiol.,. 225, 1384–1388, 1978.

**Figure 25.4**
Modified from: Bowman, R.H., The perfused rat kidney, Meth. Enzymol., 39, 3–11, 1975.

**Figure 25.5**
Modified from: Cocojel, C. et.al., Renal ultrastructure and biochemical injuries induced by aminoglycosides, Env.Health Perspect., 57, 293–299, 1984.

**Figure 25.6**
Modified from: Collier, V.U. et.al., Evidence of luminal uptake of gentamicin in the perfused rat kidney, J.Pharmacol.Exp.Ther., 210, 247–251, 1979.

**Figure 25.8**
Modified from: Autrup, H., Carcinogen metabolism in human tissues and cells, Drug Metab.Rev., 13, 603–646, 1982.

**Figure 25.9**
Modified from: Kari, F. et.al., Characterization of mutagenic glucuronide formation from benz[a]pyrene in the nonrecirculating perfused rat liver, Cancer Res., 44, 5073–5078, 1984.

**Figure 25.10**
Modified from: Bock, K.W. et.al., Release of mutagenic metabolites of benzo[a]oyrene from the perfused rat liver after inhibition of glucuronidation and sulfation by salicylamide, Chem.-Biol.Interactions, 36, 167–177, 1981.

**Figure 25.11**
Modified from: Smith, B.R. et.al., Characterization of pulmonary arene oxide biotransformation using the perfused rabbit lung, Cancer.Res., 40, 101–106, 1980.

**Figure 25.12**
Modified from: Klaus, E. et.al., Similar level of metabolic activation of benzo[a]oyrene in perfused rat lung and liver and protection of lung by liver in a combined perfusion system, Biochem.Biophys.Res.Comm., 105, 596–602, 1982.

**Figure 25.13**
Modified from: Uotila, A., Effect of cigarette smoke on glucuronide conjugation in hamster isolated lungs, Res.Comm.Chem.Pathol.Pharmacol.,. 38, 173–176, 1982.

**Figure 25.14**
Modified from: Conway, J.G. et.al., Glucuronidation of 7-hydroxycoumarin in periportal and pericentral regions of the liver lobule, Molec.Pharmacol., 25, 487–493, 1984.

**Figure 25.15**
Modified from: Wiersma.D.A. and Roth, R.A., Clearance of benzo[a]pyrene by isolated rat liver and lung: alterations in perfusion and metabolic capacity, J.Pharmacol.Exp.Ther., 225, 121–125, 1983.

**Figure 25.17**
From: Koster, A.Sj., *Glucuronidation in the rat intestinal wall in vitro and in vivo*, Thesis, University of Utrecht, Utrecht, 1985

**Figure 26.7**
Copyright: Neville Woolf, The thrombotic theory of atherogenesis, Postgraduate Medical services, Boehringer Ingelheim. With permission.

**Figure 28.10**
Modified from: Kammüller, M.E., *A toxicological approach to chemical-induced autoimmunity*, Thesis, University of Utrecht, Utrecht, 1988.

**Figure 33.2**
Modified from Figure 1 page 87, Greeff, K. and Palm, D., Einführung in die Pharmakologie des peripheren autonomen Nervensystem, in, *Allgemeine und spezielle Pharmakologie und Toxikologie*, Forth, W., Henschler, D. and Rummel, W., Eds., B.I. Wissenschaftsverlag, Mannheim, Wien, Zürich, 1983.

**Figure 33.4**
Modified from Figure 2 page 88, Greeff, K. and Palm, D., Einführung in die Pharmakologie des peripheren autonomen Nervensystem, in, *Allgemeine und spezielle Pharmakologie und Toxikologie*, Forth, W., Henschler, D. and Rummel, W., Eds., B.I. Wissenschaftsverlag, Mannheim, Wien, Zürich, 1983.

**Figure 33.5**
Modified from Figure 3 page 89, Greeff, K. and Palm, D., Einführung in die Pharmakologie des peripheren autonomen Nervensystem, in, *Allgemeine und spezielle Pharmakologie und Toxikologie*, Forth, W., Henschler, D. and Rummel, W., Eds., B.I. Wissenschaftsverlag, Mannheim, Wien, Zürich, 1983.

**Figure 33.8**
Modified from Figure 4 page 115, Palm, D., Hellenbrecht, D. and K. Quiring, Pharmakologie des noradrenergen und adrenergen Systems, in, *Allgemeine und spezielle Pharmakologie und Toxikologie*, Forth, W., Henschler, D. and Rummel, W., Eds., B.I. Wissenschaftsverlag, Mannheim, Wien, Zürich, 1983.

**Figure 33.9**

Modified from Figure 3 page 114. Palm, D. D. Hellenbrecht and K. Quiring, Pharmakologie des noradrenergen und adrenergen Systems, in, *Allgemeine und spezielle Pharmakologie und Toxikologie*, Forth, W., Henschler, D. and Rummel, W., Eds., B.I. Wissenschaftsverlag, Mannheim, Wien, Zürich, 1983.

**Figure 33.10**

Modified from: Spencer, P.S. and Schaumberg, H.H., Eds., *Experimental and clinical neurotoxicology*, William & Wilkins, Baltimore, 1980.

**Figure 34.1**

Copyright Piek, T. University of Amsterdam. With permission.

**Figure 34.6**

Modified from: Vijverberg, H.P.M., *Interaction of pyrethroids with the sodium channels in myelinated nerve fibres*, Thesis, University Utrecht, Utrecht, 1982.

**Figure 37.7**

Modified from Figure 15 page 528, Stegink, L.D., Aspartame metabolism in humans: acute dosing studies, in, Stegink L.D. and Filer Jr. L.J., Eds., *Aspartame: physiology and biochemistry*, Marcel Dekker Inc., New York-Basel, 1984, Chapter 26.

**Figure 37.8a**

Modified from Figure 27 page 543, Stegink, L.D., Aspartame metabolism in humans: acute dosing studies, in, Stegink L.D. and Filer Jr. L.J., Eds., *Aspartame: physiology and biochemistry*, Marcel Dekker Inc., New York-Basel, 1984, Chapter 26.

**Figure 37.8b**

Modified from Figure 28 page 544, Stegink, L.D., Aspartame metabolism in humans: acute dosing studies, in, Stegink L.D. and Filer Jr. L.J., Eds., *Aspartame: physiology and biochemistry*, Marcel Dekker Inc., New York-Basel, 1984, Chapter 26.

**Table 37.3**

Modified from Table 3 page 149 and Table 5 page 154, in, Stegink L.D. and Filer Jr. L.J., Eds., *Aspartame: physiology and biochemistry*, Marcel Dekker Inc., New York-Basel, 1984.

**Table 37.4**

Modified from: Stegink, L.D., Filer, L.J., Jr., and Baker, G.L., Plasma and erythrocyte concentrations of free amino acids in adult humans administered abuse doses of aspartame, J. Toxicol. Envir. Health, 7, 291–305, 1981.

**Table 37.5**

Modified from Table 9 page 544, Stegink, L.D., Aspartame metabolism in humans: acute dosing studies, in, Stegink L.D. and Filer Jr. L.J., Eds., *Aspartame: physiology and biochemistry*, Marcel Dekker Inc., New York-Basel, 1984, Chapter 26.

**Table 37.6**

Modified from: Filer, L.J. Jr., Baker, G.L. And L.D. Stegink, Effect of aspartame loading on plasma and erythrocyte free amino acid concentrations in one-year-old infants, J. Nutr. 113, 1600–1606, 1983.

**Table 37.7**

Modified from: Table 1 page 644, Fernstrom, J.D., Effects of acute aspartame ingestion on large neutral amino acids and monoamines in rat brain, in, Stegink L.D. and Filer Jr. L.J., Eds., *Aspartame: physiology and biochemistry*, Marcel Dekker Inc., New York-Basel, 1984, Chapter 33.

**Table 37.8**

Modified from: Oldendorf, W.H., Brain uptake of radiolabelled amino acids, amines, and hexoses after arterial injection, Am. J. Physiol., 221, 1629–1639, 1971.

**Table 37.10**

Modified from: Fernstrom, J.D., Effects of acute aspartame ingestion on large neutral amino acids and monoamines in rat brain, in, Stegink L.D. and Filer Jr. L.J., Eds., *Aspartame: physiology and biochemistry*, Marcel Dekker Inc., New York-Basel, 1984, Chapter 33.

**Figure 39.1**

Modified from: Koeman, J.H., *Ecologische indicatoren*, Pudoc Wageningen, 1984.

**Figure 39.3**

Modified from: Ramade, F., *Ecotoxicology*, John Wiley & Sons, Chichester, 1987.

**Figure 39.4**

Modified from: Kleiber, M., *The Fire of Life: An Introduction to Animal Energetics*, John Wiley & Sons, Chichester, 1961.

**Figure 39.6**

Modified from: Halbach, U.Siebert, M. Westermayer, M., and Wissel, C., Ecotox. Environ. Saf., 7, 484–513, 1983.

**Figure 39.7**

Modified from: Kooijman, S.A.L.M., in, *Multispecies Toxicity Testing*, Cairns, J., Jr., Ed., Pergamon Press, New York, 1985.

**Figure 39.8**

Modified from: Warwick, R.M., Mar. Biol., 92, 557–562, 1986.

**Table 39.4**

Modified from: Van Gestel, C.A.M., and Ma, W.C., Ecotox. Environ. Saf., 15, 289–297, 1988.

**Table 39.5**

Modified from: Van Der Oost, R., Heida, H., and Opperhuizen, A., Arch. Environm. Contam. Toxicol., 17, 721–729, 1988.

# Index

# C

# D

# E

# F

# G

# H

# I